Elementary Statistics

PICTURING THE WORLD

Fourth Edition

Ron Larson

The Pennsylvania State University
The Behrend College

Betsy Farber

Bucks County Community College

PEARSON

Prentice
Hall

Upper Saddle River, NJ 07458

Library of Congress Cataloging-in-Publication Data

Larson, Ron.
    Elementary statistics : picturing the world / Ron Larson, Betsy Farber.— 4th ed.
        p. cm.
    Includes index.

Editor-in-Chief, Statistics: *Deirdre Lynch*
Vice President and Editorial Director, Mathematics: *Christine Hoag*
Sponsoring Editor: *Dawn Murrin*
Project Manager, Production: *Lynn Savino Wendel*
Senior Managing Editor: *Linda Mihatov Behrens*
Senior Operations Specialist: *Diane Peirano*
Marketing Manager: *Wayne Parkins*
Project Manager, Media: *Richard Bretan*
Editorial Assistant/ Supplements Editor: *Joanne Wendelken*
Art Director: *Maureen Eide*
Interior Designer: *John Christiana*
Cover Designer: *John Christiana*
Project Manager, AV: *Thomas Benfatti*
Director, Image Resource Center: *Melinda Patelli*
Manager, Rights and Permissions: *Zina Arabia*
Manager, Visual Research: *Beth Brenzel*
Manager, Cover Visual Research & Permissions: *Karen Sanatar*
Image Permission Coordinator: *Craig A. Jones*
Photo Researcher: *Diane Austin*
Art Studio: *Precision Graphics, Inc.*
Cover Photo Courtesy of www.istockphoto.com

©2009, 2006, 2003, 2000 Pearson Education, Inc.
Pearson Prentice Hall
Pearson Education, Inc.
Upper Saddle River, New Jersey 07458

Printed in the United States of America

10 9 8 7 6 5

ISBN 13 978-0-13-600720-3 (School Edition)
ISBN 10   0-13-600720-1 (School Edition)

(ISBN 13 978-0-13-242233-2 (College Edition))
(ISBN 10   0-13-242433-9 (College Edition))

Pearson Education LTD., *London*
Pearson Education Australia PTY, Limited, *Sydney*
Pearson Education Singapore, Pte. Ltd
Pearson Education North Asia Ltd, *Hong Kong*
Pearson Education Canada, Ltd., *Toronto*
Pearson Educación de Mexico, S.A. de C.V.
Pearson Education—Japan, *Tokyo*
Pearson Education Malaysia, Pte. Ltd

About the Authors

Ron Larson
The Pennsylvania State University
The Behrend College

Ron Larson received his Ph.D. in mathematics from the University of Colorado in 1970. At that time he accepted a position with Penn State University, and he currently holds the rank of professor of mathematics at the university. Larson is the lead author of more than two dozen mathematics textbooks that range from sixth grade through calculus levels. Many of his texts, such as the eighth edition of his calculus text, are leaders in their markets. Larson is also one of the pioneers in the use of multimedia and the Internet to enhance the learning of mathematics. He has authored multimedia programs, extending from the elementary school through calculus levels. Larson is a member of several professional groups and is a frequent speaker at national and regional mathematics meetings.

Betsy Farber
Bucks County
Community College

Betsy Farber received her Bachelor's degree in mathematics from Penn State University and Master's degree in mathematics from the College of New Jersey. Since 1976, she has been teaching all levels of mathematics at Bucks County Community College in Newtown, Pennsylvania, where she currently holds the rank of professor. She is particularly interested in developing new ways to make statistics relevant and interesting to her students and has been teaching statistics in many different modes—with TI-83, with MINITAB, and by distance learning as well as in the traditional classroom. A member of the American Mathematical Association of Two-Year Colleges (AMATYC), she is an author of *The Student Edition to MINITAB* and *A Guide to MINITAB*. She served as consulting editor for *Statistics, A First Course* and has written computer tutorials for the CD-ROM correlating to the texts in the Streeter Series in mathematics.

Contents

Preface x
Supplements xiv
Acknowledgments xv
How to Study Statistics xvi
Index of Applications xviii

PART ONE

CHAPTER 1 Introduction to Statistics 2

Where You've Been 3
Where You're Going 3
1.1 An Overview of Statistics 4
1.2 Data Classification 11
■ Case Study: Rating Television Shows in the United States 17
1.3 Experimental Design 18
■ Activity: Random Numbers 28
■ Uses and Abuses 29
Chapter Summary 30
Review Exercises 31
Chapter Quiz 33
■ Real Statistics–Real Decisions—Putting It All Together 34
■ History of Statistics—Timeline 35
■ Technology: Using Technology in Statistics 36

CHAPTER 2 Descriptive Statistics 38

Where You've Been 39
Where You're Going 39
2.1 Frequency Distributions and Their Graphs 40
2.2 More Graphs and Displays 55
2.3 Measures of Central Tendency 67
■ Activity: Mean Versus Median 81
2.4 Measures of Variation 82
■ Activity: Standard Deviation 100
■ Case Study: Earnings of Athletes 101
2.5 Measures of Position 102
■ Uses and Abuses 115
Chapter Summary 116
Review Exercises 117
Chapter Quiz 121
■ Real Statistics–Real Decisions—Putting It All Together 122
■ Technology: Monthly Milk Production 123
■ Using Technology to Determine Descriptive Statistics 124
Cumulative Review: Chapters 1 and 2 126

PART TWO

CHAPTER 3

Probability   **130**

Where You've Been   131
Where You're Going   131
3.1   **Basic Concepts of Probability and Counting**   132
■ Activity: *Simulating the Stock Market*   148
3.2   **Conditional Probability and the Multiplication Rule**   149
3.3   **The Addition Rule**   160
■ Activity: *Simulating the Probability of Rolling a 3 or 4*   170
■ Case Study: *Probability and Parking Lot Strategies*   171
3.4   **Additional Topics in Probability and Counting**   172
■ Uses and Abuses   183
Chapter Summary   184
Review Exercises   185
Chapter Quiz   189
■ Real Statistics–Real Decisions— Putting It All Together   190
■ Technology: *Simulation: Composing Mozart Variations With Dice*   191

CHAPTER 4

Discrete Probability Distributions   **192**

Where You've Been   193
Where You're Going   193
4.1   **Probability Distributions**   194
4.2   **Binomial Distributions**   206
■ Activity: *Binomial Distribution*   220
■ Case Study: *Binomial Distribution of Airplane Accidents*   221
4.3   **More Discrete Probability Distributions**   222
■ Uses and Abuses   229
Chapter Summary   230
Review Exercises   231
Chapter Quiz   235
■ Real Statistics–Real Decisions— Putting It All Together   236
■ Technology: *Using Poisson Distributions as Queuing Models*   237

CHAPTER 5   **Normal Probability Distributions**   **238**

Where You've Been   238

Where You're Going   239

5.1   **Introduction to Normal Distributions and the Standard Normal Distribution**   240

5.2   **Normal Distributions: Finding Probabilities**   253

5.3   **Normal Distributions: Finding Values**   261

  ■ Case Study: *Birth Weights in America*   269

5.4   **Sampling Distributions and the Central Limit Theorem**   270

  ■ Activity: *Sampling Distributions*   284

5.5   **Normal Approximations to Binomial Distributions**   285

  ■ **Uses and Abuses**   295

  Chapter Summary   296

  Review Exercises   297

  Chapter Quiz   301

  ■ **Real Statistics–Real Decisions— Putting It All Together**   302

  ■ **Technology:** *Age Distribution in the United States*   303

  Cumulative Review: *Chapters 3–5*   304

PART THREE

CHAPTER 6   **Confidence Intervals**   **308**

Where You've Been   309

Where You're Going   309

6.1   **Confidence Intervals for the Mean (Large Samples)**   310

  ■ Case Study: *Shoulder Heights of Appalachian Black Bears*   324

6.2   **Confidence Intervals for the Mean (Small Samples)**   325

  ■ Activity: *Confidence Intervals for the Mean*   333

6.3   **Confidence Intervals for Population Proportions**   334

  ■ Activity: *Confidence Intervals for Proportions*   343

6.4   **Confidence Intervals for Variance and Standard Deviation**   344

  ■ **Uses and Abuses**   351

  Chapter Summary   352

  Review Exercises   353

  Chapter Quiz   357

  ■ **Real Statistics–Real Decisions— Putting It All Together**   358

  ■ **Technology:** *Most Admired Polls*   359

  ■ **Using Technology to Construct Confidence Intervals**   360

CHAPTER 7

Hypothesis Testing with One Sample 362

Where You've Been		363
Where You're Going		363
7.1	**Introduction to Hypothesis Testing**	364
7.2	**Hypothesis Testing for the Mean (Large Samples)**	379
	■ **Activity:** *Hypothesis Test for the Mean*	395
	■ **Case Study:** *Human Body Temperature: What's Normal?*	396
7.3	**Hypothesis Testing for the Mean (Small Samples)**	397
7.4	**Hypothesis Testing for Proportions**	407
	■ **Activity:** *Hypothesis Test for a Proportion*	413
7.5	**Hypothesis Testing for Variance and Standard Deviation**	414
	■ **Uses and Abuses**	423
	A Summary of Hypothesis Testing	424
	Chapter Summary	426
	Review Exercises	427
	Chapter Quiz	431
	■ **Real Statistics–Real Decisions— Putting It All Together**	432
	■ **Technology:** *The Case of the Vanishing Women*	433
	■ **Using Technology to Perform Hypothesis Tests**	434

CHAPTER 8

Hypothesis Testing with Two Samples 436

Where You've Been		437
Where You're Going		437
8.1	**Testing the Difference Between Means (Large Independent Samples)**	438
	■ **Case Study:** *Diets and Weight Loss*	451
8.2	**Testing the Difference Between Means (Small Independent Samples)**	452
8.3	**Testing the Difference Between Means (Dependent Samples)**	461
8.4	**Testing the Difference Between Proportions**	471
	■ **Uses and Abuses**	479
	Chapter Summary	480
	Review Exercises	481
	Chapter Quiz	485
	■ **Real Statistics–Real Decisions— Putting It All Together**	486
	■ **Technology:** *Tails Over Heads*	487
	■ **Using Technology to Perform Two-Sample Hypothesis Tests**	488
	Cumulative Review: *Chapters 6–8*	490

PART FOUR

CHAPTER 9

Correlation and Regression   494

Where You've Been   495
Where You're Going   495

9.1   **Correlation**   496
       ■ Activity: *Correlation*   512
9.2   **Linear Regression**   513
       ■ Activity: *Regression*   523
       ■ Case Study: *Correlation of Body Measurements*   524
9.3   **Measures of Regression and Prediction Intervals**   525
9.4   **Multiple Regression**   536
       ■ Uses and Abuses   541
       Chapter Summary   542
       Review Exercises   543
       Chapter Quiz   547
       ■ Real Statistics–Real Decisions— Putting It All Together   548
       ■ Technology: *Nutrients in Breakfast Cereals*   549

CHAPTER 10

Chi-Square Tests and the *F*-Distribution   550

Where You've Been   551
Where You're Going   551

10.1   **Goodness of Fit**   552
10.2   **Independence**   565
       ■ Case Study: *Traffic Safety Facts*   578
10.3   **Comparing Two Variances**   579
10.4   **Analysis of Variance**   588
       ■ Uses and Abuses   601
       Chapter Summary   602
       Review Exercises   603
       Chapter Quiz   607
       ■ Real Statistics–Real Decisions— Putting It All Together   608
       ■ Technology: *Teacher Salaries*   609

CHAPTER 11 Nonparametric Tests   610

Where You've Been   611

Where You're Going   611

11.1   **The Sign Test**   612

11.2   **The Wilcoxon Tests**   623

■ **Case Study:** *Earnings by College Degree*   632

11.3   **The Kruskal-Wallis Test**   633

11.4   **Rank Correlation**   639

11.5   **The Runs Test**   645

■ **Uses and Abuses**   653

Chapter Summary   654

Review Exercises   655

Chapter Quiz   659

■ **Real Statistics–Real Decisions— Putting It All Together**   660

■ **Technology:** *U.S. Income and Economic Research*   661

Cumulative Review: *Chapters 9–11*   662

Appendices

APPENDIX A   ALTERNATIVE PRESENTATION OF THE STANDARD NORMAL DISTRIBUTION   **A1**

Standard Normal Distribution Table (0-to-z)   A1

Alternative Presentation of the Standard Normal Distribution   A2

APPENDIX B   TABLES   **A7**

TABLE 1   *Random Numbers*   A7

TABLE 2   *Binomial Distribution*   A8

TABLE 3   *Poisson Distribution*   A11

TABLE 4   *Standard Normal Distribution*   A16

TABLE 5   *t-Distribution*   A18

TABLE 6   *Chi-Square Distribution*   A19

TABLE 7   *F-Distribution*   A20

TABLE 8   *Critical Values for the Sign Test*   A25

TABLE 9   *Critical Values for the Wilcoxon Signed-Rank Test*   A26

TABLE 10 *Critical Values for the Spearman Rank Correlation*   A27

TABLE 11 *Critical Values for the Pearson Correlation Coefficient*   A28

TABLE 12 *Critical Values for the Number of Runs*   A29

APPENDIX C   NORMAL PROBABILITY PLOTS AND THEIR GRAPHS   A30

Answers to the Try It Yourself Exercises   A32

Answers to the Odd-Numbered Exercises   A51

Index   I1

Preface

Welcome to *Elementary Statistics: Picturing the World*, Fourth Edition. We are grateful for the overwhelming acceptance and support of the first three editions. It is gratifying to know that our vision of combining theory, pedagogy, and design to exemplify how statistics is used to picture and describe the world has helped students learn about statistics and make informed decisions.

Features of the Fourth Edition

NEW! **Category Openers** The topics in the text are grouped into four parts: *Descriptive Statistics, Probability and Probability Distributions, Statistical Inference,* and *More Statistical Inference.* Each category provides a natural grouping of topics within the bigger picture of statistics.

Chapter Openers Each chapter begins with a two-page visual description of a real-life problem. *Where You've Been* shows students how the chapter fits into the bigger picture of statistics, by connecting it to topics learned in earlier chapters. *Where You're Going* gives students an overview of the chapter, exploring concepts in the context of real-world settings.

Section Organization Each section is organized by learning objectives. These objectives are presented in everyday language in *What You Should Learn.* The same objectives are then used as subsection titles throughout the section.

Titled Examples Every concept in the text is clearly illustrated with one or more step-by-step examples. Most examples have an interpretation step that shows the student how the solution may be interpreted within the real-life context of the example. This added step promotes critical thinking and writing skills. Each of the more than 210 examples is numbered and titled for easy reference.

Try It Yourself Each example is followed by a similar exercise called *Try It Yourself* so students can immediately practice the skill learned. The answers to these exercises are given in the back of the book, and the worked-out solutions are given in the *Student's Solutions Manual.* The CD Lecture Videos show clips of a teacher working out each *Try It Yourself* exercise.

Definitions Formal definitions are often followed by guidelines that explain, in everyday English, how to apply the definition.

Guidelines Throughout the book, the presentation of a statistical formula is followed by a set of step-by-step guidelines for applying the formula. The guidelines are divided into two columns titled *In Words* and *In Symbols.*

Study Tips Study tips in the margin show how to read a table, use technology, or interpret a result a graph.

Picturing the World Each section contains a real-life "mini case study" called *Picturing the World* illustrating the important concept or concepts of the section. Each *Picturing the World* concludes with a question and can be used for general class discussion or group work. The answers to these questions are included in the Annotated Instructor's Edition.

Technology Examples Many sections contain a worked example that shows how technology can be used to calculate formulas, perform tests, or display data. Screen displays from MINITAB, Excel, and TI-83/84 are given. Additional screen displays are given at the ends of selected chapters, and detailed instructions are given in separate technology manuals available with the book.

Insights   These margin notes help drive home an important interpretation or connect different concepts.

Exercises   The exercise sets in the Fourth Edition include over 2100 exercises, giving students practice in performing calculations, making decisions, providing explanations, and applying results to a real-life setting. Approximately 40% of these exercises are new or revised. The exercises are divided into three sections:

Building Basic Skills and Vocabulary   These exercises are short answer, true and false, or vocabulary carefully written to nurture student understanding.

Using and Interpreting Concepts   These exercises are skill or word problems that move from basic skill development to more challenging and interpretive problems.

Extending Concepts   These exercises go beyond the material presented in the section—they tend to be more challenging and are not required as prerequisites of subsequent sections.

NEW!
Chapter Summary   Each chapter concludes with a Chapter Summary that answers the question *What did you learn?* The objectives listed are correlated to Examples in the section as well as review exercises.

Chapter Review Exercises   A set of Review Exercises follows each Chapter Summary. The order of the exercises follows the chapter organization. Answers to all odd-numbered exercises are given in the back of the book.

Chapter Quizzes   Each chapter ends with a Chapter Quiz. The answers to all quiz questions are provided in the back of the book. For additional help, see the step-by-step video solutions on the Chapter Quiz Prep Video.

NEW!
Applet Activities   Selected sections contain activities that encourage interactive investigation of concepts in the lesson with exercises that ask students to draw conclusions. The accompanying applets are contained on the CD that accompanies new copies of the text.

Chapter Case Study   Each chapter has a full-page Case Study featuring actual data from a real-world context and questions that illustrate the important concepts of the chapter.

NEW!
Uses and Abuses: Statistics in the Real World   Each chapter features a discussion on how statistical techniques should be used, while cautioning students about common abuses. The discussion now includes ethics, where appropriate. Exercises help students to apply their knowledge.

Real Statistics–Real Decisions   This feature encourages students to think critically and make informed decisions about real-world data. Exercises guide students from interpretation to drawing conclusions.

Chapter Technology Project   Each chapter has a Technology project using MINITAB, Excel, and TI83/84 that gives students insight into the way technology is used to handle large data sets or real-life questions.

NEW!
Cumulative Review   A cumulative review, at the end of Chapters 2, 5, 8, and 11, concludes each Part of the text. Exercises in the Cumulative Review are in random order and may incorporate multiple ideas. Answers to all odd-numbered exercises are given in the back of the book.

Technology Answers NEW! The answers given in the back of the book are found using tables. Answers found using technology are also included when there are discrepancies due to rounding.

Round Off Rules Round off rules included in Study Tips guide the student during calculations.

Course Coverage NEW! In response to suggestions from statistics instructors, the following coverage is new or revised.

- **In Chapter 1,** random selection, sources of bias in sampling and surveys, treatments, control groups, experimental units, random assignments, replication, sources of bias and confounding were added. Additional coverage of experimental design has been incorporated to cover different types of experiments that can be used by experimenters.

- **In Chapter 2,** clusters and gaps were added to 2.3 **Measures of Central Tendency.**

- **In Chapter 3,** the topics were reorganized to present Counting Principles earlier in the chapter. Several probability examples have been added throughout.

- **In Chapter 6,** properties of point estimators were added.

- **In Chapter 7,** the power of the test is defined.

- **In Chapter 8,** the definitions of independent and dependent samples are now presented earlier in the chapter.

- **In Chapter 10,** the coverage of the chi-square goodness-of-fit test has been enhanced to cover chi-square distributions. Marginal and joint frequencies for contingency tables were also added.

- **In Appendix C,** we have added *normal probability plots.* This discussion focuses on how to assess normality in small data sets.

Continuing Strong Pedagogy from the Third Edition

Graphical Approach As with most introductory statistics texts, we begin the descriptive statistics chapter with a survey of different ways to display data graphically. A difference between this text and many others is that **we continue to incorporate the graphical display of data throughout the text.** For example, see the use of stem-and-leaf plots to display data on pages 394 and 396. This emphasis on graphical displays is beneficial to all students, especially those utilizing visual learning strategies.

Balanced Approach The text strikes a **balance between computation, decision making, and conceptual understanding.** We have provided many Examples, Exercises, and Try It Yourself exercises that go beyond mere computation.

Variety of Real-Life Applications We have chosen real-life applications that are representative of students taking introductory statistics courses. We want statistics to come alive and appear relevant so they understand the importance and rationale for studying statistics. We wanted the applications to be **authentic**—but they also need to be **accessible.** See the Index of Applications on page xviii.

Data and Source Lines   The data sets in the book were chosen for interest, variety, and their ability to illustrate concepts. Most of the **over 240 data sets** contain actual data with source lines. The remaining data sets contain simulated data that are representative of real-life situations. All data sets containing 20 or more entries are available in a variety of electronic forms, including CD and Internet. In the exercise sets, the data sets that are available electronically are indicated by the icon .

Flexible Technology   Although most formulas in the book are illustrated with "hand" calculations, we assume that most students have access to some form of technology tool, such as MINITAB, Excel, the TI-83, or the TI-84. Because the use of technology varies widely, we have made the text flexible. **It can be used in courses with no more technology than a scientific calculator—or it can be used in courses that require frequent use of sophisticated technology tools.** Whatever your use of technology, we are sure that you agree with us that the goal of the course is not computation. Rather, it is to gain an understanding of the basic concepts and uses of statistics.

Prerequisites   We have made every effort to keep algebraic manipulations to a minimum—often we display informal versions of formulas using words in place of or in addition to variables.

Choice of Tables   Our experience has shown that students find a **cumulative density function** (CDF) table easier to use than a "0-to-z" table. Using the CDF table to find the area under a normal curve is a topic of Section 5.1 on pages 243–247. Because we realize that some teachers prefer to use the "0-to-z" table, we have provided an alternative presentation of this topic using the "0-to-z" table in Appendix A.

Meeting the Standards

MAA, AMATYC, NCTM Standards   This text answers the call for a **student-friendly text that emphasizes the uses of statistics**. Our experience indicates that our job as teachers is not to produce statisticians but to produce informed consumers of statistical reports. For this reason, we have included exercises that require students to interpret results, provide written explanations, find patterns, and make decisions.

GAISE Recommendations   Funded by the American Statistical Association, the Guidelines for Assessment and Instruction in Statistics Education (GAISE) Project developed six recommendations for teaching introductory statistics in a college course. The recommendations are:

- Emphasize statistical literacy and develop statistical thinking
- Use real data
- Stress conceptual understanding rather than mere knowledge of procedures
- Foster active learning in the classroom
- Use technology for developing conceptual understanding and analyzing data
- Use assessments to improve and evaluate student learning

The examples, exercises, and features in this text embrace all of these recommendations.

Supplements

STUDENT RESOURCES

Chapter Quiz Prep Video (CD-ROM) Provides step-by-step video solutions to every problem in the textbook *Chapter Quizzes*. Included in Student Edition. A replacement CD (0-13-135865-0) is available for purchase.

Student Solutions Manual (0-13-601307-4) Includes complete worked-out solutions to all of the *Try It Yourself* exercises, the odd-numbered exercises, and all of the *Chapter Quiz* exercises. Available for purchase.

CD Lecture Series (0-13-603013-0) A comprehensive set of CD-ROMs, tied to the textbook, containing short video clips of an instructor working every *Try It Yourself* exercise. Available for purchase.

Technology Manual (0-13-601308-2) Tutorial instruction and worked-out examples for the TI-83/84 Calculator, Excel (including PHStat, an Excel add-in), and MINITAB. Available for purchase.

INSTRUCTOR RESOURCES

Instructor Resource Center

All of the teacher supplements and resources for this book are available electronically for preview and download on the Instructor Resource Center (IRC). Please go to pearsonschool.com/advanced and click "Online Teacher Supplements" for directions. You will be required to complete a one time registration subject to verification before being emailed access information to download materials.

Instructor CD (0-13-604428-X) Offers classroom suggestions, time-saving tips, and strategies for engaging students and presenting key topics throughout the course.

Instructor Solutions Manual (0-13-206291-7) Includes complete solutions to all of the exercises, *Try It Yourself* exercises, Case Studies, Technology pages, Uses and Abuses exercises, and Real Statistics–Real Decisions exercises.

TestGen® (0-13-603056-4) TestGen enables instructors to build, edit, print, and administer tests using a computerized bank of questions developed to cover all the objectives of the text. TestGen is algorithmically based, allowing instructors to create multiple but equivalent versions of the same question or test with the click of a button. Instructors can also modify test bank questions or add new questions. Tests can be printed or administered online. The software and testbank are available for download only from the Instructor Resource Center.

Test Item File (0-13-601309-0) A test bank derived from TestGen® (only available for download).

PowerPoint Lecture Slides Fully editable and printable slides that follow the textbook. Use during lecture or post to a website in an online course. Most slides include notes offering suggestions for how the material may effectively be presented in class. Available via download only to qualified adopters.

INTERNET RESOURCES

MathXL® for Statistics

MathXL® for Statistics is a powerful online homework, tutorial, and assessment system that accompanies Prentice Hall textbooks in statistics. With MathXL for Statistics, instructors can create, edit, and assign online homework and tests using algorithmically generated exercises correlated at the objective level to the textbook. They can also create and assign their own online exercises and import TestGen tests for added flexibility. All student work is tracked in MathXL's online gradebook. Students can take chapter tests in MathXL and receive personalized study plans based on their test results. The study plan diagnoses weaknesses and links students directly to tutorial exercises for the objective they need to study and retest. MathXL is available for purchase only to qualified adopters. For more information, visit our website at *www.mathxl.com*, or contact your sales representative.

ANNOTATED INSTRUCTOR'S EDITION

Includes:

- *Notes to Instructors* appear in the margin of the text to suggest activities that correspond to the example or concept, additional ways to present the material, common pitfalls students encounter, alternative formulas or approaches that may be used, and other helpful teaching tips for instructors
- All answers to the section and review exercises are provided with short answers (numerical, tabular, and/or graphical) appearing in the margin next to the exercise.
- Instructor Resource CD—includes Notes to the Instructor and sample syllabi, plus Chapter Quiz Prep Videos, Data Sets, and Applets.

Acknowledgments

We owe a debt of gratitude to the many reviewers who helped us shape and refine *Elementary Statistics: Picturing the World,* Fourth Edition.

Rosalie Abraham, Florida Community College at Jacksonville
Ahmed Adala, Metropolitan Community College
Polly Amstutz, University of Nebraska, Kearney
David P. Benzel, Montgomery College
Carol Curtis, Fresno City College
David DiMarco, Neumann College
Harold W. Ellingsen, Jr., SUNY—Potsdam
Michael Eurgubian, Santa Rosa Jr. College
Sandeep Holay, Southeast Community College, Lincoln Campus
M. Kazemi, University of North Carolina

Vicki L. McMillian, Ocean County College
Lyn A. Noble, Florida Community College at Jacksonville—South Campus
Eric Preibisius, Cuyamaca Community College
Melonie Rasmussen, Pierce College
John Seppala, Valdosta State University
Aileen Solomon, Trident Technical College
Deborah Swiderski, Macomb Community College
William J. Thistleton, SUNY—Institute of Technology, Utica
Clark Vangilder, DeVry University

REVIEWERS OF THE PREVIOUS EDITIONS

Frieda Ganter, California State University
David Kay, Moorpark College
Benny Lo, DeVry University, Fremont
Mike McGann, Ventura Community College
Julie Norton, California State University—Hayward
Lynn Onken, San Juan College
Agnes Tuska, California State University—Fresno
Jean Sells, Sacred Heart University
Sonja Hensler, St. Petersburg Jr. College
Nancy Johnson, Manatee Community College
Susan Kellicut, Seminole Community College
Jeffrey Linek, St. Petersburg Jr. College
Diane Long, College of DuPage
Elisabeth Schuster, Benedictine University
Carole Shapero, Oakton Community College
Ting-Xiu Wang, Oakton Community College
Sandra L. Spain, Thomas Nelson Community College
Charles Ehler, Anne Arundel Community College
Rita Kolb, Cantonsville Community College
Neal Rogness, Grand Valley State University
Jane Keller, Metropolitan Community College
Vicki McMillian, Ocean County College

Dex Whittinghall, Rowan University
Gary Egan, Monroe Community College
Hyune-Ju Kim, Syracuse University
Rowan Lindley, Westchester Community College
Lynn Meslinsky, Erie Community College
Cara DeLong, Fayetteville Technical Community College
Mohammad Kazemi, University of North Carolina—Charlotte
Rhonda Magel, North Dakota State University
G. Andy Chang, Youngstown State University
Douglas Frank, Indiana University of Pennsylvania
Michelle Strager-McCarney, Penn State—Erie, The Behrend College
Olcay Akman, College of Charleston
Ginger Dewey, York Technical College
Martin Jones, College of Charleston
Lindsay Packer, College of Charleston
Aileen Solomon, Trident Technical College
Jill Fanter, Walters State Community College
John Bernard, University of Texas—Pan American
John J. Avioli, Christopher Newport University
Sandra L. Spain, Thomas Nelson Community College
Keith J. Craswell, Western Washington University

We also give special thanks to the people at Pearson Education who worked with us in the development of *Elementary Statistics: Picturing the World,* Fourth Edition: Deirdre Lynch, Dawn Murrin, Lynn Savino Wendel, Linda Mihatov Behrens, Diane Peirano, Wayne Parkins, Joanne Wendelken, Maureen Eide, John Christiana, and Thomas Benfatti. We also thank the staff of Larson Texts, Inc., who assisted with the development and production of the book. On a personal level, we are grateful to our spouses, Deanna Gilbert Larson and Richard Farber, for their love, patience, and support. Also, a special thanks goes to R. Scott O'Neil.

We have worked hard to make *Elementary Statistics: Picturing the World,* Fourth Edition, a clean, clear, and enjoyable text from which to teach and learn statistics. Despite our best efforts to ensure accuracy and ease of use, many users will undoubtedly have suggestions for improvement. We welcome your suggestions.

Ron Larson

Betsy Farber

Ron Larson, odx@psu.edu

Betsy Farber, farberb@bucks.edu

How to Study Statistics

Study Strategies

Congratulations! You are about to begin your study of statistics. As you progress through the course, you should discover how to use statistics in your everyday life and in your career. When you are studying statistics, the material you learn each day builds on material you learned previously. There are no shortcuts—you must keep up with your studies every day. Before you begin, read through the following hints that will help you succeed.

Making a Plan Make your own course plan right now! A good rule of thumb is to study at least two hours for every hour in class. After your first major exam, you will know if your efforts were sufficient. If you did not get the grade you wanted, then you should increase your study time, improve your study efficiency, or both.

Preparing for Class Before every class, review your notes from the previous class and read the portion of the text that is to be covered. Pay special attention to the definitions and rules that are highlighted. Read the examples and work through the Try It Yourself exercises that accompany each example. These steps take self-discipline, but they pay off because you will benefit much more from your instructor's presentation.

Attending Class Attend every class. Arrive on time with your text, materials for taking notes, and your calculator. If you must miss a class, get the notes from another student, go to a tutor or your instructor for help, or view the appropriate CD Lecture Video. Try to learn the material that was covered in the missed class before attending the next class.

Participating in Class When reading the text before class, reviewing your notes from a previous class, or working on your homework, write down any questions you have about the material. Ask your instructor these questions during class. Doing so will help you (and others in your class) understand the material better.

Taking Notes During class, be sure to take notes on definitions, examples, concepts, and rules. Focus on the instructor's cues to identify important material. Then, as soon after class as possible, review your notes and add any explanations that will help to make your notes more understandable to you.

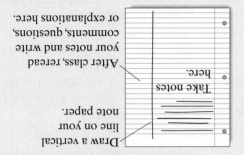

Draw a vertical line on your note paper.

Take notes here.

After class, reread your notes and write comments, questions, or explanations here.

Doing the Homework   Learning statistics is like learning to play the piano or basketball. You cannot develop skills just by watching someone do it; you must do it yourself. The best time to do your homework is right after class, when the concepts are still fresh in your mind. Doing homework at this time increases your chances of retaining the information in long-term memory.

Finding a Study Partner   When you get stuck on a problem, you may find that it helps to work with a partner. Even if you feel you are giving more help than you are getting, you will find that teaching others is an excellent way to learn.

Keeping Up with the Work   Don't let yourself fall behind in this course. If you are having trouble, seek help immediately—from your instructor, a statistics tutor, your study partner, or additional study aids such as the Chapter Quiz Prep videos on CD-ROM and the Try It Yourself video clips on the CD Lecture Series CD-ROMs. Remember: If you have trouble with one section of your statistics text, there's a good chance that you will have trouble with later sections unless you take steps to improve your understanding.

Getting Stuck   Every statistics student has had this experience: You work a problem and cannot solve it, or the answer you get does not agree with the one given in the text. When this happens, consider asking for help or taking a break to clear your thoughts. You might even want to sleep on it, or rework the problem, or reread the section in the text. Avoid getting frustrated or spending too much time on a single problem.

Preparing for Tests   Cramming for a statistics test seldom works. If you keep up with the work and follow the suggestions given here, you should be almost ready for the test. To prepare for the chapter test, review the Chapter Summary and work the Review Exercises and the Cumulative Review Exercises. Then set aside some time to take the sample Chapter Quiz. Analyze the results of your Chapter Quiz to locate and correct test-taking errors.

Taking a Test   Most instructors do not recommend studying right up to the minute the test begins. Doing so tends to make people anxious. The best cure for test-taking anxiety is to prepare well in advance. Once the test begins, read the directions carefully and work at a reasonable pace. (You might want to read the entire test first, then work the problems in the order in which you feel most comfortable.) Don't rush! People who hurry tend to make careless errors. If you finish early, take a few moments to clear your thoughts and then go over your work.

Learning from Mistakes   After your test is returned to you, go over any errors you might have made. Doing so will help you avoid repeating some systematic or conceptual errors. Don't dismiss any error as just a "dumb mistake." Take advantage of any mistakes by hunting for ways to improve your test-taking skills.

Index of Applications

Biology and Life Sciences

Air quality, 75
Air pollution, 33, 358
Alligator, 127
Atlantic croaker fish, 51, 257, 259
Beagle, 50, 257, 259
Black bears, 324
Box turtle, 239
Brown trout, 224
Cats, 186, 203
Cuckoos, 592
Dogs, 76, 118, 146, 157, 186, 203, 204
Environmentally conscious consumers, 411
Fish, 15, 538
Fisher's Iris data set, 60
Fruit flies, 112
Gray whale, 346
Green turtle migration, 298, 299
House flies, 64, 280
House wren, 251
Kangaroos, 32
Kitti's hog-nosed bat, 298, 299
Lamb, 640–641
Mice, 481
Oat, 641, 663
Pets, 96
Plants, 53, 219
Rabbits, 224
Salmon, 139, 151
Seedling, 318
Shark attacks, 234
Snapdragon flowers, 146
Soil, 584
Soybean, 26, 32
Sunflower yield, 547
Trees, 50, 174, 179, 242, 274, 280, 519, 539
Waste, 235, 331, 399, 404
Water, 350
   conductivity, 401
   consumption, 97
   pH level, 401
Wheat, 605, 641

Business

Advertisements, 64, 232, 599
Advertising expense, 497, 500, 505
Advertising and sales, 514, 516, 526, 528, 530, 535
Beverage company, 147
Board of directors, 173
Bookbinding defects, 158
Book sales, fiction, 16
Bankruptcies, 227
Clothing store purchases, 216
Consumer ratings, 469

Defective parts, 166, 180, 185, 189, 227
Disclosing personal information, 355
Free samples, 412
Inventory shrinkage, 59
Magazine advertisement, 310, 312–314, 316
Manufacturer
   claims, 250
   earnings, 111
   performance ratings, 469
Online shopping, 473
Product assembly, 179
Quality control, 26, 33, 36, 37, 133, 202
Sales, 52, 65–66, 119, 121, 162, 194, 196, 198, 199, 222–223, 227, 383, 497, 500, 505, 532, 533, 540, 592
Salesperson, 52, 109
Shipping errors, 376
Small business
   owners, 218–219
   websites, 212
Software piracy, 363
Wal-Mart shareholder's equity, 540
Warehouses, 158, 181
Web site costs, 350

Combinatorics

Answers guessing, 216
Area code, 180
Letters, 176, 179
License plate, 135, 180, 185
Number generator, 652
Password, 178, 180
Security code, 142, 173, 188, 189

Computers

Computer, 9, 10, 201, 203, 204, 213, 253, 257–259, 319, 330, 340, 376, 404
Disk drive, 600
Email addresses, 231
Internet, 33, 41, 43–48, 72, 156, 186, 233, 234, 340, 355, 377, 408, 439, 477, 509, 510, 518, 570, 575
Microchips, 228
Monitor, 455
Operating system, 9
Windows® Internet Explorer®, 290

Demographics

Age, 7, 31, 33, 62, 69, 78, 161, 165, 507, 556
Birth weights in America, 269

Bride's age, 92, 93, 622
Cars per household, 97
Children per household, 90, 202
City rent, 300
Drive to work, 201, 212
Home, 293
Education, 604, 607
Employee, 23, 67, 138, 140, 145, 180, 181, 183, 185, 188, 202, 280
Eye color, 161
Groom's age, 622
Height, 8, 507, 663
   of family, 544, 545
   of men, 78, 79, 88, 112–113, 250, 257, 267, 281, 438, 527
   of women, 50, 78, 88, 267, 281, 438
Household, 204, 304, 482
IQ, 109
Juror's age, 603
Left handed, 157, 168, 185
Marriage, 7, 139
Most admired polls, 359
Moving out, 478
New car, 134
New home prices, 121
Population
   Alaska, 89
   Florida, 89
   Japan, 98
   U.S., 11, 98
   counties, fastest growing, 3
   West Ridge County, 22–24
Race relations, 156
Retirement age, 53
Shoe size, 51, 519, 527
U.S. age distribution, 167, 185, 303
U.S. unemployment rate, 118
Weight of newborns, 247, 490, A6
Zip codes, 31

Earth Science

Clear days, May, San Francisco, CA, 214
Climate conditions, 193
Cloudy days, June, Pittsburgh, PA, 214
Environment, future, 335
Global warming, 5, 126, 341–342
   El Niños, 16
Hurricane, 204, 227, 235
   relief efforts, 26
Ice thickness, 63
Nitrogen dioxide, 393
Old Faithful, Yellowstone National Park, 46, 283, 498, 501, 503, 515, 516, 526
Pollution, opinions, 32

Precipitation, 226, 227
   Anchorage, AK, 322, 350
   Nome, AK, 323
   Sacramento, CA, 14
Rain, 659
Rainy days in July, Orlando, FL, 201
Saffir-Simpson Hurricane Scale, 235
Sea water, 318
Snowfall, 650
   Bridgeport, CT, 228
   January average, 16
   Nome, AK, 201
   New York county, 279
Sunny and rainy days, 193, 197
   Seattle, WA, 144
Temperature, 15, 65, 652
   Chicago, IL, 117
   Cleveland, OH, 49
   Mohave, AZ, 31
   Pittsburgh, PA, 618
   Sacramento, CA, 14
   San Diego, CA, 618
Tornadoes, 127, 235
UV Index, 64
   Memphis, TN, 65
Water temperatures, 636
Wet or dry, Seattle, WA, 144

Economics and Finance

Account balance, 77
ATM machine, 52, 54
Audit, 137, 166, 339
Bond, 377
Book spending, 51
Charitable donations, 339, 497, 500, 503, 514
Children's savings accounts, 300
Commission, 115
Credit card, 31, 114, 217, 277, 355, 406, 442, 560, 618
Credit card debt, 442, 619, 655
Debt and income, 642
Dividends and earnings, 509, 511
Dow Jones Industrial Average, 195
Financial debt, 619
Forecasting earnings, 7
Emergency savings, 33, 157
Ethical business leaders, 355
Expenditures, 596
Financial shape, 180–181
Franchise, 383
Home owner income, 9
Honeymoon financing, 217
IRAs, 533, 534
Income, 507, 606, 663
Missing tax deductions, 355
Money managing, 9
Monthly income, 350

Mortgage, 328
Mutual funds, 312, 662
Paycheck errors, 228
Personal income, 547, 597
    and educational attainment, 611
Primary investor in household, 9
Raising a child, cost, 388
Restaurant spending, 406, 447
Retirement income, 209, 217
Salaries, 6, 8, 9, 31, 65, 66, 74, 77, 82–85, 93, 99, 119, 121, 126, 205, 280, 299, 331, 357, 387, 392, 405, 422, 431, 449, 520, 535, 536, 538, 586, 609, 629, 630, 636, 637, 638, 657, 659
    Ann Arbor, MI, 607
    Chicago, IL, 85
    Dallas, TX, 94, 607
    Houston, TX, 94
    Long Beach, CA, 94
    Los Angeles, CA, 94
    San Jose, CA, 607
Savings, 556–557
    more money, 356
Spending before traveling, 91
Stock, 63, 75, 115, 147, 185, 232, 233, 318, 531, 533, 584, 655
    McDonald's, 539
Stock market, 148
Taxpayers' top worries, 4
U.S. exports, 79
U.S. income and economic research, 661
Utility bills, 107, 258, 259, 263
Vacation cost, 9, 402, 428, 431, 443

Education

Achievement by subject, 572
ACT, 10, 251, 257, 332, 446, 447
Ages of students, 70, 295, 315, 320
Biological science, 619
Biology, 331
Books, 318
Business majors, 166
Class size, 405
Classes, 185
College courses, 165
College graduates, 293, 366, 371, 372
    jobs, 19, 304
College major, 8
College students, 376
    hours worked, 564
Completing a test, 195
Continuing education, 573
Day care, 449
Degrees, 632
Degrees and gender, 189, 641
Doctorate degree, 619, 656, 657
Dormitory room prices, 119
Economics degrees, 331
Educational attainment, 563
    and personal income, 611
Engineering, 478, 619
Enrollment, 231
Expenditure per student, 429
Extracurricular activities, 203
Faculty hours, 405, 429
Final exam, 438
Final grade, 77, 537, 538

Genders of students, 648
GPA, 62, 76, 150, 331, 506, 541, 593, 600, 652
Grading public schools, 300
Heights of students, 120
Highest level, 145
Literary skills, 376
Majors, 484
Master's degree, 406
Mathematics assessment test, 301, 391, 491
Medical school, 153
Midterm scores, 438
Musical training, 453
Nursing major, 156, 160, 168
Physics minors, 31
Plus/minus grading, 186
Preschool, 449
Public schools, 573
Quality, 167
Quiz, 142, 203–204, 207
Reliability of testing, 159
SAT scores, 51, 54, 94, 106, 205, 251, 256, 258, 282, 331, 431, 444, 466–467, 485, 541, 605, 620, 621
School supplies, 405
Science assessment tests, 421, 586
Science assessment, 485
Secondary school students, 187
Social science, 478
Student advisory board, 176
Student ID numbers, 141
Student loans, 507, A31
Student sleep habits, 333
Student safety, 572
Study habits, 32, 448, 508, 510, 518
Tardiness, 427
Teacher salaries, 94
Teaching experience, 305
Teaching methods, 26, 459, 482
Test grades/scores, 33, 53, 63, 71, 74, 77, 78, 109, 111, 118, 120, 127, 268, 438, 508, 509, 510, 518, 564, 663
Test scores and GNP, 643
Textbooks, 278
Tuition, 75, 103, 104
U.S. history assessment tests, 421, 586
Vocabulary, 508, 518

Engineering

Aerospace engineers, 357
Bolts, 332, 349, 430
Brick mortar, 52
Building heights, Miami, FL, 117, 518
Building space, 597
Cooling capacity, 517
Gears, 260
Liquid dispenser, 260, 430, 645
Machine
    calibrations, 282
    part supplier, 144
    release valve, mints, 302
Mold, 606
Nails, 260
Nut, 448
Piston rings, 250
Plastic sheet cutting, 321

Repairs, 180
Resistors, 297
Steel pipe fitting, 605
Tensile strength, 458
Washers, 448

Entertainment

Academy Award, winning, 137
Best-selling novel, 137
Cable, 213
Concert, songs played, 195
Concert tickets, 16, 178
Daily lottery, 228
Game show, 143
Games of chance, 204–205
Guessing, 158
Home theater system, 201, 349
Horse race, 179
Lottery, 143, 176, 179, 181, 183, 216
Magazine, 10, 118, 188, 498
Monopoly game, 150
Motion Picture Association, ratings, 14
Movie ticket prices, 119
Movies, 154, 167, 278
    budget and gross, 495, 498, 501, 505, 509, 522
MP3 player, 15, 68
Music preference, 552, 553, 555
Newspaper, 51, 319
Nielsen Media ratings, 17, 27
Oscar winners, ages, 108, 114
Powerball lottery, 190
Radio stations, 14, 120, 366, 371, 373
Raffle ticket, 139, 188, 200
Reading, 211
Rock concert, fan age, 68
Satellite television, 119, 376
Song lengths, 114
Summer vacation, 155
Television, 8, 12, 110, 111, 120, 189, 232, 366, 447, 449, 477, 544, 545, 658
    high definition, 9
    Deal or No Deal, 131
    networks, Pittsburgh, PA, 12
    top ranked programs, 17
    Weather Channel, 410
Videotape or DVD rentals, 233

Food and Nutrition

Apple, 63, 267
Beef, 640–641
Breakfast, 411
Caffeine, 97, 392, 506
Calories, 377, 460, 481
Candy, 615
Carbohydrates, 460, 587
Carrots, 268
Cereal, 268, 356, 366, 371, 393, 549
Cheese, 320
Chicken wings, 232
Citrus fruits, 431
Coffee, 79, 97, 327–328, 438, 560
Cookies, 217, 293
Corn, toxin, 177
Cotton, 539
Dark chocolate, 423
Egg prices, 65
Energy bar, 427

Fat, 517
Fat substitute, 25
Fruit consumption, 299, 476
Genetically modified foods, 411
Ground beef, price, 65
Hamburger, 429
Hot dogs, 210, 519
Ice cream, 268, 281
Jelly beans, 186
Juice drinks, 318
M&M's, 233, 558–559
Meat, 226, 280, 339
Menu, 142
Milk, 417
    containers, 281
    production, 123, 543
Nuts, 217
Oranges, 267
Peanuts, 259
Pepper pungencies, 52
Pizza, 179, 382
Protein, 460, 517
Restaurant, 571, 583
    Burger King, 460, 481, 587
    Long John Silver's, 481
    McDonald's, 460, 481, 587
    serving, 418
    Wendy's, 481
Salmonella, 368
Saturated fat intake, 53
Soda consumption, 405
Soft drinks, 234, 280
Soup, 427
Sport drink, 377, 417
Storing fish, 6
Sugar, 543, 544
Supermarket, 97, 254, 614
Tea drinker, 147, 392
Tuna, 392
Vegetable consumption, 299, 476
Vending machine, 268
Water, 321, 497, 508
Wheat, 539

Government

Better Business Bureau, 59
Civil service exams, 264
Congress
    ages, 25
    gender profile, 16, 165
    issue when voting, 9
Department of Energy, gas prices, 5
Entitlements, 561
Federal employees' salaries, 441
Federal income tax, 484
Federal pension plan, 533, 534
Governor, Republicans, 10
Representative ages, 8
Legal system in U.S., 368
Registered voters, 8, 37, 165
Securities and Exchange Commission, 37
Senators, years of service, 126
Social Security Administration, 432
State tax collection, 16
Tax cuts, 561
U.S Department of Labor, 377
U.S Post Office, 377
U.S. Census, undercount, 6

Health and Medicine

Allergy medicines, 25, 347
Alternative medicines, 472, 475
Antidepressants, 476
Anxiety, 33
Appetite suppressant, 462
Arthritis
 delaying onset, 26
 medication, 479
Assisted reproductive
 technology, 156, 236
Bacteria vaccine, 29
Blood, 201
 donations, 160, 163, 202, 218
 pressure, 15, 19, 33, 338, 365,
 450, 469, 508, 517
 type, 142, 158, 218, 292
BMI, 77
Body measurements, 524
Body temperature, 13, 374, 396,
 465, 507
BRCA gene, 154–155
Breast cancer, 29
Calcium supplements, 483, 629,
 655
Cardiac surgery, walking test, 491
Cholesterol, 8, 75, 255, 256, 258,
 259, 265, 320, 460, 474, 587
Chronic fatigue syndrome, 573
Chronic medications, 491
Colds, 617
Cough syrup, 348, 350
CPR training, 102, 104, 105
Cyanosis, 216
Dentist, 249
Depression, 19, 154
Diabetes, 154, 376
Diabetic, 18
Diet, 32, 233, 451
DNA research, 301
Doctor, tell truth, 354
Doctor visits, 553
Doctors aid dying patients, 288
Drinking habits, 26
Drug testing, 143, 294, 470
Emphysema, 150
Exercise, 26, 121, 150, 226, 444,
 570
Flu, 357
Fluorouracil, 450
Generic medicine, 571
Growth of a virus, 25
Headaches, 468, 630, 657
Health care visits, 603
Health club, 258, 429
Healthy foods, 27, 187–188
Heart disease, 423
Heart medication, 377
Heart rate, 13, 77, 329, 444, 464
Heart rhythm abnormality, 9
Heart transplant, 268, 283
Herbal medicine, 470, 483, 656
HIV, 430
Hospital beds, 79
Hospital costs, 422
Hospital length of stay, 78, 421,
 596, 638
Hospital waiting times, 332, 421,
 586
Influenza vaccine, 21
Irinotecan, 450

Kidney cancer survival rate, 300
Knee surgery, 152, 208, 625
Lead levels, 33
Lower back pain, 620
Lung cancer, 376
Managed health care, 31
Medicine cabinets, 289
No trouble sleeping, 218
Nutrients entering bloodstream,
 583
Obesity, 10, 154
Organ donors, 291
Outpatient care, 26
Over-the-counter drugs, 409
Overweight, 339
Pain relievers, 591–592
Patient care, 264
Physical examination, 7
Physician practices, 663
Physicians, leaving medicine, 31
Placebo, 571
Pneumonia, 486
Pregnancy study, Cebu,
 Philippines, 32
Prescription drugs, 26
Prostate cancer, 291
Pulse rate, 349
Recovery time, 374
Registered nurse salaries, 121,
 280
Resting heart rates, 438
Sleep, 77, 154, 519, 535, 544, 545
 deprivation, 10, 26, 32
Smoking, 21, 31, 33, 147, 150,
 339, 342, 376, 392, 409, 411,
 437, 473, 474, 476, 477, 490,
 532, 533, 546
Stem cell research, 24
Stroke, reduce, 4
Sudden infant death syndrome, 9
Surgery, 216
 procedure, 207
 survival, 156
 technique, 235
Ulcers, 154
Vitamins, 126, 342, 348, 350
Weight, 74, 444, 497
Weight loss, 20, 249, 393, 451,
 462, 467, 468, 508

Housing and Construction

City house value, 300
Construction, 329
Home insurance, 637
Housing contract, 291
Prices of homes, 70, 276, 597,
 598, 615, 618
Real estate, 412, 583
Residence, rent or own, 26
Room and board, 276
Security system, 135, 144, 178, 376
Square footage, 619
Subdivision, 174
Tacoma Narrows Bridge, 167, 224
Unit size, 619

Law

Case of the vanishing women, 433
Child support, 273
Crime, 75, 509, 511

Fraudulent insurance claims, 137
Jury selection, 153, 177, 179
Repeat offenders, 617
Speeding, 150, 658
Telemarketing fraud, 608

Miscellaneous

911 calls, 204
Aggressive behavior, children, 479
Air conditioners, 545, 546, 643
Anonymous sources, news
 stories, 126
Appliances, 421, 585
MBA, average starting salary, 6
Bacteria, 522
Badge numbers, police officers,
 33
Ball, numbered, 154
Bank customers, 614
Bank waiting times, 350
Battery, 259
Beverage cans liquid content, 356
Births, 283, 564
Birthday, 133, 158, 159
Breast-feeding, 630
Calculators, defects 188
Camcorder, 340
Camera phones, 37
Candles, 33
Cards, 136, 142, 147, 149–151,
 154, 161, 162, 166, 177, 181,
 185, 187, 188, 206, 208
CD player, 354
Cell phone, 31, 53, 57, 61, 408
Charitable donations, CEOs in
 Syracuse, NY, 32
Charity, 168
Cheaters, 226
Chess, 376
Child delivery, 163
Chlorine levels in a pool, 417
Cities for best jobs, 12
Clocks, 376
Coal production, 4
Coauthored articles, 575
Coffee shop, remodeling, 20
Coin toss, 37, 132, 138, 141, 142,
 143, 150–152, 183, 185, 186,
 233, 367, 487, 651
Consumption
 energy, 598, 638
 fuel, 585
Contact with parents, 621
Crawling, 526, 548
Deck treatment, 596
Defective DVDs, 143, 203
Die roll, 37, 74, 79, 132, 136, 140,
 142, 143, 147, 150–152, 154,
 160–162, 166, 170, 185, 187,
 201
Digital camera, 280, 642
Direct-mail advertising, 339
Dishwashers, 357
 detergent, 643
Dog microchips, 652
Dreams, 377, 409
Electricity cost, 606
Electricity usage, 394
Employee salary, 50
Employment and educational
 attainment, 576–577

Energy cost, 599
Energy efficiency, 517
Eye survey, contacts, glasses, 169
Farm values, 95, 96, 299
Fitness center, 27
Fire drill, 394
Floral arrangement, 305
Fluorescent lamps, 393
Foreign oil, dependence, 31, 126
Furniture store, 376
Gas grill, 210, 318, 545, 546
Gas station, 119, 231
Gasoline, gallons purchased, 53
Gift shopping, 305, 430
Goals, 574
Greeting cards, 231
Grip strength, 468–469
Guitar, string tension, 201
Hindenburg, 10
Hotel rooms, 117, 319
Jukebox, 179
Lawn mower, 349
Life on other planets, 490
Light bulbs, 157, 332, 376, 393
Liquid volume of cans, 117
Local news broadcast, 410
Lodging cost, 349, 402, 406, 422,
 447, 586
Mail-order company, 655
Marbles, 207
Meal costs, 447
Metacarpal bone length, 663
Metal detector, 231
Microwave, 330, 404, 431, 446
Middle initial, 142
Memory, 10, 154
Months, 185
Mozart, 191
Music downloads, 363
Natural gas expenditures, 662
NASA budget, 64
New Year's resolution, 286, 288,
 289
Online bill pay, 354
Opinion poll, 15
Pages, section, 232
Paint, 376, 658
Paint cans, 281, 320
Paint sprayer, 321
Parachute assembly, 368
Perfume, 300
Phone, type, 10
Phone numbers, 12, 15
Picture development, 377
Pilot's test, 226
Post office box numbers, 33
Power failure, 75
Printing company departments,
 32
Product warning label, 25
Puzzle, 19
Queuing models, 237
Random number selection, 142,
 143
Recycling, 339
Refrigerator, 319, 377
Rent, new apartments, 659
Salesperson, 15
Slot machines, 652
Social Security numbers, 31
Socks, 186

Sound-system receivers, 277
Space shuttle
  flights, 120
  menu, 178
Speed of sound, 509
Spinner, 141, 143
Spray on water repellent, 625
Spring break, 9
Sprinkler system, 391
State troopers, 53
Statistics students, 22
Stolen identity, 137
Sudoku, 172
Survey of spectators, 8
Telephone, 78, 186, 233, 273, 455
Tent, 332
Text messages, 55–57
Toaster, 332
Toothbrush, 126
Toothpaste, 186, 229, 595
Travel concerns, 566, 569
Travel plans, 621
Typographical error, 227, 235
UFO dreams, 409
UFO sighting, 137
United Nations, 64
Vacation, 234, 339
Vacuum cleaner, 446
Vending machines, 33
Volume of bottled water, 195
Volunteering, 339, 659
Waking times, 353
Washing cars, 299
Washing machine, 143, 319
Water faucet, 366, 371
Wealthy people, 63
Weigh station, 231
Winning a prize, 227
Winter vacation, 9
Yoga, 66

Mortality

Airplane accidents, 221
Alcohol-related accidents, 485,
  574, 604
Car accident, 508, 562
Emergency response time, 51, 418
Fatal work injuries, 563
Heart disease, women, 127
Lightning deaths, 234
Motor vehicle casualties, 58, 201,
  516, 576, 604
Pedestrian motor vehicle
  collisions, 604

Motor Vehicles and Transportation

Age of vehicles, 534
Air travel, 32, 34, 67–69
Airfare, 322
Airline baggage, 64
Airplanes, 19, 76, 111, 120
Annual vehicle miles, 201
ATV, 376
Auto parts, 228, 305
Automobile insurance, 122, 400,
  628
Automobiles, 31, 374
  battery, 305, 348, 366, 371, 595
Bicycle, 561, 562

Blood alcohol content, drivers,
  32
Brakes, 282
Braking distance, 256, 264,
  298–299, 372, 446, 454, 444,
  488, 510, 520
Bumper, 457
Bus, 658
Car accident, 150, 197
Car occupancy, 167, 204, 224
Cell phone use, 63
Compact cars, consumer testing,
  80
Convertible, 543
Crash test, 457, 551
Dealership sales, 187
Diesel engines, 234
Drivers, 63, 337
Driver's license exam, 186
Driving time, 275–276
Driving to work, 294
Engine, 260, 544, 545, 646
Flights, 159, 593
Flying, 412
Footwell intrusion, 457
Fuel additive, 631
Fuel economy ratings, 309, 546
Gas prices, 207, 280, 283
Hybrid vehicle, 364, 423, 572, 585
Intersection accidents, 223–224
Mileage, 253, 364, 377, 387, 394,
  406, 421, 431, 444, 467
Motorcycles, 350
Motorcycle accidents, 201
New highway, 175
Oil tankers, 226
Parking, 171
Pickup trucks, 155
Power boats, 444
Price of a car, 11, 377, 400
Public transportation, 292
Rental car company mileage, 119
Road rage, 218
Seat belts, 376
Speed of vehicles, 62, 75, 76, 107,
  263, 382, 658
Spinal cord, injury, 4
Sports cars, 75, 332
Stressful travel, 339
SUV seating, 75
Taxi cab, 377
Tires, 112, 202, 268, 282, 305, 376,
  419, 427, 663
Top-selling vehicles, 59
Trade-in value, 615
Traffic congestion, 137, 341
Traffic safety, 578
Traffic signal, 278–279
Traffic tickets, 231
Travel concerns, 566, 569
Travel plans, 340
Type owned, 183
Vehicle
  crashes, 574
  manufacturers, 161
  owned, 572, 604
  purchased, 75
  sales, 599

Political Science

110th Congress, 15, 16

American voters, age, 145
Campaign spending, 533, 534
Candidate's approval ratings, 339
Council members, 651
Grading our leaders, 573
Gubernatorial Election,
  Pennsylvania, 144
Officers, 180, 189, 304
Political analyst, 37
Political parties, 69
Political polls, 216
President's approval ratings, 19
Supreme Court justice, ages, 119
U.S Presidents
  ages at inauguration, 105
  children, 54
  greatest, 334, 336
U.S. Senator term, 133
Voters, 220, 338, 464–465, 533, 534
Voting Democrat, 145
Voting Republican, 139

Psychology

Depression, 80
Eating disorders, 76
Experimental group, 179
IQ, 149, 543, 544
Mouthing behavior, 18
Obsessive-compulsive disorder,
  573, 576
Passive-aggressive traits, 174,
  196, 198, 199
Psychological tests, 32, 202
Psychologist, 173
Reaction times, 52

Sports

400-meter dash, women's, 96
Advertisers, 63
Baseball, 216, 217, 232
  Barry Bonds, 234
  games started, 127
  home run totals, 13
  Major League, 6, 31, 121, 172,
    255
  New York Yankees World
    Series victories, 13
Basketball, 12, 77, 188, 304
  free throws, 227
  heights, 98, A30–A31
  NBA draft, 182
  weights, 98
  women's, 32
Bicycle race, 188
Boston marathon, 33
Bowling, 52
Daytona 500, 173
Earnings, athlete, 101
Fishing, 211, 231, 419
Football, 329, 334, 336, 357
  college, 15, 201
    touchdowns, 39, 42, 43, 45,
      46, 48, 56–57, 72, 102,
      104–106, 146
  defensive player weights, 120
  National football league, 75,
    97, 164
  Super Bowl, 650
  weight, 120

Golf, 80, 93, 189, 203, 463, 488,
  603, 652
  Tiger Woods, 228
Injury, 571
Hockey, 127, 491
Lacrosse, 178
Olympic 100-meter times, 662
Skiing, 178
Soccer, 15, 109, 321, 322
Softball, 179
Sports, 294, 598
Swimming, 319
Tennis, 332, 491
Workout, 624

Work

Absenteeism, 126
Annual wage, 458
Arrangements, 567
Career advancement, 217
Career placement, 656
CEO ages, 565, 566, 568
Committee
  composition, 229
  members, 178
Department manager, 175
Earnings, 64, 165, 532, 534, 622,
  627–628, 630
Employee income, 117
Employee tenure, 265, 660
Employment, 60
Executives, ages, 113
Genders of recent hires,
  649–650
Happy at work, 339
Hourly earnings, 76, 111, 377,
  619, 620, 635–636
Injuries, 644, 648
Industry workers, 146
Job opening, 142
Job status, 567
Leaving job, 561
Lumber cutter, 281
Managers, use of digital media,
  26
Office rentals,
  Miami, FL, 86
  Seattle, WA, 86
Overtime hours, 203, 299
Phone lines in use, 202
Sick days, 76, 231
Travel time, 49, 62, 76, 353, 354
Union, 355, 562
Vacation days, 111, 217, 304, 603
Work days, 387
Work environment, 181
Work time and leisure time, 517,
  532, 533
Work weeks, 291, 293

1

PART ONE

Descriptive Statistics

CHAPTER 1   Introduction to Statistics

CHAPTER 2   Descriptive Statistics

Introduction to Statistics

1.1 An Overview of Statistics

1.2 Data Classification
- CASE STUDY

1.3 Experimental Design
- ACTIVITY
- USES AND ABUSES
- REAL STATISTICS–
  REAL DECISIONS
- HISTORY OF STATISTICS–
  TIMELINE
- TECHNOLOGY

Clark County, Nevada has one of the fastest growing populations in the United States. Las Vegas is located in this county.

◂ WHERE YOU'VE BEEN

You are already familiar with many of the practices of statistics, such as taking surveys, collecting data, and describing populations. What you may not know is that collecting accurate statistical data is often difficult and costly. Consider, for instance, the monumental task of counting and describing the entire population of the United States. If you were in charge of such a census, how would you do it? How would you ensure that your results are accurate? These and many more concerns are the responsibility of the United States Census Bureau, which conducts the census every decade.

WHERE YOU'RE GOING ➤

In Chapter 1, you will be introduced to the basic concepts and goals of statistics. For instance, statistics was used to construct the following graphs, which show the fastest growing U.S. counties with 10,000 or more people from 2000 to 2005 and the regions where the top 100 fastest growing counties from 2000 to 2005 are located. When conducting the census, the Bureau sends short forms to the entire population that ask about characteristics such as gender, age, race, and home ownership. A long form, which covers many additional topics, is sent to 17% of the population. This 17% forms a sample. In this course, you will learn how the data collected from a sample are used to infer characteristics about the entire population.

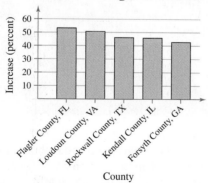

Fastest Growing U.S. Counties

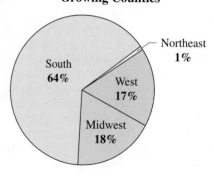

Location of the 100 Fastest Growing Counties

1.1 An Overview of Statistics

What You SHOULD LEARN

▸ The definition of statistics

▸ How to distinguish between a population and a sample and between a parameter and a statistic

▸ How to distinguish between descriptive statistics and inferential statistics

A Definition of Statistics ▸ Data Sets ▸ Branches of Statistics

▸ A Definition of Statistics

As you begin this course, you may wonder: *What is statistics? Why should I study statistics? How can studying statistics help me in my profession?* Almost every day you are exposed to statistics. For example, consider the following excerpts from recent newspapers and journals.

- "People who eat three daily servings of whole grains have been shown to reduce their risk of…stroke by 37%." *(Source: Whole Grains Council)*

- "Seventy percent of the 1500 U.S. spinal cord injuries to minors result from vehicle accidents, and 68 percent of those injured were not wearing a seatbelt." *(Source: UPI)*

- "U.S. coal production, which increased by 2.5 percent in 2006, is expected to fall by 3.1 percent in 2007." *(Source: Energy Information Administration)*

The three statements you just read are based on the collection of **data**.

DEFINITION

Data consist of information coming from observations, counts, measurements, or responses.

Sometimes data are presented graphically. If you have ever read *USA TODAY,* you have certainly seen one of that newspaper's most popular features, *USA TODAY Snapshots.* Graphics such as this present information in a way that is easy to understand.

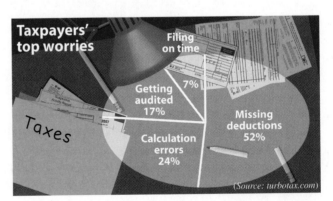

Taxpayers' top worries

Filing on time 7%

Getting audited 17%

Missing deductions 52%

Calculation errors 24%

Taxes

(Source: turbotax.com)

The use of statistics dates back to census taking in ancient Babylonia, Egypt, and later in the Roman Empire, when data were collected about matters concerning the state, such as births and deaths. In fact, the word *statistics* is derived from the Latin word *status,* meaning "state." So, what is statistics?

DEFINITION

Statistics is the science of collecting, organizing, analyzing, and interpreting data in order to make decisions.

Insight

A census consists of data from an entire population. But, unless a population is small, it is usually impractical to obtain all the population data. In most studies, information must be obtained from a sample.

▶ Data Sets

There are two types of data sets you will use when studying statistics. These data sets are called *populations* and *samples*.

DEFINITION

A **population** is the collection of all outcomes, responses, measurements, or counts that are of interest.

A **sample** is a subset of a population.

Sample data can be used to form conclusions about populations. Sample data must be collected using an appropriate method, such as *random selection*. If it is not collected using an appropriate method, the data are of no value.

EXAMPLE 1

Identifying Data Sets

In a recent survey, 1708 adults in the United States were asked if they think global warming is a problem that requires immediate government action. Nine hundred thirty-nine of the adults said yes. Identify the population and the sample. Describe the data set. *(Adapted from: Pew Research Center)*

Solution   The population consists of the responses of all adults in the United States, and the sample consists of the responses of the 1708 adults in the United States in the survey. The sample is a subset of the responses of all adults in the United States. The data set consists of 939 yes's and 769 no's.

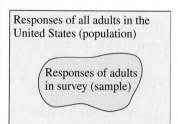

Responses of all adults in the United States (population)

Responses of adults in survey (sample)

▶ Try It Yourself 1

The U.S. Department of Energy conducts weekly surveys of approximately 800 gasoline stations to determine the average price per gallon of regular gasoline. On February 12, 2007, the average price was $2.24 per gallon. Identify the population and the sample. *(Source: Energy Information Administration)*

a. Identify the *population*.
b. Identify the *sample*.
c. What does the data set consist of?   *Answer: Page A32*

Whether a data set is a population or a sample usually depends on the context of the real-life situation. For instance, in Example 1, the population was the set of responses of all adults in the United States. Depending on the purpose of the survey, the population could have been the set of responses of all adults who live in California or who have cellular phones or who read a particular newspaper.

Two important terms that are used throughout this course are *parameter* and *statistic*.

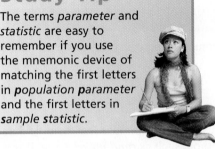

DEFINITION

A **parameter** is a numerical description of a *population* characteristic.

A **statistic** is a numerical description of a *sample* characteristic.

EXAMPLE 2

Distinguishing Between a Parameter and a Statistic

Decide whether the numerical value describes a population parameter or a sample statistic. Explain your reasoning.

1. A recent survey of a sample of MBAs reported that the average salary for an MBA is more than $82,000. *(Source: The Wall Street Journal)*
2. Starting salaries for the 667 MBA graduates from the University of Chicago Graduate School of Business increased 8.5% from the previous year.
3. In a random check of a sample of retail stores, the Food and Drug Administration found that 34% of the stores were not storing fish at the proper temperature.

Solution

1. Because the average of $82,000 is based on a subset of the population, it is a sample statistic.
2. Because the percent increase of 8.5% is based on all 667 graduates' starting salaries, it is a population parameter.
3. Because the percent of 34% is based on a subset of the population, it is a sample statistic.

▶ Try It Yourself 2

In 2006, major league baseball teams spent a total of $2,326,706,685 on players' salaries. Does this numerical value describe a population parameter or a sample statistic? *(Source: USA Today)*

a. Decide whether the numerical value is from a *population* or a *sample*.
b. Specify whether the numerical value is a *parameter* or a *statistic*.

Answer: Page A32

PICTURING the WORLD

How accurate is the U.S. census? According to a post-census evaluation conducted by the Census Bureau, the 1990 census undercounted the U.S. population by an estimated 4.0 million people. The 1990 census was the first census since at least 1940 to be less accurate than its predecessor. Notice that the undercount for the 2000 census was −1.3 million people. This means that the 2000 census *overcounted* the U.S. population by 1.3 million people.

U.S. Census Undercount

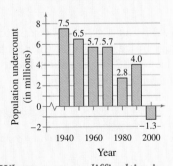

What are some difficulties in collecting population data?

In this course, you will see how the use of statistics can help you make informed decisions that affect your life. Consider the census that the U.S. government takes every decade. When taking the census, the Census Bureau attempts to contact everyone living in the United States. This is an impossible task. It is important that the census be accurate, because public officials make many decisions based on the census information. Data collected in the 2010 census will determine how to assign congressional seats and how to distribute public funds.

▶ Branches of Statistics

The study of statistics has two major branches: **descriptive statistics** and **inferential statistics.**

DEFINITION

Descriptive statistics is the branch of statistics that involves the organization, summarization, and display of data.

Inferential statistics is the branch of statistics that involves using a sample to draw conclusions about a population. A basic tool in the study of inferential statistics is probability.

EXAMPLE 3

Descriptive and Inferential Statistics

Decide which part of the study represents the descriptive branch of statistics. What conclusions might be drawn from the study using inferential statistics?

1. A large sample of men, aged 48, was studied for 18 years. For unmarried men, approximately 70% were alive at age 65. For married men, 90% were alive at age 65. *(Source: The Journal of Family Issues)*

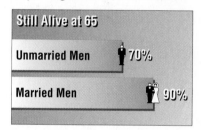

2. In a sample of Wall Street analysts, the percentage who incorrectly forecasted high-tech earnings in a recent year was 44%. *(Source: Bloomberg News)*

Solution

1. Descriptive statistics involves statements such as "For unmarried men, approximately 70% were alive at age 65" and "For married men, 90% were alive at 65." A possible inference drawn from the study is that being married is associated with a longer life for men.

2. The part of this study that represents the descriptive branch of statistics involves the statement "the percentage of Wall Street analysts who incorrectly forecasted high-tech earnings in a recent year was 44%." A possible inference drawn from the study is that the stock market is difficult to forecast, even for professionals.

▶ Try It Yourself 3

A survey conducted among 1017 men and women by Opinion Research Corporation International found that 76% of women and 60% of men had had a physical examination within the previous year. *(Source: Men's Health)*

a. Identify the descriptive aspect of the survey.
b. What inferences could be drawn from this survey?   *Answer: Page A32*

Throughout this course you will see applications of both branches. A major theme in this course will be how to use sample statistics to make inferences about unknown population parameters.

1.1 EXERCISES

For Extra Help

MyStatLab

■ Building Basic Skills and Vocabulary

1. How is a sample related to a population?

2. Why is a sample used more often than a population?

3. What is the difference between a parameter and a statistic?

4. What are the two main branches of statistics?

True or False?   *In Exercises 5–10, determine whether the statement is true or false. If it is false, rewrite it as a true statement.*

5. A statistic is a measure that describes a population characteristic.

6. A sample is a subset of a population.

7. It is impossible for the Census Bureau to obtain all the census data about the population of the United States.

8. Inferential statistics involves using a population to draw a conclusion about a corresponding sample.

9. A population is the collection of some outcomes, responses, measurements, or counts that are of interest.

10. The word *statistics* is derived from the Latin word *status*, meaning "state."

Classifying a Data Set   *In Exercises 11–16, determine whether the data set is a population or a sample. Explain your reasoning.*

11. The age of each member of the House of Representatives

12. The height of every fourth person entering an amusement park

13. A survey of 500 spectators from a stadium with 42,000 spectators

14. The annual salary for each lawyer at a firm

15. The cholesterol levels of 20 patients in a hospital with 100 patients

16. The number of televisions in each U.S. household

Graphical Analysis   *In Exercises 17–20, use the Venn diagram to identify the population and the sample.*

17.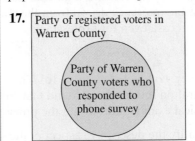

18.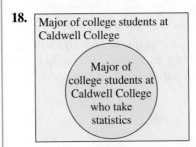

19.

```
┌─────────────────────────┐
│ Ages of adults in the United │
│ States who own computers │
│        ╭───────╮        │
│       ╱ Ages of adults ╲      │
│      │ in the U.S. who │     │
│      │  own Dell       │     │
│       ╲ computers ╱      │
│        ╰───────╯        │
└─────────────────────────┘
```

20.

```
┌─────────────────────────┐
│ Income of home          │
│ owners in Texas         │
│        ╭───────╮        │
│       ╱          ╲      │
│      │ Income of home │     │
│      │ owners in Texas │    │
│       ╲ with mortgages ╱     │
│        ╰───────╯        │
└─────────────────────────┘
```

■ Using and Interpreting Concepts

Identifying Populations and Samples   *In Exercises 21–28, identify the population and the sample.*

21. A survey of 1000 adults in the United States found that 12% prefer to take their vacation during the winter months. *(Source: Rasmussen Reports)*

22. A study of 33,043 infants in Italy was conducted to find a link between a heart rhythm abnormality and sudden infant death syndrome. *(Source: New England Journal of Medicine)*

23. A survey of 1906 households in the United States found that 13% have a high definition television.

24. A survey of 1000 computer users found that 17% plan on buying the Microsoft Windows Vista™ operating system. *(Source: Rasmussen Reports)*

25. A survey of 1045 registered voters found that 19% think the economy is the most important issue to consider when voting for Congress. *(Source: Princeton Survey Research Associates International)*

26. A survey of 496 students at a college found that 10% planned on traveling out of the country during spring break.

27. A survey of 546 women found that more than 56% are the primary investor in their household. *(Adapted from: Roper Starch Worldwide for Intuit)*

28. A survey of 791 vacationers from the United States found that they planned on spending at least $2000 for their next vacation.

Distinguishing Between a Parameter and a Statistic   *In Exercises 29–36, determine whether the numerical value is a parameter or a statistic. Explain your reasoning.*

29. The average annual salary for 35 of a company's 1200 accountants is $68,000.

30. In a survey of a sample of high school students, 43% said that their mother has taught them the most about managing money. *(Source: Harris Poll for Girls Incorporated)*

31. Sixty-two of the 97 passengers aboard the Hindenburg airship survived its explosion.

32. As of January 2007, 44% of the governors of the 50 states in the United States are Republicans.

33. In a survey of a sample of computer users, 8% said their computer had a malfunction that needed to be repaired by a service technician.

34. In a recent year, the interest category for 12% of all new magazines was sports. *(Source: Oxbridge Communications)*

35. In a recent survey of 1503 adults in the United States, 53% said they use both a landline and a cell phone. *(Source: Pew Research Center)*

36. In a recent year, the average math scores for all graduates on the ACT was 21.1. *(Source: ACT, Inc.)*

37. Which part of the survey described in Exercise 27 represents the descriptive branch of statistics? Make an inference based on the results of the survey.

38. Which part of the survey described in Exercise 28 represents the descriptive branch of statistics? Make an inference based on the results of the survey.

■ Extending Concepts

39. Identifying Data Sets in Articles Find a newspaper or magazine article that describes a survey.

(a) Identify the sample used in the survey.

(b) What is the sample's population?

40. Sleep Deprivation In a recent study, volunteers who had 8 hours of sleep were three times more likely to answer correctly on a math test than were sleep-deprived participants. *(Source: CBS News)*

(a) Identify the sample used in the study.

(b) What is the sample's population?

(c) Which part of the study represents the descriptive branch of statistics?

(d) Make an inference based on the results of the study.

41. Living in Florida A study shows that senior citizens who live in Florida have a better memory than senior citizens who do not live in Florida.

(a) Make an inference based on the results of this study.

(b) What is wrong with this type of reasoning?

42. Increase in Obesity Rates A study shows that the obesity rate among boys ages 2 to 19 has increased over the past several years. *(Source: Washington Post)*

(a) Make an inference based on the results of this study.

(b) What is wrong with this type of reasoning?

43. Writing Write an essay about the importance of statistics for one of the following.

(a) A study on the effectiveness of a new drug

(b) An analysis of a manufacturing process

(c) Making conclusions about voter opinions using surveys

1.2 Data Classification

Types of Data ▸ Levels of Measurement

▸ Types of Data

When doing a study, it is important to know the kind of data involved. The nature of the data you are working with will determine which statistical procedures can be used. In this section, you will learn how to classify data by type and by level of measurement. Data sets can consist of two types of data: *qualitative data* and *quantitative data*.

DEFINITION

Qualitative data consist of attributes, labels, or nonnumerical entries.

Quantitative data consist of numerical measurements or counts.

EXAMPLE 1

Classifying Data by Type

The base prices of several vehicles are shown in the table. Which data are qualitative data and which are quantitative data? Explain your reasoning. *(Source: Ford Motor Company)*

Model	Base Price
Fusion 14 S	$17,795
F-150 XL	$18,710
Five Hundred SEL	$23,785
Escape XLT Sport	$24,575
2007 Explorer Sport Trac Limited	$26,775
Freestar SEL	$27,500
Crown Victoria LX	$28,830
Expedition XLT	$35,480

Solution The information shown in the table can be separated into two data sets. One data set contains the names of vehicle models, and the other contains the base prices of vehicle models. The names are nonnumerical entries, so these are qualitative data. The base prices are numerical entries, so these are quantitative data.

▸ Try It Yourself 1

The populations of several U.S. cities are shown in the table. Which data are qualitative data and which are quantitative data? *(Source: U.S. Census Bureau)*

a. Identify the contents of each data set.
b. Decide whether each data set consists of numerical or nonnumerical entries.
c. Specify the qualitative data and the quantitative data.   *Answer: Page A32*

City	Population
Cleveland, OH	452,208
Detroit, MI	886,671
Houston, TX	2,016,582
Las Vegas, NV	545,147
Portland, OR	533,427
Topeka, KS	121,946

▶ Levels of Measurement

Another characteristic of data is its level of measurement. The level of measurement determines which statistical calculations are meaningful. The four levels of measurement, in order from lowest to highest, are *nominal, ordinal, interval,* and *ratio.*

DEFINITION

Data at the **nominal level of measurement** are qualitative only. Data at this level are categorized using names, labels, or qualities. No mathematical computations can be made at this level.

Data at the **ordinal level of measurement** are qualitative or quantitative. Data at this level can be arranged in order, or ranked, but differences between data entries are not meaningful.

EXAMPLE 2

Classifying Data by Level

Two data sets are shown. Which data set consists of data at the nominal level? Which data set consists of data at the ordinal level? Explain your reasoning. *(Source: Nielsen Media Research)*

Top Five TV Programs (from 2/12/07 to 2/18/07)
1. American Idol–Tuesday
2. American Idol–Wednesday
3. Grey's Anatomy
4. House
5. CSI

Network Affiliates in Pittsburgh, PA	
WTAE	(ABC)
WPXI	(NBC)
KDKA	(CBS)
WPGH	(FOX)

Solution The first data set lists the rank of five TV programs. The data consist of the ranks 1, 2, 3, 4, and 5. Because the rankings can be listed in order, these data are at the ordinal level. Note that the difference between a rank of 1 and 5 has no mathematical meaning. The second data set consists of the call letters of each network affiliate in Pittsburgh. The call letters are simply the names of network affiliates, so these data are at the nominal level.

▶ Try It Yourself 2

Consider the following data sets. For each data set, decide whether the data are at the nominal level or at the ordinal level.

1. The final standings for the Pacific Division of the National Basketball Association

2. A collection of phone numbers

a. *Identify* what each data set represents.
b. Specify the *level of measurement* and justify your answer.

Answer: Page A32

The two highest levels of measurement consist of quantitative data only.

> **DEFINITION**
>
> Data at the **interval level of measurement** can be ordered, and you can calculate meaningful differences between data entries. At the interval level, a zero entry simply represents a position on a scale; the entry is not an inherent zero.
>
> Data at the **ratio level of measurement** are similar to data at the interval level, with the added property that a zero entry is an inherent zero. A ratio of two data values can be formed so that one data value can be meaningfully expressed as a multiple of another.

An *inherent zero* is a zero that implies "none." For instance, the amount of money you have in a savings account could be zero dollars. In this case, the zero represents no money; it is an inherent zero. On the other hand, a temperature of 0°C does not represent a condition in which no heat is present. The 0°C temperature is simply a position on the Celsius scale; it is not an inherent zero.

To distinguish between data at the interval level and at the ratio level, determine whether the expression "twice as much" has any meaning in the context of the data. For instance, $2 is twice as much as $1, so these data are at the ratio level. On the other hand, 2°C is not twice as warm as 1°C so these data are at the interval level.

EXAMPLE 3

Classifying Data by Level

Two data sets are shown at the left. Which data set consists of data at the interval level? Which data set consists of data at the ratio level? Explain your reasoning. *(Source: Major League Baseball)*

Solution Both of these data sets contain quantitative data. Consider the dates of the Yankees' World Series victories. It makes sense to find differences between specific dates. For instance, the time between the Yankees' first and last World Series victories is

$$2000 - 1923 = 77 \text{ years.}$$

But it does not make sense to say that one year is a multiple of another. So, these data are at the interval level. Using the home run totals, you can find differences *and* write ratios. From the data, you can see that Detroit hit 31 more home runs than Seattle hit and that Chicago hit about twice as many home runs as Kansas City hit. So, these data are at the ratio level.

▶ **Try It Yourself 3**

Decide whether the data are at the interval level or at the ratio level.

1. The body temperatures (in degrees Fahrenheit) of an athlete during an exercise session
2. The heart rates (in beats per minute) of an athlete during an exercise session

a. *Identify* what each data set represents.
b. Specify the *level of measurement* and justify your answer.

Answer: Page A32

New York Yankees' World Series Victories (Years)
1923, 1927, 1928, 1932, 1936, 1937, 1938, 1939, 1941, 1943, 1947, 1949, 1950, 1951, 1952, 1953, 1956, 1958, 1961, 1962, 1977, 1978, 1996, 1998, 1999, 2000

2006 American League Home Run Totals (by Team)	
Baltimore	164
Boston	192
Chicago	236
Cleveland	196
Detroit	203
Kansas City	124
Los Angeles	159
Minnesota	143
New York	210
Oakland	175
Seattle	172
Tampa Bay	190
Texas	183
Toronto	199

The following tables summarize which operations are meaningful at each of the four levels of measurement. When identifying a data set's level of measurement, use the highest level that applies.

Level of measurement	Put data in categories	Arrange data in order	Subtract data values	Determine if one data value is a multiple of another
Nominal	Yes	No	No	No
Ordinal	Yes	Yes	No	No
Interval	Yes	Yes	Yes	No
Ratio	Yes	Yes	Yes	Yes

Summary of Four Levels of Measurement

	Example of a Data Set	Meaningful Calculations
Nominal Level (Qualitative data)	*Types of Music Played by a Radio Station* Pop Modern rock Contemporary jazz Hip hop	*Put in a category.* For instance, a song played by the radio station could be put into one of the four categories shown.
Ordinal Level (Qualitative or quantitative data)	*Motion Picture Association of America Ratings Description* G General Audiences PG Parental Guidance Suggested PG-13 Parents Strongly Cautioned R Restricted NC-17 No One Under 17 Admitted	Put in a category and *put in order.* For instance, a PG rating has a stronger restriction than a G rating.
Interval Level (Quantitative data)	*Average Monthly Temperature (in degrees Fahrenheit) for Sacramento, CA* Jan 46.3 Jul 75.4 Feb 51.2 Aug 74.8 Mar 54.5 Sep 71.7 Apr 58.9 Oct 64.4 May 65.5 Nov 53.3 Jun 71.5 Dec 45.8 *(Source: National Climatic Data Center)*	Put in a category, put in order, and *find differences between values.* For instance, $71.5 - 65.5 = 6°F$. So, June is 6° warmer than May.
Ratio Level (Quantitative data)	*Average Monthly Precipitation (in inches) for Sacramento, CA* Jan 3.8 Jul 0.1 Feb 3.5 Aug 0.1 Mar 2.8 Sep 0.4 Apr 1.0 Oct 0.9 May 0.5 Nov 2.2 Jun 0.2 Dec 2.5 *(Source: National Climatic Data Center)*	Put in a category, put in order, find differences between values, and *find ratios of values.* For instance, $\frac{1.0}{0.5} = 2$. So, there is twice as much rain in April as in May.

1.2   EXERCISES

For Extra Help

MyStatLab

■ Building Basic Skills and Vocabulary

1. Name each level of measurement for which data can be qualitative.

2. Name each level of measurement for which data can be quantitative.

True or False?   *In Exercises 3–6, determine whether the statement is true or false. If it is false, rewrite it as a true statement.*

3. Data at the ordinal level are quantitative only.

4. For data at the interval level, you cannot calculate meaningful differences between data entries.

5. More types of calculations can be performed with data at the nominal level than with data at the interval level.

6. Data at the ratio level cannot be put in order.

Classifying Data by Type   *In Exercises 7–12, determine whether the data are qualitative or quantitative.*

7. The telephone numbers in a telephone directory

8. The daily high temperatures for the month of July

9. The lengths of songs on an MP3 player

10. The player numbers for a soccer team

11. Responses on an opinion poll

12. Measure of diastolic blood pressure

■ Using and Interpreting Concepts

Classifying Data by Level   *In Exercises 13–18, determine whether the data are qualitative or quantitative and identify the data set's level of measurement. Explain your reasoning.*

13. **Football**   The top five teams in the final college football poll released in January 2007 are listed. *(Source: Associated Press)*

    1. Florida   2. Ohio State   3. LSU   4. USC   5. Boise State

14. **Politics**   The three political parties in the 110th Congress are listed below.

    Republican   Democrat   Independent

15. **Top Salesperson**   The region representing the top salesperson in a corporation for the past six years is given.

    Southeast   Northwest   Northeast
    Southeast   Southwest   Southwest

16. **Fish Lengths**   The lengths (in inches) of a sample of striped bass caught in Maryland waters are listed. *(Adapted from: National Marine Fisheries Service, Fisheries Statistics and Economics Division)*

    16   17.25   19   18.75   21   20.3   19.8   24   21.82

17. Best Seller List The top five hardcover fiction books on *The New York Times* Best Seller List on February 21, 2007 are shown. *(Source: The New York Times)*

1. Step on a Crack 2. Plum Lovin' 3. Natural Born Charmer
4. High Profile 5. Hannibal Rising

18. Ticket Prices The average ticket prices for 10 rock concerts in 2005 are listed. *(Source: The New York Times)*

$134 $104 $55 $63 $76 $38 $35 $81 $47 $97

Graphical Analysis *In Exercises 19–22, identify the level of measurement of the data listed on the horizontal axis in the graph.*

19. Does Global Warming Contribute to More Severe El Niños?

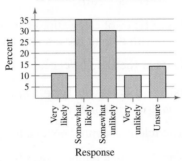

(Source: Yankelovich for the National Representatives Science Foundation, American Meteorological Society)

20. Average January Snowfall for 15 Cities

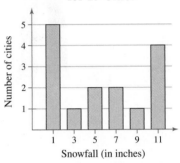

(Source: National Climatic Data Center)

21. Gender Profile of the 110th Congress

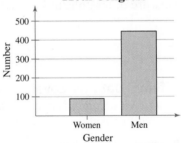

(Source: U.S. House of Representatives, Office of the Clerk)

22. State Government Tax Collections by Year

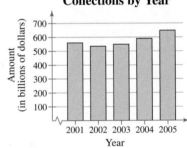

(Source: U.S. Census Bureau)

23. The following appear on a physician's intake form. Identify the level of measurement of the data.

a. Temperature   **b.** Allergies

c. Weight   **d.** Pain level (scale of 0 to 10)

24. The following appear on an employment application. Identify the level of measurement of the data.

a. Highest grade level completed   **b.** Gender

c. Year of college graduation   **d.** Number of years at last job

■ **Extending Concepts**

25. Writing What is an inherent zero? Describe three examples of data sets that have an inherent zero and three that do not.

26. Writing Describe two examples of data sets for each of the four levels of measurement. Justify your answer.

Rating Television Shows in the United States

Nielsen Media Research has been rating television programs for more than 50 years. Nielsen uses several sampling procedures, but its main one is to track the viewing patterns of 10,000 households. These contain more than 30,000 people and are chosen to form a cross section of the overall population. The households represent various locations, ethnic groups, and income brackets. The data gathered from the Nielsen sample of 10,000 households are used to draw inferences about the population of all households in the United States.

TV programs viewed by all households in the United States (111.4 million households)

TV programs viewed by Nielsen sample (10,000 households)

Top-Ranked Programs in Prime Time for the Week of 2/12/07–2/18/07

Rank	Rank Last Week	Program Name	Network	Day, Time	Rating	Share	Audience
1	1	American Idol–Tuesday	FOX	Tues., 8:00 P.M.	17.4	25	19,354,000
2	2	American Idol–Wednesday	FOX	Wed., 9:00 P.M.	16.2	24	18,045,000
3	3	Grey's Anatomy	ABC	Thu., 9:00 P.M.	16.0	23	17,809,000
4	4	House	FOX	Tues., 9:00 P.M.	14.8	22	16,469,000
5	5	CSI	CBS	Thu., 9:00 P.M.	13.8	20	15,323,000
6	7	CSI: Miami	CBS	Mon., 10:00 P.M.	12.7	21	14,093,000
7	8	Desperate Housewives	ABC	Sun., 9:00 P.M.	11.7	18	13,060,000
8	10	Deal or No Deal–Monday	NBC	Mon., 8:00 P.M.	10.0	15	11,167,000
8	8	Two and a Half Men	CBS	Mon., 9:00 P.M.	10.0	14	11,099,000
10	17	Shark	CBS	Thu., 10:00 P.M.	9.8	16	10,909,000

■ Exercises

1. **Rating Points** Each rating point represents 1,114,000 households, or 1% of the households in the United States. Does a program with a rating of 8.4 have twice the number of households as a program with a rating of 4.2? Explain your reasoning.

2. **Sampling Percent** What percentage of the total number of U.S. households is used in the Nielsen sample?

3. **Nominal Level of Measurement** Which columns in the table contain data at the nominal level?

4. **Ordinal Level of Measurement** Which columns in the table contain data at the ordinal level? Describe two ways that the data can be ordered.

5. **Interval Level of Measurement** Which column in the table contains data at the interval level? How can these data be ordered? What is the unit of measure for the difference of two entries in the data set?

6. **Ratio Level of Measurement** Which three columns contain data at the ratio level?

7. **Share** The column listed as "Share" gives the percentage of televisions in use at a given time. Does the Nielsen rating rank shows by rating or by share? Explain your reasoning.

8. **Inferences** What decisions (inferences) can be made on the basis of the Nielsen ratings?

1.3 Experimental Design

What You
SHOULD LEARN

▸ How to design a statistical study

▸ How to collect data by doing an observational study, performing an experiment, using a simulation, or using a survey

▸ How to design an experiment

▸ How to create a sample using random sampling, simple random sampling, stratified sampling, cluster sampling, and systematic sampling and how to identify a biased sample

Design of a Statistical Study ▸ Data Collection ▸ Experimental Design ▸ Sampling Techniques

▸ Design of a Statistical Study

The goal of every statistical study is to collect data and then use the data to make a decision. Any decision you make using the results of a statistical study is only as good as the process used to obtain the data. If the process is flawed, then the resulting decision is questionable.

Although you may never have to develop a statistical study, it is likely that you will have to interpret the results of one. And before you interpret the results of a study, you should determine whether the results are valid. In other words, you should be familiar with how to design a statistical study.

GUIDELINES

Designing a Statistical Study

1. Identify the variable(s) of interest (the focus) and the population of the study.
2. Develop a detailed plan for collecting data. If you use a sample, make sure the sample is representative of the population.
3. Collect the data.
4. Describe the data, using descriptive statistics techniques.
5. Interpret the data and make decisions about the population using inferential statistics.
6. Identify any possible errors.

▸ Data Collection

There are several ways you can collect data. Often, the focus of the study dictates the best way to collect data. The following is a brief summary of four methods of data collection.

- *Do an observational study* In an **observational study,** a researcher observes and measures characteristics of interest of part of a population but does not change existing conditions. For instance, an observational study was performed in which researchers observed and recorded the mouthing behavior on nonfood objects of children up to three years old. *(Source: Pediatrics Magazine)*

- *Perform an experiment* In performing an **experiment,** a **treatment** is applied to part of a population and responses are observed. Another part of the population may be used as a **control group,** in which no treatment is applied. In many cases, subjects (sometimes called **experimental units**) in the control group are given a **placebo,** which is a harmless, unmedicated treatment, that is made to look like the real treatment. The responses of the treatment group and control group can then be compared and studied. For instance, an experiment was performed in which diabetics took cinnamon extract daily while a control group took none. After 40 days, the diabetics who took the cinnamon reduced their risk of heart disease while the control group experienced no change. *(Source: Diabetes Care)*

Insight

The difference between an observational study and an experiment is that, in an observational study, a researcher does not influence the responses, whereas in an experiment, a researcher deliberately applies a treatment before observing the responses.

- *Use a simulation* A **simulation** is the use of a mathematical or physical model to reproduce the conditions of a situation or process. Collecting data often involves the use of computers. Simulations allow you to study situations that are impractical or even dangerous to create in real life, and often they save time and money. For instance, automobile manufacturers use simulations with dummies to study the effects of crashes on humans. Throughout this course, you will have the opportunity to use applets that simulate statistical processes on a computer.

- *Use a survey* A **survey** is an investigation of one or more characteristics of a population. Most often, surveys are carried out on *people* by asking them questions. The most common types of surveys are done by interview, mail, or telephone. In designing a survey, it is important to word the questions so that they do not lead to biased results. For example, a survey is conducted on a sample of female physicians to determine whether the primary reason for their career choice is financial stability. In designing the survey, it would be acceptable to make a list of reasons and ask each individual in the sample to select her first choice.

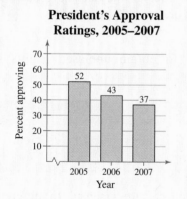

PICTURING the WORLD

The Gallup Organization conducts many polls (or surveys) regarding the president, Congress, and political and nonpolitical issues. A commonly cited Gallup poll is the public approval rating of the president. For example, the approval ratings for President George W. Bush from 2005 to 2007 are shown in the following graph. (The rating is from the first poll conducted in January of each year.)

President's Approval Ratings, 2005–2007

Discuss some ways that Gallup could select a biased sample to conduct a poll. How could Gallup select a sample that is unbiased?

EXAMPLE 1

Deciding on Methods of Data Collection

Consider the following statistical studies. Which method of data collection would you use to collect data for each study? Explain your reasoning.

1. A study of the effect of changing flight patterns on the number of airplane accidents
2. A study of the effect of eating oatmeal on lowering blood pressure
3. A study of how fourth grade students solve a puzzle
4. A study of U.S. residents' approval rating of the U.S. president

Solution

1. Because it is impractical to create this situation, use a simulation.
2. In this study, you want to measure the effect a treatment (eating oatmeal) has on patients. So, you would want to perform an experiment.
3. Because you want to observe and measure certain characteristics of part of a population, you could do an observational study.
4. You could use a survey that asks, "Do you approve of the way the president is handling his job?"

▶ **Try It Yourself 1**

Consider the following statistical studies. Which method of data collection would you use to collect data for each study?

1. A study of the effect of exercise on relieving depression
2. A study of the success of graduates of a large university finding a job within one year of graduation

a. Identify the *focus* of the study.
b. Identify the *population* of the study.
c. Choose an appropriate *method of data collection*.   *Answer: Page A32*

▶ Experimental Design

In order to produce meaningful unbiased results, experiments should be carefully designed and executed. It is important to know what steps should be taken to make the results of an experiment valid. Three key elements of a well-designed experiment are *control*, *randomization*, and *replication*.

Because experimental results can be ruined by a variety of factors, being able to *control* these influential factors in important. One such factor is a *confounding variable*.

> **DEFINITION**
>
> A **confounding variable** occurs when an experimenter cannot tell the difference between the effects of different factors on a variable.

For example, to attract more customers, a coffee shop owner experiments by remodeling her shop using bright colors. At the same time, a shopping mall nearby has its grand opening. If business at the coffee shop increases, it cannot be determined whether it is because of the new colors or the new shopping mall. The effects of the colors and the shopping mall have been confounded.

Another factor that can affect experimental results is the *placebo effect*. The **placebo effect** occurs when a subject reacts favorably to a placebo when in fact, he or she has been given no medicated treatment at all. To help control or minimize the placebo effect, a technique called **blinding** can be used.

> **DEFINITION**
>
> **Blinding** is a technique where the subject does not know whether he or she is receiving a treatment or a placebo. In a **double-blind experiment,** neither the subject nor the experimenter knows if the subject is receiving a treatment or a placebo. The experimenter is informed after all the data have been collected. This type of experimental design is preferred by researchers.

Another technique that can be used to obtain unbiased results is *randomization*.

> **DEFINITION**
>
> **Randomization** is a process of randomly assigning subjects to different treatment groups.

In a **completely randomized design,** subjects are assigned to different treatment groups through random selection. In some experiments, it may be necessary for the experimenter to use **blocks,** which are groups of subjects with similar characteristics. A commonly used experimental design is a **randomized block design.** To use a randomized block design, you should divide subjects with similar characteristics into blocks, and then within each block, randomly assign subjects to treatment groups. For example, an experimenter who is testing the effects of a new weight loss drink may first divide the subjects into age categories such as 30–39 years old, 40–49 years old, and over 50 years old. Then within each age group, randomly assign subjects to either the treatment group or control group as shown.

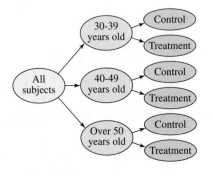

Randomized Block Design

Another type of experimental design is a **matched-pairs design,** where subjects are paired up according to a similarity. One subject in the pair is randomly selected to receive one treatment while the other subject receives a different treatment. For instance, two subjects may be paired up because of their age, geographical location, or a particular physical characteristic.

Another important part of experimental design is the sample size. To improve the validity of experimental results, *replication* is required.

> ### DEFINITION
>
> **Replication** is the repetition of an experiment using a large group of subjects.

For instance, suppose an experiment is designed to test a vaccine against a strain of influenza. In the experiment, 10,000 people are given the vaccine and another 10,000 people are given a placebo. Because of the sample size, the effectiveness of the vaccine would most likely be observed. But, if the subjects in the experiment are not selected so that both groups were similar (according to age and gender), the results are of less value.

EXAMPLE 2

Analyzing an Experimental Design

A company wants to test the effectiveness of a new gum developed to help people quit smoking. Identify a potential problem with the given experimental design and suggest a way to improve it.

1. The company identifies ten adults who are heavy smokers. Five of the subjects are given the new gum and the other five subjects are given a placebo. After two months, the subjects are evaluated and it is found that the five subjects using the new gum have quit smoking.

2. The company identifies one thousand adults who are heavy smokers. The subjects are divided into blocks according to gender. Females are given the new gum and males are given the placebo. After two months, the female group has a significant number of subjects who have quit smoking.

Solution

1. The sample size being used is not large enough to validate the results of the experiment. The experiment must be replicated to improve the validity.

2. The groups are not similar. The new gum may have a greater effect on women than men, or vice versa. The subjects can be divided into blocks according to gender, but then within each block, they must be randomly assigned to be in the treatment group or in the control group.

▶ Try It Yourself 2

Using the information in Example 2, suppose the company identifies 240 adults who are heavy smokers. The subjects are randomly assigned to be in a treatment group or control group. Each subject is also given a DVD featuring the dangers of smoking. After four months, most of the subjects in the treatment group have quit smoking.

a. Identify a *potential problem* with the experimental design.
b. How could the design be *improved*?   *Answer: Page A32*

Insight

A **biased sample** is one that is not representative of the population from which it is drawn. For instance, a sample consisting of only 18- to 22-year-old college students would not be representative of the entire 18- to 22-year-old population in the country.

To explore this topic further, see Activity 1.3 on page 28.

Study Tip

Here are instructions for using the random-integer generator on a TI-83/84 for Example 3.

[MATH]

Choose the PRB menu.

5: randInt(

[1] [,] [7] [3] [1] [,] [8] [)]

[ENTER]

```
randInt(1,731,8)
{537 33 249 728…
```

Continuing to press [ENTER] will generate more random samples of 8 integers.

▶ Sampling Techniques

A **census** is a count or measure of an *entire* population. Taking a census provides complete information, but it is often costly and difficult to perform. A **sampling** is a count or measure of *part* of a population, and is more commonly used in statistical studies. To collect unbiased data, a researcher must ensure that the sample is representative of the population. Appropriate sampling techniques must be used to ensure that inferences about the population are valid. Remember that when a study is done with faulty data, the results are questionable. Even with the best methods of sampling, a **sampling error** may occur. A sampling error is the difference between the results of a sample and those of the population. When you learn about inferential statistics, you will learn techniques of controlling these sampling errors.

A **random sample** is one in which every member of the population has an equal chance of being selected. A **simple random sample** is a sample in which every possible sample of the same size has the same chance of being selected. One way to collect a simple random sample is to assign a different number to each member of the population and then use a random number table like the one in Appendix B. Responses, counts, or measures from members of the population whose numbers correspond to those generated using the table would be in the sample. Calculators and computer software programs are also used to generate random numbers (see page 36).

Table 1—Random Numbers

92630	78240	19267	95457	53497	23894	37708	79862
79445	78735	71549	44843	26104	67318	00701	34986
59654	71966	27386	50004	05358	94031	29281	18544
31524	49587	76612	39789	13537	48086	59483	60680
06348	76938	90379	51392	55887	71015	09209	79157

Portion of Table 1 found in Appendix B

For instance, to use a simple random sample to count the number of people who live in West Ridge County households, you could assign a different number to each household, use a technology tool or table of random numbers to generate a sample of numbers, and then count the number of people living in each selected household.

EXAMPLE 3

Using a Simple Random Sample

There are 731 students currently enrolled in statistics at your school. You wish to form a sample of eight students to answer some survey questions. Select the students who will belong to the simple random sample.

Solution   Assign numbers 1 to 731 to each student in the course. On the table of random numbers, choose a starting place at random and read the digits in groups of three (because 731 is a three-digit number). For example, if you started in the third row of the table at the beginning of the second column, you would group the numbers as follows:

719│66 2│738│6 50│004│ 053│58 9│403│1 29│281│ 185│44

Ignoring numbers greater than 731, the first eight numbers are 719, 662, 650, 4, 53, 589, 403, and 129. The students assigned these numbers will make up the sample. To find the sample using a TI-83/84, follow the instructions in the margin.

> ▶ **Try It Yourself 3**

A company employs 79 people. Choose a simple random sample of five to survey.

a. On the table, randomly choose a *starting place*.
b. *Read the digits* in groups of two.
c. Write the five random numbers.   *Answer: Page A32*

When you choose members of a sample, you should decide whether it is acceptable to have the same population member selected more than once. If it is acceptable, then the sampling process is said to be *with replacement*. If it is not acceptable, then the sampling process is said to be *without replacement*.

There are several other commonly used sampling techniques. Each has advantages and disadvantages.

- **Stratified Sample**   When it is important for the sample to have members from each segment of the population, you should use a stratified sample. Depending on the focus of the study, members of the population are divided into two or more subsets, called *strata*, that share a similar characteristic such as age, gender, ethnicity, or even political preference. A sample is then randomly selected from each of the strata. Using a stratified sample ensures that each segment of the population is represented. For example, to collect a stratified sample of the number of people who live in West Ridge County households, you could divide the households into socioeconomic levels, and then randomly select households from each level.

Group 1:
Low income

Group 2:
Middle income

Group 3:
High income

Stratified Sampling

Insight

For stratified sampling, each of the strata contains members with a certain characteristic (for example, a particular age group). In contrast, clusters consist of geographic groupings, and each cluster should consist of members with all of the characteristics (for example, all age groups). With stratified samples, some of the members of each group are used. In a cluster sampling, all of the members of one or more groups are used.

- **Cluster Sample**   When the population falls into naturally occurring subgroups, each having similar characteristics, a cluster sample may be the most appropriate. To select a cluster sample, divide the population into groups, called *clusters*, and select all of the members in one or more (but not all) of the clusters. Examples of clusters could be different sections of the same course or different branches of a bank. For instance, to collect a cluster sample of the number of people who live in West Ridge County households, divide the households into groups according to zip codes, then select all the households in one or more, but not all, zip codes and count the number of people living in each household. In using a cluster sample, care must be taken to ensure that all clusters have similar characteristics. For example, if one of the zip code clusters has a greater proportion of high-income people, the data might not be representative of the population.

Zip Code Zones in West Ridge County

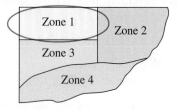

Cluster Sampling

- *Systematic Sample*   A systematic sample is a sample in which each member of the population is assigned a number. The members of the population are ordered in some way, a starting number is randomly selected, and then sample members are selected at regular intervals from the starting number. (For instance, every 3rd, 5th, or 100th member is selected.) For example, to collect a systematic sample of the number of people who live in West Ridge County households, you could assign a different number to each household, randomly choose a starting number, select every 100th household, and count the number of people living in each. An advantage of systematic sampling is that it is easy to use. In the case of any regularly occurring pattern in the data, however, this type of sampling should be avoided.

Systematic Sampling

A type of sample that often leads to biased studies (so it is not recommended) is a **convenience sample.** A convenience sample consists only of available members of the population.

EXAMPLE 4

Identifying Sampling Techniques

You are doing a study to determine the opinion of students at your school regarding stem cell research. Identify the sampling technique you are using if you select the samples listed.

1. You select a class at random and question each student in the class.
2. You divide the student population with respect to majors and randomly select and question some students in each major.
3. You assign each student a number and generate random numbers. You then question each student whose number is randomly selected.

Solution

1. Because each class is a naturally occurring subgroup (a cluster) and you question each student in the class, this is a cluster sample.
2. Because students are divided into strata (majors) and a sample is selected from each major, this is a stratified sample.
3. Each sample of the same size has an equal chance of being selected and each student has an equal chance of being selected, so this is a simple random sample.

▶ Try It Yourself 4

You want to determine the opinion of students at your school regarding stem cell research. Identify the sampling technique you are using if you select the samples listed.

1. You select students who are in your statistics class.
2. You assign each student a number and, after choosing a starting number, question every 25th student.

a. Determine *how* the sample is *selected*.
b. Identify the corresponding *sampling technique.*   *Answer: Page A32*

1.3 EXERCISES

■ Building Basic Skills and Vocabulary

1. What is the difference between an observational study and an experiment?

2. What is the difference between a census and a sampling?

3. Describe two methods you can use to generate random numbers.

4. What is replication in an experiment and why is it important?

True or False? *In Exercises 5–10, determine whether the statement is true or false. If it is false, rewrite it as a true statement.*

5. In a randomized block design, subjects with similar characteristics are divided into blocks, and then within each block, randomly assigned to treatment groups.

6. A double-blind experiment is used to increase the placebo effect.

7. Using a systematic sample guarantees that members of each group within a population will be sampled.

8. A census is a count of part of a population.

9. The method for selecting a stratified sample is to order a population in some way and then select members of the population at regular intervals.

10. To select a cluster sample, divide a population into groups and then select all of the members in at least one (but not all) of the groups.

Deciding on the Method of Data Collection *In Exercises 11–14, decide which method of data collection you would use to collect data for the study. Explain.*

11. A study of the effect on the human digestive system of potato chips made with a fat substitute

12. A study of the effect of a product's warning label to determine whether consumers still buy the product

13. A study of how fast a virus would spread in a metropolitan area

14. A study of the ages of the 535 members of the U.S. Congress

■ Using and Interpreting Concepts

15. Allergy Drug A pharmaceutical company wants to test the effectiveness of a new allergy drug. The company identifies 250 females 30–35 years old who suffer from severe allergies. The subjects are randomly assigned into two groups. One group is given the new allergy drug and the other is given a placebo that looks exactly like the new allergy drug. After six months, the subjects' symptoms are studied and compared.

(a) Identify the experimental units in this experiment.

(b) How many treatments are used in this experiment?

(c) Identify a potential problem with the experimental design being used and suggest a way to improve it.

(d) How could this experiment be designed to be double-blind?

16. **Sneakers** Nike developed a new type of sneaker designed to help delay the onset of arthritis in the knee. Eighty people with early signs of arthritis volunteered for a study. One-half of the volunteers wore the experimental sneaker and the other half wore regular Nike sneakers that looked exactly like the experimental sneakers. The individuals wore the sneakers every day. At the conclusion of the study, their symptoms were evaluated and an MRI was performed on their knees. *(Source: Washington Post)*

    (a) Identify the experimental units in this experiment.

    (b) How many treatments are used in this experiment?

    (c) Identify a potential problem with the experimental design being used and suggest a way to improve it.

    (d) The experiment is described as a placebo-controlled, double-blind study. Explain what this means.

    (e) Of the 80 volunteers, suppose 40 are men and 40 are women. How could blocking be used in designing this experiment?

Identifying Sampling Techniques   *In Exercises 17–26, identify the sampling technique used and discuss potential sources of bias (if any). Explain.*

17. Using random digit dialing, researchers called 1599 people and asked what obstacles (such as childcare) kept them from exercising. *(Source: Yankelovich Partners, Inc. for Shape Up America!)*

18. Chosen at random, 500 rural and 500 urban persons age 65 or older were asked about their health and experience with prescription drugs.

19. Questioning students as they left a university library, a researcher asked 358 students about their drinking habits.

20. After a hurricane, a disaster area is divided into 200 equal grids. Thirty of the grids are selected, and every occupied household in the grid is interviewed to help focus relief efforts on what residents require the most.

21. Chosen at random, 1210 hospital outpatients were contacted and asked their opinion of the care they received.

22. For quality assurance, every twentieth engine part is selected from an assembly line and tested for durability.

23. Soybeans are planted on a 48-acre field. The field is divided into one-acre subplots. A sample of plants is taken from each subplot to estimate the harvest.

24. Questioning teachers as they left a faculty lounge, a researcher asked 32 teachers about their teaching styles and grading methods.

25. A list of managers is compiled and ordered. After a starting number is randomly chosen, every ninth name is selected until 1000 managers are selected. The managers are questioned about the use of digital media.

26. From calls made with randomly generated telephone numbers, 1012 respondents were asked if they rented or owned their residence.

27. **Sleep Deprivation** A researcher wants to study the effects of sleep deprivation on motor skills. Eighteen people volunteer for the experiment: Jake, Maria, Mike, Lucy, Ron, Adam, Bridget, Carlos, Steve, Susan, Vanessa, Rick, Dan, Kate, Pete, Judy, Mary, and Connie. Use a random number generator to choose 9 subjects for the treatment group. The other 9 subjects will go into the control group. List the subjects in each group. Tell which method you used to generate the random numbers.

28. Random Number Generation   Volunteers for an experiment are numbered from 1 to 70. The volunteers are to be randomly assigned to two different treatment groups. Use a random number generator different from the one you used in Exercise 27 to choose 35 subjects for the treatment group. The other 35 subjects will go into the control group. List the subjects, according to number, in each group. Tell which method you used to generate the random numbers.

Choosing between a Census and a Sampling   *In Exercises 29 and 30, determine whether you would take a census or use a sampling. If you would use a sampling, decide what sampling technique you would use. Explain your reasoning.*

29. The average salary of the 50 employees of a company

30. The most popular car color among 25,000 students at a university

Recognizing a Biased Question   *In Exercises 31–34, determine whether the survey question is biased. If the question is biased, suggest a better wording.*

31. Why is drinking fruit juice good for you?

32. Why are drivers who change lanes several times dangerous?

33. How many hours of sleep do you get on an average night?

34. Do you think the media have a negative effect on teen girls' dieting habits?

35. Writing   Television program ratings by Nielsen Media Research are described on page 17. Discuss the strata used in the sample.

36. Writing   Television program ratings by Nielsen Media Research are described on page 17. Why is it important to have a stratified sample for these ratings?

■ Extending Concepts

37. Open and Closed Questions   Two types of survey questions are open questions and closed questions. An open question allows for any kind of response; a closed question allows only for a fixed response. An open question and a closed question with its possible choices are given below. List an advantage and a disadvantage of an open question. Then list an advantage and a disadvantage of a closed question.

Open Question   What can be done to get students to eat healthier foods?
Closed Question   How would you get students to eat healthier foods?
  1. Mandatory nutrition course
  2. Offer only healthy foods in the cafeteria and remove unhealthy foods
  3. Offer more healthy foods in the cafeteria and raise the prices on unhealthy foods

38. Who Picked These People?   Some polling agencies ask people to call a telephone number and give their response to a question. (a) List an advantage and a disadvantage of a survey conducted in this manner. (b) What sampling technique is used in such a survey?

39. Give an example of an experiment where confounding may occur.

40. Why is it important to use blinding in an experiment?

41. How are the placebo effect and Hawthorne effect similar? How are they different?

42. How is a randomized block design in experiments similar to a stratified sample?

43. Using Sampling Techniques   You have been asked by your school to survey 150 students who use the new fitness center. Describe your procedure for obtaining a sample of each type: random, stratified, cluster, systematic, and convenience.

ACTIVITY 1.3

APPLET

The *random numbers* applet is designed to allow you to generate random numbers from a range of values. You can specify integer values for the minimum value, maximum value, and the number of samples in the appropriate fields. You should not use decimal points when filling in the fields. When SAMPLE is clicked, the applet generates random values, which are displayed as a list in the text field.

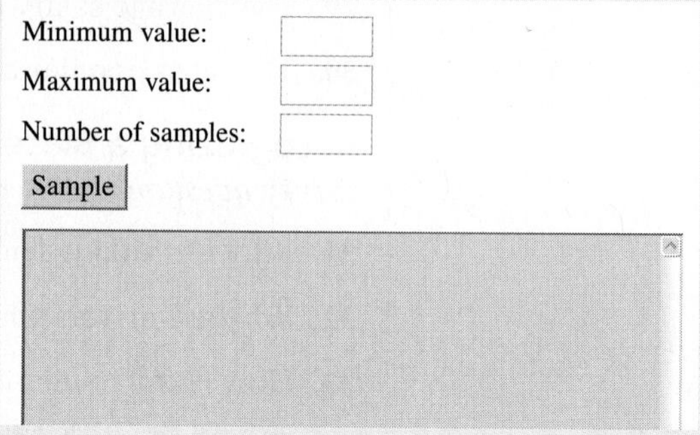

Minimum value:	
Maximum value:	
Number of samples:	

Sample

■ Explore

Step 1 Specify a minimum value.
Step 2 Specify a maximum value.
Step 3 Specify the number of samples.
Step 4 Click SAMPLE to generate a list of random values.

■ Draw Conclusions

APPLET

1. Specify the minimum, maximum, and number of samples to be 1, 20, and 8, respectively, as shown. Run the applet. Continue generating lists until you obtain one that shows that the random sample is taken with replacement. Write down this list. How do you know that the list is a random sample taken with replacement?

Minimum value:	1
Maximum value:	20
Number of samples:	8

Sample

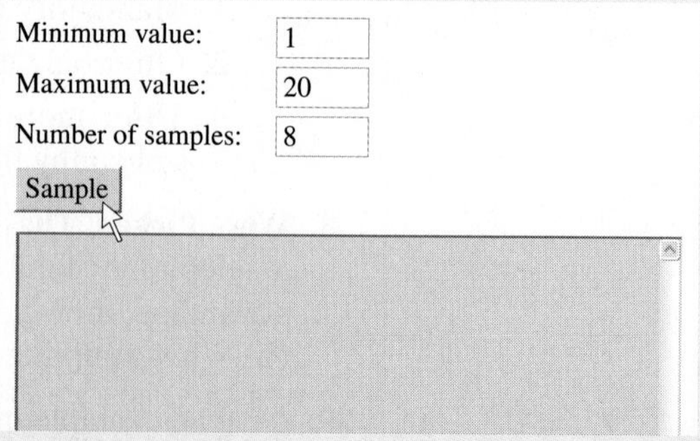

2. Use the applet to repeat Example 3 on page 22. What values did you use for the minimum, maximum, and number of samples? Which method do you prefer? Explain.

Uses & Abuses

Uses

Experiments with Favorable Results An experiment that began in March 2003 studied 321 women with advanced breast cancer. All of the women had been previously treated with other drugs, but the cancer had stopped responding to the medications. The women were then given the opportunity to take a new drug combined with a particular chemotherapy drug.

The subjects were divided into two groups, one that took the new drug combined with a chemotherapy drug, and one that took only the chemotherapy drug. After three years, results showed that the new drug in combination with the chemotherapy drug delayed the progression of cancer in the subjects. The results were so significant that the study was stopped, and the new drug was offered to all women in the study. The Food and Drug Administration has since approved use of the new drug in conjunction with a chemotherapy drug.

Abuses

Experiments with Unfavorable Results From 1988 to 1991, one hundred eighty thousand teenagers in Norway were used as subjects to test a new vaccine against the deadly bacteria *meningococcus b*. A brochure describing the possible effects of the vaccine stated, "it is unlikely to expect serious complications," while information provided to the Norwegian Parliament stated, "serious side effects can not be excluded." The vaccine trial had some disastrous results: More than 500 side effects were reported, with some considered serious, and several of the subjects developed serious neurological diseases. The results showed that the vaccine was providing immunity in only 57% of the cases. This result was not sufficient enough for the vaccine to be added to Norway's vaccination program. Compensations have since been paid to the vaccine victims.

Ethics

Experiments help us further understand the world that surrounds us. But, in some cases, they can do more harm than good. In the Norwegian experiments several ethical questions arise. Was the Norwegian experiment unethical if the best interests of the subjects were neglected? When should the experiment have been stopped? Should it have been conducted at all? If serious side effects are not reported and are withheld from subjects, there is no ethical question here, it is just wrong.

On the other hand, the breast cancer experiment would not want to deny the new drug for a group of patients with a life-threatening disease. But again, questions arise. How long must a researcher continue an experiment that shows better-than-expected results? How soon can a researcher conclude a drug is safe for the subjects involved?

■ EXERCISES

1. *Unfavorable Results* Find an example of a real-life experiment that had unfavorable results. What could have been done to avoid the outcome of the experiment?

2. *Stopping an Experiment* In your opinion, what are some problems that may arise if clinical trials of a new experimental drug or vaccine are stopped early and then distributed to other subjects or patients?

1 CHAPTER SUMMARY

What did you learn?

	EXAMPLE(S)	REVIEW EXERCISES
Section 1.1		
■ How to distinguish between a population and a sample	*1*	*1–4*
■ How to distinguish between a parameter and a statistic	*2*	*5–8*
■ How to distinguish between descriptive statistics and inferential statistics	*3*	*9, 10*
Section 1.2		
■ How to distinguish between qualitative data and quantitative data	*1*	*11–14*
■ How to classify data with respect to the four levels of measurement: nominal, ordinal, interval, and ratio	*2, 3*	*15–18*
Section 1.3		
■ How data are collected: by doing an observational study, performing an experiment, using a simulation, or using a survey	*1*	*19–22*
■ How to design an experiment	*2*	*23, 24*
■ How to create a sample using random sampling, simple random sampling, stratified sampling, cluster sampling, and systematic sampling	*3, 4*	*25–30*
■ How to identify a biased sample	*3, 4*	*31–34*

1 REVIEW EXERCISES

Section 1.1

In Exercises 1–4, identify the population and the sample.

1. A survey of 1000 U.S. adults found that 92% are worried about dependence on foreign oil. *(Source: Yale University)*

2. Thirty-eight nurses working in the San Francisco area were surveyed concerning their opinions of managed health care.

3. A study of 146 credit cards found that the average late fee is $27.46. *(Source: Consumer Action)*

4. A survey of 1205 physicians found that about 60% considered leaving the practice of medicine because they were discouraged over the state of U.S. health care. *(Source: The Physician Executive Journal of Medical Management)*

In Exercises 5–8, determine whether the numerical value describes a parameter or a statistic.

5. The 2006 team payroll of the New York Mets was $101,084,963. *(Source: U.S.A. Today)*

6. In a survey of 752 adults in the United States, 42% think there should be a law that prohibits people from talking on cell phones in public places. *(Source: University of Michigan)*

7. In a recent study of math majors at a university, 10 students were minoring in physics.

8. Nineteen percent of a sample of Indiana ninth graders surveyed said they smoked cigarettes daily. *(Source: Indiana University)*

9. Which part of the study described in Exercise 3 represents the descriptive branch of statistics? Make an inference based on the results of the study.

10. Which part of the survey described in Exercise 4 represents the descriptive branch of statistics? Make an inference based on the results of the survey.

Section 1.2

In Exercises 11–14, determine which data are qualitative data and which are quantitative data. Explain your reasoning.

11. The monthly salaries of the employees at an accounting firm

12. The Social Security numbers of the employees at an accounting firm

13. The ages of a sample of 350 employees of a software company

14. The zip codes of a sample of 350 customers at a sporting goods store

In Exercises 15–18, identify the data set's level of measurement. Explain your reasoning.

15. The daily high temperatures (in degrees Fahrenheit) for Mohave, Arizona, for a week in June are listed. *(Source: Arizona Meteorological Network)*

    93 91 86 94 103 104 103

16. The EPA size classes for a sample of automobiles are listed.

    subcompact compact midsize large compact large

17. The four departments of a printing company are listed.

Administration   Sales   Production   Billing

18. The heights (in inches) of the 2006 Los Angeles Sparks are listed. *(Source: Women's National Basketball Association)*

69   74   63   77   71   74   75   70   74   75   75   75   71

Section 1.3

In Exercises 19–22, decide which method of data collection you would use to collect data for the study. Explain your reasoning.

19. A study of charitable donations of the CEOs in Syracuse, New York

20. A study of the effect of kangaroos on the Florida Everglades ecosystem

21. A study of the effects of a fertilizer on a soybean crop

22. A study of college students' opinions on environmental pollution

In Exercises 23 and 24, an experiment is being performed to test the effects of sleep deprivation on memory recall. Two hundred students volunteer for the experiment. The students will be placed in one of five different treatment groups, including the control group.

23. Explain how you could design an experiment so that it uses a randomized block design.

24. Explain how you could design an experiment so that it uses a completely randomized design.

In Exercises 25–30, identify which sampling technique was used in the study. Explain your reasoning.

25. Calling randomly generated telephone numbers, a study asked 1001 U.S. adults which medical conditions could be prevented by their diet. *(Adapted from Wirthlin Worldwide)*

26. A student asks 18 friends to participate in a psychology experiment.

27. A pregnancy study in Cebu, Philippines, randomly selected 33 communities from the Cebu metropolitan area, then interviewed all available pregnant women in these communities. *(Adapted from Cebu Longitudinal Health and Nutrition Survey)*

28. Law enforcement officials stop and check the driver of every third vehicle for blood alcohol content.

29. Twenty-five students are randomly selected from each grade level at a high school and surveyed about their study habits.

30. A journalist interviews 154 people waiting at an airport baggage claim and asks them how safe they feel during air travel.

In Exercises 31–34, identify a bias or error that might occur in the indicated survey or study.

31. study in Exercise 25

32. experiment in Exercise 26

33. study in Exercise 27

34. sampling in Exercise 28

1 CHAPTER QUIZ

Take this quiz as you would take a quiz in class. After you are done, check your work against the answers given in the back of the book.

1. Identify the population and the sample in the following study.

   A study of 372 patients with anxiety disorders was conducted to find a link between coffee drinking and anxiety disorders.

2. Determine whether the numerical value is a parameter or a statistic.

   (a) In a survey of 798 Internet users, 19% said they have a wireless network in their home. *(Source: Pew Internet and American Life Project)*

   (b) In a vote, 84% of the employees at a company voted for new vending machines in the building.

   (c) A survey of about 1000 Americans shows that only 40% have an emergency savings account. *(Source: Consumer Federation of America)*

3. Determine whether the data are qualitative or quantitative.

   (a) A list of post office box numbers

   (b) The final exam scores in a chemistry class

4. Identify each data set's level of measurement. Explain your reasoning.

   (a) A list of badge numbers of police officers at a precinct

   (b) The number of candles sold by a candle manufacturer each quarter for the current fiscal year

   (c) The years of birth for the runners in the Boston marathon

5. Decide which method of data collection you would use to gather data for each study. Explain your reasoning.

   (a) A study on the effect of low dietary intake of vitamin C and iron on lead levels in adults

   (b) The ages of people living within 500 miles of your home

6. An experiment is being performed to test the effects of a new drug on high blood pressure. The experimenter identifies 320 people ages 35–50 years old with high blood pressure to participate in the experiment. The subjects are divided into equal groups according to age. Within each group, subjects are then randomly selected to be in either the treatment group or the control group. What type of experimental design is being used for this experiment?

7. Identify which sampling technique was used in each study. Explain your reasoning.

   (a) A journalist goes to a campground to ask people how they feel about air pollution.

   (b) For quality assurance, every tenth machine part is selected from an assembly line and measured for accuracy.

   (c) A study on attitudes about smoking is conducted at a college. The students are divided by class (freshman, sophomore, junior, and senior). Then a random sample is selected from each class and interviewed.

8. Which sampling technique used in Exercise 7 could lead to a biased study?

REAL Statistics — Real Decisions

You are a researcher for a professional research firm. Your firm has won a contract to do a study for an air travel industry publication. The editors of the publication would like to know their readers' thoughts on air travel in fields such as ticket purchase, services, safety, comfort, economic growth, and security. They would also like to know the thoughts of adults who use air travel for business as well as for recreation.

The editors have given you their readership database and 20 questions they would like to ask (two sample questions from a previous study are given at the right). You know that it is too expensive to contact all of the readers, so you need to determine a way to contact a representative sample of the entire readership population.

■ Exercises

1. *How Would You Do It?*

(a) What sampling technique would you use to select the sample for the study? Why?

(b) Will the technique you chose in part (a) give you a sample that is representative of the population?

(c) Describe the method for collecting data.

(d) Identify possible flaws or biases in your study.

2. *Data Classification*

(a) What type of data do you expect to collect: qualitative, quantitative, or both? Why?

(b) What levels of measurement do you think the data in the study will be? Why?

(c) Will the data collected for the study represent a population or a sample?

(d) Will the numerical descriptions of the data be parameters or statistics?

3. *How They Did It*

When the *Resource Systems Group* did a similar study, they used an Internet survey. They sent out 1000 invitations to participate in the survey and received 621 completed surveys.

(a) Describe some possible errors in collecting data by Internet surveys.

(b) Compare your method for collecting data in Exercise 1 to this method.

How did you acquire your ticket?

Response	Percent
Travel agent	35.1%
Directly from airline	20.9%
Online, using the airline's Web site	21.0%
Online, from a travel site other than the airline	18.5%
Other	4.5%

(Source: Resource Systems Group)

How many associates, friends, or family members traveled together in your party?

Response	Percent
1 (traveled alone)	48.7%
2 (traveled with one other person)	29.7%
3 (traveled with 2 others)	7.1%
4 (traveled with 3 others)	7.7%
5 (traveled with 4 others)	3.0%
6 or more (traveled with 5 or more others)	3.8%

(Source: Resource Systems Group)

HISTORY OF STATISTICS - TIMELINE

CONTRIBUTOR	TIME	CONTRIBUTION

John Graunt (1620–1674)

Blaise Pascal (1623–1662)
Pierre deFermat (1601–1665)

17th century

Studied records of deaths in London in the early 1600s. The first to make extensive statistical observations from massive amounts of data (Chapter 2), his work laid the foundation for modern statistics.

Pascal and Fermat corresponded about basic probability problems (Chapter 3)—especially those dealing with gaming and gambling.

Pierre Laplace (1749–1827)

Carl Friedrich Gauss (1777–1855)

18th century

Studied probability (Chapter 3) and is credited with putting probability on a sure mathematical footing.

Studied regression and the method of least squares (Chapter 9) through astronomy. In his honor, the normal distribution is sometimes called the Gaussian distribution.

Lambert Quetelet (1796–1874)

Francis Galton (1822–1911)

19th century

Used descriptive statistics (Chapter 2) to analyze crime and mortality data and studied census techniques. Described normal distributions (Chapter 5) in connection with human traits such as height.

Used regression and correlation (Chapter 9) to study genetic variation in humans. He is credited with the discovery of the Central Limit Theorem (Chapter 5).

Karl Pearson (1857–1936)

William Gosset (1876–1937)

Charles Spearman (1863–1945)

Ronald Fisher (1890–1962)

20th century

Studied natural selection using correlation (Chapter 9). Formed first academic department of statistics and helped develop chi-square analysis (Chapter 6).

Studied process of brewing and developed *t*-test to correct problems connected with small sample sizes (Chapter 6).

British psychologist who was one of the first to develop intelligence testing using factor analysis (Chapter 10).

Studied biology and natural selection and developed ANOVA (Chapter 10), stressed the importance of experimental design (Chapter 1), and was the first to identify the null and alternative hypotheses (Chapter 7).

Frank Wilcoxon (1892–1965)

John Tukey (1915–2000)

David Kendall (1918–   )

20th century (later)

Biochemist who used statistics to study plant pathology. He introduced two-sample tests (Chapter 8), which led the way to the development of nonparametric statistics.

Worked at Princeton during World War II. Introduced exploratory data analysis techniques such as stem-and-leaf plots (Chapter 2). Also, worked at Bell Laboratories and is best known for his work in inferential statistics (Chapters 6–11).

Worked at Princeton and Cambridge. Is a leading authority on applied probability and data analysis (Chapters 2 and 3).

TECHNOLOGY

USING TECHNOLOGY IN STATISTICS

With large data sets, you will find that calculators or computer software programs can help perform calculations and create graphics. Of the many calculators and statistical software programs that are available, we have chosen to incorporate the TI-83/84 graphing calculator and MINITAB and Excel software into this text.

The following example shows how to use these three technologies to generate a list of random numbers. This list of random numbers can be used to select sample members or perform simulations.

EXAMPLE

Generating a List of Random Numbers

A quality control department inspects a random sample of 15 of the 167 cars that are assembled at an auto plant. How should the cars be chosen?

Solution

One way to choose the sample is to first number the cars from 1 to 167. Then you can use technology to form a list of random numbers from 1 to 167. Each of the technology tools shown requires different steps to generate the list. Each, however, does require that you identify the minimum value as 1 and the maximum value as 167. Check your user's manual for specific instructions.

MINITAB

↓	C1
1	167
2	11
3	74
4	160
5	18
6	70
7	80
8	56
9	37
10	6
11	82
12	126
13	98
14	104
15	137

EXCEL

	A
1	41
2	16
3	91
4	58
5	151
6	36
7	96
8	154
9	2
10	113
11	157
12	103
13	64
14	135
15	90

TI-83/84

```
randInt(1, 167, 15)
{17 42 152 59 5
116 125 64 122 55
58 60 82 152 105}
```

Recall that when you generate a list of random numbers, you should decide whether it is acceptable to have numbers that repeat. If it is acceptable, then the sampling process is said to be with replacement. If it is not acceptable, then the sampling process is said to be without replacement.

With each of the three technology tools shown on page 36, you have the capability of sorting the list so that the numbers appear in order. Sorting helps you see whether any of the numbers in the list repeat. If it is not acceptable to have repeats, you should specify that the tool generate more random numbers than you need.

■ EXERCISES

1. The SEC (Securities and Exchange Commission) is investigating a financial services company. The company being investigated has 86 brokers. The SEC decides to review the records for a random sample of 10 brokers. Describe how this investigation could be done. Then use technology to generate a list of 10 random numbers from 1 to 86 and order the list.

2. A quality control department is testing 25 camera phones from a shipment of 300 camera phones. Describe how this test could be done. Then use technology to generate a list of 25 random numbers from 1 to 300 and order the list.

3. Consider the population of ten digits: 0, 1, 2, 3, 4, 5, 6, 7, 8, and 9. Select three random samples of five digits from this list. Find the average of each sample. Compare your results with the average of the entire population. Comment on your results. (*Hint:* To find the average, sum the data entries and divide the sum by the number of entries.)

4. Consider the population of 41 whole numbers from 0 to 40. What is the average of these numbers? Select three random samples of seven numbers from this list. Find the average of each sample. Compare your results with the average of the entire population. Comment on your results. (*Hint:* To find the average, sum the data entries and divide the sum by the number of entries.)

5. Use random numbers to simulate rolling a six-sided die 60 times. How many times did you obtain each number from 1 to 6? Are the results what you expected?

6. You rolled a six-sided die 60 times and got the following tally.

20 ones	20 twos	15 threes
3 fours	2 fives	0 sixes

Does this seem like a reasonable result? What inference might you draw from the result?

7. Use random numbers to simulate tossing a coin 100 times. Let 0 represent heads, and let 1 represent tails. How many times did you obtain each number? Are the results what you expected?

8. You tossed a coin 100 times and got 77 heads and 23 tails. Does this seem like a reasonable result? What inference might you draw from the result?

9. A political analyst would like to survey a sample of the registered voters in a county. The county has 47 election districts. How could the analyst use random numbers to obtain a cluster sample?

Extended solutions are given in the *Technology Supplement*. Technical instruction is provided for MINITAB, Excel, and the TI-83/84.

CHAPTER

2

Descriptive Statistics

2.1 Frequency Distributions and Their Graphs

2.2 More Graphs and Displays

2.3 Measures of Central Tendency

■ ACTIVITY

2.4 Measures of Variation

■ ACTIVITY

■ CASE STUDY

2.5 Measures of Position

■ USES AND ABUSES

■ REAL STATISTICS– REAL DECISIONS

■ TECHNOLOGY

In 2006, quarterback Colt Brennan of the University of Hawaii set an NCAA record for most touchdown passes in a single season (58).

In Chapter 1, you learned that there are many ways to collect data. Usually, researchers must work with sample data in order to analyze populations, but occasionally it is possible to collect all the data for a given population. For instance, the following represents the number of touchdowns scored by all 119 NCAA Division 1A football teams for the 2006 season.

89, 68, 65, 61, 63, 63, 61, 61, 59, 60, 54, 55, 54, 49, 53, 55, 59, 50, 52, 48, 53, 46, 55, 57, 48, 47, 48, 46, 44, 50, 55, 48, 45, 44, 46, 46, 47, 41, 39, 41, 45, 44, 45, 43, 42, 42, 48, 43, 40, 39, 44, 37, 40, 45, 43, 37, 38, 38, 36, 34, 37, 36, 35, 35, 35, 40, 31, 34, 35, 39, 38, 32, 35, 32, 32, 32, 33, 33, 33, 32, 34, 31, 31, 30, 34, 32, 31, 27, 32, 26, 28, 29, 28, 29, 31, 27, 29, 28, 27, 30, 25, 23, 24, 26, 22, 25, 20, 21, 21, 22, 21, 24, 21, 17, 15, 18, 18, 15, 15

In Chapter 2, you will learn ways to organize and describe data sets. The goal is to make the data easier to understand by describing trends, averages, and variations. For instance, in the raw data showing the number of touchdowns scored by all NCAA Division 1A football teams, it is not easy to see any patterns or special characteristics. Here are some ways you can organize and describe the data.

Make a frequency distribution table.

Class	Frequency, f
15–24	16
25–34	34
35–44	30
45–54	23
55–64	13
65–74	2
75–84	0
85–94	1

Draw a histogram.

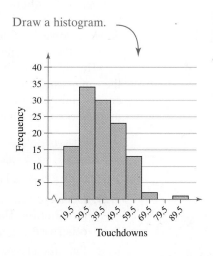

$$\text{Mean} = \frac{15 + 15 + 15 + 17 + 18 + \cdots + 63 + 65 + 68 + 89}{119}$$

$$= \frac{4624}{119}$$

$$\approx 38.9 \text{ touchdowns}$$

Find an average.

$$\text{Range} = 89 - 15$$

$$= 74 \text{ touchdowns}$$

Find how the data vary.

2.1 Frequency Distributions and Their Graphs

What You
SHOULD LEARN

▸ How to construct a frequency distribution including limits, midpoints, relative frequencies, cumulative frequencies, and boundaries

▸ How to construct frequency histograms, frequency polygons, relative frequency histograms, and ogives

Frequency Distributions ▸ Graphs of Frequency Distributions

▸ Frequency Distributions

You will learn that there are many ways to organize and describe a data set. Important characteristics to look for when organizing and describing a data set are its **center,** its **variability** (or spread), and its **shape.** Measures of center and shapes of distributions are covered in Lesson 2.3.

When a data set has many entries, it can be difficult to see patterns. In this section, you will learn how to organize data sets by grouping the data into intervals called classes and forming a frequency distribution. You will also learn how to use frequency distributions to construct graphs.

> **DEFINITION**
>
> A **frequency distribution** is a table that shows **classes** or **intervals** of data entries with a count of the number of entries in each class. The **frequency** f of a class is the number of data entries in the class.

Example of a Frequency Distribution

Class	Frequency, f
1–5	5
6–10	8
11–15	6
16–20	8
21–25	5
26–30	4

In the frequency distribution shown to the left there are six classes. The frequencies for each of the six classes are 5, 8, 6, 8, 5, and 4. Each class has a **lower class limit,** which is the least number that can belong to the class, and an **upper class limit,** which is the greatest number that can belong to the class. In the frequency distribution shown, the lower class limits are 1, 6, 11, 16, 21, and 26, and the upper class limits are 5, 10, 15, 20, 25, and 30. The **class width** is the distance between lower (or upper) limits of consecutive classes. For instance, the class width in the frequency distribution shown is $6 - 1 = 5$.

The difference between the maximum and minimum data entries is called the **range.** In the frequency table shown, suppose the maximum data entry is 29, and the minimum data entry is 1. The range then is $29 - 1 = 28$. You will learn more about the range in Section 2.4.

> **GUIDELINES**
>
> Constructing a Frequency Distribution from a Data Set
>
> 1. Decide on the number of classes to include in the frequency distribution. The number of classes should be between 5 and 20; otherwise, it may be difficult to detect any patterns.
>
> 2. Find the class width as follows. Determine the range of the data, divide the range by the number of classes, and *round up to the next convenient number*.
>
> 3. Find the class limits. You can use the minimum data entry as the lower limit of the first class. To find the remaining lower limits, add the class width to the lower limit of the preceding class. Then find the upper limit of the first class. Remember that classes cannot overlap. Find the remaining upper class limits.
>
> 4. Make a tally mark for each data entry in the row of the appropriate class.
>
> 5. Count the tally marks to find the total frequency f for each class.

Study Tip

In a frequency distribution, it is best if each class has the same width. Answers shown will use the minimum data value for the lower limit of the first class. Sometimes it may be more convenient to choose a value that is slightly lower than the minimum value. The frequency distribution produced will vary slightly.

> ### E X A M P L E 1
>
> ## Constructing a Frequency Distribution from a Data Set
>
> The following sample data set lists the number of minutes 50 Internet subscribers spent on the Internet during their most recent session. Construct a frequency distribution that has seven classes.
>
> | | | | | | | | | | | | | | | | | |
> |---|---|---|---|---|---|---|---|---|---|---|---|---|---|---|---|---|
> | 50 | 40 | 41 | 17 | 11 | 7 | 22 | 44 | 28 | 21 | 19 | 23 | 37 | 51 | 54 | 42 | 86 |
> | 41 | 78 | 56 | 72 | 56 | 17 | 7 | 69 | 30 | 80 | 56 | 29 | 33 | 46 | 31 | 39 | 20 |
> | 18 | 29 | 34 | 59 | 73 | 77 | 36 | 39 | 30 | 62 | 54 | 67 | 39 | 31 | 53 | 44 | |

Solution

1. The number of classes (7) is stated in the problem.

2. The minimum data entry is 7 and the maximum data entry is 86, so the range is $86 - 7 = 79$. Divide the range by the number of classes and round up to find the class width.

$$\text{Class width} = \frac{79}{7} \qquad \frac{\text{Range}}{\text{Number of classes}}$$

$$\approx 11.29 \qquad \text{Round up to 12.}$$

3. The minimum data entry is a convenient lower limit for the first class. To find the lower limits of the remaining six classes, add the class width of 12 to the lower limit of each previous class. The upper limit of the first class is 18, which is one less than the lower limit of the second class. The upper limits of the other classes are $18 + 12 = 30$, $30 + 12 = 42$, and so on. The lower and upper limits for all seven classes are shown.

4. Make a tally mark for each data entry in the appropriate class. For example, the data entry 51 is in the 43–54 class, so make a tally mark in that class. Continue until you have made a tally mark for each of the 50 data entries.

5. The number of tally marks for a class is the frequency for that class.

The frequency distribution is shown in the following table. The first class, 7–18, has six tally marks. So, the frequency for this class is 6. Notice that the sum of the frequencies is 50, which is the number of entries in the sample data set. The sum is denoted by $\sum f$, where $\sum$ is the uppercase Greek letter **sigma.**

Lower limit	Upper limit
7	18
19	30
31	42
43	54
55	66
67	78
79	90

Frequency Distribution for Internet Usage (in minutes)

Minutes online →

Class	Tally	Frequency, f
7–18	$\cancel{||||}\ |$	6
19–30	$\cancel{||||}\ \cancel{||||}$	10
31–42	$\cancel{||||}\ \cancel{||||}\ |||$	13
43–54	$\cancel{||||}\ |||$	8
55–66	$\cancel{||||}$	5
67–78	$\cancel{||||}\ |$	6
79–90	$||$	2
		$\sum f = 50$

← Number of subscribers

Check that the sum of the frequencies equals the number in the sample.

Insight

If you obtain a whole number when calculating the class width of a frequency distribution, use the next whole number as the class width.
Doing this ensures that you have enough space in your frequency distribution for all the data values.

Study Tip

The uppercase Greek letter sigma ($\sum$) is used throughout statistics to indicate a summation of values.

▶ Try It Yourself 1

Construct a frequency distribution using the number of touchdowns data set listed in the Chapter Opener on page 39. Use eight classes.

a. State the *number of classes*.
b. Find the minimum and maximum values and the *class width*.
c. Find the *class limits*.
d. *Tally* the data entries.
e. Write the *frequency f* for each class.   *Answer: Page A32*

After constructing a standard frequency distribution such as the one in Example 1, you can include several additional features that will help provide a better understanding of the data. These features, (the midpoint, relative frequency, and cumulative frequency of each class,) can be included as additional columns in your table.

DEFINITION

The **midpoint** of a class is the sum of the lower and upper limits of the class divided by two. The midpoint is sometimes called the *class mark*.

$$\text{Midpoint} = \frac{(\text{Lower class limit}) + (\text{Upper class limit})}{2}$$

The **relative frequency** of a class is the portion or percentage of the data that falls in that class. To find the relative frequency of a class, divide the frequency f by the sample size n.

$$\text{Relative frequency} = \frac{\text{Class frequency}}{\text{Sample size}}$$

$$= \frac{f}{n}$$

The **cumulative frequency** of a class is the sum of the frequency for that class and all previous classes. The cumulative frequency of the last class is equal to the sample size n.

After finding the first midpoint, you can find the remaining midpoints by adding the class width to the previous midpoint. For instance, if the first midpoint is 12.5 and the class width is 12, then the remaining midpoints are

$$12.5 + 12 = 24.5$$

$$24.5 + 12 = 36.5$$

$$36.5 + 12 = 48.5$$

$$48.5 + 12 = 60.5$$

and so on.

You can write the relative frequency as a fraction, decimal, or percent. The sum of the relative frequencies of all the classes must equal 1, or 100%.

EXAMPLE 2

Finding Midpoints, Relative Frequencies, and Cumulative Frequencies

Using the frequency distribution constructed in Example 1, find the midpoint, relative frequency, and cumulative frequency for each class. Identify any patterns.

Solution The midpoint, relative frequency, and cumulative frequency for the first three classes are calculated as follows.

Class	f	Midpoint	Relative frequency	Cumulative frequency
7–18	6	$\dfrac{7+18}{2}=12.5$	$\dfrac{6}{50}=0.12$	6
19–30	10	$\dfrac{19+30}{2}=24.5$	$\dfrac{10}{50}=0.2$	$6+10=16$
31–42	13	$\dfrac{31+42}{2}=36.5$	$\dfrac{13}{50}=0.26$	$16+13=29$

The remaining midpoints, relative frequencies, and cumulative frequencies are shown in the following expanded frequency distribution.

Frequency Distribution for Internet Usage (in minutes)

Minutes online

Number of subscribers

Portion of subscribers

Class	Frequency, f	Midpoint	Relative frequency	Cumulative frequency
7–18	6	12.5	0.12	6
19–30	10	24.5	0.2	16
31–42	13	36.5	0.26	29
43–54	8	48.5	0.16	37
55–66	5	60.5	0.1	42
67–78	6	72.5	0.12	48
79–90	2	84.5	0.04	50
	$\Sigma f = 50$		$\Sigma\dfrac{f}{n}=1$	

Interpretation There are several patterns in the data set. For instance, the most common time span that users spent online was 31 to 42 minutes.

▶ Try It Yourself 2

Using the frequency distribution constructed in Try It Yourself 1, find the midpoint, relative frequency, and cumulative frequency for each class. Identify any patterns.

a. Use the formulas to find each *midpoint*, *relative frequency*, and *cumulative frequency*.
b. *Organize* your results in a frequency distribution.
c. *Identify* patterns that emerge from the data.   *Answer: Page A32*

▶ Graphs of Frequency Distributions

Sometimes it is easier to identify patterns of a data set by looking at a graph of the frequency distribution. One such graph is a frequency histogram.

DEFINITION

A **frequency histogram** is a bar graph that represents the frequency distribution of a data set. A histogram has the following properties.

1. The horizontal scale is quantitative and measures the data values.
2. The vertical scale measures the frequencies of the classes.
3. Consecutive bars must touch.

Because consecutive bars of a histogram must touch, bars must begin and end at class boundaries instead of class limits. **Class boundaries** are the numbers that separate classes *without* forming gaps between them. You can mark the horizontal scale either at the midpoints or at the class boundaries, as shown in Example 3.

Study Tip

If data entries are integers, subtract 0.5 from each lower limit to find the lower class boundaries. To find the upper class boundaries, add 0.5 to each upper limit. The upper boundary of a class will equal the lower boundary of the next higher class.

EXAMPLE 3

Constructing a Frequency Histogram

Draw a frequency histogram for the frequency distribution in Example 2. Describe any patterns.

Solution First, find the class boundaries. The distance from the upper limit of the first class to the lower limit of the second class is $19 - 18 = 1$. Half this distance is 0.5. So, the lower and upper boundaries of the first class are as follows:

First class lower boundary $= 7 - 0.5 = 6.5$

First class upper boundary $= 18 + 0.5 = 18.5$

The boundaries of the remaining classes are shown in the table. Using the class midpoints or class boundaries for the horizontal scale and choosing possible frequency values for the vertical scale, you can construct the histogram.

Class	Class boundaries	Frequency, f
7–18	6.5–18.5	6
19–30	18.5–30.5	10
31–42	30.5–42.5	13
43–54	42.5–54.5	8
55–66	54.5–66.5	5
67–78	66.5–78.5	6
79–90	78.5–90.5	2

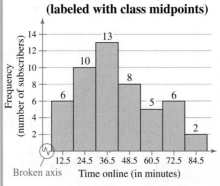

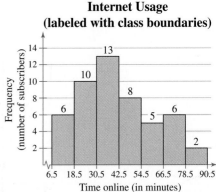

Insight

It is customary in bar graphs to have spaces between the bars, whereas with histograms, it is customary that the bars have no spaces between them.

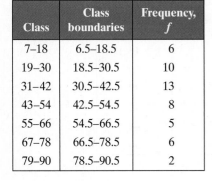

Interpretation From either histogram, you can see that more than half of the subscribers spent between 19 and 54 minutes on the Internet during their most recent session.

▶ **Try It Yourself 3**

Use the frequency distribution from Try It Yourself 1 to construct a frequency histogram that represents the number of touchdowns scored by all Division 1A football teams. Describe any patterns.

a. Find the *class boundaries*.
b. Choose appropriate *horizontal and vertical scales*.
c. Use the frequency distribution to *find the height of each bar*.
d. *Describe* any patterns for the data.   *Answer: Page A33*

Another way to graph a frequency distribution is to use a frequency polygon. A **frequency polygon** is a line graph that emphasizes the continuous change in frequencies.

EXAMPLE 4

Constructing a Frequency Polygon

Draw a frequency polygon for the frequency distribution in Example 2.

Solution   To construct the frequency polygon, use the same horizontal and vertical scales that were used in the histogram labeled with class midpoints in Example 3. Then plot points that represent the midpoint and frequency of each class and connect the points in order from left to right. Because the graph should begin and end on the horizontal axis, extend the left side to one class width before the first class midpoint and extend the right side to one class width after the last class midpoint.

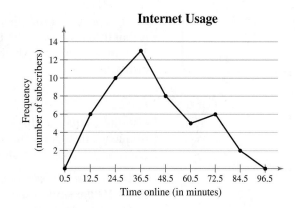

Internet Usage

Interpretation   You can see that the frequency of subscribers increases up to 36.5 minutes and then decreases.

▶ **Try It Yourself 4**

Use the frequency distribution from Try It Yourself 1 to construct a frequency polygon that represents the number of touchdowns scored by all Division 1A football teams. Describe any patterns.

a. Choose appropriate *horizontal* and *vertical scales*.
b. *Plot points* that represent the midpoint and frequency for each class.
c. *Connect the points* and extend the sides as necessary.
d. *Describe* any patterns for the data.   *Answer: Page A33*

A **relative frequency histogram** has the same shape and the same horizontal scale as the corresponding frequency histogram. The difference is that the vertical scale measures the *relative* frequencies, not frequencies.

EXAMPLE 5

Constructing a Relative Frequency Histogram

Draw a relative frequency histogram for the frequency distribution in Example 2.

Solution   The relative frequency histogram is shown. Notice that the shape of the histogram is the same as the shape of the frequency histogram constructed in Example 3. The only difference is that the vertical scale measures the relative frequencies.

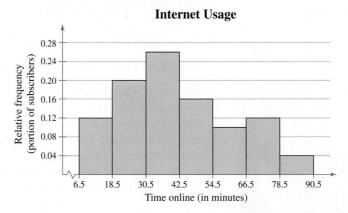

Internet Usage

Interpretation   From this graph, one piece of information you can quickly see is that 0.20 or 20% of the Internet subscribers spent between 18.5 minutes and 30.5 minutes online, which is not as immediately obvious from the frequency histogram.

▶ Try It Yourself 5

Use the frequency distribution from Try It Yourself 1 to construct a relative frequency histogram that represents the number of touchdowns scored by all Division 1A football teams.

a. *Use the same horizontal scale* as used in the frequency histogram.
b. *Revise the vertical scale* to reflect relative frequencies.
c. Use the relative frequencies to *find the height of each bar*.

Answer: Page A33

If you want to describe the number of data entries that are equal to or below a certain value, you can easily do so by constructing a cumulative frequency graph.

DEFINITION

A **cumulative frequency graph,** or **ogive** (pronounced ō′jīve), is a line graph that displays the cumulative frequency of each class at its upper class boundary. The upper boundaries are marked on the horizontal axis, and the cumulative frequencies are marked on the vertical axis.

GUIDELINES

Constructing an Ogive (Cumulative Frequency Graph)

1. Construct a frequency distribution that includes cumulative frequencies as one of the columns.
2. Specify the horizontal and vertical scales. The horizontal scale consists of upper class boundaries, and the vertical scale measures cumulative frequencies.
3. Plot points that represent the upper class boundaries and their corresponding cumulative frequencies.
4. Connect the points in order from left to right.
5. The graph should start at the lower boundary of the first class (cumulative frequency is zero) and should end at the upper boundary of the last class (cumulative frequency is equal to the sample size).

EXAMPLE 6

Constructing an Ogive

Draw an ogive for the frequency distribution in Example 2. Estimate how many subscribers spent 60 minutes or less online during their last session. Also, use the graph to estimate when the greatest increase in usage occurs.

Solution   Using the cumulative frequency distribution, you can construct the ogive shown. The upper class boundaries, frequencies, and cumulative frequencies are shown in the table. Notice that the graph starts at 6.5, where the cumulative frequency is 0, and the graph ends at 90.5, where the cumulative frequency is 50.

Upper class boundary	f	Cumulative frequency
18.5	6	6
30.5	10	16
42.5	13	29
54.5	8	37
66.5	5	42
78.5	6	48
90.5	2	50

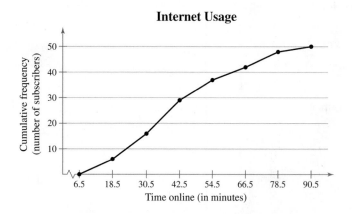

Internet Usage

Interpretation   From the ogive, you can see that about 40 subscribers spent 60 minutes or less online during their last session. It is evident that the greatest increase in usage occurs between 30.5 minutes and 42.5 minutes, as the line segment is steepest between these two class boundaries.

Another type of ogive uses percent as the vertical axis instead of frequency (see Example 5 in Section 2.5).

▶ **Try It Yourself 6**

Use the frequency distribution from Try It Yourself 1 to construct an ogive that represents the number of touchdowns scored by all Division 1A football teams. Estimate the number of teams who scored 44 or fewer touchdowns.

a. *Specify* the *horizontal* and *vertical scales*.
b. *Plot* the points given by the upper class boundaries and the cumulative frequencies.
c. *Construct* the graph.
d. *Estimate* the number of teams who scored 44 or fewer touchdowns.
e. *Interpret* the results in the context of the data. *Answer: Page A33*

E X A M P L E   7

Using Technology to Construct Histograms

Use a calculator or a computer to construct a histogram for the frequency distribution in Example 2.

Solution MINITAB, Excel, and the TI-83/84 each have features for graphing histograms. Try using this technology to draw the histograms as shown.

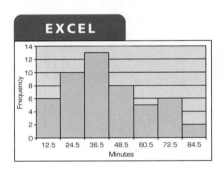

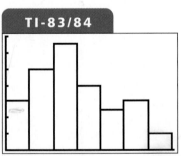

▶ **Try It Yourself 7**

Use a calculator or a computer to construct a frequency histogram that represents the number of touchdowns scored by all Division 1A football teams listed in the Chapter Opener on page 39. Use eight classes.

a. *Enter* the data.
b. *Construct* the histogram. *Answer: Page A33*

2.1 EXERCISES

For Extra Help

MyStatLab

■ Building Basic Skills and Vocabulary

1. What are some benefits of representing data sets using frequency distributions?

2. What are some benefits of representing data sets using graphs of frequency distributions?

3. What is the difference between class limits and class boundaries?

4. What is the difference between relative frequency and cumulative frequency?

True or False? *In Exercises 5–8, determine whether the statement is true or false. If it is false, rewrite it as a true statement.*

5. In a frequency distribution, the class width is the distance between the lower and upper limits of a class.

6. The midpoint of a class is the sum of its lower and upper limits divided by two.

7. An ogive is a graph that displays relative frequency.

8. Class boundaries are used to ensure that consecutive bars of a histogram touch.

In Exercises 9–12, use the given minimum and maximum data entries, and the number of classes to find the class width, the lower class limits, and the upper class limits.

9. minimum $= 7$, maximum $= 58$, 6 classes

10. minimum $= 11$, maximum $= 94$, 8 classes

11. minimum $= 15$, maximum $= 123$, 6 classes

12. minimum $= 24$, maximum $= 171$, 10 classes

Reading a Frequency Distribution *In Exercises 13 and 14, use the given frequency distribution to find the*

(a) *class width.*

(b) *class midpoints.*

(c) *class boundaries.*

13. **Cleveland, OH High Temperatures (°F)**

Class	Frequency, f
20–30	19
31–41	43
42–52	68
53–63	69
64–74	74
75–85	68
86–96	24

14. **Travel Time to Work (in minutes)**

Class	Frequency, f
0–9	188
10–19	372
20–29	264
30–39	205
40–49	83
50–59	76
60–69	32

365

15. Use the frequency distribution in Exercise 13 to construct an expanded frequency distribution, as shown in Example 2.

16. Use the frequency distribution in Exercise 14 to construct an expanded frequency distribution, as shown in Example 2.

Graphical Analysis *In Exercises 17 and 18, use the frequency histogram to*

(a) determine the number of classes.

(b) estimate the frequency of the class with the least frequency.

(c) estimate the frequency of the class with the greatest frequency.

(d) determine the class width.

17. **18.**

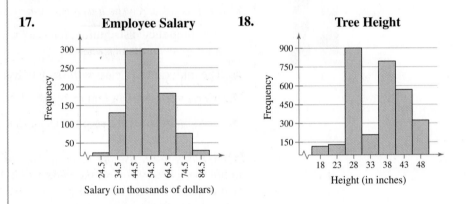

Graphical Analysis *In Exercises 19 and 20, use the ogive to approximate*

(a) the number in the sample.

(b) the location of the greatest increase in frequency.

19. **20.**

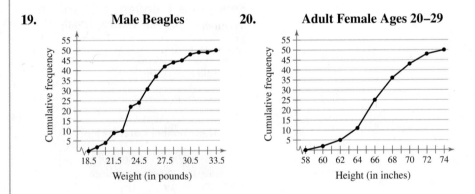

21. Use the ogive in Exercise 19 to approximate

(a) the cumulative frequency for a weight of 24.5 pounds.

(b) the weight for which the cumulative frequency is 45.

22. Use the ogive in Exercise 20 to approximate

(a) the cumulative frequency for a height of 70 inches.

(b) the height for which the cumulative frequency is 25.

Graphical Analysis *In Exercises 23 and 24, use the relative frequency histogram to*

(a) *identify the class with the greatest and the least relative frequency.*

(b) *approximate the greatest and least relative frequency.*

(c) *approximate the relative frequency of the second class.*

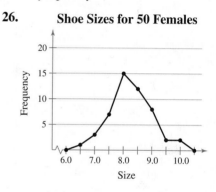

23.   **Atlantic Croaker Fish**

24.   **Emergency Response Time**

Graphical Analysis *In Exercises 25 and 26, use the frequency polygon to identify the class with the greatest and the least frequency.*

25.   **SAT Scores for 50 Students**

26.   **Shoe Sizes for 50 Females**

■ Using and Interpreting Concepts

Constructing a Frequency Distribution *In Exercises 27 and 28, construct a frequency distribution for the data set using the indicated number of classes. In the table, include the midpoints, relative frequencies, and cumulative frequencies. Which class has the greatest frequency and which has the least frequency?*

27. Newspaper Reading Times

Number of classes: 5

Data set: Time (in minutes) spent reading the newspaper in a day

7   39   13   9   25   8   22   0   2   18   2   30   7
35   12   15   8   6   5   29   0   11   39   16   15

28. Book Spending

Number of classes: 6

Data set: Amount (in dollars) spent on books for a semester

91   472   279   249   530   376   188   341   266   199
142   273   189   130   489   266   248   101   375   486
190   398   188   269   43   30   127   354   84

indicates that the data set for this exercise is available electronically.

Constructing a Frequency Distribution and a Frequency Histogram

In Exercises 29–32, construct a frequency distribution and a frequency histogram for the data set using the indicated number of classes. Describe any patterns.

29. Sales

Number of classes: 6

Data set: July sales (in dollars) for all sales representatives at a company

2114	2468	7119	1876	4105	3183	1932	1355
4278	1030	2000	1077	5835	1512	1697	2478
3981	1643	1858	1500	4608	1000		

30. Pepper Pungencies

Number of classes: 5

Data set: Pungencies (in 1000s of Scoville units) of 24 tabasco peppers

35	51	44	42	37	38	36	39	44	43	40	40
32	39	41	38	42	39	40	46	37	35	41	39

31. Reaction Times

Number of classes: 8

Data set: Reaction times (in milliseconds) of a sample of 30 adult females to an auditory stimulus

507	389	305	291	336	310	514	442	307	337
373	428	387	454	323	441	388	426	469	351
411	382	320	450	309	416	359	388	422	413

32. Fracture Times

Number of classes: 5

Data set: Amount of pressure (in pounds per square inch) at fracture time for 25 samples of brick mortar

2750	2862	2885	2490	2512	2456	2554	2532	2885
2872	2601	2877	2721	2692	2888	2755	2853	2517
2867	2718	2641	2834	2466	2596	2519		

Constructing a Frequency Distribution and a Relative Frequency Histogram

In Exercises 33–36, construct a frequency distribution and a relative frequency histogram for the data set using five classes. Which class has the greatest relative frequency and which has the least relative frequency?

33. Bowling Scores

Data set: Bowling scores of a sample of league members

154	257	195	220	182	240	177	228	235
146	174	192	165	207	185	180	264	169
225	239	148	190	182	205	148	188	

34. ATM Withdrawals

Data set: A sample of ATM withdrawals (in dollars)

35	10	30	25	75	10	30	20	20	10	40
50	40	30	60	70	25	40	10	60	20	80
40	25	20	10	20	25	30	50	80	20	

35. Plant Heights

Data set: Heights (in inches) of a sample of tomato plants

40 44 35 49 35 43 35 36 39
37 41 41 48 52 37 45 40 36
35 50 42 51 33 34 51 39

36. Years of Service

Data set: Years of service of a sample of New York state troopers

12 7 9 8 9 8 12 10 9
10 6 8 13 12 10 11 7 14
12 9 8 10 9 11 13 8

Constructing a Cumulative Frequency Distribution and an Ogive

In Exercises 37–40, construct a cumulative frequency distribution and an ogive for the data set using six classes. Then describe the location of the greatest increase in frequency.

37. Retirement Ages

Data set: Retirement ages for a sample of doctors

70 54 55 71 57 58 63 65
60 66 57 62 63 60 63 60
66 60 67 69 69 52 61 73

38. Saturated Fat Intakes

Data set: Daily saturated fat intakes (in grams) of a sample of people

38 32 34 39 40 54 32 17 29 33
57 40 25 36 33 24 42 16 31 33

39. Gasoline Purchases

Data set: Gasoline (in gallons) purchased by a sample of drivers during one fill-up

7   4   18 4   9   8   8   7   6   2
9   5   9   12 4   14 15 7   10 2
3   11 4   4   9   12 5   3

40. Cellular Phone Calls

Data set: Lengths (in minutes) of a sample of cellular phone calls

1   20 10 20 13 23 3   7
18 7   4   5   15 7   29 10
18 10 10 23 4   12 8   6

Constructing a Frequency Distribution and a Frequency Polygon

In Exercises 41 and 42, construct a frequency distribution and a frequency polygon for the data set. Describe any patterns.

41. Exam Scores

Number of classes: 5

Data set: Exam scores for all students in a statistics class

83 92 94 82 73 98 78 85 72 90
89 92 96 89 75 85 63 47 75 82

42. Children of the Presidents

Number of classes: 6

Data set: Number of children of the U.S. presidents *(Source: presidentschildren.com)*

0 5 6 0 3 4 0 4 10 15 0 6 2 3
0 4 5 4 8 7 3 5 3 2 6 3 3 1
2 2 6 1 2 3 2 2 4 4 4 6 1 2

■ Extending Concepts

43. What Would You Do?   You work at a bank and are asked to recommend the amount of cash to put in an ATM each day. You don't want to put in too much (security) or too little (customer irritation). Here are the daily withdrawals (in 100s of dollars) for a period of 30 days.

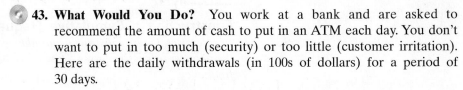

72 84 61 76 104 76 86 92 80 88
98 76 97 82 84 67 70 81 82 89
74 73 86 81 85 78 82 80 91 83

(a) Construct a relative frequency histogram for the data using eight classes.

(b) If you put $9000 in the ATM each day, what percent of the days in a month should you expect to run out of cash? Explain your reasoning.

(c) If you are willing to run out of cash for 10% of the days, how much cash, in hundreds of dollars, should you put in the ATM each day? Explain your reasoning.

44. What Would You Do?   You work in the admissions department for a college and are asked to recommend the minimum SAT scores that the college will accept for a position as a full-time student. Here are the SAT scores for a sample of 50 applicants.

1325	1072	982	996	872	849	785	706	669	1049
885	1367	935	980	1188	869	1006	1127	979	1034
1052	1165	1359	667	1264	727	808	955	544	1202
1051	1173	410	1148	1195	1141	1193	768	812	887
1211	1266	830	672	917	988	791	1035	688	700

(a) Construct a relative frequency histogram for the data using 10 classes.

(b) If you set the minimum score at 986, what percent of the applicants will meet this requirement? Explain your reasoning.

(c) If you want to accept the top 88% of the applicants, what should the minimum score be? Explain your reasoning.

45. Writing   What happens when the number of classes is increased for a frequency histogram? Use the data set listed and a technology tool to create frequency histograms with 5, 10, and 20 classes. Which graph displays the data best?

2 7 3 2 11 3 15 8 4 9 10 13 9
7 11 10 1 2 12 5 6 4 2 9 15

2.2 More Graphs and Displays

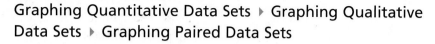

Graphing Quantitative Data Sets ▸ Graphing Qualitative Data Sets ▸ Graphing Paired Data Sets

What You SHOULD LEARN

▸ How to graph and interpret quantitative data sets using stem-and-leaf plots and dot plots

▸ How to graph and interpret qualitative data sets using pie charts and Pareto charts

▸ How to graph and interpret paired data sets using scatter plots and time series charts

▸ Graphing Quantitative Data Sets

In Section 2.1, you learned several traditional ways to display quantitative data graphically. In this section, you will learn a newer way to display quantitative data, called a **stem-and-leaf plot.** Stem-and-leaf plots are examples of **exploratory data analysis (EDA),** which was developed by John Tukey in 1977.

In a stem-and-leaf plot, each number is separated into a **stem** (for instance, the entry's leftmost digits) and a **leaf** (for instance, the rightmost digit). You should have as many leaves as there are entries in the original data set. A stem-and-leaf plot is similar to a histogram but has the advantage that the graph still contains the original data values. Another advantage of a stem-and-leaf plot is that it provides an easy way to sort data.

EXAMPLE 1

Constructing a Stem-and-Leaf Plot

The following are the numbers of text messages sent last month by the cellular phone users on one floor of a college dormitory.

155 159 144 129 105 145 126 116 130 114 122 112 112 142 126
118 118 108 122 121 109 140 126 119 113 117 118 109 109 119
139 139 122 78 133 126 123 145 121 134 124 119 132 133 124
129 112 126 148 147

Solution   Because the data entries go from a low of 78 to a high of 159, you should use stem values from 7 to 15. To construct the plot, list these stems to the left of a vertical line. For each data entry, list a leaf to the right of its stem. For instance, the entry 155 has a stem of 15 and a leaf of 5. The resulting stem-and-leaf plot will be unordered. To obtain an ordered stem-and-leaf plot, rewrite the plot with the leaves in increasing order from left to right. It is important to include a key for the display to identify the values of the data.

Number of Text Messages Sent

7	8	Key: 15|5 = 155
8		
9		
10	5 8 9 9 9	
11	6 4 2 2 8 8 9 3 7 8 9 9 2	
12	9 6 2 6 2 1 6 2 6 3 1 4 4 9 6	
13	0 9 9 3 4 2 3	
14	4 5 2 0 5 8 7	
15	5 9	

Unordered Stem-and-Leaf Plot

Number of Text Messages Sent

7	8	Key: 15|5 = 155
8		
9		
10	5 8 9 9 9	
11	2 2 2 3 4 6 7 8 8 8 9 9 9	
12	1 1 2 2 2 3 4 4 6 6 6 6 6 9 9	
13	0 2 3 3 4 9 9	
14	0 2 4 5 5 7 8	
15	5 9	

Ordered Stem-and-Leaf Plot

Interpretation   From the ordered stem-and-leaf plot, you can conclude that more than 50% of the cellular phone users sent between 110 and 130 text messages.

Insight

You can use stem-and-leaf plots to identify unusual data values called **outliers.** In Example 1, the data value 78 is an outlier. You will learn more about outliers in Section 2.3.

▶ **Try It Yourself 1**

Use a stem-and-leaf plot to organize the number of touchdowns data set listed in the Chapter Opener on page 39. What can you conclude?

a. List all possible *stems*.
b. List the leaf of each data entry to the right of its stem and include a key.
c. Rewrite the stem-and-leaf plot so that the leaves are ordered.
d. Use the plot to make a conclusion. *Answer: Page A33*

EXAMPLE 2

Constructing Variations of Stem-and-Leaf Plots

Organize the data given in Example 1 using a stem-and-leaf plot that has two rows for each stem. What can you conclude?

Solution Construct the stem-and-leaf plot as described in Example 1, except now list each stem twice. Use the leaves 0, 1, 2, 3, and 4 in the first stem row and the leaves 5, 6, 7, 8, and 9 in the second stem row. The revised stem-and-leaf plot is shown.

<table>
<tr><td colspan="2">**Number of Text Messages Sent**</td><td colspan="2">**Number of Text Messages Sent**</td></tr>
<tr><td>7</td><td>Key: 15|5 = 155</td><td>7</td><td>Key: 15|5 = 155</td></tr>
<tr><td>7</td><td>8</td><td>7</td><td>8</td></tr>
<tr><td>8</td><td></td><td>8</td><td></td></tr>
<tr><td>8</td><td></td><td>8</td><td></td></tr>
<tr><td>9</td><td></td><td>9</td><td></td></tr>
<tr><td>9</td><td></td><td>9</td><td></td></tr>
<tr><td>10</td><td></td><td>10</td><td></td></tr>
<tr><td>10</td><td>5 8 9 9 9</td><td>10</td><td>5 8 9 9 9</td></tr>
<tr><td>11</td><td>4 2 2 3 2</td><td>11</td><td>2 2 2 3 4</td></tr>
<tr><td>11</td><td>6 8 8 9 7 8 9 9</td><td>11</td><td>6 7 8 8 8 9 9 9</td></tr>
<tr><td>12</td><td>2 2 1 2 3 1 4 4</td><td>12</td><td>1 1 2 2 2 3 4 4</td></tr>
<tr><td>12</td><td>9 6 6 6 6 9 6</td><td>12</td><td>6 6 6 6 6 9 9</td></tr>
<tr><td>13</td><td>0 3 4 2 3</td><td>13</td><td>0 2 3 3 4</td></tr>
<tr><td>13</td><td>9 9</td><td>13</td><td>9 9</td></tr>
<tr><td>14</td><td>4 2 0</td><td>14</td><td>0 2 4</td></tr>
<tr><td>14</td><td>5 5 8 7</td><td>14</td><td>5 5 7 8</td></tr>
<tr><td>15</td><td></td><td>15</td><td></td></tr>
<tr><td>15</td><td>5 9</td><td>15</td><td>5 9</td></tr>
<tr><td colspan="2">**Unordered Stem-and-Leaf Plot**</td><td colspan="2">**Ordered Stem-and-Leaf Plot**</td></tr>
</table>

Interpretation From the display, you can conclude that most of the cellular phone users sent between 105 and 135 text messages.

▶ **Try It Yourself 2**

Using two rows for each stem, revise the stem-and-leaf plot you constructed in Try It Yourself 1.

a. List each stem *twice*.
b. List all leaves *using the appropriate stem row*. *Answer: Page A34*

Insight

Compare Examples 1 and 2. Notice that by using two rows per stem, you obtain a more detailed picture of the data.

You can also use a dot plot to graph quantitative data. In a **dot plot,** each data entry is plotted, using a point, above a horizontal axis. Like a stem-and-leaf plot, a dot plot allows you to see how data are distributed, determine specific data entries, and identify unusual data values.

EXAMPLE 3

Constructing a Dot Plot

Use a dot plot to organize the text messaging data given in Example 1.

```
155  159  144  129  105  145
126  116  130  114  122  112
112  142  126  118  118  108
122  121  109  140  126  119
113  117  118  109  109  119
139  139  122   78  133  126
123  145  121  134  124  119
132  133  124  129  112  126
148  147
```

Solution   So that each data entry is included in the dot plot, the horizontal axis should include numbers between 70 and 160. To represent a data entry, plot a point above the entry's position on the axis. If an entry is repeated, plot another point above the previous point.

Number of Text Messages Sent

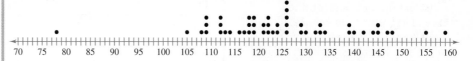

Interpretation   From the dot plot, you can see that most values cluster between 105 and 148 and the value that occurs the most is 126. You can also see that 78 is an unusual data value.

▶ Try It Yourself 3

Use a dot plot to organize the number of touchdowns data set listed in the Chapter Opener on page 39. What can you conclude from the graph?

a. Choose an appropriate scale for the *horizontal axis*.
b. Represent each data entry by *plotting a point*.
c. *Describe* any patterns for the data.   *Answer: Page A34*

Technology can be used to construct stem-and-leaf plots and dot plots. For instance, a MINITAB dot plot for the text messaging data is shown.

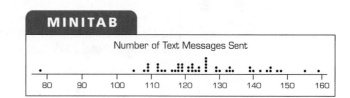

▶ Graphing Qualitative Data Sets

Pie charts provide a convenient way to present qualitative data graphically as percents of a whole. A **pie chart** is a circle that is divided into sectors that represent categories. The area of each sector is proportional to the frequency of each category. In most cases, you will be interpreting a pie chart or constructing one using technology. Example 4 shows how to construct a pie chart by hand.

Motor Vehicle Occupants Killed in 2005

Vehicle type	Killed
Cars	18,440
Trucks	13,778
Motorcycles	4,553
Other	823

EXAMPLE 4

Constructing a Pie Chart

The numbers of motor vehicle occupants killed in crashes in 2005 are shown in the table. Use a pie chart to organize the data. What can you conclude? *(Source: U.S. Department of Transportation, National Highway Traffic Safety Administration)*

Solution   Begin by finding the relative frequency, or percent, of each category. Then construct the pie chart using the central angle that corresponds to each category. To find the central angle, multiply 360° by the category's relative frequency. For example, the central angle for cars is $360°(0.49) \approx 176°$. To construct a pie chart in Excel, follow the instructions in the margin.

	f	Relative frequency	Angle
Cars	18,440	0.49	176°
Trucks	13,778	0.37	133°
Motorcycles	4,553	0.12	43°
Other	823	0.02	7°

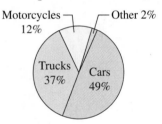

Motor Vehicle Occupants Killed in 2005

Interpretation   From the pie chart, you can see that most fatalities in motor vehicle crashes were those involving the occupants of cars.

▶ Try It Yourself 4

The numbers of motor vehicle occupants killed in crashes in 1995 are shown in the table. Use a pie chart to organize the data. Compare the 1995 data with the 2005 data. *(Source: U.S. Department of Transportation, National Highway Safety Administration)*

Motor Vehicle Occupants Killed in 1995

Vehicle type	Killed
Cars	22,423
Trucks	10,216
Motorcycles	2,227
Other	425

a. Find the *relative frequency* of each category.
b. Use the *central angle* to find the portion that corresponds to each category.
c. Compare the 1995 data with the 2005 data.   *Answer: Page A34*

Answer: Page A34

Study Tip

Here are instructions for constructing a pie chart using Excel. First, enter the vehicle types and their corresponding relative frequencies (written as percents) in two separate columns. Then highlight the two columns, click on the Chart Wizard, and select *Pie* as your chart type. Click *Next* throughout the Chart Wizard while constructing your pie chart.

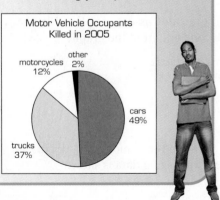

Another way to graph qualitative data is to use a Pareto chart. A **Pareto chart** is a vertical bar graph in which the height of each bar represents frequency or relative frequency. The bars are positioned in order of decreasing height, with the tallest bar positioned at the left. Such positioning helps highlight important data and is used frequently in business.

EXAMPLE 5

Constructing a Pareto Chart

In a recent year, the retail industry lost $41.0 million in inventory shrinkage. Inventory shrinkage is the loss of inventory through breakage, pilferage, shoplifting, and so on. The causes of the inventory shrinkage are administrative error ($7.8 million), employee theft ($15.6 million), shoplifting ($14.7 million), and vendor fraud ($2.9 million). If you were a retailer, which causes of inventory shrinkage would you address first? *(Source: National Retail Federation and Center for Retailing Education, University of Florida)*

Solution   Using frequencies for the vertical axis, you can construct the Pareto chart as shown.

Causes of Inventory Shrinkage

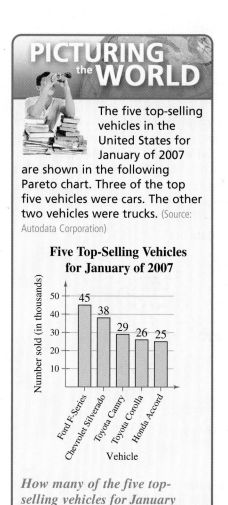

Interpretation   From the graph, it is easy to see that the causes of inventory shrinkage that should be addressed first are employee theft and shoplifting.

▶ **Try It Yourself 5**

Every year, the Better Business Bureau (BBB) receives complaints from customers. In a recent year, the BBB received the following complaints.

    7792 complaints about home furnishing stores
    5733 complaints about computer sales and service stores
    14,668 complaints about auto dealers
    9728 complaints about auto repair shops
    4649 complaints about dry cleaning companies

Use a Pareto chart to organize the data. What source is the greatest cause of complaints? *(Source: Council of Better Business Bureaus)*

a. Find the *frequency or relative frequency* for each data entry.
b. *Position the bars in decreasing order* according to frequency or relative frequency.
c. *Interpret* the results in the context of the data.   *Answer: Page A34*

▶ Graphing Paired Data Sets

When each entry in one data set corresponds to one entry in a second data set, the sets are called **paired data sets.** For instance, suppose a data set contains the costs of an item and a second data set contains sales amounts for the item at each cost. Because each cost corresponds to a sales amount, the data sets are paired. One way to graph paired data sets is to use a **scatter plot,** where the ordered pairs are graphed as points in a coordinate plane. A scatter plot is used to show the relationship between two quantitative variables.

EXAMPLE 6

Interpreting a Scatter Plot

The British statistician Ronald Fisher (see page 35) introduced a famous data set called Fisher's Iris data set. This data set describes various physical characteristics, such as petal length and petal width (in millimeters), for three species of iris. In the scatter plot shown, the petal lengths form the first data set and the petal widths form the second data set. As the petal length increases, what tends to happen to the petal width? *(Source: Fisher, R. A., 1936)*

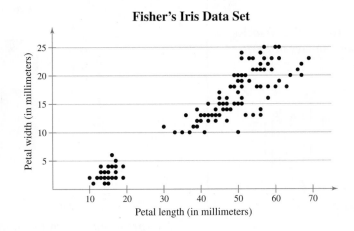

Fisher's Iris Data Set

Solution The horizontal axis represents the petal length, and the vertical axis represents the petal width. Each point in the scatter plot represents the petal length and petal width of one flower.

Interpretation From the scatter plot, you can see that as the petal length increases, the petal width also tends to increase.

▶ Try It Yourself 6

The lengths of employment and the salaries of 10 employees are listed in the table at the left. Graph the data using a scatter plot. What can you conclude?

a. Label the *horizontal and vertical axes.*
b. *Plot* the paired data.
c. *Describe* any trends.

Answer: Page A34

Length of employment (in years)	Salary (in dollars)
5	32,000
4	32,500
8	40,000
4	27,350
2	25,000
10	43,000
7	41,650
6	39,225
9	45,100
3	28,000

You will learn more about scatter plots and how to analyze them in Chapter 9.

A data set that is composed of quantitative entries taken at regular intervals over a period of time is a **time series.** For instance, the amount of precipitation measured each day for one month is an example of a time series. You can use a **time series chart** to graph a time series.

EXAMPLE 7

Constructing a Time Series Chart

See MINITAB and TI-83/84 steps on pages 124 and 125.

The table lists the number of cellular telephone subscribers (in millions) and a subscriber's average local monthly bill for service (in dollars) for the years 1995 through 2005. Construct a time series chart for the number of cellular subscribers. What can you conclude? *(Source: Cellular Telecommunications & Internet Association)*

Year	Subscribers (in millions)	Average bill (in dollars)
1995	33.8	51.00
1996	44.0	47.70
1997	55.3	42.78
1998	69.2	39.43
1999	86.0	41.24
2000	109.5	45.27
2001	128.4	47.37
2002	140.8	48.40
2003	158.7	49.91
2004	182.1	50.64
2005	207.9	49.98

Solution   Let the horizontal axis represent the years and the vertical axis represent the number of subscribers (in millions). Then plot the paired data and connect them with line segments.

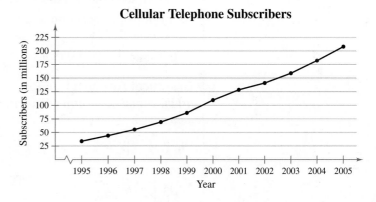

Cellular Telephone Subscribers

Interpretation   The graph shows that the number of subscribers has been increasing since 1995, with greater increases recently.

▶ Try It Yourself 7

Use the table in Example 7 to construct a time series chart for a subscriber's average local monthly cellular telephone bill for the years 1995 through 2005. What can you conclude?

a. Label the *horizontal and vertical axes.*
b. *Plot* the paired data and *connect* them with line segments.
c. *Describe* any patterns you see.

Answer: Page A34

2.2 EXERCISES

■ Building Basic Skills and Vocabulary

1. Name some ways to display quantitative data graphically. Name some ways to display qualitative data graphically.

2. What is an advantage of using a stem-and-leaf plot instead of a histogram? What is a disadvantage?

3. In terms of displaying data, how is a stem-and-leaf plot similar to a dot plot?

4. How is a Pareto chart different from a standard vertical bar graph?

Putting Graphs in Context *In Exercises 5–8, match the plot with the description of the sample.*

5.
```
0 | 8          Key: 0|8 = 0.8
1 | 5 6 8
2 | 1 3 4 5
3 | 0 9
4 | 0 0
```

6.
```
6 | 7 8          Key: 6|7 = 67
7 | 4 5 5 8 8 8
8 | 1 3 5 5 8 8 9
9 | 0 0 0 2 4
```

7.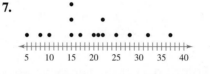

8.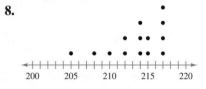

(a) Time (in minutes) it takes a sample of employees to drive to work

(b) Grade point averages of a sample of students with finance majors

(c) Top speeds (in miles per hour) of a sample of high-performance sports cars

(d) Ages (in years) of a sample of residents of a retirement home

Graphical Analysis *In Exercises 9–12, use the stem-and-leaf plot or dot plot to list the actual data entries. What is the maximum data entry? What is the minimum data entry?*

9. Key: 2|7 = 27

```
2 | 7
3 | 2
4 | 1 3 3 4 7 7 8
5 | 0 1 1 2 3 3 3 4 4 4 4 5 6 6 8 9
6 | 8 8 8
7 | 3 8 8
8 | 5
```

10. Key: 12|9 = 12.9

```
12 |
12 | 9
13 | 3
13 | 6 7 7
14 | 1 1 1 1 3 4 4
14 | 6 9 9
15 | 0 0 0 1 2 4
15 | 6 7 8 8 8 9
16 | 1
16 | 6 7
```

11.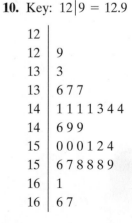

12.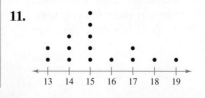

■ Using and Interpreting Concepts

Graphical Analysis   *In Exercises 13–16, what can you conclude from the graph?*

13.   **Top Five Sports Advertisers**

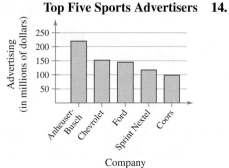

(Source: Nielsen Media Research)

14.   **Stock Portfolio**

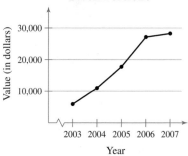

15.   **How Other Drivers Irk Us**

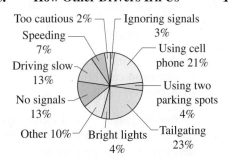

(Adapted from Reuters/Zogby)

16.   **Driving and Cell Phone Use**

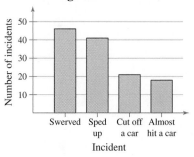

(Adapted from USA TODAY)

Graphing Data Sets   *In Exercises 17–32, organize the data using the indicated type of graph. What can you conclude about the data?*

17. Exam Scores   Use a stem-and-leaf plot to display the data. The data represent the scores of a biology class on a midterm exam.

75 85 90 80 87 67 82 88 95 91 73 80
83 92 94 68 75 91 79 95 87 76 91 85

18. World's Richest People   Use a stem-and-leaf plot to display the data. The data represent the ages of the top 25 wealthiest people in the world. *(Source: Forbes)*

51 76 67 80 56 73 58 71 78 49 62 84 50
49 87 40 59 47 54 84 61 79 59 52 63

19. Ice Thickness   Use a stem-and-leaf plot to display the data. The data represent the thicknesses (in centimeters) of ice measured at 20 different locations on a frozen lake.

5.8 6.4 6.9 7.2 5.1 4.9 4.3 5.8 7.0 6.8
8.1 7.5 7.2 6.9 5.8 7.2 8.0 7.0 6.9 5.9

20. Apple Prices   Use a stem-and-leaf plot to display the data. The data represent the price (in cents per pound) paid to 28 farmers for apples.

19.2 19.6 16.4 17.1 19.0 17.4 17.3 20.1 19.0 17.5
17.6 18.6 18.4 17.7 19.5 18.4 18.9 17.5 19.3 20.8
19.3 18.6 18.6 18.3 17.1 18.1 16.8 17.9

21. Advertisements Use a dot plot to display the data. The data represent the number of advertisements seen or heard in one week by a sample of 30 people from the United States.

598 494 441 595 728 690 684 486 735 808 734 590 673 545 702
481 298 135 846 764 317 649 732 582 637 588 540 727 486 703

22. Life Spans of House Flies Use a dot plot to display the data. The data represent the life spans (in days) of 40 house flies.

9 9 4 4 8 11 10 5 8 13 9 6 7 11
13 11 6 9 8 14 10 6 10 10 8 7 14 11
7 8 6 11 13 10 14 14 8 13 14 10

23. United Nations Use a pie chart to display the data. The data represent the number of countries in the United Nations by continent. *(Source: United Nations)*

North America	23	Europe	43	Africa	53
South America	12	Oceania	14	Asia	47

24. NASA Budget Use a pie chart to display the data. The data represent the 2007 NASA budget (in millions of dollars) divided among three categories. *(Source: NASA)*

Science, aeronautics, and exploration	10,651
Exploration capabilities	6108
Inspector General	34

25. Airline Baggage Use a Pareto chart to display the data. The data represent the results of a 2005 worldwide study of all airlines on the causes for baggage delay. *(Source: Société International de Télécommunications Aéronautiques)*

Transfer baggage mishandling	61%
Loading/offloading error	4%
Failure to load at originating airport	15%
Space-weight restriction	5%
Arrival station mishandling	3%
Other	12%

26. UV Index Use a Pareto chart to display the data. The data represent the ultraviolet index for five cities at noon on a recent date. *(Source: National Oceanic and Atmospheric Administration)*

Atlanta, GA	Boise, ID	Concord, NH	Denver, CO	Miami, FL
9	7	8	7	10

27. Hourly Wages Use a scatter plot to display the data in the table. The data represent the number of hours worked and the hourly wages (in dollars) for a sample of 12 production workers. Describe any trends shown.

Hours	Hourly wage
33	12.16
37	9.98
34	10.79
40	11.71
35	11.80
33	11.51
40	13.65
33	12.05
28	10.54
45	10.33
37	11.57
28	10.17

Number of students per teacher	Average teacher's salary
17.1	28.7
17.5	47.5
18.9	31.8
17.1	28.1
20.0	40.3
18.6	33.8
14.4	49.8
16.5	37.5
13.3	42.5
18.4	31.9

TABLE FOR EXERCISE 28

28. **Salaries**   Use a scatter plot to display the data shown in the table. The data represent the number of students per teacher and the average teacher salary (in thousands of dollars) for a sample of 10 school districts. Describe any trends shown.

29. **UV Index**   Use a time series chart to display the data. The data represent the ultraviolet index for Memphis, TN, on June 14–23 during a recent year. *(Source: Weather Services International)*

June 14	June 15	June 16	June 17	June 18
9	4	10	10	10

June 19	June 20	June 21	June 22	June 23
10	10	10	9	9

30. **Daily High Temperatures**   Use a time series chart to display the data. The data represent the daily high temperatures for a city for a period of 12 days.

May 1	May 2	May 3	May 4	May 5	May 6
77°	77°	79°	81°	82°	82°

May 7	May 8	May 9	May 10	May 11	May 12
85°	87°	90°	88°	89°	82°

31. **Egg Prices**   Use a time series chart to display the data. The data represent the prices of Grade A eggs (in dollars per dozen) for the indicated years. *(Source: U.S. Bureau of Labor Statistics)*

1994	1995	1996	1997	1998	1999
0.87	1.16	1.31	1.17	1.09	0.92

2000	2001	2002	2003	2004	2005
0.96	0.93	1.18	1.56	1.20	1.35

32. **Ground Beef Prices**   Use a time series chart to display the data. The data represent the prices of 100% ground beef (in dollars per pound) for the indicated years. *(Source: U.S. Bureau of Labor Statistics)*

1994	1995	1996	1997	1998	1999
1.38	1.40	1.42	1.39	1.39	1.53

2000	2001	2002	2003	2004	2005
1.63	1.71	1.69	2.23	2.14	2.30

■ Extending Concepts

A Misleading Graph?   *In Exercises 33 and 34,*

(a) explain why the graph is misleading.

(b) redraw the graph so that it is not misleading.

33.

34.

Sales for Company B

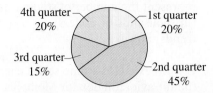

4th quarter 20%
1st quarter 20%
3rd quarter 15%
2nd quarter 45%

1st quarter	2nd quarter	3rd quarter	4th quarter
20%	15%	45%	20%

35. Law Firm Salaries   A **back-to-back stem-and-leaf plot** compares two data sets by using the same stems for each data set. Leaves for the first data set are on one side while leaves for the second data set are on the other side. The back-to-back stem-and-leaf plot shows the salaries (in thousands) of all lawyers at two small law firms.

Law Firm A		Law Firm B
5 0	9	0 3
8 5 2 2 2	10	5 7
9 9 7 0 0	11	0 0 5
1 1	12	0 3 3 5
	13	2 2 5 9
	14	1 3 3 3 9
	15	5 5 5 6
	16	4 9 9
9 9 5 1 0	17	1 2 5
5 5 5 2 1	18	9
9 9 8 7 5	19	0
3	20	

Key: 5|19|0 = $195,000 for Law Firm A and $190,000 for Law Firm B

(a) What are the lowest and highest salaries at Law Firm A? at Law Firm B?

(b) How many lawyers are in each firm?

(c) Compare the distribution of salaries at each law firm. What do you notice?

36. Yoga Classes   The back-to-back stem-and-leaf plot shows the ages of all participants in two yoga classes.

3:00 P.M. Class		8:00 P.M. Class
	1	8 8 8 8 8 9 9 9 9 9
	2	0 0 0 2 3 4 4 5 5 8 9 9
8 5	3	1 1 9
0	4	3 4 4
9 7 5 3 1	5	6
9 8 8 8 8 4 2 0	6	
7 7 6 5 5 5 3 3	7	1
5 4	8	

Key: 5|3|1 = 35-year-old in 3:00 P.M. class and 31-year-old in 8:00 P.M. class

(a) What are the lowest and highest ages of participants in the 3:00 P.M. class? in the 8:00 P.M. class?

(b) How many participants are in each class?

(c) Compare the distribution of ages in each class. What conclusion(s) can you make based on your observations?

2.3 Measures of Central Tendency

What You SHOULD LEARN

▸ How to find the mean, median, and mode of a population and of a sample

▸ How to find a weighted mean of a data set and the mean of a frequency distribution

▸ How to describe the shape of a distribution as symmetric, uniform, or skewed and how to compare the mean and median for each

Mean, Median, and Mode ▸ Weighted Mean and Mean of Grouped Data ▸ The Shape of Distributions

▸ Mean, Median, and Mode

In Sections 2.1 and 2.2, you learned about the graphical representations of quantitative data. In Sections 2.3 and 2.4, you will learn how to supplement graphical representations with numerical statistics that describe the center and variability of a data set.

A **measure of central tendency** is a value that represents a typical, or central, entry of a data set. The three most commonly used measures of central tendency are the mean, the median, and the mode.

DEFINITION

The **mean** of a data set is the sum of the data entries divided by the number of entries. To find the mean of a data set, use one of the following formulas.

$$\text{Population Mean: } \mu = \frac{\sum x}{N} \qquad \text{Sample Mean: } \bar{x} = \frac{\sum x}{n}$$

The lowercase Greek letter μ (pronounced mu) represents the population mean and $\bar{x}$ (read as "x bar") represents the sample mean. Note that N represents the number of entries in a *population* and n represents the number of entries in a *sample*. Recall that the uppercase Greek letter sigma (Σ) indicates a summation of values.

EXAMPLE 1

Finding a Sample Mean

The prices (in dollars) for a sample of roundtrip flights from Chicago, Illinois to Cancun, Mexico are listed. What is the mean price of the flights?

872   432   397   427   388   782   397

Solution   The sum of the flight prices is

$$\sum x = 872 + 432 + 397 + 427 + 388 + 782 + 397 = 3695.$$

To find the mean price, divide the sum of the prices by the number of prices in the sample.

$$\bar{x} = \frac{\sum x}{n} = \frac{3695}{7} \approx 527.9$$

So, the mean price of the flights is about $527.90.

▸**Try It Yourself 1**

The ages of employees in a department are listed. What is the mean age?

34   27   50   45   41   37   24
57   40   38   62   44   39   40

a. *Find the sum* of the data entries.
b. *Divide the sum* by the number of data entries.
c. *Interpret* the results in the context of the data.

Answer: Page A34

Study Tip

Notice that the mean in Example 1 has one more decimal place than the original set of data values. This *round-off rule* will be used throughout the text. Another important *round-off rule* is that rounding should not be done until the final answer of a calculation.

DEFINITION

The **median** of a data set is the value that lies in the middle of the data when the data set is ordered. The median measures the center of an ordered data set by dividing it into two equal parts. If the data set has an odd number of entries, the median is the middle data entry. If the data set has an even number of entries, the median is the mean of the two middle data entries.

Study Tip

In a data set, there are the same number of data values above the median as there are below the median. For instance, in Example 2, three of the prices are below $427 and three are above $427.

EXAMPLE 2

Finding the Median

Find the median of the flight prices given in Example 1.

Solution To find the median price, first order the data.

388 397 397 427 432 782 872

Because there are seven entries (an odd number), the median is the middle, or fourth, data entry. So, the median flight price is $427.

▶ **Try It Yourself 2**

The ages for a sample of fans at a rock concert are listed. Find the median age.

24 27 19 21 18 23 21 20 19 33 30 29 21
18 24 26 38 19 35 34 33 30 21 27 30

a. *Order* the data entries.
b. *Find the middle* data entry.
c. *Interpret* the results in the context of the data. *Answer: Page A34*

EXAMPLE 3

Finding the Median

In Example 2, the flight priced at $432 is no longer available. What is the median price of the remaining flights?

Solution The remaining prices, in order, are

388, 397, 397, 427, 782, and 872.

Because there are six entries (an even number), the median is the mean of the two middle entries.

$$\text{Median} = \frac{397 + 427}{2}$$
$$= 412$$

So, the median price of the remaining flights is $412.

▶ **Try It Yourself 3**

The prices (in dollars) for a sample of MP3 players are listed. Find the median price of the MP3 players.

80 250 200 150 270 140 70 100 130 160

a. *Order* the data entries.
b. *Find the mean* of the two middle data entries.
c. *Interpret* the results in the context of the data. *Answer: Page A34*

DEFINITION

The **mode** of a data set is the data entry that occurs with the greatest frequency. If no entry is repeated, the data set has no mode. If two entries occur with the same greatest frequency, each entry is a mode and the data set is called **bimodal.**

Insight

The mode is the only measure of central tendency that can be used to describe data at the nominal level of measurement. But when working with quantitative data, the mode is rarely used.

EXAMPLE 4

Finding the Mode

Find the mode of the flight prices given in Example 1.

Solution   Ordering the data helps to find the mode.

388   397   397   427   432   782   872

From the ordered data, you can see that the entry of 397 occurs twice, whereas the other data entries occur only once. So, the mode of the flight prices is $397.

▶ Try It Yourself 4

Find the mode of the ages of the residents of a small town. The data are given below.

25, 5, 18, 12, 60, 44, 24, 22, 2, 7, 15, 39, 58, 53, 36, 42,
16, 20, 1, 5, 39, 51, 44, 23, 3, 13, 37, 56, 58, 13, 47, 23,
1, 17, 39, 13, 24, 0, 39, 10, 41, 1, 48, 17, 18, 3, 72, 20, 3,
9, 0, 12, 33, 21, 40, 68, 25, 40, 59, 4, 67, 29, 13, 18, 19,
13, 16, 41, 19, 26, 68, 49, 5, 26, 49, 26, 45, 41, 19, 49

a. Write the data in *order*.
b. Identify the entry, or entries, that occur with the *greatest frequency*.
c. *Interpret* the results in the context of the data.   *Answer: Page A35*

EXAMPLE 5

Finding the Mode

At a political debate a sample of audience members was asked to name the political party to which they belong. Their responses are shown in the table. What is the mode of the responses?

Political party	Frequency, f
Democrat	34
Republican	56
Other	21
Did not respond	9

Solution   The response occurring with the greatest frequency is Republican. So, the mode is Republican.

Interpretation   In this sample, there were more Republicans than people of any other single affiliation.

▶ Try It Yourself 5

In a survey, 240 U.S. adults were asked if the United States will ever have a female president. Of those surveyed, 171 responded "yes," 45 responded "no," and 24 "didn't know." What is the mode of the responses?

a. Identify the entry that occurs with the *greatest frequency*.
b. *Interpret* the results in the context of the data.   *Answer: Page A35*

Although the mean, the median, and the mode each describe a typical entry of a data set, there are advantages and disadvantages of using each. The mean is a reliable measure because it takes into account every entry of a data set. But, the mean can be greatly affected when the data set contains outliers.

DEFINITION

An **outlier** is a data entry that is far removed from the other entries in the data set.

A data set can have one or more outliers, causing **gaps** in a distribution. Conclusions that are drawn from a data set that contains outliers may be flawed.

Ages in a class						
20	20	20	20	20	20	21
21	21	21	22	22	22	23
23	23	23	24	24	65	

Outlier

EXAMPLE 6

Comparing the Mean, the Median, and the Mode

Find the mean, the median, and the mode of the sample ages of a class shown at the left. Which measure of central tendency best describes a typical entry of this data set? Are there any outliers?

Solution

Mean: $\bar{x} = \dfrac{\sum x}{n} = \dfrac{475}{20} \approx 23.8$ years

Median: Median $= \dfrac{21 + 22}{2} = 21.5$ years

Mode: The entry occurring with the greatest frequency is 20 years.

Interpretation The mean takes every entry into account but is influenced by the outlier of 65. The median also takes every entry into account, and it is not affected by the outlier. In this case the mode exists, but it doesn't appear to represent a typical entry. Sometimes a graphical comparison can help you decide which measure of central tendency best represents a data set. The histogram shows the distribution of the data and the location of the mean, the median, and the mode. In this case, it appears that the median best describes the data set.

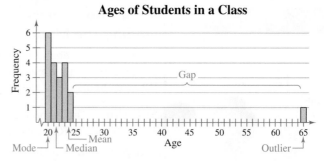

Ages of Students in a Class

▶ **Try It Yourself 6**

Remove the data entry of 65 from the preceding data set. Then rework the example. How does the absence of this outlier change each of the measures?

a. Find the *mean*, the *median*, and the *mode*.
b. Compare these measures of central tendency with those found in Example 6.

Answer: Page A35

PICTURING the **WORLD**

The National Association of Realtors keeps a databank of existing-home sales. One list uses the *median* price of existing homes sold and another uses the *mean* price of existing homes sold. The sales for the first quarter of 2006 are shown in the double-bar graph. (Source: National Association of Realtors)

2006 U.S. Existing-Home Sales

Notice in the graph that each month the mean price is about $45,000 more than the median price. What factors would cause the mean price to be greater than the median price?

▶ Weighted Mean and Mean of Grouped Data

Sometimes data sets contain entries that have a greater effect on the mean than do other entries. To find the mean of such data sets, you must find the weighted mean.

DEFINITION

A **weighted mean** is the mean of a data set whose entries have varying weights. A weighted mean is given by

$$\bar{x} = \frac{\sum (x \cdot w)}{\sum w}$$

where w is the weight of each entry x.

EXAMPLE 7

Finding a Weighted Mean

You are taking a class in which your grade is determined from five sources: 50% from your test mean, 15% from your midterm, 20% from your final exam, 10% from your computer lab work, and 5% from your homework. Your scores are 86 (test mean), 96 (midterm), 82 (final exam), 98 (computer lab), and 100 (homework). What is the weighted mean of your scores? If the minimum average for an A is 90, did you get an A?

Solution   Begin by organizing the scores and the weights in a table.

Source	Score, x	Weight, w	xw
Test Mean	86	0.50	43.0
Midterm	96	0.15	14.4
Final Exam	82	0.20	16.4
Computer Lab	98	0.10	9.8
Homework	100	0.05	5.0
		$\sum w = 1$	$\sum (x \cdot w) = 88.6$

$$\bar{x} = \frac{\sum (x \cdot w)}{\sum w}$$
$$= \frac{88.6}{1}$$
$$= 88.6$$

Your weighted mean for the course is 88.6. So, you did not get an A.

▶ Try It Yourself 7

An error was made in grading your final exam. Instead of getting 82, you scored 98. What is your new weighted mean?

a. Multiply each score by its weight and *find the sum of these products.*
b. Find the *sum of the weights.*
c. Find the *weighted mean.*
d. *Interpret* the results in the context of the data.   *Answer: Page A35*

If data are presented in a frequency distribution, you can approximate the mean as follows.

DEFINITION

The **mean of a frequency distribution** for a sample is approximated by

$$\bar{x} = \frac{\Sigma(x \cdot f)}{n}$$ Note that $n = \Sigma f$

where x and f are the midpoints and frequencies of a class, respectively.

GUIDELINES

Finding the Mean of a Frequency Distribution

In Words	*In Symbols*
1. Find the midpoint of each class.	$x = \dfrac{(\text{Lower limit}) + (\text{Upper limit})}{2}$
2. Find the sum of the products of the midpoints and the frequencies.	$\Sigma(x \cdot f)$
3. Find the sum of the frequencies.	$n = \Sigma f$
4. Find the mean of the frequency distribution.	$\bar{x} = \dfrac{\Sigma(x \cdot f)}{n}$

EXAMPLE 8

Finding the Mean of a Frequency Distribution

Use the frequency distribution at the left to approximate the mean number of minutes that a sample of Internet subscribers spent online during their most recent session.

Solution

$$\bar{x} = \frac{\Sigma(x \cdot f)}{n} = \frac{2089}{50} \approx 41.8$$

So, the mean time spent online was approximately 41.8 minutes.

▶ **Try It Yourself 8**

Use a frequency distribution to approximate the mean number of touchdowns scored by all Division 1A football teams. (See Try It Yourself 2 on page 43.)

a. Find the *midpoint* of each class.
b. Find the *sum of the products* of each midpoint and corresponding frequency.
c. Find the *sum of the frequencies*.
d. Find the *mean of the frequency distribution*. *Answer: Page A35*

Class midpoint, x	Frequency, f	$(x \cdot f)$
12.5	6	75.0
24.5	10	245.0
36.5	13	474.5
48.5	8	388.0
60.5	5	302.5
72.5	6	435.0
84.5	2	169.0
	$n = 50$	$\Sigma = 2089.0$

▶ The Shape of Distributions

A graph reveals several characteristics of a frequency distribution. One such characteristic is the shape of the distribution.

DEFINITION

A frequency distribution is **symmetric** when a vertical line can be drawn through the middle of a graph of the distribution and the resulting halves are approximately mirror images.

A frequency distribution is **uniform** (or **rectangular**) when all entries, or classes, in the distribution have equal or approximately equal frequencies. A uniform distribution is also symmetric.

A frequency distribution is skewed if the "tail" of the graph elongates more to one side than to the other. A distribution is **skewed left (negatively skewed)** if its tail extends to the left. A distribution is **skewed right (positively skewed)** if its tail extends to the right.

To explore this topic further, see Activity 2.3 on page 81.

When a distribution is symmetric and unimodal, the mean, median, and mode are equal. If a distribution is skewed left, the mean is less than the median and the median is usually less than the mode. If a distribution is skewed right, the mean is greater than the median and the median is usually greater than the mode. Examples of these commonly occurring distributions are shown.

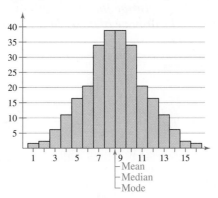

Symmetric Distribution

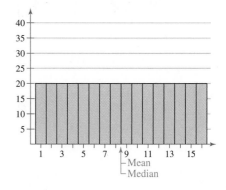

Uniform Distribution

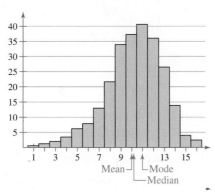

Skewed-Left Distribution

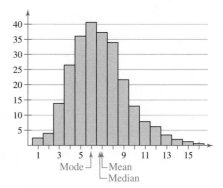

Skewed-Right Distribution

The mean will always fall in the direction the distribution is skewed. For instance, when a distribution is skewed left, the mean is to the left of the median.

Insight

Be aware that there are many different shapes of distributions. In some cases, the shape cannot be classified as symmetric, uniform, or skewed. A distribution can have several gaps caused by outliers, or **clusters** of data. Clusters occur when several types of data are included in the one data set.

2.3 EXERCISES

■ Building Basic Skills and Vocabulary

True or False? *In Exercises 1–6, determine whether the statement is true or false. If it is false, rewrite it as a true statement.*

1. The mean is the measure of central tendency most likely to be affected by an extreme value (an outlier).

2. Every data set must have a mode.

3. Some quantitative data sets do not have a median.

4. The mean is the only measure of central tendency that can be used for data at the nominal level of measurement.

5. When each data class has the same frequency, the distribution is skewed right.

6. When the mean is greater than the median, the distribution is skewed left.

7. Construct a data set in which the mean is *not* representative of a typical number in the data set.

8. Construct a data set in which the median and the mode are the same.

Graphical Analysis *In Exercises 9–12, determine whether the approximate shape of the distribution in the histogram is symmetric, uniform, skewed left, skewed right, or none of these. Justify your answer.*

9.
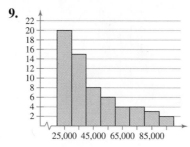

10.
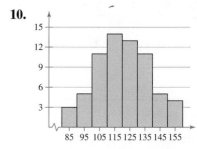

11.
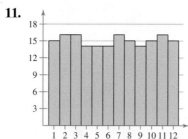

12.
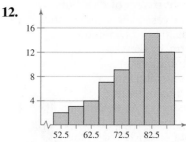

Matching *In Exercises 13–16, match the distribution with one of the graphs in Exercises 9–12. Justify your decision.*

13. The frequency distribution of 180 rolls of a dodecagon (a 12-sided die)

14. The frequency distribution of salaries at a company where a few executives make much higher salaries than the majority of employees

15. The frequency distribution of scores on a 90-point test where a few students scored much lower than the majority of students

16. The frequency distribution of weights for a sample of seventh grade boys

■ Using and Interpreting Concepts

Finding and Discussing the Mean, Median, and Mode   *In Exercises 17–34, find the mean, median, and mode of the data, if possible. If any of these measures cannot be found or a measure does not represent the center of the data, explain why.*

17. SUVs   The maximum number of seats in a sample of 13 sport utility vehicles

6   6   9   9   6   5   5   5   7   5   5   5   8

18. Education   The education cost per student (in thousands of dollars) from a sample of 10 liberal arts colleges

30   35   19   22   22   20   23   21   35   25

19. Sports Cars   The times (in seconds) for a sample of seven sports cars to go from 0 to 60 miles per hour

3.7   4.0   4.8   4.8   4.8   4.8   5.1

20. Cholesterol   The cholesterol levels of a sample of 10 female employees

154   240   171   188   235   203   184   173   181   275

21. NFL   The average points per game scored by each NFL team during the 2006 regular season   *(Source: NFL)*

19.6   18.2   22.1   18.8   16.9   26.7   23.3   14.9
26.6   19.9   19.1   18.8   16.7   26.7   23.2   20.7
16.2   17.6   24.1   25.8   19.8   22.2   10.5   24.9
22.1   30.8   18.6   20.9   22.9   13.2   20.2   19.2

22. Power Failures   The durations (in minutes) of power failures at a residence in the last 10 years

18   26   45   75   125   80   33   40   44   49
89   80   96   125   12   61   31   63   103   28

23. Air Quality   The responses of a sample of 1040 people who were asked if the air quality in their community is better or worse than it was 10 years ago

Better: 346   Worse: 450   Same: 244

24. Crime   The responses of a sample of 1019 people who were asked how they felt when they thought about crime

Unconcerned: 34   Watchful: 672   Nervous: 125   Afraid: 188

25. Top Speeds   The top speeds (in miles per hour) for a sample of seven sports cars

187.3   181.8   180.0   169.3   162.2   158.1   155.7

26. Purchase Preference   The responses of a sample of 1001 people who were asked if their next vehicle purchase will be foreign or domestic

Domestic: 704   Foreign: 253   Don't know: 44

27. Stocks   The recommended prices (in dollars) for several stocks that analysts predict should produce at least 10% annual returns   *(Source: Money)*

41   20   22   14   15   25   18   40   17   14

28. Eating Disorders   The number of weeks it took to reach a target weight for a sample of five patients with eating disorders treated by psychodynamic psychotherapy *(Source: The Journal of Consulting and Clinical Psychology)*

15.0   31.5   10.0   25.5   1.0

29. Eating Disorders   The number of weeks it took to reach a target weight for a sample of 14 patients with eating disorders treated by psychodynamic psychotherapy and cognitive behavior techniques *(Source: The Journal of Consulting and Clinical Psychology)*

2.5   20.0   11.0   10.5   17.5   16.5   13.0
15.5   26.5   2.5   27.0   28.5   1.5   5.0

30. Aircraft   The number of aircraft 11 airlines have in their fleets *(Source: Airline Transport Association)*

699   480   25   35   110   445
458   374   93   356   380

31. Weights (in pounds) of Dogs at a Kennel

```
 1 | 0 2     Key: 1|0 = 10
 2 | 1 4 7
 3 | 7 8
 4 | 1 5 5
 5 | 0 7
 6 | 5
 7 |
 8 |
 9 |
10 | 6
```

32. Grade Point Averages of Students in a Class

```
0 | 8       Key:  0|8 = 0.8
1 | 5 6 8
2 | 1 3 4 5
3 | 0 9
4 | 0 0
```

33.   Time (in minutes) it Takes Employees to Drive to Work

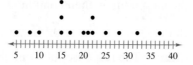

34.   Top Speeds (in miles per hour) of High-Performance Sports Cars

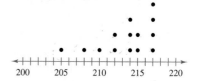

Graphical Analysis   *In Exercises 35 and 36, the letters A, B, and C are marked on the horizontal axis. Describe the shape of the data. Then determine which is the mean, which is the median, and which is the mode. Justify your answers.*

35.   Sick Days Used by Employees

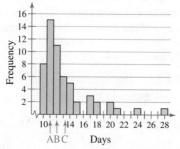

36.   Hourly Wages of Employees

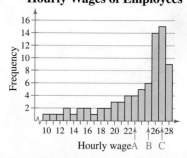

In Exercises 37–40, without performing any calculations, determine which measure of central tendency best represents the graphed data. Explain your reasoning.

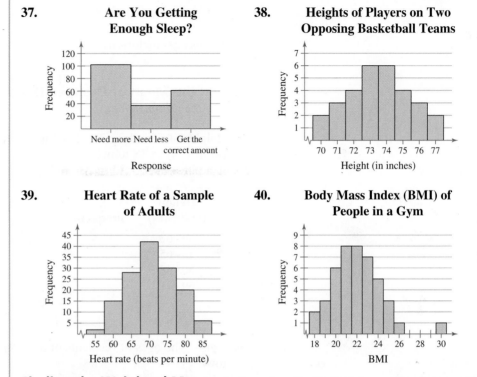

37.   **Are You Getting Enough Sleep?**

38.   **Heights of Players on Two Opposing Basketball Teams**

39.   **Heart Rate of a Sample of Adults**

40.   **Body Mass Index (BMI) of People in a Gym**

Finding the Weighted Mean   *In Exercises 41–46, find the weighted mean of the data.*

41. Final Grade   The scores and their percents of the final grade for a statistics student are given. What is the student's mean score?

	Score	Percent of final grade
Homework	85	5%
Quizzes	80	35%
Project	100	20%
Speech	90	15%
Final Exam	93	25%

42. Salaries   The average starting salaries (by degree attained) for 25 employees at a company are given. What is the mean starting salary for these employees?

8 with MBAs: $45,500
17 with BAs in business: $32,000

43. Account Balance   For the month of April, a checking account has a balance of $523 for 24 days, $2415 for 2 days, and $250 for 4 days. What is the account's mean daily balance for April?

44. Account Balance   For the month of May, a checking account has a balance of $759 for 15 days, $1985 for 5 days, $1410 for 5 days, and $348 for 6 days. What is the account's mean daily balance for May?

45. Grades   A student receives the following grades, with an A worth 4 points, a B worth 3 points, a C worth 2 points, and a D worth 1 point. What is the student's mean grade point score?

B in 2 three-credit classes   D in 1 two-credit class
A in 1 four-credit class   C in 1 three-credit class

46. Scores   The mean scores for a statistics course (by major) are given. What is the mean score for the class?

9 engineering majors: 85
5 math majors: 90
13 business majors: 81

Finding the Mean of Grouped Data   *In Exercises 47–50, approximate the mean of the grouped data.*

47. Heights of Females   The heights (in inches) of 18 female students in a physical education class

Height (in inches)	Frequency
60–62	4
63–65	5
66–68	8
69–71	1

48. Heights of Males   The heights (in inches) of 23 male students in a physical education class

Height (in inches)	Frequency
63–65	3
66–68	6
69–71	7
72–74	4
75–77	3

49. Ages   The ages of residents of a town

Age	Frequency
0–9	55
10–19	70
20–29	35
30–39	56
40–49	74
50–59	42
60–69	38
70–79	17
80–89	10

50. Phone Calls   The lengths of long-distance calls (in minutes) made by one person in one year

Length of call	Number of calls
1–5	12
6–10	26
11–15	20
16–20	7
21–25	11
26–30	7
31–35	4
36–40	4
41–45	1

Identifying the Shape of a Distribution   *In Exercises 51–54, construct a frequency distribution and a frequency histogram of the data using the indicated number of classes. Describe the shape of the histogram as symmetric, uniform, negatively skewed, positively skewed, or none of these.*

 51. Hospitalization

Number of classes: 6

Data set: The number of days 20 patients remained hospitalized

6	9	7	14	4
5	6	8	4	11
10	6	8	6	5
7	6	6	3	11

52. Hospital Beds

Number of classes: 5

Data set: The number of beds in a sample of 24 hospitals

149 167 162 127 130 180 160 167
221 145 137 194 207 150 254 262
244 297 137 204 166 174 180 151

53. Height of Males

Number of classes: 5

Data set: The heights (to the nearest inch) of 30 males

67 76 69 68 72 68 65 63 75 69
66 72 67 66 69 73 64 62 71 73
68 72 71 65 69 66 74 72 68 69

54. Six-Sided Die

Number of classes: 6

Data set: The results of rolling a six-sided die 30 times

1 4 6 1 5 3 2 5 4 6
1 2 4 3 5 6 3 2 1 1
5 6 2 4 4 3 1 6 2 4

55. Coffee Content   During a quality assurance check, the actual coffee content (in ounces) of six jars of instant coffee was recorded as 6.03, 5.59, 6.40, 6.00, 5.99, and 6.02.

(a) Find the mean and the median of the coffee content.

(b) The third value was incorrectly measured and is actually 6.04. Find the mean and median of the coffee content again.

(c) Which measure of central tendency, the mean or the median, was affected more by the data entry error?

56. U.S. Exports   The following data are the U.S. exports (in billions of dollars) to 19 countries for a recent year. *(Source: U.S. Department of Commerce)*

Canada	230.3	Japan	59.6
Mexico	134.2	United Kingdom	45.4
Germany	41.3	South Korea	32.5
Taiwan	23.0	Singapore	24.7
Netherlands	31.1	France	24.2
China	55.2	Brazil	19.2
Australia	17.8	Belgium	21.3
Malaysia	12.6	Italy	12.6
Switzerland	14.4	Thailand	8.2
Saudi Arabia	7.8		

(a) Find the mean and median.

(b) Find the mean and median without the U.S. exports to Canada.

(c) Which measure of central tendency, the mean or the median, was affected more by the elimination of the Canadian export data?

■ Extending Concepts

57. Golf The distances (in yards) for nine holes of a golf course are listed.

336 393 408 522 147 504 177 375 360

(a) Find the mean and median of the data.

(b) Convert the distances to feet. Then rework part (a).

(c) Compare the measures you found in part (b) with those found in part (a). What do you notice?

(d) Use your results from part (c) to explain how to quickly find the mean and median of the given data set if the distances are measured in inches.

58. Data Analysis A consumer testing service obtained the following miles per gallon in five test runs performed with three types of compact cars.

	Run 1	Run 2	Run 3	Run 4	Run 5
Car A:	28	32	28	30	34
Car B:	31	29	31	29	31
Car C:	29	32	28	32	30

(a) The manufacturer of Car A wants to advertise that its car performed best in this test. Which measure of central tendency—mean, median, or mode—should be used for its claim? Explain your reasoning.

(b) The manufacturer of Car B wants to advertise that its car performed best in this test. Which measure of central tendency—mean, median, or mode—should be used for its claim? Explain your reasoning.

(c) The manufacturer of Car C wants to advertise that its car performed best in this test. Which measure of central tendency—mean, median, or mode—should be used for its claim? Explain your reasoning.

59. Midrange Another measure of central tendency that is rarely used but is easy to calculate is the **midrange**. It can be found by the formula

$$\frac{(\text{Maximum data entry}) + (\text{Minimum data entry})}{2}.$$

Which of the manufacturers in Exercise 58 would prefer to use the midrange statistic in their ads? Explain your reasoning.

60. Data Analysis Students in an experimental psychology class did research on depression as a sign of stress. A test was administered to a sample of 30 students. The scores are given.

44 51 11 90 76 36 64 37 43 72 53 62 36 74 51
72 37 28 38 61 47 63 36 41 22 37 51 46 85 13

(a) Find the mean and median of the data.

(b) Draw a stem-and-leaf plot for the data using one row per stem. Locate the mean and median on the display.

(c) Describe the shape of the distribution.

61. Trimmed Mean To find the 10% **trimmed mean** of a data set, order the data, delete the lowest 10% of the entries and the highest 10% of the entries, and find the mean of the remaining entries.

(a) Find the 10% trimmed mean for the data in Exercise 60.

(b) Compare the four measures of central tendency, including the midrange.

(c) What is the benefit of using a trimmed mean versus using a mean found using all data entries? Explain your reasoning.

APPLET

The *mean versus median* applet is designed to allow you to interactively investigate the mean and the median as measures of the center of a data set. Points can be added to the plot by clicking the mouse above the horizontal axis. The mean of the points is shown as a green arrow and the median is shown as a red arrow. If the two values are the same, then a single yellow arrow is displayed. Numeric values for the mean and median are shown above the plot. Points on the plot can be removed by clicking on the point and then dragging the point into the trash can. All of the points on the plot can be removed by simply clicking inside the trash can. The range of values for the horizontal axis can be specified by inputting lower and upper limits and then clicking UPDATE.

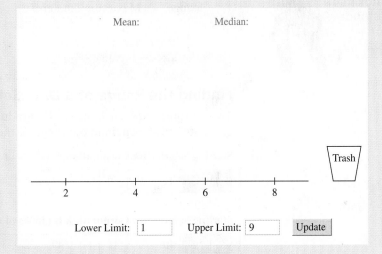

■ Explore

Step 1 Specify a lower limit.
Step 2 Specify an upper limit.
Step 3 Add 15 points to the plot.
Step 4 Remove all of the points from the plot.

■ Draw Conclusions

APPLET

1. Specify the lower limit to be 1 and the upper limit to be 50. Add at least ten points that range from 20 to 40 so that the mean and the median are the same. What is the shape of the distribution? What happens at first to the mean and median when you add a few points that are less than 10? What happens over time as you continue to add points that are less than 10?

2. Specify the lower limit to be 0 and the upper limit to be 0.75. Place ten points on the plot. Then change the upper limit to 25. Add ten more points that are greater than 20 to the plot. Can the mean be any one of the points that was plotted? Can the median be any one of the points that was plotted? Explain.

2.4 Measures of Variation

What You SHOULD LEARN

▸ How to find the range of a data set

▸ How to find the variance and standard deviation of a population and of a sample

▸ How to use the Empirical Rule and Chebychev's Theorem to interpret standard deviation

▸ How to approximate the sample standard deviation for grouped data

Range ▸ Deviation, Variance, and Standard Deviation ▸ Interpreting Standard Deviation ▸ Standard Deviation for Grouped Data

▸ Range

In this section, you will learn different ways to measure the variation of a data set. The simplest measure is the range of the set.

DEFINITION

The **range** of a data set is the difference between the maximum and minimum data entries in the set. To find the range, the data must be quantitative.

Range = (Maximum data entry) − (Minimum data entry)

EXAMPLE 1

Finding the Range of a Data Set

Two corporations each hired 10 graduates. The starting salaries for each graduate are shown. Find the range of the starting salaries for Corporation A.

Starting Salaries for Corporation A (1000s of dollars)

Salary	41	38	39	45	47	41	44	41	37	42

Starting Salaries for Corporation B (1000s of dollars)

Salary	40	23	41	50	49	32	41	29	52	58

Solution Ordering the data helps to find the least and greatest salaries.

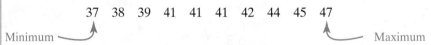

37 38 39 41 41 41 42 44 45 47

Minimum ⌣   Maximum

Range = (Maximum salary) − (Minimum salary)

= 47 − 37

= 10

So, the range of the starting salaries for Corporation A is 10, or $10,000.

▸Try It Yourself 1

Find the range of the starting salaries for Corporation B.

a. Identify the *minimum* and *maximum* salaries.
b. Find the *range*.
c. Compare your answer with that for Example 1.

Answer: Page A35

Insight

Both data sets in Example 1 have a mean of 41.5, a median of 41, and a mode of 41. And yet the two sets differ significantly.

The difference is that the entries in the second set have greater variation. Your goal in this section is to learn how to measure the variation of a data set.

▶ Deviation, Variance, and Standard Deviation

As a measure of variation, the range has the advantage of being easy to compute. Its disadvantage, however, is that it uses only two entries from the data set. Two measures of variation that use all the entries in a data set are the variance and the standard deviation. However, before you learn about these measures of variation, you need to know what is meant by the deviation of an entry in a data set.

DEFINITION

The **deviation** of an entry x in a population data set is the difference between the entry and the mean μ of the data set.

$$\text{Deviation of } x = x - \mu$$

Deviations of Starting Salaries for Corporation A

Salary (1000s of dollars) x	Deviation (1000s of dollars) $x - \mu$
41	−0.5
38	−3.5
39	−2.5
45	3.5
47	5.5
41	−0.5
44	2.5
41	−0.5
37	−4.5
42	0.5
$\Sigma x = 415$	$\Sigma(x - \mu) = 0$

EXAMPLE 2

Finding the Deviations of a Data Set

Find the deviation of each starting salary for Corporation A given in Example 1.

Solution   The mean starting salary is $\mu = 415/10 = 41.5$. To find out how much each salary deviates from the mean, subtract 41.5 from the salary. For instance, the deviation of 41 (or $41,000) is

$$41 - 41.5 = -0.5 \text{ (or } -\$500). \qquad \text{Deviation of } x = x - \mu$$

The table at the left lists the deviations of each of the 10 starting salaries.

▶ Try It Yourself 2

Find the deviation of each starting salary for Corporation B given in Example 1.

a. Find the *mean* of the data set.
b. *Subtract* the mean from each salary. *Answer: Page A35*

In Example 2, notice that the sum of the deviations is zero. Because this is true for any data set, it doesn't make sense to find the average of the deviations. To overcome this problem, you can square each deviation. When you add the squares of the deviations, you compute a quantity called the **sum of squares,** denoted SS_x. In a population data set, the mean of the squares of the deviations is called the **population variance.**

DEFINITION

The **population variance** of a population data set of N entries is

$$\text{Population variance} = \sigma^2 = \frac{\Sigma(x - \mu)^2}{N}$$

The symbol σ is the lowercase Greek letter sigma.

DEFINITION

The **population standard deviation** of a population data set of N entries is the square root of the population variance.

$$\text{Population standard deviation} = \sigma = \sqrt{\sigma^2} = \sqrt{\frac{\Sigma(x-\mu)^2}{N}}$$

GUIDELINES

Finding the Population Variance and Standard Deviation

In Words	*In Symbols*
1. Find the mean of the population data set.	$\mu = \dfrac{\Sigma x}{N}$
2. Find the deviation of each entry.	$x - \mu$
3. Square each deviation.	$(x - \mu)^2$
4. Add to get the **sum of squares**.	$SS_x = \Sigma(x-\mu)^2$
5. Divide by N to get the **population variance**.	$\sigma^2 = \dfrac{\Sigma(x-\mu)^2}{N}$
6. Find the square root of the variance to get the **population standard deviation**.	$\sigma = \sqrt{\dfrac{\Sigma(x-\mu)^2}{N}}$

Sum of Squares of Starting Salaries for Corporation A

Salary x	Deviation $x - \mu$	Squares $(x-\mu)^2$
41	−0.5	0.25
38	−3.5	12.25
39	−2.5	6.25
45	3.5	12.25
47	5.5	30.25
41	−0.5	0.25
44	2.5	6.25
41	−0.5	0.25
37	−4.5	20.25
42	0.5	0.25
	$\Sigma = 0$	$SS_x = 88.5$

EXAMPLE 3

Finding the Population Standard Deviation

Find the population variance and standard deviation of the starting salaries for Corporation A given in Example 1.

Solution   The table at the left summarizes the steps used to find SS_x.

$$SS_x = 88.5, \qquad N = 10, \qquad \sigma^2 = \frac{88.5}{10} \approx 8.9, \qquad \sigma = \sqrt{8.85} \approx 3.0$$

So, the population variance is about 8.9, and the population standard deviation is about 3.0, or $3000.

▶ **Try It Yourself 3**

Find the population standard deviation of the starting salaries for Corporation B given in Example 1.

a. Find the *mean* and each *deviation,* as you did in Try It Yourself 2.
b. *Square* each deviation and *add* to get the sum of squares.
c. *Divide* by N to get the population variance.
d. Find the *square root* of the population variance.
e. *Interpret* the results by giving the population standard deviation in dollars.

Answer: Page A35

Study Tip

Notice that the variance and standard deviation in Example 3 have one more decimal place than the original set of data values has. This is the same *round-off rule* that was used to calculate the mean.

Symbols in Variance and Standard Deviation Formulas

	Population	Sample
Variance	σ^2	s^2
Standard deviation	σ	s
Mean	μ	$\bar{x}$
Number of entries	N	n
Deviation	$x - \mu$	$x - \bar{x}$
Sum of squares	$\Sigma(x - \mu)^2$	$\Sigma(x - \bar{x})^2$

See MINITAB and TI-83/84 steps on pages 124 and 125.

DEFINITION

The **sample variance** and **sample standard deviation** of a sample data set of *n* entries are listed below.

$$\text{Sample variance} = s^2 = \frac{\Sigma(x - \bar{x})^2}{n - 1}$$

$$\text{Sample standard deviation} = s = \sqrt{s^2} = \sqrt{\frac{\Sigma(x - \bar{x})^2}{n - 1}}$$

GUIDELINES

Finding the Sample Variance and Standard Deviation

In Words	*In Symbols*
1. Find the mean of the sample data set.	$\bar{x} = \dfrac{\Sigma x}{n}$
2. Find the deviation of each entry.	$x - \bar{x}$
3. Square each deviation.	$(x - \bar{x})^2$
4. Add to get the **sum of squares**.	$SS_x = \Sigma(x - \bar{x})^2$
5. Divide by $n - 1$ to get the **sample variance**.	$s^2 = \dfrac{\Sigma(x - \bar{x})^2}{n - 1}$
6. Find the square root of the variance to get the **sample standard deviation**.	$s = \sqrt{\dfrac{\Sigma(x - \bar{x})^2}{n - 1}}$

EXAMPLE 4

Finding the Sample Standard Deviation

The starting salaries given in Example 1 are for the Chicago branches of Corporations A and B. Each corporation has several other branches, and you plan to use the starting salaries of the Chicago branches to estimate the starting salaries for the larger populations. Find the *sample* standard deviation of the starting salaries for the Chicago branch of Corporation A.

Solution

$$SS_x = 88.5, \qquad n = 10, \qquad s^2 = \frac{88.5}{9} \approx 9.8, \qquad s = \sqrt{\frac{88.5}{9}} \approx 3.1$$

So, the sample variance is about 9.8, and the sample standard deviation is about 3.1, or $3100.

▶ Try It Yourself 4

Find the sample standard deviation of the starting salaries for the Chicago branch of Corporation B.

a. Find the *sum of squares*, as you did in Try It Yourself 3.
b. *Divide* by $n - 1$ to get the sample variance.
c. Find the *square root* of the sample variance.   *Answer: Page A35*

Office Rental Rates		
35.00	33.50	37.00
23.75	26.50	31.25
36.50	40.00	32.00
39.25	37.50	34.75
37.75	37.25	36.75
27.00	35.75	26.00
37.00	29.00	40.50
24.50	33.00	38.00

Study Tip

Here are instructions for calculating the sample mean and sample standard deviation on a TI-83/84 for Example 5.

STAT

Choose the EDIT menu.

1: Edit

Enter the sample office rental rates into L1.

STAT

Choose the CALC menu.

1: 1–Var Stats

ENTER

  2nd L1 ENTER

EXAMPLE 5

Using Technology to Find the Standard Deviation

Sample office rental rates (in dollars per square foot per year) for Miami's central business district are shown in the table. Use a calculator or a computer to find the mean rental rate and the sample standard deviation. *(Adapted from Cushman & Wakefield Inc.)*

Solution MINITAB, Excel, and the TI-83/84 each have features that automatically calculate the mean and the standard deviation of data sets. Try using this technology to find the mean and the standard deviation of the office rental rates. From the displays, you can see that $\bar{x} \approx 33.73$ and $s \approx 5.09$.

MINITAB

Descriptive Statistics

Variable	N	Mean	Median	TrMean	StDev
Rental Rates	24	33.73	35.38	33.88	5.09

Variable	SE Mean	Minimum	Maximum	Q1	Q3
Rental Rates	1.04	23.75	40.50	29.56	37.44

EXCEL

	A	B
1	Mean	33.72917
2	Standard Error	1.038864
3	Median	35.375
4	Mode	37
5	Standard Deviation	5.089373
6	Sample Variance	25.90172
7	Kurtosis	-0.74282
8	Skewness	-0.70345
9	Range	16.75
10	Minimum	23.75
11	Maximum	40.5
12	Sum	809.5
13	Count	24

TI-83/84

1-Var Stats
$\bar{x}=33.72916667$
$\Sigma x=809.5$
$\Sigma x^2=27899.5$
$Sx=5.089373342$
$\sigma x=4.982216639$

$n=24$

Sample Mean

Sample Standard Deviation

▶ Try It Yourself 5

Sample office rental rates (in dollars per square foot per year) for Seattle's central business district are listed. Use a calculator or a computer to find the mean rental rate and the sample standard deviation. *(Adapted from Cushman & Wakefield Inc.)*

40.00	43.00	46.00	40.50	35.75	39.75	32.75
36.75	35.75	38.75	38.75	36.75	38.75	39.00
29.00	35.00	42.75	32.75	40.75	35.25	

a. *Enter* the data.
b. *Calculate* the sample mean and the sample standard deviation.

Answer: Page A35

▸ Interpreting Standard Deviation

When interpreting the standard deviation, remember that it is a measure of the typical amount an entry deviates from the mean. The more the entries are spread out, the greater the standard deviation.

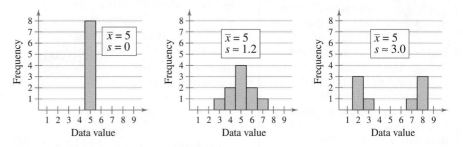

To explore this topic further, see Activity 2.4 on page 100.

EXAMPLE 6

Estimating Standard Deviation

Without calculating, estimate the population standard deviation of each data set.

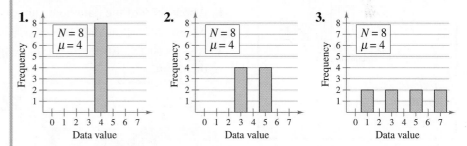

Solution

1. Each of the eight entries is 4. So, each deviation is 0, which implies that

$$\sigma = 0.$$

2. Each of the eight entries has a deviation of ± 1. So, the population standard deviation should be 1. By calculating, you can see that

$$\sigma = 1.$$

3. Each of the eight entries has a deviation of ± 1 or ± 3. So, the population standard deviation should be about 2. By calculating, you can see that

$$\sigma \approx 2.24.$$

▸ Try It Yourself 6

Write a data set that has 10 entries, a mean of 10, and a population standard deviation that is approximately 3. (There are many correct answers.)

a. *Write* a data set that has five entries that are three units less than 10 and five entries that are three units more than 10.

b. *Calculate* the population standard deviation to check that σ is approximately 3.

Answer: Page A35

PICTURING the WORLD

A survey was conducted by the National Center for Health Statistics to find the mean height of males in the U.S. The histogram shows the distribution of heights for the 724 men examined in the 20–29 age group. In this group, the mean was 69.6 inches and the standard deviation was 3.0 inches. (Source: National Center for Health Statistics)

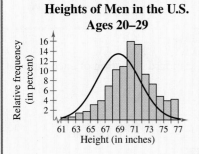

Heights of Men in the U.S. Ages 20–29

Roughly which two heights contain the middle 95% of the data?

Many real-life data sets have distributions that are approximately symmetric and bell shaped. Later in the text, you will study this type of distribution in detail. For now, however, the following *Empirical Rule* can help you see how valuable the standard deviation can be as a measure of variation.

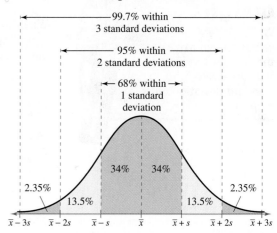

Bell-Shaped Distribution

EMPIRICAL RULE (OR 68-95-99.7 RULE)

For data with a (symmetric) bell-shaped distribution, the standard deviation has the following characteristics.

1. About 68% of the data lie within one standard deviation of the mean.
2. About 95% of the data lie within two standard deviations of the mean.
3. About 99.7% of the data lie within three standard deviations of the mean.

EXAMPLE 7

Using the Empirical Rule

In a survey conducted by the National Center for Health Statistics, the sample mean height of women in the United States (ages 20–29) was 64 inches, with a sample standard deviation of 2.71 inches. Estimate the percent of the women whose heights are between 64 inches and 69.42 inches.

Solution The distribution of the women's heights is shown. Because the distribution is bell shaped, you can use the Empirical Rule. The mean height is 64, so when you add two standard deviations to the mean height, you get

$$\overline{x} + 2s = 64 + 2(2.71) = 69.42.$$

Because 69.42 is two standard deviations above the mean height, the percent of the heights between 64 inches and 69.42 inches is 34% + 13.5% = 47.5%.

Interpretation So, 47.5% of women are between 64 and 69.42 inches tall.

▶ **Try It Yourself 7**

Estimate the percent of the heights that are between 61.29 and 64 inches.

a. How many standard deviations is 61.29 to the left of 64?
b. Use the Empirical Rule to estimate the percent of the data between $\overline{x} - s$ and $\overline{x}$.
c. *Interpret* the result in the context of the data. *Answer: Page A35*

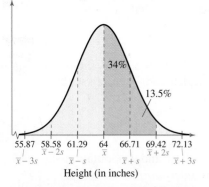

Heights of Women in the U.S. Ages 20–29

Insight

Data values that lie more than two standard deviations from the mean are considered unusual. Data values that lie more than three standard deviations from the mean are very unusual.

The Empirical Rule applies only to (symmetric) bell-shaped distributions. What if the distribution is not bell-shaped, or what if the shape of the distribution is not known? The following theorem gives an inequality statement that applies to *all* distributions. It is named after the Russian statistician Pafnuti Chebychev (1821–1894).

CHEBYCHEV'S THEOREM

The portion of any data set lying within k standard deviations ($k > 1$) of the mean is at least

$$1 - \frac{1}{k^2}.$$

- $k = 2$: In any data set, at least $1 - \frac{1}{2^2} = \frac{3}{4}$, or 75%, of the data lie within 2 standard deviations of the mean.
- $k = 3$: In any data set, at least $1 - \frac{1}{3^2} = \frac{8}{9}$, or 88.9%, of the data lie within 3 standard deviations of the mean.

EXAMPLE 8

Using Chebychev's Theorem

The age distributions for Alaska and Florida are shown in the histograms. Decide which is which. Apply Chebychev's Theorem to the data for Florida using $k = 2$. What can you conclude?

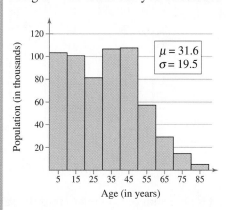
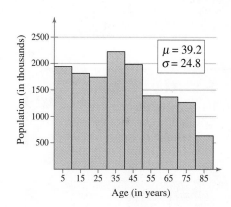

Solution   The histogram on the right shows Florida's age distribution. You can tell because the population is greater and older. Moving two standard deviations to the left of the mean puts you below 0, because $\mu - 2\sigma = 39.2 - 2(24.8) = -10.4$. Moving two standard deviations to the right of the mean puts you at $\mu + 2\sigma = 39.2 + 2(24.8) = 88.8$. By Chebychev's Theorem, you can say that at least 75% of the population of Florida is between 0 and 88.8 years old.

▶ Try It Yourself 8

Apply Chebychev's Theorem to the data for Alaska using $k = 2$.

a. *Subtract* two standard deviations from the mean.
b. *Add* two standard deviations to the mean.
c. *Apply* Chebychev's Theorem for $k = 2$ and *interpret* the results.

Answer: Page A35

Insight

In Example 8, Chebychev's Theorem gives you an inequality statement that says that at least 75% of the population of Florida is under the age of 88.8. This is a true statement, but it is not nearly as strong a statement as could be made from reading the histogram.

In general, Chebychev's Theorem gives the minimum percent of data values that fall within the given number of standard deviations of the mean. Depending on the distribution, there is probably a higher percent of data falling in the given range.

▶ **Standard Deviation for Grouped Data**

In Section 2.1, you learned that large data sets are usually best represented by a frequency distribution. The formula for the sample standard deviation for a frequency distribution is

$$\text{Sample standard deviation} = s = \sqrt{\frac{\sum (x - \bar{x})^2 f}{n - 1}}$$

where $n = \sum f$ is the number of entries in the data set.

Number of Children in 50 Households				
1	3	1	1	1
1	2	2	1	0
1	1	0	0	0
1	5	0	3	6
3	0	3	1	1
1	1	6	0	1
3	6	6	1	2
2	3	0	1	1
4	1	1	2	2
0	3	0	2	4

EXAMPLE 9

Finding the Standard Deviation for Grouped Data

You collect a random sample of the number of children per household in a region. The results are shown at the left. Find the sample mean and the sample standard deviation of the data set.

Solution   These data could be treated as 50 individual entries, and you could use the formulas for mean and standard deviation. Because there are so many repeated numbers, however, it is easier to use a frequency distribution.

x	f	xf		$x - \bar{x}$	$(x - \bar{x})^2$	$(x - \bar{x})^2 f$
0	10	0		−1.8	3.24	32.40
1	19	19		−0.8	0.64	12.16
2	7	14		0.2	0.04	0.28
3	7	21		1.2	1.44	10.08
4	2	8		2.2	4.84	9.68
5	1	5		3.2	10.24	10.24
6	4	24		4.2	17.64	70.56
	$\Sigma = 50$	$\Sigma = 91$				$\Sigma = 145.40$

$$\bar{x} = \frac{\sum xf}{n} = \frac{91}{50} \approx 1.8 \qquad \text{Sample mean}$$

Use the sum of squares to find the sample standard deviation.

$$s = \sqrt{\frac{\sum (x - \bar{x})^2 f}{n - 1}} = \sqrt{\frac{145.4}{49}} \approx 1.7 \qquad \text{Sample standard deviation}$$

So, the sample mean is about 1.8 children, and the standard deviation is about 1.7 children.

▶ **Try It Yourself 9**

Change three of the 6s in the data set to 4s. How does this change affect the sample mean and sample standard deviation?

a. Write the first three columns of a *frequency distribution*.
b. Find the *sample mean*.
c. Complete the *last three columns* of the frequency distribution.
d. Find the *sample standard deviation*.   *Answer: Page A36*

When a frequency distribution has classes, you can estimate the sample mean and standard deviation by using the midpoint of each class.

EXAMPLE 10

Using Midpoints of Classes

The circle graph at the right shows the results of a survey in which 1000 adults were asked how much they spend in preparation for personal travel each year. Make a frequency distribution for the data. Then use the table to estimate the sample mean and the sample standard deviation of the data set. *(Adapted from Travel Industry Association of America)*

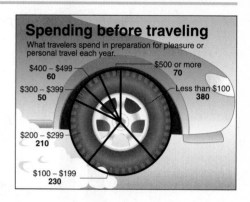

Spending before traveling
What travelers spend in preparation for pleasure or personal travel each year.

$400 – $499 — 60
$500 or more — 70
$300 – $399 — 50
Less than $100 — 380
$200 – $299 — 210
$100 – $199 — 230

Solution Begin by using a frequency distribution to organize the data.

Class	x	f	xf	$x - \bar{x}$	$(x - \bar{x})^2$	$(x - \bar{x})^2 f$
0–99	49.5	380	18,810	−142.5	20,306.25	7,716,375.0
100–199	149.5	230	34,385	−42.5	1,806.25	415,437.5
200–299	249.5	210	52,395	57.5	3,306.25	694,312.5
300–399	349.5	50	17,475	157.5	24,806.25	1,240,312.5
400–499	449.5	60	26,970	257.5	66,306.25	3,978,375.0
500+	599.5	70	41,965	407.5	166,056.25	11,623,937.5
		$\Sigma = 1,000$	$\Sigma = 192,000$			$\Sigma = 25,668,750.0$

$$\bar{x} = \frac{\Sigma xf}{n} = \frac{192,000}{1,000} = 192 \qquad \text{Sample mean}$$

Use the sum of squares to find the sample standard deviation.

$$s = \sqrt{\frac{\Sigma (x - \bar{x})^2 f}{n - 1}} = \sqrt{\frac{25,668,750}{999}} \approx 160.3 \qquad \text{Sample standard deviation}$$

So, the sample mean is $192 per year, and the sample standard deviation is about $160.3 per year.

▶ Try It Yourself 10

In the frequency distribution, 599.5 was chosen to represent the class of $500 or more. How would the sample mean and standard deviation change if you used 650 to represent this class?

a. Write the first four columns of a *frequency distribution*.
b. Find the *sample mean*.
c. Complete the *last three columns* of the frequency distribution.
d. Find the *sample standard deviation*.

Answer: Page A36

Study Tip

When a class is open, as in the last class, you must assign a single value to represent the midpoint. For this example, we selected 599.5.

2.4 EXERCISES

■ Building Basic Skills and Vocabulary

In Exercises 1 and 2, find the range, mean, variance, and standard deviation of the population data set.

1. 12   9   7   5   7   8   10   4   11   6

2. 15   24   17   19   20   18   20
     16   21   23   17   18   22   14

In Exercises 3 and 4, find the range, mean, variance, and standard deviation of the sample data set.

3. 17   8   13   18   15   9   10   11   6

4. 28   25   21   15   7   14   9
     27   21   24   14   17   16

Graphical Reasoning   *In Exercises 5 and 6, find the range of the data set represented by the display or graph.*

5.

2	3 9	Key: 2|3 = 23
3	0 0 2 3 6 7	
4	0 1 2 3 3 8	
5	0 1 1 9	
6	1 2 9 9	
7	5 9	
8	4 8	
9	0 2 5 6	

6.   **Bride's Age at First Marriage**

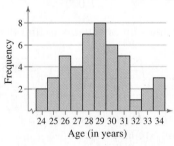

7. Explain how to find the range of a data set. What is an advantage of using the range as a measure of variation? What is a disadvantage?

8. Explain how to find the deviation of an entry in a data set. What is the sum of all the deviations in any data set?

9. Why is the standard deviation used more frequently than the variance? (*Hint:* Consider the units of the variance.)

10. Explain the relationship between variance and standard deviation. Can either of these measures be negative? Explain. Find a data set for which $n = 5$, $\bar{x} = 7$, and $s = 0$.

11. **Marriage Ages**   The ages of 10 brides at their first marriage are given below.

    31.8   24.5   26.7   21.3   45.6   35.9   22.5   33.1   42.3   30.6

    (a) Find the range of the data set.

    (b) Change 45.6 to 65.6 and find the range of the new data set.

    (c) Compare your answer to part (a) with your answer to part (b).

12. Find a population data set that contains six entries, has a mean of 5, and has a standard deviation of 2.

■ Using and Interpreting Concepts

13. **Graphical Reasoning**   Both data sets have a mean of 165. One has a standard deviation of 16, and the other has a standard deviation of 24. Which is which? Explain your reasoning.

(a)

Stem	Leaf
12	8 9
13	5 5 8
14	1 2
15	0 0 6 7
16	4 5 9
17	1 3 6 8
18	0 8 9
19	6
20	3 5 7

Key: 12|8 = 128

(b)

Stem	Leaf
12	
13	1
14	2 3 5
15	0 4 5 6 8
16	1 1 2 3 3 3
17	1 5 8 8
18	2 3 4 5
19	0 2
20	

14. **Graphical Reasoning**   Both data sets represented below have a mean of 50. One has a standard deviation of 2.4, and the other has a standard deviation of 5. Which is which? Explain your reasoning.

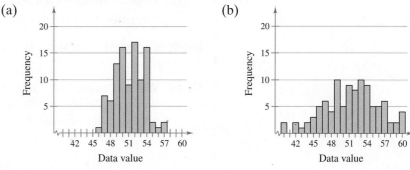

(a)   (b)

15. **Writing**   Describe the difference between the calculation of population standard deviation and that of sample standard deviation.

16. **Writing**   Given a data set, how do you know whether to calculate σ or s?

17. **Salary Offers**   You are applying for a job at two companies. Company A offers starting salaries with $\mu = \$31{,}000$ and $\sigma = \$1000$. Company B offers starting salaries with $\mu = \$31{,}000$ and $\sigma = \$5000$. From which company are you more likely to get an offer of $33,000 or more?

18. **Golf Strokes**   An Internet site compares the strokes per round of two professional golfers. Which golfer is more consistent: Player A with $\mu = 71.5$ strokes and $\sigma = 2.3$ strokes, or Player B with $\mu = 70.1$ strokes and $\sigma = 1.2$ strokes?

Comparing Two Data Sets   *In Exercises 19–22, you are asked to compare two data sets and interpret the results.*

19. Annual Salaries   Sample annual salaries (in thousands of dollars) for municipal employees in Los Angeles and Long Beach are listed.

Los Angeles: 20.2 26.1 20.9 32.1 35.9 23.0 28.2 31.6 18.3
Long Beach: 20.9 18.2 20.8 21.1 26.5 26.9 24.2 25.1 22.2

(a) Find the range, variance, and standard deviation of each data set.

(b) Interpret the results in the context of the real-life setting.

20. Annual Salaries   Sample annual salaries (in thousands of dollars) for municipal employees in Dallas and Houston are listed.

Dallas: 34.9 25.7 17.3 16.8 26.8 24.7 29.4 32.7 25.5
Houston: 25.6 23.2 26.7 27.7 25.4 26.4 18.3 26.1 31.3

(a) Find the range, variance, and standard deviation of each data set.

(b) Interpret the results in the context of the real-life setting.

21. SAT Scores   Sample SAT scores for eight males and eight females are listed.

Male SAT scores: 1059 1328 1175 1123   923 1017 1214 1042
Female SAT scores: 1226   965   841 1053 1056 1393 1312 1222

(a) Find the range, variance, and standard deviation of each data set.

(b) Interpret the results in the context of the real-life setting.

22. Annual Salaries   Sample annual salaries (in thousands of dollars) for public and private elementary school teachers are listed.

Public teachers: 38.6 38.1 38.7 36.8 34.8 35.9 39.9 36.2
Private teachers: 21.8 18.4 20.3 17.6 19.7 18.3 19.4 20.8

(a) Find the range, variance, and standard deviation of each data set.

(b) Interpret the results in the context of the real-life setting.

Reasoning with Graphs   *In Exercises 23–26, you are asked to compare three data sets.*

23. (a) Without calculating, determine which data set has the greatest sample standard deviation. Which has the least sample standard deviation? Explain your reasoning.

(i) (ii) (iii)

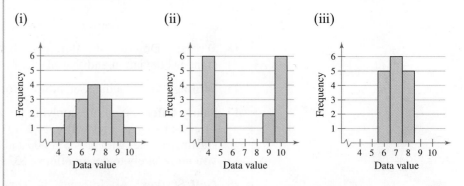

(b) How are the data sets the same? How do they differ?

24. (a) Without calculating, determine which data set has the greatest sample standard deviation. Which has the least sample standard deviation? Explain your reasoning.

(i)

0	9
1	5 8
2	3 3 7 7
3	2 5
4	1

Key: 4|1 = 41

(ii)

0	9
1	5
2	3 3 3 7 7 7
3	5
4	1

Key: 4|1 = 41

(iii)

0	
1	5
2	3 3 3 3 7 7 7 7
3	5
4	

Key: 4|1 = 41

(b) How are the data sets the same? How do they differ?

25. (a) Without calculating, determine which data set has the greatest sample standard deviation. Which has the least sample standard deviation? Explain your reasoning.

(i)   (ii)   (iii)

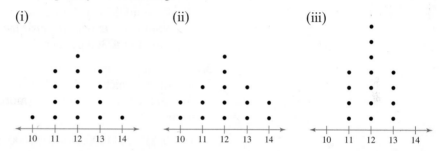

(b) How are the data sets the same? How do they differ?

26. (a) Without calculating, determine which data set has the greatest sample standard deviation. Which has the least sample standard deviation? Explain your reasoning.

(i)   (ii)   (iii)

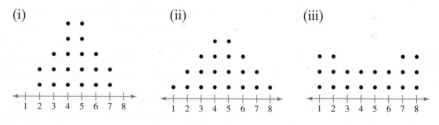

(b) How are the data sets the same? How do they differ?

27. Writing Discuss the similarities and the differences between the Empirical Rule and Chebychev's Theorem.

28. Writing What must you know about a data set before you can use the Empirical Rule?

Using the Empirical Rule *In Exercises 29–34, you are asked to use the Empirical Rule.*

29. The mean value of land and buildings per acre from a sample of farms is $1500, with a standard deviation of $200. The data set has a bell-shaped distribution. Estimate the percent of farms whose land and building values per acre are between $1300 and $1700.

30. The mean value of land and buildings per acre from a sample of farms is $2400, with a standard deviation of $450. Between what two values do about 95% of the data lie? (Assume the data set has a bell-shaped distribution.)

31. Using the sample statistics from Exercise 29, do the following. (Assume the number of farms in the sample is 75.)

(a) Use the Empirical Rule to estimate the number of farms whose land and building values per acre are between $1300 and $1700.

(b) If 25 additional farms were sampled, about how many of these farms would you expect to have land and building values between $1300 per acre and $1700 per acre?

32. Using the sample statistics from Exercise 30, do the following. (Assume the number of farms in the sample is 40.)

(a) Use the Empirical Rule to estimate the number of farms whose land and building values per acre are between $1500 and $3300.

(b) If 20 additional farms were sampled, about how many of these farms would you expect to have land and building values between $1500 per acre and $3300 per acre?

33. Using the sample statistics from Exercise 29 and the Empirical Rule, determine which of the following farms, whose land and building values per acre are given, are outliers (more than two standard deviations from the mean).

$1150, $1775, $1000, $1475, $2000, $1850

34. Using the sample statistics from Exercise 30 and the Empirical Rule, determine which of the following farms, whose land and building values per acre are given, are outliers (more than two standard deviations from the mean).

$3325, $2450, $3200, $1490, $1675, $2950

35. Chebychev's Theorem Old Faithful is a famous geyser at Yellowstone National Park. From a sample with $n = 32$, the mean duration of Old Faithful's eruptions is 3.32 minutes and the standard deviation is 1.09 minutes. Using Chebychev's Theorem, determine at least how many of the eruptions lasted between 1.14 minutes and 5.5 minutes. *(Source: Yellowstone National Park)*

36. Chebychev's Theorem The mean time in a women's 400-meter dash is 57.07 seconds, with a standard deviation of 1.05. Apply Chebychev's Theorem to the data using $k = 2$. Interpret the results.

Calculating Using Grouped Data
In Exercises 37–44, use the grouped data formulas to find the indicated mean and standard deviation.

37. Pets per Household The results of a random sample of the number of pets per household in a region are shown in the histogram. Estimate the sample mean and the sample standard deviation of the data set.

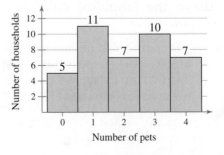

38. Cars per Household   A random sample of households in a region and the number of cars per household are shown in the histogram. Estimate the sample mean and the sample deviation of the data set.

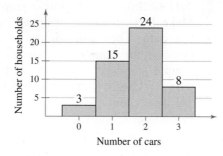

39. Football Wins   The number of wins for each National Football League team in 2006 are listed. Make a frequency distribution (using five classes) for the data set. Then approximate the population mean and the population standard deviation of the data set. *(Source: National Football League)*

```
12  10  7  6  13  8  8  4  12  8  8  6
14   9  9  2  10  9  8  5  13  8  6  3
10   8  7  4   9  8  7  5
```

40. Water Consumption   The number of gallons of water consumed per day by a small village are listed. Make a frequency distribution (using five classes) for the data set. Then approximate the population mean and the population standard deviation of the data set.

```
167  180  192  173  145  151  174
175  178  160  195  224  244  146
162  146  177  163  149  188
```

41. Amount of Caffeine   The amount of caffeine in a sample of five-ounce servings of brewed coffee is shown in the histogram. Make a frequency distribution for the data. Then use the table to estimate the sample mean and the sample standard deviation of the data set.

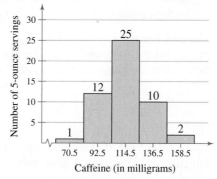

FIGURE FOR EXERCISE 41

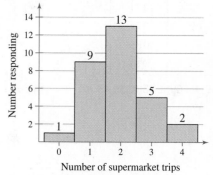

FIGURE FOR EXERCISE 42

42. Supermarket Trips   Thirty people were randomly selected and asked how many trips to the supermarket they made in the past week. The responses are shown in the histogram. Make a frequency distribution for the data. Then use the table to estimate the sample mean and the sample standard deviation of the data set.

43. U.S. Population The estimated distribution (in millions) of the U.S. population by age for the year 2011 is shown in the circle graph. Make a frequency distribution for the data. Then use the table to estimate the sample mean and the sample standard deviation of the data set. Use 70 as the midpoint for "65 years and over." *(Source: U.S. Census Bureau)*

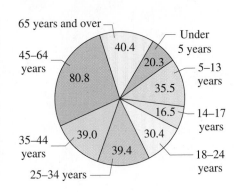

44. Japan's Population Japan's estimated population for the year 2014 is shown in the bar graph. Make a frequency distribution for the data. Then use the table to estimate the sample mean and the sample standard deviation of the data set. *(Source: U.S. Census Bureau, International Data Base)*

Heights	Weights
72	180
74	168
68	225
76	201
74	189
69	192
72	197
79	162
70	174
69	171
77	185
73	210

TABLE FOR EXERCISE 45

■ Extending Concepts

45. Coefficient of Variation The **coefficient of variation** CV describes the standard deviation as a percent of the mean. Because it has no units, you can use the coefficient of variation to compare data with different units.

$$CV = \frac{\text{Standard deviation}}{\text{Mean}} \times 100\%$$

The table to the left shows the heights (in inches) and weights (in pounds) of the members of a basketball team. Find the coefficient of variation for each data set. What can you conclude?

46. Shortcut Formula You used $SS_x = \sum (x - \bar{x})^2$ when calculating variance and standard deviation. An alternative formula that is sometimes more convenient for hand calculations is

$$SS_x = \sum x^2 - \frac{(\sum x)^2}{n}.$$

You can find the sample variance by dividing the sum of squares by $n - 1$ and the sample standard deviation by finding the square root of the sample variance.

(a) Use the shortcut formula to calculate the sample standard deviation for the data set given in Exercise 21.

(b) Compare your results with those obtained in Exercise 21.

47. Scaling Data   Sample annual salaries (in thousands of dollars) for employees at a company are listed.

42   36   48   51   39   39   42   36   48   33   39   42   45

(a) Find the sample mean and sample standard deviation.

(b) Each employee in the sample is given a 5% raise. Find the sample mean and sample standard deviation for the revised data set.

(c) To calculate the monthly salary, divide each original salary by 12. Find the sample mean and sample standard deviation for the revised data set.

(d) What can you conclude from the results of (a), (b), and (c)?

48. Shifting Data   Sample annual salaries (in thousands of dollars) for employees at a company are listed.

40   35   49   53   38   39   40   37   49   34   38   43   47

(a) Find the sample mean and sample standard deviation.

(b) Each employee in the sample is given a $1000 raise. Find the sample mean and sample standard deviation for the revised data set.

(c) Each employee in the sample takes a pay cut of $2000 from their original salary. Find the sample mean and sample standard deviation for the revised data set.

(d) What can you conclude from the results of (a), (b), and (c)?

49. Mean Absolute Deviation   Another useful measure of variation for a data set is the **mean absolute deviation** MAD. It is calculated by the formula

$$\frac{\Sigma|x - \bar{x}|}{n}.$$

(a) Find the mean absolute deviations of the data sets in Exercise 21. Compare your results with the sample standard deviation.

(b) Find the mean absolute deviations of the data sets in Exercise 22. Compare your results with the sample standard deviation.

50. Chebychev's Theorem   At least 99% of the data in any data set lie within how many standard deviations of the mean? Explain how you obtained your answer.

51. Pearson's Index of Skewness   The English statistician Karl Pearson (1857–1936) introduced a formula for the skewness of a distribution.

$$P = \frac{3(\bar{x} - \text{median})}{s} \qquad \text{Pearson's index of skewness}$$

Most distributions have an index of skewness between -3 and 3. When $P > 0$, the data are skewed right. When $P < 0$, the data are skewed left. When $P = 0$, the data are symmetric. Calculate the coefficient of skewness for each distribution. Describe the shape of each.

(a) $\bar{x} = 17$, $s = 2.3$, median $= 19$

(b) $\bar{x} = 32$, $s = 5.1$, median $= 25$

APPLET

The *standard deviation* applet is designed to allow you to interactively investigate the standard deviation as a measure of spread for a data set. Points can be added to the plot by clicking the mouse above the horizontal axis. The mean of the points is shown as a green arrow. A numeric value for the standard deviation is shown above the plot. Points on the plot can be removed by clicking on the point and then dragging the point into the trash can. All of the points on the plot can be removed by simply clicking inside the trash can. The range of values for the horizontal axis can be specified by inputting lower and upper limits and then clicking UPDATE.

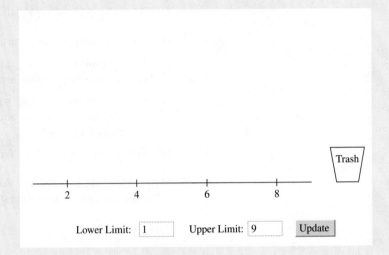

■ **Explore**

Step 1 Specify a lower limit.
Step 2 Specify an upper limit.
Step 3 Add 15 points to the plot.
Step 4 Remove all of the points from the plot.

■ **Draw Conclusions**

APPLET

1. Specify the lower limit to be 10 and the upper limit to be 20. Plot 10 points that have a mean of about 15 and a standard deviation of about 3. Write the estimates of the values of the points. Plot a point with a value of 15. What happens to the mean and standard deviation? Plot a point with a value of 20. What happens to the mean and standard deviation?

2. Specify the lower limit to be 30 and the upper limit to be 40. How can you plot eight points so that the points have the largest possible standard deviation? Use the applet to plot the set of points and then use the formula for standard deviation to confirm the value given in the applet. How can you plot eight points so that the points have the lowest possible standard deviation? Explain.

CASE STUDY

Earnings of Athletes

The earnings of professional athletes in different sports can vary. An athlete can be paid a base salary, earn signing bonuses upon signing a new contract, or even earn money by finishing in a certain position in a race or tournament. The data shown below are the earnings (for performance only, no endorsements) from Major League Baseball (MLB), Major League Soccer (MLS), the National Basketball Association (NBA), the National Football League (NFL), the National Hockey League (NHL), the National Association for Stock Car Auto Racing (NASCAR), and the Professional Golf Association Tour (PGA) for a recent year.

Organization	Number of players
MLB	824
MLS	321
NBA	444
NFL	1877
NHL	727
NASCAR	78
PGA	263

Number of Players Separated into Earnings Ranges

Organization	$0–$500,000	$500,001–$2,000,000	$2,000,001–$6,000,000	$6,000,001–$10,000,000	$10,000,001+
MLB	299	207	189	73	56
MLS	316	5	0	0	0
NBA	31	166	147	58	42
NFL	760	758	274	70	15
NHL	85	448	177	17	0
NASCAR	27	13	33	5	0
PGA	115	117	29	2	0

■ Exercises

1. **Revenue** Which organization had the greatest total player earnings? Explain your reasoning.

2. **Mean Earnings** Estimate the mean earnings of a player in each organization. Use $16,500,000 as the midpoint for $10,000,001+.

3. **Revenue** Which organization had the greatest earnings per player? Explain your reasoning.

4. **Standard Deviation** Estimate the standard deviation for the earnings of a player in each organization. Use $16,500,000 as the midpoint for $10,000,001+.

5. **Standard Deviation** Which organization had the greatest standard deviation? Explain your reasoning.

6. **Bell-Shaped Distribution** Of the seven organizations, which is more bell shaped? Explain your reasoning.

2.5 Measures of Position

What You SHOULD LEARN

▸ How to find the first, second, and third quartiles of a data set

▸ How to find the interquartile range of a data set

▸ How to represent a data set graphically using a box-and-whisker plot

▸ How to interpret other fractiles such as percentiles

▸ How to find and interpret the standard score (z-score)

Quartiles ▸ Percentiles and Other Fractiles ▸ The Standard Score

▸ Quartiles

In this section, you will learn how to use fractiles to specify the position of a data entry within a data set. **Fractiles** are numbers that partition, or divide, an ordered data set into equal parts. For instance, the median is a fractile because it divides an ordered data set into two equal parts.

DEFINITION

The three **quartiles**, Q_1, Q_2, and Q_3, approximately divide an ordered data set into four equal parts. About one quarter of the data fall on or below the **first quartile** Q_1. About one half of the data fall on or below the **second quartile** Q_2 (the second quartile is the same as the median of the data set). About three quarters of the data fall on or below the **third quartile** Q_3.

EXAMPLE 1

Finding the Quartiles of a Data Set

The test scores of 15 employees enrolled in a CPR training course are listed. Find the first, second, and third quartiles of the test scores.

13 9 18 15 14 21 7 10 11 20 5 18 37 16 17

Solution

First, order the data set and find the median Q_2. Once you find Q_2, divide the data set into two halves. The first and third quartiles are the medians of the lower and upper halves of the data set.

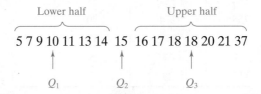

Lower half   Upper half

5 7 9 10 11 13 14   15   16 17 18 18 20 21 37

Q_1 Q_2 Q_3

Interpretation About one fourth of the employees scored 10 or less; about one half scored 15 or less; and about three fourths scored 18 or less.

▸ Try It Yourself 1

Find the first, second, and third quartiles for the number of touchdowns scored by all Division 1A football teams using the data set listed in the Chapter Opener on page 39.

a. *Order* the data set.
b. Find the median Q_2.
c. Find the first and third quartiles Q_1 and Q_3.

Answer: Page A36

EXAMPLE 2

Using Technology to Find Quartiles

The tuition costs (in thousands of dollars) for 25 liberal arts colleges are listed. Use a calculator or a computer to find the first, second, and third quartiles.

23 25 30 23 20 22 21 15 25 24 30 25 30
20 23 29 20 19 22 23 29 23 28 22 28

Solution   MINITAB, Excel, and the TI-83/84 each have features that automatically calculate quartiles. Try using this technology to find the first, second, and third quartiles of the tuition data. From the displays, you can see that $Q_1 = 21.5$, $Q_2 = 23$, and $Q_3 = 28$.

MINITAB

Descriptive Statistics

Variable	N	Mean	SE Mean	TrMean	StDev
Tuition	25	23.960	0.788	24.087	3.942

Variable	Minimum	Q1	Median	Q3	Maximum
Tuition	15.000	21.500	23.000	28.000	30.000

EXCEL

	A	B	C	D
1	23			
2	25		Quartile(A1:A25,1)	
3	30		22	
4	23			
5	20		Quartile(A1:A25,2)	
6	22		23	
7	21			
8	15		Quartile(A1:A25,3)	
9	25		28	
10	24			
11	30			
12	25			
13	30			
14	20			
15	23			
16	29			
17	20			
18	19			
19	22			
20	23			
21	29			
22	23			
23	28			
24	22			
25	28			

TI-83/84

```
1-Var Stats
↑n=25
minX=15
Q₁=21.5
Med=23
Q₃=28
maxX=30
```

Interpretation   About one quarter of these colleges charge tuition of $21,500 or less; one half charge $23,000 or less; and about three quarters charge $28,000 or less.

▶ Try It Yourself 2

The tuition costs (in thousands of dollars) for 25 universities are listed. Use a calculator or a computer to find the first, second, and third quartiles.

20 26 28 25 31 14 23 15 12 26 29 24 31
19 31 17 15 17 20 31 32 16 21 22 28

a. *Enter* the data.
b. *Calculate* the first, second, and third quartiles.
c. What can you conclude? *Answer: Page A36*

After finding the quartiles of a data set, you can find the interquartile range.

DEFINITION

The **interquartile range (IQR)** of a data set is the difference between the third and first quartiles.

$$\text{Interquartile range (IQR)} = Q_3 - Q_1$$

EXAMPLE 3

Finding the Interquartile Range

Find the interquartile range of the 15 test scores given in Example 1. What can you conclude from the result?

Solution From Example 1, you know that $Q_1 = 10$ and $Q_3 = 18$. So, the interquartile range is

$$\text{IQR} = Q_3 - Q_1 = 18 - 10 = 8.$$

Interpretation The test scores in the middle portion of the data set vary by at most 8 points.

Try It Yourself 3

Find the interquartile range for the number of touchdowns scored by all Division 1A football teams listed in the Chapter Opener on page 39.

a. Find the first and third quartiles, Q_1 and Q_3.
b. *Subtract* Q_1 from Q_3.
c. *Interpret* the result in the context of the data. *Answer: Page A36*

The IQR is a measure of variation that gives you an idea of how much the middle 50% of the data varies. It can also be used to identify outliers. Any data value that lies more than 1.5 IQRs to the left of Q_1 or to the right of Q_3 is an outlier. For instance, the IQR in Example 1 is $18 - 10 = 8$. So, 1.5 IQRs to the right of Q_3 is $Q_3 + 1.5(8) = 18 + 12 = 30$. Because $37 > 30$, 37 is an outlier.

Another important application of quartiles is to represent data sets using box-and-whisker plots. A **box-and-whisker plot** is an exploratory data analysis tool that highlights the important features of a data set. To graph a box-and-whisker plot, you must know the following values.

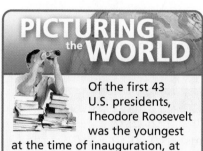
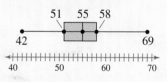
1. The minimum entry
2. The first quartile Q_1
3. The median Q_2
4. The third quartile Q_3
5. The maximum entry

These five numbers are called the **five-number summary** of the data set.

GUIDELINES

Drawing a Box-and-Whisker Plot

1. Find the five-number summary of the data set.
2. Construct a horizontal scale that spans the range of the data.
3. Plot the five numbers above the horizontal scale.
4. Draw a box above the horizontal scale from Q_1 to Q_3 and draw a vertical line in the box at Q_2.
5. Draw whiskers from the box to the minimum and maximum entries.

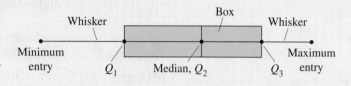

EXAMPLE 4

Drawing a Box-and-Whisker Plot

Draw a box-and-whisker plot that represents the 15 test scores given in Example 1. What can you conclude from the display?

> See MINITAB and TI-83/84 steps on pages 124 and 125.

Solution   The five-number summary of the test scores is below. Using these five numbers, you can construct the box-and-whisker plot shown.

$$\text{Min} = 5 \qquad Q_1 = 10 \qquad Q_2 = 15 \qquad Q_3 = 18 \qquad \text{Max} = 37$$

Test Scores in CPR Class

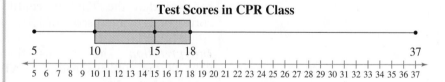

Interpretation   You can make several conclusions from the display. One is that about half the scores are between 10 and 18. By looking at the length of the right whisker, you can also conclude that the score of 37 is a possible outlier.

▶ **Try It Yourself 4**

Draw a box-and-whisker plot that represents the number of touchdowns scored by all Division 1A football teams listed in the chapter opener on page 39.

a. Find the *five-number summary* of the data set.
b. Construct a *horizontal scale* and *plot* the five numbers above it.
c. Draw the *box*, the *vertical line*, and the *whiskers*.
d. Make some conclusions.

Answer: Page A36

▶ Percentiles and Other Fractiles

In addition to using quartiles to specify a measure of position, you can also use percentiles and deciles. These common fractiles are summarized as follows.

Fractiles	Summary	Symbols
Quartiles	Divide a data set into 4 equal parts.	Q_1, Q_2, Q_3
Deciles	Divide a data set into 10 equal parts.	$D_1, D_2, D_3, \ldots, D_9$
Percentiles	Divide a data set into 100 equal parts.	$P_1, P_2, P_3, \ldots, P_{99}$

Percentiles are often used in education and health-related fields to indicate how one individual compares with others in a group. They can also be used to identify unusually high or unusually low values. For instance, test scores and children's growth measurements are often expressed in percentiles. Scores or measurements in the 95th percentile and above are unusually high, while those in the 5th percentile and below are unusually low.

EXAMPLE 5

Interpreting Percentiles

The ogive represents the cumulative frequency distribution for SAT test scores of college-bound students in a recent year. What test score represents the 72nd percentile? How should you interpret this? (*Source: College Board Online*)

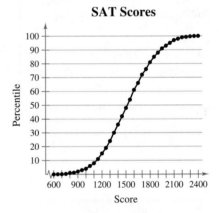

SAT Scores

Solution From the ogive, you can see that the 72nd percentile corresponds to a test score of 1700.

Interpretation This means that 72% of the students had an SAT score of 1700 or less.

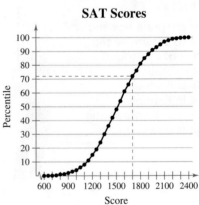

SAT Scores

▶ Try It Yourself 5

The number of touchdowns scored by all Division 1A football teams are represented in the cumulative frequency graph at the left. At what percentile is a team that scores 40 touchdowns?

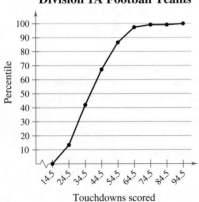

Touchdowns Scored by Division 1A Football Teams

a. *Use the graph* to find the percentile that corresponds to the given touchdowns scored.
b. *Interpret* the results in the context of the data.

Answer: Page A36

The Standard Score

When you know the mean and standard deviation of a data set, you can measure a data value's position in the data set with a standard score, or z-score.

DEFINITION

The **standard score,** or **z-score,** represents the number of standard deviations a given value x falls from the mean μ. To find the z-score for a given value, use the following formula.

$$z = \frac{\text{Value} - \text{Mean}}{\text{Standard deviation}} = \frac{x - \mu}{\sigma}$$

A z-score can be negative, positive, or zero. If z is negative, the corresponding x-value is below the mean. If z is positive, the corresponding x-value is above the mean. And if $z = 0$, the corresponding x-value is equal to the mean. A z-score can be used to identify an unusual value of a data set that is approximately bell-shaped.

EXAMPLE 6

Finding z-Scores

The mean speed of vehicles along a stretch of highway is 56 miles per hour with a standard deviation of 4 miles per hour. You measure the speed of three cars traveling along this stretch of highway as 62 miles per hour, 47 miles per hour, and 56 miles per hour. Find the z-score that corresponds to each speed. What can you conclude?

Solution   The z-score that corresponds to each speed is calculated below.

$$x = 62 \text{ mph} \qquad x = 47 \text{ mph} \qquad x = 56 \text{ mph}$$

$$z = \frac{62 - 56}{4} = 1.5 \qquad z = \frac{47 - 56}{4} = -2.25 \qquad z = \frac{56 - 56}{4} = 0$$

Interpretation   From the z-scores, you can conclude that a speed of 62 miles per hour is 1.5 standard deviations above the mean; a speed of 47 miles per hour is 2.25 standard deviations below the mean; and a speed of 56 miles per hour is equal to the mean. If the distribution of the speeds is approximately bell-shaped, the car traveling 47 miles per hour is said to be traveling unusually slowly, because its speed corresponds to a z-score of -2.25.

▶ Try It Yourself 6

The monthly utility bills in a city have a mean of $70 and a standard deviation of $8. Find the z-scores that correspond to utility bills of $60, $71, and $92. What can you conclude?

a. *Identify* μ and σ of the nonstandard normal distribution.
b. *Transform* each value to a z-score.
c. *Interpret* the results.   *Answer: Page A36*

When a distribution is approximately bell shaped, you know from the Empirical Rule that about 95% of the data lie within 2 standard deviations of the mean. So, when this distribution's values are transformed to z-scores, about 95% of the z-scores should fall between -2 and 2. A z-score outside of this range will occur about 5% of the time and would be considered unusual. So, according to the Empirical Rule, a z-score less than -3 or greater than 3 would be *very* unusual, with such a score occurring about 0.3% of the time.

Very unusual scores

Unusual scores

Usual scores

-3 -2 -1 0 1 2 3

z-score

In Example 6, you used z-scores to compare data values within the same data set. You can also use z-scores to compare data values from different data sets.

EXAMPLE 7

Comparing z-Scores from Different Data Sets

In 2007, Forest Whitaker won the Best Actor Oscar at age 45 for his role in the movie *The Last King of Scotland*. Helen Mirren won the Best Actress Oscar at age 61 for her role in *The Queen*. The mean age of all best actor winners is 43.7, with a standard deviation of 8.8. The mean age of all best actress winners is 36, with a standard deviation of 11.5. Find the z-score that corresponds to the age for each actor or actress. Then compare your results.

Solution

The z-score that corresponds to the age of each actor or actress is calculated below.

$$\textbf{\textit{Forest Whitaker}} \quad z = \frac{x - \mu}{\sigma}$$

$$= \frac{45 - 43.7}{8.8}$$

$$\approx 0.15$$

$$\textbf{\textit{Helen Mirren}} \quad z = \frac{x - \mu}{\sigma}$$

$$= \frac{61 - 36}{11.5}$$

$$\approx 2.17$$

The age of Forest Whitaker is 0.15 standard deviation above the mean, and the age of Helen Mirren is 2.17 standard deviations above the mean.

Interpretation   The z-score corresponding to the age of Helen Mirren is more than two standard deviations from the mean, so it is considered unusual. Compared to other Best Actress winners, she is relatively older, whereas the age of Forest Whitaker is only slightly higher than the average age of other Best Actor winners.

▶ Try It Yourself 7

In 2007, Alan Arkin won the Best Supporting Actor Oscar at age 72 for his role in the movie *Little Miss Sunshine*. Jennifer Hudson won the Best Supporting Actress Oscar at age 25 for her role in *Dreamgirls*. The mean age of all best supporting actor winners is 50.1, with a standard deviation of 13.9. The mean age of all best supporting actress winners is 39.7, with a standard deviation of 14. Find the z-score that corresponds to the age for each actor or actress. Then compare your results.

a. *Identify* μ and σ of each nonstandard normal distribution.
b. *Transform* each value to a z-score.
c. *Compare* your results.   *Answer: Page A36*

2.5   EXERCISES

MyStatLab

■ Building Basic Skills and Vocabulary

In Exercises 1 and 2, (a) find the three quartiles and (b) draw a box-and-whisker plot of the data.

1. 4 7 7 5 2 9 7 6 8 5 8 4 1 5 2 8 7 6 6 9

2. 2 7 1 3 1 2 8 9 9 2 5 4
    7 3 7 5 4 7 2 3 5 9 5 6
    3 9 3 4 9 8 8 2 3 9 5

3. The goals scored per game by a soccer team represent the first quartile for all teams in a league. What can you conclude about the team's goals scored per game?

4. A salesperson at a company sold $6,903,435 of hardware equipment last year, a figure that represented the eighth decile of sales performance at the company. What can you conclude about the salesperson's performance?

5. A student's score on an actuarial exam is in the 78th percentile. What can you conclude about the student's exam score?

6. A counselor tells a child's parents that their child's IQ is in the 93rd percentile for the child's age group. What can you conclude about the child's IQ?

True or False?   *In Exercises 7–10, determine whether the statement is true or false. If it is false, rewrite it as a true statement.*

7. The second quartile is the median of an ordered data set.

8. The five numbers you need to graph a box-and-whisker plot are the minimum, the maximum, Q_1, Q_3, and the mean.

9. The 50th percentile is equivalent to Q_1.

10. It is impossible to have a z-score of 0.

■ Using and Interpreting Concepts

Graphical Analysis   *In Exercises 11–16, use the box-and-whisker plot to identify*

(a) the minimum entry.   *(d) the second quartile.*

(b) the maximum entry.   *(e) the third quartile.*

(c) the first quartile.   *(f) the interquartile range.*

11.
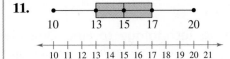

12.
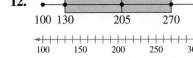

13.
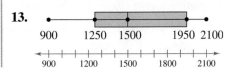

14.
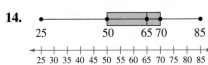

15.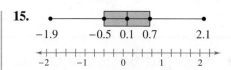

16.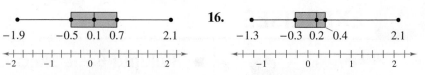

Interpreting Graphs *In Exercises 17–20, use the box-and-whisker plot to determine if the shape of the distribution represented is symmetric, skewed left, skewed right, or none of these. Justify your answer.*

17.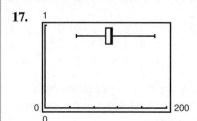

18.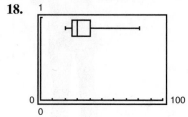

19.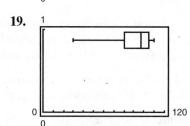

20.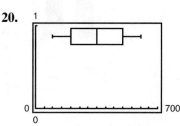

21. Graphical Analysis The letters A, B, and C are marked on the histogram. Match them to Q_1, Q_2 (the median), and Q_3. Justify your answer.

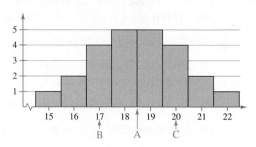

22. Graphical Analysis The letters R, S, and T are marked on the histogram. Match them to P_{10}, P_{50}, and P_{80}. Justify your answer.

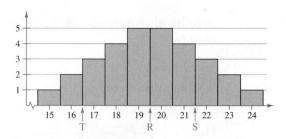

Using Technology to Find Quartiles and Draw Graphs *In Exercises 23–26, use a calculator or a computer to (a) find the data set's first, second, and third quartiles, and (b) draw a box-and-whisker plot that represents the data set.*

23. TV Viewing The number of hours of television watched per day by a sample of 28 people

2 4 1 5 7 2 5 4 4 2 3 6 4 3
5 2 0 3 5 9 4 5 2 1 3 6 7 2

24. Vacation Days   The number of vacation days used by a sample of 20 employees in a recent year

3	9	2	1	7	5	3	2	2	6
4	0	10	0	3	5	7	8	6	5

25. Airplane Distances   The distances (in miles) from an airport of a sample of 22 inbound and outbound airplanes

2.8	2.0	3.0	3.0	3.2	5.9	3.5	3.6
1.8	5.5	3.7	5.2	3.8	3.9	6.0	2.5
4.0	4.1	4.6	5.0	5.5	6.0		

26. Hourly Earnings   The hourly earnings (in dollars) of a sample of 25 railroad equipment manufacturers

15.60	18.75	14.60	15.80	14.35	13.90	17.50	17.55	13.80
14.20	19.05	15.35	15.20	19.45	15.95	16.50	16.30	15.25
15.05	19.10	15.20	16.22	17.75	18.40	15.25		

27. TV Viewing   Refer to the data set given in Exercise 23 and the box-and-whisker plot you drew that represents the data set.

(a) About 75% of the people watched no more than how many hours of television per day?

(b) What percent of the people watched more than 4 hours of television per day?

(c) If you randomly selected one person from the sample, what is the likelihood that the person watched less than 2 hours of television per day? Write your answer as a percent.

28. Manufacturer Earnings   Refer to the data set given in Exercise 26 and the box-and-whisker plot you drew that represents the data set.

(a) About 75% of the manufacturers made less than what amount per hour?

(b) What percent of the manufacturers made more than $15.80 per hour?

(c) If you randomly selected one manufacturer from the sample, what is the likelihood that the manufacturer made less than $15.80 per hour? Write your answer as a percent.

Graphical Analysis   *In Exercises 29 and 30, the midpoints A, B, and C are marked on the histogram. Match them to the indicated z-scores. Which z-scores, if any, would be considered unusual?*

29. $z = 0$

$z = 2.14$

$z = -1.43$

30. $z = 0.77$

$z = 1.54$

$z = -1.54$

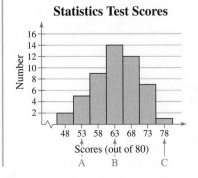

Comparing Test Scores *For the statistics test scores in Exercise 29, the mean is 63 and the standard deviation is 7.0, and for the biology test scores in Exercise 30 the mean is 23 and the standard deviation is 3.9. In Exercises 31–34, you are given the test scores of a student who took both tests.*

(a) *Transform each test score to a z-score.*

(b) *Determine on which test the student had a better score.*

31. A student gets a 73 on the statistics test and a 26 on the biology test.

32. A student gets a 60 on the statistics test and a 20 on the biology test.

33. A student gets a 78 on the statistics test and a 29 on the biology test.

34. A student gets a 63 on the statistics test and a 23 on the biology test.

35. Life Spans of Tires A certain brand of automobile tire has a mean life span of 35,000 miles and a standard deviation of 2250 miles. (Assume the life spans of the tires have a bell-shaped distribution.)

    (a) The life spans of three randomly selected tires are 34,000 miles, 37,000 miles, and 31,000 miles. Find the z-score that corresponds to each life span. According to the z-scores, would the life spans of any of these tires be considered unusual?

    (b) The life spans of three randomly selected tires are 30,500 miles, 37,250 miles, and 35,000 miles. Using the Empirical Rule, find the percentile that corresponds to each life span.

36. Life Spans of Fruit Flies The life spans of a species of fruit fly have a bell-shaped distribution, with a mean of 33 days and a standard deviation of 4 days.

    (a) The life spans of three randomly selected fruit flies are 34 days, 30 days, and 42 days. Find the z-score that corresponds to each life span and determine if any of these life spans are unusual.

    (b) The life spans of three randomly selected fruit flies are 29 days, 41 days, and 25 days. Using the Empirical Rule, find the percentile that corresponds to each life span.

Interpreting Percentiles *In Exercises 37–42, use the cumulative frequency distribution to answer the questions. The cumulative frequency distribution represents the heights of males in the United States in the 20–29 age group. The heights have a bell-shaped distribution (see Picturing the World, page 88) with a mean of 69.6 inches and a standard deviation of 3.0 inches.* (Source: National Center for Health Statistics)

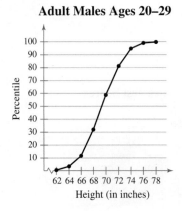

Adult Males Ages 20–29

37. What height represents the 40th percentile? How should you interpret this?

38. What percentile is a height of 76 inches? How should you interpret this?

39. Three adult males in the 20–29 age group are randomly selected. Their heights are 74 inches, 62 inches, and 80 inches. Use z-scores to determine which heights, if any, are unusual.

40. Three adult males in the 20–29 age group are randomly selected. Their heights are 70 inches, 66 inches, and 68 inches. Use z-scores to determine which heights, if any, are unusual.

41. Find the z-score for a male in the 20–29 age group whose height is 71.1 inches. What percentile is this?

42. Find the z-score for a male in the 20–29 age group whose height is 66.3 inches. What percentile is this?

■ Extending Concepts

43. Ages of Executives The ages of a sample of 100 executives are listed.

```
31 62 51 44 61 47 49 45 40 52
60 51 67 47 63 54 59 43 63 52
50 54 61 41 48 49 51 54 39 54
47 52 36 53 74 33 53 68 44 40
60 42 50 48 42 42 36 57 42 48
56 51 54 42 27 43 43 41 54 49
49 47 51 28 54 36 36 41 60 55
42 59 35 65 48 56 82 39 54 49
61 56 57 32 38 48 64 51 45 46
62 63 59 63 32 47 40 37 49 57
```

Over the hill or on top?
Number of 100 top executives in the following age groups:

TOP EXECUTIVES

(a) Order the data and find the first, second, and third quartiles.

(b) Draw a box-and-whisker plot that represents the data set.

(c) Interpret the results in the context of the data.

(d) On the basis of this sample, at what age would you expect to be an executive? Explain your reasoning.

(e) Which age groups, if any, can be considered unusual? Explain your reasoning.

Midquartile   *Another measure of position is called the* **midquartile.** *You can find the midquartile of a data set by using the following formula.*

$$Midquartile = \frac{Q_1 + Q_3}{2}$$

In Exercises 44–47, find the midquartile of the given data set.

44. 5   7   1   2   3   10   8   7   5   3

45. 23   36   47   33   34   40   39   24   32   22   38   41

46. 12.3   9.7   8.0   15.4   16.1   11.8   12.7   13.4
    12.2   8.1   7.9   10.3   11.2

47. 21.4   20.8   19.7   15.2   31.9   18.7   15.6   16.7
    19.8   13.4   22.9   28.7   19.8   17.2   30.1

48. Song Lengths   Side-by-side box-and-whisker plots can be used to compare two or more different data sets. Each box-and-whisker plot is drawn on the same number line to compare the data sets more easily. The song lengths (in seconds) from two different compact discs are given.

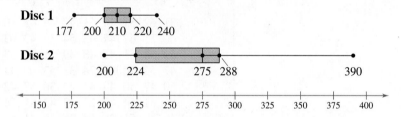

(a) Describe the shape of each distribution. Which disc has less variation in song lengths?

(b) Which distribution is more likely to have outliers? Explain your reasoning.

(c) Which disc do you think has a standard deviation of 16.3? Explain your reasoning.

49. Credit Card Purchases   The monthly credit card purchases (rounded to the nearest dollar) over the last two years for you and a friend are listed.

You: 60   95   102   110   130   130   162   200   215   120   124   28
    58   40   102   105   141   160   130   210   145   90   46   76

Friend: 100   125   132   90   85   75   140   160   180   190   160   105
    145   150   151   82   78   115   170   158   140   130   165   125

Use a calculator or a computer to draw a side-by-side box-and-whisker plot that represents the data sets. Then describe the shapes of the distributions.

Finding Percentiles   *You can find the percentile that corresponds to a specific data value x by using the following formula, then rounding the result to the nearest whole number.*

$$Percentile\ of\ x = \frac{number\ of\ data\ values\ less\ than\ x}{total\ number\ of\ data\ values} \cdot 100$$

In Exercises 50 and 51, use the information from Example 7 and the fact that there have been 80 Best Actor Oscars and 80 Best Actress Oscars awarded.

50. Fifty-one winners were younger than Forest Whitaker when they won the Best Actor Oscar. Find the percentile that corresponds to Forest Whitaker's age.

51. Only four winners were older than Helen Mirren when they won the Best Actress Oscar. Find the percentile that corresponds to Helen Mirren's age.

Uses & Abuses

Uses

Descriptive statistics helps you see trends or patterns from a set of raw data. A good description of a data set consists of (1) a measure of the center of the data, (2) a measure of the variability (or spread) of the data, and (3) the shape (or distribution) of the data. When you read reports, news items, or advertisements prepared by other people, you are seldom given the raw data used for a study. Instead you see graphs, measures of central tendency, and measures of variability. To be a discerning reader, you need to understand the terms and techniques of descriptive statistics.

Abuses

Knowing how statistics are calculated can help you analyze questionable statistics. For example, suppose you are interviewing for a sales position and the company reports that the average yearly commission earned by the five people in its sales force is $60,000. This is a misleading statement if it is based on four commissions of $25,000 and one of $200,000. The median would more accurately describe the yearly commission, but they used the mean because it is a greater amount.

Statistical graphs can also be misleading. Compare the two time series charts below that show the year-end stock prices for Kellogg Company. The data are the same for each. The first graph, however, has a cropped vertical axis, which makes it appear that the stock price has increased greatly from 1999 to 2006. In the second graph, the scale on the vertical axis begins at zero. This graph correctly shows that the stock prices increased only modestly during this time period. *(Source: Kellogg Company)*

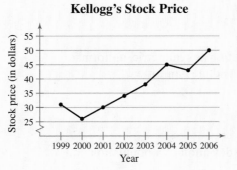

Kellogg's Stock Price

Kellogg's Stock Price

Ethics

Mark Twain helped popularize the saying, "There are three kinds of lies: lies, damned lies, and statistics." In short, even the most accurate statistics can be used to support studies or statements that are incorrect. Unscrupulous people can use misleading statistics to "prove" their point. Being informed about how statistics are calculated and questioning the data are ways to avoid being misled.

■ EXERCISES

1. In a newspaper or magazine, find an example of a graph that might lead to incorrect conclusions.

2. Describe a situation in which a statistic could be used to make a conclusion misleading.

2 CHAPTER SUMMARY

What did you learn?

	EXAMPLE(S)	REVIEW EXERCISES
Section 2.1		
■ How to construct a frequency distribution including limits, midpoints, relative frequencies, cumulative frequencies, and boundaries	1, 2	1
■ How to construct frequency histograms, frequency polygons, relative frequency histograms, and ogives	3–7	2–6
Section 2.2		
■ How to graph quantitative data sets using the exploratory data analysis tools of stem-and-leaf plots and dot plots	1–3	7, 8
■ How to graph and interpret paired data sets using scatter plots and time series charts	6, 7	9, 10
■ How to graph qualitative data sets using pie charts and Pareto charts	4, 5	11, 12
Section 2.3		
■ How to find the mean, median, and mode of a population and a sample $$\mu = \frac{\Sigma x}{N}, \bar{x} = \frac{\Sigma x}{n}$$	1–6	13, 14
■ How to find a weighted mean of a data set and the mean of a frequency distribution $$\bar{x} = \frac{\Sigma(x \cdot w)}{\Sigma w}, \bar{x} = \frac{\Sigma(x \cdot f)}{n}$$	7, 8	15–18
■ How to describe the shape of a distribution as symmetric, uniform, or skewed and how to compare the mean and median for each		19–24
Section 2.4		
■ How to find the range of a data set	1	25, 26
■ How to find the variance and standard deviation of a population and a sample $$\sigma = \sqrt{\frac{\Sigma(x - \mu)^2}{N}}, s = \sqrt{\frac{\Sigma(x - \bar{x})^2}{n - 1}}$$	2–5	27–30
■ How to use the Empirical Rule and Chebychev's Theorem to interpret standard deviation	6–8	31–34
■ How to approximate the sample standard deviation for grouped data $$s = \sqrt{\frac{\Sigma(x - \bar{x})^2 f}{n - 1}}$$	9, 10	35, 36
Section 2.5		
■ How to find the quartiles and interquartile range of a data set	1–3	37–39, 41
■ How to draw a box-and-whisker plot	4	40, 42
■ How to interpret other fractiles such as percentiles	5	43, 44
■ How to find and interpret the standard score (z-score) $z = (x - \mu)/\sigma$	6, 7	45–48

2 REVIEW EXERCISES

Section 2.1

In Exercises 1 and 2, use the following data set. The data set represents the incomes (in thousands of dollars) of 20 employees at a small business.

30 28 26 39 34 33 20 39 28 33
26 39 32 28 31 39 33 31 33 32

1. Make a frequency distribution of the data set using five classes. Include the class midpoints, limits, boundaries, frequencies, relative frequencies, and cumulative frequencies.

2. Make a relative frequency histogram using the frequency distribution in Exercise 1. Then determine which class has the greatest relative frequency and which has the least relative frequency.

In Exercises 3 and 4, use the following data set. The data represent the actual liquid volumes (in ounces) in 24 twelve-ounce cans.

11.95 11.91 11.86 11.94 12.00 11.93 12.00 11.94
12.10 11.95 11.99 11.94 11.89 12.01 11.99 11.94
11.92 11.98 11.88 11.94 11.98 11.92 11.95 11.93

3. Make a frequency histogram using seven classes.

4. Make a relative frequency histogram of the data set using seven classes.

In Exercises 5 and 6, use the following data set. The data represent the number of rooms reserved during one night's business at a sample of hotels.

153 104 118 166 89 104 100 79
93 96 116 94 140 84 81 96
108 111 87 126 101 111 122 108
126 93 108 87 103 95 129 93

5. Make a frequency distribution with six classes and draw a frequency polygon.

6. Make an ogive of the data set using six classes.

Section 2.2

In Exercises 7 and 8, use the following data set. The data represent the average daily high temperatures (in degrees Fahrenheit) during the month of January for Chicago, Illinois. (*Source: National Oceanic and Atmospheric Administration*)

33 31 25 22 38 51 32 23
23 34 44 43 47 37 29 25
28 35 21 24 20 19 23 27
24 13 18 28 17 25 31

7. Make a stem-and-leaf plot of the data set. Use one line per stem.

8. Make a dot plot of the data set.

9. The following are the heights (in feet) and the number of stories of nine notable buildings in Miami. Use the data to construct a scatter plot. What type of pattern is shown in the scatter plot? (*Source: Emporis Buildings*)

Height (in feet)	764	625	520	510	484	492	450	430	410
Number of stories	55	47	51	28	34	39	33	31	40

10. The U.S. unemployment rate over a 12-year period is given. Use the data to construct a time series chart. *(Source: U.S. Bureau of Labor Statistics)*

Year	1995	1996	1997	1998	1999	2000
Unemployment rate	5.6	5.4	4.9	4.5	4.2	4.0

Year	2001	2002	2003	2004	2005	2006
Unemployment rate	4.7	5.8	6.0	5.5	5.1	4.6

In Exercises 11 and 12, use the following data set. The data set represents the top seven American Kennel Club registrations (in thousands) in 2006. (Source: American Kennel Club)

Breed	Labrador Retriever	Yorkshire Terrier	German Shepherd	Golden Retriever	Beagle	Dachshund	Boxer
Number registered (in thousands)	124	48	44	43	39	36	35

11. Make a Pareto chart of the data set.

12. Make a pie chart of the data set.

Section 2.3

13. Find the mean, median, and mode of the data set.

   3   5   12   16   7   9   13   7   8   11

14. Find the mean, median, and mode of the data set.

   42   36   39   42   44   45   42   42   36   38

15. Estimate the mean of the frequency distribution you made in Exercise 1.

16. The following frequency distribution shows the number of magazine subscriptions per household for a sample of 60 households. Find the mean number of subscriptions per household.

Number of magazines	0	1	2	3	4	5	6
Frequency	13	9	19	8	5	2	4

17. Six test scores are given. The first 5 test scores are 15% of the final grade, and the last test score is 25% of the final grade. Find the weighted mean of the test scores.

   78   72   86   91   87   80

18. Four test scores are given. The first 3 test scores are 20% of the final grade, and the last test score is 40% of the final grade. Find the weighted mean of the test scores.

   96   85   91   86

19. Describe the shape of the distribution in the histogram you made in Exercise 3. Is the distribution symmetric, uniform, or skewed?

20. Describe the shape of the distribution in the histogram you made in Exercise 4. Is the distribution symmetric, uniform, or skewed?

In Exercises 21 and 22, determine whether the approximate shape of the distribution in the histogram is skewed right, skewed left, or symmetric.

21.

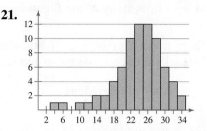

22.

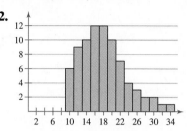

23. For the histogram in Exercise 21, which is greater, the mean or the median?

24. For the histogram in Exercise 22, which is greater, the mean or the median?

Section 2.4

25. The data set represents the mean price of a movie ticket (in U.S. dollars) for a sample of 12 U.S. cities. Find the range of the data set.

    7.82 7.38 6.42 6.76 6.34 7.44 6.15 5.46 7.92 6.58 8.26 7.17

26. The data set represents the mean price of a movie ticket (in U.S. dollars) for a sample of 12 Japanese cities. Find the range of the data set.

    19.73 16.48 19.10 18.56 17.68 17.19
    16.63 15.99 16.66 19.59 15.89 16.49

27. The mileage (in thousands) for a rental car company's fleet is listed. Find the population mean and standard deviation of the data.

    4 2 9 12 15 3 6 8 1 4 14 12 3 3

28. The age of each Supreme Court justice as of March 19, 2007 is listed. Find the population mean and standard deviation of the data. *(Source: Supreme Court of the United States)*

    52 86 71 70 67 58 74 68 56

29. Dormitory room prices (in dollars for one school year) for a sample of four-year universities are listed. Find the sample mean and the sample standard deviation of the data.

    2445 2940 2399 1960 2421 2940 2657 2153
    2430 2278 1947 2383 2710 2761 2377

30. Sample salaries (in dollars) of high school teachers are listed. Find the sample mean and standard deviation of the data.

    49,632 54,619 58,298 48,250 51,842 50,875 53,219 49,924

31. The mean rate for satellite television from a sample of households was $49.00 per month, with a standard deviation of $2.50 per month. Between what two values do 99.7% of the data lie? (Assume a bell-shaped distribution.)

32. The mean rate for satellite television from a sample of households was $49.50 per month, with a standard deviation of $2.75 per month. Estimate the percent of satellite television rates between $46.75 and $52.25. (Assume that the data set has a bell-shaped distribution.)

33. The mean sale per customer for 40 customers at a gas station is $36.00, with a standard deviation of $8.00. On the basis of Chebychev's Theorem, at least how many of the customers spent between $20.00 and $52.00?

34. The mean length of the first 20 space shuttle flights was about 7 days, and the standard deviation was about 2 days. On the basis of Chebychev's Theorem, at least how many of the flights lasted between 3 days and 11 days? *(Source: NASA)*

35. From a random sample of households, the number of television sets are listed. Find the sample mean and standard deviation of the data.

Number of televisions	0	1	2	3	4	5
Number of households	1	8	13	10	5	3

36. From a random sample of airplanes, the number of defects found in their fuselages are listed. Find the sample mean and standard deviation of the data.

Number of defects	0	1	2	3	4	5	6
Number of airplanes	4	5	2	9	1	3	1

Section 2.5

In Exercises 37–40, use the following data set. The data represent the heights (in inches) of students in a statistics class.

52 54 55 56 56 56 58 59 60 61
61 63 65 67 68 68 70 71 72

37. Find the height that corresponds to the first quartile.

38. Find the height that corresponds to the third quartile.

39. Find the interquartile range.

40. Make a box-and-whisker plot of the data.

41. Find the interquartile range of the data from Exercise 14.

42. The weights (in pounds) of the defensive players on a high school football team are given. Make a box-and-whisker plot of the data.

173 145 205 192 197 227 156 240 172 185
208 185 190 167 212 228 190 184 195

43. A student's test grade of 68 represents the 77th percentile of the grades. What percent of students scored higher than 68?

44. In 2007 there were 768 "oldies" radio stations in the United States. If one station finds that 84 stations have a larger daily audience than it has, what percentile does this station come closest to in the daily audience rankings? *(Source: Radio-locator.com)*

In Exercises 45–48, use the following information. The weights of 19 high school football players have a bell-shaped distribution, with a mean of 186 pounds and a standard deviation of 18 pounds. Use z-scores to determine if the weights of the following randomly selected football players are unusual.

45. 213 pounds

46. 141 pounds

47. 178 pounds

48. 249 pounds

2 CHAPTER QUIZ

Take this quiz as you would take a quiz in class. After you are done, check your work against the answers given in the back of the book.

 1. The data set is the number of minutes a sample of 25 people exercise each week.

108	139	120	123	120	132	123	131	131
157	150	124	111	101	135	119	116	117
127	128	139	119	118	114	127

(a) Make a frequency distribution of the data set using five classes. Include class limits, midpoints, frequencies, boundaries, relative frequencies, and cumulative frequencies.

(b) Display the data using a frequency histogram and a frequency polygon on the same axes.

(c) Display the data using a relative frequency histogram.

(d) Describe the distribution's shape as symmetric, uniform, or skewed.

(e) Display the data using a box-and-whisker plot.

(f) Display the data using an ogive.

2. Use frequency distribution formulas to approximate the sample mean and standard deviation of the data set in Exercise 1.

3. U.S. sporting goods sales (in billions of dollars) can be classified in four areas: clothing (11.7), footwear (15.7), equipment (24.0), and recreational transport (38.5). Display the data using (a) a pie chart and (b) a Pareto chart. *(Source: National Sporting Goods Association)*

4. Weekly salaries (in dollars) for a sample of registered nurses are listed.

774   446   1019   795   908   667   444   960

(a) Find the mean, the median, and the mode of the salaries. Which best describes a typical salary?

(b) Find the range, variance, and standard deviation of the data set. Interpret the results in the context of the real-life setting.

5. The mean price of new homes from a sample of houses is $155,000 with a standard deviation of $15,000. The data set has a bell-shaped distribution. Between what two prices do 95% of the houses fall?

6. Refer to the sample statistics from Exercise 5 and use z-scores to determine which, if any, of the following house prices is unusual.

(a) $200,000   (b) $55,000   (c) $175,000   (d) $122,000

7. The number of wins for each Major League Baseball team in 2006 are listed. *(Source: Major League Baseball)*

97	87	86	70	61	96	95	90	78	62
93	89	80	78	97	85	79	78	71	83
82	80	75	67	66	88	88	76	76	76

(a) Find the quartiles of the data set.

(b) Find the interquartile range.

(c) Draw a box-and-whisker plot.

REAL Statistics — Real Decisions

You are a consumer journalist for a newspaper. You have received several letters and e-mails from readers who are concerned about the cost of their automobile insurance premiums. One of the readers wrote the following:

"I think, on the average, a driver in our city pays a higher automobile insurance premium than drivers in other cities like ours in this state."

Your editor asks you to investigate the costs of insurance premiums and write an article about it. You have gathered the data shown at the right (your city is City A). The data represent the automobile insurance premiums paid annually (in dollars) by a random sample of drivers in your city and three other cities of similar size in your state. (The prices of the premiums from the sample include comprehensive, collision, bodily injury, property damage, and uninsured motorist coverage.)

The Prices, in Dollars, of Automobile Insurance Premiums Paid by 10 Randomly Selected Drivers in 4 Cities

City A	City B	City C	City D
2465	2514	2030	2345
1984	1600	1450	2152
2545	1545	2715	1570
1640	2716	2145	1850
1983	1987	1600	1450
2302	2200	1430	1745
2542	2005	1545	1590
1875	1945	1792	1800
1920	1380	1645	2575
2655	2400	1368	2016

(Adapted from: Runzheimer International)

■ Exercises

1. How Would You Do It?

(a) How would you investigate the statement about the price of automobile insurance premiums?

(b) What statistical measures in this chapter would you use?

2. Displaying the Data

(a) What type of graph would you choose to display the data? Why?

(b) Construct the graph from part (a).

(c) On the basis of what you did in part (b), does it appear that the average automobile insurance premium in your city, City A, is higher than in any of the other cities? Explain.

3. Measuring the Data

(a) What statistical measures discussed in this chapter would you use to analyze the automobile insurance premium data?

(b) Calculate the measures from part (a).

(c) Compare the measures from part (b) with the graph you made in Exercise 2. Do the measurements support your conclusion in Exercise 2? Explain.

4. Discussing the Data

(a) What would you tell your readers? Is the average automobile insurance premium in your city more than in the other cities?

(b) What reasons might you give to your readers as to why the prices of automobile insurance premiums vary from city to city?

Lowest auto insurance premiums
AVERAGE PER CITY

Eau Claire, WI	$869
Norfolk, VA	$954
Raleigh, NC	$966
Bismarck, ND	$989

TECHNOLOGY   MINITAB   EXCEL   T1-83/84

Dairy Farmers of America is an association that provides help to dairy farmers. Part of this help is gathering and distributing statistics on milk production.

www.dfamilk.com

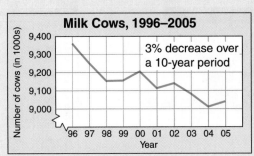

(Source: National Agricultural Statistics Service)

MONTHLY MILK PRODUCTION

The following data set was supplied by a dairy farmer. It lists the monthly milk production (in pounds) for 50 Holstein dairy cows. *(Source: Matlink Dairy, Clymer, NY)*

2825	2072	2733	2069	2484
4285	2862	3353	1449	2029
1258	2982	2045	1677	1619
2597	3512	2444	1773	2284
1884	2359	2046	2364	2669
3109	2804	1658	2207	2159
2207	2882	1647	2051	2202
3223	2383	1732	2230	1147
2711	1874	1979	1319	2923
2281	1230	1665	1294	2936

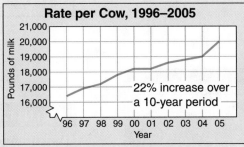

(Source: National Agricultural Statistics Service)

From 1996 to 2005, the number of dairy cows in the United States decreased and the yearly milk production increased.

■ EXERCISES

In Exercises 1–4, use a computer or calculator. If possible, print your results.

1. Find the sample mean of the data.

2. Find the sample standard deviation of the data.

3. Make a frequency distribution for the data. Use a class width of 500.

4. Draw a histogram for the data. Does the distribution appear to be bell shaped?

5. What percent of the distribution lies within one standard deviation of the mean? Within two standard deviations of the mean? How do these results agree with the Empirical Rule?

In Exercises 6–8, use the frequency distribution found in Exercise 3.

6. Use the frequency distribution to estimate the sample mean of the data. Compare your results with Exercise 1.

7. Use the frequency distribution to find the sample standard deviation for the data. Compare your results with Exercise 2.

8. **Writing** Use the results of Exercises 6 and 7 to write a general statement about the mean and standard deviation for grouped data. Do the formulas for grouped data give results that are as accurate as the individual entry formulas?

Extended solutions are given in the *Technology Supplement*.
Technical instruction is provided for MINITAB, Excel, and the TI-83/84.

Here are some MINITAB and TI-83/84 printouts for three examples in this chapter.

Graph

Plot...
Time Series Plot...
Chart...
Histogram...
Boxplot...
Matrix Plot...
Draftsman Plot...
Contour Plot...

(See Example 7, page 61.)

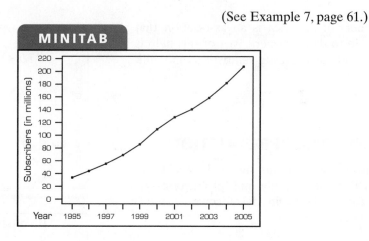

MINITAB

Display Descriptive Statistics...
Store Descriptive Statistics...

1-Sample Z...
1-Sample t...
2-Sample t...
Paired t...

1 Proportion...
2 Proportions...

2 Variances...

Correlation...
Covariance...

Normality Test...

(See Example 4, page 85.)

MINITAB

Descriptive Statistics

Variable	N	Mean	SE Mean	TrMean	StDev
Salaries	10	41.500	0.992	41.375	3.136

Variable	Minimum	Q1	Median	Q3	Maximum
Salaries	37.000	38.750	41.000	44.250	47.000

Graph

Plot...
Time Series Plot...
Chart...
Histogram...
Boxplot...
Matrix Plot...
Draftsman Plot...
Contour Plot...

(See Example 4, page 105.)

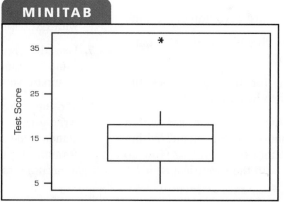

MINITAB

(See Example 7, page 61.)

TI-83/84

STAT PLOTS

1: Plot1...Off
    L1 L2 □
2: Plot2...Off
    L1 L2 □
3: Plot3...Off
    L1 L2 □

TI-83/84

Plot1 Plot2 Plot3
On Off
Type:

Xlist: L1
Ylist: L2
Mark: ■ + .

TI-83/84

ZOOM MEMORY

4↑ ZDecimal
5: ZSquare
6: ZStandard
7: ZTrig
8: ZInteger
9: ZoomSta
0: ZoomFit

TI-83/84

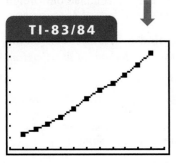

(See Example 4, page 85.)

TI-83/84

EDIT **CALC** TESTS

1: 1-Var Stats
2: 2-Var Stats
3: Med-Med
4: LinReg(ax+b)
5: QuadReg
6: CubicReg
7↓ QuartReg

TI-83/84

1-Var Stats L1

TI-83/84

1-Var Stats
$\bar{x}$= 41.5
$\sum x$= 415
$\sum x^2$= 17311
Sx= 3.13581462
σx= 2.974894956
↓n= 10

(See Example 4, page 105.)

TI-83/84

STAT PLOTS

1: Plot1...Off
    L1 L2 □
2: Plot2...Off
    L1 L2 □
3: Plot3...Off
    L1 L2 □
4↓ PlotsOff

TI-83/84

Plot1 Plot2 Plot3
On Off
Type:
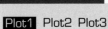

Xlist: L1
Freq: 1

TI-83/84

ZOOM MEMORY

4↑ ZDecimal
5: ZSquare
6: ZStandard
7: ZTrig
8: ZInteger
9: ZoomStat
0: ZoomFit

TI-83/84

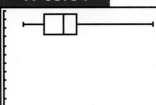

Cumulative Review

CHAPTERS 1 AND 2

In Exercises 1 and 2, identify the sampling technique used and discuss potential sources of bias (if any). Explain.

1. For quality assurance, every fortieth toothbrush is taken from each of 4 assembly lines and tested to make sure the bristles stay in the toothbrush.

2. Using random digit dialing, researchers asked 1200 U.S. adults their thoughts on global warming.

3. In a recent year, unscheduled absenteeism at U.S. companies and organizations reached a rate of 2.5%, which is the highest since 1999. It was found that the unscheduled absences were due to entitlement mentality (11%), family issues (24%), personal illness (35%), personal needs (18%), and stress (12%). Use a Pareto chart to organize the data. *(Source: Harris Interactive)*

In Exercises 4 and 5, determine whether the numerical value is a parameter or a statistic. Explain your reasoning.

4. The average annual salary for the 43 employees of a company is $42,500.

5. In a recent survey of 1000 adults from the United States, 28% said it is ethical for reporters to publish news stories based on anonymous sources. *(Source: Rasmussen Reports)*

6. The mean annual salary from a sample of electrical engineers is $83,500, with a standard deviation of $1500. The data set has a bell-shaped distribution.

   (a) Use the Empirical Rule to estimate the number of electrical engineers whose annual salaries are between $80,500 and $86,500.

   (b) If 40 additional electrical engineers were sampled, about how many of these electrical engineers would you expect to have annual salaries between $80,500 and $86,500?

In Exercises 7 and 8, identify the population and the sample.

7. A survey of 1498 U.S. adults found that 52% believe that alternate energy sources are the best way for the United States to reduce reliance on foreign oil. *(Source: Bloomberg Poll)*

8. A study of 232,606 people was conducted to find a link between taking antioxidant vitamins and living a longer life. *(Source: Journal of the American Medical Association)*

In Exercises 9 and 10, decide which method of data collection you would use to collect data for the study. Explain.

9. A study of the years of service of the 100 members of the Senate

10. A study of the effects of removing recess from schools

In Exercises 11 and 12, determine whether the data are qualitative or quantitative and identify the data set's level of measurement.

11. The number of games started by each pitcher with at least one start for the Houston Astros in 2006 is listed. *(Source: Major League Baseball)*

2 8 19 19 9 11 32 35 24 3

12. The regions typically used for calculating average house prices are listed.

Northeast Midwest South West

13. The number of tornadoes by state in a recent year is listed. Find the data set's first, second, and third quartiles, and draw a box-and-whisker plot that represents the data set. *(Source: National Climatic Data Center)*

81	1	8	69	30	34	0	0	56	54
2	6	21	14	46	136	17	23	2	0
1	5	71	105	39	10	40	1	0	7
4	0	23	53	4	27	1	11	0	14
19	23	105	4	0	24	4	0	63	6

14. Five test scores are given. The first four test scores are 15% of the final grade, and the last test score is 40% of the final grade. Find the weighted mean of the test scores.

85 92 84 89 91

15. Tail lengths (in feet) for a sample of American alligators are listed.

6.5 3.4 4.2 7.1 5.4 6.8 7.5 3.9 4.6

(a) Find the mean, the median, and the mode of the tail lengths. Which best describes a typical American alligator tail length? Explain your reasoning.

(b) Find the range, variance, and standard deviation of the data set. Interpret the results in the context of the real-life setting.

16. A study shows that the number of deaths due to heart disease for women has decreased every year for the past five years.

(a) Make an inference based on the results of the study.

(b) What is wrong with this type of reasoning?

In Exercises 17–19, use the following data set. The data set represents the points scored by each player on the Detroit Red Wings in a recent NHL season. (Source: National Hockey League)

11	15	8	87	32	1	8	16	59
0	0	9	62	12	80	15	2	11
15	0	45	59	81	58	19	34	85

17. Make a frequency distribution using eight classes. Include the class midpoints, limits, boundaries, frequencies, relative frequencies, and cumulative frequencies.

18. Describe the shape of the distribution.

19. Make a relative frequency histogram using the frequency distribution in Exercise 17. Then determine which class has the greatest relative frequency and which has the least relative frequency.

Probability & Probability Distributions

CHAPTER 3   Probability

CHAPTER 4   Discrete Probability Distributions

CHAPTER 5   Normal Probability Distributions

129

CHAPTER

3

Probability

3.1 Basic Concepts of Probability and Counting
■ ACTIVITY

3.2 Conditional Probability and the Multiplication Rule

3.3 The Addition Rule
■ ACTIVITY
■ CASE STUDY

3.4 Additional Topics in Probability and Counting
■ USES AND ABUSES
■ REAL STATISTICS– REAL DECISIONS
■ TECHNOLOGY

The television game show *Deal or No Deal* gives contestants a chance to win $1,000,000. Contestants can use their knowledge of probability to determine when to accept a deal for less than $1,000,000.

In Chapters 1 and 2, you learned how to collect and describe data. Once the data are collected and described, you can use the results to write summaries, form conclusions, and make decisions. For instance, in the game show *Deal or No Deal,* contestants play and deal for up to $1,000,000. By collecting and analyzing data, you can determine the chances of winning $1,000,000.

Each game consists of 26 sealed briefcases containing dollar amounts ranging from $.01 to $1,000,000. Without knowing the amount in each briefcase, the contestant chooses one briefcase, which remains sealed until the end of the game. In each round, a predetermined number of the remaining briefcases are opened revealing the amount in each. At the end of each round, the "Banker" offers the contestant an amount of cash based on the amounts still left in the unopened briefcases, in exchange for the contestant's briefcase. The contestant can either accept the Banker's offer and end the game or continue to the next round. If the contestant never accepts an offer and all other briefcases have been opened, then the contestant receives what is in the briefcase he or she chose at the beginning of the game.

WHERE YOU'RE GOING →

In Chapter 3, you will learn how to determine the probability that an event will occur. For instance, the probability that the first briefcase chosen by the contestant contains $1,000,000 is $\frac{1}{26}$, because there are 26 briefcases at the start of the game and only 1 briefcase has $1,000,000. The table below shows the probability of the contestant's briefcase containing $1,000,000 if the briefcase with $1,000,000 has not been opened yet.

Round		1	2	3	4	5	6	7	8	9
Total cases opened	0	6	11	15	18	20	21	22	23	24
Probability	$\frac{1}{26}$	$\frac{1}{20}$	$\frac{1}{15}$	$\frac{1}{11}$	$\frac{1}{8}$	$\frac{1}{6}$	$\frac{1}{5}$	$\frac{1}{4}$	$\frac{1}{3}$	$\frac{1}{2}$

You can also find the probability of a contestant choosing a briefcase that has at least $100,000. (Seven briefcases have at least $100,000.)

Probability of at least $100,000 in briefcase $= \dfrac{7}{26} \approx 0.269$

Then, you can find the probability of a contestant choosing a briefcase that has less than $100,000 by subtracting the probability of choosing a briefcase that has at least $100,000 from 1.

Probability of less than $100,000 in briefcase $= 1 -$ Probability of at least $100,000 in briefcase

$$= 1 - \frac{7}{26} = \frac{19}{26} \approx 0.731$$

So, the probability that a contestant chooses a briefcase that contains at least $100,000 is about 0.269, or 26.9%. The probability that a contestant chooses a briefcase that contains less than $100,000 is about 0.731, or 73.1%.

3.1 Basic Concepts of Probability and Counting

What You
SHOULD LEARN

▸ How to identify the sample space of a probability experiment and how to identify simple events

▸ How to use the Fundamental Counting Principle to find the number of ways two or more events can occur

▸ How to distinguish among classical probability, empirical probability, and subjective probability

▸ How to find the probability of the complement of an event

▸ How to use a tree diagram and the Fundamental Counting Principle to find more probabilities

Probability Experiments ▸ The Fundamental Counting Principle ▸ Types of Probability ▸ Complementary Events ▸ Probability Applications

▸ Probability Experiments

When weather forecasters say that there is a 90% chance of rain or a physician says there is a 35% chance for a successful surgery, they are stating the likelihood, or *probability*, that a specific event will occur. Decisions such as "should you go golfing" or "should you proceed with surgery" are often based on these probabilities. In the previous chapter, you learned about the role of the descriptive branch of statistics. Because probability is the foundation of inferential statistics, it is necessary to learn about probability before proceeding to the second branch—inferential statistics.

DEFINITION

A **probability experiment** is an action, or trial, through which specific results (counts, measurements, or responses) are obtained. The result of a single trial in a probability experiment is an **outcome.** The set of all possible outcomes of a probability experiment is the **sample space.** An **event** is a subset of the sample space. It may consist of one or more outcomes.

Study Tip

Here is a simple example of the use of the terms *probability experiment*, *sample space*, *event*, and *outcome*.

Probability Experiment:
   Roll a six-sided die.

Sample Space:
   {1, 2, 3, 4, 5, 6}

Event:
   Roll an even number,
   {2, 4, 6}

Outcome:
   Roll a 2, {2}

EXAMPLE 1

Identifying the Sample Space of a Probability Experiment

A probability experiment consists of tossing a coin and then rolling a six-sided die. Determine the number of outcomes and identify the sample space.

Solution

There are two possible outcomes when tossing a coin: a head (H) or a tail (T). For each of these, there are six possible outcomes when rolling a die: 1, 2, 3, 4, 5, or 6. One way to list outcomes for actions occurring in a sequence is to use a **tree diagram.**

Tree Diagram for Coin and Die Experiment

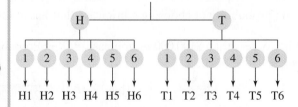

From the tree diagram, the sample space has 12 outcomes.

   {H1, H2, H3, H4, H5, H6, T1, T2, T3, T4, T5, T6}

SURVEY

There should be a limit to the number of terms a U.S. senator can serve.

Check one response:

☐ Agree

☐ Disagree

☐ No opinion

▶ **Try It Yourself 1**

For each probability experiment, determine the number of outcomes and identify the sample space.

1. A probability experiment consists of recording a response to the survey statement at the left *and* the gender of the respondent.

2. A probability experiment consists of recording a response to the survey statement at the left *and* the political party (Democrat, Republican, or Other) of the respondent.

a. Start a tree diagram by forming a branch for each possible response to the survey.

b. At the end of each survey response branch, draw a new branch for each possible outcome.

c. Find the *number of outcomes* in the sample space.

d. List the *sample space*.   *Answer: Page A37*

In the rest of this chapter, you will learn how to calculate the probability or likelihood of an event. Events are often represented by uppercase letters, such as A, B, and C. An event that consists of a single outcome is called a **simple event**. In Example 1, the event "tossing heads and rolling a 3" is a simple event and can be represented as $A = \{H3\}$. In contrast, the event "tossing heads and rolling an even number" is not simple because it consists of three possible outcomes $B = \{H2, H4, H6\}$.

E X A M P L E   2

Identifying Simple Events

Determine the number of outcomes in each event. Then decide whether each event is simple or not. Explain your reasoning.

1. For quality control, you randomly select a machine part from a batch that has been manufactured that day. Event A is selecting a specific defective machine part.

2. You roll a six-sided die. Event B is rolling at least a 4.

Solution

1. Event A has only one outcome: choosing the specific defective machine part. So, the event is a simple event.

2. Event B has three outcomes: rolling a 4, a 5, or a 6. Because the event has more than one outcome, it is not simple.

▶ **Try It Yourself 2**

You ask for a student's age at his or her last birthday. Decide whether each event is simple or not.

1. Event C: The student's age is between 18 and 23, inclusive.

2. Event D: The student's age is 20.

a. Determine the number of outcomes in the event.

b. State whether the event is *simple* or not.   *Answer: Page A37*

▶ The Fundamental Counting Principle

In some cases, an event can occur in so many different ways that it is not practical to write out all the outcomes. When this occurs, you can rely on the Fundamental Counting Principal. The Fundamental Counting Principle can be used to find the number of ways two or more events can occur in sequence.

> ### THE FUNDAMENTAL COUNTING PRINCIPLE
>
> If one event can occur in m ways and a second event can occur in n ways, the number of ways the two events can occur in sequence is $m \cdot n$. This rule can be extended for any number of events occurring in sequence.

In words, the number of ways that events can occur in sequence is found by multiplying the number of ways one event can occur by the number of ways the other event(s) can occur.

EXAMPLE 3

Using the Fundamental Counting Principle

You are purchasing a new car. The possible manufacturers, car sizes, and colors are listed.

Manufacturer: Ford, GM, Honda
Car size: compact, midsize
Color: white (W), red (R), black (B), green (G)

How many different ways can you select one manufacturer, one car size, and one color? Use a tree diagram to check your result.

Solution There are three choices of manufacturers, two car sizes, and four colors. Using the Fundamental Counting Principle, you can conclude that the number of ways to select one manufacturer, one car size, and one color is

$3 \cdot 2 \cdot 4 = 24$ ways.

Using a tree diagram, you can see why there are 24 options.

Tree Diagram for Car Selections

Try It Yourself 3

Your choices now include a Toyota, a large car, or a tan or gray car. How many different ways can you select one manufacturer, one car size, and one color?

a. Find the *number of ways* each event can occur.
b. Use the *Fundamental Counting Principle*.
c. Use a *tree diagram* to check your result.

Answer: Page A37

EXAMPLE 4

Using the Fundamental Counting Principle

The access code for a car's security system consists of four digits. Each digit can be 0 through 9.

Access Code

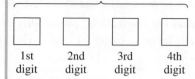

| 1st | 2nd | 3rd | 4th |
| digit | digit | digit | digit |

How many access codes are possible if

1. each digit can be used only once and not repeated?
2. each digit can be repeated?
3. each digit can be repeated but the first digit cannot be 0 or 1?

Solution

1. Because each digit can be used only once, there are 10 choices for the first digit, 9 choices left for the second digit, 8 choices left for the third digit, and 7 choices left for the fourth digit. Using the Fundamental Counting Principle, you can conclude that there are

   $$10 \cdot 9 \cdot 8 \cdot 7 = 5040$$

   possible access codes.

2. Because each digit can be repeated, there are 10 choices for each of the four digits. So, there are

   $$10 \cdot 10 \cdot 10 \cdot 10 = 10^4$$
   $$= 10,000$$

   possible access codes.

3. Because the first digit cannot be 0 or 1, there are 8 choices for the first digit. Then there are 10 choices for each of the other three digits. So, there are

   $$8 \cdot 10 \cdot 10 \cdot 10 = 8000$$

   possible access codes.

▶ Try It Yourself 4

How many license plates can you make if a license plate consists of

1. six (out of 26) alphabetical letters each of which can be repeated?
2. six (out of 26) alphabetical letters each of which cannot be repeated?
3. six (out of 26) alphabetical letters each of which can be repeated but the first letter cannot be A, B, C, or D?

a. *Identify* each event and the *number of ways* each event can occur.
b. Use the *Fundamental Counting Principle*.   *Answer: Page A37*

▶ Types of Probability

The method you will use to calculate a probability depends on the type of probability. There are three types of probability: classical probability, empirical probability, and subjective probability. The probability that event E will occur is written as $P(E)$ and is read "the probability of event E."

DEFINITION

Classical (or **theoretical**) **probability** is used when each outcome in a sample space is equally likely to occur. The classical probability for an event E is given by

$$P(E) = \frac{\text{Number of outcomes in event } E}{\text{Total number of outcomes in sample space}}.$$

EXAMPLE 5

Finding Classical Probabilities

You roll a six-sided die. Find the probability of each event.

1. Event A: rolling a 3
2. Event B: rolling a 7
3. Event C: rolling a number less than 5

Solution When a six-sided die is rolled, the sample space consists of six outcomes: $\{1, 2, 3, 4, 5, 6\}$.

1. There is one outcome in event $A = \{3\}$. So,

$$P(\text{rolling a 3}) = \frac{1}{6} \approx 0.167.$$

2. Because 7 is not in the sample space, there are no outcomes in event B. So,

$$P(\text{rolling a 7}) = \frac{0}{6} = 0.$$

3. There are four outcomes in event $C = \{1, 2, 3, 4\}$. So,

$$P(\text{rolling a number less than 5}) = \frac{4}{6} = \frac{2}{3} \approx 0.667.$$

▶ Try It Yourself 5

You select a card from a standard deck. Find the probability of each event.

1. Event D: Selecting a seven of diamonds
2. Event E: Selecting a diamond
3. Event F: Selecting a diamond, heart, club, or spade

a. Identify the *total number of outcomes* in the sample space.
b. Find the *number of outcomes* in the event.
c. Use the *classical probability formula.*   *Answer: Page A37*

Standard Deck of Playing Cards

Hearts	Diamonds	Spades	Clubs
A ♥	A ♦	A ♠	A ♣
K ♥	K ♦	K ♠	K ♣
Q ♥	Q ♦	Q ♠	Q ♣
J ♥	J ♦	J ♠	J ♣
10 ♥	10 ♦	10 ♠	10 ♣
9 ♥	9 ♦	9 ♠	9 ♣
8 ♥	8 ♦	8 ♠	8 ♣
7 ♥	7 ♦	7 ♠	7 ♣
6 ♥	6 ♦	6 ♠	6 ♣
5 ♥	5 ♦	5 ♠	5 ♣
4 ♥	4 ♦	4 ♠	4 ♣
3 ♥	3 ♦	3 ♠	3 ♣
2 ♥	2 ♦	2 ♠	2 ♣

When an experiment is repeated many times, regular patterns are formed. These patterns make it possible to find empirical probability. Empirical probability can be used even if each outcome of an event is not equally likely to occur.

PICTURING the WORLD

It seems as if no matter how strange an event is, somebody wants to know the probability that it will occur. The following table lists the probability that some intriguing events will happen. (Adapted from Life: The Odds)

What are the chances?

Event	Probability
Being audited by the IRS	0.6%
Writing a *New York Times* best seller	0.0045
Winning an Academy Award	0.000087
Having your identity stolen	0.5%
Spotting a UFO	0.0000003

Which of these events is most likely to occur? Least likely?

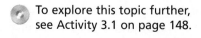

To explore this topic further, see Activity 3.1 on page 148.

DEFINITION

Empirical (or **statistical**) **probability** is based on observations obtained from probability experiments. The empirical probability of an event E is the relative frequency of event E.

$$P(E) = \frac{\text{Frequency of event } E}{\text{Total frequency}}$$

$$= \frac{f}{n}.$$

EXAMPLE 6

Finding Empirical Probabilities

A company is conducting an online survey of randomly selected individuals to determine if traffic congestion is a problem in their community. So far, 320 people have responded to the survey. The frequency distribution shows the results. What is the probability that the next person that responds to the survey says that traffic congestion is a serious problem in their community?

Response	Number of times, f
It is a serious problem.	123
It is a moderate problem.	115
It is not a problem.	82
	$\Sigma f = 320$

Solution The event is a response of "It is a serious problem." The frequency of this event is 123. Because the total of the frequencies is 320, the empirical probability of the next person saying that traffic congestion is a serious problem in their community is

$$P(\text{serious problem}) = \frac{123}{320}$$

$$= 0.384.$$

▶ **Try It Yourself 6**

An insurance company determines that in every 100 claims, 4 are fraudulent. What is the probability that the next claim the company processes will be fraudulent?

a. *Identify* the event. Find the *frequency* of the event.
b. *Find the total frequency for the experiment.*
c. Find the *relative frequency* of the event.

Answer: Page A37

As you increase the number of times a probability experiment is repeated, the empirical probability (relative frequency) of an event approaches the theoretical probability of the event. This is known as the **law of large numbers.**

LAW OF LARGE NUMBERS

As an experiment is repeated over and over, the empirical probability of an event approaches the theoretical (actual) probability of the event.

Probability of Tossing a Head

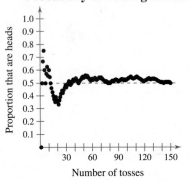

As an example of this law, suppose you want to determine the probability of tossing a head with a fair coin. If you toss the coin 10 times and get only 3 heads, you obtain an empirical probability of $\frac{3}{10}$. Because you tossed the coin only a few times, your empirical probability is not representative of the theoretical probability, which is $\frac{1}{2}$. If, however, you toss the coin several thousand times, then the law of large numbers tells you that the empirical probability will be very close to the theoretical or actual probability.

The scatter plot at the left shows the results of simulating a coin toss 150 times. Notice that, as the number of tosses increases, the probability of tossing a head gets closer and closer to the theoretical probability of 0.5.

EXAMPLE 7

Using Frequency Distributions to Find Probabilities

You survey a sample of 1000 employees at a company and record the age of each. The results are shown at the left in the frequency distribution. If you randomly select another employee, what is the probability that the employee will be between 25 and 34 years old?

Solution

The event is selecting an employee who is between 25 and 34 years old. In your survey, the frequency of this event is 366. Because the total of the frequencies is 1000, the probability of selecting an employee between the ages of 25 and 34 years old is

$$P(\text{age } 25 \text{ to } 34) = \frac{366}{1000} = 0.366.$$

Employee ages	Frequency, f
15 to 24	54
25 to 34	366
35 to 44	233
45 to 54	180
55 to 64	125
65 and over	42
	$\Sigma f = 1000$

▶ **Try It Yourself 7**

Find the probability that an employee chosen at random will be between 15 and 24 years old.

a. Find the *frequency* of the event.
b. Find the *total of the frequencies.*
c. Find the relative frequency of the event.   *Answer: Page A37*

The third type of probability is **subjective probability.** Subjective probabilities result from intuition, educated guesses, and estimates. For instance, given a patient's health and extent of injuries, a doctor may feel that the patient has a 90% chance of a full recovery. Or a business analyst may predict that the chance of the employees of a certain company going on strike is 0.25.

EXAMPLE 8

Classifying Types of Probability

Classify each statement as an example of classical probability, empirical probability, or subjective probability. Explain your reasoning.

1. The probability that you will be married by age 30 is 0.5.
2. The probability that a voter chosen at random will vote Republican is 0.45.
3. The probability of winning a 1000-ticket raffle with one ticket is $\frac{1}{1000}$.

Solution

1. This probability is most likely based on an educated guess. It is an example of subjective probability.
2. This statement is most likely based on a survey of a sample of voters, so it is an example of empirical probability.
3. Because you know the number of outcomes and each is equally likely, this is an example of classical probability.

▶ Try It Yourself 8

Based on previous counts, the probability of a salmon successfully passing through a dam on the Columbia River is 0.85. Is this statement an example of classical probability, empirical probability, or subjective probability? *(Source: Army Corps of Engineers)*

a. Identify the *event*.
b. Decide whether the probability is *determined* by knowing all possible outcomes, whether the probability is *estimated* from the results of an experiment, or whether the probability is an *educated guess*.
c. Make a *conclusion*.   *Answer: Page A37*

A probability cannot be negative or greater than 1. So, the probability of an event *E* is between 0 and 1, inclusive, as stated in the following rule.

RANGE OF PROBABILITIES RULE

The probability of an event *E* is between 0 and 1, inclusive. That is,

$$0 \leq P(E) \leq 1.$$

If the probability of an event is 1, the event is certain to occur. If the probability of an event is 0, the event is impossible. A probability of 0.5 indicates that an event has an even chance of occurring.

The following graph shows the possible range of probabilities and their meanings.

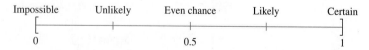

An event that occurs with a probability of 0.05 or less is typically considered unusual. Unusual events are highly unlikely to occur. Later in this course you will identify unusual events when studying inferential statistics.

▶ Complementary Events

The sum of the probabilities of all outcomes in a sample space is 1 or 100%. An important result of this fact is that if you know the probability of an event E, you can find the probability of the *complement of event E.*

DEFINITION

The **complement of event E** is the set of all outcomes in a sample space that are not included in event E. The complement of event E is denoted by E' and is read as "E prime."

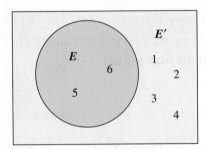

The area of the rectangle represents the total probability of the sample space (1 = 100%). The area of the circle represents the probability of event E, and the area outside the circle represents the probability of the complement of event E.

For instance, if you roll a die and let E be the event "the number is at least 5," then the complement of E is the event "the number is less than 5." In symbols, $E = \{5, 6\}$ and $E' = \{1, 2, 3, 4\}$.

Using the definition of the complement of an event and the fact that the sum of the probabilities of all outcomes is 1, you can determine the following formulas:

$$P(E) + P(E') = 1 \qquad P(E) = 1 - P(E') \qquad P(E') = 1 - P(E)$$

The Venn diagram illustrates the relationship between the sample space, an event E, and its complement E'.

EXAMPLE 9

Finding the Probability of the Complement of an Event

Use the frequency distribution in Example 7 to find the probability of randomly choosing an employee who is not between 25 and 34 years old.

Solution

From Example 7, you know that

$$P(\text{age 25 to 34}) = \frac{366}{1000}$$

$$= 0.366.$$

So, the probability that an employee is not between 25 and 34 years old is

$$P(\text{age is not 25 to 34}) = 1 - \frac{366}{1000}$$

$$= \frac{634}{1000}$$

$$= 0.634.$$

▶ Try It Yourself 9

Use the frequency distribution in Example 7 to find the probability of randomly choosing an employee who is not between 45 and 54 years old.

a. *Find the probability* of randomly choosing an employee who is between 45 and 54 years old.
b. *Subtract* the resulting probability from 1.
c. State the probability as a fraction and as a decimal.   *Answer: Page A37*

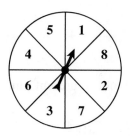

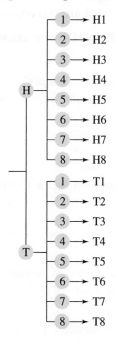

Tree Diagram for Coin and Spinner Experiment

H
- 1 → H1
- 2 → H2
- 3 → H3
- 4 → H4
- 5 → H5
- 6 → H6
- 7 → H7
- 8 → H8

T
- 1 → T1
- 2 → T2
- 3 → T3
- 4 → T4
- 5 → T5
- 6 → T6
- 7 → T7
- 8 → T8

▶ Probability Applications

Using a Tree Diagram

A probability experiment consists of tossing a coin and spinning the spinner shown to the left. The spinner is equally likely to land on each number. Use a tree diagram to find the probability of each event.

1. Event *A*: tossing a tail and spinning an odd number
2. Event *B*: tossing a head or spinning a number greater than 3

Solution From the tree diagram to the left, you can see that there are 16 outcomes.

1. There are four outcomes in event $A = \{T1, T3, T5, T7\}$. So,

$$P(\text{tossing a tail and spinning an odd number}) = \frac{4}{16} = \frac{1}{4} = 0.25.$$

2. There are 13 outcomes in event $B = \{H1, H2, H3, H4, H5, H6, H7, H8, T4, T5, T6, T7, T8\}$. So,

$$P(\text{tossing a head or spinning a number greater than 3}) = \frac{13}{16} \approx 0.813.$$

▶ Try It Yourself 10

Find the probability of tossing a tail and spinning a number less than 6.

a. Determine the *total number* of outcomes.
b. Find the number of outcomes in the *event*.
c. Find the *probability of the event*.   *Answer: Page A37*

Using the Fundamental Counting Principle

Your college identification number consists of 8 digits. Each digit can be 0 through 9 and each digit can be repeated. What is the probability of getting your college identification number when randomly generating eight digits?

Solution Because each digit can be repeated, there are 10 choices for each of the 8 digits. So, using the Fundamental Counting Principle, there are $10 \cdot 10 \cdot 10 \cdot 10 \cdot 10 \cdot 10 \cdot 10 \cdot 10 = 10^8 = 100,000,000$ possible identification numbers.

But only one of those numbers corresponds to your college identification number. So, the probability of randomly generating 8 digits and getting your college identification number is 1/100,000,000.

▶ Try It Yourself 11

Your college identification number consists of 9 digits. The first two digits of each number will be the last two digits of the year you graduate. The other digits can be 0 through 9 and each digit can be repeated. What is the probability of getting your college identification number when randomly generating the other seven digits?

a. Find the *total number* of possible identification numbers. Assume that you are scheduled to graduate in 2012.
b. Find the *probability* of randomly generating your identification number.

Answer: Page A37

3.1 EXERCISES

■ Building Basic Skills and Vocabulary

1. Determine which of the following numbers could not represent the probability of an event. Explain your reasoning.

   (a) 0   (b) 0.001   (c) -1 (d) 50%   (e) $\frac{745}{1262}$ (f) $\frac{45}{31}$

2. Explain why the following statement is incorrect:

   The probability of rain tomorrow is 150%.

3. When you use the Fundamental Counting Principle, what are you counting?

4. Use your own words to describe the law of large numbers. Give an example.

Identifying a Sample Space   *In Exercises 5–8, identify the sample space of the probability experiment and determine the number of outcomes in the sample space. Draw a tree diagram if it is appropriate.*

5. Guessing the initial of a student's middle name

6. Tossing three coins

7. Determining a person's blood type (A, B, AB, O) and Rh-factor (positive, negative)

8. Rolling a pair of six-sided dice

Recognizing Simple Events   *In Exercises 9–12, determine the number of outcomes in each event. Then decide whether the event is a simple event or not. Explain your reasoning.*

9. A computer is used to randomly select a number between 1 and 2000. Event A is selecting 359.

10. A computer is used to randomly select a number between 1 and 2000. Event B is selecting a number less than 200.

11. You randomly select one card from a standard deck. Event A is selecting a king.

12. You randomly select one card from a standard deck. Event B is selecting a four of hearts.

13. **Job Openings**   An insurance company is hiring for two positions: an actuary and a claims adjuster. How many ways can these positions be filled if there are 9 people applying for the actuarial position and 15 people applying for the claims adjuster position?

14. **Menu**   A menu has three choices for salad, six main dishes, and four desserts. How many different meals are available if you select a salad, a main dish, and a dessert?

15. **Security System**   The access code for a car's security system consists of four digits. The first digit cannot be zero and the last digit must be odd. How many different codes are available?

16. **True or False Quiz**   Assuming that no questions are left unanswered, in how many ways can a six-question true-false quiz be answered?

True or False?   *In Exercises 17–20, determine whether the statement is true or false. If it is false, rewrite it as a true statement.*

17. If you roll a six-sided die six times, you will roll an even number at least once.

18. You flip a fair coin nine times and it lands tails up each time. The probability it will land heads up on the tenth flip is greater than 0.5.

19. A probability of 0.25 indicates an unusual event.

20. If an event is almost certain to happen, its complement will be an unusual event.

Matching Probabilities   *In Exercises 21–24, match the event with its probability.*

(a) 0.95   (b) 0.05   (c) 0.25   (d) 0

21. You toss a coin and randomly select a number from 0 to 9. What is the probability of getting tails and selecting a 3?

22. A random number generator is used to select a number from 1 to 100. What is the probability of selecting the number 153?

23. A game show contestant must randomly select a door. One door doubles her money while the other three doors leave her bankrupt. What is the probability she selects the door that doubles her money?

24. Five of the 100 DVD players in an inventory are known to be defective. What is the probability you randomly select an item that is not defective?

Classifying Types of Probability   *In Exercises 25 and 26, classify the statement as an example of classical probability, empirical probability, or subjective probability. Explain your reasoning.*

25. According to company records, the probability that a washing machine will need repairs during a six-year period is 0.10.

26. The probability of choosing 6 numbers from 1 to 40 that match the 6 numbers drawn by a state lottery is $1/3,838,380 \approx 0.00000026$.

Finding Probabilities   *In Exercises 27–30, consider a company that selects employees for random drug tests. The company uses a computer to randomly select employee numbers that range from 1 to 6296.*

27. Find the probability of selecting a number less than 1000.

28. Find the probability of selecting a number greater than 1000.

29. Find the probability of selecting a number divisible by 1000.

30. Find the probability of selecting a number that is not divisible by 1000.

Probability Experiment   *In Exercises 31–34, a probability experiment consists of rolling a six-sided die and spinning the spinner shown. The spinner is equally likely to land on each color. Use a tree diagram to find the probability of each event.*

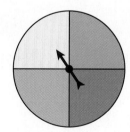

31. Event *A*: rolling a 5 and the spinner landing on blue

32. Event *B*: rolling an odd number and the spinner landing on green

33. Event *C*: rolling a number less than 6 and the spinner landing on yellow

34. Event *D*: not rolling a number less than 6 and the spinner landing on yellow

35. Security System   The access code for a garage door consists of three digits. Each digit can be 0 through 9 and each digit can be repeated.

(a) Find the number of possible access codes.

(b) What is the probability of randomly selecting the correct access code?

(c) What is the probability of not selecting the correct access code?

36. Security System   An access code consists of a letter followed by four digits. Any letter can be used, the first digit cannot be 0, and the last digit must be even.

(a) Find the number of possible access codes.

(b) What is the probability of randomly selecting the correct access code on the first try?

(c) What is the probability of not selecting the correct access code on the first try?

■ Using and Interpreting Concepts

Wet or Dry?   *You are planning a three-day trip to Seattle, Washington, in October. Use the following tree diagram to answer each question.*

37. List the sample space.

38. List the outcome(s) of the event "It rains all three days."

39. List the outcome(s) of the event "It rains on exactly one day."

40. List the outcome(s) of the event "It rains on at least one day."

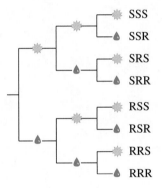

Day 1   Day 2   Day 3

SSS
SSR
SRS
SRR
RSS
RSR
RRS
RRR

41. Sunny and Rainy Days   You are planning a four-day trip to Seattle, Washington, in October.

(a) Make a sunny day/rainy day tree diagram for your trip.

(b) List the sample space.

(c) List the outcome(s) of the event "It rains on exactly one day."

42. Machine Part Suppliers   Your company buys machine parts from three different suppliers. Make a tree diagram that shows the three suppliers and whether the parts they supply are defective.

Graphical Analysis   *In Exercises 43 and 44, use the diagram to answer the question.*

43. What is the probability that a registered voter in Pennsylvania voted in the 2006 gubernatorial election? *(Source: Pennsylvania Department of State)*

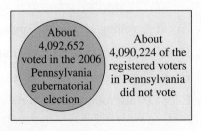

About 4,092,652 voted in the 2006 Pennsylvania gubernatorial election

About 4,090,224 of the registered voters in Pennsylvania did not vote

44. What is the probability that a voter chosen at random did not vote for a Democratic representative in the 2004 election? *(Source: Federal Election Commission)*

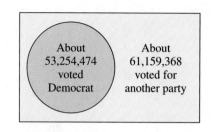

About 53,254,474 voted Democrat

About 61,159,368 voted for another party

Using a Frequency Distribution to Find Probabilities *In Exercises 45–48, use the frequency distribution, which shows the number of American voters (in millions) according to age.* (Source: U.S. Bureau of the Census)

Ages of voters	Frequency (in millions)
18 to 20 years old	5.8
21 to 24 years old	8.5
25 to 34 years old	21.7
35 to 44 years old	27.7
45 to 64 years old	51.7
65 years old and over	26.7

= 142.1 mil

Find the probability that a voter chosen at random is

45. between 21 and 24 years old.

46. between 35 and 44 years old.

47. not between 18 and 20 years old.

48. not between 25 and 34 years old.

Using a Bar Graph to Find Probabilities *In Exercises 49–52, use the following bar graph, which shows the highest level of education received by employees of a company.*

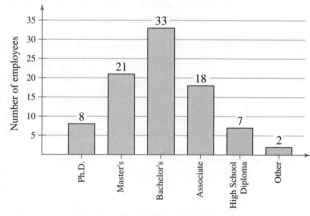

Level of Education

Find the probability that the highest level of education for an employee chosen at random is

49. a Ph.D.

50. an Associate degree.

51. a Master's degree.

52. a Bachelor's degree.

53. Genetics When two pink snapdragon flowers (RW) are crossed, there are four equally likely possible outcomes for the genetic makeup of the offspring: red (RR), pink (RW), pink (WR), and white (WW). If two pink snapdragons are crossed, what is the probability that the offspring will be (a) pink, (b) red, and (c) white?

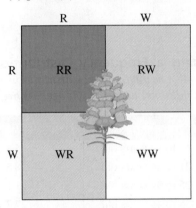

Parents
Ssmm and SsMm

	SM	Sm
Sm	SSMm	SSmm
Sm	SSMm	SSmm
sm	SsMm	Ssmm
sm	SsMm	Ssmm

	sM	sm
Sm	SsMm	Ssmm
Sm	SsMm	Ssmm
sm	ssMm	ssmm
sm	ssMm	ssmm

54. Genetics There are six basic types of coloring in registered collies: sable (SSmm), tricolor (ssmm), trifactored sable (Ssmm), blue merle (ssMm), sable merle (SSMm), and trifactored sable merle (SsMm). The *Punnett square* at the left shows the possible coloring of the offspring of a trifactored sable merle collie and a trifactored sable collie. What is the probability that the offspring will have the same coloring as one of its parents?

Using a Pie Chart to Find Probabilities *In Exercises 55–58, use the pie chart at the left, which shows the number of workers (in thousands) by industry for the United States.* (*Source: U.S. Bureau of Labor Statistics*)

55. Find the probability that a worker chosen at random was employed in the services industry.

56. Find the probability that a worker chosen at random was employed in the manufacturing industry.

57. Find the probability that a worker chosen at random was not employed in the services industry.

58. Find the probability that a worker chosen at random was not employed in the agriculture, forestry, fishing, and hunting industry.

Workers (in thousands) by Industry for the U.S.

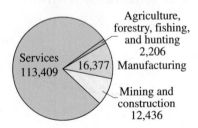

59. College Football A stem-and-leaf plot for the number of touchdowns scored by all Division 1A football teams is shown. If a team is selected at random, find the probability the team scored (a) at least 31 touchdowns, (b) between 40 and 50 touchdowns inclusive, and (c) more than 69 touchdowns.

```
1 | 5 5 5 7 8 8                          Key: 1|5 = 15
2 | 0 1 1 1 1 2 2 3 4 4 5 5 6 6 7 7 7 8 8 8 9 9 9
3 | 0 0 1 1 1 1 1 2 2 2 2 2 2 2 3 3 3 3 4 4 4 4 5 5 5 5 5 6 6 7 7 7 8 8 8 9 9 9
4 | 0 0 0 1 1 2 2 3 3 3 3 4 4 4 4 5 5 5 5 6 6 6 6 7 7 8 8 8 8 8 9
5 | 0 0 2 3 3 4 4 5 5 5 5 7 9 9
6 | 0 1 1 1 3 3 5 8
7 |
8 | 9
```

60. Individual Stock Price   An individual stock is selected at random from the portfolio represented by the box-and-whisker plot shown. Find the probability that the stock price is (a) less than $21, (b) between $21 and $50, and (c) $30 or more.

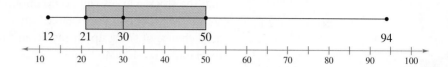

Writing   *In Exercises 61 and 62, write a statement that represents the complement of the given probability.*

61. The probability of randomly choosing a tea drinker who has a college degree (Assume that you are choosing from the population of all tea drinkers.)

62. The probability of randomly choosing a smoker whose mother also smoked (Assume that you are choosing from the population of all smokers.)

■ Extending Concepts

63. Rolling a Pair of Dice   You roll a pair of six-sided dice and record the sum.

(a) List all of the possible sums and determine the probability of rolling each sum.

(b) Use a technology tool to simulate rolling a pair of dice and recording the sum 100 times. Make a tally of the 100 sums and use these results to list the probability of rolling each sum.

(c) Compare the probabilities in part (a) with the probabilities in part (b). Explain any similarities or differences.

Odds   *In Exercises 64–67, use the following information. In gambling, the chances of winning are often written in terms of odds rather than probabilities. The **odds of winning** is the ratio of the number of successful outcomes to the number of unsuccessful outcomes. The **odds of losing** is the ratio of the number of unsuccessful outcomes to the number of successful outcomes. For example, if the number of successful outcomes is 2 and the number of unsuccessful outcomes is 3, the odds of winning are 2 : 3 (read "2 to 3") or $\frac{2}{3}$. (Note: The probability of success is $\frac{2}{5}$.)*

64. A beverage company puts game pieces under the caps of its drinks and claims that one in six game pieces wins a prize. The official rules of the contest state that the odds of winning a prize are 1 : 6. Is the claim "one in six game pieces wins a prize" correct? Why or why not?

65. The odds of an event occurring are 4 : 5. Find (a) the probability that the event will occur and (b) the probability that the event will not occur.

66. A card is picked at random from a standard deck of 52 playing cards. Find the odds that it is a spade.

67. A card is picked at random from a standard deck of 52 playing cards. Find the odds that it is not a spade.

APPLET

ACTIVITY 3.1

The *simulating the stock market* applet allows you to investigate the probability that the stock market will go up on any given day. The plot in the top left corner shows the probability associated with each outcome. In this case, the market has a 50% chance of going up on any given day. When SIMULATE is clicked, outcomes for *n* days are simulated. The results of the simulations are shown in the frequency plot. If the animate option is checked, the display will show each outcome dropping into the frequency plot as the simulation runs. To stop an animation, uncheck the animate option. The individual outcomes are shown in the text field to the far right of the applet. The center plot shows in red the cumulative proportion of times that the market went up. The green line in the plot reflects the true probability of the market going up. As the experiment is conducted more and more, the cumulative proportion should converge to the true value.

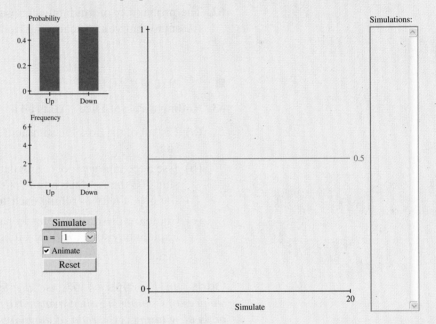

■ Explore

Step 1 Specify a value for *n*.
Step 2 Click SIMULATE four times.
Step 3 Click RESET.
Step 4 Specify another value for *n*.
Step 5 Click SIMULATE.

■ Draw Conclusions

APPLET

1. Run the simulation using *n* = 1 without clicking RESET. How many days did it take until there were three straight days when the stock market went up? How many days did it take until there were three straight days when the stock market went down?

2. Run the applet to simulate the stock market activity over the last 35 business days. Find the empirical probability that the market goes up on day 36.

3.2 Conditional Probability and the Multiplication Rule

What You SHOULD LEARN

▸ How to find the probability of an event given that another event has occurred

▸ How to distinguish between independent and dependent events

▸ How to use the Multiplication Rule to find the probability of two events occurring in sequence

▸ How to use the Multiplication Rule to find conditional probabilities

Conditional Probability ▸ Independent and Dependent Events ▸ The Multiplication Rule

▸ Conditional Probability

In this section, you will learn how to find the probability that two events occur in sequence. Before you can find this probability, however, you must know how to find conditional probabilities.

DEFINITION

A **conditional probability** is the probability of an event occurring, given that another event has already occurred. The conditional probability of event B occurring, given that event A has occurred, is denoted by $P(B|A)$ and is read as "probability of B, given A."

EXAMPLE 1

Finding Conditional Probabilities

1. Two cards are selected in sequence from a standard deck. Find the probability that the second card is a queen, given that the first card is a king. (Assume that the king is not replaced.)

2. The table at the left shows the results of a study in which researchers examined a child's IQ and the presence of a specific gene in the child. Find the probability that a child has a high IQ, given that the child has the gene. *(Source: Psychological Science)*

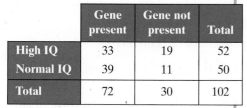

	Gene present	Gene not present	Total
High IQ	33	19	52
Normal IQ	39	11	50
Total	72	30	102

Sample Space

	Gene present
High IQ	33
Normal IQ	39
Total	72

Solution

1. Because the first card is a king and is not replaced, the remaining deck has 51 cards, 4 of which are queens. So,

$$P(B|A) = \frac{4}{51} \approx 0.078.$$

So, the probability that the second card is a queen, given that the first card is a king, is about 0.078.

2. There are 72 children who have the gene. So, the sample space consists of these 72 children, as shown at the left. Of these, 33 have a high IQ. So,

$$P(B|A) = \frac{33}{72} \approx 0.458.$$

So, the probability that a child has a high IQ, given that the child has the gene, is about 0.458.

▸ Try It Yourself 1

1. Find the probability that a child does not have the gene.
2. Find the probability that a child does not have the gene, given that the child has a normal IQ.

a. Find the *number of outcomes* in the event and in the sample space.
b. *Divide* the number of outcomes in the event by the number of outcomes in the sample space.

Answer: Page A37

▶ Independent and Dependent Events

In some experiments, one event does not affect the probability of another. For instance, if you roll a die and flip a coin, the outcome of the roll of the die does not affect the probability of the coin landing on heads. These two events are independent. The question of the independence of two or more events is important to researchers in fields such as marketing, medicine, and psychology. You can use conditional probabilities to determine whether events are independent.

DEFINITION

Two events are **independent** if the occurrence of one of the events does not affect the probability of the occurrence of the other event. Two events A and B are independent if

$$P(B|A) = P(B) \quad \text{or if} \quad P(A|B) = P(A).$$

Events that are not independent are **dependent.**

To determine if A and B are independent, first calculate $P(B)$, the probability of event B. Then calculate $P(B|A)$, the probability of B, given A. If the values are equal, the events are independent. If $P(B) \neq P(B|A)$, then A and B are dependent events.

EXAMPLE 2

Classifying Events as Independent or Dependent

Decide whether the events are independent or dependent.

1. Selecting a king from a standard deck (A), not replacing it, and then selecting a queen from the deck (B)
2. Tossing a coin and getting a head (A), and then rolling a six-sided die and obtaining a 6 (B)
3. Driving over 85 miles per hour (A), and then getting in a car accident (B)

Solution

1. $P(B|A) = \frac{4}{51}$ and $P(B) = \frac{4}{52}$. The occurrence of A changes the probability of the occurrence of B, so the events are dependent.

2. $P(B|A) = \frac{1}{6}$ and $P(B) = \frac{1}{6}$. The occurrence of A does not change the probability of the occurrence of B, so the events are independent.

3. If you drive over 85 miles per hour, the chances of getting in a car accident are greatly increased, so these events are dependent.

▶ Try It Yourself 2

Decide whether the events are independent or dependent.

1. Smoking a pack of cigarettes per day (A) and developing emphysema, a chronic lung disease (B)
2. Exercising frequently (A) and having a 4.0 grade point average (B)

a. *Decide* whether the occurrence of the first event affects the probability of the second event.
b. State if the events are *independent* or *dependent*. *Answer: Page A38*

▶ The Multiplication Rule

To find the probability of two events occurring in sequence, you can use the Multiplication Rule.

> **THE MULTIPLICATION RULE FOR THE PROBABILITY OF A AND B**
>
> The probability that two events A and B will occur in sequence is
>
> $$P(A \text{ and } B) = P(A) \cdot P(B|A).$$
>
> If events A and B are independent, then the rule can be simplified to $P(A \text{ and } B) = P(A) \cdot P(B)$. This simplified rule can be extended for any number of independent events.

EXAMPLE 3

Using the Multiplication Rule to Find Probabilities

1. Two cards are selected, without replacing the first card, from a standard deck. Find the probability of selecting a king and then selecting a queen.
2. A coin is tossed and a die is rolled. Find the probability of getting a head and then rolling a 6.

Solution

1. Because the first card is not replaced, the events are dependent.

$$\begin{aligned} P(K \text{ and } Q) &= P(K) \cdot P(Q|K) \\ &= \frac{4}{52} \cdot \frac{4}{51} \\ &= \frac{16}{2652} \\ &\approx 0.006 \end{aligned}$$

So, the probability of selecting a king and then a queen is about 0.006.

2. The events are independent.

$$\begin{aligned} P(H \text{ and } 6) &= P(H) \cdot P(6) \\ &= \frac{1}{2} \cdot \frac{1}{6} \\ &= \frac{1}{12} \\ &\approx 0.083 \end{aligned}$$

So, the probability of tossing a head and then rolling a 6 is about 0.083.

▶ Try It Yourself 3

1. The probability that a salmon swims successfully through a dam is 0.85. Find the probability that two salmon successfully swim through the dam.
2. Two cards are selected from a standard deck without replacement. Find the probability that they are both hearts.

a. Decide if the events are *independent* or *dependent*.
b. Use the *Multiplication Rule* to find the probability.   *Answer: Page A38*

E X A M P L E   4

Using the Multiplication Rule to Find Probabilities

1. A coin is tossed and a die is rolled. Find the probability of getting a tail and then rolling a 2.
2. The probability that a particular knee surgery is successful is 0.85. Find the probability that three knee surgeries are successful.
3. Find the probability that none of the three knee surgeries is successful.
4. Find the probability that at least one of the three knee surgeries is successful.

Solution

1. $P(T) = \frac{1}{2}$. Whether or not the coin is a tail, $P(2) = \frac{1}{6}$. The events are independent.

$$P(T \text{ and } 2) = P(T) \cdot P(2) = \frac{1}{2} \cdot \frac{1}{6} = \frac{1}{12} \approx 0.083$$

So, the probability of tossing a tail and then rolling a 2 is about 0.083.

2. The probability that each knee surgery is successful is 0.85. The chance of success for one surgery is independent of the chances for the other surgeries.

$$P(3 \text{ surgeries are successful}) = (0.85)(0.85)(0.85)$$
$$\approx 0.614$$

So, the probability that all three surgeries are successful is about 0.614.

3. Because the probability of success for one surgery is 0.85, the probability of failure for one surgery is $1 - 0.85 = 0.15$.

$$P(\text{none of the three is successful}) = (0.15)(0.15)(0.15)$$
$$\approx 0.003$$

So, the probability that none of the surgeries is successful is about 0.003.

4. The phrase "at least one" means one or more. The complement to the event "at least one is successful" is the event "none are successful." Using the rule of complements,

$$P(\text{at least 1 is successful}) = 1 - P(\text{none are successful})$$
$$\approx 1 - 0.003$$
$$= 0.997.$$

There is about a 0.997 probability that at least one of the three surgeries is successful.

▶ Try It Yourself 4

The probability that the knee surgery is successful has increased to 0.9.

1. Find the probability that three knee surgeries are successful.
2. Find the probability that at least one of three knee surgeries is successful..

a. Determine whether to find the probability of the event or its complement.
b. Use the *Multiplication Rule* to find the probability. If necessary, use the *Complement Rule*.   *Answer: Page A38*

Insight

In Example 4, you were asked to find a probability using the phrase "at least one." Notice that it was easier to find the probability of its complement, "none," and then use the Complement Rule.

Medical School

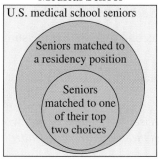

Jury Selection

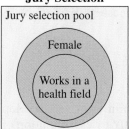

EXAMPLE 5

Using the Multiplication Rule to Find Probabilities

More than 15,000 U.S. medical school seniors applied to residency programs in 2007. Of those, 93% were matched to a residency position. Seventy-four percent of the seniors matched to a residency position were matched to one of their top two choices. Medical students electronically rank the residency programs in their order of preference and program directors across the United States do the same. The term "match" refers to the process where a student's preference list and a program director's preference list overlap, resulting in the placement of the student for a residency position. *(Source: National Resident Matching Program)*

1. Find the probability that a randomly selected senior was matched to a residency position *and* it was one of the senior's top two choices.

2. Find the probability that a randomly selected senior that was matched to a residency position did *not* get matched with one of the senior's top two choices.

3. Would it be unusual for a randomly selected senior to result in a senior that was matched to a residency position and it was one of the senior's top two choices?

Solution Let $A = \{$matched to residency position$\}$ and $B = \{$matched to one of two top choices$\}$. So, $P(A) = 0.93$ and $P(B|A) = 0.74$.

1. These events are dependent.

$$P(A \text{ and } B) = P(A) \cdot P(B|A) = (0.93) \cdot (0.74) \approx 0.688$$

So, the probability that a randomly selected senior was matched to one of the top two choices is about 0.688.

2. To find this probability, use the complement.

$$P(B'|A) = 1 - P(B|A) = 1 - 0.74 = 0.26$$

So, the probability that a randomly selected senior was matched to a residency position that was not one of the top two choices is 0.26.

3. It is not unusual because the probability of a senior being matched to a residency position and it was one of the top two choices is about 0.688.

▶ **Try It Yourself 5**

In a jury selection pool, 65% of the people are female. Of these 65%, one out of four works in a health field.

1. Find the probability that a randomly selected person from the jury pool is female and works in a health field.

2. Find the probability that a randomly selected person from the jury pool is female and does not work in a health field.

a. Determine *events A* and *B*.

b. Use the *Multiplication Rule* to write a formula to find the probability. If necessary, use the *Complement Rule*.

c. *Calculate* the probability.   *Answer: Page A38*

3.2 EXERCISES

■ Building Basic Skills and Vocabulary

1. What is the difference between independent and dependent events?

2. List examples of the following types of events.

   (a) Two events that are independent
   (b) Two events that are dependent

True or False?   *In Exercises 3 and 4, determine whether the statement is true or false. If it is false, rewrite it as a true statement.*

3. If two events are not independent, $P(A|B) = P(B)$.

4. If events A and B are dependent, then $P(A \text{ and } B) = P(A) \cdot P(B)$.

Classifying Events   *In Exercises 5–8, decide whether the events are independent or dependent. Explain your reasoning.*

5. Selecting a king from a standard deck, replacing it, and then selecting a queen from the deck

6. Returning a rented movie after the due date and receiving a late fee

7. Rolling a six-sided die and then rolling the die a second time so that the sum of the two rolls is seven

8. A numbered ball between 1 and 52 is selected from a bin, *replaced*, and then a second numbered ball is selected from the bin.

Classifying Events Based on Studies   *In Exercises 9–12, identify the two events described in the study. Do the results indicate that the events are independent or dependent? Explain your reasoning.*

9. Researchers found that people with depression are five times more likely to have a breathing-related sleep disorder than people who are not depressed. *(Source: Journal of Clinical Psychiatry)*

10. Stress causes the body to produce higher amounts of acid, which can irritate already existing ulcers. But, stress does not cause stomach ulcers. *(Source: Baylor College of Medicine)*

11. Studies found that Aspartame, an artificial sweetener, does not cause memory loss. *(Source: Food and Drug Administration)*

12. According to researchers, diabetes is rare in societies in which obesity is rare. In societies in which obesity has been common for at least 20 years, diabetes is also common. *(Source: American Diabetes Association)*

■ Using and Interpreting Concepts

13. **BRCA Gene**   In the general population, one woman in eight will develop breast cancer. Research has shown that 1 woman in 600 carries a mutation of the BRCA gene. Eight out of 10 women with this mutation develop breast cancer. *(Source: Susan G. Komen Breast Cancer Foundation)*

    (a) Find the probability that a randomly selected woman will develop breast cancer given that she has a mutation of the BRCA gene.

(b) Find the probability that a randomly selected woman will carry the mutation of the BRCA gene and will develop breast cancer.

(c) Are the events of carrying this mutation and developing breast cancer independent or dependent? Explain.

Breast Cancer and the BRCA Gene

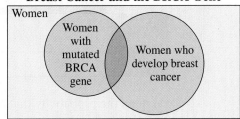

14. Pickup Trucks In a survey, 510 adults were asked if they drive a pickup truck and if they drive a Ford. The results showed that one in six adults surveyed drives a pickup truck, and three in ten adults surveyed drives a Ford. Of the adults surveyed that drive Fords, two in nine drive a pickup truck.

(a) Find the probability that a randomly selected adult drives a pickup truck given that he or she drives a Ford.

(b) Find the probability that a randomly selected adult drives a Ford and drives a pickup truck.

What Do You Drive?

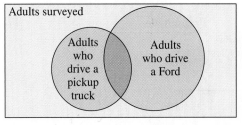

(c) Are the events driving a Ford and driving a pickup truck independent or dependent? Explain.

15. Summer Vacation The table shows the results of a survey in which 146 families were asked if they own a computer and if they will be taking a summer vacation this year.

		Summer Vacation This Year		
		Yes	No	Total
Own a Computer	Yes	46	11	57
	No	55	34	89
	Total	101	45	146

(a) Find the probability that a randomly selected family is not taking a summer vacation this year.

(b) Find the probability that a randomly selected family owns a computer.

(c) Find the probability a randomly selected family is taking a summer vacation this year given that they own a computer.

(d) Find the probability a randomly selected family is taking a summer vacation this year and owns a computer.

(e) Are the events of owning a computer and taking a summer vacation this year independent or dependent events? Explain.

16. Nursing Majors The table shows the number of male and female students enrolled in nursing at the University of Oklahoma Health Sciences Center for a recent semester. *(Adapted from University of Oklahoma Health Center Office of Admissions and Records)*

	Nursing majors	Non-nursing majors	Total
Males	95	1015	1110
Females	700	1727	2427
Total	795	2742	3537

(a) Find the probability that a randomly selected student is a nursing major.

(b) Find the probability that a randomly selected student is male.

(c) Find the probability that a randomly selected student is a nursing major given that the student is male.

(d) Find the probability that a randomly selected student is a nursing major and male.

(e) Are the events being a male student and being a nursing major independent or dependent events? Explain.

17. Assisted Reproductive Technology A study found that 35% of the assisted reproductive technology (ART) cycles resulted in a pregnancy. Twenty-eight percent of the ART pregnancies resulted in multiple births. *(Source: National Center for Chronic Disease Prevention and Health Promotion)*

(a) Find the probability that a randomly selected ART cycle resulted in a pregnancy *and* produced a multiple birth.

(b) Find the probability that a randomly selected ART cycle that resulted in a pregnancy did *not* produce a multiple birth.

(c) Would it be unusual for a randomly selected ART cycle to result in a pregnancy and produce a multiple birth? Explain.

18. Race Relations In a survey, 60% of adults in the United States think race relations have improved since the death of Martin Luther King Jr. Of these 60%, 4 out of 10 said the rate of civil rights progress is too slow. *(Source: Marist Institute for Public Opinion)*

(a) Find the probability that a randomly selected adult thinks race relations have improved since the death of Martin Luther King Jr. *and* thinks the rate of civil rights progress is too slow.

(b) Given that a randomly selected adult thinks race relations have improved since the death of Martin Luther King Jr., find the probability that he or she thinks the rate of civil rights progress is *not* too slow.

(c) Would it be unusual for a randomly selected adult to think race relations have improved since the death of Martin Luther King Jr. and think the rate of civil rights progress is too slow? Explain.

19. Computers and Internet Access A study found that 62% of households in the United States have a computer. Of those 62%, 88% have Internet access. Find the probability that a U.S. household selected at random has a computer and has Internet access. *(Source: U.S. Census Bureau)*

20. Surviving Surgery A doctor gives a patient a 60% chance of surviving bypass surgery after a heart attack. If the patient survives the surgery, he has a 50% chance that the heart damage will heal. Find the probability that the patient survives surgery and the heart damage heals.

Pregnancies

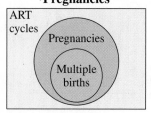

Race Relations

21. **Left-Handed People**   In a sample of 1000 people, 120 are left-handed. Two unrelated people are selected at random without replacement.

    (a) Find the probability that both people are left-handed.
    (b) Find the probability that neither person is left-handed.
    (c) Find the probability that at least one of the two people is left-handed.

22. **Light Bulbs**   Twelve light bulbs are tested to see if they last as long as the manufacturer claims they do. Three light bulbs fail the test. Two light bulbs are selected at random without replacement.

    (a) Find the probability that both light bulbs failed the test.
    (b) Find the probability that both light bulbs passed the test.
    (c) Find the probability that at least one light bulb failed the test.

23. **Emergency Savings**   The table shows the results of a survey in which 142 men and 145 women workers ages 25 to 64 were asked if they have at least one month's income set aside for emergencies.

	Men	Women	Total
Less than one month's income	66	83	149
One month's income or more	76	62	138
Total	142	145	287

    (a) Find the probability that a randomly selected worker has one month's income or more set aside for emergencies.
    (b) Given that a randomly selected worker is a male, find the probability that the worker has less than one month's income.
    (c) Given that a randomly selected worker has one month's income or more, find the probability that the worker is a female.
    (d) Are the events "having less than one month's income saved" and "being male" independent or dependent? Explain.

24. **Health Care for Dogs**   The table shows the results of a survey in which 90 dog owners were asked how much they have spent in the last year for their dog's health care, and whether their dogs were purebred or mixed breeds.

		Type of Dog		
		Purebred	Mixed breed	Total
Health Care	Less than $100	19	21	40
	$100 or more	35	15	50
	Total	54	36	90

    (a) Find the probability that $100 or more was spent on a randomly selected dog's health care in the last year.
    (b) Given that a randomly selected dog owner spent less than $100, find the probability that the dog was a mixed breed.
    (c) Find the probability that a randomly selected dog owner spent $100 or more on health care and the dog was a mixed breed.
    (d) Are the events "spending $100 or more on health care" and "having a mixed breed dog" independent or dependent? Explain.

25. Blood Types　The probability that a person in the United States has type AB^+ blood is 3%. Five unrelated people in the United States are selected at random. *(Source: American Association of Blood Banks)*

(a) Find the probability that all five have type AB^+ blood.

(b) Find the probability that none of the five has type AB^+ blood.

(c) Find the probability that at least one of the five has type AB^+ blood.

26. Blood Types　The probability that a person in the United States has type O^+ blood is 38%. Three unrelated people in the United States are selected at random. *(Source: American Association of Blood Banks)*

(a) Find the probability that all three have type O^+ blood.

(b) Find the probability that none of the three has type O^+ blood.

(c) Find the probability that at least one of the three has type O^+ blood.

27. Guessing　A multiple-choice quiz has three questions, each with five answer choices. Only one of the choices is correct. You have no idea what the answer is to any question and have to guess each answer.

(a) Find the probability of answering the first question correctly.

(b) Find the probability of answering the first two questions correctly.

(c) Find the probability of answering all three questions correctly.

(d) Find the probability of answering none of the questions correctly.

(e) Find the probability of answering at least one of the questions correctly.

28. Bookbinding Defects　A printing company's bookbinding machine has a probability of 0.005 of producing a defective book. This machine is used to bind three books.

(a) Find the probability that none of the books is defective.

(b) Find the probability that at least one of the books is defective.

(c) Find the probability that all of the books are defective.

29. Warehouses　A distribution center receives shipments of a product from three different factories in the following quantities: 50, 35, and 25. Three times a product is selected at random, each time without a replacement. Find the probability that all three products came from the third factory.

30. Birthdays　Three people are selected at random. Find the probability that (a) all three share the same birthday and (b) none of the three shares the same birthday. Assume 365 days in a year.

■ Extending Concepts

*According to **Bayes's Theorem**, the probability of event A, given that event B has occurred, is*

$$P(A|B) = \frac{P(A) \cdot P(B|A)}{P(A) \cdot P(B|A) + P(A') \cdot P(B|A')}.$$

In Exercises 31–34, use Bayes's Theorem to find $P(A|B)$.

31. $P(A) = \frac{2}{3}$, $P(A') = \frac{1}{3}$, $P(B|A) = \frac{1}{5}$, and $P(B|A') = \frac{1}{2}$

32. $P(A) = \frac{3}{8}$, $P(A') = \frac{5}{8}$, $P(B|A) = \frac{2}{3}$, and $P(B|A') = \frac{3}{5}$

33. $P(A) = 0.25$, $P(A') = 0.75$, $P(B|A) = 0.3$, and $P(B|A') = 0.5$

34. $P(A) = 0.62$, $P(A') = 0.38$, $P(B|A) = 0.41$, and $P(B|A') = 0.17$

35. Reliability of Testing   A certain virus infects one in every 200 people. A test used to detect the virus in a person is positive 80% of the time if the person has the virus and 5% of the time if the person does not have the virus. (This 5% result is called a *false positive*.) Let A be the event "the person is infected" and B be the event "the person tests positive."

(a) Using Bayes's Theorem, if a person tests positive, determine the probability that the person is infected.

(b) Using Bayes's Theorem, if a person tests negative, determine the probability that the person is *not* infected.

36. Birthday Problem   You are in a class that has 24 students. You want to find the probability that at least two of the students share the same birthday.

(a) First, find the probability that each student has a different birthday.

$$\overbrace{P(\text{different birthdays}) = \frac{365}{365} \cdot \frac{364}{365} \cdot \frac{363}{365} \cdot \frac{362}{365} \cdots \frac{343}{365} \cdot \frac{342}{365}}^{24 \text{ factors}}$$

(b) The probability that at least two students have the same birthday is the complement of the probability in part (a). What is this probability?

(c) We used a technology tool to generate 24 random numbers between 1 and 365. Each number represents a birthday. Did we get at least two people with the same birthday?

228	348	181	317	81	183
52	346	177	118	315	273
252	168	281	266	285	13
118	360	8	193	57	107

(d) Use a technology tool to simulate the "Birthday Problem." Repeat the simulation 10 times. How many times did you get "at least two people" with the same birthday?

The Multiplication Rule and Conditional Probability   *By rewriting the formula for the Multiplication Rule, you can write a formula for finding conditional probabilities. The conditional probability of event B occurring, given that event A has occurred, is*

$$P(B|A) = \frac{P(A \text{ and } B)}{P(A)}.$$

In Exercises 37 and 38, use the following information.

- *The probability that an airplane flight departs on time is 0.89.*

- *The probability that a flight arrives on time is 0.87.*

- *The probability that a flight departs and arrives on time is 0.83.*

37. Find the probability that a flight departed on time given that it arrives on time.

38. Find the probability that a flight arrives on time given that it departed on time.

3.3 The Addition Rule

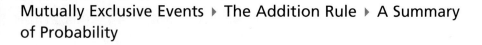

What You SHOULD LEARN

▸ How to determine if two events are mutually exclusive

▸ How to use the Addition Rule to find the probability of two events

Mutually Exclusive Events ▸ The Addition Rule ▸ A Summary of Probability

▸ Mutually Exclusive Events

In Section 3.2, you learned how to find the probability of two events, A and B, occurring in sequence. Such probabilities are denoted by $P(A \text{ and } B)$. In this section, you will learn how to find the probability that at least one of two events will occur. Probabilities such as these are denoted by $P(A \text{ or } B)$ and depend on whether the events are mutually exclusive.

DEFINITION

Two events A and B are **mutually exclusive** if A and B cannot occur at the same time.

The Venn diagrams show the relationship between events that are mutually exclusive and events that are not mutually exclusive.

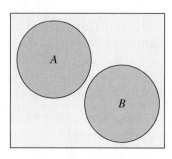

A and B are mutually exclusive.

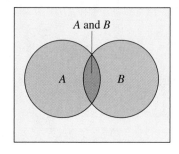

A and B are not mutually exclusive.

Study Tip

In probability and statistics, the word *or* is usually used as an "inclusive or" rather than an "exclusive or." For instance, there are three ways for "Event A or B" to occur.

(1) A occurs and B does not occur.

(2) B occurs and A does not occur.

(3) A and B both occur.

EXAMPLE 1

Mutually Exclusive Events

Decide if the events are mutually exclusive. Explain your reasoning.

1. Event A: Roll a 3 on a die.
   Event B: Roll a 4 on a die.
2. Event A: Randomly select a male student.
   Event B: Randomly select a nursing major.
3. Event A: Randomly select a blood donor with type O blood.
   Event B: Randomly select a female blood donor.

Solution

1. The first event has one outcome, a 3. The second event also has one outcome, a 4. These outcomes cannot occur at the same time, so the events are mutually exclusive.
2. Because the student can be a male nursing major, the events are not mutually exclusive.
3. Because the donor can be a female with type O blood, the events are not mutually exclusive.

▶ **Try It Yourself 1**

Decide if the events are mutually exclusive.

1. Event *A*: Randomly select a jack from a standard deck of cards.
   Event *B*: Randomly select a face card from a standard deck of cards.
2. Event *A*: Randomly select a 20-year-old student.
   Event *B*: Randomly select a student with blue eyes.
3. Event *A*: Randomly select a vehicle that is a Ford.
   Event *B*: Randomly select a vehicle that is a Toyota.

a. Decide if one of the following statements is true.

- Events *A* and *B* cannot occur at the same time.
- Events *A* and *B* have no outcomes in common.
- $P(A \text{ and } B) = 0$

b. Make a conclusion.

Answer: Page A38

▶ The Addition Rule

Study Tip

By subtracting *P*(*A* and *B*) you avoid double counting the probability of outcomes that occur in both *A* and *B*

To explore this topic further, see Activity 3.3 on page 170.

THE ADDITION RULE FOR THE PROBABILITY OF *A* OR *B*

The probability that events *A* or *B* will occur, $P(A \text{ or } B)$, is given by

$$P(A \text{ or } B) = P(A) + P(B) - P(A \text{ and } B).$$

If events *A* and *B* are mutually exclusive, then the rule can be simplified to $P(A \text{ or } B) = P(A) + P(B)$. This simplified rule can be extended to any number of mutually exclusive events.

In words, to find the probability one event or the other will occur, add the individual probabilities of each event and subtract the probability they both occur.

EXAMPLE 2

Using the Addition Rule to Find Probabilities

1. You select a card from a standard deck. Find the probability that the card is a 4 or an ace.
2. You roll a die. Find the probability of rolling a number less than three or rolling an odd number.

Solution

1. If the card is a 4, it cannot be an ace. So, the events are mutually exclusive as shown in the Venn diagram. The probability of selecting a 4 or an ace is

$$P(4 \text{ or ace}) = P(4) + P(\text{ace}) = \frac{4}{52} + \frac{4}{52} = \frac{8}{52} = \frac{2}{13} \approx 0.154.$$

2. The events are not mutually exclusive because 1 is an outcome of both events as shown in the Venn diagram. So, the probability of rolling a number less than 3 or an odd number is

$$P(\text{less than 3 or odd}) = P(\text{less than 3}) + P(\text{odd})$$
$$- P(\text{less than 3 and odd})$$
$$= \frac{2}{6} + \frac{3}{6} - \frac{1}{6} = \frac{4}{6} = \frac{2}{3} \approx 0.667.$$

Deck of 52 Cards

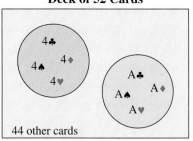

44 other cards

Roll a Die

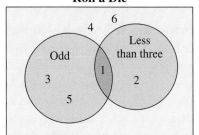

▶ Try It Yourself 2

1. A die is rolled. Find the probability of rolling a 6 or an odd number.
2. A card is selected from a standard deck. Find the probability that the card is a face card or a heart.

a. Decide whether the events are *mutually exclusive.*
b. Find $P(A)$, $P(B)$, and, if necessary, $P(A \text{ and } B)$.
c. Use the *Addition Rule* to find the probability.   *Answer: Page A38*

EXAMPLE 3

Finding Probabilities of Mutually Exclusive Events

The frequency distribution shows the volume of sales (in dollars) and the number of months a sales representative reached each sales level during the past three years. If this sales pattern continues, what is the probability that the sales representative will sell between $75,000 and $124,999 next month?

Sales volume ($)	Months
0–24,999	3
25,000–49,999	5
50,000–74,999	6
75,000–99,999	7
100,000–124,999	9
125,000–149,999	2
150,000–174,999	3
175,000–199,999	1

Solution   To solve this problem, define events A and B as follows.

A = monthly sales between $75,000 and $99,999

B = monthly sales between $100,000 and $124,999

Because events A and B are mutually exclusive, the probability that the sales representative will sell between $75,000 and $124,999 next month is

$$P(A \text{ or } B) = P(A) + P(B)$$
$$= \frac{7}{36} + \frac{9}{36}$$
$$= \frac{16}{36}$$
$$= \frac{4}{9} \approx 0.444.$$

Try It Yourself 3

Find the probability that the sales representative will sell between $0 and $49,999.

a. *Identify* events A and B.
b. Verify that A and B are *mutually exclusive.*
c. Find the *probability* of each event.
d. Use the *Addition Rule* to find the probability.   *Answer: Page A38*

Using the Addition Rule to Find Probabilities

A blood bank catalogs the types of blood, including positive or negative Rh-factor, given by donors during the last five days. The number of donors who gave each blood type is shown in the table. A donor is selected at random.

1. Find the probability that the donor has type O or type A blood.
2. Find the probability that the donor has type B blood or is Rh-negative.

		Blood Type				
		O	**A**	**B**	**AB**	**Total**
RH-factor	**Positive**	156	139	37	12	344
	Negative	28	25	8	4	65
	Total	184	164	45	16	409

Solution

1. Because a donor cannot have type O blood and type A blood, these events are mutually exclusive. So, on the basis of the Addition Rule, the probability that a randomly chosen donor has type O or type A blood is

$$P(\text{type O or type A}) = P(\text{type O}) + P(\text{type A})$$

$$= \frac{184}{409} + \frac{164}{409}$$

$$= \frac{348}{409}$$

$$\approx 0.851.$$

2. Because a donor can have type B blood and be Rh-negative, these events are not mutually exclusive. So, on the basis of the Addition Rule, the probability that a randomly chosen donor has type B blood or is Rh-negative is

$$P(\text{type B or Rh-neg}) = P(\text{type B}) + P(\text{Rh-neg}) - P(\text{type B and Rh-neg})$$

$$= \frac{45}{409} + \frac{65}{409} - \frac{8}{409}$$

$$= \frac{102}{409}$$

$$\approx 0.249.$$

▶ **Try It Yourself 4**

1. Find the probability that the donor has type B or type AB blood.
2. Find the probability that the donor has type O blood or is Rh-positive.

a. Decide if the events are *mutually exclusive*.
b. Use the *Addition Rule*.   *Answer: Page A38*

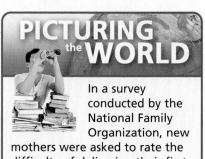

PICTURING the WORLD

In a survey conducted by the National Family Organization, new mothers were asked to rate the difficulty of delivering their first child compared with what they expected. (Source: National Family Organization Research for CNS)

How Difficult Was the Delivery?

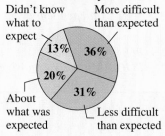

Didn't know what to expect — 13%
More difficult than expected — 36%
About what was expected — 20%
Less difficult than expected — 31%

If you selected a new mother at random and asked her to compare the difficulty of her delivery with what she expected, what is the probability that she would say that it was the same or more difficult than what she expected?

▸ A Summary of Probability

Type of Probability and Probability Rules	In Words	In Symbols
Classical Probability	The number of outcomes in the sample space is known and each outcome is equally likely to occur.	$P(E) = \dfrac{\text{Number of outcomes in event } E}{\text{Number of outcomes in sample space}}$
Empirical Probability	The frequency of outcomes in the sample space is estimated from experimentation.	$P(E) = \dfrac{\text{Frequency of event } E}{\text{Total frequency}} = \dfrac{f}{n}$
Range of Probabilities Rule	The probability of an event is between 0 and 1, inclusive.	$0 \le P(E) \le 1$
Complementary Events	The complement of event E is the set of all outcomes in a sample space that are not included in E, denoted by E'.	$P(E') = 1 - P(E)$
Multiplication Rule	The Multiplication Rule is used to find the probability of two events occurring in a sequence.	$P(A \text{ and } B) = P(A) \cdot P(B\|A)$ $P(A \text{ and } B) = P(A) \cdot P(B)$ *Independent events*
Addition Rule	The Addition Rule is used to find the probability of at least one of two events occurring.	$P(A \text{ or } B) = P(A) + P(B) - P(A \text{ and } B)$ $P(A \text{ or } B) = P(A) + P(B)$ *Mutually exclusive events*

EXAMPLE 5

Combining Rules to Find Probabilities

Use the graph at the right to find the probability that a randomly selected draft pick is not a running back or a wide receiver.

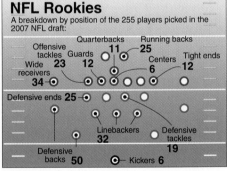

NFL Rookies
A breakdown by position of the 255 players picked in the 2007 NFL draft:

(Source: NFL.com)

Solution Define events A and B.

   A: Draft pick is a running back.
   B: Draft pick is a wide receiver.

These events are mutually exclusive, so the probability that the draft pick is a running back or wide receiver is

$$P(A \text{ or } B) = P(A) + P(B) = \tfrac{25}{255} + \tfrac{34}{255} = \tfrac{59}{255} \approx 0.231.$$

By taking the complement of $P(A \text{ or } B)$, you can determine that the probability of randomly selecting a draft pick who is not a running back or wide receiver is

$$1 - P(A \text{ or } B) = 1 - \tfrac{59}{255} = \tfrac{196}{255} \approx 0.769.$$

▸ **Try It Yourself 5**

Find the probability that a randomly selected draft pick is not a linebacker or a quarterback.

a. Find the *probability* that the draft pick is a linebacker or a quarterback.
b. Find the *complement* of the event. *Answer: Page A38*

3.3 EXERCISES

■ Building Basic Skills and Vocabulary

1. If two events are mutually exclusive, why is $P(A \text{ and } B) = 0$?

2. List examples of

   (a) two events that are mutually exclusive.

   (b) two events that are not mutually exclusive.

True or False? *In Exercises 3–6, determine whether the statement is true or false. If it is false, explain why.*

3. If two events are mutually exclusive, they have no outcomes in common.

4. If two events are independent, then they are also mutually exclusive.

5. The probability that event *A* or event *B* will occur is

$$P(A \text{ or } B) = P(A) + P(B) - P(A \text{ or } B).$$

6. If events *A* and *B* are mutually exclusive, then

$$P(A \text{ or } B) = P(A) + P(B).$$

Graphical Analysis *In Exercises 7 and 8, decide if the events shown in the Venn diagram are mutually exclusive. Explain your reasoning.*

7.

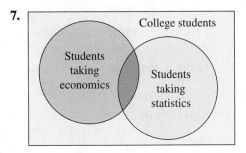

8.

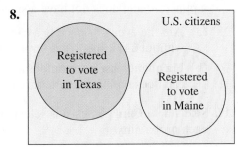

Recognizing Mutually Exclusive Events *In Exercises 9–12, decide if the events are mutually exclusive. Explain your reasoning.*

9. Event *A*: Randomly select a female worker.
   Event *B*: Randomly select a worker with a college degree.

10. Event *A*: Randomly select a member of U.S. Congress.
   Event *B*: Randomly select a male U.S. Senator.

11. Event *A*: Randomly select a person between 18 and 24 years old.
   Event *B*: Randomly select a person between 25 and 34 years old.

12. Event *A*: Randomly select a person between 18 and 24 years old.
   Event *B*: Randomly select a person earning between $20,000 and $29,999.

■ **Using and Interpreting Concepts**

13. **Audit**   During a 52-week period, a company paid overtime wages for 18 weeks and hired temporary help for 9 weeks. During 5 weeks, the company paid overtime *and* hired temporary help.

    (a) Are the events "selecting a week that contained overtime wages" and "selecting a week that contained temporary help wages" mutually exclusive? Explain.

    (b) If an auditor randomly examined the payroll records for only one week, what is the probability that the payroll for that week contained overtime wages or temporary help wages?

14. **Newspaper Survey**   A college has an undergraduate enrollment of 3500. Of these, 860 are business majors and 1800 are women. Of the business majors, 425 are women.

    (a) Are the events "selecting a woman student" and "selecting a business major" mutually exclusive? Explain.

    (b) If a college newspaper conducts a poll and selects students at random to answer a survey, find the probability that a selected student is a woman or a business major.

15. **Carton Defects**   A company that makes cartons finds the probability of producing a carton with a puncture is 0.05, the probability that a carton has a smashed corner is 0.08, and the probability that a carton has a puncture and has a smashed corner is 0.004.

    (a) Are the events "selecting a carton with a puncture" and "selecting a carton with a smashed corner" mutually exclusive? Explain.

    (b) If a quality inspector randomly selects a carton, find the probability that the carton has a puncture or has a smashed corner.

16. **Can Defects**   A company that makes soda pop cans finds the probability of producing a can without a puncture is 0.96, the probability that a can does not have a smashed edge is 0.93, and the probability that a can does not have a puncture and does not have a smashed edge is 0.893.

    (a) Are the events "selecting a can without a puncture" and "selecting a can without a smashed edge" mutually exclusive? Explain.

    (b) If a quality inspector randomly selects a can, find the probability that the can does not have a puncture or does not have a smashed edge.

17. **Selecting a Card**   A card is selected at random from a standard deck. Find each probability.

    (a) Randomly selecting a diamond or a 7

    (b) Randomly selecting a red suit or a queen

    (c) Randomly selecting a 3 or a face card

18. **Rolling a Die**   You roll a die. Find each probability.

    (a) Rolling a 6 or a number greater than 4

    (b) Rolling a number less than 5 or an odd number

    (c) Rolling a 3 or an even number

19. U.S. Age Distribution The estimated percent distribution of the U.S. population for 2015 is shown in the pie chart. Find each probability. (*Source: U.S. Census Bureau*)

(a) Randomly selecting someone under five years old

(b) Randomly selecting someone who is not 65 years or over

(c) Randomly selecting someone who is between 18 and 34 years old

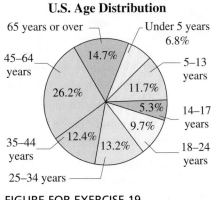

U.S. Age Distribution

FIGURE FOR EXERCISE 19

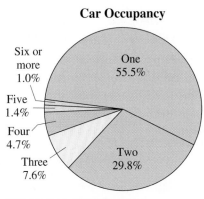

Car Occupancy

FIGURE FOR EXERCISE 20

20. Tacoma Narrows Bridge The percent distribution of the number of occupants in vehicles crossing the Tacoma Narrows Bridge in Washington is shown in the pie chart. Find each probability. (*Source: Washington State Department of Transportation*)

(a) Randomly selecting a car with two occupants

(b) Randomly selecting a car with two or more occupants

(c) Randomly selecting a car with between two and five occupants, inclusive

21. Education The number of responses to a survey are shown in the Pareto chart. The survey asked 1017 U.S. adults how they feel about the quality of education students receive in kindergarten through grade twelve. Each person gave one response. Find each probability. (*Adapted from Gallup Poll*)

(a) Randomly selecting a person from the sample who is not completely satisfied with the quality of education

(b) Randomly selecting a person from the sample who is somewhat dissatisfied or completely dissatisfied with the quality of education

22. Movies The number of responses to a survey are shown in the Pareto chart. The survey asked 1005 U.S. adults what they feel is the biggest problem with movies. Each person gave one response. Find each probability. (*Source: Associated Press*)

(a) Randomly selecting a person from the sample who feels the biggest problem with movies is that movies are not as good as they used to be

(b) Randomly selecting a person from the sample who feels the biggest problem is other than movies have too much violence or that the tickets cost too much.

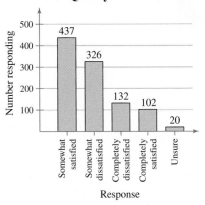

How Satisfied Are You with the Quality of Education

FIGURE FOR EXERCISE 21

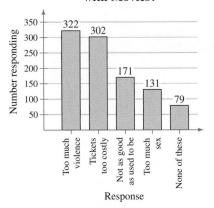

What Is the Biggest Problem with Movies?

FIGURE FOR EXERCISE 22

23. **Nursing Majors**　The table shows the number of male and female students enrolled in nursing at the University of Oklahoma Health Sciences Center for a recent semester. A student is selected at random. Find the probability of each event. *(Adapted from University of Oklahoma Health Center Office of Admissions and Records)*

	Nursing majors	Non-nursing majors	Total
Males	95	1015	1110
Females	700	1727	2427
Total	795	2742	3537

(a) The student is male or a nursing major.

(b) The student is female or not a nursing major.

(c) The student is not female or a nursing major.

(d) Are the events "being male" and "being a nursing major" mutually exclusive? Explain.

24. **Left-Handed People**　In a sample of 1000 people (525 men and 475 women), 113 are left-handed (63 men and 50 women). The results of the sample are shown in the table. A person is selected at random from the sample. Find the probability of each event.

		Gender		
		Men	Women	Total
Dominant Hand	Left	63	50	113
	Right	462	425	887
	Total	525	475	1000

(a) The person is left-handed or a woman.

(b) The person is right-handed or a man.

(c) The person is not right-handed or a man.

(d) The person is a right-handed woman.

(e) Are the events "being right-handed" and "being a woman" mutually exclusive? Explain.

25. **Charity**　The table shows the results of a survey that asked 2850 people whether they are involved in any type of charity work. A person is selected at random from the sample. Find the probability of each event.

	Frequently	Occasionally	Not at all	Total
Male	221	456	795	1472
Female	207	430	741	1378
Total	428	886	1536	2850

(a) The person is frequently or occasionally involved in charity work.

(b) The person is female or not involved in charity work at all.

(c) The person is male or frequently involved in charity work.

(d) The person is female or not frequently involved in charity work.

(e) Are the events "being female" and "being frequently involved in charity work" mutually exclusive? Explain.

26. Eye Survey   The table shows the results of a survey that asked 3203 people whether they wear contacts or glasses. A person is selected at random from the sample. Find the probability of each event.

	Contacts only	Glasses only	Both contacts and glasses	Neither	Total
Male	64	841	177	456	1538
Female	189	427	368	681	1665
Total	253	1268	545	1137	3203

(a) The person wears contacts or glasses only.

(b) The person is male or wears both contacts and glasses.

(c) The person is female or wears neither contacts or glasses.

(d) The person is male or does not wear glasses.

(e) Are the events "wearing contacts" and "wearing both contacts and glasses" mutually exclusive? Explain.

■ Extending Concepts

27. Writing   Is there a relationship between independence and mutual exclusivity? To decide, find examples of the following, if possible.

(a) Describe two events that are dependent and mutually exclusive.

(b) Describe two events that are independent and mutually exclusive.

(c) Describe two events that are dependent and not mutually exclusive.

(d) Describe two events that are independent and not mutually exclusive.

Use your results to write a conclusion about the relationship between independence and mutual exclusivity.

Addition Rule for Three Events   *The Addition Rule for the probability that events A or B or C will occur, P(A or B or C), is given by*

$$P(A \text{ or } B \text{ or } C) = P(A) + P(B) + P(C) - P(A \text{ and } B) - P(A \text{ and } C)$$
$$- P(B \text{ and } C) + P(A \text{ and } B \text{ and } C).$$

In the Venn diagram shown, P(A or B or C) is represented by the blue areas.

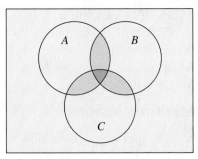

In Exercises 28 and 29, find P(A or B or C) for the given probabilities.

28. $P(A) = 0.40$, $P(B) = 0.10$, $P(C) = 0.50$,
$P(A \text{ and } B) = 0.05$, $P(A \text{ and } C) = 0.25$, $P(B \text{ and } C) = 0.10$,
$P(A \text{ and } B \text{ and } C) = 0.03$

29. $P(A) = 0.38$, $P(B) = 0.26$, $P(C) = 0.14$,
$P(A \text{ and } B) = 0.12$, $P(A \text{ and } C) = 0.03$, $P(B \text{ and } C) = 0.09$,
$P(A \text{ and } B \text{ and } C) = 0.01$

APPLET

APPLET

ACTIVITY 3.3

The *simulating the probability of rolling a 3 or 4* applet allows you to investigate the probability of rolling a 3 or 4 on a fair die. The plot in the top left corner shows the probability associated with each outcome of a die roll. When ROLL is clicked, *n* simulations of the experiment of rolling a die are performed. The results of the simulations are shown in the frequency plot. If the animate option is checked, the display will show each outcome dropping into the frequency plot as the simulation runs. To stop an animation, uncheck the animate option. The individual outcomes are shown in the text field to the far right of the applet. The center plot shows in blue the cumulative proportion of times that an event of rolling a 3 or 4 occurs. The green line in the plot reflects the true probability of rolling a 3 or 4. As the experiment is conducted more and more, the cumulative proportion should converge to the true value.

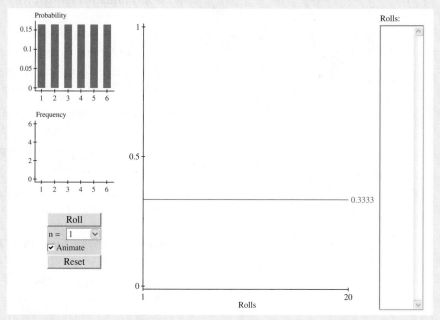

■ Explore

Step 1   Specify a value for *n*.
Step 2   Click ROLL four times.
Step 3   Click RESET.
Step 4   Specify another value for *n*.
Step 5   Click ROLL.

■ Draw Conclusions

1. What is the theoretical probability of rolling a 3 or 4?

2. Run the simulation using each value of *n* one time. Clear the results after each trial. Compare the cumulative proportion of rolling a 3 or 4 for each trial to the theoretical probability of rolling a 3 or 4.

3. Suppose you want to modify the applet so you can find the probability of rolling a number less than 4. Describe the placement of the green line.

CASE STUDY

Probability and Parking Lot Strategies

The Institute for Operations Research and the Management Sciences (INFORMS) is an international scientific society with more than 12,000 members. It is dedicated to the application of scientific methods to improve decision making, management, and operations. Members of the institute work primarily in business, government, and education. They represent fields as diverse as airlines, health care, law enforcement, the military, the stock market, and telecommunications.

One study published by INFORMS was the result of research conducted by Dr. C. Richard Cassady of Mississippi State University and Dr. John Kobza of Virginia Polytechnic Institute. The parking space study was conducted at a mall that has 4 entrances, 7 rows with 72 spaces each, and directional restrictions. The researchers compared several parking lot strategies to see which strategy saves the most time. The two best strategies are called *Pick a Row* and *Cycling*. The results are shown in the table.

Pick a Row
Choose a row. Enter it and select the closest available space.

Cycling
Enter the closest row. Park in any of the 20 closest spaces. If all are full, cycle to next row.

Store entrance

Time or Distance	Pick a Row	Cycling
Time from lot entrance to parking space	37.7 seconds	52.5 seconds
Time from lot entrance to store's door	61.3 seconds	70.7 seconds
Average walking distance to store	257 feet	208 feet

■ Exercises

1. In a parking lot study, is each parking space equally likely to be empty? Explain your reasoning.

2. According to the results of the study, are you more likely to spend less time using the Pick-a-Row strategy or the Cycling strategy? Explain.

3. According to the results of the study, are you more likely to walk less using the Pick-a-Row strategy or the Cycling strategy? Explain.

4. A key assumption in the study was that the drivers can see which spaces are available as soon as they enter a lane. Why is that important?

5. The parking lot is completely full, and one car leaves. What is the probability that the car was in the first row? Explain your reasoning.

6. A person is leaving from a row that is full. What is the probability that the person was parked in one of the 20 spaces that are closest to the store?

7. Draw a diagram of the parking lot. Color code the parking spaces into three categories of 168 spaces each: most desirable, moderately desirable, and least desirable. Assume that the parking lot is half full. Estimate the probability that you can find a parking space in the most desirable category. Explain your reasoning.

171

3.4 Additional Topics in Probability and Counting

Permutations ▸ Combinations ▸ Applications of Counting Principles

▸ Permutations

In Section 3.1, you learned that the Fundamental Counting Principle is used to find the number of ways two or more events can occur in sequence. In this section, you will study several other techniques for counting the number of ways an event can occur. An important application of the Fundamental Counting Principle is determining the number of ways that n objects can be arranged in order or in a permutation.

> **DEFINITION**
>
> A **permutation** is an ordered arrangement of objects. The number of different permutations of n distinct objects is $n!$.

The expression $n!$ is read as n **factorial** and is defined as follows.

$$n! = n \cdot (n-1) \cdot (n-2) \cdot (n-3) \cdots 3 \cdot 2 \cdot 1$$

As a special case, $0! = 1$. Here are several other values of $n!$.

$$1! = 1, \ 2! = 2 \cdot 1 = 2, \ 3! = 3 \cdot 2 \cdot 1 = 6, \ 4! = 4 \cdot 3 \cdot 2 \cdot 1 = 24$$

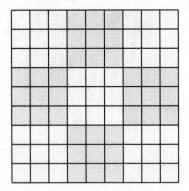

Sudoku Number Puzzle

> **EXAMPLE 1**
>
> ### Finding the Number of Permutations of n Objects
>
> The objective of a 9×9 Sudoku number puzzle is to fill the grid so that each row, each column, and each 3×3 grid contain the digits 1 to 9. How many different ways can the first row of a blank 9×9 Sudoku grid be filled?
>
> **Solution**
>
> The number of permutations is $9! = 9 \cdot 8 \cdot 7 \cdot 6 \cdot 5 \cdot 4 \cdot 3 \cdot 2 \cdot 1 = 362{,}880$. So, there are 362,880 different ways the first row can be filled.
>
> ▸ **Try It Yourself 1**
>
> The teams in the National League Central Division are listed at the left. How many different final standings are possible?
>
> **a.** Determine *how many teams*, n, are in the Central Division.
> **b.** Evaluate $n!$.   *Answer: Page A38*

National League Central Division

Chicago Cubs	Cincinnati Reds
Houston Astros	Milwaukee Brewers
Pittsburgh Pirates	St. Louis Cardinals

Suppose you want to choose some of the objects in a group and put them in order. Such an ordering is called a **permutation of n objects taken r at a time.**

> **PERMUTATIONS OF n OBJECTS TAKEN r AT A TIME**
>
> The number of permutations of n distinct objects taken r at a time is
>
> $$_nP_r = \frac{n!}{(n-r)!}, \text{ where } r \leq n.$$

EXAMPLE 2

Finding $_nP_r$

Find the number of ways of forming three-digit codes in which no digit is repeated.

Solution

To form a three-digit code with no repeating digits, you need to select 3 digits from a group of 10, so $n = 10$ and $r = 3$.

$$_nP_r = {}_{10}P_3 = \frac{10!}{(10-3)!} = \frac{10!}{7!} = \frac{10 \cdot 9 \cdot 8 \cdot \cancel{7} \cdot \cancel{6} \cdot \cancel{5} \cdot \cancel{4} \cdot \cancel{3} \cdot \cancel{2} \cdot \cancel{1}}{\cancel{7} \cdot \cancel{6} \cdot \cancel{5} \cdot \cancel{4} \cdot \cancel{3} \cdot \cancel{2} \cdot \cancel{1}} = 720$$

So, there are 720 possible three-digit codes that do not have repeating digits.

▸ Try It Yourself 2

A psychologist shows a list of eight activities to her subject. How many ways can the subject pick a first, second, and third activity?

a. Find the quotient of $n!$ and $(n - r)!$. (List the factors and divide out.)
b. Write the result as a sentence. *Answer: Page A38*

EXAMPLE 3

Permutations of n Objects Taken r at a Time

Forty-three race cars started the 2007 Daytona 500. How many ways can the cars finish first, second, and third? *(Source: NASCAR.com)*

Solution You need to select three race cars from a group of 43, so $n = 43$ and $r = 3$. Because the order is important, the number of ways the cars can finish first, second, and third is

$$_nP_r = {}_{43}P_3 = \frac{43!}{(43-3)!} = \frac{43!}{40!} = 43 \cdot 42 \cdot 41 = 74{,}046.$$

▸ Try It Yourself 3

The board of directors for a company has 12 members. One member is the president, another is the vice president, another is the secretary, and another is the treasurer. How many ways can can these positions be assigned?

a. *Identify* the total number of objects n and the number of objects r being chosen in order.
b. *Evaluate* $_nP_r$. *Answer: Page A38*

You may want to order a group of n objects in which some of the objects are the same. For instance, consider a group of letters consisting of four As, two Bs, and one C. How many ways can you order such a group? Using the previous formula, you might conclude that there are $_7P_7 = 7!$ possible orders. However, because some of the objects are the same, not all of these permutations are *distinguishable*. How many distinguishable permutations are possible? The answer can be found using the following formula.

DISTINGUISHABLE PERMUTATIONS

The number of **distinguishable permutations** of n objects, where n_1 are of one type, n_2 are of another type, and so on is

$$\frac{n!}{n_1! \cdot n_2! \cdot n_3! \cdots n_k!}, \text{ where } n_1 + n_2 + n_3 + \cdots + n_k = n.$$

Insight

Notice that the Fundamental Counting Principle can be used in Example 3 to obtain the same result. You can see that there are 43 choices for first place, 42 choices for second place, and 41 choices for third place. You can then conclude that there are

$$43 \cdot 42 \cdot 41 = 74{,}046$$

ways the cars can finish first, second, and third.

Study Tip

The letters *AAAABBC* can be rearranged in 7! orders, but many of these are not distinguishable. The number of distinguishable orders is

$$\frac{7!}{4! \cdot 2! \cdot 1!} = \frac{7 \cdot 6 \cdot 5}{2}$$
$$= 105.$$

EXAMPLE 4

Distinguishable Permutations

A building contractor is planning to develop a subdivision. The subdivision is to consist of 6 one-story houses, 4 two-story houses, and 2 split-level houses. In how many distinguishable ways can the houses be arranged?

Solution   There are to be 12 houses in the subdivision, 6 of which are of one type (one-story), 4 of another type (two-story), and 2 of a third type (split-level). So, there are

$$\frac{12!}{6! \cdot 4! \cdot 2!} = \frac{12 \cdot 11 \cdot 10 \cdot 9 \cdot 8 \cdot 7 \cdot 6!}{6! \cdot 4! \cdot 2!}$$

$$= 13,860 \text{ distinguishable ways.}$$

Interpretation   There are 13,860 distinguishable ways to arrange the houses in the subdivision.

Try It Yourself 4

The contractor wants to plant six oak trees, nine maple trees, and five poplar trees along the subdivision street. The trees are to be spaced evenly apart. In how many distinguishable ways can they be planted?

a. *Identify* the total number of objects, n, and the number of each type of object in the group, n_1, n_2, and n_3.

b. *Evaluate* $\dfrac{n!}{n_1! \cdot n_2! \cdots n_k!}$. *Answer: Page A38*

▶ Combinations

You want to buy three CDs from a selection of five CDs. There are 10 ways to make your selections.

> *ABC, ABD, ABE,*
> *ACD, ACE,*
> *ADE,*
> *BCD, BCE,*
> *BDE,*
> *CDE*

In each selection, order does not matter (*ABC* is the same set as *BAC*). The number of ways to choose r objects from n objects without regard to order is called the number of **combinations of n objects taken r at a time.**

Insight

You can think of a combination of n objects chosen r at a time as a permutation of n objects in which the r selected objects are alike and the remaining $n - r$ (not selected) objects are alike.

COMBINATION OF n OBJECTS TAKEN r AT A TIME

A combination is a selection of r objects from a group of n objects without regard to order and is denoted by $_nC_r$. The number of combinations of r objects selected from a group of n objects is

$$_nC_r = \frac{n!}{(n - r)!r!}.$$

> # EXAMPLE 5

Finding the Number of Combinations

A state's department of transportation plans to develop a new section of interstate highway and receives 16 bids for the project. The state plans to hire four of the bidding companies. How many different combinations of four companies can be selected from the 16 bidding companies?

Solution   The state is selecting four companies from a group of 16, so $n = 16$ and $r = 4$. Because order is not important, there are

$$
\begin{aligned}
{}_nC_r = {}_{16}C_4 &= \frac{16!}{(16 - 4)!4!} \\
&= \frac{16!}{12!4!} \\
&= \frac{16 \cdot 15 \cdot 14 \cdot 13 \cdot 12!}{12! \cdot 4!} \\
&= 1820 \text{ different combinations.}
\end{aligned}
$$

Interpretation   There are 1820 different combinations of four companies that can be selected from the 16 bidding companies.

▶ Try It Yourself 5

The manager of an accounting department wants to form a three-person advisory committee from the 20 employees in the department. In how many ways can the manager form this committee?

a. *Identify* the number of objects in the group n and the number of objects to be selected r.
b. *Evaluate* ${}_nC_r$.
c. *Write* the results as a sentence.   *Answer: Page A38*

The table summarizes the counting principles.

Principle	Description	Formula
Fundamental Counting Principle	If one event can occur in m ways and a second event can occur in n ways, the number of ways the two events can occur in sequence is $m \cdot n$.	$m \cdot n$
Permutation	The number of different ordered arrangements of n distinct objects	$n!$
	The number of permutations of n distinct objects taken r at a time, where $r \leq n$	${}_nP_r = \dfrac{n!}{(n - r)!}$
	The number of distinguishable permutations of n objects where n_1 are of one type, n_2 are of another type, and so on	$\dfrac{n!}{n_1! \cdot n_2! \cdots n_k!}$
Combinations	The number of combinations of r objects selected from a group of n objects without regard to order	${}_nC_r = \dfrac{n!}{(n - r)!r!}$

▶ Applications of Counting Principles

EXAMPLE 6

Finding Probabilities

A student advisory board consists of 17 members. Three members serve as the board's chair, secretary, and webmaster. Each member is equally likely to serve any of the positions. What is the probability of selecting at random the three members that hold each position?

Solution

There is one favorable outcome and there are

$$_{17}P_3 = \frac{17!}{(17-3)!} = \frac{17!}{14!} = 17 \cdot 16 \cdot 15 = 4080$$

ways the three positions can be filled. So, the probability of correctly selecting the three members that hold each position is

$$P(\text{selecting the three members}) = \frac{1}{4080} \approx 0.0002.$$

▶ Try It Yourself 6

A student advisory board consists of 20 members. Two members serve as the board's chair and secretary. Each member is equally likely to serve either of the positions. What is the probability of selecting at random the two members that hold each position?

a. Find the *number of ways* the two positions can be filled.
b. Find the *probability* of correctly selecting the two members.

Answer: Page A38

EXAMPLE 7

Finding Probabilities

You have 11 letters consisting of one M, four Is, four Ss, and two Ps. If the letters are randomly arranged in order, what is the probability that the arrangement spells the word *Mississippi*?

Solution   There is one favorable outcome and there are

$$\frac{11!}{1! \cdot 4! \cdot 4! \cdot 2!} = 34{,}650 \qquad \text{11 letters with 1, 4, 4, and 2 like letters}$$

distinguishable permutations of the given letters. So, the probability that the arrangement spells the word *Mississippi* is

$$P(\text{Mississippi}) = \frac{1}{34{,}650} \approx 0.000029.$$

▶ Try It Yourself 7

You have 6 letters consisting of one L, two Es, two Ts, and one R. If the letters are randomly arranged in order, what is the probability that the arrangement spells the word *letter*?

a. *Find* the number of favorable outcomes and the number of distinguishable permutations.
b. *Divide* the number of favorable outcomes by the number of distinguishable permutations.

Answer: Page A38

EXAMPLE 8

Finding Probabilities

Find the probability of being dealt five diamonds from a standard deck of playing cards. (In poker, this is a diamond flush.)

Solution   The possible number of ways of choosing 5 diamonds out of 13 is $_{13}C_5$. The number of possible five-card hands is $_{52}C_5$. So, the probability of being dealt 5 diamonds is

$$P(\text{diamond flush}) = \frac{_{13}C_5}{_{52}C_5} = \frac{1287}{2,598,960} \approx 0.0005.$$

▶ Try It Yourself 8

Find the probability of being dealt five diamonds from a standard deck of playing cards that also includes two jokers. In this case, the joker is considered to be a wild card that can be used to represent any card in the deck.

a. Find the *number of ways* of choosing 5 diamonds out of 15.
b. *Find* the number of possible five-card hands.
c. *Divide* the result of part a by the result of part b.   *Answer: Page A38*

EXAMPLE 9

Finding Probabilities

A food manufacturer is analyzing a sample of 400 corn kernels for the presence of a toxin. In this sample, three kernels have dangerously high levels of the toxin. If four kernels are randomly selected from the sample, what is the probability that exactly one kernel contains a dangerously high level of the toxin?

Solution

The possible number of ways of choosing one toxic kernel out of three toxic kernels is $_3C_1$. The possible number of ways of choosing 3 nontoxic kernels from 397 nontoxic kernels is $_{397}C_3$. So, using the Fundamental Counting Principle, the number of ways of choosing one toxic kernel and three nontoxic kernels is

$$_3C_1 \cdot {_{397}C_3} = 3 \cdot 10,349,790$$
$$= 31,049,370.$$

The number of possible ways of choosing 4 kernels from 400 kernels is $_{400}C_4 = 1,050,739,900$. So, the probability of selecting exactly 1 toxic kernel is

$$P(1 \text{ toxic kernel}) = \frac{_3C_1 \cdot {_{397}C_3}}{_{400}C_4} = \frac{31,049,370}{1,050,739,900} \approx 0.0296.$$

▶ Try It Yourself 9

A jury consists of five men and seven women. Three are selected at random for an interview. Find the probability that all three are men.

a. *Find* the product of the number of ways to choose three men from five and the number of ways to choose zero women from seven.
b. *Find* the number of ways to choose 3 jury members from 12.
c. *Divide* the result of part a by the result of part b.   *Answer: Page A38*

3.4 EXERCISES

■ Building Basic Skills and Vocabulary

1. When you calculate the number of permutations of n distinct objects taken r at a time, what are you counting? Give an example.

2. When you calculate the number of combinations of r objects taken from a group of n objects, what are you counting? Give an example.

True or False? *In Exercises 3–6, determine whether the statement is true or false. If it is false, rewrite it as a true statement.*

3. A combination is an ordered arrangement of objects.

4. The number of different ordered arrangements of n distinct objects is $n!$.

5. If you divide the number of permutations of 11 objects taken 3 at a time by 3!, you will get the number of combinations of 11 objects taken 3 at a time.

6. $_7C_5 = {_7}C_2$

In Exercises 7–14, perform the indicated calculation.

7. $_7P_3$

8. $_{14}P_2$

9. $_7C_4$

10. $_8P_6$

11. $_{24}C_6$

12. $\dfrac{_8C_4}{_{12}C_6}$

13. $\dfrac{_6P_2}{_{10}P_4}$

14. $\dfrac{_8C_3}{_{12}C_3}$

In Exercises 15–18, decide if the situation involves permutations, combinations, or neither. Explain your reasoning.

15. The number of ways 15 people can line up in a row for concert tickets

16. The number of ways a four-member committee can be chosen from 10 people

17. The number of ways 2 captains can be chosen from 28 players on a lacrosse team.

18. The number of four-letter passwords that can be created when no letter can be repeated.

■ Using and Interpreting Concepts

19. **Space Shuttle Menu** Space shuttle astronauts each consume an average of 3000 calories per day. One meal normally consists of a main dish, a vegetable dish, and two different desserts. The astronauts can choose from 10 main dishes, 8 vegetable dishes, and 13 desserts. How many different meals are possible? *(Source: NASA)*

20. **Skiing** Eight people compete in a downhill ski race. Assuming that there are no ties, in how many different orders can the skiers finish?

21. **Security Code** In how many ways can the letters A, B, C, D, E, and F be arranged for a six-letter security code?

22. Starting Lineup The starting lineup for a softball team consists of 10 players. How many different batting orders are possible using the starting lineup?

23. Lottery Number Selection A lottery has 52 numbers. In how many different ways can 6 of the numbers be selected? (Assume that order of selection is not important.)

24. Assembly Process There are four processes involved in assembling a certain product. These processes can be performed in any order. Management wants to find which order is the least time-consuming. How many different orders will have to be tested?

25. Tree Planting A landscaper wants to plant four oak trees, eight maple trees, and six poplar trees along the border of a lawn. The trees are to be spaced evenly apart. In how many distinguishable ways can they be planted?

26. Experimental Group In order to conduct an experiment, 4 subjects are randomly selected from a group of 20 subjects. How many different groups of four subjects are possible?

27. Letters In how many distinguishable ways can the letters in the word *statistics* be written?

28. Jury Selection From a group of 40 people, a jury of 12 people is selected. In how many different ways can a jury of 12 people be selected?

Word Jumble *In Exercises 29–34, do the following.*

(a) Find the number of distinguishable ways the letters can be arranged.

(b) There is one arrangement that spells an important term used throughout the course. Find the term.

(c) If the letters are randomly arranged in order, what is the probability that the arrangement spells the word from part b?

29. palmes

30. nevte

31. etre

32. ediman

33. unoppolati

34. sidtbitoiurn

35. Horse Race A horse race has 12 entries. Assuming that there are no ties, what is the probability that the three horses owned by one person finish first, second, and third?

36. Pizza Toppings A pizza shop offers nine toppings. No topping is used more than once. What is the probability that the toppings on a pizza are pepperoni, onions, and mushrooms?

37. Jukebox You look over the songs on a jukebox and determine that you like 15 of the 56 songs.

  (a) What is the probability that you like the next three songs that are played? Assume a song cannot be repeated.

  (b) What is the probability that you do not like the next three songs that are played? Assume a song cannot be repeated.

38. Officers The offices of president, vice president, secretary, and treasurer for an environmental club will be filled from a pool of 14 candidates. Six of the candidates are members of the debate team.

(a) What is the probability that all of the offices are filled by members of the debate team?

(b) What is the probability that none of the offices are filled by members of the debate team?

39. Employee Selection Four sales representatives for a company are to be chosen to participate in a training program. The company has eight sales representatives, two in each of four regions. In how many ways can the four sales representatives be chosen if (a) there are no restrictions and (b) the selection must include a sales representative from each region? (c) What is the probability that the four sales representatives chosen to participate in the training program will be from only two of the four regions if they are chosen at random?

40. License Plates In a certain state, each automobile license plate number consists of two letters followed by a four-digit number. How many distinct license plate numbers can be formed if (a) there are no restrictions and (b) the letters O and I are not used? (c) What is the probability of selecting at random a license plate that ends in an even number?

41. Password A password consists of two letters followed by a five-digit number. How many passwords are possible if (a) there are no restrictions and (b) none of the letters or digits can be repeated? (c) What is the probability of guessing the password in one trial if there are no restrictions?

42. Area Code An area code consists of three digits. How many area codes are possible if (a) there are no restrictions and (b) the first digit cannot be a 1 or a 0? (c) What is the probability of selecting an area code at random that ends in an odd number if the first digit cannot be a 1 or a 0?

43. Repairs In how many orders can three broken computers and two broken printers be repaired if (a) there are no restrictions, (b) the printers must be repaired first, and (c) the computers must be repaired first? (d) If the order of repairs has no restrictions and the order of repairs is done at random, what is the probability that a printer will be repaired first?

44. Defective Units A shipment of 10 microwave ovens contains two defective units. In how many ways can a restaurant buy three of these units and receive (a) no defective units, (b) one defective unit, and (c) at least two nondefective units? (d) What is the probability of the restaurant buying at least two defective units?

Financial Shape *In Exercises 45–48, use the pie chart, which shows how U.S. adults rate their financial shape.* (Source: Pew Research Center)

Rate Your Financial Shape

45. Suppose 4 people are chosen at random from a group of 1200. What is the probability that all four would rate their financial shape as excellent? (Make the assumption that the 1200 people are represented by the pie chart.)

46. Suppose 10 people are chosen at random from a group of 1200. What is the probability that all 10 would rate their financial shape as poor? (Make the assumption that the 1200 people are represented by the pie chart.)

47. Suppose 80 people are chosen at random from a group of 500. What is the probability that none of the 80 people would rate their financial shape as fair? (Make the assumption that the 500 people are represented by the pie chart.)

48. Suppose 55 people are chosen at random from a group of 500. What is the probability that none of the 55 people would rate their financial shape as good? (Make the assumption that the 500 people are represented by the pie chart.)

49. Probability   In a state lottery, you must select 5 numbers (in any order) out of 40 correctly to win the top prize.

   (a) How many ways can 5 numbers be chosen from 40 numbers?

   (b) You purchase one lottery ticket. What is the probability of winning the top prize?

50. Probability   A company that has 200 employees chooses a committee of 15 to represent employee retirement issues. When the committee was formed, none of the 56 minority employees were selected.

   (a) Use a technology tool to find the number of ways 15 employees can be chosen from 200.

   (b) Use a technology tool to find the number of ways 15 employees can be chosen from 144 nonminorities.

   (c) If the committee was chosen randomly (without bias), what is the probability that it contained no minorities?

   (d) Does your answer to part (c) indicate that the committee selection was biased? Explain your reasoning.

51. Cards   You are dealt a hand of five cards from a standard deck of playing cards. Find the probability of being dealt a hand consisting of

   (a) four-of-a-kind.

   (b) a full house, which consists of 1 three-of-a-kind and 1 two-of-a-kind.

   (c) three-of-a-kind. (The other two cards are different from each other.)

   (d) two clubs and one of each other three suits.

52. Warehouse   A warehouse employs 24 workers on first shift and 17 workers on second shift. Eight workers are chosen at random to be interviewed about the work environment. Find the probability of choosing

   (a) all first-shift workers.

   (b) all second-shift workers.

   (c) six first-shift workers.

   (d) four second-shift workers.

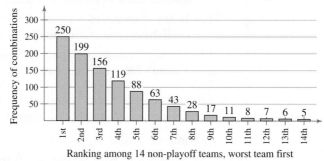

■ Extending Concepts

NBA Draft Lottery   *In Exercises 53–58, use the following information. The National Basketball Association (NBA) uses a lottery to determine which team gets the first pick in its annual draft. The teams eligible for the lottery are the 14 non-playoff teams. Fourteen Ping-Pong balls numbered 1 through 14 are placed in a drum. Each of the 14 teams is assigned several of the possible four-number combinations that correspond to the numbers on the Ping-Pong balls, such as 3, 8, 10, and 12. Four balls are then drawn out to determine the first pick in the draft. The order in which the balls are drawn is not important. All of the four-number combinations are assigned to the 14 teams by computer except for one four-number combination. When this four-number combination is drawn, the balls are put back in the drum and another drawing takes place. For instance, if Team A has been assigned the four-number combination 3, 8, 10, 12 and the balls shown at the left are drawn, then Team A wins the first pick.*

After the first pick of the draft is determined, the process continues to choose the teams that will select second and third picks. The remaining order of the draft is determined by the number of losses of each team.

53. In how many ways can 4 of the numbers 1 to 14 be selected if order is *not* important? How many sets of 4 numbers are assigned to the 14 teams?

54. In how many ways can four of the numbers be selected if order is important?

In the Pareto chart, the number of combinations assigned to each of the 14 teams is shown. The team with the most losses (the worst team) gets the most chances to win the lottery. So, the worst team receives the greatest frequency of four-number combinations, 250. The team with the best record of the 14 non-playoff teams has the fewest chances, with 5 four-number combinations.

Frequency of Four-Number Combinations Assigned in the NBA Draft Lottery

Frequency of combinations

300 — 250, 199, 156, 119, 88, 63, 43, 28, 17, 11, 8, 7, 6, 5

Ranking among 14 non-playoff teams, worst team first (1st through 14th)

55. For each team, find the probability that the team will win the first pick.

56. What is the probability that the team with the worst record will win the second pick, given that the team with the best record, ranked 14th, wins the first pick?

57. What is the probability that the team with the worst record will win the third pick, given that the team with the best record, ranked 14th, wins the first pick and the team ranked 2nd wins the second pick?

58. What is the probability that neither the first- nor the second-worst team will get the first pick?

Uses & Abuses

Uses

Probability affects decisions when the weather is forecast, when marketing strategies are determined, when medications are selected, and even when players are selected for professional sports teams. Although intuition is often used for determining probabilities, you will be better able to assess the likelihood that an event will occur by applying the rules of classical probability and empirical probability.

For instance, suppose you work for a real estate company and are asked to estimate the likelihood that a particular house will sell for a particular price within the next 90 days. You could use your intuition, but you could better assess the probability by looking at sales records for similar houses.

Abuses

One common abuse of probability is thinking that probabilities have "memories." For example, if a coin is tossed eight times, the probability that it will land heads up all eight times is only about 0.004. However, if the coin has already been tossed seven times and has landed heads up each time, the probability that it will land heads up on the eighth time is 0.5. Each toss is independent of all other tosses. The coin does not "remember" that it has already landed heads up seven times.

Ethics

A human resources director for a company with 100 employees wants to show that her company is an equal opportunity employer of women and minorities. There are 40 women employees and 20 minority employees in the company. Nine of the women employees are minorities. Despite this fact, the director reports that 60% of the company is either a woman or a minority. If one employee is selected at random, the probability that the employee is a woman is 0.4 and the probability that the employee is a minority is 0.2. This does not mean, however, that the probability that a randomly selected employee is a woman or a minority is 0.4 + 0.2 or 0.6, because nine employees belong to both groups. In this case, it would be ethically incorrect to omit this information from her report because these individuals would have been counted twice.

■ EXERCISES

1. **Assuming Probability Has a "Memory"** A "Daily Number" lottery has a three-digit number from 000 to 999. You buy one ticket each day. Your number is 389.

   a. What is the probability of winning next Tuesday and Wednesday?

   b. You won on Tuesday. What's the probability of winning on Wednesday?

   c. You didn't win on Tuesday. What's the probability of winning on Wednesday?

2. **Adding Probabilities Incorrectly** A town has a population of 500 people. Suppose that the probability that a randomly chosen person owns a pickup is 0.25 and the probability that a randomly chosen person owns an SUV is 0.30. What can you say about the probability that a randomly chosen person owns a pickup or an SUV? Could this probability be 0.55? Could it be 0.60? Explain your reasoning.

3 CHAPTER SUMMARY

What did you learn?

	EXAMPLE(S)	REVIEW EXERCISES
Section 3.1		
■ How to identify the sample space of a probability experiment and to identify simple events	*1, 2*	*1–4*
■ How to use the Fundamental Counting Principle to find the number of ways two or more events can occur	*3, 4*	*5, 6*
■ How to distinguish among classical probability, empirical probability, and subjective probability	*5–8*	*7–12*
■ How to find the probability of the complement of an event and how to find other probabilities using tree diagrams and the Fundamental Counting Principle	*9–11*	*13–16*
Section 3.2		
■ How to find conditional probabilities	*1*	*17, 18*
■ How to distinguish between independent and dependent events	*2*	*19, 20*
■ How to use the Multiplication Rule to find the probability of two events occurring in sequence	*3–5*	*21, 22*

$P(A \text{ and } B) = P(A) \cdot P(B|A)$ if events are dependent

$P(A \text{ and } B) = P(A) \cdot P(B)$ if events are independent

	EXAMPLE(S)	REVIEW EXERCISES
Section 3.3		
■ How to determine if two events are mutually exclusive	*1*	*23, 24*
■ How to use the Addition Rule to find the probability of two events	*2–5*	*25–34*

$P(A \text{ or } B) = P(A) + P(B) - P(A \text{ and } B)$

$P(A \text{ or } B) = P(A) + P(B)$ if events are mutually exclusive

	EXAMPLE(S)	REVIEW EXERCISES
Section 3.4		
■ How to find the number of ways a group of objects can be arranged in order and the number of ways to choose several objects from a group without regard to order	*1–5*	*35–38*

$$_nP_r = \frac{n!}{(n-r)!}, \quad \frac{n!}{n_1! \cdot n_2! \cdot n_3! \cdots n_k!}, \quad _nC_r = \frac{n!}{(n-r)!r!}$$

	EXAMPLE(S)	REVIEW EXERCISES
■ How to use counting principles to find probabilities	*6–9*	*39–42*

3 REVIEW EXERCISES

Section 3.1

In Exercises 1–4, identify the sample space of the probability experiment and determine the number of outcomes in the event. Draw a tree diagram if it is appropriate.

1. *Experiment:* Tossing four coins
   Event: Getting three heads

2. *Experiment:* Rolling 2 six-sided dice
   Event: Getting a sum of 4 or 5

3. *Experiment:* Choosing a month of the year
   Event: Choosing a month that begins with the letter J

4. *Experiment:* Guessing the gender of the three children in a family
   Event: The family has two boys

In Exercises 5 and 6, use the Fundamental Counting Principle.

5. A student must choose between 7 classes to take at 8:00 A.M., 4 classes to take at 9:00 A.M., and 3 classes to take at 10:00 A.M. How many ways can the student arrange the schedule?

6. The state of Virginia's license plate has three letters followed by four digits. Assuming that any letter or digit can be used, how many different license plates are possible?

In Exercises 7–12, classify the statement as an example of classical probability, empirical probability, or subjective probability.

7. On the basis of prior counts, a quality control officer says there is a 0.05 probability that a randomly chosen part is defective.

8. The probability of randomly selecting five cards of the same suit (a flush) from a standard deck is about 0.0005.

9. The chance that Corporation A's stock price will fall today is 75%.

10. The probability of a person from the United States being left-handed is 11%.

11. The probability of rolling 2 six-sided dice and getting a sum greater than nine is $\frac{1}{6}$.

12. The chance that a randomly selected person in the United States is between 15 and 24 years old is about 14%. *(Source: U.S. Census Bureau)*

In Exercises 13 and 14, the table shows the approximate distribution of the sizes of firms for 2004. Use the table to determine the probability of the event. (Source: U.S. Small Business Administration)

Number of Employees	0 to 4	5 to 9	10 to 19	20 to 99	100 or more
Percent of Firms	60.8%	17.7%	10.8%	8.9%	1.8%

13. What is the probability that a randomly selected firm will have at least 10 employees?

14. What is the probability that a randomly selected firm will have fewer than 20 employees?

Telephone Numbers *The telephone numbers for a region of a state have an area code of 570. The next seven digits represent the local telephone numbers for that region. A local telephone number cannot begin with a 0 or 1. Your cousin lives within the given area code.*

15. What is the probability of randomly generating your cousin's telephone number?

16. What is the probability of not randomly generating your cousin's telephone number?

Section 3.2

In Exercises 17 and 18, the list shows the results of a study on the use of plus/minus grading at North Carolina State University. It shows the percents of graduate and undergraduate students who received grades with pluses and minuses (for example, C+, A−, etc.). (Source: North Carolina State University)

- *Of all students who received one or more plus grades, 92% were undergraduates and 8% were graduates.*
- *Of all students who received one or more minus grades, 93% were undergraduates and 7% were graduates.*

17. Find the probability that a student is an undergraduate student, given that the student received a plus grade.

18. Find the probability that a student is a graduate student, given that the student received a minus grade.

In Exercises 19 and 20, decide whether the events are independent or dependent.

19. Tossing a coin four times, getting four heads, and tossing it a fifth time and getting a head

20. Taking a driver's education course and passing the driver's license exam

In Exercises 21 and 22, find the probability of the sequence of events.

21. You are shopping, and your roommate has asked you to pick up toothpaste and dental rinse. However, your roommate did not tell you which brands to get. The store has eight brands of toothpaste and five brands of dental rinse. What is the probability that you will purchase the correct brands of both products?

22. Your sock drawer has 18 folded pairs of socks, with 8 pairs of white, 6 pairs of black, and 4 pairs of blue. What is the probability, without looking in the drawer, that you will first select and remove a black pair, then select either a blue or a white pair?

Section 3.3

In Exercises 23 and 24, decide if the events are mutually exclusive.

23. Event *A*: Randomly select a red jelly bean from a jar.

Event *B*: Randomly select a yellow jelly bean from the same jar.

24. Event *A*: Randomly select a person who loves cats.

Event *B*: Randomly select a person who owns a dog.

25. A random sample of 250 working adults found that 37% access the Internet at work, 44% access the Internet at home, and 21% access the Internet at both work and home. What is the probability that a person in this sample selected at random accesses the Internet at home or at work?

26. A sample of automobile dealerships found that 19% of automobiles sold are silver, 22% of automobiles sold are sports utility vehicles (SUVs), and 16% of automobiles sold are silver SUVs. What is the probability that a randomly chosen sold automobile from this sample is silver or an SUV?

In Exercises 27–30, determine the probability.

27. A card is randomly selected from a standard deck. Find the probability that the card is between 4 and 8 (inclusive) or is a club.

28. A card is randomly selected from a standard deck. Find the probability that the card is red or a queen.

29. A 12-sided die, numbered 1–12, is rolled. Find the probability that the roll results in an odd number or a number less than 4.

30. An eight-sided die, numbered 1–8, is rolled. Find the probability that the roll results in an even number or a number greater than 6.

In Exercises 31 and 32, use the pie chart, which shows the percent distribution of the number of students in traditional U.S. secondary schools. (Adapted from U.S. National Center for Education Statistics)

Students in Secondary Schools

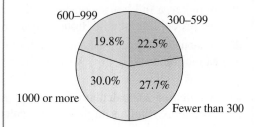

600–999   19.8%

300–599   22.5%

1000 or more   30.0%

27.7%   Fewer than 300

31. Find the probability of randomly selecting a school with 600 or more students.

32. Find the probability of randomly selecting a school with between 300 and 999 students, inclusive.

In Exercises 33 and 34, use the Pareto chart, which shows the results of a survey in which 500 adults were asked why they don't always eat healthy foods.

Why Don't You Eat Healthy Foods?

Number responding

- No time to cook: 175
- Can't take food on the go: 95
- High cost: 85
- Poor taste: 60
- Hard to find: 55
- Confusion about nutrition: 30

Response

33. Find the probability of randomly selecting an adult from the sample who feels that healthy foods have poor taste or are hard to find.

34. Find the probability of randomly selecting an adult from the sample who doesn't always eat healthy foods because he or she has no time to cook or is confused about nutrition.

Section 3.4

In Exercises 35–38, use combinations and permutations.

35. Fifteen cyclists enter a race. In how many ways can they finish first, second, and third?

36. Five players on a basketball team must choose a player on the opposing team to defend. In how many ways can they choose their defensive assignments?

37. A literary magazine editor must choose 4 short stories for this month's issue from 17 submissions. In how many ways can the editor choose this month's stories?

38. An employer must hire 2 people from a list of 13 applicants. In how many ways can the employer choose to hire 2 people?

In Exercises 39–42, use counting principles to find the probability.

39. In poker, a full house consists of a three-of-a-kind and a two-of-a-kind. Find the probability of a full house consisting of three kings and two queens.

40. A security code consists of three letters followed by one digit. The first letter cannot be an A, B, or C. What is the probability of guessing the security code in one trial?

41. A batch of 200 calculators contains three defective calculators. What is the probability that a sample of three calculators will have

(a) no defective calculators?

(b) all defective calculators?

(c) at least one defective calculator?

(d) at least one nondefective calculator?

42. A batch of 350 raffle tickets contains four winning tickets. You buy four tickets. What is the probability that you have

(a) no winning tickets?

(b) all of the winning ticket?

(c) at least one winning ticket?

(d) at least one nonwinning ticket?

3 CHAPTER QUIZ

Take this quiz as you would take a quiz in class. After you are done, check your work against the answers given in the back of the book.

1. The table shows the number (in thousands) of earned degrees conferred in the United States in the year 2004 by level and gender. *(Source: National Center for Education Statistics)*

<table>
<tr><td colspan="2" rowspan="2"></td><td colspan="3">Gender</td></tr>
<tr><td>Male</td><td>Female</td><td>Total</td></tr>
<tr><td rowspan="4">Level of Degree</td><td>Associate</td><td>260</td><td>405</td><td>665</td></tr>
<tr><td>Bachelor's</td><td>595</td><td>804</td><td>1399</td></tr>
<tr><td>Master's</td><td>230</td><td>329</td><td>559</td></tr>
<tr><td>Doctorate</td><td>25</td><td>23</td><td>48</td></tr>
<tr><td>Total</td><td>1110</td><td>1561</td><td>2671</td></tr>
</table>

A person who earned a degree in the year 2004 is randomly selected. Find the probability of selecting someone who

   (a) earned a bachelor's degree.

   (b) earned a bachelor's degree given that the person is a female.

   (c) earned a bachelor's degree given that the person is not a female.

   (d) earned an associate degree or a bachelor's degree.

   (e) earned a doctorate given that the person is a male.

   (f) earned a master's degree or is a female.

   (g) earned an associate degree and is a male.

   (h) is a female given that the person earned a bachelor's degree.

2. Decide if the events are mutually exclusive. Then decide if the events are independent or dependent. Explain your reasoning.

   Event *A*: A golfer scoring the best round in a four-round tournament
   Event *B*: Losing the golf tournament

3. A shipment of 150 television sets contains 3 defective units. Determine how many ways a vending company can buy three of these units and receive (a) no defective units, (b) all defective units, and (c) at least one good unit.

4. In Exercise 3, find the probability of the vending company receiving (a) no defective units, (b) all defective units, and (c) at least one good unit.

5. The access code for a warehouse's security system consists of six digits. The first digit cannot be 0 and the last digit must be even. How many different codes are available?

6. From a pool of 30 candidates, the offices of president, vice president, secretary, and treasurer will be filled. In how many different ways can the offices be filled?

Putting It All Together

REAL Statistics — Real Decisions

www.musl.com

You work for the company that runs the Powerball lottery. Powerball is a lottery game in which five white balls are chosen from a drum containing 55 balls and one red ball is chosen from a drum containing 42 balls. To win the jackpot, a player must match all five white balls and the red ball. Other winners and their prizes are also shown in the table.

Working in the public relations department, you handle many inquiries from the media and from lottery players. You receive the following e-mail.

> *You list the probability of matching only the red ball as 1/69. I know from my statistics class that the probability of winning is the ratio of the number of successful outcomes to the total number of outcomes. Could you please explain why the probability of matching only the red ball is 1/69?*

Your job is to answer this question, using the probability techniques you have learned in this chapter to justify your answer. In answering the question, assume only one ticket is purchased.

Powerball Winners and Prizes

Match	Prize	Approximate Probability
5 white, 1 red	Jackpot	1/146,107,962
5 white	$100,000	1/3,563,609
4 white, 1 red	$5,000	1/584,432
4 white	$100	1/14,254
3 white, 1 red	$100	1/11,927
3 white	$7	1/291
2 white, 1 red	$7	1/745
1 white	$4	1/127
1 red	$3	1/69

(Source: Multi-State Lottery Association)

■ Exercises

1. How Would You Do It?

(a) How would you investigate the question about the probability of matching only the red ball?

(b) What statistical methods taught in this chapter would you use?

2. Answering the Question

Write an explanation that answers the question about the probability of matching only the red ball. Include in your explanation any probability formulas that justify your explanation.

3. Another Question

You receive another question asking how the overall probability of winning a prize in the Powerball lottery is determined. The overall probability of winning a prize in the Powerball lottery is 1/37. Write an explanation that answers the question and include any probability formulas that justify your explanation.

Where Is Powerball Played?
Powerball is played in 29 states, Washington, D.C., and the U.S. Virgin Islands

U.S Virgin Islands

(Source: Multi-State Lottery Association)

TECHNOLOGY

SIMULATION: COMPOSING MOZART VARIATIONS WITH DICE

Wolfgang Mozart (1756–1791) composed a wide variety of musical pieces. In his Musical Dice Game, he wrote a Wiener minuet with an almost endless number of variations. Each minuet has 16 bars. In the eighth and sixteenth bars, the player has a choice of two musical phrases. In each of the other 14 bars, the player has a choice of 11 phrases.

To create a minuet, Mozart suggested that the player toss 2 six-sided dice 16 times. For the eighth and sixteenth bars, choose Option 1 if the dice total is odd and Option 2 if it is even. For each of the other 14 bars, subtract 1 from the dice total. The following minuet is the result of the following sequence of numbers.

5	7	1	6	4	10	5	1
6	6	2	4	6	8	8	2

■ EXERCISES

1. How many phrases did Mozart write to create the Musical Dice Game minuet? Explain.

2. How many possible variations are there in Mozart's Musical Dice Game minuet? Explain.

3. Use technology to randomly select a number from 1 to 11.

  (a) What is the theoretical probability of each number from 1 to 11 occurring?

  (b) Use this procedure to select 100 integers between 1 and 11. Tally your results and compare them with the probabilities in part (a).

4. What is the probability of randomly selecting options 6, 7, or 8 for the first bar? For all 14 bars? Find each probability using (a) theoretical probability and (b) the results of Exercise 3(b).

5. Use technology to randomly select two numbers from 1, 2, 3, 4, 5, and 6. Find the sum and subtract 1 to obtain a total.

  (a) What is the theoretical probability of each total from 1 to 11?

  (b) Use this procedure to select 100 totals between 1 and 11. Tally your results and compare them with the probabilities in part (a).

6. What is the probability of randomly selecting options 6, 7, or 8 for the first bar? For all 14 bars? Find each probability using (a) theoretical probability and (b) the results of Exercise 5(b).

Extended solutions are given in the *Technology Supplement.* Technical instruction is provided for MINITAB, Excel, and the TI-83/84.

CHAPTER

4

Discrete Probability Distributions

4.1 Probability Distributions

4.2 Binomial Distributions
- ACTIVITY
- CASE STUDY

4.3 More Discrete Probability Distributions
- USES AND ABUSES
- REAL STATISTICS–REAL DECISIONS
- TECHNOLOGY

The National Center for Atmospheric Research (NCAR) is located in Boulder, Colorado. It is part of the complex system of organizations that gathers and analyzes data about weather and other climatic conditions.

In Chapters 1 through 3, you learned how to collect and describe data and how to find the probability of an event. These skills are used in many different types of careers. For example, data about climatic conditions are used to analyze and forecast the weather throughout the world. On a typical day, 5000 weather stations, 800 to 1100 upper-air balloon stations, 2000 ships, 600 aircraft, several polar-orbiting and geostationary satellites, and a variety of other data-collection devices work together to provide meteorologists with data that are used to forecast the weather. Even with this much data, meteorologists cannot forecast the weather with certainty. Instead, they assign probabilities to certain weather conditions. For instance, a meteorologist might determine that there is a 40% chance of rain (based on the relative frequency of rain under similar weather conditions).

WHERE YOU'RE GOING →

In Chapter 4, you will learn how to create and use probability distributions. Knowing the shape, center, and variability of a probability distribution will enable you to make decisions in inferential statistics. You are a meteorologist working on a three-day forecast. Assuming that having rain on one day is independent of having rain on another day, you have determined that there is a 40% probability of rain on each of the three days (and 60% probability of no rain). What is the probability that it will rain on 0, 1, 2, or 3 of the days? To answer this, you can create a probability distribution for the possible outcomes.

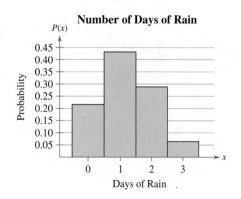

Day 1	Day 2	Day 3	Probability	Days of Rain
0.6	0.6	0.6	$P(\ast,\ast,\ast) = 0.216$	0
		0.4	$P(\ast,\ast,\blacklozenge) = 0.144$	1
	0.4	0.6	$P(\ast,\blacklozenge,\ast) = 0.144$	1
		0.4	$P(\ast,\blacklozenge,\blacklozenge) = 0.096$	2
0.4	0.6	0.6	$P(\blacklozenge,\ast,\ast) = 0.144$	1
		0.4	$P(\blacklozenge,\ast,\blacklozenge) = 0.096$	2
	0.4	0.6	$P(\blacklozenge,\blacklozenge,\ast) = 0.096$	2
		0.4	$P(\blacklozenge,\blacklozenge,\blacklozenge) = 0.064$	3

Using the *Addition Rule* with the probabilities in the tree diagram, you can determine the probability of having rain on various numbers of days. You can then use this information to graph a probability distribution.

Probability Distribution

Days of rain	Tally	Probability
0	1	0.216
1	3	0.432
2	3	0.288
3	1	0.064

Number of Days of Rain

P(x)

Probability

0.45
0.40
0.35
0.30
0.25
0.20
0.15
0.10
0.05

0   1   2   3   *x*

Days of Rain

4.1 Probability Distributions

What You SHOULD LEARN

▸ How to distinguish between discrete random variables and continuous random variables

▸ How to construct a discrete probability distribution and its graph

▸ How to determine if a distribution is a probability distribution

▸ How to find the mean, variance, and standard deviation of a discrete probability distribution

▸ How to find the expected value of a discrete probability distribution

Random Variables ▸ Discrete Probability Distributions ▸ Mean, Variance, and Standard Deviation ▸ Expected Value

▸ Random Variables

The outcome of a probability experiment is often a count or a measure. When this occurs, the outcome is called a random variable.

> ### DEFINITION
>
> A **random variable** x represents a numerical value associated with each outcome of a probability experiment.

The word *random* indicates that x is determined by chance. There are two types of random variables: discrete and continuous.

> ### DEFINITION
>
> A random variable is **discrete** if it has a finite or countable number of possible outcomes that can be listed.
>
> A random variable is **continuous** if it has an uncountable number of possible outcomes, represented by an interval on the number line.

You conduct a study of the number of calls a salesperson makes in one day. The possible values of the random variable x are 0, 1, 2, 3, 4, and so on. Because the set of possible outcomes

$$\{0, 1, 2, 3, \dots\}$$

can be listed, x is a discrete random variable. You can represent its values as points on a number line.

Number of Sales Calls (Discrete)

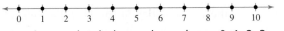

x can have only whole number values: 0, 1, 2, 3, ...

A different way to conduct the study would be to measure the time (in hours) a salesperson spends making calls in one day. Because the time spent making sales calls can be any number from 0 to 24 (including fractions and decimals), x is a continuous random variable. You can represent its values with an interval on a number line, but you cannot list all the possible values.

Hours Spent on Sales Calls (Continuous)

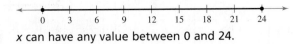

x can have any value between 0 and 24.

When a random variable is discrete, you can list the possible values it can assume. However, it is impossible to list all values for a continuous random variable.

EXAMPLE 1

Discrete Variables and Continuous Variables

Decide whether the random variable x is discrete or continuous. Explain your reasoning.

1. x represents the number of stocks in the Dow Jones Industrial Average that have share price increases on a given day.

2. x represents the volume of water in a 32-ounce container.

Solution

1. The number of stocks whose share price increases can be counted.

$$\{0, 1, 2, 3, \dots, 30\}$$

So, x is a *discrete* random variable.

2. The amount of water in the container can be any volume between 0 ounces and 32 ounces. So, x is a continuous random variable.

▶ Try It Yourself 1

Decide whether the random variable x is discrete or continuous.

1. x represents the length of time it takes to complete a test.
2. x represents the number of songs played by a band at a rock festival.

a. Decide if x represents counted data or measured data.
b. Make a conclusion and *explain* your reasoning.   *Answer: Page A38*

It is important that you can distinguish between discrete and continuous random variables because different statistical techniques are used to analyze each. The remainder of this chapter focuses on discrete random variables and their probability distributions. You will study continuous distributions later.

▶ Discrete Probability Distributions

Each value of a discrete random variable can be assigned a probability. By listing each value of the random variable with its corresponding probability, you are forming a probability distribution.

DEFINITION

A **discrete probability distribution** lists each possible value the random variable can assume, together with its probability. A probability distribution must satisfy the following conditions.

In Words	*In Symbols*
1. The probability of each value of the discrete random variable is between 0 and 1, inclusive.	$0 \leq P(x) \leq 1$
2. The sum of all the probabilities is 1.	$\sum P(x) = 1$

Because probabilities represent relative frequencies, a discrete probability distribution can be graphed with a relative frequency histogram.

Constructing a Discrete Probability Distribution

Let x be a discrete random variable with possible outcomes $x_1, x_2, \ldots, x_n$.

1. Make a frequency distribution for the possible outcomes.
2. Find the sum of the frequencies.
3. Find the probability of each possible outcome by dividing its frequency by the sum of the frequencies.
4. Check that each probability is between 0 and 1, inclusive, and that the sum is 1.

Frequency Distribution

Score, x	Frequency, $P(x)$
1	24
2	33
3	42
4	30
5	21

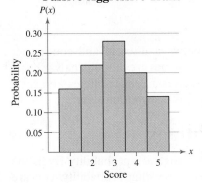

Passive-Aggressive Traits

Frequency Distribution

Sales per day, x	Number of days, f
0	16
1	19
2	15
3	21
4	9
5	10
6	8
7	2

EXAMPLE 2

Constructing and Graphing a Discrete Probability Distribution

An industrial psychologist administered a personality inventory test for passive-aggressive traits to 150 employees. Individuals were given a score from 1 to 5, where 1 was extremely passive and 5 extremely aggressive. A score of 3 indicated neither trait. The results are shown at the left. Construct a probability distribution for the random variable x. Then graph the distribution using a histogram.

Solution Divide the frequency of each score by the total number of individuals in the study to find the probability for each value of the random variable.

$$P(1) = \frac{24}{150} = 0.16 \qquad P(2) = \frac{33}{150} = 0.22 \qquad P(3) = \frac{42}{150} = 0.28$$

$$P(4) = \frac{30}{150} = 0.20 \qquad P(5) = \frac{21}{150} = 0.14$$

The discrete probability distribution is shown in the following table.

x	1	2	3	4	5
$P(x)$	0.16	0.22	0.28	0.20	0.14

Note that $0 \leq P(x) \leq 1$ and $\sum P(x) = 1$.

The histogram is shown at the left. Because the width of each bar is one, the area of each bar is equal to the probability of a particular outcome. Also, the probability of an event corresponds to the sum of the areas of the outcomes included in the event. For instance, the probability of the event "having a score of 2 or 3" is equal to the sum of the areas of the second and third bars,

$$(1)(0.22) + (1)(0.28) = 0.22 + 0.28 = 0.50.$$

Interpretation You can see that the distribution is approximately symmetric.

▶ **Try It Yourself 2**

A company tracks the number of sales new employees make each day during a 100-day probationary period. The results for one new employee are shown at the left. Construct and graph a probability distribution.

a. *Find* the probability of each outcome.
b. *Organize* the probabilities in a probability distribution.
c. *Graph* the probability distribution using a histogram. *Answer: Page A38*

Probability Distribution

Days of rain, x	Probability, $P(x)$
0	0.216
1	0.432
2	0.288
3	0.064

PICTURING the WORLD

In a recent year in the United States, nearly 11 million traffic accidents were reported to the police. A histogram of traffic accidents for various age groups from 16 to 84 is shown. (Source: National Safety Council)

U.S. Traffic Accidents by Age

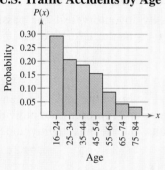

Estimate the probability that a randomly selected person involved in a traffic accident is in the 16 to 34 age group.

EXAMPLE 3

Verifying Probability Distributions

Verify that the distribution at the left (see page 193) is a probability distribution.

Solution If the distribution is a probability distribution, then (1) each probability is between 0 and 1, inclusive, and (2) the sum of the probabilities equals 1.

1. Each probability is between 0 and 1.

2. $\sum P(x) = 0.216 + 0.432 + 0.288 + 0.064$

$\qquad = 1.$

Interpretation Because both conditions are met, the distribution is a probability distribution.

▶ **Try It Yourself 3**

Verify that the distribution you constructed in Try It Yourself 2 is a probability distribution.

a. Verify that the *probability* of each outcome is between 0 and 1, inclusive.
b. Verify that the *sum* of all the probabilities is 1.
c. Make a *conclusion*.   *Answer: Page A38*

EXAMPLE 4

Probability Distributions

Decide whether each distribution is a probability distribution.

1.

x	5	6	7	8
$P(x)$	0.28	0.21	0.43	0.15

2.

x	1	2	3	4
$P(x)$	$\frac{1}{2}$	$\frac{1}{4}$	$\frac{5}{4}$	-1

Solution

1. Each probability is between 0 and 1, but the sum of the probabilities is 1.07, which is greater than 1. So, it is *not* a probability distribution.

2. The sum of the probabilities is equal to 1, but $P(3)$ and $P(4)$ are not between 0 and 1. So, it is *not* a probability distribution. Probabilities can never be negative or greater than 1.

▶ **Try It Yourself 4**

Decide whether the distribution is a probability distribution. Explain your reasoning.

1.

x	5	6	7	8
$P(x)$	$\frac{1}{16}$	$\frac{5}{8}$	$\frac{1}{4}$	$\frac{1}{16}$

2.

x	1	2	3	4
$P(x)$	0.09	0.36	0.49	0.06

a. Verify that the *probability* of each outcome is between 0 and 1.
b. Verify that the *sum* of all the probabilities is 1.
c. Make a *conclusion*.   *Answer: Page A38*

▶ Mean, Variance, and Standard Deviation

You can measure the center of a probability distribution with its mean and measure the variability with its variance and standard deviation. The mean of a discrete random variable is defined as follows.

MEAN OF A DISCRETE RANDOM VARIABLE

The **mean** of a discrete random variable is given by

$$\mu = \sum x P(x).$$

Each value of x is multiplied by its corresponding probability and the products are added.

The mean of the random variable represents the "theoretical average" of a probability experiment and sometimes is not a possible outcome. If the experiment were performed many thousands of times, the mean of all the outcomes would be close to the mean of the random variable.

x	$P(x)$
1	0.16
2	0.22
3	0.28
4	0.20
5	0.14

EXAMPLE 5

Finding the Mean of a Probability Distribution

The probability distribution for the personality inventory test for passive-aggressive traits discussed in Example 2 is given at the left. Find the mean score. What can you conclude?

Solution

Use a table to organize your work, as shown below. From the table, you can see that the mean score is approximately 2.9. A score of 3 represents an individual who exhibits neither passive nor aggressive traits. The mean is slightly under 3.

x	$P(x)$	$xP(x)$
1	0.16	$1(0.16) = 0.16$
2	0.22	$2(0.22) = 0.44$
3	0.28	$3(0.28) = 0.84$
4	0.20	$4(0.20) = 0.80$
5	0.14	$5(0.14) = 0.70$
	$\sum P(x) = 1$	$\sum xP(x) = 2.94$ ◀—— Mean

Interpretation   You can conclude that the mean personality trait is neither extremely passive nor extremely aggressive, but is slightly closer to passive.

▶ Try It Yourself 5

Find the mean of the probability distribution you constructed in Try It Yourself 2. What can you conclude?

a. *Find the product* of each random outcome and its corresponding probability.
b. *Find the sum* of the products.
c. *What* can you conclude?

Answer: Page A38

Study Tip

Notice that the mean in Example 5 is rounded to one decimal place. This rounding was done because the mean of a probability distribution should be rounded to one more decimal place than was used for the random variable x. This *round-off rule* is also used for the variance and standard deviation of a probability distribution.

Although the mean of the random variable of a probability distribution describes a typical outcome, it gives no information about how the outcomes vary. To study the variation of the outcomes, you can use the variance and standard deviation of the random variable of a probability distribution.

Study Tip

A shortcut formula for the variance of a probability distribution is

$$\sigma^2 = [\Sum x^2 P(x)] - \mu^2.$$

STANDARD DEVIATION OF A DISCRETE RANDOM VARIABLE

The **variance** of a discrete random variable is

$$\sigma^2 = \sum(x - \mu)^2 P(x).$$

The **standard deviation** is

$$\sigma = \sqrt{\sigma^2} = \sqrt{\sum(x - \mu)^2 P(x)}.$$

x	$P(x)$
1	0.16
2	0.22
3	0.28
4	0.20
5	0.14

EXAMPLE 6

Finding the Variance and Standard Deviation

The probability distribution for the personality inventory test for passive-aggressive traits discussed in Example 2 is given at the left. Find the variance and standard deviation of the probability distribution.

Solution   From Example 5, you know that before rounding, the mean of the distribution is $\mu = 2.94$. Use a table to organize your work, as shown below.

x	$P(x)$	$x - \mu$	$(x - \mu)^2$	$P(x)(x - \mu)^2$
1	0.16	−1.94	3.764	0.602
2	0.22	−0.94	0.884	0.194
3	0.28	0.06	0.004	0.001
4	0.20	1.06	1.124	0.225
5	0.14	2.06	4.244	0.594
	$\sum P(x) = 1$			$\sum P(x)(x - \mu)^2 = 1.616$

Variance

So, the variance is

$$\sigma^2 = 1.616 \approx 1.6$$

and the standard deviation is

$$\sigma = \sqrt{\sigma^2} = \sqrt{1.616} \approx 1.3.$$

Interpretation   Most of the data values differ from the mean by no more than 1.3 points.

▶ Try It Yourself 6

Find the variance and standard deviation for the probability distribution constructed in Try It Yourself 2.

a. *For each value of* x, *find the square* of the deviation from the mean and multiply that by the corresponding probability of x.
b. *Find the sum* of the products found in part (a) for the variance.
c. *Take the square root* of the variance for the standard deviation.
d. *Interpret* the results.   *Answer: Page A39*

▶ Expected Value

The mean of a random variable represents what you would expect to happen for thousands of trials. It is also called the *expected value*.

DEFINITION

The **expected value** of a discrete random variable is equal to the mean of the random variable.

$$\text{Expected Value} = E(x) = \mu = \sum xP(x)$$

Although probabilities can never be negative, the expected value of a random variable can be negative.

EXAMPLE 7

Finding an Expected Value

At a raffle, 1500 tickets are sold at $2 each for four prizes of $500, $250, $150, and $75. You buy one ticket. What is the expected value of your gain?

Solution

To find the gain for each prize, subtract the price of the ticket from the prize. For instance, your gain for the $500 prize is

$$\$500 - \$2 = \$498$$

and your gain for the $250 prize is

$$\$250 - \$2 = \$248.$$

Write a probability distribution for the possible gains (or outcomes).

Gain, x	$498	$248	$148	$73	$-\$2$
Probability, $P(x)$	$\frac{1}{1500}$	$\frac{1}{1500}$	$\frac{1}{1500}$	$\frac{1}{1500}$	$\frac{1496}{1500}$

Then, using the probability distribution, you can find the expected value.

$$E(x) = \sum xP(x)$$

$$= \$498 \cdot \frac{1}{1500} + \$248 \cdot \frac{1}{1500} + \$148 \cdot \frac{1}{1500} + \$73 \cdot \frac{1}{1500} + (-\$2) \cdot \frac{1496}{1500}$$

$$= -\$1.35$$

Interpretation Because the expected value is negative, you can expect to lose an average of $1.35 for each ticket you buy.

▶ Try It Yourself 7

At a raffle, 2000 tickets are sold at $5 each for five prizes of $2000, $1000, $500, $250, and $100. You buy one ticket. What is the expected value of your gain?

a. Find the *gain* for each prize.
b. Write a *probability distribution* for the possible gains.
c. Find the *expected value*.
d. *Interpret* the results.

Answer: Page A39

Insight

In most applications, an expected value of 0 has a practical interpretation. For instance, in gambling games, an expected value of 0 implies that a game is a fair game (an unlikely occurrence!). In a profit and loss analysis, an expected value of 0 represents the break-even point.

4.1 EXERCISES

■ Building Basic Skills and Vocabulary

1. What is a random variable? Give an example of a discrete random variable and a continuous random variable. Justify your answer.

2. What is a discrete probability distribution? What are the two conditions that determine a probability distribution?

3. The expected value of an accountant's profit and loss analysis is 0. Explain what this means.

4. What is the significance of the mean of a probability distribution?

True or False? *In Exercises 5–8, determine whether the statement is true or false. If it is false, rewrite it as a true statement.*

5. In most applications, continuous random variables represent counted data, while discrete random variables represent measured data.

6. For a random variable x the word *random* indicates that the value of x is determined by chance.

7. The mean of a random variable represents the "theoretical average" of a probability experiment and sometimes is not a possible outcome.

8. The expected value of a discrete random variable is equal to the standard deviation of the random variable.

Graphical Analysis *In Exercises 9–12, decide whether the graph represents a discrete random variable or a continuous random variable. Explain your reasoning.*

9. The home attendance for football games at a university

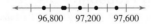

10. The length of time students use a computer each week

11. The annual vehicle-miles driven in the United States. *(Source: U.S. Federal Highway Administration)*

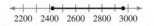

12. The annual traffic fatalities in the United States. *(Source: National Highway Traffic Safety Administration)*

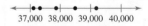

Distinguishing Between Discrete and Continuous Random Variables

In Exercises 13–20, decide whether the random variable x is discrete or continuous. Explain your reasoning.

13. x represents the number of motorcycle accidents in one year in California.

14. x represents the length of time it takes to get to work.

15. x represents the volume of blood drawn for a blood test.

16. x represents the number of rainy days in the month of July in Orlando, Florida.

17. x represents the number of home theater systems sold per month at an electronics store.

18. x represents the tension at which a randomly selected guitar's strings have been strung.

19. x represents the amount of snow (in inches) that fell in Nome, Alaska last winter.

20. x represents the total number of die rolls required for an individual to roll a five.

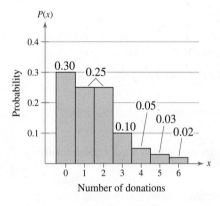

FIGURE FOR EXERCISE 21

FIGURE FOR EXERCISE 22

■ Using and Interpreting Concepts

21. Employee Testing A company gave psychological tests to prospective employees. The random variable x represents the possible test scores. Use the histogram to find the probability that a person selected at random from the survey's sample had a test score of (a) more than two and (b) less than four.

22. Blood Donations A survey asked a sample of people how many times they donate blood each year. The random variable x represents the number of donations for one year. Use the histogram to find the probability that a person selected at random from the survey's sample donated blood (a) more than once in a year and (b) less than three times in a year.

Determining a Missing Probability *In Exercises 23 and 24, determine the probability distribution's missing probability value.*

23. Dependent Children A sociologist surveyed the households in a small town. The random variable x represents the number of dependent children in the households.

x	0	1	2	3	4
$P(x)$	0.07	0.20	0.38	?	0.13

24. Dependent Children The sociologist in Exercise 23 surveyed the households in a neighboring town. The random variable x represents the number of dependent children in the households.

x	0	1	2	3	4	5	6
$P(x)$	0.05	?	0.23	0.21	0.17	0.11	0.08

Identifying Probability Distributions *In Exercises 25–28, decide whether the distribution is a probability distribution. If it is not a probability distribution, identify the property (or properties) that are not satisfied.*

25. Tires A mechanic checked the tire pressures on each car that he worked on for one week. The random variable x represents the number of tires that were underinflated.

x	0	1	2	3	4
$P(x)$	0.30	0.25	0.25	0.15	0.05

26. Phone Lines A company recorded the number of phone lines in use per hour during one work day. The random variable x represents the number of phone lines in use.

x	0	1	2	3	4	5	6
$P(x)$	0.135	0.186	0.226	0.254	0.103	0.64	0.032

27. Quality Control A quality inspector checked for imperfections in rolls of fabric for one week. The random variable x represents the number of imperfections found.

x	0	1	2	3	4	5
$P(x)$	$\frac{3}{4}$	$\frac{1}{10}$	$\frac{1}{20}$	$\frac{1}{25}$	$\frac{1}{50}$	$-\frac{1}{100}$

28. Golf Putts   A golf tournament director recorded the number of putts needed on a hole for the four rounds of a tournament. The random variable *x* represents the number of putts needed on the hole.

x	0	1	2	3	4	5
P(x)	0.007	0.292	0.394	0.245	0.058	0.004

Constructing Probability Distributions   *In Exercises 29–34, (a) use the frequency distribution to construct a probability distribution, find the (b) mean, (c) variance, and (d) standard deviation of the probability distribution, and (e) interpret the results in the context of the real-life situation.*

29. Dogs   The number of dogs per household in a small town

Dogs	0	1	2	3	4	5
Households	1491	425	168	48	29	14

30. Cats   The number of cats per household in a small town

Cats	0	1	2	3	4	5
Households	1941	349	203	78	57	40

31. Computers   The number of computers per household in a small town

Computers	0	1	2	3
Households	300	280	95	20

32. DVDs   The number of defects per batch of DVDs inspected

Defects	0	1	2	3	4	5
Batches	95	113	87	64	13	8

33. Overtime Hours   The number of overtime hours worked in one week per employee

Overtime hours	0	1	2	3	4	5	6
Employees	6	12	29	57	42	30	16

34. Extracurricular Activities   The number of school-related extracurricular activities per student

Activities	0	1	2	3	4	5	6	7
Students	19	39	52	57	68	41	27	17

Finding Expected Value   *In Exercises 35–40, use the probability distribution or histogram to find the (a) mean, (b) variance, (c) standard deviation, and (d) expected value of the probability distribution, and (e) interpret the results.*

35. Quiz   Students in a class take a quiz with eight questions. The number *x* of questions answered correctly can be approximated by the following probability distribution.

x	0	1	2	3	4	5	6	7	8
$P(x)$	0.02	0.02	0.06	0.06	0.08	0.22	0.30	0.16	0.08

36. 911 Calls   A 911 service center recorded the number of calls received per hour. The number of calls per hour for one week can be approximated by the following probability distribution.

x	0	1	2	3	4	5	6	7
$P(x)$	0.01	0.10	0.26	0.33	0.18	0.06	0.03	0.03

37. Hurricanes   The histogram shows the distribution of hurricanes that have hit the U.S. mainland by category, with 1 the weakest level and 5 the strongest. (*Source: National Hurricane Center*)

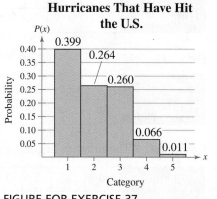

Hurricanes That Have Hit the U.S.

FIGURE FOR EXERCISE 37

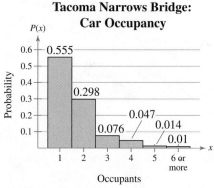

Tacoma Narrows Bridge: Car Occupancy

FIGURE FOR EXERCISE 38

38. Car Occupancy   The histogram shows the distribution of occupants in cars crossing the Tacoma Narrows Bridge in Washington each week. (*Adapted from Washington State Department of Transportation*)

39. Household Size   The histogram shows the distribution of household sizes in the United States for a recent year. (*Adapted from United States Census Bureau*)

40. Car Occupancy   The histogram shows the distribution of carpooling by the number of cars per household. (*Adapted from Federal Highway Administration*)

41. Finding Probabilities   Use the probability distribution you made for Exercise 29 to find the probability of randomly selecting a household that has (a) fewer than two dogs, (b) at least one dog, and (c) between one and three dogs, inclusive.

42. Finding Probabilities   Use the probability distribution you made for Exercise 31 to find the probability of randomly selecting a household that has (a) no computers, (b) at least one computer, and (c) between zero and two computers, inclusive.

43. Unusual Values   A person lives in a household with three dogs and claims that having three dogs is not unusual. Use the information in Exercise 29 to determine if this person is correct. Explain your reasoning.

44. Unusual Values   A person lives in a household with no computer and claims that not having a computer is not unusual. Use the information in Exercise 31 to determine if this person is correct. Explain your reasoning.

Games of Chance   *In Exercises 45 and 46, find the expected net gain to the player for one play of the game. If x is the net gain to a player in a game of chance, then E(x) is usually negative. This value gives the average amount per game the player can expect to lose.*

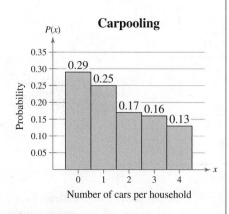

Size of Household

FIGURE FOR EXERCISE 39

Carpooling

FIGURE FOR EXERCISE 40

45. In American roulette, the wheel has the 38 numbers

$$00, 0, 1, 2, \ldots, 34, 35, \text{ and } 36$$

marked on equally spaced slots. If a player bets $1 on a number and wins, then the player keeps the dollar and receives an additional 35 dollars. Otherwise, the dollar is lost.

46. A charity organization is selling $4 raffle tickets as part of a fund-raising program. The first prize is a boat valued at $3150, and the second prize is a camping tent valued at $450. The remaining 15 prizes are $25 gift certificates. The number of tickets sold is 5000.

■ Extending Concepts

Linear Transformation of a Random Variable   *In Exercises 47 and 48, use the following information.*

*For a random variable x, a new random variable y can be created by applying a **linear transformation** $y = a + bx$, where a and b are constants. If the random variable x has mean μ_x and standard deviation σ_x, then the mean, variance, and standard deviation of y are given by the following formulas.*

$$\mu_y = a + b\mu_x \qquad \sigma_y{}^2 = b^2\sigma_x{}^2 \qquad \sigma_y = |b|\sigma_x$$

47. The mean annual salary for employees at a company is $36,000. At the end of the year, each employee receives a $1000 bonus and a 5% raise (based on salary). What is the new annual salary (including the bonus and raise) for the employees?

48. The mean annual salary for employees at a company is $36,000 with a variance of 15,202,201. At the end of the year, each employee receives a $2000 bonus and a 4% raise (based on salary). What is the standard deviation of the new salaries?

Independent and Dependent Random Variables   *Two random variables x and y are **independent** if the value of x does not affect the value of y. If the variables are not independent, they are **dependent**. A new random variable can be formed by finding the sum or difference of random variables. If a random variable x has mean μ_x and a random variable y has mean μ_y, then the mean of the sum and difference of the variables are given by the following equations.*

$$\mu_{x+y} = \mu_x + \mu_y \qquad\qquad \mu_{x-y} = \mu_x - \mu_y$$

If random variables are independent, then the variance and standard deviation of the sum or difference of the random variables can be found. So, if a random variable x has variance $\sigma^2{}_x$ and a random variable y has variance $\sigma^2{}_y$, then the variances of the sum and difference of the variables are given by the following equations. Note that the variance of the difference is the sum of the variances.

$$\sigma^2{}_{x+y} = \sigma^2{}_x + \sigma^2{}_y \qquad\qquad \sigma^2{}_{x-y} = \sigma^2{}_x + \sigma^2{}_y$$

In Exercises 49 and 50, the distribution of SAT scores for college-bound male seniors has mean of 1532 and a standard deviation of 312. The distribution of SAT scores for college-bound female seniors has a mean of 1506 and a standard deviation of 304. One male and one female are randomly selected. Assume their scores are independent. (Source: College Board Online)

49. What is the average sum of their scores? What is the average difference of their scores?

50. What is the standard deviation of the difference in their scores?

4.2 Binomial Distributions

What You SHOULD LEARN

▸ How to determine if a probability experiment is a binomial experiment

▸ How to find binomial probabilities using the binomial probability formula

▸ How to find binomial probabilities using technology, formulas, and a binomial probability table

▸ How to graph a binomial distribution

▸ How to find the mean, variance, and standard deviation of a binomial probability distribution

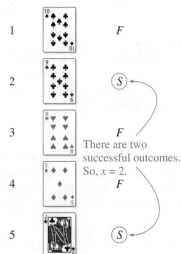

Binomial Experiments ▸ Binomial Probability Formula ▸ Finding Binomial Probabilities ▸ Graphing Binomial Distributions ▸ Mean, Variance, and Standard Deviation

▸ Binomial Experiments

There are many probability experiments for which the results of each trial can be reduced to two outcomes: success and failure. For instance, when a basketball player attempts a free throw, he or she either makes the basket or does not. Probability experiments such as these are called binomial experiments.

DEFINITION

A **binomial experiment** is a probability experiment that satisfies the following conditions.

1. The experiment is repeated for a fixed number of trials, where each trial is independent of the other trials.
2. There are only two possible outcomes of interest for each trial. The outcomes can be classified as a success (S) or as a failure (F).
3. The probability of a success $P(S)$ is the same for each trial.
4. The random variable x counts the number of successful trials.

NOTATION FOR BINOMIAL EXPERIMENTS

Symbol	Description
n	The number of times a trial is repeated
$p = P(S)$	The probability of success in a single trial
$q = P(F)$	The probability of failure in a single trial ($q = 1 - p$)
x	The random variable represents a count of the number of successes in n trials: $x = 0, 1, 2, 3, \ldots, n$.

Here is a simple example of a binomial experiment. From a standard deck of cards, you pick a card, note whether it is a club or not, and replace the card. You repeat the experiment five times, so $n = 5$. The outcomes for each trial can be classified in two categories: S = selecting a club and F = selecting another suit. The probabilities of success and failure are

$$p = P(S) = \frac{1}{4} \quad \text{and} \quad q = P(F) = \frac{3}{4}.$$

The random variable x represents the number of clubs selected in the five trials. So, the possible values of the random variable are

0, 1, 2, 3, 4, and 5.

For instance, if $x = 2$, then exactly two of the five cards are clubs and the other three are not clubs. An example of an experiment with $x = 2$ is shown at the left. Note that x is a discrete random variable because its possible values can be listed.

Trial Outcome   S or F?

Trial	Outcome	S or F?
1		F
2		S
3		F
4		F
5		S

There are two successful outcomes. So, $x = 2$.

PICTURING the WORLD

A recent survey of vehicle owners in the United States asked whether they have cut back on any products or services because of the increase in gas prices. The respondents' answers were either yes or no. (Source: Harris Interactive)

Survey question: Have you cut back on any products or services in order to pay the increased price of gasoline?

Yes 44%
No 56%

Why is this a binomial experiment? Identify the probability of success, p. Identify the probability of failure, q.

EXAMPLE 1

Binomial Experiments

Decide whether the experiment is a binomial experiment. If it is, specify the values of n, p, and q, and list the possible values of the random variable x. If it is not, explain why.

1. A certain surgical procedure has an 85% chance of success. A doctor performs the procedure on eight patients. The random variable represents the number of successful surgeries.

2. A jar contains five red marbles, nine blue marbles, and six green marbles. You randomly select three marbles from the jar, *without replacement*. The random variable represents the number of red marbles.

Solution

1. The experiment is a binomial experiment because it satisfies the four conditions of a binomial experiment. In the experiment, each surgery represents one trial. There are eight surgeries, and each surgery is independent of the others. There are only two possible outcomes for each surgery—either the surgery is a success or it is a failure. Also, the probability of success for each surgery is 0.85. Finally, the random variable x represents the number of successful surgeries.

$$n = 8$$
$$p = 0.85$$
$$q = 1 - 0.85 = 0.15$$
$$x = 0, 1, 2, 3, 4, 5, 6, 7, 8$$

2. The experiment is not a binomial experiment because it does not satisfy all four conditions of a binomial experiment. In the experiment, each marble selection represents one trial, and selecting a red marble is a success. When the first marble is selected, the probability of success is 5/20. However, because the marble is not replaced, the probability of success for subsequent trials is no longer 5/20. So, the trials are not independent, and the probability of a success is not the same for each trial.

▶ Try It Yourself 1

Decide whether the following is a binomial experiment. If it is, specify the values of n, p, and q, and list the possible values of the random variable x. If it is not, explain why.

You take a multiple-choice quiz that consists of 10 questions. Each question has four possible answers, only one of which is correct. To complete the quiz, you randomly guess the answer to each question. The random variable represents the number of correct answers.

a. Identify a *trial* of the experiment and what is a "success."
b. Decide if the experiment *satisfies the four conditions* of a binomial experiment.
c. *Make a conclusion* and *identify n, p, q,* and the possible values of *x*.

Answer: Page A39

▶ Binomial Probability Formula

There are several ways to find the probability of x successes in n trials of a binomial experiment. One way is to use a tree diagram and the Multiplication Rule. Another way is to use the binomial probability formula.

BINOMIAL PROBABILITY FORMULA

In a binomial experiment, the probability of exactly x successes in n trials is

$$P(x) = {}_nC_x\, p^x q^{n-x} = \frac{n!}{(n-x)!\,x!}\, p^x q^{n-x}.$$

EXAMPLE 2

Finding Binomial Probabilities

Microfracture knee surgery has a 75% chance of success on patients with degenerative knees. The surgery is performed on three patients. Find the probability of the surgery being successful on exactly two patients. *(Source: Illinois Orthopaedic and Sportsmedicine Centers)*

Solution

Method 1: Draw a tree diagram and use the Multiplication Rule.

1st Surgery	2nd Surgery	3rd Surgery	Outcome	Number of Successes	Probability
S	S	S	SSS	3	$\frac{3}{4} \cdot \frac{3}{4} \cdot \frac{3}{4} = \frac{27}{64}$
		F	SSF	2	$\frac{3}{4} \cdot \frac{3}{4} \cdot \frac{1}{4} = \frac{9}{64}$
	F	S	SFS	2	$\frac{3}{4} \cdot \frac{1}{4} \cdot \frac{3}{4} = \frac{9}{64}$
		F	SFF	1	$\frac{3}{4} \cdot \frac{1}{4} \cdot \frac{1}{4} = \frac{3}{64}$
F	S	S	FSS	2	$\frac{1}{4} \cdot \frac{3}{4} \cdot \frac{3}{4} = \frac{9}{64}$
		F	FSF	1	$\frac{1}{4} \cdot \frac{3}{4} \cdot \frac{1}{4} = \frac{3}{64}$
	F	S	FFS	1	$\frac{1}{4} \cdot \frac{1}{4} \cdot \frac{3}{4} = \frac{3}{64}$
		F	FFF	0	$\frac{1}{4} \cdot \frac{1}{4} \cdot \frac{1}{4} = \frac{1}{64}$

There are three outcomes that have exactly two successes, and each has a probability of $\frac{9}{64}$. So, the probability of a successful surgery on exactly two patients is $3\left(\frac{9}{64}\right) \approx 0.422$.

Method 2: Use the binomial probability formula.

In this binomial experiment, the values for n, p, q, and x are $n = 3$, $p = \frac{3}{4}$, $q = \frac{1}{4}$, and $x = 2$. The probability of exactly two successful surgeries is

$$P(2 \text{ successful surgeries}) = \frac{3!}{(3-2)!\,2!}\left(\frac{3}{4}\right)^2\left(\frac{1}{4}\right)^1$$

$$= 3\left(\frac{9}{16}\right)\left(\frac{1}{4}\right) = 3\left(\frac{9}{64}\right) = \frac{27}{64} \approx 0.422.$$

▶ Try It Yourself 2

A card is selected from a standard deck and replaced. This experiment is repeated a total of five times. Find the probability of selecting exactly three clubs.

a. *Identify* a trial, a success, and a failure.
b. *Identify* n, p, q, and x.
c. Use the *binomial probability formula*.

Answer: Page A39

By listing the possible values of x with the corresponding probability of each, you can construct a **binomial probability distribution.**

EXAMPLE 3

Constructing a Binomial Distribution

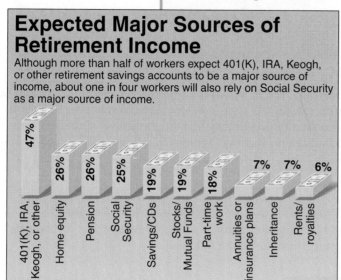

Expected Major Sources of Retirement Income

Although more than half of workers expect 401(K), IRA, Keogh, or other retirement savings accounts to be a major source of income, about one in four workers will also rely on Social Security as a major source of income.

47% | 26% | 26% | 25% | 19% | 19% | 18% | 7% | 7% | 6%

401(K), IRA, Keogh, or other | Home equity | Pension | Social Security | Savings/CDs | Stocks/ Mutual Funds | Part-time work | Annuities or insurance plans | Inheritance | Rents/ royalties

(Source: The Gallup Organization)

In a survey, workers in the United States were asked to name their expected sources of retirement income. The results are shown in the graph. Seven workers who participated in the survey are randomly selected and asked whether they expect to rely on Social Security for retirement income. Create a binomial probability distribution for the number of workers who respond yes.

x	$P(x)$
0	0.1335
1	0.3115
2	0.3115
3	0.1730
4	0.0577
5	0.0115
6	0.0013
7	0.0001
	$\Sigma P(x) = 1$

Solution

From the graph, you can see that 25% of working Americans expect to rely on Social Security for retirement income. So, $p = 0.25$ and $q = 0.75$. Because $n = 7$, the possible values of x are 0, 1, 2, 3, 4, 5, 6, and 7.

$$P(0) = {}_7C_0(0.25)^0(0.75)^7 = 1(0.25)^0(0.75)^7 \approx 0.1335$$

$$P(1) = {}_7C_1(0.25)^1(0.75)^6 = 7(0.25)^1(0.75)^6 \approx 0.3115$$

$$P(2) = {}_7C_2(0.25)^2(0.75)^5 = 21(0.25)^2(0.75)^5 \approx 0.3115$$

$$P(3) = {}_7C_3(0.25)^3(0.75)^4 = 35(0.25)^3(0.75)^4 \approx 0.1730$$

$$P(4) = {}_7C_4(0.25)^4(0.75)^3 = 35(0.25)^4(0.75)^3 \approx 0.0577$$

$$P(5) = {}_7C_5(0.25)^5(0.75)^2 = 21(0.25)^5(0.75)^2 \approx 0.0115$$

$$P(6) = {}_7C_6(0.25)^6(0.75)^1 = 7(0.25)^6(0.75)^1 \approx 0.0013$$

$$P(7) = {}_7C_7(0.25)^7(0.75)^0 = 1(0.25)^7(0.75)^0 \approx 0.0001$$

Notice in the table at the left that all the probabilities are between 0 and 1 and that the sum of the probabilities is $1.0001 \approx 1$.

▶ Try It Yourself 3

Seven workers who participated in the survey are randomly selected and asked whether they expect to rely on a pension for retirement income. Create a binomial distribution for the number of retirees who respond yes.

a. *Identify* a trial, a success, and a failure.
b. *Identify* n, p, q, and possible values for x.
c. Use the *binomial probability formula* for each value of x.
d. *Use a table* to show that the properties of a probability distribution are satisfied.

Answer: Page A39

Study Tip

When probabilities are rounded to a fixed number of decimal places, the sum of the probabilities may differ slightly from 1.

▶ Finding Binomial Probabilities

In Examples 2 and 3 you used the binomial probability formula to find the probabilities. A more efficient way to find binomial probabilities is to use a calculator or a computer. For instance, you can find binomial probabilities using MINITAB, Excel, and the TI-83/84.

EXAMPLE 4

Finding a Binomial Probability Using Technology

The results of a recent survey indicate that when grilling, 59% of households in the United States use a gas grill. If you randomly select 100 households, what is the probability that exactly 65 households use a gas grill? Use a technology tool to find the probability. *(Source: Greenfield Online for Weber-Stephens Products Company)*

Solution

MINITAB, Excel, and the TI-83/84 each have features that allow you to find binomial probabilities automatically. Try using these technologies. You should obtain results similar to the following.

MINITAB

Probability Distribution Function

Binomial with n = 100 and p = 0.590000

x	P(X=x)
65.00	0.0391072

TI-83/84

binompdf(100,.59,65)
.0391071795

EXCEL

	A	B	C	D
1	BINOMDIST(65,100,0.59,FALSE)			
2				0.039107

From the displays, you can see that the probability that exactly 65 households use a gas grill is about 0.04.

▶ Try It Yourself 4

The results of a recent survey indicate that 71% of people in the United States use more than one topping on their hot dogs. If you randomly select 250 people, what is the probability that exactly 178 of them will use more than one topping? Use a technology tool to find the probability. *(Source: ICR Survey Research Group for Hebrew International)*

a. *Identify* n, p, and x.
b. *Calculate* the binomial probability.
c. *Write* the result as a sentence.

Answer: Page A39

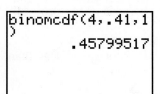

Using a TI-83/84, you can find the probability automatically.

Study Tip

The complement of "x is at least 2" is "x is less than 2." So, another way to find the probability in part (3) is

$$P(x < 2) = 1 - P(x \geq 2)$$
$$\approx 1 - 0.542$$
$$= 0.458.$$

binomcdf(4,.41,1
)
        .45799517

The cumulative density function (CDF) computes the probability of "x or fewer" successes. The CDF adds the areas for the given x-value and all those to its left.

EXAMPLE 5

Finding Binomial Probabilities Using Formulas

A survey indicates that 41% of women in the United States consider reading their favorite leisure-time activity. You randomly select four U.S. women and ask them if reading is their favorite leisure-time activity. Find the probability that (1) exactly two of them respond yes, (2) at least two of them respond yes, and (3) fewer than two of them respond yes. *(Source: Louis Harris & Associates)*

Solution

1. Using $n = 4$, $p = 0.41$, $q = 0.59$, and $x = 2$, the probability that exactly two women will respond yes is

$$P(2) = {}_4C_2(0.41)^2(0.59)^2 = 6(0.41)^2(0.59)^2 \approx 0.351.$$

2. To find the probability that at least two women will respond yes, find the sum of $P(2)$, $P(3)$, and $P(4)$.

$$P(2) = {}_4C_2(0.41)^2(0.59)^2 = 6(0.41)^2(0.59)^2 \approx 0.351094$$
$$P(3) = {}_4C_3(0.41)^3(0.59)^1 = 4(0.41)^3(0.59)^1 \approx 0.162654$$
$$P(4) = {}_4C_4(0.41)^4(0.59)^0 = 1(0.41)^4(0.59)^0 \approx 0.028258$$

So, the probability that at least two will respond yes is

$$P(x \geq 2) = P(2) + P(3) + P(4)$$
$$\approx 0.351094 + 0.162654 + 0.028258$$
$$\approx 0.542.$$

3. To find the probability that fewer than two women will respond yes, find the sum of $P(0)$ and $P(1)$.

$$P(0) = {}_4C_0(0.41)^0(0.59)^4 = 1(0.41)^0(0.59)^4 \approx 0.121174$$
$$P(1) = {}_4C_1(0.41)^1(0.59)^3 = 4(0.41)^1(0.59)^3 \approx 0.336822$$

So, the probability that fewer than two will respond yes is

$$P(x < 2) = P(0) + P(1)$$
$$\approx 0.121174 + 0.336822$$
$$\approx 0.458.$$

▶ Try It Yourself 5

A survey indicates that 21% of men in the United States consider fishing their favorite leisure-time activity. You randomly select five U.S. men and ask them if fishing is their favorite leisure-time activity. Find the probability that (1) exactly two of them respond yes, (2) at least two of them respond yes, and (3) fewer than two of them respond yes. *(Source: Louis Harris & Associates)*

a. Determine the appropriate *values of x* for each situation.
b. Find the *binomial probability* for each value of x. Then find the sum, if necessary.
c. *Write* the result as a sentence.

Answer: Page A39

Finding binomial probabilities with the binomial probability formula can be a tedious process. To make this process easier, you can use a binomial probability table. Table 2 in Appendix B lists the binomial probability for selected values of n and p.

EXAMPLE 6

Finding a Binomial Probability Using a Table

About thirty percent of working adults spend less than 15 minutes each way commuting to their jobs. You randomly select six working adults. What is the probability that exactly three of them spend less than 15 minutes each way commuting to work? Use a table to find the probability. *(Source: U.S. Census Bureau)*

Solution A portion of Table 2 in Appendix B is shown here. Using the distribution for $n = 6$ and $p = 0.3$, you can find the probability that $x = 3$, as shown by the highlighted areas in the table.

								p						
n	***x***	**.01**	**.05**	**.10**	**.15**	**.20**	**.25**	**.30**	**.35**	**.40**	**.45**	**.50**	**.55**	**.60**
2	0	.980	.902	.810	.723	.640	.563	.490	.423	.360	.303	.250	.203	.160
	1	.020	.095	.180	.255	.320	.375	.420	.455	.480	.495	.500	.495	.480
	2	.000	.002	.010	.023	.040	.063	.090	.123	.160	.203	.250	.303	.360
3	0	.970	.857	.729	.614	.512	.422	.343	.275	.216	.166	.125	.091	.064
	1	.029	.135	.243	.325	.384	.422	.441	.444	.432	.408	.375	.334	.288
	2	.000	.007	.027	.057	.096	.141	.189	.239	.288	.334	.375	.408	.432
	3	.000	.000	.001	.003	.008	.016	.027	.043	.064	.091	.125	.166	.216
6	0	.941	.735	.531	.377	.262	.178	.118	.075	.047	.028	.016	.008	.004
	1	.057	.232	.354	.399	.393	.356	.303	.244	.187	.136	.094	.061	.037
	2	.001	.031	.098	.176	.246	.297	.324	.328	.311	.278	.234	.186	.138
	3	.000	.002	.015	.042	.082	.132	.185	.236	.276	.303	.312	.303	.276
	4	.000	.000	.001	.006	.015	.033	.060	.095	.138	.186	.234	.278	.311
	5	.000	.000	.000	.000	.002	.004	.010	.020	.037	.061	.094	.136	.187
	6	.000	.000	.000	.000	.000	.000	.001	.002	.004	.008	.016	.028	.047

To explore this topic further, see Activity 4.2 on page 220.

So, the probability that exactly three of the six workers spend less than 15 minutes each way commuting to work is 0.185.

▶ Try It Yourself 6

Forty-five percent of all small businesses in the United States have a Web site. If you randomly select 10 small businesses, what is the probability that exactly four of them have a Web site? Use a table to find the probability. *(Source: Hewlett-Packard Company)*

a. *Identify* a trial, a success, and a failure.
b. Identify n, p, and x.
c. *Use Table 2* in Appendix B to find the binomial probability.
d. *Write* the result as a sentence. *Answer: Page A39*

▶ Graphing Binomial Distributions

In Section 4.1, you learned how to graph discrete probability distributions. Because a binomial distribution is a discrete probability distribution, you can use the same process.

EXAMPLE 7

Graphing a Binomial Distribution

Fifty-nine percent of households in the United States subscribe to cable TV. You randomly select six households and ask each if they subscribe to cable TV. Construct a probability distribution for the random variable x. Then graph the distribution. *(Source: Kagan Research, LLC)*

Solution

To construct the binomial distribution, find the probability for each value of x. Using $n = 6$, $p = 0.59$, and $q = 0.41$, you can obtain the following.

x	0	1	2	3	4	5	6
$P(x)$	0.005	0.041	0.148	0.283	0.306	0.176	0.042

You can graph the probability distribution using a histogram as shown below.

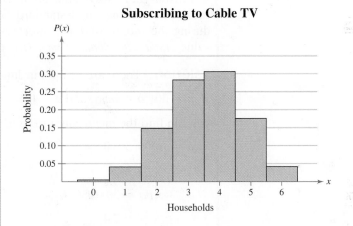

Subscribing to Cable TV

Interpretation   From the histogram, you can see that it would be unusual if none or only one of the households subscribes to cable TV because of the low probabilities.

▶ Try It Yourself 7

Sixty-two percent of households in the United States own a computer. You randomly select six households and ask if they own a computer. Construct a probability distribution for the random variable x. Then graph the distribution. *(Source: U.S. Department of Commerce)*

a. *Find* the binomial probability for each value of the random variable x.
b. *Organize* the values of x and their corresponding probability in a binomial distribution.
c. Use a histogram to *graph* the binomial distribution.

Answer: Page A40

Notice in Example 7 that the histogram is skewed left. The graph of a binomial distribution with $p > 0.5$ is skewed left, whereas the graph of a binomial distribution with $p < 0.5$ is skewed right. The graph of a binomial distribution with $p = 0.5$ is symmetric.

Recall that if a probability is 0.05 or less, it is typically considered unusual.

▶ Mean, Variance, and Standard Deviation

Although you can use the formulas learned in Section 4.1 for mean, variance, and standard deviation of a discrete probability distribution, the properties of a binomial distribution enable you to use much simpler formulas.

POPULATION PARAMETERS OF A BINOMIAL DISTRIBUTION

Mean: $\mu = np$

Variance: $\sigma^2 = npq$

Standard deviation: $\sigma = \sqrt{npq}$

EXAMPLE 8

Finding and Interpreting Mean, Variance, and Standard Deviation

In Pittsburgh, Pennsylvania, about 56% of the days in a year are cloudy. Find the mean, variance, and standard deviation for the number of cloudy days during the month of June. Interpret the results and determine any unusual values. *(Source: National Climatic Data Center)*

Solution   There are 30 days in June. Using

$n = 30$, $p = 0.56$, and $q = 0.44$

you can find the mean, variance, and standard deviation as shown below.

$$\mu = np = 30 \cdot 0.56$$
$$= 16.8$$
$$\sigma^2 = npq = 30 \cdot 0.56 \cdot 0.44$$
$$\approx 7.4$$
$$\sigma = \sqrt{npq} = \sqrt{30 \cdot 0.56 \cdot 0.44}$$
$$\approx 2.7$$

Interpretation   On average, there are 16.8 cloudy days during the month of June. The standard deviation is about 2.7 days. Values that are more than two standard deviations from the mean are considered unusual. Because $16.8 - 2(2.7) = 11.4$, a June with 11 cloudy days would be unusual. Similarly, because $16.8 + 2(2.7) = 22.2$, a June with 23 cloudy days would also be unusual.

▶ Try It Yourself 8

In San Francisco, California, 44% of the days in a year are clear. Find the mean, variance, and standard deviation for the number of clear days during the month of May. Interpret the results and determine any unusual values. *(Source: National Climatic Data Center)*

a. *Identify* a success and the values of n, p, and q.
b. *Find the product* of n and p to calculate the mean.
c. *Find the product* of n, p, and q for the variance.
d. *Find the square root* of the variance for the standard deviation.
e. *Interpret* the results.

Answer: Page A40

4.2 EXERCISES

■ Building Basic Skills and Vocabulary

Graphical Analysis   *In Exercises 1 and 2, match the given probabilities with the correct graph. The histograms each represent binomial distributions. Each distribution has the same number of trials n but different probabilities of success p.*

1. $p = 0.20$, $p = 0.50$, $p = 0.80$

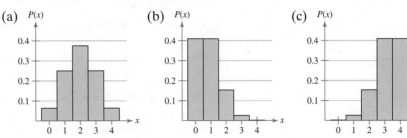

2. $p = 0.25$, $p = 0.50$, $p = 0.75$

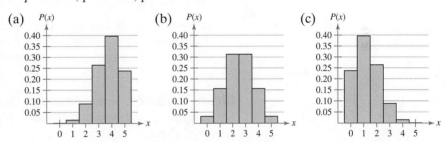

Graphical Analysis   *In Exercises 3 and 4, match the given values of n with the correct graph. Each histogram shown represents part of a binomial distribution. Each distribution has the same probability of success p but different numbers of trials n. What happens as the value of n increases and the probability of success remains the same?*

3. $n = 4$, $n = 8$, $n = 12$

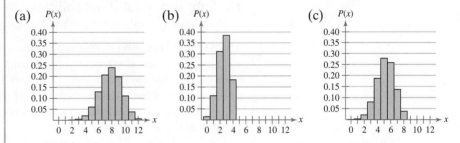

4. $n = 5$, $n = 10$, $n = 15$

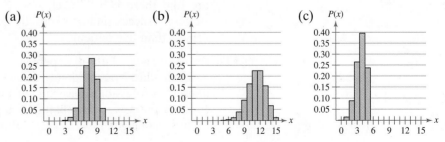

5. Identify the unusual values of x in each histogram in Exercise 2.

6. Identify the unusual values of x in each histogram in Exercise 4.

Identifying and Understanding Binomial Experiments *In Exercises 7–10, decide whether the experiment is a binomial experiment. If it is, identify a success, specify the values of n, p, and q, and list the possible values of the random variable x. If it is not a binomial experiment, explain why.*

7. **Cyanosis** Cyanosis is the condition of having bluish skin due to insufficient oxygen in the blood. About 80% of babies born with cyanosis recover fully. A hospital is caring for five babies born with cyanosis. The random variable represents the number of babies that recover fully. *(Source: The World Book Encyclopedia)*

8. **Clothing Store Purchases** From past records, a clothing store finds that 26% of the people who enter the store will make a purchase. During a one-hour period, 18 people enter the store. The random variable represents the number of people who do not make a purchase.

9. **Political Polls** A survey asks 1000 adults, "Do tax cuts help or hurt the economy?" Twenty-one percent of those surveyed said tax cuts hurt the economy. Fifteen adults who participated in the survey are randomly selected. The random variable represents the number of adults who think tax cuts hurt the economy. *(Source: Rasmussen Reports)*

10. **Lottery** A state lottery randomly chooses 6 balls numbered from 1 to 40. You choose six numbers and purchase a lottery ticket. The random variable represents the number of matches on your ticket to the numbers drawn in the lottery.

Mean, Variance, and Standard Deviation *In Exercises 11–14, find the mean, variance, and standard deviation of the binomial distribution with the given values of n and p.*

11. $n = 80, p = 0.3$

12. $n = 64, p = 0.85$

13. $n = 124, p = 0.26$

14. $n = 316, p = 0.72$

■ Using and Interpreting Concepts

Finding Binomial Probabilities *In Exercises 15–24, find the indicated probabilities. If convenient, use technology to find the probabilities.*

15. **Answer Guessing** You are taking a multiple-choice quiz that consists of five questions. Each question has four possible answers, only one of which is correct. To complete the quiz, you randomly guess the answer to each question. Find the probability of guessing (a) exactly three answers correctly, (b) at least three answers correctly, and (c) less than three answers correctly.

16. **Surgery Success** A surgical technique is performed on seven patients. You are told there is a 70% chance of success. Find the probability that the surgery is successful for (a) exactly five patients, (b) at least five patients, and (c) less than five patients.

17. **Baseball Fans** Fifty-nine percent of men consider themselves professional baseball fans. You randomly select 10 men and ask each if he considers himself a professional baseball fan. Find the probability that the number who consider themselves baseball fans is (a) exactly eight, (b) at least eight, and (c) less than eight. *(Source: Gallup Poll)*

18. **Favorite Cookie**   Ten percent of adults say oatmeal raisin is their favorite cookie. You randomly select 12 adults and ask each to name his or her favorite cookie. Find the probability that the number who say oatmeal raisin is their favorite cookie is (a) exactly four, (b) at least four, and (c) less than four. *(Source: WEAREVER)·*

19. **Vacation Purpose**   Twenty-one percent of vacationers say the primary purpose of their vacation is outdoor recreation. You randomly select 10 vacationers and ask each to name the primary purpose of his or her vacation. Find the probability that the number who say outdoor recreation is the primary purpose of their vacation is (a) exactly three, (b) more than three, and (c) at most three. *(Source: Travel Industry Association)*

20. **Honeymoon Financing**   Seventy percent of married couples paid for their honeymoon themselves. You randomly select 20 married couples and ask each if they paid for their honeymoon themselves. Find the probability that the number of couples who say they paid for their honeymoon themselves is (a) exactly one, (b) more than one, and (c) at most one. *(Source: Bride's Magazine)*

21. **Favorite Nut**   Fifty-five percent of adults say cashews are their favorite kind of nut. You randomly select 12 adults and ask each to name his or her favorite nut. Find the probability that the number who say cashews are their favorite nut is (a) exactly three, (b) at least four, and (c) at most two. *(Source: Harris Interactive)*

22. **Retirement**   Fourteen percent of workers believe they will need less than $250,000 when they retire. You randomly select 10 workers and ask each how much money he or she thinks they will need for retirement. Find the probability that the number of workers who say they will need less than $250,000 when they retire is (a) exactly two, (b) more than six, and (c) at most five. *(Source: Retirement Corporation of America)*

23. **Credit Cards**   Twenty-eight percent of college students say they use credit cards because of the rewards program. You randomly select 10 college students and ask each to name the reason he or she uses credit cards. Find the probability that the number of college students who say they use credit cards because of the rewards program is (a) exactly two, (b) more than two, and (c) between two and five inclusive. *(Source: Experience.com)*

24. **Career Advancement**   Twenty-four percent of executives say that older workers have blocked their career advancement. You randomly select 12 executives and ask if they feel that older workers have blocked their career advancement. Find the probability that the number who say older workers have blocked their career advancement is (a) exactly four, (b) more than four, and (c) between four and eight inclusive. *(Source: Korn/Ferry International)*

Constructing Binomial Distributions   *In Exercises 25–28, (a) construct a binomial distribution, (b) graph the binomial distribution using a histogram, (c) describe the shape of the histogram, find the (d) mean, (e) variance, and (f) standard deviation of the binomial distribution, and (g) interpret the results in the context of the real-life situation. What values of the random variable x would you consider unusual? Explain your reasoning.*

25. **Women Baseball Fans**   Thirty-seven percent of women consider themselves fans of professional baseball. You randomly select six women and ask each if she considers herself a fan of professional baseball. *(Source: Gallup Poll)*

26. No Trouble Sleeping One in four adults says he or she has no trouble sleeping at night. You randomly select five adults and ask each if he or she has no trouble sleeping at night. *(Source: Marist Institute for Public Opinion)*

27. Blood Donors Five percent of people in the United States eligible to donate blood actually do. You randomly select four eligible blood donors and ask if they donate blood. *(Adapted from American Association of Blood Banks)*

28. Blood Types Thirty-eight percent of people in the United States have type O^+ blood. You randomly select five Americans and ask them if their blood type is O^+. *(Source: American Association of Blood Banks)*

29. Road Rage The graph shows the results of a survey of drivers who were asked to name the most annoying habit of other drivers. You randomly select six people who participated in the survey and ask each one of them to name the most annoying habit of other drivers. Let x represent the number who named talking on cell phones as the most annoying habit. *(Source: Hagerty Insurance)*

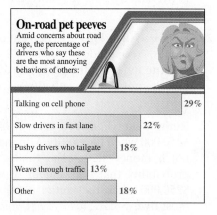

On-road pet peeves
Amid concerns about road rage, the percentage of drivers who say these are the most annoying behaviors of others:

Talking on cell phone	29%
Slow drivers in fast lane	22%
Pushy drivers who tailgate	18%
Weave through traffic	13%
Other	18%

(a) Construct a binomial distribution.

(b) Find the probability that exactly two people will name "talking on cell phones."

(c) Find the probability that at least five people will name "talking on cell phones."

30. Small-Business Owners The graph shows the results of a survey of small-business owners who were asked which business skills they would like to develop further. You randomly select five owners who participated in the survey and ask each one of them which business skills he or she wants to develop further. Let x represent the number who said financial management was the skill they wanted to develop further. *(Source: American Express)*

Small-business owners want better customer service skills
Which business skills would you like to develop further? Top responses:

Customer service	63%
Marketing/sales	58%
Financial management	48%
Decision making	40%
Negotiation	30%

Note: Multiple responses allowed
Source: OPEN from American Express Small Business Monitor survey of 625 small-business owners with fewer than 100 employees.
Margin of error ±4 percentage points.

(a) Construct a binomial distribution.

(b) Find the probability that exactly two owners will say "financial management."

(c) Find the probability that fewer than four owners will say "financial management."

31. Writing   Find the mean and standard deviation of the binomial distribution in Exercise 29 and interpret the results in the context of the real-life situation. What values of x would you consider unusual? Explain your reasoning.

32. Writing   Find the mean and standard deviation of the binomial distribution in Exercise 30 and interpret the results in the context of the real-life situation. What values of x would you consider unusual? Explain your reasoning.

■ Extending Concepts

Multinomial Experiments   *In Exercises 33 and 34, use the following information.*

A **multinomial experiment** is a probability experiment that satisfies the following conditions.

1. The experiment is repeated a fixed number of times n where each trial is independent of the other trials.

2. Each trial has k possible mutually exclusive outcomes: $E_1, E_2, E_3, \ldots, E_k$.

3. Each outcome has a fixed probability. Therefore, $P(E_1) = p_1$, $P(E_2) = p_2$, $P(E_3) = p_3, \ldots, P(E_k) = p_k$. The sum of the probabilities for all outcomes is

$$p_1 + p_2 + p_3 + \cdots + p_k = 1.$$

4. x_1 is the number of times E_1 will occur; x_2 is the number of times E_2 will occur; x_3 is the number of times E_3 will occur; and so on.

5. The discrete random variable x counts the number of times $x_1, x_2, x_3, \ldots, x_k$ occurs in n independent trials where

$$x_1 + x_2 + x_3 + \cdots + x_k = n.$$

The probability that x will occur is

$$P(x) = \frac{n!}{x_1!x_2!x_3! \cdots x_k!} \, p_1{}^{x_1} p_2{}^{x_2} p_3{}^{x_3} \cdots p_k{}^{x_k}.$$

33. Genetics   According to a theory in genetics, if tall and colorful plants are crossed with short and colorless plants, four types of plants will result: tall and colorful, tall and colorless, short and colorful, and short and colorless, with corresponding probabilities of $\frac{9}{16}$, $\frac{3}{16}$, $\frac{3}{16}$, and $\frac{1}{16}$. If 10 plants are selected, find the probability that five will be tall and colorful, two will be tall and colorless, two will be short and colorful, and one will be short and colorless.

34. Genetics   Another proposed theory in genetics gives the corresponding probabilities for the four types of plants described as $\frac{5}{16}$, $\frac{4}{16}$, $\frac{1}{16}$, and $\frac{6}{16}$. If 10 plants are selected, find the probability that five will be tall and colorful, two will be tall and colorless, two will be short and colorful, and one will be short and colorless.

APPLET

The *binomial distribution* applet allows you to simulate values from a binomial distribution. You can specify the parameters for the binomial distribution (*n* and *p*) and the number of values to be simulated (N). When you click SIMULATE, N values from the specified binomial distribution will be plotted to the right. The frequency of each outcome is shown in the plot.

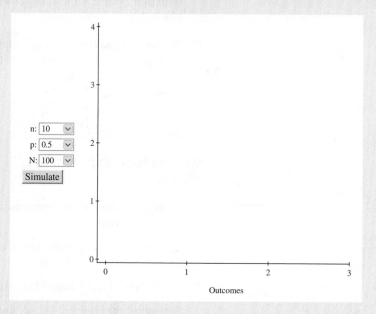

■ Explore

Step 1 Specify a value of n.
Step 2 Specify a value of p.
Step 3 Specify a value of N.
Step 4 Click SIMULATE.

■ Draw Conclusions

APPLET

1. During a Presidential election year, 70% of a county's eligible voters actually vote. Simulate selecting $n = 10$ eligible voters $N = 10$ times (for 10 of the communities in the county). Use the results of the simulation to estimate the probability that the number who voted in this election is (a) exactly 5, (b) at least 8, and (c) at most 7.

2. During a non-Presidential election year, 20% of the eligible voters in the same county as in Exercise 1 actually vote. Simulate selecting $n = 10$ eligible voters $N = 10$ times (for 10 of the communities in the county). Use the results of the simulation to estimate the probability that the number who voted in this election is (a) exactly 4, (b) at least 5, and (c) less than 4.

3. Suppose in Exercise 1 you select $n = 10$ eligible voters $N = 100$ times. Estimate the probability that the number who voted in this election is exactly 5. Compare this result to the result in Exercise 1 part a. Which of these is closer to the probability found using the binomial probability formula?

CASE STUDY

Binomial Distribution of Airplane Accidents

The Air Transport Association of America (ATA) is a support organization for the principal U.S. airlines. Some of the ATA's activities include promoting the air transport industry and conducting industry-wide studies.

The ATA also keeps statistics about commercial airline flights, including those that involve accidents. From 1977 through 2006 for aircraft with 10 or more seats, there were 91 fatal commercial airplane accidents involving U.S. airlines. The distribution of these accidents is shown in the histogram at the right.

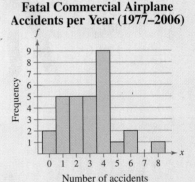

Fatal Commercial Airplane Accidents per Year (1977–2006)

Year	1977	1978	1979	1980	1981	1982	1983	1984	1985	1986	1987	1988	1989	1990	1991
Accidents	3	5	4	0	4	4	4	1	4	2	4	3	8	6	4

Year	1992	1993	1994	1995	1996	1997	1998	1999	2000	2001	2002	2003	2004	2005	2006
Accidents	4	1	4	1	3	3	1	2	2	6	0	2	1	3	2

■ Exercises

1. In 2006, there were about 11 million commercial flights in the United States. If one is selected at random, what is the probability that it involved a fatal accident?

2. Suppose that the probability of a fatal accident in a given year is 0.0000004. A binomial probability distribution for $n = 11,000,000$ and $p = 0.0000004$ with $x = 0$ to 12 is shown.

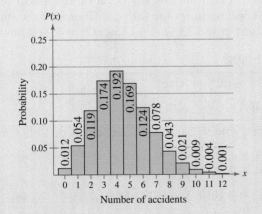

What is the probability that there will be (a) 4 fatal accidents in a year? (b) 10 fatal accidents? (c) between 1 and 5, inclusive?

3. Construct a binomial distribution for $n = 11,000,000$ and $p = 0.0000008$ with $x = 0$ to 12. Compare your results with the distribution in Exercise 2.

4. Is a binomial distribution a good model for determining the probability of various numbers of fatal accidents during a year? Explain your reasoning and include a discussion of the four criteria for a binomial experiment.

5. According to analysis by *USA TODAY*, air flight is so safe that a person "would have to fly every day for more than 64,000 years before dying in an accident." How can such a statement be justified?

221

4.3 More Discrete Probability Distributions

What You SHOULD LEARN

▸ How to find probabilities using the geometric distribution

▸ How to find probabilities using the Poisson distribution

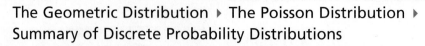

The Geometric Distribution ▸ The Poisson Distribution ▸ Summary of Discrete Probability Distributions

▸ The Geometric Distribution

In this section, you will study two more discrete probability distributions—the geometric distribution and the Poisson distribution.

Many actions in life are repeated until a success occurs. For instance, a CPA candidate might take the CPA exam several times before receiving a passing score, or you might have to dial a cellular phone number several times before successfully being connected. Situations such as these can be represented by a geometric distribution.

DEFINITION

A **geometric distribution** is a discrete probability distribution of a random variable x that satisfies the following conditions.

1. A trial is repeated until a success occurs.
2. The repeated trials are independent of each other.
3. The probability of success p is constant for each trial.

The **probability that the first success will occur on trial number x** is

$$P(x) = p(q)^{x-1}, \text{ where } q = 1 - p.$$

In other words, when the first success occurs on the third trial, the outcome is FFS, and the probability is $P(3) = q \cdot q \cdot p$, or $P(3) = p \cdot q^2$.

Study Tip

Detailed instructions for finding a geometric probability on a TI-83/84.

[2nd] DISTR

D: geometpdf(

Enter the values of p and x separated by commas.

[ENTER]

```
geometpdf(.23,4)
         .10500259
geometpdf(.23,5)
       .0808519943
```

Using a TI-83/84, you can find the probabilities used in Example 1 automatically.

EXAMPLE 1

Finding Probabilities Using the Geometric Distribution

From experience, you know that the probability that you will make a sale on any given telephone call is 0.23. Find the probability that your first sale on any given day will occur on your fourth or fifth sales call.

Solution To find the probability that your first sale will occur on the fourth or fifth call, first find the probability that the sale will occur on the fourth call and the probability that the sale will occur on the fifth call. Then find the sum of the resulting probabilities. Using $p = 0.23$, $q = 0.77$, and $x = 4$, you have

$$P(4) = 0.23 \cdot (0.77)^3 \approx 0.105003.$$

Using $p = 0.23$, $q = 0.77$, and $x = 5$, you have

$$P(5) = 0.23 \cdot (0.77)^4 \approx 0.080852.$$

So, the probability that your first sale will occur on the fourth or fifth sales call is

$$P(\text{sale on fourth or fifth call}) = P(4) + P(5)$$
$$\approx 0.105003 + 0.080852$$
$$\approx 0.186.$$

> ▶ **Try It Yourself 1**

Find the probability that your first sale will occur before your fourth sales call.

a. *Use the geometric distribution* to find $P(1)$, $P(2)$, and $P(3)$.
b. *Find the sum* of $P(1)$, $P(2)$, and $P(3)$.
c. *Write* the result as a sentence.   *Answer: Page A40*

Even though theoretically a success may never occur, the geometric distribution is a discrete probability distribution because the values of x can be listed—1, 2, 3, ... Notice that as x becomes larger, $P(x)$ gets closer to zero. For instance

$$P(50) = 0.23(0.77)^{49}$$
$$\approx 0.0000006306.$$

▶ The Poisson Distribution

In a binomial experiment you are interested in finding the probability of a specific number of successes in a given number of trials. Suppose instead that you want to know the probability that a specific number of occurrences takes place within a given unit of time or space. For instance, to determine the probability that an employee will take 15 sick days within a year, you can use the Poisson distribution.

DEFINITION

The **Poisson distribution** is a discrete probability distribution of a random variable x that satisfies the following conditions.

1. The experiment consists of counting the number of times, x, an event occurs in a given interval. The interval can be an interval of time, area, or volume.

2. The probability of the event occurring is the same for each interval.

3. The number of occurrences in one interval is independent of the number of occurrences in other intervals.

The probability of exactly x occurrences in an interval is

$$P(x) = \frac{\mu^x e^{-\mu}}{x!}$$

where e is an irrational number approximately equal to 2.71828 and μ is the mean number of occurrences per interval unit.

EXAMPLE 2

Using the Poisson Distribution

The mean number of accidents per month at a certain intersection is three. What is the probability that in any given month four accidents will occur at this intersection?

Solution   Using $x = 4$ and $\mu = 3$, the probability that 4 accidents will occur in any given month at the intersection is

$$P(4) = \frac{3^4 (2.71828)^{-3}}{4!}$$

$$\approx 0.168.$$

▶ **Try It Yourself 2**

What is the probability that more than four accidents will occur in any given month at the intersection?

a. *Use the Poisson distribution* to find $P(0)$, $P(1)$, $P(2)$, $P(3)$, and $P(4)$.
b. *Find the sum* of $P(0)$, $P(1)$, $P(2)$, $P(3)$, and $P(4)$.
c. *Subtract* the sum from 1.
d. *Write* the result as a sentence.   *Answer: Page A40*

In Example 2 you used a formula to determine a Poisson probability. You can also use a table to find Poisson probabilities. Table 3 in Appendix B lists the Poisson probability for selected values of x and μ. You can use technology tools, such as MINITAB, Excel, and the TI-83/84, to find Poisson probabilities as well. For example, on a TI-83/84, the DISTR menu can be used to find binomial, geometric, and Poisson probabilities. The solution for Example 2 is shown in the margin.

EXAMPLE 3

Finding Poisson Probabilities Using a Table

A population count shows that there is an average of 3.6 rabbits per acre living in a field. Use a table to find the probability that two rabbits are found on any given acre of the field.

Solution   A portion of Table 3 in Appendix B is shown here. Using the distribution for $\mu = 3.6$ and $x = 2$, you can find the Poisson probability as shown by the highlighted areas in the table.

| | | | | μ | | | |
x	3.1	3.2	3.3	3.4	3.5	3.6	3.7
0	.0450	.0408	.0369	.0334	.0302	.0273	.0247
1	.1397	.1304	.1217	.1135	.1057	.0984	.0915
2	.2165	.2087	.2008	.1929	.1850	.1771	.1692
3	.2237	.2226	.2209	.2186	.2158	.2125	.2087
4	.1734	.1781	.1823	.1858	.1888	.1912	.1931
5	.1075	.1140	.1203	.1264	.1322	.1377	.1429
6	.0555	.0608	.0662	.0716	.0771	.0826	.0881
7	.0246	.0278	.0312	.0348	.0385	.0425	.0466
8	.0095	.0111	.0129	.0148	.0169	.0191	.0215
9	.0033	.0040	.0047	.0056	.0066	.0076	.0089
10	.0010	.0013	.0016	.0019	.0023	.0028	.0033

So, the probability that two rabbits are found on any given acre is 0.1771.

▶ **Try It Yourself 3**

Two thousand brown trout are introduced into a small lake. The lake has a volume of 20,000 cubic meters. Use a table to find the probability that three brown trout are found in any given cubic meter of the lake.

a. *Find the average* number of brown trout per cubic meter.
b. *Identify* μ and x.
c. *Use Table 3* in Appendix B to find the Poisson probability.
d. *Write* the result as a sentence.   *Answer: Page A40*

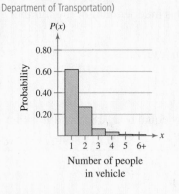

PICTURING the WORLD

The first successful suspension bridge built in the United States, the Tacoma Narrows Bridge, spans the Tacoma Narrows in Washington State. The average occupancy of vehicles that travel across the bridge is 1.6. The following probability distribution represents the vehicle occupancy on the bridge during a five-day period. (Source: Washington State Department of Transportation)

What is the probability that a randomly selected vehicle has two occupants or fewer?

▶ Summary of Discrete Probability Distributions

The following table summarizes the discrete probability distributions discussed in this chapter.

Distribution	Summary	Formulas
Binomial Distribution	A binomial experiment satisfies the following conditions. 1. The experiment is repeated for a fixed number (n) of independent trials. 2. There are only two possible outcomes for each trial. Each outcome can be classified as a success or as a failure. 3. The probability of a success must remain constant for each trial. 4. The random variable x counts the number of successful trials out of the n trials. The parameters of a binomial distribution are n and p.	x = the number of successes in n trials p = probability of success in a single trial q = probability of failure in a single trial $q = 1 - p$ The probability of exactly x successes in n trials is $$P(x) = {}_nC_x\, p^x q^{n-x}$$ $$= \frac{n!}{(n-x)!x!}\, p^x q^{n-x}.$$
Geometric Distribution	A geometric distribution is a discrete probability distribution of a random variable x that satisfies the following conditions. 1. A trial is repeated until a success occurs. 2. The repeated trials are independent of each other. 3. The probability of success p is constant for each trial. 4. The random variable x represents the number of the trial in which the first success occurs. The parameter of a geometric distribution is p.	x = the number of the trial in which the first success occurs p = probability of success in a single trial q = probability of failure in a single trial $q = 1 - p$ The probability that the first success occurs on trial number x is $$P(x) = p(q)^{x-1}.$$
Poisson Distribution	The Poisson distribution is a discrete probability distribution of a random variable x that satisfies the following conditions. 1. The experiment consists of counting the number of times, x, an event occurs over a specified interval of time, area, or volume. 2. The probability of the event occurring is the same for each interval. 3. The number of occurrences in one interval is independent of the number of occurrences in other intervals. The parameter of a Poisson distribution is μ.	x = the number of occurrences in the given interval μ = the mean number of occurrences in a given time or space unit The probability of exactly x occurrences in an interval is $$P(x) = \frac{\mu^x e^{-\mu}}{x!}.$$

4.3 EXERCISES

■ Building Basic Skills and Vocabulary

In Exercises 1–4, assume the geometric distribution applies. Use the given probability of success p to find the indicated probability.

1. Find $P(2)$ when $p = 0.60$.　　　**2.** Find $P(1)$ when $p = 0.25$.

3. Find $P(6)$ when $p = 0.09$.　　　**4.** Find $P(5)$ when $p = 0.38$.

In Exercises 5–8, assume the Poisson distribution applies. Use the given mean μ to find the indicated probability.

5. Find $P(3)$ when $\mu = 4$.　　　**6.** Find $P(5)$ when $\mu = 6$.

7. Find $P(2)$ when $\mu = 1.5$.　　　**8.** Find $P(4)$ when $\mu = 8.1$.

9. In your own words, describe the difference between the value of x in a binomial distribution and in a geometric distribution.

10. In your own words, describe the difference between the value of x in a binomial distribution and in a Poisson distribution.

Deciding on a Distribution *In Exercises 11–16, decide which probability distribution—binomial, geometric, or Poisson—applies to the question. You do not need to answer the question. Instead, justify your choice.*

11. Pilot's Test *Given:* The probability that a student passes the written test for a private pilot's license is 0.75. *Question:* What is the probability that a student will fail the test on the first attempt and pass it on the second attempt?

12. Precipitation *Given:* In Rapid City, South Dakota, the mean number of days with 0.01 inch or more precipitation for May is 12. *Question:* What is the probability that Rapid City has 18 days with 0.01 inch or more precipitation next May? *(Source: National Climatic Data Center)*

13. Oil Tankers *Given:* The mean number of oil tankers at a port city is 8 per day. The port has facilities to handle up to 12 oil tankers in a day. *Question:* What is the probability that too many tankers will arrive on a given day?

14. Exercise *Given:* Forty percent of adults in the United States exercise at least 30 minutes a week. In a survey of 120 randomly chosen adults, people were asked, "Do you exercise at least 30 minutes a week?" *Question:* What is the probability that exactly 50 of the people answer yes?

15. Cheaters *Given:* Of students ages 16 to 18 with A or B averages who plan to attend college after graduation, 78% cheated to get higher grades. Ten randomly chosen students with A or B averages who plan to attend college after graduation were asked, "Did you cheat to get higher grades?" *Question:* What is the probability that exactly two students answered no? *(Source: Who's Who Among American High School Students)*

16. No Meat? *Given:* About 21% of Americans say they could not go one week without eating meat. You select at random 20 Americans. *Question:* What is the probability that the first person who says he or she cannot go one week without eating meat is the fifth person selected? *(Source: Reuters/Zogby)*

■ Using and Interpreting Concepts

Using a Geometric Distribution to Find Probabilities   *In Exercises 17–20, find the indicated probabilities using the geometric distribution. If convenient, use technology to find the probabilities.*

17. Telephone Sales   Assume the probability that you will make a sale on any given telephone call is 0.19. Find the probability that you (a) make your first sale on the fifth call, (b) make your first sale on the first, second, or third call, and (c) do not make a sale on the first three calls.

18. Free Throws   Basketball player Shaquille O'Neal makes a free-throw shot about 52.6% of the time. Find the probability that (a) the first shot O'Neal makes is the second shot, (b) the first shot O'Neal makes is the first or second shot, and (c) O'Neal does not make two shots. *(Source: National Basketball Association)*

19. Glass Manufacturer   A glass manufacturer finds that 1 in every 500 glass items produced is warped. Find the probability that (a) the first warped glass item is the tenth item produced, (b) the first warped glass item is the first, second, or third item produced, and (c) none of the first 10 glass items produced are defective.

20. Winning a Prize   A cereal maker places a game piece in its cereal boxes. The probability of winning a prize in the game is 1 in 4. Find the probability that you (a) win your first prize with your fourth purchase, (b) win your first prize with your first, second, or third purchase, and (c) do not win a prize with your first four purchases.

Using a Poisson Distribution to Find Probabilities   *In Exercises 21–24, find the indicated probabilities using the Poisson distribution. If convenient, use a Poisson probability table or technology tool to find the probabilities.*

21. Bankruptcies   The mean number of bankruptcies filed per minute in the United States in a recent year was about three. Find the probability that (a) exactly five businesses will file bankruptcy in any given minute, (b) at least five businesses will file bankruptcy in any given minute, and (c) more than five businesses will file bankruptcy in any given minute. *(Source: Administrative Office of the U.S. Courts)*

22. Typographical Errors   A newspaper finds that the mean number of typographical errors per page is four. Find the probability that (a) exactly three typographical errors will be found on a page, (b) at most three typographical errors will be found on a page, and (c) more than three typographical errors will be found on a page.

23. Major Hurricanes   A major hurricane is a hurricane with wind speeds of 111 miles per hour or greater. During the 20th century, the mean number of major hurricanes to strike the U.S. mainland per year was about 0.6. Find the probability that in a given year (a) exactly one major hurricane will strike the U.S. mainland, (b) at most one major hurricane will strike the U.S. mainland, and (c) more than one major hurricane will strike the U.S. mainland. *(Source: National Hurricane Center)*

24. Precipitation   The mean number of days with 0.01 inch or more precipitation per month for Lewistown, Idaho, is about 8.7. Find the probability that in a given month (a) there are exactly 9 days with 0.01 inch or more precipitation, (b) there are at most 9 days with 0.01 inch or more precipitation, and (c) there are more than 9 days with 0.01 inch or more precipitation. *(Source: National Climatic Data Center)*

■ Extending Concepts

25. Approximating the Binomial Distribution An automobile manufacturer finds that 1 in every 2500 automobiles produced has a particular manufacturing defect. (a) Use a binomial distribution to find the probability of finding four cars with the defect in a random sample of 6000 cars. (b) The Poisson distribution can be used to approximate the binomial distribution for large values of n and small values of p. Repeat (a) using a Poisson distribution and compare the results.

26. Hypergeometric Distribution Binomial experiments require that any sampling be done with replacement because each trial must be independent of the others. The **hypergeometric distribution** also has two outcomes—success and failure. However, the sampling is done without replacement. Given a population of N items having k successes and $N - k$ failures, the probability of selecting a sample of size n that has x successes and $n - x$ failures is given by

$$P(x) = \frac{(_kC_x)(_{N-k}C_{n-x})}{_NC_n}.$$

In a shipment of 15 microchips, 2 are defective and 13 are not defective. A sample of three microchips is chosen at random. Find the probability that (a) all three microchips are not defective, (b) one microchip is defective and two are not defective, and (c) two microchips are defective and one is not defective.

Geometric Distribution: Mean and Variance
In Exercises 27 and 28, use the fact that the mean of a geometric distribution is $\mu = 1/p$ and the variance is $\sigma^2 = q/p^2$.

27. Daily Lottery A daily number lottery chooses three balls numbered 0 to 9. The probability of winning the lottery is 1/1000. Let x be the number of times you play the lottery before winning the first time. (a) Find the mean, variance, and standard deviation. Interpret the results. (b) How many times would you expect to have to play the lottery before winning? Assume that it costs $1 to play and winners are paid $500. Would you expect to make or lose money playing this lottery? Explain.

28. Paycheck Errors A company assumes that 0.5% of the paychecks for a year were calculated incorrectly. The company has 200 employees and examines the payroll records from one month. (a) Find the mean, variance, and standard deviation. Interpret the results. (b) How many employee payroll records would you expect to examine before finding one with an error?

Poisson Distribution: Variance
In Exercises 29 and 30, use the fact that the variance of a Poisson distribution is $\sigma^2 = \mu$.

29. Tiger Woods In a recent year, the mean number of strokes per hole for golfer Tiger Woods was about 3.8. (a) Find the variance and standard deviation. Interpret the results. (b) How likely is Woods to play an 18-hole round and have more than 72 strokes? *(Source: PGATour.com)*

30. Snowfall The mean snowfall in January for Bridgeport, Connecticut is 7.6 inches. (a) Find the variance and standard deviation. Interpret the results. (b) Find the probability that the snowfall in January for Bridgeport, Connecticut will exceed 12 inches. *(Source: National Climatic Data Center)*

Uses & Abuses

Uses

There are countless occurrences of binomial probability distributions in business, science, engineering, and many other fields.

For example, suppose you work for a marketing agency and are in charge of creating a television ad for Brand A toothpaste. The toothpaste manufacturer claims that 40% of toothpaste buyers prefer its brand. To check whether the manufacturer's claim is reasonable, your agency conducts a survey. Of 100 toothpaste buyers selected at random, you find that only 35 (or 35%) prefer Brand A. Could the manufacturer's claim still be true? What if your random sample of 100 found only 25 people (or 25%) who express a preference for Brand A? Would you still be justified in running the advertisement?

Knowing the characteristics of binomial probability distributions will help you answer this type of question. By the time you have completed this course, you will be able make educated decisions about the reasonableness of the manufacturer's claim.

Ethics

Suppose the toothpaste manufacturer also claims that four out of five dentists recommend Brand A toothpaste. Your agency wants to mention this fact in the television ad, but when determining how the sample of dentists was formed, you find that the dentists were paid to recommend the toothpaste. Including this statement when running the advertisement would be unethical.

Abuses

Interpreting the "Most Likely" Outcome A common misuse of binomial probability distributions is to think that the "most likely" outcome is the outcome that will occur most of the time. For instance, suppose you randomly choose a committee of four from a large population that is 50% women and 50% men. The most likely composition of the committee is that it will contain two men and two women. Although this is the most likely outcome, the probability that it will occur is only 0.375. There is a 0.5 chance that the committee will contain one man and three women or three men and one woman. So, if either of these outcomes occurs, you should not assume that the selection was unusual or biased.

■ EXERCISES

In Exercises 1 and 2, suppose that the manufacturer's claim is true—40% of toothpaste buyers prefer Brand A toothpaste. Use the graph and technology to answer the questions.

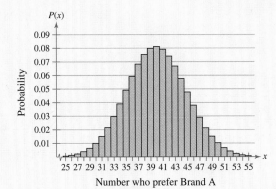

Number who prefer Brand A

1. ***Interpreting the "Most Likely" Outcome*** In a random sample of 100, what is the most likely outcome? How likely is it?

2. ***Interpreting the "Most Likely" Outcome*** In a random sample of 100, what is the probability that between 35 and 45 people, inclusive, prefer Brand A? Explain your reasoning.

3. Suppose in a random sample of 100, you found 36 who prefer Brand A. Would the manufacturer's claim be believable? Explain your reasoning.

4. Suppose in a random sample of 100, you found 25 who prefer Brand A. Would the manufacturer's claim be believable? Explain your reasoning.

Statistics in the Real World

4 CHAPTER SUMMARY

What did you **learn?**	EXAMPLE(S)	REVIEW EXERCISES
Section 4.1		
■ How to distinguish between discrete random variables and continuous random variables	*1*	*1–4*
■ How to determine if a distribution is a probability distribution	*3–4*	*5–10*
■ How to construct a discrete probability distribution and its graph and find the mean, variance, and standard deviation of a discrete probability distribution $$\mu = \Sigma x P(x)$$ $$\sigma^2 = \Sigma(x - \mu)^2 P(x)$$ $$\sigma = \sqrt{\sigma^2} = \sqrt{\Sigma(x - \mu)^2 P(x)}.$$	*2, 5, 6*	*11–14*
■ How to find the expected value of a discrete probability distribution	*7*	*15, 16*
Section 4.2		
■ How to determine if a probability experiment is a binomial experiment	*1*	*17, 18*
■ How to find binomial probabilities using the binomial probability formula, a binomial probability table, and technology $$P(x) = {}_nC_x p^x q^{n-x} = \frac{n!}{(n-x)!x!} p^x q^{n-x}$$	*2, 4–6*	*19–22*
■ How to construct a binomial distribution and its graph and find the mean, variance, and standard deviation of a binomial probability distribution $$\mu = np$$ $$\sigma^2 = npq$$ $$\sigma = \sqrt{npq}$$	*3, 7, 8*	*23–26*
Section 4.3		
■ How to find probabilities using the geometric distribution $$P(x) = pq^{x-1}$$	*1*	*27, 28*
■ How to find probabilities using the Poisson distribution $$P(x) = \frac{\mu^x e^{-\mu}}{x!}$$	*2, 3*	*29, 30*

4 REVIEW EXERCISES

Section 4.1

In Exercises 1–4, decide whether the random variable x is discrete or continuous.

1. x represents the number of pumps in use at a gas station.

2. x represents the weight of a truck at a weigh station.

3. x represents the amount of gas pumped at a gas station.

4. x represents the number of people that activate a metal detector at an airport each hour.

In Exercises 5–10, decide whether the distribution is a probability distribution. If it is not, identify the property that is not satisfied.

5. The daily limit for catching bass at a lake is four. The random variable x represents the number of fish caught in a day.

x	0	1	2	3	4
$P(x)$	0.36	0.23	0.08	0.14	0.29

6. The random variable x represents the number of tickets a police officer writes out each shift.

x	0	1	2	3	4	5
$P(x)$	0.09	0.23	0.29	0.16	0.21	0.02

7. A greeting card shop keeps records of customers' buying habits. The random variable x represents the number of cards sold to an individual customer in a shopping visit.

x	1	2	3	4	5	6	7
$P(x)$	0.68	0.14	0.08	0.05	0.02	0.02	0.01

8. The random variable x represents the number of classes in which a student is enrolled in a given semester at a university.

x	1	2	3	4	5	6	7	8
$P(x)$	$\frac{1}{80}$	$\frac{2}{75}$	$\frac{1}{10}$	$\frac{12}{25}$	$\frac{27}{20}$	$\frac{1}{5}$	$\frac{2}{25}$	$\frac{1}{120}$

9. In a survey, Internet users were asked how many e-mail addresses they have. The random variable x represents the number of e-mail addresses.

x	1	2	3
$P(x)$	0.26	0.31	0.43

10. The random variable x represents the number of employees at a company that call in sick per day.

x	0	1	2	3	4	5	6
$P(x)$	0.156	0.318	0.227	0.091	0.136	0.045	0.045

In Exercises 11–14,

(a) use the frequency distribution table to construct a probability distribution.

(b) graph the probability distribution using a histogram.

(c) find the mean, variance, and standard deviation of the probability distribution.

11. The number of pages in a section from a sample of statistics texts

Pages	Sections
2	3
3	12
4	72
5	115
6	169
7	120
8	83
9	48
10	22
11	6

12. The number of hits per game played by a baseball player during a recent season

Hits	Games
0	29
1	62
2	33
3	12
4	3
5	1

13. A survey asked 200 households how many televisions they owned.

Televisions	Households
0	3
1	38
2	83
3	52
4	18
5	5
6	1

14. A television station sells advertising in 15-, 30-, 60-, 90-, and 120-second blocks. The distribution of sales for one 24-hour day is given.

Length (in seconds)	Number
15	76
30	445
60	30
90	3
120	12

In Exercises 15 and 16, find the expected value of the random variable.

15. A person has shares of eight different stocks. The random variable x represents the number of stocks showing a loss on a selected day.

x	0	1	2	3	4	5	6	7	8
$P(x)$	0.02	0.11	0.18	0.32	0.15	0.09	0.05	0.05	0.03

16. A local pub has a chicken wing special on Tuesdays. The pub owners purchase wings in cases of 300. The random variable x represents the number of cases used during the special.

x	1	2	3	4
$P(x)$	$\frac{1}{9}$	$\frac{1}{3}$	$\frac{1}{2}$	$\frac{1}{18}$

Section 4.2

In Exercises 17 and 18, decide whether the experiment is a binomial experiment. If it is not, identify the property that is not satisfied. If it is, list the values of n, p, and q and the values that x can assume.

17. Bags of plain M&M's contain 24% blue candies. One candy is selected from each of 12 bags. The random variable represents the number of blue candies selected. *(Source: Mars, Inc.)*

18. A fair coin is tossed repeatedly until 15 heads are obtained. The random variable *x* counts the number of tosses.

In Exercises 19–22, find the indicated probabilities.

19. One in four adults is currently on a diet. In a random sample of eight adults, what is the probability that the number currently on a diet is

    (a) exactly three?

    (b) at least three?

    (c) more than three? *(Source: Wirthlin Worldwide)*

20. One in four people in the United States owns individual stocks. In a random sample of 12 people, what is the probability that the number owning individual stocks is

    (a) exactly two?

    (b) at least two?

    (c) more than two? *(Source: Pew Research Center)*

21. Forty-three percent of adults in the United States receive fewer than five phone calls a day. In a random sample of seven adults, what is the probability that the number receiving fewer than five calls a day is

    (a) exactly three?

    (b) at least three?

    (c) more than three? *(Source: Wirthlin Worldwide)*

22. In a typical day, 31% of people in the United States with Internet access go online to get news. In a random sample of five people in the United States with Internet access, what is the probability that the number going online to get news is

    (a) exactly two?

    (b) at least two?

    (c) more than two? *(Source: Pew Research Center)*

In Exercises 23–26,

(a) construct a binomial distribution.

(b) graph the binomial distribution using a histogram.

(c) find the mean, variance, and standard deviation of the binomial distribution.

23. Sixty-three percent of adults in the United States rent videotapes or DVDs at least once a month. Consider a random sample of five Americans who are asked if they rent at least one videotape or DVD a month.

24. Sixty-eight percent of families say that their children have an influence on their vacation destinations. Consider a random sample of six families who are asked if their children have an influence on their vacation destinations. *(Source: YPB&R)*

25. In a recent year, forty percent of trucks sold by a company had diesel engines. Consider a random sample of four trucks sold by the company

26. In a typical day, 15% of people in the United States with Internet access check the weather while online. Consider a random sample of five people in the United States with Internet access who are asked if they check the weather while online. *(Source: Pew Research Center)*

Section 4.3

In Exercises 27 and 28, find the indicated probabilities using the geometric distribution. If convenient, use technology to find the probabilities.

27. During a promotional contest, a soft drink company places winning caps on one of every six bottles. If you purchase one bottle a day, find the probability that you find your first winning cap

(a) on the fourth day.

(b) within four days.

(c) sometime after three days.

28. In a recent year, Barry Bonds hit 73 home runs in the 153 games he played. Assume that his home run production stayed at that level the following season. What is the probability that he would hit his first home run

(a) on the first game of the season.

(b) on the second game of the season.

(c) on the first or second game of the season.

(d) within the first three games of the season. *(Source: Major League Baseball)*

In Exercises 29 and 30, find the indicated probabilities using the Poisson distribution. If convenient, use a Poisson probability table or technology tool to find the probabilities.

29. During a 36-year period, lightning killed 2457 people in the United States. Assume that this rate holds true today and is constant throughout the year. Find the probability that tomorrow

(a) no one in the United States will be struck and killed by lightning.

(b) one person will be struck and killed.

(c) more than one person will be struck and killed. *(Source: National Weather Service)*

30. It is estimated that sharks kill 10 people each year worldwide. Find the probability that at least three people are killed by sharks this year

(a) assuming that this rate is true.

(b) if the rate is actually five people a year.

(c) if the rate is actually 15 people a year. *(Source: International Shark Attack File)*

4 CHAPTER QUIZ

Take this quiz as you would take a quiz in class. After you are done, check your work against the answers given in the back of the book.

1. Decide if the random variable, x, is discrete or continuous. Explain your reasoning.

    (a) x represents the number of tornadoes that occur in Kansas during the month of May.

    (b) x represents the amount of waste (in pounds) generated each day in the United States.

2. The table lists the number of U.S. mainland hurricane strikes (from 1901 to 2004) for various intensities according to the Saffir-Simpson Hurricane Scale. *(Source: National Hurricane Center)*

Intensity	Number of hurricanes
1	70
2	41
3	49
4	13
5	3

    (a) Construct a probability distribution of the data.

    (b) Graph the discrete probability distribution using a probability histogram.

    (c) Find the mean, variance, and standard deviation of the probability distribution and interpret the results.

    (d) Find the probability that a hurricane selected at random for further study has an intensity of at least four.

3. A surgical technique is performed on eight patients. You are told there is an 80% chance of success.

    (a) Construct a binomial distribution.

    (b) Graph the binomial distribution using a probability histogram.

    (c) Find the mean, variance, and standard deviation of the probability distribution and interpret the results.

    (d) Find the probability that the surgery is successful for exactly two patients.

    (e) Find the probability that the surgery is successful for fewer than two patients.

4. A newspaper finds that the mean number of typographical errors per page is five. Find the probability that

    (a) exactly five typographical errors will be found on a page.

    (b) fewer than five typographical errors will be found on a page.

    (c) no typographical errors will be found on a page.

REAL Statistics — Real Decisions

The Centers for Disease Control and Prevention (CDC) is required by law to publish a report on assisted reproductive technologies (ART). ART includes all fertility treatments in which both the egg and the sperm are used. These procedures generally involve removing eggs from a woman's ovaries, combining them with sperm in the laboratory, and returning them to the woman's body or giving them to another woman.

You are helping to prepare the CDC report and select at random 10 ART cycles for a special review. None of the cycles resulted in a clinical pregnancy. Your manager feels it is impossible to select at random 10 ART cycles that did not result in a clinical pregnancy. Use the information provided at the right and your knowledge of statistics to determine if your manager is correct.

■ Exercises

1. **How Would You Do It?**

    (a) How would you determine if your manager's view is correct, that it is impossible to select at random 10 ART cycles that did not result in a clinical pregnancy?

    (b) What probability distribution do you think best describes the situation? Do you think the distribution of the number of clinical pregnancies is discrete or continuous? Why?

2. **Answering the Question**

    Write an explanation that answers the question, "Is it possible to select at random 10 ART cycles that did not result in a clinical pregnancy?" Include in your explanation the appropriate probability distribution and your calculation of the probability of no clinical pregnancies in 10 ART cycles.

3. **Suspicious Samples?**

    Which of the following samples would you consider suspicious if someone told you that the sample was selected at random? Would you believe that the samples were selected at random? Why or why not?

    (a) Selecting at random 10 ART cycles among women of age 40, eight of which resulted in clinical pregnancies.

    (b) Selecting at random 10 ART cycles among women of age 41, none of which resulted in clinical pregnancies.

Results of ART Cycles

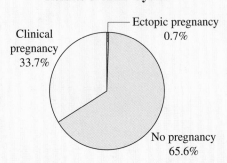

(Source: Centers for Disease Control and Prevention)

Pregnancy and Live Birth Rates for ART Cycles Among Women of Age 40 and Older

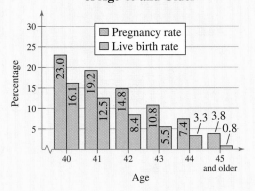

(Source: Centers for Disease Control and Prevention)

TECHNOLOGY

MINITAB   **EXCEL**   **T1-83/84**

USING POISSON DISTRIBUTIONS AS QUEUING MODELS

Queuing means waiting in line to be served. There are many examples of queuing in everyday life: waiting at a traffic light, waiting in line at a grocery checkout counter, waiting for an elevator, holding for a telephone call, and so on.

Poisson distributions are used to model and predict the number of people (calls, computer programs, vehicles) arriving at the line. In the following exercises, you are asked to use Poisson distributions to analyze the queues at a grocery store checkout counter.

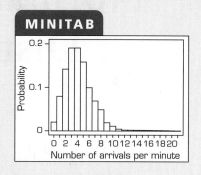

■ **EXERCISES**

In Exercises 1–6, consider a grocery store that can process a total of four customers at its checkout counters each minute.

1. Suppose that the mean number of customers who arrive at the checkout counters each minute is 4. Create a Poisson distribution with $\mu = 4$ for $x = 0$ to 20. Compare your results with the histogram shown at the upper right.

2. MINITAB was used to generate 20 random numbers with a Poisson distribution for $\mu = 4$. Let the random number represent the number of arrivals at the checkout counter each minute for 20 minutes.

   3 3 3 3 5 5 6 7 3 6
   3 5 6 3 4 6 2 2 4 1

   During each of the first four minutes, only three customers arrived. These customers could all be processed, so there were no customers waiting after four minutes.

   (a) How many customers were waiting after 5 minutes? 6 minutes? 7 minutes? 8 minutes?

   (b) Create a table that shows the number of customers waiting at the end of 1 through 20 minutes.

3. Generate a list of 20 random numbers with a Poisson distribution for $\mu = 4$. Create a table that shows the number of customers waiting at the end of 1 through 20 minutes.

4. Suppose that the mean increases to 5 arrivals per minute. You can still process only four per minute. How many would you expect to be waiting in line after 20 minutes?

5. Simulate the setting in Exercise 4. Do this by generating a list of 20 random numbers with a Poisson distribution for $\mu = 5$. Then create a table that shows the number of customers waiting at the end of 20 minutes.

6. Suppose that the mean number of arrivals per minute is 5. What is the probability that 10 customers will arrive during the first minute?

7. Suppose that the mean number of arrivals per minute is 4.

   (a) What is the probability that three, four, or five customers will arrive during the third minute?

   (b) What is the probability that more than four customers will arrive during the first minute?

   (c) What is the probability that more than four customers will arrive during each of the first four minutes?

Extended solutions are given in the *Technology Supplement.* Technical instruction is provided for MINITAB, Excel, and the TI-83/84.

CHAPTER 5

Normal Probability Distributions

5.1 Introduction to Normal Distributions and the Standard Normal Distribution

5.2 Normal Distributions: Finding Probabilities

5.3 Normal Distributions: Finding Values

■ CASE STUDY

5.4 Sampling Distributions and the Central Limit Theorem

■ ACTIVITY

5.5 Normal Approximations to Binomial Distributions

■ USES AND ABUSES

■ REAL STATISTICS– REAL DECISIONS

■ TECHNOLOGY

The North Carolina Zoo is the largest walk-through natural-habitat zoo in the United States. It is one of only two state zoos in the United States, with the other located in Minnesota.

©1992 Susan Middleton & David Liittschwager

In Chapters 1 through 4, you learned how to collect and describe data, find the probability of an event, and analyze discrete probability distributions. You also learned that if a sample is used to make inferences about a population, then it is critical that the sample not be biased. Suppose, for instance, that you wanted to determine the rate of clinical mastitis (infections caused by bacteria that can alter milk production) in dairy herds. How would you organize the study? When the Animal Health Service performed this study, it used random sampling and then classified the results according to breed, housing, hygiene, health, milking management, and milking machine. One conclusion from the study was that herds with Red and White cows as the predominant breed had a higher rate of clinical mastitis than herds with Holstein-Friesian cows as the main breed.

WHERE YOU'RE GOING →

In Chapter 5, you will learn how to recognize normal (bell-shaped) distributions and how to use their properties in real-life applications. Suppose that you worked for the North Carolina Zoo and were collecting data about various physical traits of Eastern Box Turtles at the zoo. Which of the following would you expect to have bell-shaped, symmetric distributions: carapace (top shell) length, plastral (bottom shell) length, carapace width, plastral width, weight, total length? For instance, the four graphs below show the carapace length and plastral length of male and female Eastern Box Turtles in the North Carolina Zoo. Notice that the male Eastern Box Turtle carapace length distribution is bell shaped, but the other three distributions are skewed left.

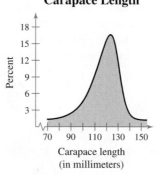

Female Eastern Box Turtle Carapace Length

Carapace length (in millimeters)

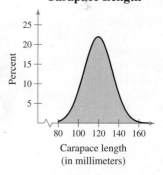

Male Eastern Box Turtle Carapace Length

Carapace length (in millimeters)

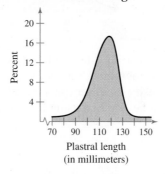

Female Eastern Box Turtle Plastral Length

Plastral length (in millimeters)

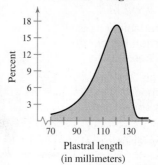

Male Eastern Box Turtle Plastral Length

Plastral length (in millimeters)

Introduction to Normal Distributions and the Standard Normal Distribution

Properties of a Normal Distribution ▸ The Standard Normal Distribution

▸ Properties of a Normal Distribution

In Section 4.1, you distinguished between discrete and continuous random variables, and learned that a **continuous random variable** has an infinite number of possible values that can be represented by an interval on the number line. Its probability distribution is called a **continuous probability distribution.** In this chapter, you will study the most important continuous probability distribution in statistics—the normal distribution. Normal distributions can be used to model many sets of measurements in nature, industry, and business. For instance, the systolic blood pressure of humans, the lifetime of television sets, and even housing costs are all normally distributed random variables.

Insight

To learn how to determine if a random sample is taken from a normal distribution, see Appendix C.

> ### GUIDELINES
>
> Properties of a Normal Distribution
>
> A **normal distribution** is a continuous probability distribution for a random variable x. The graph of a normal distribution is called the **normal curve.** A normal distribution has the following properties.
>
> 1. The mean, median, and mode are equal.
> 2. The normal curve is bell-shaped and is symmetric about the mean.
> 3. The total area under the normal curve is equal to one.
> 4. The normal curve approaches, but never touches, the x-axis as it extends farther and farther away from the mean.
> 5. Between $\mu - \sigma$ and $\mu + \sigma$ (in the center of the curve), the graph curves downward. The graph curves upward to the left of $\mu - \sigma$ and to the right of $\mu + \sigma$. The points at which the curve changes from curving upward to curving downward are called *inflection points*.
>
>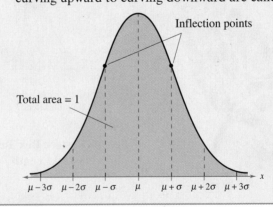

Insight

A probability density function has two requirements.

1. The total area under the curve is equal to one.

2. The function can never be negative.

You have learned that a discrete probability distribution can be graphed with a histogram. For a continuous probability distribution, you can use a **probability density function (pdf).** A normal curve with mean μ and standard deviation σ can be graphed using the normal probability density function.

$$y = \frac{1}{\sigma\sqrt{2\pi}}\, e^{-(x-\mu)^2/2\sigma^2}.$$

A normal curve depends completely on the two parameters μ and σ because $e \approx 2.718$ and $\pi \approx 3.14$ are constants.

A normal distribution can have any mean and any positive standard deviation. These two parameters, μ and σ, completely determine the shape of the normal curve. The mean gives the location of the line of symmetry, and the standard deviation describes how much the data are spread out.

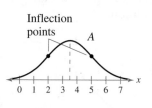

Mean: $\mu = 3.5$
Standard deviation:
$\sigma = 1.5$

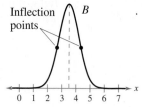

Mean: $\mu = 3.5$
Standard deviation:
$\sigma = 0.7$

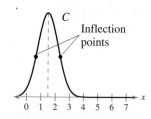

Mean: $\mu = 1.5$
Standard deviation:
$\sigma = 0.7$

Notice that curve *A* and curve *B* above have the same mean, and curve *B* and curve *C* have the same standard deviation. The total area under each curve is 1.

EXAMPLE 1

Understanding Mean and Standard Deviation

1. Which normal curve has a greater mean?
2. Which normal curve has a greater standard deviation?

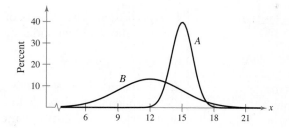

Solution

1. The line of symmetry of curve *A* occurs at $x = 15$. The line of symmetry of curve *B* occurs at $x = 12$. So, curve *A* has a greater mean.

2. Curve *B* is more spread out than curve *A*; so, curve *B* has a greater standard deviation.

▶ Try It Yourself 1

Consider the normal curves shown at the left. Which normal curve has the greatest mean? Which normal curve has the greatest standard deviation? Justify your answers.

a. Find the location of the *line of symmetry* of each curve. Make a conclusion about which mean is greatest.

b. Determine which normal curve is *more spread out*. Make a conclusion about which standard deviation is greatest.

Answer: Page A40

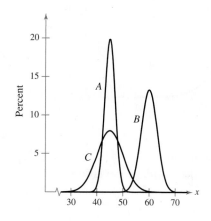

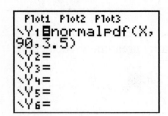

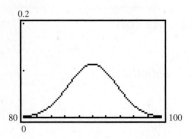

Once you determine the mean and standard deviation, you can use a TI-83/84 to graph the normal curve in Example 2.

EXAMPLE 2

Interpreting Graphs of Normal Distributions

The heights (in feet) of fully grown white oak trees are normally distributed. The normal curve shown below represents this distribution. What is the mean height of a fully grown white oak tree? Estimate the standard deviation of this normal distribution.

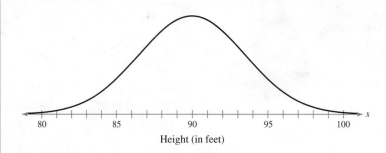

Height (in feet)

Solution

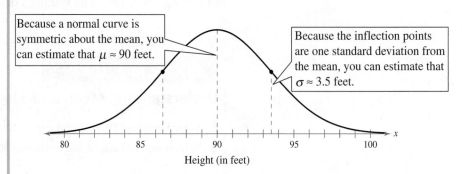

Because a normal curve is symmetric about the mean, you can estimate that $\mu \approx 90$ feet.

Because the inflection points are one standard deviation from the mean, you can estimate that $\sigma \approx 3.5$ feet.

Height (in feet)

Interpretation   The heights of the oak trees are normally distributed with a mean of about 90 feet and a standard deviation of about 3.5 feet.

▶ Try It Yourself 2

The diameters (in feet) of fully grown white oak trees are normally distributed. The normal curve shown below represents this distribution. What is the mean diameter of a fully grown white oak tree? Estimate the standard deviation of this normal distribution.

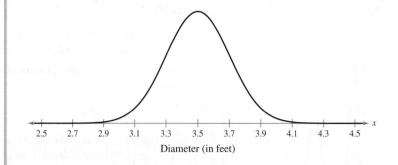

Diameter (in feet)

a. Find the *line of symmetry* and identify the mean.
b. Estimate the *inflection points* and identify the standard deviation.

Answer: Page A40

▶ The Standard Normal Distribution

There are infinitely many normal distributions, each with its own mean and standard deviation. The normal distribution with a mean of 0 and a standard deviation of 1 is called **the standard normal distribution.** The horizontal scale of the graph of the standard normal distribution corresponds to z-scores. In Section 2.5, you learned that a z-score is a measure of position that indicates the number of standard deviations a value lies from the mean. Recall that you can transform an x-value to a z-score using the formula

$$z = \frac{\text{Value} - \text{Mean}}{\text{Standard deviation}}$$

$$= \frac{x - \mu}{\sigma}. \qquad \text{Round to the nearest hundredth.}$$

DEFINITION

The **standard normal distribution** is a normal distribution with a mean of 0 and a standard deviation of 1.

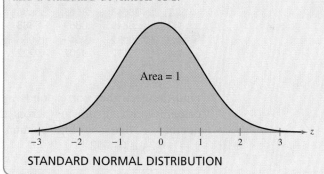

STANDARD NORMAL DISTRIBUTION

If each data value of a normally distributed random variable x is transformed into a z-score, the result will be the standard normal distribution. When this transformation takes place, the area that falls in the interval under the nonstandard normal curve is the *same* as that under the standard normal curve within the corresponding z-boundaries.

In Section 2.4, you learned to use the Empirical Rule to approximate areas under a normal curve when the values of the random variable x corresponded to −3, −2, −1, 0, 1, 2, or 3 standard deviations from the mean. Now, you will learn to calculate areas corresponding to other x-values. After you use the formula given above to transform an x-value to a z-score, you can use the Standard Normal Table in Appendix B. The table lists the cumulative area under the standard normal curve to the left of z for z-scores from −3.49 to 3.49. As you examine the table, notice the following.

PROPERTIES OF THE STANDARD NORMAL DISTRIBUTION

1. The cumulative area is close to 0 for z-scores close to $z = -3.49$.

2. The cumulative area increases as the z-scores increase.

3. The cumulative area for $z = 0$ is 0.5000.

4. The cumulative area is close to 1 for z-scores close to $z = 3.49$.

EXAMPLE 3

Using the Standard Normal Table

1. Find the cumulative area that corresponds to a z-score of 1.15.
2. Find the cumulative area that corresponds to a z-score of -0.24.

Solution

1. Find the area that corresponds to $z = 1.15$ by finding 1.1 in the left column and then moving across the row to the column under 0.05. The number in that row and column is 0.8749. So, the area to the left of $z = 1.15$ is 0.8749.

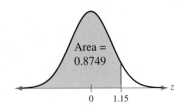

Area = 0.8749

z	.00	.01	.02	.03	.04	.05	.06
0.0	.5000	.5040	.5080	.5120	.5160	.5199	.5239
0.1	.5398	.5438	.5478	.5517	.5557	.5596	.5636
0.2	.5793	.5832	.5871	.5910	.5948	.5987	.6026
0.9	.8159	.8186	.8212	.8238	.8264	.8289	.8315
1.0	.8413	.8438	.8461	.8485	.8508	.8531	.8554
1.1	.8643	.8665	.8686	.8708	.8729	.8749	.8770
1.2	.8849	.8869	.8888	.8907	.8925	.8944	.8962
1.3	.9032	.9049	.9066	.9082	.9099	.9115	.9131
1.4	.9192	.9207	.9222	.9236	.9251	.9265	.9279

2. Find the area that corresponds to $z = -0.24$ by finding -0.2 in the left column and then moving across the row to the column under 0.04. The number in that row and column is 0.4052. So, the area to the left of $z = -0.24$ is 0.4052.

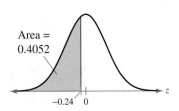

Area = 0.4052

z	.09	.08	.07	.06	.05	.04	.03
−3.4	.0002	.0003	.0003	.0003	.0003	.0003	.0003
−3.3	.0003	.0004	.0004	.0004	.0004	.0004	.0004
−3.2	.0005	.0005	.0005	.0006	.0006	.0006	.0006
−0.5	.2776	.2810	.2843	.2877	.2912	.2946	.2981
−0.4	.3121	.3156	.3192	.3228	.3264	.3300	.3336
−0.3	.3483	.3520	.3557	.3594	.3632	.3669	.3707
−0.2	.3859	.3897	.3936	.3974	.4013	.4052	.4090
−0.1	.4247	.4286	.4325	.4364	.4404	.4443	.4483
−0.0	.4641	.4681	.4721	.4761	.4801	.4840	.4880

You can also use a computer or calculator to find the cumulative area that corresponds to a z-score, as shown in the margin.

▸ Try It Yourself 3

1. Find the area under the curve to the left of a z-score of -2.19.
2. Find the area under the curve to the left of a z-score of 2.17.

Locate the given z-score and *find the area* that corresponds to it in the Standard Normal Table. *Answer: Page A40*

When the z-score is not in the table, use the entry closest to it. If the given z-score is exactly midway between two z-scores, then use the area midway between the corresponding areas.

Study Tip

Here are instructions for finding the area that corresponds to $z = -0.24$ on a TI-83/84.

To specify the lower bound in this case, use $-10,000$.

2nd DISTR

2: normalcdf(

−10000, −.24)

ENTER

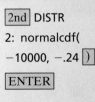

normalcdf(-10000
,-.24
          .405165175

You can use the following guidelines to find various types of areas under the standard normal curve.

GUIDELINES

Finding Areas Under the Standard Normal Curve

1. Sketch the standard normal curve and shade the appropriate area under the curve.

2. Find the area by following the directions for each case shown.

   a. To find the area to the *left* of z, find the area that corresponds to z in the Standard Normal Table.

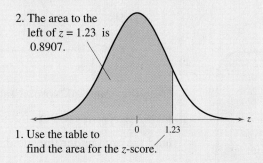

2. The area to the left of $z = 1.23$ is 0.8907.

1. Use the table to find the area for the z-score.

   b. To find the area to the *right* of z, use the Standard Normal Table to find the area that corresponds to z. Then subtract the area from 1.

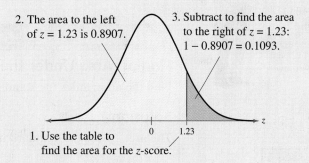

2. The area to the left of $z = 1.23$ is 0.8907.

3. Subtract to find the area to the right of $z = 1.23$: $1 - 0.8907 = 0.1093$.

1. Use the table to find the area for the z-score.

   c. To find the area *between* two z-scores, find the area corresponding to each z-score in the Standard Normal Table. Then subtract the smaller area from the larger area.

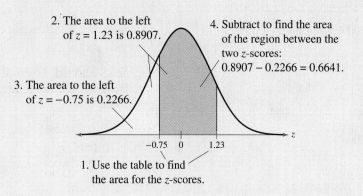

2. The area to the left of $z = 1.23$ is 0.8907.

4. Subtract to find the area of the region between the two z-scores: $0.8907 - 0.2266 = 0.6641$.

3. The area to the left of $z = -0.75$ is 0.2266.

1. Use the table to find the area for the z-scores.

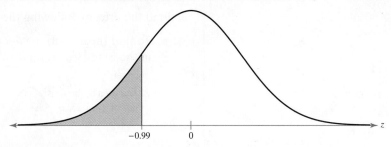

Using a TI-83/84, you can find the area automatically

Insight

Because the normal distribution is a continuous probability distribution, the area under the standard normal curve to the left of a z-score gives the probability that z is less than that z-score. For instance, in Example 4, the area to the left of $z = -0.99$ is 0.1611. So, $P(z < -0.99) = 0.1611$, which is read as "the probability that z is less than -0.99 is 0.1611."

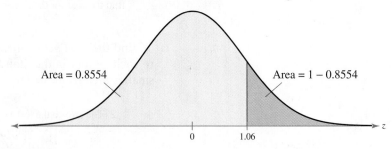

Use 10,000 for the upper bound.

EXAMPLE 4

Finding Area Under the Standard Normal Curve

Find the area under the standard normal curve to the left of $z = -0.99$.

Solution

The area under the standard normal curve to the left of $z = -0.99$ is shown.

From the Standard Normal Table, this area is equal to 0.1611.

▶ **Try It Yourself 4**

Find the area under the standard normal curve to the left of $z = 2.13$.

a. *Draw* the standard normal curve and shade the area under the curve and to the left of $z = 2.13$.

b. Use the Standard Normal Table to *find the area* that corresponds to $z = 2.13$.

Answer: Page A40

EXAMPLE 5

Finding Area Under the Standard Normal Curve

Find the area under the standard normal curve to the right of $z = 1.06$.

Solution

The area under the standard normal curve to the right of $z = 1.06$ is shown.

From the Standard Normal Table, the area to the left of $z = 1.06$ is 0.8554. Because the total area under the curve is 1, the area to the right of $z = 1.06$ is

$$\text{Area} = 1 - 0.8554$$
$$= 0.1446.$$

▶ **Try It Yourself 5**

Find the area under the standard normal curve to the right of $z = -2.16$.

a. *Draw* the standard normal curve and shade the area below the curve and to the right of $z = -2.16$.
b. Use the Standard Normal Table to *find the area* to the left of $z = -2.16$.
c. *Subtract* the area from 1.   *Answer: Page A40*

EXAMPLE 6

Finding Area Under the Standard Normal Curve

Find the area under the standard normal curve between $z = -1.5$ and $z = 1.25$.

Solution

The area under the standard normal curve between $z = -1.5$ and $z = 1.25$ is shown.

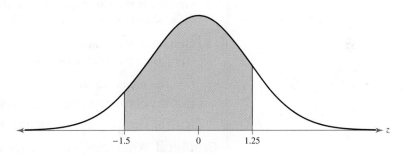

From the Standard Normal Table, the area to the left of $z = 1.25$ is 0.8944 and the area to the left of $z = -1.5$ is 0.0668. So, the area between $z = -1.5$ and $z = 1.25$ is

  Area $= 0.8944 - 0.0668$

      $= 0.8276$.

Interpretation   So, 82.76% of the area under the curve falls between $z = -1.5$ and $z = 1.25$.

▶ **Try It Yourself 6**

Find the area under the standard normal curve between $z = -2.16$ and $z = -1.35$.

a. Use the Standard Normal Table to *find the area* to the left of $z = -1.35$.
b. Use the Standard Normal Table to *find the area* to the left of $z = -2.16$.
c. *Subtract* the smaller area from the larger area.   *Answer: Page A40*

  Recall in Section 2.4 you learned, using the Empirical Rule, that values lying more than two standard deviations from the mean are considered unusual. Values lying more than three standard deviations from the mean are considered *very* unusual. So if a z-score is greater than 2 or less than -2, it is unusual. If a z-score is greater than 3 or less than -3, it is *very* unusual.

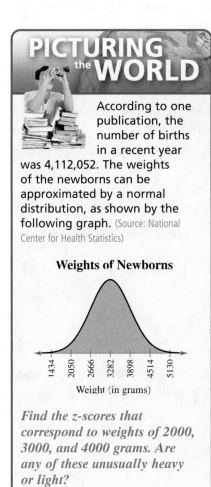

PICTURING the WORLD

According to one publication, the number of births in a recent year was 4,112,052. The weights of the newborns can be approximated by a normal distribution, as shown by the following graph. (Source: National Center for Health Statistics)

Weights of Newborns

Weight (in grams)

Find the z-scores that correspond to weights of 2000, 3000, and 4000 grams. Are any of these unusually heavy or light?

```
normalcdf(-1.5,1
.25)
      .8275429323
```

When using technology, your answers may differ slightly from those found using the Standard Normal Table.

5.1 EXERCISES

■ Building Basic Skills and Vocabulary

1. Find three real-life examples of a continuous variable. Which do you think may be normally distributed? Why?

2. What is the total area under the normal curve?

3. Draw two normal curves that have the same mean but different standard deviations. Describe the similarities and differences.

4. Draw two normal curves that have different means but the same standard deviations. Describe the similarities and differences.

5. What is the mean of the standard normal distribution? What is the standard deviation of the standard normal distribution?

6. Describe how you can transform a nonstandard normal distribution to a standard normal distribution.

7. Getting at the Concept   Why is it correct to say "a" normal distribution and "the" standard normal distribution?

8. Getting at the Concept   If a z-score is zero, which of the following must be true? Explain your reasoning.

(a) The mean is zero.

(b) The corresponding x-value is zero.

(c) The corresponding x-value is equal to the mean.

Graphical Analysis   *In Exercises 9–14, determine whether the graph could represent a variable with a normal distribution. Explain your reasoning.*

9.

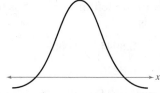

10.

11.

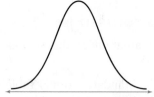

12.

13.

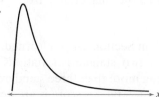

14.

Graphical Analysis   *In Exercises 15 and 16, determine whether the histogram represents data with a normal distribution. Explain your reasoning.*

15.

Waiting Time in a Dentist's Office

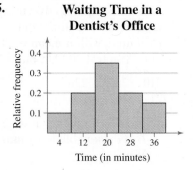

16.

Weight Loss

Graphical Analysis   *In Exercises 17–20, find the area of the indicated region under the standard normal curve. If convenient, use technology to find the area.*

17.

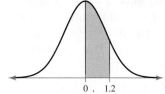

18.

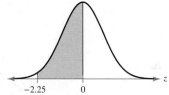

19.

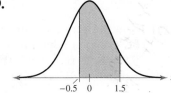

20.

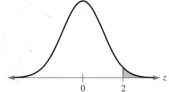

Finding Area   *In Exercises 21–40, find the indicated area under the standard normal curve. If convenient, use technology to find the area.*

21. To the left of $z = 1.36$

22. To the left of $z = 0.08$

23. To the left of $z = 1.96$

24. To the left of $z = 1.28$

25. To the right of $z = -0.65$

26. To the right of $z = -1.95$

27. To the right of $z = 1.28$

28. To the right of $z = 3.25$

29. To the left of $z = -2.575$

30. To the left of $z = -3.16$

31. To the right of $z = 1.615$

32. To the right of $z = 2.51$

33. Between $z = 0$ and $z = 1.54$

34. Between $z = 0$ and $z = 2.86$

35. Between $z = -1.53$ and $z = 0$

36. Between $z = -0.51$ and $z = 0$

37. Between $z = -1.96$ and $z = 1.96$

38. Between $z = -2.33$ and $z = 2.33$

39. To the left of $z = -1.28$ or to the right of $z = 1.28$

40. To the left of $z = -1.96$ or to the right of $z = 1.96$

■ Using and Interpreting Concepts

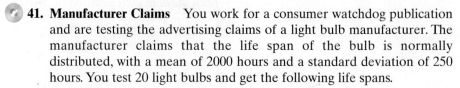 **41. Manufacturer Claims** You work for a consumer watchdog publication and are testing the advertising claims of a light bulb manufacturer. The manufacturer claims that the life span of the bulb is normally distributed, with a mean of 2000 hours and a standard deviation of 250 hours. You test 20 light bulbs and get the following life spans.

2210, 2406, 2267, 1930, 2005, 2502, 1106, 2140, 1949, 1921,
2217, 2121, 2004, 1397, 1659, 1577, 2840, 1728, 1209, 1639

(a) Draw a frequency histogram to display these data. Use five classes. Is it reasonable to assume that the life span is normally distributed? Why?

(b) Find the mean and standard deviation of your sample.

(c) Compare the mean and standard deviation of your sample with those in the manufacturer's claim. Discuss the differences.

42. Heights of Men You are performing a study about the height of 20- to 29-year-old men. A previous study found the height to be normally distributed, with a mean of 69.6 inches and a standard deviation of 3.0 inches. You randomly sample 30 men and find their heights to be as follows. *(Adapted from National Center for Health Statistics)*

72.1, 71.2, 67.9, 67.3, 69.5, 68.6, 68.8, 69.4, 73.5, 67.1,
69.2, 75.7, 71.1, 69.6, 70.7, 66.9, 71.4, 62.9, 69.2, 64.9,
68.2, 65.2, 69.7, 72.2, 67.5, 66.6, 66.5, 64.2, 65.4, 70.0

(a) Draw a frequency histogram to display these data. Use seven classes with midpoints of 63.85, 65.85, 67.85, 69.85, 71.85, 73.85, and 75.85. Is it reasonable to assume that the heights are normally distributed? Why?

(b) Find the mean and standard deviation of your sample.

(c) Compare the mean and standard deviation of your sample with those in the previous study. Discuss the differences.

Computing and Interpreting z-Scores of Normal Distributions *In Exercises 43–46, you are given a normal distribution, the distribution's mean and standard deviation, four values from that distribution, and a graph of the Standard Normal Distribution. (a) Without converting to z-scores, match each value with the letters A, B, C, and D on the given graph of the Standard Normal Distribution. (b) Find the z-score that corresponds to each value and check your answers to part (a). (c) Determine whether any of the values are unusual.*

43. Piston Rings Your company manufactures piston rings for cars. The inside diameters of the piston rings are normally distributed, with a mean of 93.01 millimeters and a standard deviation of 0.005 millimeter. The inside diameters of four piston rings selected at random are 93.014 millimeters, 93.018 millimeters, 93.004 millimeters, and 92.994 millimeters.

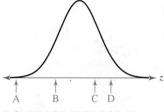

FIGURE FOR EXERCISE 43

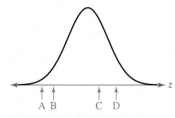

FIGURE FOR EXERCISE 44

44. House Wren Eggs   The incubation period for the eggs of a House Wren is normally distributed with a mean time of 336 hours and a standard deviation of 3.5 hours. The incubation times for four eggs selected at random are 328 hours, 338 hours, 330 hours, and 341 hours.

45. SAT I Scores   The SAT is an exam used by colleges and universities to evaluate undergraduate applicants. The test scores are normally distributed. In a recent year, the mean test score was 1518 and the standard deviation was 308. The test scores of four students selected at random are 1406, 1848, 2177, and 1186. *(Source: College Board Online)*

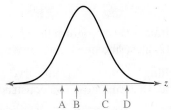   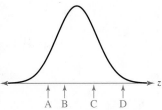

FIGURE FOR EXERCISE 45   FIGURE FOR EXERCISE 46

46. ACT Scores   The ACT is an exam used by colleges and universities to evaluate undergraduate applicants. The test scores are normally distributed. In a recent year, the mean test score was 21.0 and the standard deviation was 4.8. The test scores of four students selected at random are 18, 32, 14, and 25. *(Source: ACT, Inc.)*

Graphical Analysis   *In Exercises 47–52, find the probability of z occurring in the indicated region. If convenient, use technology to find the probability.*

47.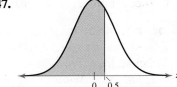

48.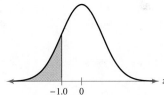

49.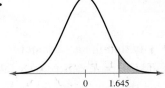

50.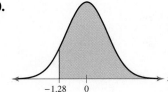

51.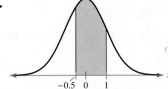

52.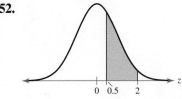

Finding Probabilities *In Exercises 53–62, find the indicated probability using the standard normal distribution. If convenient, use technology to find the probability.*

53. $P(z < 1.45)$ **54.** $P(z < 0.45)$ **55.** $P(z > -0.95)$

56. $P(z > -1.85)$ **57.** $P(-0.89 < z < 0)$ **58.** $P(-2.08 < z < 0)$

59. $P(-1.65 < z < 1.65)$ **60.** $P(-1.54 < z < 1.54)$

61. $P(z < -2.58 \text{ or } z > 2.58)$ **62.** $P(z < -1.54 \text{ or } z > 1.54)$

■ Extending Concepts

63. Writing Draw a normal curve with a mean of 60 and a standard deviation of 12. Describe how you constructed the curve and discuss its features.

64. Writing Draw a normal curve with a mean of 450 and a standard deviation of 50. Describe how you constructed the curve and discuss its features.

65. Uniform Distribution Another continuous distribution is the **uniform distribution.** An example is $f(x) = 1$ for $0 \le x \le 1$. The mean of this distribution for this example is 0.5 and the standard deviation is approximately 0.29. The graph of this distribution for this example is a square with the height and width both equal to 1 unit. In general, the density function for a uniform distribution on the interval from $x = a$ to $x = b$ is given by

$$f(x) = \frac{1}{b - a}.$$

The mean is

$$\frac{a + b}{2}$$

and the variance is

$$\frac{(b - a)^2}{12}.$$

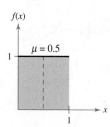

(a) Verify that the area under the curve is 1.

(b) Find the probability that x falls between 0.25 and 0.5.

(c) Find the probability that x falls between 0.3 and 0.7.

66. Uniform Distribution Consider the uniform density function $f(x) = 0.1$ for $10 \le x \le 20$. The mean of this distribution is 15 and the standard deviation is about 2.89.

(a) Draw a graph of the distribution and show that the area under the curve is 1.

(b) Find the probability that x falls between 12 and 15.

(c) Find the probability that x falls between 13 and 18.

5.2 Normal Distributions: Finding Probabilities

Probability and Normal Distributions

▸ Probability and Normal Distributions

If a random variable x is normally distributed, you can find the probability that x will fall in a given interval by calculating the area under the normal curve for the given interval. To find the area under any normal curve, you can first convert the upper and lower bounds of the interval to z-scores. Then use the standard normal distribution to find the area. For instance, consider a normal curve with $\mu = 500$ and $\sigma = 100$, as shown at the upper left. The value of x one standard deviation above the mean is $\mu + \sigma = 500 + 100 = 600$. Now consider the standard normal curve shown at the lower left. The value of z one standard deviation above the mean is $\mu + \sigma = 0 + 1 = 1$. Because a z-score of 1 corresponds to an x-value of 600, and areas are not changed with a transformation to a standard normal curve, the shaded areas in the graphs are equal.

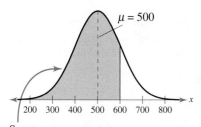

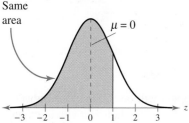

Same area

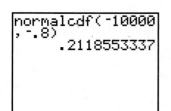

In Example 1, you can use a TI-83/84 to find the probability once the upper bound is converted to a z-score.

EXAMPLE 1

Finding Probabilities for Normal Distributions

A survey indicates that people use their computers an average of 2.4 years before upgrading to a new machine. The standard deviation is 0.5 year. A computer owner is selected at random. Find the probability that he or she will use it for fewer than 2 years before upgrading. Assume that the variable x is normally distributed.

Solution   The graph shows a normal curve with $\mu = 2.4$ and $\sigma = 0.5$ and a shaded area for x less than 2. The z-score that corresponds to 2 years is

$$z = \frac{x - \mu}{\sigma} = \frac{2 - 2.4}{0.5} = -0.80.$$

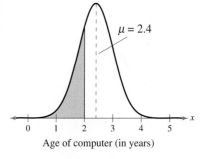

The Standard Normal Table shows that $P(z < -0.8) = 0.2119$. The probability that the computer will be upgraded in fewer than 2 years is 0.2119.

Interpretation   So, 21.19% of computer owners will upgrade in fewer than 2 years.

▸ Try It Yourself 1

A Ford Focus manual transmission gets an average of 24 miles per gallon (mpg) in city driving with a standard deviation of 1.6 mpg. A Focus is selected at random. What is the probability that it will get more than 28 mpg? Assume that gas mileage is normally distributed. *(Adapted from U.S. Department of Energy)*

a. *Sketch* a graph.
b. *Find the z-score* that corresponds to 28 miles per gallon.
c. *Find the area* to the right of that z-score.
d. *Write* the result as a sentence.   *Answer: Page A40*

EXAMPLE 2

Finding Probabilities for Normal Distributions

A survey indicates that for each trip to the supermarket, a shopper spends an average of 45 minutes with a standard deviation of 12 minutes in the store. The length of time spent in the store is normally distributed and is represented by the variable x. A shopper enters the store. (a) Find the probability that the shopper will be in the store for each interval of time listed below. (b) Interpret your answer if 200 shoppers enter the store. How many shoppers would you expect to be in the store for each interval of time listed below?

1. Between 24 and 54 minutes   **2.** More than 39 minutes

Solution

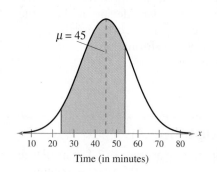

Time (in minutes)

1. (a) The graph at the left shows a normal curve with $\mu = 45$ minutes and $\sigma = 12$ minutes. The area for x between 24 and 54 minutes is shaded. The z-scores that correspond to 24 minutes and to 54 minutes are

$$z_1 = \frac{24 - 45}{12} = -1.75 \quad \text{and} \quad z_2 = \frac{54 - 45}{12} = 0.75.$$

So, the probability that a shopper will be in the store between 24 and 54 minutes is

$$P(24 < x < 54) = P(-1.75 < z < 0.75)$$
$$= P(z < 0.75) - P(z < -1.75)$$
$$= 0.7734 - 0.0401 = 0.7333.$$

(b) **Interpretation**   So, 73.33% of the shoppers will be in the store between 24 and 54 minutes. If 200 shoppers enter the store, then you would expect $200(0.7333) = 146.66$ (or about 147) shoppers to be in the store between 24 and 54 minutes.

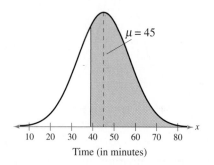

Time (in minutes)

2. (a) The graph at the left shows a normal curve with $\mu = 45$ minutes and $\sigma = 12$ minutes. The area for x greater than 39 minutes is shaded. The z-score that corresponds to 39 minutes is

$$z = \frac{39 - 45}{12} = -0.5.$$

So, the probability that a shopper will be in the store more than 39 minutes is

$$P(x > 39) = P(z > -0.5) = 1 - P(z < -0.5) = 1 - 0.3085 = 0.6915.$$

(b) **Interpretation**   If 200 shoppers enter the store, then you would expect $200(0.6915) = 138.3$ (or about 138) shoppers to be in the store more than 39 minutes.

▶ Try It Yourself 2

What is the probability that the shopper in Example 2 will be in the supermarket between 33 and 60 minutes?

a. *Sketch* a graph.
b. *Find z-scores* that correspond to 60 minutes and 33 minutes.
c. *Find the cumulative area* for each z-score and *subtract* the smaller area from the larger.
d. *Interpret* your answer if 150 shoppers enter the store. How many shoppers would you expect to be in the store between 33 and 60 minutes?

Answer: Page A40

Another way to find normal probabilities is to use a calculator or a computer. You can find normal probabilities using MINITAB, Excel, and the TI-83/84.

EXAMPLE 3

Using Technology to Find Normal Probabilities

Assume that cholesterol levels of men in the United States are normally distributed, with a mean of 215 milligrams per deciliter and a standard deviation of 25 milligrams per deciliter. You randomly select a man from the United States. What is the probability that his cholesterol level is less than 175? Use a technology tool to find the probability.

Solution   MINITAB, Excel, and the TI-83/84 each have features that allow you to find normal probabilities without first converting to standard z-scores. For each, you must specify the mean and standard deviation of the population, as well as the x-value(s) that determine the interval.

MINITAB

Cumulative Distribution Function

Normal with mean = 215.000 and standard deviation = 25.0000

x	P[X <= x]
175.0000	0.0548

EXCEL

	A	B	C
1	NORMDIST(175,215,25,TRUE)		
2			0.054799

TI-83/84

normalcdf(0,175,215,25)
            .0547992894

From the displays, you can see that the probability that his cholesterol level is less than 175 is about 0.0548, or 5.48%.

▶ Try It Yourself 3

A man from the United States is selected at random. What is the probability that his cholesterol is between 190 and 225? Use a technology tool.

a. *Read the user's guide* for the technology tool you are using.
b. *Enter the appropriate data* to obtain the probability.
c. *Write* the result as a sentence.   *Answer: Page A40*

Example 3 shows only one of several ways to find normal probabilities using MINITAB, Excel, and the TI-83/84.

PICTURING the WORLD

In baseball, a batting average is the number of hits divided by the number of at-bats. The batting averages of the more than 750 Major League Baseball players in a recent year can be approximated by a normal distribution, as shown in the following graph. The mean of the batting averages is 0.269 and the standard deviation is 0.009.

Major League Baseball

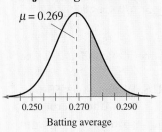

$\mu = 0.269$

Batting average

What percent of the players have a batting average of 0.275 or greater? If there are 40 players on a roster, how many would you expect to have a batting average of 0.275 or greater?

5.2 EXERCISES

■ Building Basic Skills and Vocabulary

Computing Probabilities *In Exercises 1–6, assume the random variable x is normally distributed with mean μ = 86 and standard deviation σ = 5. Find the indicated probability.*

1. $P(x < 80)$ **2.** $P(x < 100)$

3. $P(x > 92)$ **4.** $P(x > 75)$

5. $P(70 < x < 80)$ **6.** $P(85 < x < 95)$

Graphical Analysis *In Exercises 7–12, assume a member is selected at random from the population represented by the graph. Find the probability that the member selected at random is from the shaded area of the graph. Assume the variable x is normally distributed.*

7. SAT Critical Reading Scores

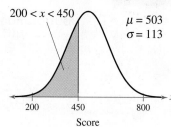

$200 < x < 450$

$\mu = 503$
$\sigma = 113$

Score

(Source: College Board Online)

8. SAT Math Scores

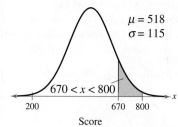

$670 < x < 800$

$\mu = 518$
$\sigma = 115$

Score

(Source: College Board Online)

9. U.S. Women Ages 20–34: Total Cholesterol

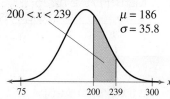

$200 < x < 239$

$\mu = 186$
$\sigma = 35.8$

Total cholesterol level (in mg/dL)

(Adapted from National Center for Health Statistics)

10. U.S. Women Ages 55–64: Total Cholesterol

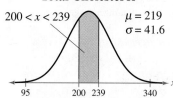

$200 < x < 239$

$\mu = 219$
$\sigma = 41.6$

Total cholesterol level (in mg/dL)

(Adapted from National Center for Health Statistics)

11. Toyota Camry: Braking Distance on a Dry Surface

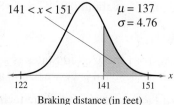

$141 < x < 151$

$\mu = 137$
$\sigma = 4.76$

Braking distance (in feet)

(Adapted from Consumer Reports)

12. Toyota Camry: Braking Distance on a Wet Surface

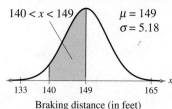

$140 < x < 149$

$\mu = 149$
$\sigma = 5.18$

Braking distance (in feet)

(Adapted from Consumer Reports)

■ Using and Interpreting Concepts

Finding Probabilities   *In Exercises 13–20, find the indicated probabilities. If convenient, use technology to find the probabilities.*

13. **Heights of Men**   A survey was conducted to measure the height of U.S. men. In the survey, respondents were grouped by age. In the 20–29 age group, the heights were normally distributed, with a mean of 69.6 inches and a standard deviation of 3.0 inches. A study participant is randomly selected. *(Adapted from U.S. National Center for Health Statistics)*

    (a) Find the probability that his height is less than 66 inches.

    (b) Find the probability that his height is between 66 and 72 inches.

    (c) Find the probability that his height is more than 72 inches.

14. **Fish Lengths**   The lengths of Atlantic croaker fish are normally distributed, with a mean of 10 inches and a standard deviation of 2 inches. An Atlantic croaker fish is randomly selected. *(Adapted from National Marine Fisheries Service, Fisheries Statistics and Economics Division)*

    (a) Find the probability that the length of the fish is less than 7 inches.

    (b) Find the probability that the length of the fish is between 7 and 15 inches.

    (c) Find the probability that the length of the fish is more than 15 inches.

15. **ACT Scores**   In a recent year, the ACT scores for high school students with a 3.50 to 4.00 grade point average were normally distributed, with a mean of 24.2 and a standard deviation of 4.3. A student with a 3.50 to 4.00 grade point average who took the ACT during this time is randomly selected. *(Source: ACT, Inc.)*

    (a) Find the probability that the student's ACT score is less than 17.

    (b) Find the probability that the student's ACT score is between 20 and 29.

    (c) Find the probability that the student's ACT score is more than 32.

16. **Beagles**   The weights of adult male beagles are normally distributed, with a mean of 25 pounds and a standard deviation of 3 pounds. A beagle is randomly selected.

    (a) Find the probability that the beagle's weight is less than 23 pounds.

    (b) Find the probability that the weight is between 23 and 25 pounds.

    (c) Find the probability that the beagle's weight is more than 27 pounds.

17. **Computer Usage**   A survey was conducted to measure the number of hours per week adults in the United States spend on home computers. In the survey, the number of hours were normally distributed, with a mean of 7 hours and a standard deviation of 1 hour. A survey participant is randomly selected.

    (a) Find the probability that the hours spent on the home computer by the participant are less than 5 hours per week.

    (b) Find the probability that the hours spent on the home computer by the participant are between 5.5 and 9.5 hours per week.

    (c) Find the probability that the hours spent on the home computer by the participant are more than 10 hours per week.

18. Utility Bills The monthly utility bills in a city are normally distributed, with a mean of $100 and a standard deviation of $12. A utility bill is randomly selected.

(a) Find the probability that the utility bill is less than $70.

(b) Find the probability that the utility bill is between $90 and $120.

(c) Find the probability that the utility bill is more than $140.

19. Computer Lab Schedule The time per week a student uses a lab computer is normally distributed, with a mean of 6.2 hours and a standard deviation of 0.9 hour. A student is randomly selected.

(a) Find the probability that the student uses a lab computer less than 4 hours per week.

(b) Find the probability that the student uses a lab computer between 5 and 7 hours per week.

(c) Find the probability that the student uses a lab computer more than 8 hours per week.

20. Health Club Schedule The time per workout an athlete uses a stairclimber is normally distributed, with a mean of 20 minutes and a standard deviation of 5 minutes. An athlete is randomly selected.

(a) Find the probability that the athlete uses a stairclimber for less than 17 minutes.

(b) Find the probability that the athlete uses a stairclimber between 20 and 28 minutes.

(c) Find the probability that the athlete uses a stairclimber for more than 30 minutes.

Using Normal Distributions *In Exercises 21–30, answer the questions about the specified normal distribution.*

21. SAT Critical Reading Scores Use the normal distribution of SAT critical reading scores in Exercise 7 for which the mean is 503 and the standard deviation is 113.

(a) What percent of the SAT verbal scores are less than 600?

(b) If 1000 SAT verbal scores are randomly selected, about how many would you expect to be greater than 550?

22. SAT Math Scores Use the normal distribution of SAT math scores in Exercise 8 for which the mean is 518 and the standard deviation is 115.

(a) What percent of the SAT math scores are less than 500?

(b) If 1500 SAT math scores are randomly selected, about how many would you expect to be greater than 600?

23. Cholesterol Use the normal distribution of women's total cholesterol levels in Exercise 9 for which the mean is 186 milligrams per deciliter and the standard deviation is 35.8 milligrams per deciliter.

(a) What percent of the women have a total cholesterol level less than 200 milligrams per deciliter of blood?

(b) If 250 U.S. women in the 20–34 age group are randomly selected, about how many would you expect to have a total cholesterol level greater than 240 milligrams per deciliter of blood?

24. Cholesterol Use the normal distribution of women's total cholesterol levels in Exercise 10 for which the mean is 219 milligrams per deciliter and the standard deviation is 41.6 milligrams per deciliter.

(a) What percent of the women have a total cholesterol level less than 239 milligrams per deciliter of blood?

(b) If 200 U.S. women in the 55–64 age group are randomly selected, about how many would you expect to have a total cholesterol level greater than 200 milligrams per deciliter of blood?

25. Fish Lengths Use the normal distribution of fish lengths in Exercise 14 for which the mean is 10 inches and the standard deviation is 2 inches.

(a) What percent of the fish are longer than 11 inches?

(b) If 200 Atlantic croakers are randomly selected, about how many would you expect to be shorter than 8 inches?

26. Beagles Use the normal distribution of beagle weights in Exercise 16 for which the mean is 25 pounds and the standard deviation is 3 pounds.

(a) What percent of the beagles have a weight that is greater than 30 pounds?

(b) If 50 beagles are randomly selected, about how many would you expect to weigh less than 22 pounds?

27. Computer Usage Use the normal distribution of computer usage in Exercise 17 for which the mean is 7 hours and the standard deviation is 1 hour.

(a) What percent of the adults spend more than 4 hours per week on a home computer?

(b) If 35 adults in the United States are randomly selected, about how many would you expect to say they spend less than 5 hours per week on a home computer?

28. Utility Bills Use the normal distribution of utility bills in Exercise 18 for which the mean is $100 and the standard deviation is $12.

(a) What percent of the utility bills are more than $125?

(b) If 300 utility bills are randomly selected, about how many would you expect to be less than $90?

29. Battery Life Spans The life span of a battery is normally distributed, with a mean of 2000 hours and a standard deviation of 30 hours. What percent of batteries have a life span that is more than 2065 hours? Would it be unusual for a battery to have a life span that is more than 2065 hours? Explain your reasoning.

30. Peanuts Assume the mean annual consumption of peanuts is normally distributed, with a mean of 5.9 pounds per person and a standard deviation of 1.8 pounds per person. What percent of people annually consume less than 3.1 pounds of peanuts per person? Would it be unusual for a person to consume less than 3.1 pounds of peanuts in a year? Explain your reasoning.

■ Extending Concepts

Control Charts *Statistical process control (SPC) is the use of statistics to monitor and improve the quality of a process, such as manufacturing an engine part. In SPC, information about a process is gathered and used to determine if a process is meeting all of the specified requirements. One tool used in SPC is a* **control chart.** *When individual measurements of a variable x are normally distributed, a control chart can be used to detect processes that are possibly out of statistical control. Three warning signals that a control chart uses to detect a process that may be out of control are as follows:*

(1) A point lies beyond three standard deviations of the mean.

(2) There are nine consecutive points that fall on one side of the mean.

(3) At least two of three consecutive points lie more than two standard deviations from the mean.

In Exercises 31–34, a control chart is shown. Each chart has horizontal lines drawn at the mean μ, at μ ± 2σ, and at μ ± 3σ. Determine if the process shown is in control or out of control. Explain.

31. A gear has been designed to have a diameter of 3 inches. The standard deviation of the process is 0.2 inch.

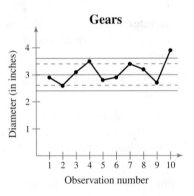

Gears

32. A nail has been designed to have a length of 4 inches. The standard deviation of the process is 0.12 inch.

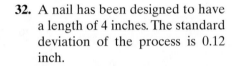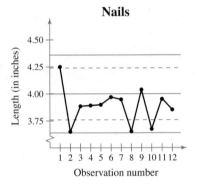

Nails

33. A liquid-dispensing machine has been designed to fill bottles with 1 liter of liquid. The standard deviation of the process is 0.1 liter.

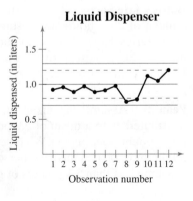

Liquid Dispenser

34. An engine part has been designed to have a diameter of 55 millimeters. The standard deviation of the process is 0.001 millimeter.

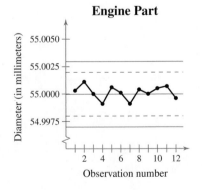

Engine Part

5.3 Normal Distributions: Finding Values

Finding *z*-Scores ▸ Transforming a *z*-Score to an *x*-Value ▸ Finding a Specific Data Value for a Given Probability

▸ Finding *z*-Scores

In Section 5.2, you were given a normally distributed random variable *x* and you found the probability that *x* would fall in a given interval by calculating the area under the normal curve for the given interval.

But what if you are given a probability and want to find a value? For instance, a university might want to know what is the lowest test score a student can have on an entrance exam and still be in the top 10%, or a medical researcher might want to know the cutoff values to select the middle 90% of patients by age. In this section, you will learn how to find a value given an area under a normal curve (or a probability), as shown in the following example.

EXAMPLE 1

Finding a *z*-Score Given an Area

1. Find the *z*-score that corresponds to a cumulative area of 0.3632.
2. Find the *z*-score that has 10.75% of the distribution's area to its right.

Solution

1. Find the *z*-score that corresponds to an area of 0.3632 by locating 0.3632 in the Standard Normal Table. The values at the beginning of the corresponding row and at the top of the corresponding column give the *z*-score. For this area, the row value is -0.3 and the column value is 0.05. So, the *z*-score is -0.35.

z	.09	.08	.07	.06	.05	.04	.03
−3.4	.0002	.0003	.0003	.0003	.0003	.0003	.0003
−0.5	.2776	.2810	.2843	.2877	.2912	.2946	.2981
−0.4	.3121	.3156	.3192	.3228	.3264	.3300	.3336
−0.3	.3483	.3520	.3557	.3594	.3632	.3669	.3707
−0.2	.3859	.3897	.3936	.3974	.4013	.4052	.4090

2. Because the area to the right is 0.1075, the cumulative area is $1 - 0.1075 = 0.8925$. Find the *z*-score that corresponds to an area of 0.8925 by locating 0.8925 in the Standard Normal Table. For this area, the row value is 1.2 and the column value is 0.04. So, the *z*-score is 1.24.

z	.00	.01	.02	.03	.04	.05	.06
0.0	.5000	.5040	.5080	.5120	.5160	.5199	.5239
1.0	.8413	.8438	.8461	.8485	.8508	.8531	.8554
1.1	.8643	.8665	.8686	.8708	.8729	.8749	.8770
1.2	.8849	.8869	.8888	.8907	.8925	.8944	.8962
1.3	.9032	.9049	.9066	.9082	.9099	.9115	.9131

You can also use a computer or calculator to find the *z*-scores that correspond to the given cumulative areas, as shown in the margin.

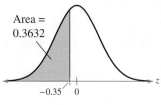

Area = 0.3632

-0.35 0   *z*

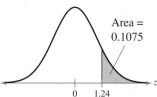

Area = 0.1075

0   1.24   *z*

▶ **Try It Yourself 1**

1. Find the z-score that has 96.16% of the distribution's area to the right.
2. Find the z-score for which 95% of the distribution's area lies between $-z$ and z.

a. *Determine* the cumulative area.
b. *Locate* the area in the Standard Normal Table.
c. *Find the z-score* that corresponds to the area.   *Answer: Page A40*

Study Tip

In most cases, the given area will not be found in the table, so use the entry closest to it. If the given area is halfway between two area entries, use the z-score halfway between the corresponding z-scores. For instance, in part 1 of Example 2, the z-score between -1.64 and -1.65 is -1.645.

In Section 2.5, you learned that percentiles divide a data set into one hundred equal parts. To find a z-score that corresponds to a percentile, you can use the Standard Normal Table. Recall that if a value x represents the 83rd percentile P_{83}, then 83% of the data values are below x and 17% of the data values are above x.

EXAMPLE 2

Finding a z-Score Given a Percentile

Find the z-score that corresponds to each percentile.

1. P_5 2. P_{50} 3. P_{90}

Solution

1. To find the z-score that corresponds to P_5, find the z-score that corresponds to an area of 0.05 (see figure) by locating 0.05 in the Standard Normal Table. The areas closest to 0.05 in the table are 0.0495 ($z = -1.65$) and 0.0505 ($z = -1.64$). Because 0.05 is halfway between the two areas in the table, use the z-score that is halfway between -1.64 and -1.65. So, the z-score that corresponds to an area of 0.05 is -1.645.

2. To find the z-score that corresponds to P_{50}, find the z-score that corresponds to an area of 0.5 (see figure) by locating 0.5 in the Standard Normal Table. The area closest to 0.5 in the table is 0.5000, so the z-score that corresponds to an area of 0.5 is 0.00.

3. To find the z-score that corresponds to P_{90}, find the z-score that corresponds to an area of 0.9 (see figure) by locating 0.9 in the Standard Normal Table. The area closest to 0.9 in the table is 0.8997, so the z-score that corresponds to an area of 0.9 is 1.28.

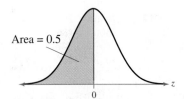

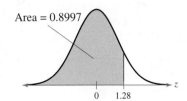

▶ **Try It Yourself 2**

Find the z-score that corresponds to each percentile.

1. P_{10} 2. P_{20} 3. P_{99}

a. *Write* the percentile as an area. If necessary, draw a graph of the area to visualize the problem.
b. *Locate* the area in the Standard Normal Table. If the area is not in the table, use the closest area. (See Study Tip above.)
c. *Identify* the z-score that corresponds to the area.   *Answer: Page A40*

▶ Transforming a z-Score to an x-Value

Recall that to transform an x-value to a z-score, you can use the formula

$$z = \frac{x - \mu}{\sigma}.$$

This formula gives z in terms of x. If you solve this formula for x, you get a new formula that gives x in terms of z.

$$z = \frac{x - \mu}{\sigma} \qquad \text{Formula for } z \text{ in terms of } x$$

$$z\sigma = x - \mu \qquad \text{Multiply each side by } \sigma.$$

$$\mu + z\sigma = x \qquad \text{Add } \mu \text{ to each side.}$$

$$x = \mu + z\sigma \qquad \text{Interchange sides.}$$

TRANSFORMING A Z-SCORE TO AN X-VALUE

To transform a standard z-score to a data value x in a given population, use the formula

$$x = \mu + z\sigma.$$

EXAMPLE 3

Finding an x-Value Corresponding to a z-Score

The speeds of vehicles along a stretch of highway are normally distributed, with a mean of 67 miles per hour and a standard deviation of 4 miles per hour. Find the speeds x corresponding to z-scores of 1.96, −2.33, and 0. Interpret your results.

Solution   The x-value that corresponds to each standard score is calculated using the formula $x = \mu + z\sigma$.

$z = 1.96$: $x = 67 + 1.96(4) = 74.84$ miles per hour

$z = -2.33$: $x = 67 + (-2.33)(4) = 57.68$ miles per hour

$z = 0$: $x = 67 + 0(4) = 67$ miles per hour

Interpretation   You can see that 74.84 miles per hour is above the mean, 57.68 is below the mean, and 67 is equal to the mean.

▶ Try It Yourself 3

The monthly utility bills in a city are normally distributed, with a mean of $70 and a standard deviation of $8. Find the x-values that correspond to z-scores of −0.75, 4.29, and −1.82. What can you conclude?

a. *Identify* μ and σ of the nonstandard normal distribution.
b. *Transform* each z-score to an x-value.
c. *Interpret* the results.   *Answer: Page A40*

PICTURING the **WORLD**

According to the American Medical Association, the mean number of hours all physicians spend in patient care each week is about 52.8 hours. The hours spent in patient care each week by physicians can be approximated by a normal distribution. Assume the standard deviation is 3 hours.

Hours Physicians Spend in Patient Care

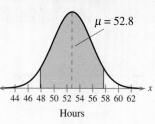

Between what two values does the middle 90% of the data lie?

Study Tip

Here are instructions for finding a specific *x*-value for a given probability on a TI-83/84.

[2nd] [DISTR]

3: invNorm(

Enter the values for the area under the normal distribution, the specified mean, and the specified standard deviation separated by commas.

[ENTER]

```
invNorm(.95,75,6
.5)
        85.69154857
```

▶ Finding a Specific Data Value for a Given Probability

You can also use the normal distribution to find a specific data value (*x*-value) for a given probability, as shown in Example 4.

E X A M P L E 4

Finding a Specific Data Value

Scores for a civil service exam are normally distributed, with a mean of 75 and a standard deviation of 6.5. To be eligible for civil service employment, you must score in the top 5%. What is the lowest score you can earn and still be eligible for employment?

Solution Exam scores in the top 5% correspond to the shaded region shown.

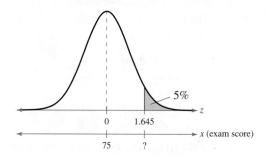

An exam score in the top 5% is any score above the 95th percentile. To find the score that represents the 95th percentile, you must first find the *z*-score that corresponds to a cumulative area of 0.95. From the Standard Normal Table, you can find that the areas closest to 0.95 are 0.9495 ($z = 1.64$) and 0.9505 ($z = 1.65$). Because 0.95 is halfway between the two areas in the table, use the *z*-score that is halfway between 1.64 and 1.65. That is, $z = 1.645$. Using the equation $x = \mu + z\sigma$, you have

$$x = \mu + z\sigma$$
$$= 75 + 1.645(6.5)$$
$$\approx 85.69.$$

Interpretation The lowest score you can earn and still be eligible for employment is 86.

▶ Try It Yourself 4

The braking distances of a sample of Honda Accords are normally distributed. On a dry surface, the mean braking distance was 142 feet and the standard deviation was 6.51 feet. What is the longest braking distance on a dry surface one of these Honda Accords could have and still be in the top 1%? *(Adapted from Consumer Reports)*

a. *Sketch* a graph.
b. *Find the z-score* that corresponds to the given area.
c. *Find x* using the equation $x = \mu + z\sigma$.
d. *Interpret* the result.

Answer: Page A40

EXAMPLE 5

Finding a Specific Data Value

In a randomly selected sample of 1169 men ages 35–44, the mean total cholesterol level was 210 milligrams per deciliter with a standard deviation of 38.6 milligrams per deciliter. Assume the total cholesterol levels are normally distributed. Find the highest total cholesterol level a man in this 35–44 age group can have and be in the lowest 1%. *(Adapted from National Center for Health Statistics)*

Solution

Total cholesterol levels in the lowest 1% correspond to the shaded region shown.

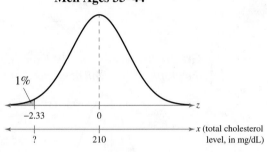

Total Cholesterol Levels in Men Ages 35–44

A total cholesterol level in the lowest 1% is any level below the 1st percentile. To find the level that represents the 1st percentile, you must first find the z-score that corresponds to a cumulative area of 0.01. From the Standard Normal Table, you can find that the area closest to 0.01 is 0.0099. So, the z-score that corresponds to an area of 0.01 is $z = -2.33$. Using the equation $x = \mu + z\sigma$, you have

$$x = \mu + z\sigma$$
$$= 210 + (-2.33)(38.6)$$
$$\approx 120.06.$$

Interpretation   The value that separates the lowest 1% of total cholesterol levels for men in the 35–44 age group from the highest 99% is about 120.

▶ Try It Yourself 5

The length of time employees have worked at a corporation is normally distributed, with a mean of 11.2 years and a standard deviation of 2.1 years. In a company cutback, the lowest 10% in seniority are laid off. What is the maximum length of time an employee could have worked and still be laid off?

a. *Sketch* a graph.
b. *Find the z-score* that corresponds to the given area.
c. *Find x* using the equation $x = \mu + z\sigma$.
d. *Interpret* the result.

Answer: Page A41

```
invNorm(.01,210,
38.6)
        120.2029719
```

Using a TI-83/84, you can find the highest total cholesterol level automatically.

5.3 EXERCISES

■ Building Basic Skills and Vocabulary

In Exercises 1–24, use the Standard Normal Table to find the z-score that corresponds to the given cumulative area or percentile. If the area is not in the table, use the entry closest to the area. If the area is halfway between two entries, use the z-score halfway between the corresponding z-scores. If convenient, use technology to find the z-score.

1. 0.7580	**2.** 0.2090	**3.** 0.6331	**4.** 0.0918
5. 0.4364	**6.** 0.0080	**7.** 0.9916	**8.** 0.7995
9. 0.05	**10.** 0.85	**11.** 0.94	**12.** 0.01
13. P_1	**14.** P_{15}	**15.** P_{20}	**16.** P_{55}
17. P_{88}	**18.** P_{67}	**19.** P_{25}	**20.** P_{50}
21. P_{75}	**22.** P_{90}	**23.** P_{35}	**24.** P_{65}

Graphical Analysis *In Exercises 25–30, find the indicated z-score(s) shown in the graph. If convenient, use technology to find the z-score(s).*

25.

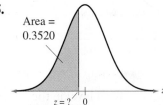

Area = 0.3520

$z = ?$ 0

26.

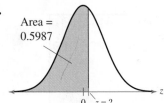

Area = 0.5987

0   $z = ?$

27.

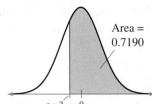

Area = 0.7190

$z = ?$ 0

28.

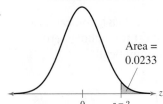

Area = 0.0233

0   $z = ?$

29.

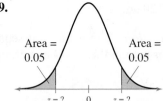

Area = 0.05   Area = 0.05

$z = ?$ 0 $z = ?$

30.

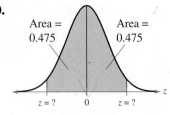

Area = 0.475   Area = 0.475

$z = ?$ 0 $z = ?$

In Exercises 31–38, find the indicated z-score.

31. Find the z-score that has 11.9% of the distribution's area to its left.

32. Find the z-score that has 78.5% of the distribution's area to its left.

33. Find the z-score that has 11.9% of the distribution's area to its right.

34. Find the z-score that has 78.5% of the distribution's area to its right.

35. Find the z-score for which 80% of the distribution's area lies between −z and z.

36. Find the z-score for which 99% of the distribution's area lies between $-z$ and z.

37. Find the z-score for which 5% of the distribution's area lies between $-z$ and z.

38. Find the z-score for which 12% of the distribution's area lies between $-z$ and z.

■ Using and Interpreting Concepts

Using Normal Distributions   *In Exercises 39–44, answer the questions about the specified normal distribution.*

39. Heights of Women   In a survey of women in the United States (ages 20–29), the mean height was 64.1 inches with a standard deviation of 2.71 inches. *(Adapted from National Center for Health Statistics)*

(a) What height represents the 95th percentile?

(b) What height represents the first quartile?

40. Heights of Men   In a survey of men in the United States (ages 20–29), the mean height was 69.6 inches with a standard deviation of 3.0 inches. *(Adapted from National Center for Health Statistics)*

(a) What height represents the 90th percentile?

(b) What height represents the first quartile?

41. Apples   The annual per capita utilization of apples (in pounds) in the United States can be approximated by a normal distribution, as shown in the graph. *(Adapted from U.S. Department of Agriculture)*

(a) What annual per capita utilization of apples represents the 10th percentile?

(b) What annual per capita utilization of apples represents the third quartile?

Annual U.S. per Capita Apple Utilization

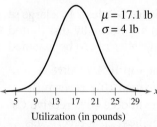

$\mu = 17.1$ lb
$\sigma = 4$ lb

Utilization (in pounds)

FIGURE FOR EXERCISE 41

Annual U.S. per Capita Orange Utilization

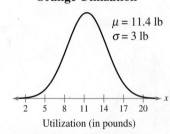

$\mu = 11.4$ lb
$\sigma = 3$ lb

Utilization (in pounds)

FIGURE FOR EXERCISE 42

42. Oranges   The annual per capita utilization of oranges (in pounds) in the United States can be approximated by a normal distribution, as shown in the graph. *(Adapted from U.S. Department of Agriculture)*

(a) What annual per capita utilization of oranges represents the 5th percentile?

(b) What annual per capita utilization of oranges represents the third quartile?

Time Spent Waiting for a Heart

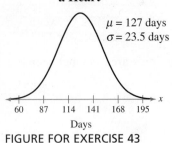

$\mu = 127$ days
$\sigma = 23.5$ days

60   87   114   141   168   195
Days

FIGURE FOR EXERCISE 43

Annual U.S. per Capita Ice Cream Consumption

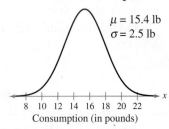

$\mu = 15.4$ lb
$\sigma = 2.5$ lb

8   10   12   14   16   18   20   22
Consumption (in pounds)

FIGURE FOR EXERCISE 44

Final Exam Grades

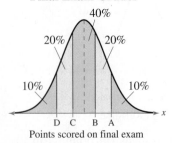

40%
20%   20%
10%   10%

D   C   B   A
Points scored on final exam

FIGURE FOR EXERCISE 48

43. Heart Transplant Waiting Times   The time spent (in days) waiting for a heart transplant in Ohio and Michigan for patients with type A⁺ blood can be approximated by a normal distribution, as shown in the graph. *(Adapted from Organ Procurement and Transplant Network)*

(a) What is the shortest time spent waiting for a heart that would still place a patient in the top 30% of waiting times?

(b) What is the longest time spent waiting for a heart that would still place a patient in the bottom 10% of waiting times?

44. Ice Cream   The annual per capita consumption of ice cream (in pounds) in the United States can be approximated by a normal distribution, as shown in the graph. *(Adapted from U.S. Department of Agriculture)*

(a) What is the smallest annual per capita consumption of ice cream that can be in the top 25% of consumptions?

(b) What is the largest annual per capita consumption of ice cream that can be in the bottom 15% of consumptions?

45. Cereal Boxes   The weights of the contents of a cereal box are normally distributed with a mean weight of 20 ounces and a standard deviation of 0.07 ounce. Boxes in the lower 5% do not meet the minimum weight requirements and must be repackaged. What is the minimum weight requirement for a cereal box?

46. Bags of Baby Carrots   The weights of bags of baby carrots are normally distributed with a mean of 32 ounces and a standard deviation of 0.36 ounce. Bags in the upper 4.5% are too heavy and must be repackaged. What is the most a bag of baby carrots can weigh and not need to be repackaged?

■ Extending Concepts

47. Writing a Guarantee   You sell a brand of automobile tire that has a life expectancy that is normally distributed, with a mean life of 30,000 miles and a standard deviation of 2500 miles. You want to give a guarantee for free replacement of tires that don't wear well. How should you word your guarantee if you are willing to replace approximately 10% of the tires you sell?

48. Statistics Grades   In a large section of a statistics class, the points for the final exam are normally distributed with a mean of 72 and a standard deviation of 9. Grades are to be assigned according to the following rule.

• The top 10% receive As
• The next 20% receive Bs
• The middle 40% receive Cs
• The next 20% receive Ds
• The bottom 10% receive Fs

Find the lowest score on the final exam that would qualify a student for an A, a B, a C, and a D.

49. Vending Machine   A vending machine dispenses coffee into an eight-ounce cup. The amount of coffee dispensed into the cup is normally distributed with a standard deviation of 0.03 ounce. You can allow the cup to overfill 1% of the time. What amount should you set as the mean amount of coffee to be dispensed?

CASE STUDY

Birth Weights in America

The National Center for Health Statistics (NCHS) keeps records of many health-related aspects of people, including the birth weights of all babies born in the United States.

The birth weight of a baby is related to its gestation period (the time between conception and birth). For a given gestation period, the birth weights can be approximated by a normal distribution. The means and standard deviations of the birth weights for various gestation periods are shown at the right.

One of the many goals of the NCHS is to reduce the percentage of babies born with low birth weights. As you can see from the graph at the upper right, the problem of low birth weights increased from 1990 to 2004.

Gestation period	Mean birth weight	Standard deviation
Under 28 Weeks	1.88 lb	1.20 lb
28 to 31 Weeks	4.08 lb	1.85 lb
32 to 35 Weeks	5.71 lb	1.47 lb
36 Weeks	6.44 lb	1.19 lb
37 to 39 Weeks	7.31 lb	1.09 lb
40 Weeks	7.69 lb	1.04 lb
41 Weeks	7.79 lb	1.08 lb
42 Weeks and over	7.61 lb	1.11 lb

■ Exercises

1. The distributions of birth weights for three gestation periods are shown. Match the curves with the gestation periods. Explain your reasoning.

(a)
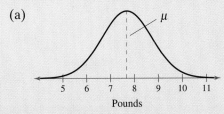

(b)
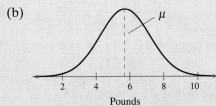

(c)
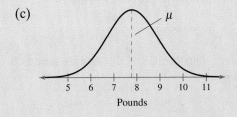

2. What percent of the babies born within each gestation period have a low birth weight (under 5.5 pounds)? Explain your reasoning.

(a) Under 28 weeks   (b) 32 to 35 weeks

(c) 37 to 39 weeks   (d) 42 weeks and over

3. Describe the weights of the top 10% of the babies born with each gestation period. Explain your reasoning.

(a) 37 to 39 weeks   (b) 42 weeks and over

4. For each gestation period, what is the probability that a baby will weigh between 6 and 9 pounds at birth?

(a) 32 to 35 weeks   (b) 37 to 39 weeks

(c) 42 weeks and over

5. A birth weight of less than 3.3 pounds is classified by the NCHS as a "very low birth weight." What is the probability that a baby has a very low birth weight for each gestation period?

(a) Under 28 weeks   (b) 32 to 35 weeks

(c) 37 to 39 weeks

269

5.4 Sampling Distributions and the Central Limit Theorem

Sampling Distributions ▸ The Central Limit Theorem ▸ Probability and the Central Limit Theorem

▸ Sampling Distributions

In previous sections, you studied the relationship between the mean of a population and values of a random variable. In this section, you will study the relationship between a population mean and the means of samples taken from the population.

> ### DEFINITION
>
> A **sampling distribution** is the probability distribution of a sample statistic that is formed when samples of size n are repeatedly taken from a population. If the sample statistic is the sample mean, then the distribution is the **sampling distribution of sample means.** Every sample statistic has a sampling distribution.

Insight

Sample means can vary from one another and can also vary from the population mean. This type of variation is to be expected and is called *sampling error.*

For instance, consider the following Venn diagram. The rectangle represents a large population, and each circle represents a sample of size n. Because the sample entries can differ, the sample means can also differ. The mean of Sample 1 is $\bar{x}_1$; the mean of Sample 2 is $\bar{x}_2$; and so on. The sampling distribution of the sample means for samples of size n for this population consists of $\bar{x}_1$, $\bar{x}_2$, $\bar{x}_3$, and so on. If the samples are drawn with replacement, an infinite number of samples can be drawn from the population.

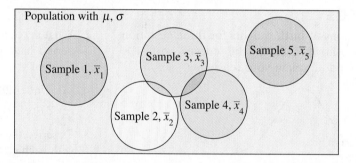

> ### PROPERTIES OF SAMPLING DISTRIBUTIONS OF SAMPLE MEANS
>
> **1.** The mean of the sample means $\mu_{\bar{x}}$ is equal to the population mean μ.
>
> $$\mu_{\bar{x}} = \mu$$
>
> **2.** The standard deviation of the sample means $\sigma_{\bar{x}}$ is equal to the population standard deviation σ divided by the square root of n.
>
> $$\sigma_{\bar{x}} = \frac{\sigma}{\sqrt{n}}$$
>
> The standard deviation of the sampling distribution of the sample means is called the **standard error of the mean.**

**Probability Histogram
of Population of x**

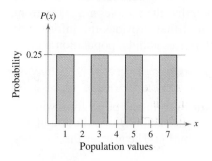

**Probability Distribution
of Sample Means**

$\bar{x}$	f	Probability
1	1	0.0625
2	2	0.1250
3	3	0.1875
4	4	0.2500
5	3	0.1875
6	2	0.1250
7	1	0.0625

**Probability Histogram of
Sampling Distribution of $\bar{x}$**

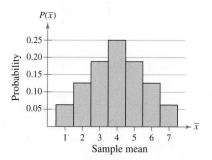

To explore this topic further,
see Activity 5.4 on page 284.

EXAMPLE 1

A Sampling Distribution of Sample Means

You write the population values $\{1, 3, 5, 7\}$ on slips of paper and put them in a box. Then you randomly choose two slips of paper, with replacement. List all possible samples of size $n = 2$ and calculate the mean of each. These means form the sampling distribution of the sample means. Find the mean, variance, and standard deviation of the sample means. Compare your results with the mean $\mu = 4$, variance $\sigma^2 = 5$, and standard deviation $\sigma = \sqrt{5} \approx 2.236$ of the population.

Solution List all 16 samples of size 2 from the population and the mean of each sample.

Sample	Sample mean, $\bar{x}$	Sample	Sample mean, $\bar{x}$
1, 1	1	5, 1	3
1, 3	2	5, 3	4
1, 5	3	5, 5	5
1, 7	4	5, 7	6
3, 1	2	7, 1	4
3, 3	3	7, 3	5
3, 5	4	7, 5	6
3, 7	5	7, 7	7

After constructing a probability distribution of the sample means, you can graph the sampling distribution using a probability histogram as shown at the left. Notice that the shape of the histogram is bell shaped and symmetric, similar to a normal curve. The mean, variance, and standard deviation of the 16 sample means are

$$\mu_{\bar{x}} = 4$$

$$(\sigma_{\bar{x}})^2 = \frac{5}{2} = 2.5 \quad \text{and} \quad \sigma_{\bar{x}} = \sqrt{\frac{5}{2}} = \sqrt{2.5} \approx 1.581.$$

These results satisfy the properties of sampling distributions because

$$\mu_{\bar{x}} = \mu = 4 \quad \text{and} \quad \sigma_{\bar{x}} = \frac{\sigma}{\sqrt{n}} = \frac{\sqrt{5}}{\sqrt{2}} \approx \frac{2.236}{\sqrt{2}} \approx 1.581.$$

▶ Try It Yourself 1

List all possible samples of $n = 3$, with replacement, from the population $\{1, 3, 5, 7\}$. Calculate the mean, variance, and standard deviation of the sample means. Compare these values with the corresponding population parameters.

a. *Form* all possible samples of size 3 and find the mean of each.
b. *Make* a probability distribution of the sample means and *find* the mean, variance, and standard deviation.
c. *Compare* the mean, variance, and standard deviation of the sample means with those for the population.

Answer: Page A41

▸ The Central Limit Theorem

The Central Limit Theorem forms the foundation for the inferential branch of statistics. This theorem describes the relationship between the sampling distribution of sample means and the population that the samples are taken from. The Central Limit Theorem is an important tool that provides the information you'll need to use sample statistics to make inferences about a population mean.

THE CENTRAL LIMIT THEOREM

1. If samples of size n, where $n \geq 30$, are drawn from any population with a mean μ and a standard deviation σ, then the sampling distribution of sample means approximates a normal distribution. The greater the sample size, the better the approximation.

2. If the population itself is normally distributed, the sampling distribution of sample means is normally distributed for *any* sample size n.

In either case, the sampling distribution of sample means has a mean equal to the population mean.

$$\mu_{\bar{x}} = \mu \qquad \text{Mean}$$

The sampling distribution of sample means has a variance equal to $1/n$ times the variance of the population and a standard deviation equal to the population standard deviation divided by the square root of n.

$$\sigma_{\bar{x}}^2 = \frac{\sigma^2}{n} \qquad \text{Variance}$$

$$\sigma_{\bar{x}} = \frac{\sigma}{\sqrt{n}} \qquad \text{Standard deviation}$$

The standard deviation of the sampling distribution of the sample means, $\sigma_{\bar{x}}$, is also called the **standard error of the mean.**

Insight

The distribution of sample means has the same mean as the population. But its standard deviation is less than the standard deviation of the population. This tells you that the distribution of sample means has the same center as the population, but it is not as spread out.

Moreover, the distribution of sample means becomes less and less spread out (tighter concentration about the mean) as the sample size n increases.

1. Any Population Distribution

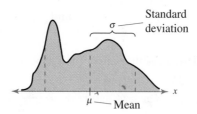

Distribution of Sample Means, $n \geq 30$

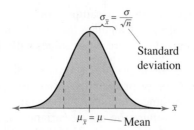

2. Normal Population Distribution

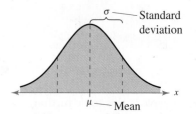

Distribution of Sample Means (any n)

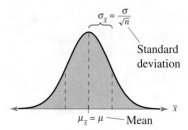

PICTURING the WORLD

In a recent year, there were more than 5 million parents in the United States who received child support payments. The following histogram shows the distribution of children per custodial parent. The mean number of children was 1.7 and the standard deviation was 0.9. (Adapted from: U.S. Census Bureau)

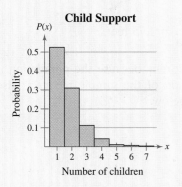

Child Support

You randomly select 35 parents who receive child support and ask how many children in their custody are receiving child support payments. What is the probability that the mean of the sample is between 1.5 and 1.9 children?

EXAMPLE 2

Interpreting the Central Limit Theorem

Phone bills for residents of a city have a mean of $64 and a standard deviation of $9, as shown in the following graph. Random samples of 36 phone bills are drawn from this population and the mean of each sample is determined. Find the mean and standard error of the mean of the sampling distribution. Then sketch a graph of the sampling distribution of sample means.

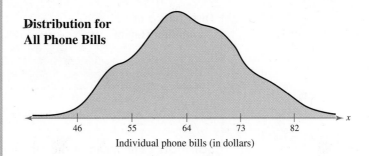

Distribution for All Phone Bills

Individual phone bills (in dollars)

Solution   The mean of the sampling distribution is equal to the population mean, and the standard error of the mean is equal to the population standard deviation divided by $\sqrt{n}$. So,

$$\mu_{\bar{x}} = \mu = 64 \quad \text{and} \quad \sigma_{\bar{x}} = \frac{\sigma}{\sqrt{n}} = \frac{9}{\sqrt{36}} = 1.5.$$

Interpretation   From the Central Limit Theorem, because the sample size is greater than 30, the sampling distribution can be approximated by a normal distribution with $\mu = \$64$ and $\sigma = \$1.50$, as shown in the graph below.

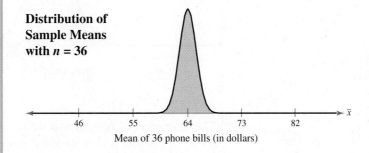

Distribution of Sample Means with n = 36

Mean of 36 phone bills (in dollars)

▶ Try It Yourself 2

Suppose random samples of size 100 are drawn from the population in Example 2. Find the mean and standard error of the mean of the sampling distribution. Sketch a graph of the sampling distribution and compare it with the sampling distribution in Example 2.

a. *Find* $\mu_{\bar{x}}$ and $\sigma_{\bar{x}}$.
b. *Identify* the sample size. If $n \geq 30$, *sketch* a normal curve with mean $\mu_{\bar{x}}$ and standard deviation $\sigma_{\bar{x}}$.
c. *Compare* the results with those in Example 2.   *Answer: Page A41*

EXAMPLE 3

Interpreting the Central Limit Theorem

The heights of fully grown white oak trees are normally distributed, with a mean of 90 feet and standard deviation of 3.5 feet, as shown in the following graph. Random samples of size 4 are drawn from this population, and the mean of each sample is determined. Find the mean and standard error of the mean of the sampling distribution. Then sketch a graph of the sampling distribution of sample means.

Distribution of Population Heights

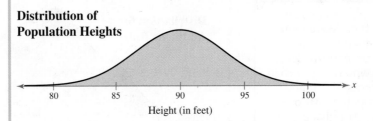

Height (in feet)

Solution   The mean of the sampling distribution is equal to the population mean, and the standard error of the mean is equal to the population standard deviation divided by $\sqrt{n}$. So,

$$\mu_{\bar{x}} = \mu = 90 \text{ feet} \quad \text{and} \quad \sigma_{\bar{x}} = \frac{\sigma}{\sqrt{n}} = \frac{3.5}{\sqrt{4}} = 1.75 \text{ feet}.$$

Interpretation   From the Central Limit Theorem, because the population is normally distributed, the sampling distribution of the sample means is also normally distributed, as shown in the graph below.

Distribution of Sample Means with $n = 4$

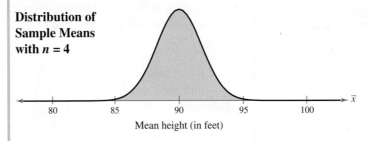

Mean height (in feet)

▶ Try It Yourself 3

The diameters of fully grown white oak trees are normally distributed, with a mean of 3.5 feet and a standard deviation of 0.2 foot, as shown in the graph below. Random samples of size 16 are drawn from this population, and the mean of each sample is determined. Find the mean and standard error of the mean of the sampling distribution. Then sketch a graph of the sampling distribution.

Distribution of Population Diameters

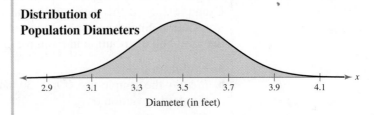

Diameter (in feet)

a. *Find* $\mu_{\bar{x}}$ and $\sigma_{\bar{x}}$.
b. *Sketch* a normal curve with mean $\mu_{\bar{x}}$ and standard deviation $\sigma_{\bar{x}}$.

Answer: Page A41

▶ Probability and the Central Limit Theorem

In Section 5.2, you learned how to find the probability that a random variable x will fall in a given interval of population values. In a similar manner, you can find the probability that a sample mean $\bar{x}$ will fall in a given interval of the $\bar{x}$ sampling distribution. To transform $\bar{x}$ to a z-score, you can use the formula

$$z = \frac{\text{Value} - \text{Mean}}{\text{Standard error}} = \frac{\bar{x} - \mu_{\bar{x}}}{\sigma_{\bar{x}}} = \frac{\bar{x} - \mu}{\sigma/\sqrt{n}}.$$

Distribution of Sample Means with $n = 50$

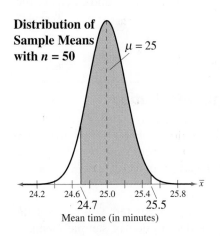

$\mu = 25$

24.2 24.6 25.0 25.4 25.8
       24.7   25.5
Mean time (in minutes)

z-score Distribution of Sample Means with $n = 50$

−1.41   0   2.36

```
normalcdf(24.7,2
5.5,25,.21213)
        .9121418524
```

In Example 4, you can use a TI-83/84 to find the probability automatically once the standard error of the mean is calculated.

EXAMPLE 4

Finding Probabilities for Sampling Distributions

The graph at the right shows the length of time people spend driving each day. You randomly select 50 drivers ages 15 to 19. What is the probability that the mean time they spend driving each day is between 24.7 and 25.5 minutes? Assume that $\sigma = 1.5$ minutes.

Solution The sample size is greater than 30, so you can use the Central Limit Theorem to conclude that the distribution of sample means is approximately normal with a mean and a standard deviation of

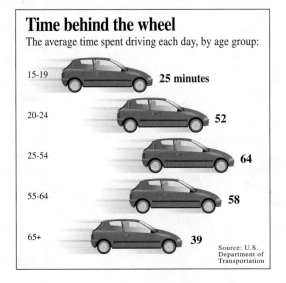

Time behind the wheel
The average time spent driving each day, by age group:

15-19   **25 minutes**

20-24   **52**

25-54   **64**

55-64   **58**

65+   **39**

Source: U.S. Department of Transportation

$$\mu_{\bar{x}} = \mu = 25 \text{ minutes} \quad \text{and} \quad \sigma_{\bar{x}} = \frac{\sigma}{\sqrt{n}} = \frac{1.5}{\sqrt{50}} \approx 0.21213 \text{ minute}.$$

The graph of this distribution is shown at the left with a shaded area between 24.7 and 25.5 minutes. The z-scores that correspond to sample means of 24.7 and 25.5 minutes are

$$z_1 = \frac{24.7 - 25}{1.5/\sqrt{50}} \approx \frac{-0.3}{0.21213} \approx -1.41 \quad \text{and}$$

$$z_2 = \frac{25.5 - 25}{1.5/\sqrt{50}} \approx \frac{0.5}{0.21213} \approx 2.36.$$

So, the probability that the mean time the 50 people spend driving each day is between 24.7 and 25.5 minutes is

$$P(24.7 < \bar{x} < 25.5) = P(-1.41 < z < 2.36)$$
$$= P(z < 2.36) - P(z < -1.41)$$
$$= 0.9909 - 0.0793 = 0.9116.$$

Interpretation Of the samples of 50 drivers ages 15 to 19, 91.16% will have a mean driving time that is between 24.7 and 25.5 minutes, as shown in the graph at the left. This implies that, assuming the value of $\mu = 25$ is correct, only 8.84% of such sample means will lie outside the given interval.

▶ **Try It Yourself 4**

You randomly select 100 drivers ages 15 to 19 from Example 4. What is the probability that the mean time they spend driving each day is between 24.7 and 25.5 minutes? Use $\mu = 25$ and $\sigma = 1.5$ minutes.

a. Use the Central Limit Theorem to *find* $\mu_{\bar{x}}$ and $\sigma_{\bar{x}}$ and *sketch* the sampling distribution of the sample means.
b. *Find the z-scores* that correspond to $\bar{x} = 24.7$ minutes and $\bar{x} = 25.5$ minutes.
c. *Find the cumulative area* that corresponds to each z-score and calculate the probability. *Answer: Page A41*

EXAMPLE 5

Finding Probabilities for Sampling Distributions

The mean room and board expense per year of four-year colleges is $6803. You randomly select 9 four-year colleges. What is the probability that the mean room and board is less than $7088? Assume that the room and board expenses are normally distributed, with a standard deviation of $1125. *(Source: National Center for Education Statistics)*

Solution Because the population is normally distributed, you can use the Central Limit Theorem to conclude that the distribution of sample means is normally distributed, with a mean of $6803 and a standard deviation of $375.

$$\mu_{\bar{x}} = \mu = 6803 \quad \text{and} \quad \sigma_{\bar{x}} = \frac{\sigma}{\sqrt{n}} = \frac{1125}{\sqrt{9}} = 375$$

The graph of this distribution is shown at the left. The area to the left of $7088 is shaded. The z-score that corresponds to $7088 is

$$z = \frac{7088 - 6803}{1125/\sqrt{9}} = \frac{285}{375} = 0.76.$$

So, the probability that the mean room and board expense is less than $7088 is

$$P(\bar{x} < 7088) = P(z < 0.76) = 0.7764.$$

Interpretation So, 77.64% of such samples with $n = 9$ will have a mean less than $7088 and 22.36% of these sample means will lie outside this interval.

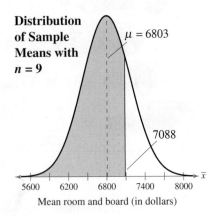

Distribution of Sample Means with $n = 9$

$\mu = 6803$

7088

5600   6200   6800   7400   8000
Mean room and board (in dollars)

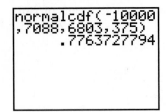

```
normalcdf(-10000
,7088,6803,375)
        .7763727794
```

In Example 5, you can use a TI-83/84 to find the probability automatically.

▶ **Try It Yourself 5**

The average sales price of a single-family house in the United States is $306,258. You randomly select 12 single-family houses. What is the probability that the mean sales price is more than $280,000? Assume that the sales prices are normally distributed with a standard deviation of $44,000. *(Source: Federal Housing Finance Board)*

a. Use the Central Limit Theorem to *find* $\mu_{\bar{x}}$ and $\sigma_{\bar{x}}$ and *sketch* the sampling distribution of the sample means.
b. *Find the z-score* that corresponds to $\bar{x} = \$280,000$.
c. *Find the cumulative area* that corresponds to the z-score and calculate the probability. *Answer: Page A41*

The Central Limit Theorem can also be used to investigate unusual events. An unusual event is one that occurs with a probability of less than 5%.

EXAMPLE 6

Finding Probabilities for *x* and $\bar{x}$

A bank auditor claims that credit card balances are normally distributed, with a mean of $2870 and a standard deviation of $900.

1. What is the probability that a randomly selected credit card holder has a credit card balance less than $2500?
2. You randomly select 25 credit card holders. What is the probability that their mean credit card balance is less than $2500?
3. Compare the probabilities from (1) and (2) and interpret your answer in terms of the auditor's claim.

Solution

1. In this case, you are asked to find the probability associated with a certain value of the random variable *x*. The *z*-score that corresponds to *x* = $2500 is

$$z = \frac{x - \mu}{\sigma}$$

$$= \frac{2500 - 2870}{900} \approx -0.41.$$

So, the probability that the card holder has a balance less than $2500 is

$$P(x < 2500) = P(z < -0.41) = 0.3409.$$

2. Here, you are asked to find the probability associated with a sample mean $\bar{x}$. The *z*-score that corresponds to $\bar{x}$ = $2500 is

$$z = \frac{\bar{x} - \mu_{\bar{x}}}{\sigma_{\bar{x}}} = \frac{\bar{x} - \mu}{\sigma/\sqrt{n}}$$

$$= \frac{2500 - 2870}{900/\sqrt{25}} = \frac{-370}{180} \approx -2.06.$$

So, the probability that the mean credit card balance of the 25 card holders is less than $2500 is

$$P(\bar{x} < 2500) = P(z < -2.06) = 0.0197.$$

3. *Interpretation*   Although there is a 34% chance that an individual will have a balance less than $2500, there is only a 2% chance that the mean of a sample of 25 will have a balance less than $2500. Because there is only a 2% chance that the mean of a sample of 25 will have a balance less than $2500, this is an unusual event. So, it is possible that the sample is unusual, or it is possible that the auditor's claim that the mean is $2870 is incorrect.

▶ Try It Yourself 6

A consumer price analyst claims that prices for sound-system receivers are normally distributed, with a mean of $625 and a standard deviation of $150. (1) What is the probability that a randomly selected receiver costs less than $700? (2) You randomly select 10 receivers. What is the probability that their mean cost is less than $700? (3) Compare these two probabilities.

a. *Find* the *z*-scores that correspond to *x* and $\bar{x}$.
b. *Use* the Standard Normal Table to *find the probability* associated with each *z*-score.
c. *Compare* the probabilities and *interpret* your answer.   *Answer: Page A41*

Study Tip

To find probabilities for individual members of a population with a normally distributed random variable *x*, use the formula

$$z = \frac{x - \mu}{\sigma}.$$

To find probabilities for the mean $\bar{x}$ of a sample size *n*, use the formula

$$z = \frac{\bar{x} - \mu_{\bar{x}}}{\sigma_{\bar{x}}}.$$

5.4 EXERCISES

For Extra Help

MyStatLab

■ Building Basic Skills and Vocabulary

In Exercises 1–4, a population has a mean $\mu = 100$ and a standard deviation $\sigma = 15$. Find the mean and standard deviation of a sampling distribution of sample means with the given sample size n.

1. $n = 50$

2. $n = 100$

3. $n = 250$

4. $n = 1000$

True or False? *In Exercises 5–8, determine whether the statement is true or false. If it is false, rewrite it as a true statement.*

5. As the size of a sample increases, the mean of the distribution of sample means increases.

6. As the size of a sample increases, the standard deviation of the distribution of sample means increases.

7. A sampling distribution is normal only if the population is normal.

8. If the size of a sample is at least 30, you can use z-scores to determine the probability that a sample mean falls in a given interval of the sampling distribution.

Verifying Properties of Sampling Distributions *In Exercises 9 and 10, find the mean and standard deviation of the population. List all samples (with replacement) of the given size from that population. Find the mean and standard deviation of the sampling distribution and compare them with the mean and standard deviation of the population.*

9. The number of movies that all four people in a family have seen in the past month is 4, 2, 8, and 0. Use a sample size of 3.

10. Four people in a carpool paid the following amounts for textbooks this semester: $120, $140, $180, and $220. Use a sample size of 2.

Graphical Analysis *In Exercises 11 and 12, the graph of a population distribution is shown with its mean and standard deviation. Assume that a sample size of 100 is drawn from each population. Decide which of the graphs labeled (a)–(c) would most closely resemble the sampling distribution of the sample means for each graph. Explain your reasoning.*

11. The waiting time (in seconds) at a traffic signal during a red light

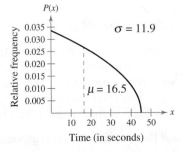

Time (in seconds)

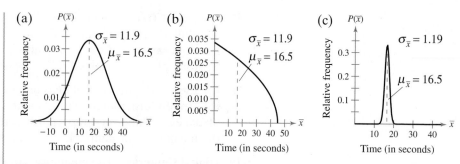

12. The annual snowfall (in feet) for a central New York State county

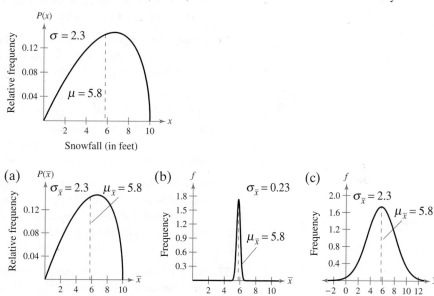

Finding Probabilities
In Exercises 13–16, the population mean and standard deviation are given. Find the required probability and determine whether the given sample mean would be considered unusual. If convenient, use technology to find the probability.

13. For a sample of $n = 36$, find the probability of a sample mean being less than 12.2 if $\mu = 12$ and $\sigma = 0.95$.

14. For a sample of $n = 100$, find the probability of a sample mean being greater than 12.2 if $\mu = 12$ and $\sigma = 0.95$.

15. For a sample of $n = 75$, find the probability of a sample mean being greater than 221 if $\mu = 220$ and $\sigma = 3.9$.

16. For a sample of $n = 36$, find the probability of a sample mean being less than 12,750 or greater than 12,753 if $\mu = 12,750$ and $\sigma = 1.7$.

■ Using and Interpreting Concepts

Using the Central Limit Theorem   *In Exercises 17–22, use the Central Limit Theorem to find the mean and standard error of the mean of the indicated sampling distribution. Then sketch a graph of the sampling distribution.*

17. **Heights of Trees** The heights of fully grown sugar maple trees are normally distributed, with a mean of 87.5 feet and a standard deviation of 6.25 feet. Random samples of size 12 are drawn from the population and the mean of each sample is determined.

18. **Fly Eggs** The number of eggs female house flies lay during their lifetimes is normally distributed, with a mean of 800 eggs and a standard deviation of 100 eggs. Random samples of size 15 are drawn from this population and the mean of each sample is determined.

19. **Digital Cameras** The mean price of digital cameras at an electronics store is $224, with a standard deviation of $8. Random samples of size 40 are drawn from this population and the mean of each sample is determined.

20. **Employees' Ages** The mean age of employees at a large corporation is 47.2 years, with a standard deviation of 3.6 years. Random samples of size 36 are drawn from this population and the mean of each sample is determined.

21. **Red Meat Consumed** The per capita consumption of red meat by people in the United States in a recent year was normally distributed, with a mean of 110 pounds and a standard deviation of 38.5 pounds. Random samples of size 20 are drawn from this population and the mean of each sample is determined. *(Adapted from U.S. Department of Agriculture)*

22. **Soft Drinks** The per capita consumption of soft drinks by people in the United States in a recent year was normally distributed, with a mean of 51.5 gallons and a standard deviation of 17.1 gallons. Random samples of size 25 are drawn from this population and the mean of each sample is determined. *(Adapted from U.S. Department of Agriculture)*

23. Repeat Exercise 17 for samples of size 24 and 36. What happens to the mean and standard deviation of the distribution of sample means as the size of the sample increases?

24. Repeat Exercise 18 for samples of size 30 and 45. What happens to the mean and to the standard deviation of the distribution of sample means as the size of the sample increases?

Finding Probabilities *In Exercises 25–30, find the probabilities. If convenient, use technology to find the probabilities.*

25. **Plumber Salaries** The population mean annual salary for plumbers is $46,700. A random sample of 42 plumbers is drawn from this population. What is the probability that the mean salary of the sample is less than $44,000? Assume $\sigma = \$5600$. *(Adapted from Salary.com)*

26. **Nurse Salaries** The population mean annual salary for registered nurses is $59,100 A random sample of 35 registered nurses is selected from this population. What is the probability that the mean annual salary of the sample is less than $55,000? Assume $\sigma = \$1700$. *(Adapted from Salary.com)*

27. **Gas Prices: New England** During a certain week the mean price of gasoline in the New England region was $2.818 per gallon. A random sample of 32 gas stations is drawn from this population. What is the probability that the mean price for the sample was between $2.768 and $2.918 that week? Assume $\sigma = \$0.045$. *(Adapted from Energy Information Administration)*

28. **Gas Prices: California** During a certain week the mean price of gasoline in California was $3.305 per gallon. A random sample of 38 gas stations is drawn from this population. What is the probability that the mean price for the sample was between $3.310 and $3.320 that week? Assume $\sigma = \$0.049$. *(Adapted from Energy Information Administration)*

29. Heights of Women The mean height of women in the United States (ages 20–29) is 64.1 inches. A random sample of 60 women in this age group is selected. What is the probability that the mean height for the sample is greater than 66 inches? Assume $\sigma = 2.71$ inches. (*Source: National Center for Health Statistics*)

30. Heights of Men The mean height of men in the United States (ages 20–29) is 69.6 inches. A random sample of 60 men in this age group is selected. What is the probability that the mean height for the sample is greater than 70 inches? Assume $\sigma = 3.0$ inches. (*Source: National Center for Health Statistics*)

31. Which Is More Likely? Assume that the heights given in Exercise 29 are normally distributed. Are you more likely to randomly select 1 woman with a height less than 70 inches or are you more likely to select a sample of 20 women with a mean height less than 70 inches? Explain.

32. Which Is More Likely? Assume that the heights given in Exercise 30 are normally distributed. Are you more likely to randomly select 1 man with a height less than 65 inches or are you more likely to select a sample of 15 men with a mean height less than 65 inches? Explain.

33. Make a Decision A machine used to fill gallon-sized paint cans is regulated so that the amount of paint dispensed has a mean of 128 ounces and a standard deviation of 0.20 ounce. You randomly select 40 cans and carefully measure the contents. The sample mean of the cans is 127.9 ounces. Does the machine need to be reset? Explain your reasoning.

34. Make a Decision A machine used to fill half-gallon-sized milk containers is regulated so that the amount of milk dispensed has a mean of 64 ounces and a standard deviation of 0.11 ounce. You randomly select 40 containers and carefully measure the contents. The sample mean of the containers is 64.05 ounces. Does the machine need to be reset? Explain your reasoning.

35. Lumber Cutter Your lumber company has bought a machine that automatically cuts lumber. The seller of the machine claims that the machine cuts lumber to a mean length of 8 feet (96 inches) with a standard deviation of 0.5 inch. Assume the lengths are normally distributed. You randomly select 40 boards and find that the mean length is 96.25 inches.

(a) Assuming the seller's claim is correct, what is the probability the mean of the sample is 96.25 inches or more?

(b) Using your answer from part (a), what do you think of the seller's claim?

(c) Would it be unusual to have an individual board with a length of 96.25 inches? Why or why not?

36. Ice Cream Carton Weights A manufacturer claims that the mean weight of its ice cream cartons is 10 ounces with a standard deviation of 0.5 ounce. Assume the weights are normally distributed. You test 25 cartons and find their mean weight is 10.21 ounces.

(a) Assuming the manufacturer's claim is correct, what is the probability the mean of the sample is 10.21 ounces or more?

(b) Using your answer from part (a), what do you think of the manufacturer's claim?

(c) Would it be unusual to have an individual carton with a weight of 10.21 ounces? Why or why not?

37. Life of Tires   A manufacturer claims that the life span of its tires is 50,000 miles. You work for a consumer protection agency and you are testing this manufacturer's tires. Assume the life spans of the tires are normally distributed. You select 100 tires at random and test them. The mean life span is 49,721 miles. Assume $\sigma = 800$ miles.

(a) Assuming the manufacturer's claim is correct, what is the probability the mean of the sample is 49,721 miles or less?

(b) Using your answer from part (a), what do you think of the manufacturer's claim?

(c) Would it be unusual to have an individual tire with a life span of 49,721 miles? Why or why not?

38. Brake Pads   A brake pad manufacturer claims its brake pads will last for 38,000 miles. You work for a consumer protection agency and you are testing this manufacturer's brake pads. Assume the life spans of the brake pads are normally distributed. You randomly select 50 brake pads. In your tests, the mean life of the brake pads is 37,650 miles. Assume $\sigma = 1000$ miles.

(a) Assuming the manufacturer's claim is correct, what is the probability the mean of the sample is 37,650 miles or less?

(b) Using your answer from part (a), what do you think of the manufacturer's claim?

(c) Would it be unusual to have an individual brake pad last for 37,650 miles? Why or why not?

■ **Extending Concepts**

39. SAT Scores   The average math SAT score is 518 with a standard deviation of 115. A particular high school claims that its students have unusually high math SAT scores. A random sample of 50 students from this school was selected, and the mean math SAT score was 530. Is the high school justified in its claim? Explain. *(Source: College Board Online)*

40. Machine Calibrations   A machine in a manufacturing plant is calibrated to produce a bolt that has a mean diameter of 4 inches and a standard deviation of 0.5 inch. An engineer takes a random sample of 100 bolts from this machine and finds the mean diameter is 4.2 inches. What are some possible consequences from these findings?

Finite Correction Factor   *The formula for the standard error of the mean*

$$\sigma_{\bar{x}} = \frac{\sigma}{\sqrt{n}}$$

given in the Central Limit Theorem is based on an assumption that the population has infinitely many members. This is the case whenever sampling is done with replacement (each member is put back after it is selected) because the sampling process could be continued indefinitely. The formula is also valid if the sample size is small in comparison to the population. However, when sampling is done without replacement and the sample size n is more than 5% of the finite population of size

$$N\left(\frac{n}{N} > 0.05\right),$$

*there is a finite number of possible samples. A **finite correction factor,***

$$\sqrt{\frac{N-n}{N-1}}$$

should be used to adjust the standard error. The sampling distribution of the sample means will be normal with a mean equal to the population mean, and the standard error of the mean will be

$$\sigma_{\bar{x}} = \frac{\sigma}{\sqrt{n}} \sqrt{\frac{N - n}{N - 1}}.$$

In Exercises 41 and 42, determine if the finite correction factor should be used. If so, use it in your calculations when you find the probability.

41. Gas Prices   In a sample of 800 gas stations, the mean price for regular gasoline at the pump was \$2.876 per gallon and the standard deviation was \$0.009 per gallon. A random sample of size 55 is drawn from this population. What is the probability that the mean price per gallon is less than \$2.871? *(Adapted from U.S. Department of Energy)*

42. Old Faithful   In a sample of 500 eruptions of the Old Faithful geyser at Yellowstone National Park, the mean duration of the eruptions was 3.32 minutes and the standard deviation was 1.09 minutes. A random sample of size 30 is drawn from this population. What is the probability that the mean duration of eruptions is between 2.5 minutes and 4 minutes? *(Adapted from Yellowstone National Park)*

Sampling Distribution of Sample Proportions   *The sample mean is not the only statistic with a sampling distribution. Every sample statistic, such as the sample median, the sample standard deviation, and the sample proportion, has a sampling distribution. For a random sample of size n, the **sample proportion** is the number of individuals in the sample with a specified characteristic divided by the sample size. The **sampling distribution of sample proportions** is the distribution formed when sample proportions of size n are repeatedly taken from a population where the probability of an individual with a specified characteristic is p.*

In Exercises 43–45, suppose three births are randomly selected. There are two equally possible outcomes for each birth, a boy (b) or a girl (g). The number of boys can equal 0, 1, 2, or 3. These correspond to sample proportions of 0, 1/3, 2/3, and 1.

43. List the eight possible samples when randomly selecting three births. For instance, let bbb represents a sample of three boys. Make a table that shows each sample, the number of boys in each sample, and the proportion of boys in each sample.

44. Use the table from Exercise 43 to construct the sampling distribution of the sample proportion of boys from three births. What do you notice about the spread of the histogram as compared to the binomial probability distribution for the number of boys in each sample?

45. Let $x = 1$ represent a boy and $x = 0$ represent a girl. Using these values, find the sample mean for each sample. What do you notice?

46. Construct a sampling distribution of the sample proportion of boys from four births.

47. Heart Transplants   About 75% of all female heart transplant patients will survive for at least 3 years. Ninety female heart transplant patients are randomly selected. What is the probability that the sample proportion surviving for at least 3 years will be less than 70%? Assume the sampling distribution of sample proportions is a normal distribution. The mean of the sample proportion is equal to the population proportion p and the standard deviation is equal to $\sqrt{\dfrac{pq}{n}}$. *(Source: American Heart Association)*

ACTIVITY 5.4

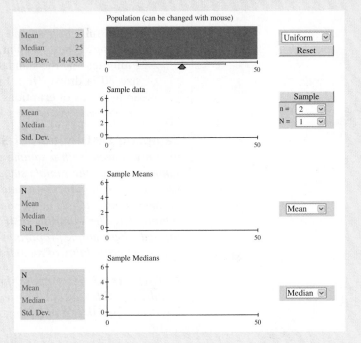

APPLET

The *sampling distributions* applet allows you to investigate sampling distributions by repeatedly taking samples from a population. The top plot displays the distribution of a population. Several options are available for the population distribution (Uniform, Bell-shaped, Skewed, Binary, and Custom). When SAMPLE is clicked, *N* random samples of size *n* will be repeatedly selected from the population. The sample statistics specified in the bottom two plots will be updated for each sample. If *N* is set to 1 and *n* is less than or equal to 50, the display will show, in an animated fashion, the points selected from the population dropping into the second plot and the corresponding summary statistic values dropping into the third and fourth plots. Click RESET to stop an animation and clear existing results. Summary statistics for each plot are shown in the panel to the left of the plot.

■ Explore

Step 1 Specify a distribution.
Step 2 Specify a value for *n*.
Step 3 Specify a value for *N*.
Step 4 Specify what to display in the bottom two graphs.
Step 5 Click SAMPLE to generate the sampling distributions.

■ Draw Conclusions

APPLET

1. Run the simulation using *n* = 30 and *N* = 10 for a uniform, a bell-shaped, and a skewed distribution. What is the mean of the sampling distribution of the sample means for each distribution? For each distribution, is this what you would expect?

2. Run the simulation using *n* = 50 and *N* = 10 for a bell-shaped distribution. What is the standard deviation of the sampling distribution of the sample means? According to the formula, what should the standard deviation of the sampling distribution of the sample means be? Is this what you would expect?

5.5 Normal Approximations to Binomial Distributions

Approximating a Binomial Distribution ▸ Correction for Continuity ▸ Approximating Binomial Probabilities

▸ Approximating a Binomial Distribution

In Section 4.2, you learned how to find binomial probabilities. For instance, if a surgical procedure has an 85% chance of success and a doctor performs the procedure on 10 patients, it is easy to find the probability of exactly two successful surgeries.

But what if the doctor performs the surgical procedure on 150 patients and you want to find the probability of *fewer than 100* successful surgeries? To do this using the techniques described in Section 4.2, you would have to use the binomial formula 100 times and find the sum of the resulting probabilities. This approach is not practical, of course. A better approach is to use a normal distribution to approximate the binomial distribution.

> ### NORMAL APPROXIMATION TO A BINOMIAL DISTRIBUTION
>
> If $np \geq 5$ and $nq \geq 5$, then the binomial random variable x is approximately normally distributed, with mean
>
> $$\mu = np$$
>
> and standard deviation
>
> $$\sigma = \sqrt{npq}.$$

To see why this result is valid, look at the following binomial distributions for $p = 0.25$ and $n = 4$, $n = 10$, $n = 25$, and $n = 50$. Notice that as n increases, the histogram approaches a normal curve.

Study Tip

Properties of a binomial experiment

- n independent trials

- Two possible outcomes: success or failure

- Probability of success is p; probability of failure is $1 - p = q$

- p is constant for each trial

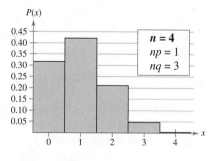

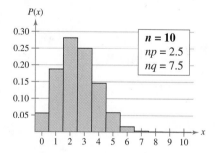

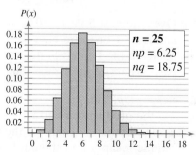

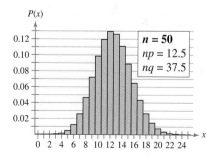

EXAMPLE 1

Approximating the Binomial Distribution

Two binomial experiments are listed. Decide whether you can use the normal distribution to approximate x, the number of people who reply yes. If you can, find the mean and standard deviation. If you cannot, explain why. *(Source: Opinion Research Corporation)*

1. Fifty-one percent of adults in the United States whose New Year's resolution was to exercise more achieved their resolution. You randomly select 65 adults in the United States whose resolution was to exercise more and ask each if he or she achieved that resolution.

2. Fifteen percent of adults in the United States do not make New Year's resolutions. You randomly select 15 adults in the United States and ask each if he or she made a New Year's resolution.

Solution

1. In this binomial experiment, $n = 65$, $p = 0.51$, and $q = 0.49$. So,

$$np = (65)(0.51) = 33.15$$

and

$$nq = (65)(0.49) = 31.85.$$

Because np and nq are greater than 5, you can use the normal distribution with

$$\mu = 33.15$$

and

$$\sigma = \sqrt{npq} = \sqrt{65 \cdot 0.51 \cdot 0.49} \approx 4.03$$

to approximate the distribution of x.

2. In this binomial experiment, $n = 15$, $p = 0.15$, and $q = 0.85$. So,

$$np = (15)(0.15) = 2.25.$$

and

$$np = (15)(0.85) = 12.75.$$

Because $np < 5$, you cannot use the normal distribution to approximate the distribution of x.

▶ Try It Yourself 1

Consider the following binomial experiment. Decide whether you can use the normal distribution to approximate x, the number of people who reply yes. If you can, find the mean and standard deviation. If you cannot, explain why. *(Source: Opinion Research Corporation)*

> Over the past 5 years, 80% of adults in the United States have made and kept 1 or more New Year's resolutions. You randomly select 70 adults in the United States who made a New Year's resolution in the past 5 years and ask each if he or she kept at least 1 resolution.

a. *Identify* n, p, and q.
b. *Find* the products np and nq.
c. *Decide* whether you can use the normal distribution to approximate x.
d. *Find* the mean μ and standard deviation σ, if appropriate.

Answer: Page A41

▶ Correction for Continuity

The binomial distribution is discrete and can be represented by a probability histogram. To calculate *exact* binomial probabilities, you can use the binomial formula for each value of *x* and add the results. Geometrically, this corresponds to adding the areas of bars in the probability histogram. Remember that each bar has a width of one unit and *x* is the midpoint of the interval.

When you use a *continuous* normal distribution to approximate a binomial probability, you need to move 0.5 unit to the left and right of the midpoint to include all possible *x*-values in the interval. When you do this, you are making a **correction for continuity.**

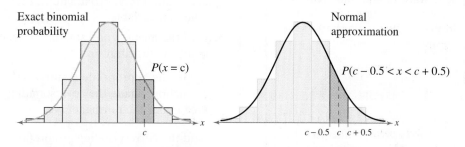

Study Tip

To use a correction for continuity, simply subtract 0.5 from the lowest value and add 0.5 to the highest.

EXAMPLE 2

Using a Correction for Continuity

Use a correction for continuity to convert each of the following binomial intervals to a normal distribution interval.

1. The probability of getting between 270 and 310 successes, inclusive
2. The probability of at least 158 successes
3. The probability of getting less than 63 successes

Solution

1. The discrete midpoint values are 270, 271,..., 310. The corresponding interval for the continuous normal distribution is

   $269.5 < x < 310.5$.

2. The discrete midpoint values are 158, 159, 160,.... The corresponding interval for the continuous normal distribution is

   $x > 157.5$.

3. The discrete midpoint values are ..., 60, 61, 62. The corresponding interval for the continuous normal distribution is

   $x < 62.5$.

▶ Try It Yourself 2

Use a correction for continuity to convert each of the following binomial intervals to a normal distribution interval.

1. The probability of getting between 57 and 83 successes, inclusive
2. The probability of getting at most 54 successes

a. List the *midpoint values* for the binomial probability.
b. Use a *correction for continuity* to write the normal distribution interval.

Answer: Page A42

▸ **Approximating Binomial Probabilities**

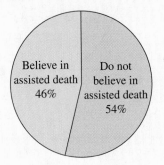

In a survey of U.S. adults, people were asked if the law should allow doctors to aid dying patients who want to end their lives. The results of the survey are shown in the following pie chart. (Adapted from Pew Research Center)

Believe in assisted death **46%**

Do not believe in assisted death **54%**

Assume that this survey is a true indication of the proportion of the population who believe in assisted death for terminally ill patients. If you sampled 50 adults at random, what is the probability that between 21 and 25, inclusive, would believe in assisted death?

GUIDELINES

Using the Normal Distribution to Approximate Binomial Probabilities

In Words	*In Symbols*
1. Verify that the binomial distribution applies.	Specify n, p, and q.
2. Determine if you can use the normal distribution to approximate x, the binomial variable.	Is $np \geq 5$? Is $nq \geq 5$?
3. Find the mean μ and standard deviation σ for the distribution.	$\mu = np$ $\sigma = \sqrt{npq}$
4. Apply the appropriate continuity correction. Shade the corresponding area under the normal curve.	Add or subtract 0.5 from endpoints.
5. Find the corresponding z-score(s).	$z = \dfrac{x - \mu}{\sigma}$
6. Find the probability.	Use the Standard Normal Table.

EXAMPLE 3

Approximating a Binomial Probability

Fifty-one percent of adults in the United States whose New Year's resolution was to exercise more achieved their resolution. You randomly select 65 adults in the United States whose resolution was to exercise more and ask each if he or she achieved that resolution. What is the probability that fewer than 40 of them respond yes? *(Source: Opinion Research Corporation)*

Solution From Example 1, you know that you can use a normal distribution with $\mu = 33.15$ and $\sigma \approx 4.03$ to approximate the binomial distribution. Remember to apply the continuity correction for the value of x. In the binomial distribution, the possible midpoint values for "fewer than 40" are

$$\ldots 37, 38, 39.$$

To use the normal distribution, add 0.5 to the right-hand boundary 39 to get $x = 39.5$. The graph at the left shows a normal curve with $\mu = 33.15$ and $\sigma \approx 4.03$ and a shaded area to the left of 39.5. The z-score that corresponds to $x = 39.5$ is

$$z = \frac{39.5 - 33.15}{\sqrt{65 \cdot 0.51 \cdot 0.49}}$$

$$\approx 1.58.$$

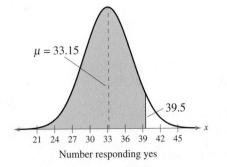

$\mu = 33.15$

39.5

21 24 27 30 33 36 39 42 45 → x
Number responding yes

Using the Standard Normal Table,

$$P(z < 1.58) = 0.9429.$$

Interpretation The probability that fewer than forty people respond yes is approximately 0.9429, or about 94%.

▶ **Try It Yourself 3**

Over the past 5 years, 80% of adults in the United States have made and kept 1 or more New Year's resolutions. You randomly select 70 adults in the United States who made a New Year's resolution in the past 5 years and ask each if he or she kept at least 1 resolution. What is the probability that more than 50 respond yes? (See Try it Yourself 1.) *(Source: Opinion Research Corporation)*

a. *Determine* whether you can use the normal distribution to approximate the binomial variable (see part c of Try It Yourself 1).
b. *Find* the mean μ and the standard deviation σ for the distribution (see part d of Try It Yourself 1).
c. *Apply* the appropriate continuity correction and sketch a graph.
d. *Find* the corresponding z-score.
e. *Use* the Standard Normal Table to find the area to the left of z and calculate the probability.   *Answer: Page A42*

EXAMPLE 4

Approximating a Binomial Probability

Thirty-eight percent of people in the United States admit that they snoop in other people's medicine cabinets. You randomly select 200 people in the United States and ask each if he or she snoops in other people's medicine cabinets. What is the probability that at least 70 will say yes? *(Source: USA TODAY)*

Solution   Because $np = 200 \cdot 0.38 = 76$ and $nq = 200 \cdot 0.62 = 124$, the binomial variable x is approximately normally distributed with

$$\mu = np = 76 \quad \text{and} \quad \sigma = \sqrt{200 \cdot 0.38 \cdot 0.62} \approx 6.86.$$

Using the correction for continuity, you can rewrite the discrete probability $P(x \geq 70)$ as the continuous probability $P(x \geq 69.5)$. The graph shows a normal curve with $\mu = 76$ and $\sigma = 6.86$ and a shaded area to the right of 69.5. The z-score that corresponds to 69.5 is

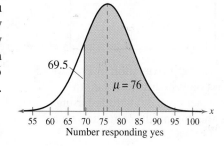

$$z = \frac{(69.5 - 76)}{6.86} \approx -0.95.$$

So, the probability that at least 70 will say yes is

$$P(x \geq 69.5) = P(z \geq -0.95)$$

$$= 1 - P(z \leq -0.95) = 1 - 0.1711 = 0.8289.$$

▶ **Try It Yourself 4**

In Example 4, what is the probability that at most 85 people will say yes?

a. *Determine* whether you can use the normal distribution to approximate the binomial variable (see Example 4).
b. *Find* the mean μ and the standard deviation σ for the distribution (see Example 4).
c. *Apply* a continuity correction to rewrite $P(x \leq 85)$ and sketch a graph.
d. *Find* the corresponding z-score.
e. *Use* the Standard Normal Table to *find the area* to the left of z and calculate the probability.   *Answer: Page A42*

Study Tip

In a discrete distribution, there is a difference between $P(x \geq c)$ and $P(x > c)$. This is true because the probability that x is exactly c is not zero. In a continuous distribution, however, there is no difference between $P(x \geq c)$ and $P(x > c)$ because the probability that x is exactly c is zero.

EXAMPLE 5

Approximating a Binomial Probability

A survey reports that 86% of Internet users use Windows® Internet Explorer® as their browser. You randomly select 200 Internet users and ask each whether he or she uses Internet Explorer as his or her browser. What is the probability that exactly 176 will say yes? *(Source: OneStat.com)*

Solution Because $np = 200 \cdot 0.86 = 172$ and $nq = 200 \cdot 0.14 = 28$, the binomial variable x is approximately normally distributed with

$$\mu = np = 172 \quad \text{and} \quad \sigma = \sqrt{npq} = \sqrt{200 \cdot 0.86 \cdot 0.14} \approx 4.91.$$

Using the correction for continuity, you can rewrite the discrete probability $P(x = 176)$ as the continuous probability $P(175.5 < x < 176.5)$. The following graph shows a normal curve with $\mu = 172$ and $\sigma = 4.91$ and a shaded area between 175.5 and 176.5.

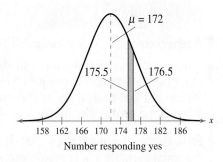

Number responding yes

The z-scores that correspond to 175.5 and 176.5 are

$$z_1 = \frac{175.5 - 172}{\sqrt{200 \cdot 0.86 \cdot 0.14}} \quad \text{and} \quad z_2 = \frac{176.5 - 172}{\sqrt{200 \cdot 0.86 \cdot 0.14}}.$$

So, the probability that exactly 176 Internet users will say they use Internet Explorer is

$$
\begin{aligned}
P(175.5 < x < 176.5) &= P(0.71 < z < 0.92) \\
&= P(z < 0.92) - P(z < 0.71) \\
&= 0.8212 - 0.7611 \\
&= 0.0601.
\end{aligned}
$$

Interpretation The probability that exactly 176 of the Internet users will say they use Internet Explorer is approximately 0.0601, or about 6%.

▶ Try It Yourself 5

In Example 5, what is the probability that exactly 170 people will say yes?

a. *Determine* whether you can use the normal distribution to approximate the binomial variable (see Example 5).
b. *Find* the mean μ and the standard deviation σ for the distribution (see Example 5).
c. *Apply* a continuity correction to rewrite $P(x = 170)$ and sketch a graph.
d. *Find* the corresponding z-scores.
e. *Use* the Standard Normal Table to *find the area* to the left of each z-score and calculate the probability. *Answer: Page A42*

---

binompdf(200,.86
,176)
      .0611688936

The approximation in Example 5 is only slightly less than the exact probability found using the binompdf(command on a TI-83/84.

5.5 EXERCISES

MyStatLab

■ Building Basic Skills and Vocabulary

In Exercises 1–4, the sample size n, probability of success p, and probability of failure q are given for a binomial experiment. Decide whether you can use the normal distribution to approximate the random variable x.

1. $n = 24$, $p = 0.85$, $q = 0.15$ **2.** $n = 15$, $p = 0.70$, $q = 0.30$

3. $n = 18$, $p = 0.90$, $q = 0.10$ **4.** $n = 20$, $p = 0.65$, $q = 0.35$

Approximating a Binomial Distribution   *In Exercises 5–8, a binomial experiment is given. Decide whether you can use the normal distribution to approximate the binomial distribution. If you can, find the mean and standard deviation. If you cannot, explain why.*

5. House Contract   A survey of U.S. adults found that 85% read every word or at least enough to understand a contract for buying or selling a home before signing. You ask 10 adults selected at random if he or she reads every word or at least enough to understand a contract for buying or selling a home before signing. *(Source: FindLaw.com)*

6. Organ Donors   A survey of U.S. adults found that 63% would want their organs transplanted into a patient who needs them if they were killed in an accident. You randomly select 20 adults and ask each if he or she would want their organs transplanted into a patient who needs them if they were killed in an accident. *(Source: USA TODAY)*

7. Prostate Cancer   In a recent year, the American Cancer Society said that the five-year survival rate for all men diagnosed with prostate cancer was 99%. You randomly select 10 men who were diagnosed with prostate cancer and calculate their five-year survival rate. *(Source: American Cancer Society)*

8. Work Weeks   A survey of workers in the United States found that 8.6% work fewer than 40 hours per week. You randomly select 30 workers in the United States and ask each if he or she works fewer than 40 hours per week.

In Exercises 9–12, match the binomial probability with the correct statement.

Probability	Statement
9. $P(x \geq 65)$	(a) P(there are fewer than 65 successes)
10. $P(x \leq 65)$	(b) P(there are at most 65 successes)
11. $P(x < 65)$	(c) P(there are more than 65 successes)
12. $P(x > 65)$	(d) P(there are at least 65 successes)

In Exercises 13–16, use the correction for continuity and match the binomial probability statement with the corresponding normal distribution statement.

Binomial Probability	Normal Probability
13. $P(x > 109)$	(a) $P(x > 109.5)$
14. $P(x \geq 109)$	(b) $P(x < 108.5)$
15. $P(x \leq 109)$	(c) $P(x \leq 109.5)$
16. $P(x < 109)$	(d) $P(x \geq 108.5)$

■ **Using and Interpreting Concepts**

Graphical Analysis *In Exercises 17 and 18, write the binomial probability and the normal probability for the shaded region of the graph. Find the value of each probability and compare the results.*

17.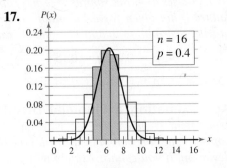

18.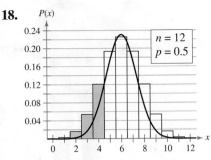

Approximating Binomial Probabilities *In Exercises 19–24, decide whether you can use the normal distribution to approximate the binomial distribution. If you can, use the normal distribution to approximate the indicated probabilities and sketch their graphs. If you cannot, explain why and use the binomial distribution to find the indicated probabilities.*

19. Blood Type O⁻ Seven percent of people in the United States have type O⁻ blood. You randomly select 30 people in the United States and ask them if their blood type is O⁻. *(Source: American Association of Blood Banks)*

  (a) Find the probability that exactly 10 people say they have O⁻ blood.

  (b) Find the probability that at least 10 people say they have O⁻ blood.

  (c) Find the probability that fewer than 10 people say they have O⁻ blood.

  (d) A blood drive would like to get at least five donors with O⁻ blood. There are 100 donors. What is the probability that there will not be enough O⁻ blood donors?

20. Blood Type A⁺ Thirty-four percent of people in the United States have type A⁺ blood. You randomly select 32 people in the United States and ask them if their blood type is A⁺. *(Source: American Association of Blood Banks)*

  (a) Find the probability that exactly 12 people say they have A⁺ blood.

  (b) Find the probability that at least 12 people say they have A⁺ blood.

  (c) Find the probability that fewer than 12 people say they have A⁺ blood.

  (d) A blood drive would like to get at least 60 donors with A⁺ blood. There are 150 donors. What is the probability that there will not be enough A⁺ blood donors?

21. Public Transportation Five percent of workers in the United States use public transportation to get to work. You randomly select 250 workers and ask them if they use public transportation to get to work. *(Source: U.S. Census Bureau)*

  (a) Find the probability that exactly 16 workers will say yes.

  (b) Find the probability that at least 9 workers will say yes.

  (c) Find the probability that fewer than 16 workers will say yes.

  (d) A transit authority offers discount rates to companies that have at least 30 employees who use public transportation to get to work. There are 500 employees in a company. What is the probability that the company will not get the discount?

22. College Graduates   Thirty-two percent of workers in the United States are college graduates. You randomly select 50 workers and ask each if he or she is a college graduate. *(Source: U.S. Bureau of Labor Statistics)*

(a) Find the probability that exactly 12 workers are college graduates.

(b) Find the probability that at least 14 workers are college graduates.

(c) Find the probability that fewer than 18 workers are college graduates.

(d) A committee is looking for 30 working college graduates to volunteer at a career fair. The committee randomly selects 150 workers. What is the probability that there will not be enough college graduates?

23. Favorite Cookie   Fifty-two percent of adults say chocolate chip is their favorite cookie. You randomly select 40 adults and ask each if chocolate chip is his or her favorite cookie. *(Source: Wearever)*

(a) Find the probability that at most 23 people say chocolate chip is their favorite cookie.

(b) Find the probability that at least 18 people say chocolate chip is their favorite cookie.

(c) Find the probability that more than 20 people say chocolate chip is their favorite cookie.

(d) A community bake sale has prepared 350 chocolate chip cookies. The bake sale attracts 650 customers, and they each buy their favorite cookie. What is the probability there will not be enough chocolate chip cookies?

24. Long Work Weeks   A survey of workers in the United States found that 2.9% work more than 70 hours per week. You randomly select 10 workers in the U.S. and ask each if he or she works more than 70 hours per week.

(a) Find the probability that at most 3 people say they work more than 70 hours per week.

(b) Find the probability that at least 1 person says he or she works more than 70 hours per week.

(c) Find the probability that more than 2 people say they work more than 70 hours per week.

(d) A large company is concerned about overworked employees who work more than 70 hours per week. The company randomly selects 50 employees. What is the probability there will be no employee working more than 70 hours?

25. Bigger Home   A survey of homeowners in the United States found that 24% feel their home is too small for their family. You randomly select 25 homeowners and ask them if they feel their home is too small for their family.

(a) Verify that the normal distribution can be used to approximate the binomial distribution.

(b) Find the probability that more than eight homeowners say their home is too small for their family.

(c) Is it unusual for 8 out of 25 homeowners to say their home is too small? Why or why not?

26. Driving to Work A survey of workers in the United States found that 80% rely on their own vehicle to get to work. You randomly select 40 workers and ask them if they rely on their own vehicle to get to work.

(a) Verify that the normal distribution can be used to approximate the binomial distribution.

(b) Find the probability that at most 26 workers say they rely on their own vehicle to get to work.

(c) Is it unusual for 26 out of 40 workers to say they rely on their own vehicle to get to work? Why or why not?

■ **Extending Concepts**

Getting Physical *In Exercises 27 and 28, use the following information. The graph shows the results of a survey of adults in the United States ages 33 to 51 who were asked if they participated in a sport. Seventy percent of adults said they regularly participate in at least one sport, and they gave their favorite sport.*

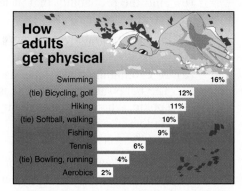

27. You randomly select 250 people in the United States ages 33 to 51 and ask each if he or she regularly participates in at least one sport. You find that 60% say no. How likely is this result? Do you think the sample is a good one? Explain your reasoning.

28. You randomly select 300 people in the United States ages 33 to 51 and ask each if he or she regularly participates in at least one sport. Of the 200 who say yes, 9% say they participate in hiking. How likely is this result? Is the sample a good one? Explain your reasoning.

Testing a Drug *In Exercises 29 and 30, use the following information. A drug manufacturer claims that a drug cures a rare skin disease 75% of the time. The claim is checked by testing the drug on 100 patients. If at least 70 patients are cured, the claim will be accepted.*

29. Find the probability that the claim will be rejected assuming that the manufacturer's claim is true.

30. Find the probability that the claim will be accepted assuming that the actual probability that the drug cures the skin disease is 65%.

Uses & Abuses

Uses

Normal Distributions Normal distributions can be used to describe many real-life situations and are widely used in the fields of science, business, and psychology. They are the most important probability distributions in statistics and can be used to approximate other distributions, such as discrete binomial distributions.

The most incredible application of the normal distribution lies in the Central Limit Theorem. This theorem states that no matter what type of distribution a population may have, as long as the sample size is at least 30, the distribution of sample means will be approximately normal. If the population is itself normal, then the distribution of sample means will be normal no matter how small the sample is.

The normal distribution is essential to sampling theory. Sampling theory forms the basis of statistical inference, which you will begin to study in the next chapter.

Abuses

Unusual Events Suppose a population is normally distributed with a mean of 100 and standard deviation of 15. It would not be unusual for an individual value taken from this population to be 115 or more. In fact, this will happen almost 16% of the time. It *would* be, however, highly unusual to take random samples of 100 values from that population and obtain a sample with a mean of 115 or more. Because the population is normally distributed, the mean of the sample distribution will be 100, and the standard deviation will be 1.5. A mean of 115 lies 10 standard deviations above the mean. This would be an extremely unusual event. When an event this unusual occurs, it is a good idea to question the original claimed value of the mean.

Although normal distributions are common in many populations, people try to make *non-normal* statistics fit the normal distribution. The statistics used for normal distributions are often inappropriate when the distribution is obviously non-normal.

■ EXERCISES

1. ***Is It Unusual?*** A population is normally distributed with a mean of 100 and a standard deviation of 15. Determine if the following event is unusual. Explain your reasoning.

   a. mean of a sample of 3 is 115 or more

   b. mean of a sample of 20 is 105 or more

2. ***Find the Error*** The mean age of students at a high school is 16.5 with a standard deviation of 0.7. You use the Standard Normal Table to help you determine that the probability of selecting one student at random and finding his or her age to be more than 17.5 years is about 8%. What is the error in this problem?

3. Give an example of a distribution that might be non-normal.

5 CHAPTER SUMMARY

What did you learn?	EXAMPLE(S)	REVIEW EXERCISES
Section 5.1		
■ How to interpret graphs of normal probability distributions	*1, 2*	*1, 2*
■ How to find and interpret z-scores $$z = \frac{x - \mu}{\sigma}$$	*3*	*3, 4*
■ How to find areas under the standard normal curve	*4–6*	*5–16*
Section 5.2		
■ How to find probabilities for normally distributed variables	*1–3*	*17–24*
Section 5.3		
■ How to find a z-score given the area under the normal curve	*1, 2*	*25–30*
■ How to transform a z-score to an x-value $$x = \mu + z\sigma$$	*3*	*31, 32*
■ How to find a specific data value of a normal distribution given the probability	*4, 5*	*33–36*
Section 5.4		
■ How to find sampling distributions and verify their properties	*1*	*37, 38*
■ How to interpret the Central Limit Theorem $$\mu_{\bar{x}} = \mu, \ \sigma_{\bar{x}} = \frac{\sigma}{\sqrt{n}}$$	*2, 3*	*39, 40*
■ How to apply the Central Limit Theorem to find the probability of a sample mean	*4–6*	*41–46*
Section 5.5		
■ How to decide when the normal distribution can approximate the binomial distribution $$\mu = np, \sigma = \sqrt{npq}$$	*1*	*47, 48*
■ How to find the correction for continuity	*2*	*49–52*
■ How to use the normal distribution to approximate binomial probabilities	*3–5*	*53, 54*

5 REVIEW EXERCISES

Section 5.1

In Exercises 1 and 2, use the graph to estimate μ and σ.

1.

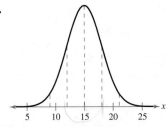

2.

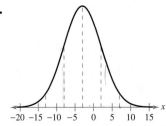

In Exercises 3 and 4, use the following information and standard scores to investigate observations about a normal population. A batch of 2500 resistors is normally distributed, with a mean resistance of 1.5 ohms and a standard deviation of 0.08 ohm. Four resistors are randomly selected and tested. Their resistances were measured at 1.32, 1.54, 1.66, and 1.78 ohms.

3. How many standard deviations from the mean are these observations?

4. Are there any unusual observations?

In Exercises 5–16, use the Standard Normal Table to find the indicated area under the standard normal curve. If convenient, use technology to find the area.

5. To the left of $z = 0.33$

6. To the left of $z = 2.55$

7. To the left of $z = -0.27$

8. To the left of $z = 1.72$

9. To the right of $z = 1.68$

10. To the right of $z = 0.12$

11. Between $z = -1.64$ and the mean

12. Between $z = -1.55$ and $z = 1.04$

13. Between $z = 0.05$ and $z = 1.71$

14. Between $z = -1.96$ and $z = 1.96$

15. To the left of $z = -1.5$ and to the right of $z = 1.5$

16. To the left of $z = 0.64$ and to the right of $z = 2.16$

Section 5.2

In Exercises 17–22, find the indicated probabilities. If convenient, use technology to find the probability.

17. $P(z < 1.28)$

18. $P(z > -0.74)$

19. $P(-2.15 < z < 1.55)$

20. $P(0.42 < z < 3.15)$

21. $P(z < -2.50$ or $z > 2.50)$

22. $P(z < 0$ or $z > 1.68)$

In Exercises 23 and 24, find the indicated probabilities.

23. A study found that the mean migration distance of the green turtle was 2200 kilometers and the standard deviation was 625 kilometers. Assuming that the distances are normally distributed, find the probability that a randomly selected green turtle migrates a distance of

(a) less than 1900 kilometers.

(b) between 2000 kilometers and 2500 kilometers.

(c) greater than 2450 kilometers.

(Adapted from Dorling Kindersley Visual Encyclopedia)

24. The world's smallest mammal is the Kitti's hog-nosed bat, with a mean weight of 1.5 grams and a standard deviation of 0.25 gram. Assuming that the weights are normally distributed, find the probability of randomly selecting a bat that weighs

(a) between 1.0 gram and 2.0 grams.

(b) between 1.6 grams and 2.2 grams.

(c) more than 2.2 grams.

(Adapted from Dorling Kindersley Visual Encyclopedia)

Section 5.3

In Exercises 25–30, use the Standard Normal Table to find the z-score that corresponds to the given cumulative area or percentile. If the area is not in the table, use the entry closest to the area. If convenient, use technology to find the z-score.

25. 0.4721   **26.** 0.1   **27.** 0.8708

28. P_2 **29.** P_{85} **30.** P_{20}

In Exercises 31–36, use the following information. On a dry surface, the braking distance (in meters) of a Ford Expedition can be approximated by a normal distribution, as shown in the graph. (Source: National Highway Traffic Safety Administration)

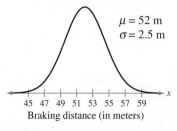

**Braking Distance of a
Ford Expedition**

$\mu = 52$ m
$\sigma = 2.5$ m

45 47 49 51 53 55 57 59
Braking distance (in meters)

31. Find the braking distance of a Ford Expedition that corresponds to $z = -2.4$.

32. Find the braking distance of a Ford Expedition that corresponds to $z = 1.2$.

33. What braking distance of a Ford Expedition represents the 95th percentile?

34. What braking distance of a Ford Expedition represents the third quartile?

35. What is the shortest braking distance of a Ford Expedition that can be in the top 10% of braking distances?

36. What is the longest braking distance of a Ford Expedition that can be in the bottom 5% of braking distances?

Section 5.4

In Exercises 37 and 38, use the given population to find the mean and standard deviation of the population and the mean and standard deviation of the sampling distribution. Compare the values.

37. A corporation has five executives. The number of minutes of overtime a week reported by each is 90, 300, 120, 160, and 210. Draw three executives' names from this population, with replacement.

38. There are four residents sharing a house. The number of times each washes his or her car each month is 1, 2, 0, and 3. Draw two names from this population, with replacement.

In Exercises 39 and 40, use the Central Limit Theorem to find the mean and standard error of the mean of the indicated sampling distribution. Then sketch a graph of the sampling distribution.

39. The consumption of processed fruits by people in the United States in a recent year was normally distributed, with a mean of 144.3 pounds and a standard deviation of 51.6 pounds. Random samples of size 35 are drawn from this population. *(Adapted from U.S. Department of Agriculture)*

40. The consumption of processed vegetables by people in the United States in a recent year was normally distributed, with a mean of 218.2 pounds and a standard deviation of 68.1 pounds. Random samples of size 40 are drawn from this population. *(Adapted from U.S. Department of Agriculture)*

In Exercises 41–46, find the probabilities for the sampling distributions.

41. Refer to Exercise 23. A sample of 12 green turtles is randomly selected. Find the probability that the sample mean of the distance migrated is (a) less than 1900 kilometers, (b) between 2000 kilometers and 2500 kilometers, and (c) greater than 2450 kilometers. Compare your answers with those in Exercise 23.

42. Refer to Exercise 24. A sample of seven Kitti's hog-nosed bats is randomly selected. Find the probability that the sample mean is (a) between 1.0 gram and 2.0 grams, (b) between 1.6 grams and 2.2 grams, and (c) more than 2.2 grams. Compare your answers with those in Exercise 24.

43. The mean annual salary for chauffeurs is $29,200. A random sample of size 45 is drawn from this population. What is the probability that the mean annual salary is (a) less than $29,000 and (b) more than $31,000? Assume $\sigma = \$1500$. *(Source: Salary.com)*

44. The mean value of land and buildings per acre for farms is $1300. A random sample of size 36 is drawn. What is the probability that the mean value of land and buildings per acre is (a) less than $1400 and (b) more than $1150? Assume $\sigma = \$250$.

45. The mean price of houses in a city is $1.5 million with a standard deviation of $500,000. The house prices are normally distributed. You randomly select 15 houses in this city. What is the probability that the mean price will be less than $1.125 million?

46. Mean rent in a city is $500 per month with a standard deviation of $30. The rents are normally distributed. You randomly select 15 apartments in this city. What is the probability that the mean price will be more than $525?

Section 5.5

In Exercises 47 and 48, a binomial experiment is given. Decide whether you can use the normal distribution to approximate the binomial distribution. If you can, find the mean and standard deviation. If you cannot, explain why.

47. In a recent year, the American Cancer Society said that the five-year survival rate for new cases of stage 1 kidney cancer is 95%. You randomly select 12 men who were new stage 1 kidney cancer cases this year and calculate their five-year survival rate. *(Source: American Cancer Society)*

48. A survey indicates that 59% of men purchased perfume in the past year. You randomly select 15 men and ask them if they have purchased perfume in the past year. *(Source: USA TODAY)*

In Exercises 49–52, write the binomial probability as a normal probability using the continuity correction.

Binomial Probability	Normal Probability
49. $P(x \geq 25)$	$P(x > ?)$
50. $P(x \leq 36)$	$P(x < ?)$
51. $P(x = 45)$	$P(? < x < ?)$
52. $P(x = 50)$	$P(? < x < ?)$

In Exercises 53 and 54, decide whether you can use the normal distribution to approximate the binomial distribution. If you can, use the normal distribution to approximate the indicated probabilities and sketch their graphs. If you cannot, explain why and use the binomial distribution to find the indicated probabilities.

53. Seventy percent of children ages 12 to 17 keep at least part of their savings in a savings account. You randomly select 45 children and ask each if he or she keeps at least part of his or her savings in a savings account. Find the probability that at most 20 children will say yes. *(Source: International Communications Research for Merrill Lynch)*

54. Thirty-three percent of adults graded public schools as excellent or good at preparing students for college. You randomly select 12 adults and ask them if they think public schools are excellent or good at preparing students for college. Find the probability that more than five adults will say yes. *(Source: Marist Institute for Public Opinion)*

5 CHAPTER QUIZ

Take this quiz as you would take a quiz in class. After you are done, check your work against the answers given in the back of the book.

1. Find each standard normal probability.

    (a) $P(z > -2.10)$
    (b) $P(z < 3.22)$
    (c) $P(-2.33 < z < 2.33)$
    (d) $P(z < -1.75 \text{ or } z > -0.75)$

2. Find each normal probability for the given parameters.

    (a) $\mu = 5.5$, $\sigma = 0.08$, $P(5.36 < x < 5.64)$
    (b) $\mu = -8.2$, $\sigma = 7.84$, $P(-5.00 < x < 0)$
    (c) $\mu = 18.5$, $\sigma = 9.25$, $P(x < 0 \text{ or } x > 37)$

In Exercises 3–10, use the following information. In a recent year, grade 8 Minnesota State public school students taking a mathematics assessment test had a mean score of 290 with a standard deviation of 37. Possible test scores could range from 0 to 500. Assume that the scores are normally distributed. (Source: National Center for Educational Statistics)

3. Find the probability that a student had a score higher than 320.

4. Find the probability that a student had a score between 250 and 300.

5. What percent of the students had a test score that is greater than 250?

6. If 2000 students are randomly selected, how many would be expected to have a test score that is less than 280?

7. What is the lowest score that would still place a student in the top 5% of the scores?

8. What is the highest score that would still place a student in the bottom 25% of the scores?

9. A random sample of 60 students is drawn from this population. What is the probability that the mean test score is greater than 300?

10. Are you more likely to randomly select one student with a test score greater than 300 or are you more likely to select a sample of 15 students with a mean test score greater than 300? Explain.

In Exercises 11 and 12, use the following information. In a survey of adults, 75% strongly support using DNA research by scientists to find new ways to prevent or treat diseases. You randomly select 24 adults and ask each if they strongly support using DNA research by scientists to find new ways to prevent or treat diseases. (Source: Harris Interactive)

11. Decide whether you can use the normal distribution to approximate the binomial distribution. If you can, find the mean and standard deviation. If you cannot, explain why.

12. Find the probability that at most 15 people say they strongly support using DNA research by scientists to find new ways to prevent or treat diseases.

Putting It All Together

REAL Statistics — Real Decisions

You work for a candy company as a statistical process analyst. Your job is to analyze processes and make sure they are in statistical control. In one process, a machine is supposed to drop 11.4 ounces of mints into a bag. (Assume this process can be approximated by a normal distribution.) The acceptable range of weights for the bags of mints is 11.25 ounces to 11.55 ounces, inclusive.

Because of an error with the release valve, the setting on the mint release machine "shifts" from 11.4 ounces. To check that the machine is placing the correct weight of mints into the bags, you select at random three samples of five bags of mints and find the mean weight (in ounces) of each sample. A coworker asks why you take three samples of size 5 and find the mean instead of randomly choosing and measuring 15 bags of mints individually to check the machine's settings. (*Note:* Both samples are chosen without replacement.)

■ Exercises

1. *Sampling Individuals*

You select one bag of mints and measure its weight. Assume the machine shifts and is filling the bags with a mean weight of 11.56 ounces and a standard deviation of 0.05 ounces.

(a) What is the probability that you select a bag of mints that is *not* outside the acceptable range (in other words, you do not detect that the machine has shifted)? (See figure.)

(b) You randomly select 15 bags of mints. What is the probability that you select at least one bag that is *not* outside the acceptable range?

2. *Sampling Groups of Five*

You select five bags of mints and find their mean weight. Assume the machine shifts and is filling the bags with a mean weight of 11.56 ounces and a standard deviation of 0.05 ounces.

(a) What is the probability that you select a sample of five bags of mints that has a mean that is *not* outside the acceptable range? (See figure.)

(b) You randomly select three samples of five bags of mints. What is the probability that you select at least one sample of five bags of mints that has a mean that is *not* outside the acceptable range?

(c) What is more sensitive to change—an individual measure or the mean?

3. *Writing an Explanation*

Write a paragraph to your coworker explaining why you take 3 samples of size 5 and find the mean of each sample instead of randomly choosing and measuring 15 bags of mints individually to check the machine's settings.

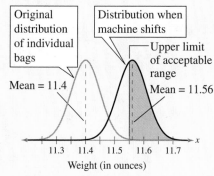

FIGURE FOR EXERCISE 1

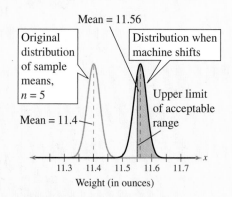

FIGURE FOR EXERCISE 2

TECHNOLOGY

U.S. Census Bureau

www.census.gov

Class boundaries	Class midpoint	Relative frequency
0–4	2	6.8%
5–9	7	6.6%
10–14	12	7.0%
15–19	17	7.1%
20–24	22	7.1%
25–29	27	6.8%
30–34	32	6.8%
35–39	37	7.1%
40–44	42	7.7%
45–49	47	7.6%
50–54	52	6.7%
55–59	57	5.9%
60–64	62	4.4%
65–69	67	3.4%
70–74	72	2.9%
75–79	77	2.5%
80–84	82	1.9%
85–89	87	1.1%
90–94	92	0.5%
95–99	97	0.1%

AGE DISTRIBUTION IN THE UNITED STATES

One of the jobs of the U.S. Census Bureau is to keep track of the age distribution in the country. The age distribution in 2005 is shown below.

Age Distribution in the U.S.

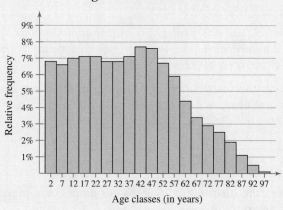

■ EXERCISES

We used a technology tool to select random samples with n = 40 from the age distribution of the United States. The means of the 36 samples were as follows.

28.14, 31.56, 36.86, 32.37, 36.12, 39.53,
36.19, 39.02, 35.62, 36.30, 34.38, 32.98,
36.41, 30.24, 34.19, 44.72, 38.84, 42.87,
38.90, 34.71, 34.13, 38.25, 38.04, 34.07,
39.74, 40.91, 42.63, 35.29, 35.91, 34.36,
36.51, 36.47, 32.88, 37.33, 31.27, 35.80

1. Enter the age distribution of the United States into a technology tool. Use the tool to find the mean age in the United States.

2. Enter the set of sample means into a technology tool. Find the mean of the set of sample means. How does it compare with the mean age in the United States? Does this agree with the result predicted by the Central Limit Theorem?

3. Are the ages of people in the United States normally distributed? Explain your reasoning.

4. Sketch a relative frequency histogram for the 36 sample means. Use nine classes. Is the histogram approximately bell-shaped and symmetric? Does this agree with the result predicted by the Central Limit Theorem?

5. Use a technology tool to find the standard deviation of the ages of people in the United States.

6. Use a technology tool to find the standard deviation of the set of 36 sample means. How does it compare with the standard deviation of the ages? Does this agree with the result predicted by the Central Limit Theorem?

Extended solutions are given in the *Technology Supplement*. Technical instruction is provided for MINITAB, Excel, and the TI-83/84.

Cumulative Review

CHAPTERS 3 – 5

1. A survey of employees in the United States found that 56% do not use all of their vacation time. You randomly select 30 employees and ask them if they use all of their vacation time. *(Source: Rasmussen Reports)*

   (a) Verify that the normal distribution can be used to approximate the binomial distribution.

   (b) Find the probability that at most 14 employees say they do not use all of their vacation time.

   (c) Is it unusual for 14 out of 30 employees to say they do not use all of their vacation time? Why or why not?

In Exercises 2 and 3, use the probability distribution to find the (a) mean, (b) variance, (c) standard deviation, and (d) expected value of the probability distribution, and (e) interpret the results.

2. The table shows the distribution of family household sizes in the United States for a recent year. *(Source: U.S. Census Bureau)*

x	2	3	4	5	6	7
$P(x)$	0.421	0.233	0.202	0.093	0.033	0.017

3. The table shows the distribution of fouls per game for a player in a recent NBA season. *(Source: NBA.com)*

x	0	1	2	3	4	5	6
$P(x)$	0.012	0.049	0.159	0.256	0.244	0.195	0.085

4. Use the probability distribution in Exercise 3 to find the probability of randomly selecting a game in which the player had (a) fewer than four fouls, (b) at least three fouls, and (c) between two and four fouls, inclusive.

5. From a pool of 16 candidates, 9 men and 7 women, the offices of president, vice president, secretary, and treasurer will be filled. (a) In how many different ways can the offices be filled? (b) What is the probability that all four of the offices are filled by women?

In Exercises 6–11, use the Standard Normal Table to find the indicated area under the standard normal curve.

6. To the left of $z = 1.54$

7. To the left of $z = -3.08$

8. To the right of $z = -0.84$

9. Between $z = 0$ and $z = 3.09$

10. Between $z = -1.22$ and $z = -0.26$

11. To the left of $z = 0.12$ or to the right of $z = 1.72$

12. Seventy-eight percent of college graduates say they spent two years or less at their first full-time job after graduating college. You randomly select 10 college graduates and ask each how long they stayed at their first full-time job after graduating college. Find the probability that the number who say they spent less than two years at their first full-time job after graduating college is (a) exactly six, (b) at least six, and (c) less than six. *(Source: Experience.com)*

13. An auto parts seller finds that 1 in every 200 parts sold is defective. Use the geometric distribution to find the probability that (a) the first defective part is the tenth part sold, (b) the first defective part is the first, second, or third part sold, and (c) none of the first ten parts sold are defective.

14. The table shows the results of a survey in which 3,188,100 public and 438,800 private school teachers were asked about their full-time teaching experience. *(Adapted from U.S. National Center for Education Statistics)*

	Public	Private	Total
Less than 3 years	388,500	106,600	495,100
3 to 9 years	1,048,000	144,900	1,192,900
10 to 20 years	833,350	98,300	931,800
20 years or more	918,100	89,000	1,007,100
Total	3,188,100	438,800	3,626,900

(a) Find the probability that a randomly selected private school teacher has 10 to 20 years of full-time teaching experience.

(b) Given that a randomly selected teacher has 3 to 9 years of full-time teaching experience, find the probability that the teacher is at a public school.

(c) Are the events "being a public school teacher" and "having 20 years or more of full-time teaching experience" independent or dependent? Explain.

(d) Find the probability that a randomly selected teacher is either at a public school or has less than 3 years of full-time teaching experience.

(e) Find the probability that a randomly selected teacher has 3 to 9 years of full-time teaching experience or is at a private school.

15. The initial pressure for bicycle tires when first filled is normally distributed, with a mean of 70 pounds per square inch (psi) and a standard deviation of 1.2 psi.

(a) Random samples of size 40 are drawn from this population and the mean of each sample is determined. Use the Central Limit Theorem to find the mean and standard error of the mean of the sampling distribution. Then sketch a graph of the sampling distribution of sample means.

(b) A random sample of 15 tires is drawn from this population. What is the probability that the mean tire pressure of the sample, $\bar{x}$, is less than 69 psi?

16. The life span of a car battery is normally distributed, with a mean of 44 months and a standard deviation of 5 months.

(a) A car battery is selected at random. Find the probability that the life span of the battery is less than 36 months.

(b) A car battery is selected at random. Find the probability that the life span of the battery is between 42 and 60 months.

(c) What is the shortest life expectancy a car battery can have and still be in the top 5% of life expectancies?

17. A florist has 12 different flowers from which floral arrangements can be made. (a) If a centerpiece is to be made using four different flowers, how many different centerpieces can be made? (b) What is the probability that the four flowers in the centerpiece are roses, gerbers, hydrangeas, and callas?

18. Forty-one percent of adults say they shop for a gift within a week of an event. You randomly select 20 adults and ask each how far in advance he or she shops for a gift. Use the binomial formula to find the probability that the number who say they shop for a gift within a week of the event is (a) exactly eight, (b) at least six, and (c) at most thirteen. *(Source: Harris Interactive)*

3
PART THREE

Statistical Inference

CHAPTER 6   Confidence Intervals

CHAPTER 7   Hypothesis Testing with One Sample

CHAPTER 8   Hypothesis Testing with Two Samples

CHAPTER 6

Confidence Intervals

6.1 Confidence Intervals for the Mean (Large Samples)
  ■ CASE STUDY

6.2 Confidence Intervals for the Mean (Small Samples)
  ■ ACTIVITY

6.3 Confidence Intervals for Population Proportions
  ■ ACTIVITY

6.4 Confidence Intervals for Variance and Standard Deviation
  ■ USES AND ABUSES

  ■ REAL STATISTICS– REAL DECISIONS

  ■ TECHNOLOGY

The Energy Policy Conservation Act (EPCA) was enacted into law in 1975. This act established the Corporate Average Fuel Economy (CAFE) standards for passenger cars and light trucks. These standards have been increased over the years despite the efforts of the automotive industry. They require that the fuel economy rating for a manufacturer's entire line of passenger cars must average at least 27.5 miles per gallon, and the fuel economy rating for a manufacturer's entire line of light trucks must average at least 22.2 miles per gallon.

In Chapters 1 through 5, you studied descriptive statistics (how to collect and describe data) and probability (how to find probabilities and analyze discrete and continuous probability distributions). Automobile manufacturers use descriptive statistics to analyze the data collected during vehicle tests conducted in their laboratories.

To meet the CAFE certification, either the automobile manufacturer provides its own fuel economy test data or the EPA obtains a vehicle and tests it. The EPA tests the mean fuel economy rating of about 30% of the existing vehicle lines. In a recent year, the EPA tested a sample of 18 cars from an automobile manufacturer's line of passenger cars. The mean fuel economy rating was 31.1 miles per gallon.

In this chapter, you will begin your study of inferential statistics—the second major branch of statistics. For instance, from the mean of the sample of a manufacturer's line of passenger cars, the EPA can estimate the mean fuel economy rating to be 31.1 miles per gallon for the manufacturer's *entire* line of passenger cars. Because this estimate consists of a single number represented by a point on a number line, it is called a point estimate. The problem with using a point estimate is that it is rarely equal to the exact parameter (mean, standard deviation, or proportion) of the population.

In this chapter, you will learn how to make a more meaningful estimate by specifying an interval of values on a number line, together with a statement of how confident you are that your interval contains the population parameter. Suppose the EPA wanted to be 90% confident of its estimate for the mean fuel economy rating for the manufacturer's entire line of passenger cars. Here is an overview of how to construct an interval estimate.

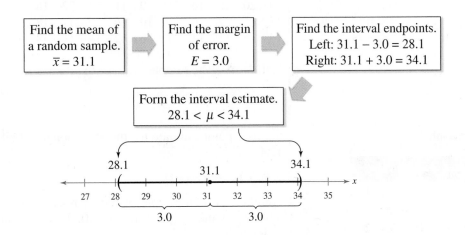

So, the EPA can be 90% confident that the mean fuel economy rating for the manufacturer's entire line of passenger cars is between 28.1 and 34.1 miles per gallon.

6.1 Confidence Intervals for the Mean (Large Samples)

Estimating Population Parameters ▸ Confidence Intervals for the Population Mean ▸ Sample Size

▸ Estimating Population Parameters

In this chapter, you will learn an important technique of statistical inference—to use sample statistics to estimate the value of an unknown population parameter. In this section, you will learn how to use sample statistics to make an estimate of the population parameter μ when the sample size is at least 30 or when the population is normally distributed and the standard deviation σ is known. To make such an inference, begin by finding a point estimate.

> **DEFINITION**
>
> A **point estimate** is a single value estimate for a population parameter. The most unbiased point estimate of the population mean μ is the sample mean $\overline{x}$.

The validity of an estimation method is increased if a sample statistic is unbiased and has low variability. A statistic is unbiased if it does not overestimate or underestimate the population parameter. In Chapter 5, you learned that the mean of all possible sample means of the same size equals the population mean. As a result, $\overline{x}$ is an unbiased estimator of μ. When the standard error, $\sigma/\sqrt{n}$, of a sample mean is decreased by increasing n, it becomes less variable.

> **EXAMPLE 1**
>
> ### Finding a Point Estimate
>
> Market researchers use the number of sentences per advertisement as a measure of readability for magazine advertisements. The following represents a random sample of the number of sentences found in 50 advertisements. Find a point estimate of the population mean μ. *(Source: Journal of Advertising Research)*
>
> | 9 | 20 | 18 | 16 | 9 | 9 | 11 | 13 | 22 | 16 | 5 | 18 | 6 | 6 | 5 | 12 | 25 |
> |---|----|----|----|---|---|----|----|----|----|---|----|---|---|---|----|----|
> | 17 | 23 | 7 | 10 | 9 | 10 | 10 | 5 | 11 | 18 | 18 | 9 | 9 | 17 | 13 | 11 | 7 |
> | 14 | 6 | 11 | 12 | 11 | 6 | 12 | 14 | 11 | 9 | 18 | 12 | 12 | 17 | 11 | 20 | |
>
> **Solution** The sample mean of the data is
>
> $$\overline{x} = \frac{\Sigma x}{n} = \frac{620}{50} = 12.4.$$
>
> So, your point estimate for the mean length of all magazine advertisements is 12.4 sentences.
>
> ### ▸ Try It Yourself 1
>
> Another random sample of the number of sentences found in 30 magazine advertisements is listed at the left. Use this sample to find another point estimate for μ.
>
> **a.** *Find* the sample mean.
> **b.** *Estimate* the mean sentence length of the population. *Answer: Page A42*

Sample Data

Number of Sentences					
16	9	14	11	17	12
99	18	13	12	5	9
17	6	11	17	18	20
6	14	7	11	12	12
5	11	18	6	4	13

In Example 1, the probability that the population mean is exactly 12.4 is virtually zero. So, instead of estimating μ to be exactly 12.4 using a *point estimate*, you can estimate that μ lies in an *interval*. This is called *making an interval estimate*.

> ## DEFINITION
>
> An **interval estimate** is an interval, or range of values, used to estimate a population parameter.

Although you can assume that the point estimate in Example 1 is not equal to the actual population mean, it is probably close to it. To form an interval estimate, use the point estimate as the center of the interval, then add and subtract a margin of error. For instance, if the margin of error is 2.1, then an interval estimate would be given by 12.4 ± 2.1 or $10.3 < \mu < 14.5$. The point estimate and interval estimate are as follows.

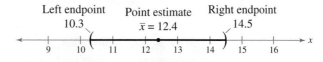

Interval estimate

Before finding a margin of error for an interval estimate, you should first determine how confident you need to be that your interval estimate contains the population mean μ.

> ## DEFINITION
>
> The **level of confidence c** is the probability that the interval estimate contains the population parameter.

You know from the Central Limit Theorem that when $n \geq 30$, the sampling distribution of sample means is a normal distribution. The level of confidence c is the area under the standard normal curve between the **critical values,** $-z_c$ and z_c. You can see from the graph that c is the percent of the area under the normal curve between $-z_c$ and z_c. The area remaining is $1 - c$, so the area in each tail is $\frac{1}{2}(1 - c)$. For instance, if $c = 90\%$, then 5% of the area lies to the left of $-z_c = -1.645$ and 5% lies to the right of $z_c = 1.645$.

Study Tip

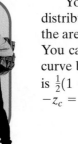

In this course, you will usually use 90%, 95%, and 99% levels of confidence. The following z-scores correspond to these levels of confidence.

Level of Confidence	z_c
90%	1.645
95%	1.96
99%	2.575

Insight

Critical values are values that separate sample statistics that are probable from sample statistics that are improbable, or unusual.

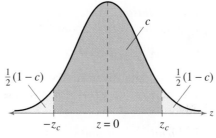

	If $c = 90\%$:
$c = 0.90$	Area in blue region
$1 - c = 0.10$	Area in yellow regions
$\frac{1}{2}(1 - c) = 0.05$	Area in each tail
$-z_c = -1.645$	Critical value separating left tail
$z_c = 1.645$	Critical value separating right tail

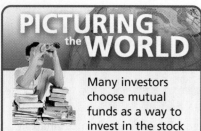
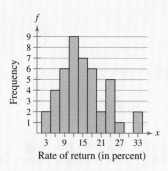
The difference between the point estimate and the actual parameter value is called the **sampling error.** When μ is estimated, the sampling error is the difference $\overline{x} - \mu$. In most cases, of course, μ is unknown, and $\overline{x}$ varies from sample to sample. However, you can calculate a maximum value for the error if you know the level of confidence and the sampling distribution.

DEFINITION

Given a level of confidence c, the **margin of error** (sometimes also called the maximum error of estimate or error tolerance) E is the greatest possible distance between the point estimate and the value of the parameter it is estimating.

$$E = z_c \sigma_{\overline{x}} = z_c \frac{\sigma}{\sqrt{n}}$$

In order to use this technique, it is assumed that the population standard deviation is known. This is rarely the case, but when $n \geq 30$, the sample standard deviation s can be used in place of σ.

EXAMPLE 2

Finding the Margin of Error

Use the data in Example 1 and a 95% confidence level to find the margin of error for the mean number of sentences in all magazine advertisements. Assume that the sample standard deviation is about 5.0.

Solution   The z-score that corresponds to a 95% confidence level is 1.96. This implies that 95% of the area under the standard normal curve falls within 1.96 standard deviations of the mean. (You can approximate the distribution of the sample means with a normal curve by the Central Limit Theorem, because $n = 50 \geq 30$.) You don't know the population standard deviation σ. But because $n \geq 30$, you can use s in place of σ.

Using the values $z_c = 1.96$, $\sigma \approx s \approx 5.0$, and $n = 50$,

$$E = z_c \frac{\sigma}{\sqrt{n}}$$

$$\approx 1.96 \cdot \frac{5.0}{\sqrt{50}}$$

$$\approx 1.4.$$

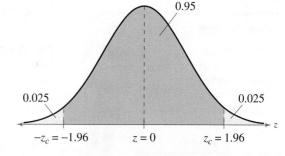

Interpretation   You are 95% confident that the margin of error for the population mean is about 1.4 sentences.

▶ Try It Yourself 2

Use the data given in Try It Yourself 1 and a 95% confidence level to find the margin of error for the mean number of sentences in a magazine advertisement.

a. *Identify* z_c, n, and s.
b. *Find* E using z_c, $\sigma \approx s$, and n.
c. *State* the margin of error.

Answer: Page A42

▶ Confidence Intervals for the Population Mean

Using a point estimate and a margin of error, you can construct an interval estimate of a population parameter such as μ. This interval estimate is called a confidence interval.

DEFINITION

A *c*-**confidence interval** for the population mean μ is

$$\bar{x} - E < \mu < \bar{x} + E.$$

The probability that the confidence interval contains μ is c.

GUIDELINES

Finding a Confidence Interval for a Population Mean ($n \geq 30$ or σ known with a normally distributed population)

In Words	*In Symbols*
1. Find the sample statistics n and $\bar{x}$.	$\bar{x} = \dfrac{\sum x}{n}$
2. Specify σ, if known. Otherwise, if $n \geq 30$, find the sample standard deviation s and use it as an estimate for σ.	$s = \sqrt{\dfrac{\sum (x - \bar{x})^2}{n - 1}}$
3. Find the critical value z_c that corresponds to the given level of confidence.	Use the Standard Normal Table or technology.
4. Find the margin of error E.	$E = z_c \dfrac{\sigma}{\sqrt{n}}$
5. Find the left and right endpoints and form the confidence interval.	Left endpoint: $\bar{x} - E$ Right endpoint: $\bar{x} + E$ Interval: $\bar{x} - E < \mu < \bar{x} + E$

EXAMPLE 3

Constructing a Confidence Interval

Construct a 95% confidence interval for the mean number of sentences in all magazine advertisements.

> See MINITAB steps on page 360.

Solution   In Examples 1 and 2, you found that $\bar{x} = 12.4$ and $E = 1.4$. The confidence interval is as follows.

Left Endpoint   Right Endpoint

$\bar{x} - E = 12.4 - 1.4 = 11.0$ $\bar{x} + E = 12.4 + 1.4 = 13.8$

$11.0 < \mu < 13.8$

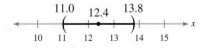

Interpretation   With 95% confidence, you can say that the population mean number of sentences is between 11.0 and 13.8.

Answer: Page A42

Answer: Page A42

Insight

The width of a confidence interval is $2E$. Examine the formula for E to see why a larger sample size tends to give you a narrower confidence interval for the same level of confidence.

Study Tip

Using a TI-83/84, you can either enter the original data into a list to construct the confidence interval or enter the descriptive statistics.

| STAT |

Choose the TESTS menu.

7: ZInterval…

Select the *Data* input option if you have entered the original data. Select the *Stats* input option if you entered the descriptive statistics. In each case, enter the appropriate values, then select *Calculate*. Your results may differ slightly depending on the method you use. For Example 4, the original data values were entered.

```
ZInterval
 (10.579,14.221)
 x̄=12.4
 Sx=5.010193691
 n=50
```

▶ Try It Yourself 3

Use the data given in Try It Yourself 1 to construct a 95% confidence interval for the mean number of sentences in all magazine advertisements. Compare your result with the interval found in Example 3.

a. *Find* $\bar{x}$ and E.
b. *Find* the left and right endpoints of the confidence interval.
c. *State* the 95% confidence interval and compare it with Example 3.

EXAMPLE 4

Constructing a Confidence Interval Using Technology

Use a technology tool to construct a 99% confidence interval for the mean number of sentences in all magazine advertisements, using the sample in Example 1.

Solution To use a technology tool to solve the problem, enter the data and recall that the sample standard deviation is $s \approx 5.0$. Then, use the confidence interval command to calculate the confidence interval (*1-Sample Z* for MINITAB). The display should look like the one shown below. To construct a confidence interval using a TI-83/84, follow the instructions in the margin.

MINITAB

Z Confidence Intervals

The assumed sigma = 5

Variable	N	Mean	StDev	SE Mean	99.0 % CI
C1	50	12.4	5.010	0.709	(10.579, 14.221)

So, a 99% confidence interval for μ is $(10.6, 14.2)$.

Interpretation With 99% confidence, you can say that the population mean number of sentences is between 10.6 and 14.2.

▶ Try It Yourself 4

Use the sample data in Example 1 and a technology tool to construct 75%, 85%, and 99% confidence intervals for the mean number of sentences in all magazine advertisements. How does the width of the confidence interval change as the level of confidence increases?

a. *Enter* the data.
b. *Use* the appropriate command to construct each confidence interval.
c. *Compare* the widths of the confidence intervals for $c = 0.75, 0.85$, and 0.99.

In Example 4 and Try It Yourself 4, the same sample data were used to construct confidence intervals with different levels of confidence. Notice that as the level of confidence increases, the width of the confidence interval also increases. In other words, when the same sample data are used, *the greater the level of confidence, the wider the interval.*

If the population is normally distributed and the population standard deviation σ is known, you may use the normal sampling distribution for any sample size, as shown in Example 5.

EXAMPLE 5

Constructing a Confidence Interval, σ Known

See TI-83/84 steps on page 361.

A college admissions director wishes to estimate the mean age of all students currently enrolled. In a random sample of 20 students, the mean age is found to be 22.9 years. From past studies, the standard deviation is known to be 1.5 years, and the population is normally distributed. Construct a 90% confidence interval of the population mean age.

Solution

Using $n = 20$, $\overline{x} = 22.9$, $\sigma = 1.5$, and $z_c = 1.645$, the margin of error at the 90% confidence interval is

$$E = z_c \frac{\sigma}{\sqrt{n}} = 1.645 \cdot \frac{1.5}{\sqrt{20}} \approx 0.6.$$

The 90% confidence interval can be written as $\overline{x} \pm E = 22.9 \pm 0.6$ or as follows.

Left Endpoint   Right Endpoint

$\overline{x} - E = 22.9 - 0.6 = 22.3$ $\overline{x} + E = 22.9 + 0.6 = 23.5$

$22.3 < \mu < 23.5$

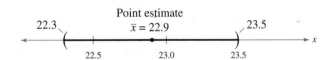

Interpretation   With 90% confidence, you can say that the mean age of all the students is between 22.3 and 23.5 years.

▶ Try It Yourself 5

Construct a 90% confidence interval of the population mean age for the college students in Example 5 if the sample size is increased to 30 students. Compare your answer with Example 5.

a. *Identify* n, $\overline{x}$, σ, and z_c, and *find* E.
b. *Find* the left and right endpoints of the confidence interval.
c. *Specify* the 90% confidence interval and compare your answer with Example 5.   *Answer: Page A42*

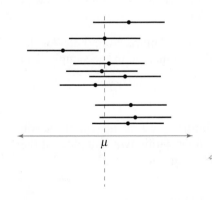

The horizontal segments represent 90% confidence intervals for different samples of the same size. In the long run, 9 of every 10 such intervals will contain μ.

After constructing a confidence interval, it is important that you interpret the results correctly. Consider the 90% confidence interval constructed in Example 5. Because μ already exists, it is either in the interval or not. It is *not* correct to say "There is a 90% probability that the actual mean is in the interval $(22.3, 23.5)$." The correct way to interpret your confidence interval is "If a large number of samples is collected and a confidence interval is created for each sample, approximately 90% of these intervals will contain μ."

▶ **Sample Size**

For the same sample statistics, as the level of confidence increases, the confidence interval widens. As the confidence interval widens, the precision of the estimate decreases. One way to improve the precision of an estimate without decreasing the level of confidence is to increase the sample size. But how large a sample size is needed to guarantee a certain level of confidence for a given margin of error?

FIND A MINIMUM SAMPLE SIZE TO ESTIMATE μ

Given a c-confidence level and a margin of error E, the minimum sample size n needed to estimate the population mean μ is

$$n = \left(\frac{z_c \sigma}{E}\right)^2.$$

If σ is unknown, you can estimate it using s, provided you have a preliminary sample with at least 30 members.

EXAMPLE 6

Determining a Minimum Sample Size

You want to estimate the mean number of sentences in a magazine advertisement. How many magazine advertisements must be included in the sample if you want to be 95% confident that the sample mean is within one sentence of the population mean?

Solution   Using $c = 0.95$, $z_c = 1.96$, $\sigma \approx s \approx 5.0$ (from Example 2), and $E = 1$, you can solve for the minimum sample size n.

$$n = \left(\frac{z_c \sigma}{E}\right)^2$$

$$\approx \left(\frac{1.96 \cdot 5.0}{1}\right)^2$$

$$= 96.04$$

When necessary, round up to obtain a whole number. So, you should include at least 97 magazine advertisements in your sample.

Interpretation   You already have 50, so you need 47 more. Note that 97 is the *minimum* number of magazines advertisements to include in the sample. You could include more, if desired.

▶ **Try It Yourself 6**

How many magazine advertisements must be included in the sample if you want to be 95% confident that the sample mean is within two sentences of the population mean? Compare your answer with Example 6.

a. *Identify* z_c, E, and s.
b. *Use* z_c, E, and $\sigma \approx s$ to find the minimum sample size n.
c. *State* how many magazine advertisements must be included in the sample and compare your answer with Example 6.   *Answer: Page A42*

6.1 EXERCISES

For Extra Help

MyStatLab

■ Building Basic Skills and Vocabulary

1. When estimating a population mean, are you more likely to be correct if you use a point estimate or an interval estimate? Explain your reasoning.

2. Which statistic is the best unbiased estimator for μ?

(a) s (b) $\bar{x}$ (c) the median   (d) the mode

3. Given the same sample statistics, which level of confidence would produce the widest confidence interval? Explain your reasoning.

(a) 90%   (b) 95%   (c) 98%   (d) 99%

4. What is the effect on the width of the confidence interval when the sample size is increased? Explain your reasoning.

(a) The width increases   (b) The width decreases   (c) No effect

In Exercises 5–8, find the critical value z_c necessary to form a confidence interval at the given level of confidence.

5. $c = 0.80$ **6.** $c = 0.85$ **7.** $c = 0.75$ **8.** $c = 0.97$

Graphical Analysis   *In Exercises 9–14, use the values on the number line to find the sampling error.*

9. $\bar{x} = 3.8$ $\mu = 4.27$
3.4 3.6 3.8 4.0 4.2 4.4 4.6

10. $\mu = 8.76$ $\bar{x} = 9.5$
8.6 8.8 9.0 9.2 9.4 9.6 9.8

11. $\mu = 24.67$ $\bar{x} = 26.43$
24   25   26   27

12. $\bar{x} = 46.56$ $\mu = 48.12$
46   47   48   49

13. $\bar{x} = 0.7$ $\mu = 1.3$
0.0   0.5   1.0   1.5   2.0

14. $\mu = 80.9$ $\bar{x} = 86.4$
80   82   84   86   88

In Exercises 15–18, find the margin of error for the given values of c, s, and n.

15. $c = 0.90, s = 2.5, n = 36$ **16.** $c = 0.95, s = 3.0, n = 60$

17. $c = 0.80, s = 1.3, n = 75$ **18.** $c = 0.975, s = 4.6, n = 100$

Matching   *In Exercises 19–22, match the level of confidence c, with its representation on the number line, given $\bar{x} = 57.2$, $s = 7.1$, and $n = 50$.*

19. $c = 0.88$ **20.** $c = 0.90$ **21.** $c = 0.95$ **22.** $c = 0.98$

(a)   54.9   57.2   59.5
54 55 56 57 58 59 60

(b)   55.2   57.2   59.2
54 55 56 57 58 59 60

(c)   55.6   57.2   58.8
54 55 56 57 58 59 60

(d)   55.5   57.2   58.9
54 55 56 57 58 59 60

In Exercises 23–26, construct the indicated confidence interval for the population mean μ. If convenient, use technology to construct the confidence interval.

23. $c = 0.90, \bar{x} = 15.2, s = 2.0, n = 60$

24. $c = 0.95, \bar{x} = 31.39, s = 0.8, n = 82$

25. $c = 0.95, \bar{x} = 4.27, s = 0.3, n = 42$

26. $c = 0.99, \bar{x} = 13.5, s = 1.5, n = 100$

In Exercises 27–30, use the given confidence interval to find the margin of error and the sample mean.

27. $(0.264, 0.494)$ **28.** $(3.144, 3.176)$

29. $(1.71, 2.05)$ **30.** $(21.61, 30.15)$

In Exercises 31–34, find the minimum sample size n needed to estimate μ for the given values of c, s, and E.

31. $c = 0.90, s = 6.8, E = 1$ **32.** $c = 0.95, s = 2.5, E = 1$

33. $c = 0.80, s = 4.1, E = 2$ **34.** $c = 0.98, s = 10.1, E = 2$

■ Using and Interpreting Concepts

Finding the Margin of Error *In Exercises 35 and 36, use the given confidence interval to find the estimated margin of error. Then find the sample mean.*

35. Seedlings A biologist reports a confidence interval of $(2.1, 3.5)$ when estimating the mean height (in centimeters) of a sample of seedlings.

36. Book Prices A store manager reports a confidence interval of $(44.07, 80.97)$ when estimating the mean price (in dollars) of a sample of textbooks.

Constructing Confidence Intervals *In Exercises 37–40, you are given the sample mean and the sample standard deviation. Use this information to construct the 90% and 95% confidence intervals for the population mean. Which interval is wider? If convenient, use technology to construct the confidence intervals.*

37. Gas Grills A random sample of 32 gas grills has a mean price of $630.90 and a standard deviation of $56.70.

38. Stock Prices From a random sample of 35 days in a recent year, the closing stock prices for Hasbro had a mean of $23.20 and a standard deviation of $4.34. *(Source: Marketwatch, Inc.)*

39. Juice Drinks A random sample of 31 eight-ounce servings of different juice drinks has a mean of 99.3 calories and a standard deviation of 41.5 calories. *(Adapted from The Beverage Institute for Health and Wellness)*

40. Sodium Chloride Concentration In 36 randomly selected seawater samples, the mean sodium chloride concentration was 23 cubic centimeters per cubic meter and the standard deviation was 6.7 cubic centimeters per cubic meter. *(Adapted from Dorling Kindersley Visual Encyclopedia)*

41. Repair Costs: Washing Machines   You work for a consumer advocate agency and want to find the mean repair cost of a washing machine. As part of your study, you randomly select 40 repair costs and find the mean to be $120.00. The sample standard deviation is $17.50. Construct a 95% confidence interval for the population mean repair cost. *(Adapted from Consumer Reports)*

42. Repair Costs: Refrigerators   In a random sample of 60 refrigerators, the mean repair cost was $150.00 and the standard deviation was $15.50. Construct a 99% confidence interval for the population mean repair cost. *(Adapted from Consumer Reports)*

43. Repeat Exercise 41, changing the sample size to $n = 80$. Which confidence interval is wider? Explain.

44. Repeat Exercise 42, changing the sample size to $n = 40$. Which confidence interval is wider? Explain.

45. Swimming Times   A random sample of forty-eight 200-meter swims has a mean time of 3.12 minutes and a standard deviation of 0.09 minutes. Construct a 95% confidence interval for the population mean time.

46. Hotels   A random sample of 61 single-bed hotel rooms in the Phoenix, AZ area has a mean cost of $107.05 and a standard deviation of $28.10. Construct a 99% confidence interval for the population mean cost.

47. Repeat Exercise 45, using a standard deviation of $s = 0.06$ minutes. Which confidence interval is wider? Explain.

48. Repeat Exercise 46, using a standard deviation of $s = \$32.50$. Which confidence interval is wider? Explain.

49. If all other quantities remain the same, how does the indicated change affect the width of a confidence interval?

(a) Increase in the level of confidence

(b) Increase in the sample size

(c) Increase in the standard deviation

50. Describe how you would form a 90% confidence interval to estimate the population mean age for students at your school.

Constructing Confidence Intervals   *In Exercises 51 and 52, use the given information to construct the 90% and 99% confidence intervals for the population mean. Which interval is wider? If convenient, use technology to construct the confidence intervals.*

51. Newspaper Reading Times   A publisher wants to estimate the mean length of time (in minutes) all adults spend reading newspapers. To determine this estimate, the publisher takes a random sample of 15 people and obtains the following results.

11, 9, 8, 10, 10, 9, 7, 11, 11, 7, 6, 9, 10, 8, 10

From past studies, the publisher assumes σ is 1.5 minutes and that the population of times is normally distributed.

52. Computer Usage   A computer company wants to estimate the mean number of hours per day all adults use computers at home. In a random sample of 21 adults, the mean length of time a computer was used at home was 1.7 hours. From past studies, the company assumes σ is 0.6 hour and that the population of times is normally distributed. *(Adapted from National Association for Sport & Physical Education)*

53. Determine the minimum required sample size if you want to be 95% confident that the sample mean is within one unit of the population mean given $\sigma = 4.8$. Assume the population is normally distributed.

54. Determine the minimum required sample size if you want to be 99% confident that the sample mean is within two units of the population mean given $\sigma = 1.4$. Assume the population is normally distributed.

55. Cholesterol Contents of Cheese A cheese processing company wants to estimate the mean cholesterol content of all one-ounce servings of cheese. The estimate must be within 0.5 milligram of the population mean.

(a) Determine the minimum required sample size to construct a 95% confidence interval for the population mean. Assume the population standard deviation is 2.8 milligrams.

(b) Repeat part (a) using a 99% confidence interval.

(c) Which level of confidence requires a larger sample size? Explain.

56. Ages of College Students An admissions director wants to estimate the mean age of all students enrolled at a college. The estimate must be within 1 year of the population mean. Assume the population of ages is normally distributed.

(a) Determine the minimum required sample size to construct a 90% confidence interval for the population mean. Assume the population standard deviation is 1.2 years.

(b) Repeat part (a) using a 99% confidence interval.

(c) Which level of confidence requires a larger sample size? Explain.

57. Paint Can Volumes A paint manufacturer uses a machine to fill gallon cans with paint (see figure).

Error tolerance = 0.25 oz

Volume = 1 gal. (128 oz)

(a) The manufacturer wants to estimate the mean volume of paint the machine is putting in the cans within 0.25 ounce. Determine the minimum sample size required to construct a 90% confidence interval for the population mean. Assume the population standard deviation is 0.85 ounce.

(b) Repeat part (a) using an error tolerance of 0.15 ounce. Which error tolerance requires a larger sample size? Explain.

58. Water Dispensing Machine   A beverage company uses a machine to fill one-liter bottles with water (see figure). Assume that the population of volumes is normally distributed.

Error tolerance = 1 mL

Fresh
Spring
Water

Volume = 1 liter
(1000 mL)

(a) The company wants to estimate the mean volume of water the machine is putting in the bottles within 1 milliliter. Determine the minimum sample size required to construct a 95% confidence interval for the population mean. Assume the population standard deviation is 3 milliliters.

(b) Repeat part (a) using an error tolerance of 2 milliliters. Which error tolerance requires a larger sample size? Explain.

59. Plastic Sheet Cutting   A machine cuts plastic into sheets that are 50 feet (600 inches) long. Assume that the population of lengths is normally distributed.

(a) The company wants to estimate the mean length the machine is cutting the plastic within 0.125 inch. Determine the minimum sample size required to construct a 95% confidence interval for the population mean. Assume the population standard deviation is 0.25 inch.

(b) Repeat part (a) using an error tolerance of 0.0625 inch. Which error tolerance requires a larger sample size? Explain.

60. Paint Sprayer   A company uses an automated sprayer to apply paint to metal furniture. The company sets the sprayer to apply the paint one-mil (1/1000 of an inch) thick.

(a) The company wants to estimate the mean thickness the sprayer is applying the paint within 0.0425 mil. Determine the minimum sample size required to construct a 90% confidence interval for the population mean. Assume the population standard deviation is 0.15 mil.

(b) Repeat part (a) using an error tolerance of 0.02125 mil. Which error tolerance requires a larger sample size? Explain.

61. Soccer Balls   A soccer ball manufacturer wants to estimate the mean circumference of soccer balls within 0.1 inch.

(a) Determine the minimum sample size required to construct a 99% confidence interval for the population mean. Assume the population standard deviation is 0.25 inch.

(b) Repeat part (a) using a standard deviation of 0.3 inch. Which standard deviation requires a larger sample size? Explain.

62. **Mini-Soccer Balls**   A soccer ball manufacturer wants to estimate the mean circumference of mini-soccer balls within 0.15 inch. Assume that the population of circumferences is normally distributed.

    (a) Determine the minimum sample size required to construct a 99% confidence interval for the population mean. Assume the population standard deviation is 0.20 inch.

    (b) Repeat part (a) using a standard deviation of 0.10 inch. Which standard deviation requires a larger sample size? Explain.

63. If all other quantities remain the same, how does the indicated change affect the minimum sample size requirement?

    (a) Increase in the level of confidence

    (b) Increase in the error tolerance

    (c) Increase in the standard deviation

64. When estimating the population mean, why not construct a 99% confidence interval every time?

Using Technology   *In Exercises 65–68, you are given a data sample. Use a technology tool to construct a 95% confidence interval for the population mean. Interpret your answer.*

65. **Airfare**   A random sample of airfare prices (in dollars) for a one-way ticket from Atlanta, GA to Pittsburgh, PA *(Adapted from Newsweek)*

    ```
    21 | 4  4                      Key: 21|4 = 214
    22 | 3  3  4  4  4  6  6  8
    23 | 6  6  6  9  9  9  9  9
    24 | 5  5  9  9  9
    25 | 3  3  4  4  4  6  6  6
    ```

66. **Airfare**   A random sample of airfare prices (in dollars) for a one-way ticket from Chicago, IL to Minneapolis, MN *(Adapted from Newsweek)*

    ```
     8 | 1  1  1  1               Key: 8|1 = 81
     8 | 6  6  6  9  9  9  9  9
     9 | 4  4  4  4  4
     9 | 8  8  9  9
    10 | 3  3  3  4  4
    10 | 9  9  9  9
    11 | 5  5  5  5
    11 | 9  9
    12 | 4
    ```

67. **Annual Precipitation**   A random sample of the annual precipitation (in inches) for Anchorage, Alaska *(Source: Alaska Climate Research Center)*

13.24	16.13	16.10	16.23	19.27
16.50	12.25	19.16	12.08	13.09
13.42	14.54	15.51	14.75	19.17
17.68	14.97	15.51	14.93	17.31
16.89	13.12	11.65	18.30	14.37
12.52	18.79	16.68	19.53	19.81

68. Annual Precipitation   A random sample of the annual precipitation (in inches) for Nome, Alaska *(Source: Alaska Climate Research Center)*

18.31	19.87	19.76	17.10	19.06	14.93	9.08	20.66	12.29
20.14	24.38	22.15	24.25	13.67	20.80	14.30	7.39	20.09
9.93	14.97	17.13	10.44	22.06	19.25	14.92	13.05	14.17
15.46	16.27	15.23	13.43	17.62	17.49			

■ Extending Concepts

Finite Population Correction Factor   *In Exercises 69 and 70, use the following information.*

In this section, you studied the formation of a confidence interval to estimate a population mean when the population is large or infinite. When a population is finite, the formula that determines the standard error of the mean $\sigma_{\bar{x}}$ needs to be adjusted. If N is the size of the population and n is the size of the sample (where $n \geq 0.05\,N$), the standard error of the mean is

$$\sigma_{\bar{x}} = \frac{\sigma}{\sqrt{n}}\sqrt{\frac{N-n}{N-1}}.$$

The expression $\sqrt{(N-n)/(N-1)}$ is called the *finite population correction factor*. The margin of error is

$$E = z_c\frac{\sigma}{\sqrt{n}}\sqrt{\frac{N-n}{N-1}}.$$

69. Determine the finite population correction factor for each of the following.

(a) $N = 1000$ and $n = 500$

(b) $N = 1000$ and $n = 100$

(c) $N = 1000$ and $n = 75$

(d) $N = 1000$ and $n = 50$

(e) What happens to the finite population correction factor as the sample size n decreases but the population size N remains the same?

70. Determine the finite population correction factor for each of the following.

(a) $N = 100$ and $n = 50$

(b) $N = 400$ and $n = 50$

(c) $N = 700$ and $n = 50$

(d) $N = 1000$ and $n = 50$

(e) What happens to the finite population correction factor as the population size N increases but the sample size n remains the same?

71. Sample Size   The equation for determining the sample size

$$n = \left(\frac{z_c\sigma}{E}\right)^2$$

can be obtained by solving the equation for the margin of error

$$E = \frac{z_c\sigma}{\sqrt{n}}$$

for n. Show that this is true and justify each step.

CASE STUDY

Shoulder Heights of Appalachian Black Bears

Appalachian Bear Rescue (ABR) is a not-for-profit organization located near the Great Smoky Mountains National Park. ABR's programs include the rehabilitation of orphaned and injured black bears, as well as research and education about Appalachian black bears. ABR provides the most natural environment possible for rehabilitating black bears before their release back into the wild.

Recently, Katie Settlage performed a study to learn more about the Appalachian black bear population in the Great Smoky Mountains National Park. She and a team of researchers found 68 black bears in the park and took measurements such as paw size, weight, and shoulder height. The stem-and-leaf plots below show the shoulder heights (in centimeters) of the 40 male and 28 female bears from the study.

Shoulder Heights (in cm) of Male Bears

Key: 4|9 = 49

```
 4 | 9
 5 | 7
 6 | 8 9
 7 | 1 1 2 2 2 2 2 3 3 3 4 4 5 5 6 6 7 8 8
 8 | 1 2 3 4 4 5 6 7 9
 9 | 0 0 3 6 7 9
10 | 2
11 | 4
```

Shoulder Heights (in cm) of Female Bears

Key: 5|0 = 50

```
5 | 0
6 | 7 8
7 | 1 2 3 3 3 3 3 4 4 5 5 5 5 5 5 6 9
8 | 1 2 2 3 3 4 5
9 | 3
```

■ Exercises

1. Use the sample to find a point estimate for the mean shoulder height of

   (a) male bears.   (b) female bears.

2. Find the standard deviation of the sample of shoulder heights for the

   (a) male bears.   (b) female bears.

3. Use the sample to construct a 95% confidence interval for the mean shoulder height of

   (a) male bears.   (b) female bears.

4. Use the sample to construct a 95% confidence interval for the mean shoulder height of all bears in the study. How do your results differ from those in Exercise 3? Explain.

5. A researcher wants to estimate the mean shoulder heights for both male and female bears within 0.5 centimeter. Determine the minimum sample size required to construct a 99% confidence interval for the population mean shoulder height of

   (a) male bears. Assume the population standard deviation is 12.4 centimeters.

   (b) female bears. Assume the population standard deviation is 7.8 centimeters.

324

6.2 Confidence Intervals for the Mean (Small Samples)

What You SHOULD LEARN

▸ How to interpret the *t*-distribution and use a *t*-distribution table

▸ How to construct confidence intervals when $n < 30$, the population is normally distributed, and σ is unknown

The *t*-Distribution ▸ Confidence Intervals and *t*-Distributions

▸ The *t*-Distribution

In many real-life situations, the population standard deviation is unknown. Moreover, because of various constraints such as time and cost, it is often not practical to collect samples of size 30 or more. So, how can you construct a confidence interval for a population mean given such circumstances? If the random variable is normally distributed (or approximately normally distributed), you can use a *t*-distribution.

DEFINITION

If the distribution of a random variable x is approximately normal, then

$$t = \frac{\overline{x} - \mu}{\dfrac{s}{\sqrt{n}}}$$

follows a ***t*-distribution.**

Critical values of t are denoted by t_c. Several properties of the *t*-distribution are as follows.

1. The *t*-distribution is bell-shaped and symmetric about the mean.

2. The *t*-distribution is a family of curves, each determined by a parameter called the degrees of freedom. The **degrees of freedom** are the number of free choices left after a sample statistic such as $\overline{x}$ is calculated. When you use a *t*-distribution to estimate a population mean, the degrees of freedom are equal to one less than the sample size.

   $$\text{d.f.} = n - 1 \qquad \text{Degrees of freedom}$$

3. The total area under a *t*-curve is 1 or 100%.

4. The mean, median, and mode of the *t*-distribution are equal to zero.

5. As the degrees of freedom increase, the *t*-distribution approaches the normal distribution. After 30 d.f., the *t*-distribution is very close to the standard normal *z*-distribution.

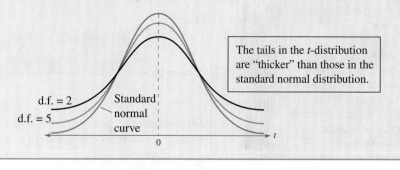

d.f. = 2
d.f. = 5
Standard normal curve

The tails in the *t*-distribution are "thicker" than those in the standard normal distribution.

Historical Reference

William S. Gosset (1876–1937)

Developed the *t*-distribution while employed by the Guinness Brewing Company in Dublin, Ireland. Gosset published his findings using the pseudonym Student. The *t*-distribution is sometimes referred to as Student's *t*-distribution. (See page 35 for others who were important in the history of statistics.)

Table 5 of Appendix B lists critical values of t for selected confidence intervals and degrees of freedom.

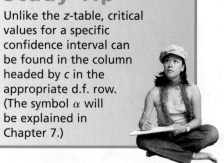

EXAMPLE 1

Finding Critical Values of t

Find the critical value t_c for a 95% confidence when the sample size is 15.

Solution

Because $n = 15$, the degrees of freedom are

d.f. $= n - 1 = 15 - 1 = 14$.

A portion of Table 5 is shown. Using d.f. $= 14$ and $c = 0.95$, you can find the critical value t_c as shown by the highlighted areas in the table.

	Level of confidence, c	0.50	0.80	0.90	0.95	0.98
	One tail, α	0.25	0.10	0.05	0.025	0.01
d.f.	Two tails, α	0.50	0.20	0.10	0.05	0.02
1		1.000	3.078	6.314	12.706	31.821
2		.816	1.886	2.920	4.303	6.965
3		.765	1.638	2.353	3.182	4.541
12		.695	1.356	1.782	2.179	2.681
13		.694	1.350	1.771	2.160	2.650
14		.692	1.345	1.761	2.145	2.624
15		.691	1.341	1.753	2.131	2.602
16		.690	1.337	1.746	2.120	2.583
28		.683	1.313	1.701	2.048	2.467
29		.683	1.311	1.699	2.045	2.462
∞		.674	1.282	1.645	1.960	2.326

From the table, you can see that $t_c = 2.145$. The graph shows the t-distribution for 14 degrees of freedom, $c = 0.95$, and $t_c = 2.145$.

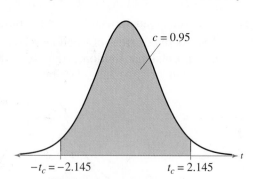

$c = 0.95$

$-t_c = -2.145$ $t_c = 2.145$

Interpretation   So, 95% of the area under the t-distribution curve with 14 degrees of freedom lies between $t = \pm2.145$.

▶ Try It Yourself 1

Find the critical value t_c for a 90% confidence when the sample size is 22.

a. *Identify* the degrees of freedom.
b. *Identify* the level of confidence c.
c. *Use* Table 5 of Appendix B to find t_c.   *Answer: Page A42*

▶ Confidence Intervals and *t*-Distributions

Constructing a confidence interval using the *t*-distribution is similar to constructing a confidence interval using the normal distribution—both use a point estimate $\bar{x}$ and a margin of error E.

GUIDELINES

Constructing a Confidence Interval for the Mean: *t*-Distribution

In Words	*In Symbols*
1. Identify the sample statistics n, $\bar{x}$, and s.	$\bar{x} = \dfrac{\sum x}{n}$, $s = \sqrt{\dfrac{\sum (x - \bar{x})^2}{n - 1}}$
2. Identify the degrees of freedom, the level of confidence c, and the critical value t_c.	d.f. $= n - 1$
3. Find the margin of error E.	$E = t_c \dfrac{s}{\sqrt{n}}$
4. Find the left and right endpoints and form the confidence interval.	Left endpoint: $\bar{x} - E$ Right endpoint: $\bar{x} + E$ Interval: $\bar{x} - E < \mu < \bar{x} + E$

EXAMPLE 2

Constructing a Confidence Interval

See MINITAB steps on page 360.

You randomly select 16 coffee shops and measure the temperature of the coffee sold at each. The sample mean temperature is 162.0°F with a sample standard deviation of 10.0°F. Find the 95% confidence interval for the mean temperature. Assume the temperatures are approximately normally distributed.

Solution Because the sample size is less than 30, σ is unknown, and the temperatures are approximately normally distributed, you can use the *t*-distribution. Using $n = 16$, $\bar{x} = 162.0$, $s = 10.0$, $c = 0.95$, and d.f. $= 15$, you can use Table 5 to find that $t_c = 2.131$. The margin of error at the 95% confidence interval is

$$E = t_c \frac{s}{\sqrt{n}} = 2.131 \cdot \frac{10}{\sqrt{16}} \approx 5.3.$$

The confidence interval is as follows.

Left Endpoint	Right Endpoint
$\bar{x} - E = 162 - 5.3 = 156.7$	$\bar{x} + E = 162 + 5.3 = 167.3$

$$156.7 < \mu < 167.3$$

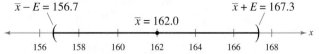

$\bar{x} - E = 156.7$ \qquad $\bar{x} = 162.0$ \qquad $\bar{x} + E = 167.3$

Interpretation With 95% confidence, you can say that the mean temperature of coffee sold is between 156.7°F and 167.3°F.

Study Tip

For a TI-83/84, constructing a confidence interval using the *t*-distribution is similar to constructing a confidence interval using the normal distribution.

STAT

Choose the TESTS menu.

8: TInterval...

Select the *Data* input option if you have entered the original data. Select the *Stats* input option if you are entering the descriptive statistics. In each case, enter the appropriate values, then select *Calculate*. For Example 2, the descriptive statistics were entered.

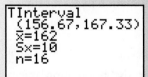

```
TInterval
 (156.67,167.33)
 x̄=162
 Sx=10
 n=16
```

▶ **Try It Yourself 2**

Find the 90% and 99% confidence intervals for the mean temperature.

a. *Find* t_c *and* E *for each level of confidence.*
b. *Use* $\bar{x}$ *and* E *to find the left and right endpoints.*
c. *State* the 90% and 99% confidence intervals for the mean temperature.

Answer: Page A42

To explore this topic further, see Activity 6.2 on page 333.

EXAMPLE 3

Constructing a Confidence Interval

See TI-83/84 steps on page 361.

You randomly select 20 mortgage institutions and determine the current mortgage interest rate at each. The sample mean rate is 6.22% with a sample standard deviation of 0.42%. Find the 99% confidence interval for the population mean mortgage interest rate. Assume the interest rates are approximately normally distributed.

Solution Because the sample size is less than 30, σ is unknown, and the interest rates are approximately normally distributed, you can use the *t*-distribution. Using $n = 20$, $\bar{x} = 6.22$, $s = 0.42$, $c = 0.99$, and d.f. $= 19$, you can use Table 5 to find that $t_c = 2.861$. The margin of error at the 99% confidence interval is

$$E = t_c \frac{s}{\sqrt{n}}$$

$$= 2.861 \cdot \frac{0.42}{\sqrt{20}}$$

$$\approx 0.27.$$

The confidence interval is as follows.

Left Endpoint   Right Endpoint
$\bar{x} - E = 6.22 - 0.27 = 5.95$ $\bar{x} + E = 6.22 + 0.27 = 6.49$

$$5.95 < \mu < 6.49$$

Interpretation With 99% confidence, you can say that the population mean mortgage interest rate is between 5.95% and 6.49%.

▶ **Try It Yourself 3**

Find the 90% and 95% confidence intervals for the population mean mortgage interest rate. Compare the widths of the intervals.

a. *Find* t_c *and* E *for each level of confidence.*
b. *Use* $\bar{x}$ *and* E *to find the left and right endpoints.*
c. *State* the 90% and 95% confidence intervals for the population mean mortgage interest rate and compare their widths.

Answer: Page A42

PICTURING the WORLD

Two footballs, one filled with air and the other filled with helium, were kicked on a windless day at Ohio State University. The footballs were alternated with each kick. After 10 practice kicks, each football was kicked 29 more times. The distances (in yards) are listed. (Source: The Columbus Dispatch)

Air Filled

1	9
2	0 0 2 2 2
2	5 5 5 5 6 6
2	7 7 7 8 8 8 8 8 9 9 9
3	1 1 1 2
3	3 4 Key: 1|9 = 19

Helium Filled

1	1 2
1	4
1	
2	2
2	3 4 6 6 6
2	7 8 8 8 9 9 9 9
3	0 0 0 0 1 1 2 2
3	3 4 5
3	9 Key: 1|1 = 11

Assume that the distances are normally distributed for each football. Apply the flowchart at the right to each sample. Find a 95% confidence interval for the mean distance each football traveled. Do the confidence intervals overlap? What does this result tell you?

The flowchart describes when to use the normal distribution to construct a confidence interval for the population mean and when to use a *t*-distribution.

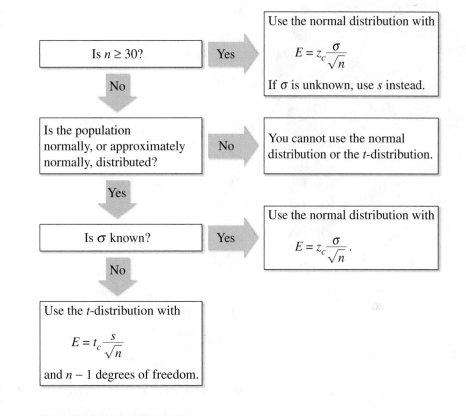

Is $n \geq 30$? — Yes → Use the normal distribution with $E = z_c \dfrac{\sigma}{\sqrt{n}}$ If σ is unknown, use s instead.

No ↓

Is the population normally, or approximately normally, distributed? — No → You cannot use the normal distribution or the *t*-distribution.

Yes ↓

Is σ known? — Yes → Use the normal distribution with $E = z_c \dfrac{\sigma}{\sqrt{n}}$.

No ↓

Use the *t*-distribution with $E = t_c \dfrac{s}{\sqrt{n}}$ and $n - 1$ degrees of freedom.

EXAMPLE 4

Choosing the Normal or *t*-Distribution

You randomly select 25 newly constructed houses. The sample mean construction cost is $181,000 and the population standard deviation is $28,000. Assuming construction costs are normally distributed, should you use the normal distribution, the *t*-distribution, or neither to construct a 95% confidence interval for the population mean construction cost? Explain your reasoning.

Solution

Because the population is normally distributed and the population standard deviation is known, you should use the normal distribution.

▶ Try It Yourself 4

You randomly select 18 adult male athletes and measure the resting heart rate of each. The sample mean heart rate is 64 beats per minute with a sample standard deviation of 2.5 beats per minute. Assuming the heart rates are normally distributed, should you use the normal distribution, the *t*-distribution, or neither to construct a 90% confidence interval for the mean heart rate? Explain your reasoning.

Use the flowchart to determine which distribution you should use to construct the 90% confidence interval for the mean heart rate.

Answer: Page A42

6.2   EXERCISES

■ Building Basic Skills and Vocabulary

In Exercises 1–4, find the critical value t_c for the given confidence level c and sample size n.

1. $c = 0.90$, $n = 10$
2. $c = 0.95$, $n = 12$
3. $c = 0.99$, $n = 16$
4. $c = 0.98$, $n = 20$

In Exercises 5–8, find the margin of error for the given values of c, s, and n.

5. $c = 0.95$, $s = 5$, $n = 16$
6. $c = 0.99$, $s = 3$, $n = 6$
7. $c = 0.90$, $s = 2.4$, $n = 12$
8. $c = 0.98$, $s = 4.7$, $n = 9$

In Exercises 9–12, construct the indicated confidence interval for the population mean μ using (a) a t-distribution. (b) If you had incorrectly used a normal distribution, which interval would be wider?

9. $c = 0.90$, $\bar{x} = 12.5$, $s = 2.0$, $n = 6$

10. $c = 0.95$, $\bar{x} = 13.4$, $s = 0.85$, $n = 8$

11. $c = 0.98$, $\bar{x} = 4.3$, $s = 0.34$, $n = 14$

12. $c = 0.99$, $\bar{x} = 24.7$, $s = 4.6$, $n = 10$

■ Using and Interpreting Concepts

Constructing Confidence Intervals *In Exercises 13 and 14, you are given the sample mean and the sample standard deviation. Assume the variable is normally distributed and use a t-distribution to construct a 95% confidence interval for the population mean μ. What is the margin of error of μ? If convenient, use technology to construct the confidence interval.*

13. **Repair Costs: Microwaves** In a random sample of five microwave ovens, the mean repair cost was $75.00 and the standard deviation was $12.50. *(Adapted from Consumer Reports)*

14. **Repair Costs: Computers** In a random sample of seven computers, the mean repair cost was $100.00 and the standard deviation was $42.50. *(Adapted from Consumer Reports)*

15. You did some research on repair costs of microwave ovens and found that the standard deviation is $\sigma = \$15$. Repeat Exercise 13, using a normal distribution with the appropriate calculations for a standard deviation that is known. Compare the results.

16. You did some research on repair costs of computers and found that the standard deviation is $\sigma = \$50$. Repeat Exercise 14, using a normal distribution with the appropriate calculations for a standard deviation that is known. Compare the results.

Constructing Confidence Intervals *In Exercises 17 and 18, you are given the sample mean and the sample standard deviation. Assume the variable is normally distributed and use a normal distribution or a t-distribution to construct a 90% confidence interval for the population mean μ. If convenient, use technology to construct the confidence intervals.*

17. Waste Generated   (a) In a random sample of 10 adults from the United States, the mean waste generated per person per day was 4.54 pounds and the standard deviation was 1.21 pounds. (b) Repeat part (a), assuming the same statistics came from a sample size of 500. Compare the results. *(Adapted from U.S. Environmental Protection Agency)*

18. Waste Recycled   (a) In a random sample of 12 adults from the United States, the mean waste recycled per person per day was 1.46 pounds and the standard deviation was 0.28 pound. (b) Repeat part (a), assuming the same statistics came from a sample size of 600. Compare the results. *(Adapted from U.S. Environmental Protection Agency)*

Constructing Confidence Intervals   *In Exercises 19–22, a data set is given. For each data set, (a) find the sample mean, (b) find the sample standard deviation, and (c) construct a 99% confidence interval for the population mean μ. Assume the population of each data set is normally distributed. If convenient, use a technology tool.*

19. Biology   The monthly incomes for 10 randomly selected people, each with a bachelor's degree in biology *(Adapted from U.S. Bureau of Labor Statistics)*

4625.68   4289.72   4461.22   4519.46   4714.27
4408.73   4391.45   4318.54   4576.12   4296.41

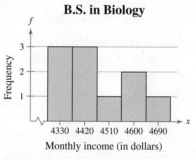

FIGURE FOR EXERCISE 19

FIGURE FOR EXERCISE 20

20. Economics   The monthly incomes for 14 randomly selected people, each with a bachelor's degree in economics *(Adapted from U.S. Bureau of Labor Statistics)*

5418.76   5278.63   5912.05   6118.35   5647.86   5714.38   5365.19
5524.91   5761.57   4924.16   5494.66   5619.74   6205.64   5801.23

21. SAT Scores   The SAT scores for 12 randomly selected high school seniors

1704   1940   1518   2005   1432   1872
1998   1658   1825   1670   2210   1380

22. GPA   The grade point averages (GPA) for 15 randomly selected college students

2.3   3.3   2.6   1.8   0.2   3.1   4.0   0.7
2.3   2.0   3.1   3.4   1.3   2.6   2.6

Choosing a Distribution   *In Exercises 23–28, use a normal distribution or a t-distribution to construct a 95% confidence interval for the population mean. Justify your decision. If neither distribution can be used, explain why. If convenient, use technology to construct the confidence interval.*

23. Lengths of Bolts In a random sample of 70 bolts, the mean length was 1.25 inches and the standard deviation was 0.05 inch.

24. Prices of Toasters You took a random sample of 12 two-slice toasters and found the mean price was $57.79 and the standard deviation was $19.05. Assume the prices are normally distributed.

25. Sports Cars: Miles per Gallon You take a random survey of 25 sports cars and record the miles per gallon for each. The data are listed below. Assume the miles per gallon are normally distributed.

```
15  27  24  24  20  21  24  14  21
25  21  13  21  25  22  21  25  24
22  24  24  22  21  24  24
```

26. ACT Scores In a recent year, the standard deviation of ACT scores for all students was 4.8. The ACT scores for 20 randomly selected students are listed below. Assume the test scores are normally distributed. *(Source: ACT, Inc.)*

```
26  22  23  12  19  25  23  21  25  10
17  26  23  24  20  14  21  23  20  22
```

27. Hospital Waiting Times In a random sample of 19 patients at a hospital's minor emergency department, the mean waiting time (in minutes) before seeing a medical professional was 23 minutes and the standard deviation was 11 minutes. Assume the waiting times are not normally distributed.

28. Solo Tent Costs In a random sample of 18 one-person tents, the mean price was $144.19 and the standard deviation was $61.32. Assume the prices are normally distributed.

■ Extending Concepts

29. Tennis Ball Manufacturing A company manufactures tennis balls. When its tennis balls are dropped onto a concrete surface from a height of 100 inches, the company wants the mean height the balls bounce upward to be 55.5 inches. This average is maintained by periodically testing random samples of 25 tennis balls. If the t-value falls between $-t_{0.99}$ and $t_{0.99}$, the company will be satisfied that it is manufacturing acceptable tennis balls. A sample of 25 balls is randomly selected and tested. The mean bounce height of the sample is 56.0 inches and the standard deviation is 0.25 inch. Assume the bounce heights are approximately normally distributed. Is the company making acceptable tennis balls? Explain your reasoning.

30. Light Bulb Manufacturing A company manufactures light bulbs. The company wants the bulbs to have a mean life span of 1000 hours. This average is maintained by periodically testing random samples of 16 light bulbs. If the t-value falls between $-t_{0.99}$ and $t_{0.99}$, the company will be satisfied that it is manufacturing acceptable light bulbs. A sample of 16 light bulbs is randomly selected and tested. The mean life span of the sample is 1015 hours and the standard deviation is 25 hours. Assume the life spans are approximately normally distributed. Is the company making acceptable light bulbs? Explain your reasoning.

APPLET

The *confidence intervals for a mean (the impact of not knowing the standard deviation)* applet allows you to visually investigate confidence intervals for a population mean. You can specify the sample size *n*, the shape of the distribution (Normal or Right-skewed), the true population mean (Mean), and the true population standard deviation (Std. Dev.). When you click SIMULATE, 100 separate samples of size *n* will be selected from a population with these population parameters. For each of the 100 samples, a 95% Z confidence interval (known standard deviation) and a 95% T confidence interval (unknown standard deviation) are displayed in the plot to the right. The 95% Z confidence interval is displayed in green and the 95% T confidence interval is displayed in blue. If an interval does not contain the true mean, it is displayed in red. Additional simulations can be carried out by clicking SIMULATE multiple times. The cumulative number of times that each type of interval contains the true mean is also shown. Press CLEAR to clear existing results and start a new simulation.

■ Explore

Step 1 Specify a value for *n*.
Step 2 Specify a distribution.
Step 3 Specify a value for the mean.
Step 4 Specify a value for the standard deviation.
Step 5 Click SIMULATE to generate the confidence intervals.

n:	10
Distribution:	Normal ⌄
Mean:	50
Std. Dev.:	10

Simulate

Cumulative results:

	95% Z CI	95% T CI
Contained mean		
Did not contain mean		
Prop. contained		

Clear

■ Draw Conclusions

APPLET

1. Set *n* = 30, Mean = 25, Std. Dev. = 5, and the distribution to Normal. Run the simulation so that at least 1000 confidence intervals are generated. Compare the proportion of the 95% Z confidence intervals and 95% T confidence intervals that contain the population mean. Is this what you would expect? Explain.

2. In a random sample of 24 high school students, the mean number of hours of sleep per night during the school week was 7.26 hours and the standard deviation was 1.19 hours. Assume the sleep times are normally distributed. Run the simulation for *n* = 10 so that at least 500 confidence intervals are generated. What proportion of the 95% Z confidence intervals and 95% T confidence intervals contain the population mean? Should you use a Z confidence interval or a T confidence interval for the mean number of hours of sleep? Explain.

6.3 Confidence Intervals for Population Proportions

Point Estimate for the Population Proportion p ▸ Confidence Intervals for a Population Proportion p ▸ Increasing Sample Size to Increase Precision

▸ Point Estimate for the Population Proportion p

Recall from Section 4.2 that the probability of success in a single trial of a binomial experiment is p. This probability is a population **proportion**. In this section, you will learn how to estimate a population proportion p using a confidence interval. As with confidence intervals for μ, you will start with a point estimate.

DEFINITION

The point estimate for p, the population proportion of successes, is given by the proportion of successes in a sample and is denoted by

$$\hat{p} = \frac{x}{n}$$

where x is the number of successes in the sample and n is the number in the sample. The point estimate for the proportion of failures is $\hat{q} = 1 - \hat{p}$. The symbols $\hat{p}$ and $\hat{q}$ are read as "p hat" and "q hat."

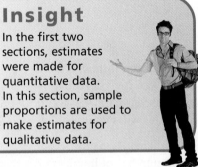

EXAMPLE 1

Finding a Point Estimate for p

In a survey of 1219 U.S. adults, 354 said that their favorite sport to watch is football. Find a point estimate for the population proportion of U.S. adults who say their favorite sport to watch is football. *(Adapted from The Harris Poll)*

Solution Using $n = 1219$ and $x = 354$,

$$\hat{p} = \frac{x}{n}$$

$$= \frac{354}{1219}$$

$$\approx 0.290402$$

$$\approx 29.0\%.$$

Try It Yourself 1

In a survey of 1006 adults from the U.S., 181 said that Abraham Lincoln was the greatest president. Find a point estimate for the population proportion of adults who say Abraham Lincoln was the greatest president. *(Adapted from The Gallup Poll)*

a. *Identify x and n.*
b. *Use x and n to find $\hat{p}$.*

Answer: Page A42

Insight

In the first two sections, estimates were made for quantitative data. In this section, sample proportions are used to make estimates for qualitative data.

PICTURING the WORLD

A poll surveyed 1002 adults in the United States about the environment. Of those surveyed, 551 said that in 10 years or so, they think the natural environment in the world will be worse than it is today. (Adapted from PollingReport.com)

551 think natural environment will be worse

451 do not think natural environment will be worse

Find a 90% confidence interval for the proportion of adults in the United States that think the natural environment will be worse.

Study Tip

Here are instructions for constructing a confidence interval for a population proportion on a TI-83/84.

STAT

Choose the TESTS menu.

A: 1–PropZInt

Enter the values for x, n, and the level of confidence c (C-Level). Then select *Calculate*.

▶ Confidence Intervals for a Population Proportion p

Constructing a confidence interval for a population proportion p is similar to constructing a confidence interval for a population mean. You start with a point estimate and calculate a margin of error.

DEFINITION

A **c-confidence interval** for the population proportion p is

$$\hat{p} - E < p < \hat{p} + E$$

where

$$E = z_c \sqrt{\frac{\hat{p}\hat{q}}{n}}.$$

The probability that the confidence interval contains p is c.

In Section 5.5, you learned that a binomial distribution can be approximated by the normal distribution if $np \geq 5$ and $nq \geq 5$. When $n\hat{p} \geq 5$ and $n\hat{q} \geq 5$, the sampling distribution for $\hat{p}$ is approximately normal with a mean of

$$\mu_{\hat{p}} = p$$

and a standard error of

$$\sigma_{\hat{p}} = \sqrt{\frac{pq}{n}}.$$

GUIDELINES

Constructing a Confidence Interval for a Population Proportion

In Words	*In Symbols*
1. Identify the sample statistics n and x.	
2. Find the point estimate $\hat{p}$.	$\hat{p} = \dfrac{x}{n}$
3. Verify that the sampling distribution of $\hat{p}$ can be approximated by the normal distribution.	$n\hat{p} \geq 5$, $n\hat{q} \geq 5$
4. Find the critical value z_c that corresponds to the given level of confidence c.	Use the Standard Normal Table.
5. Find the margin of error E.	$E = z_c \sqrt{\dfrac{\hat{p}\hat{q}}{n}}$
6. Find the left and right endpoints and form the confidence interval.	Left endpoint: $\hat{p} - E$ Right endpoint: $\hat{p} + E$ Interval: $\hat{p} - E < p < \hat{p} + E$

MINITAB and TI-83/84 steps are shown on pages 360 and 361.

EXAMPLE 2

Constructing a Confidence Interval for *p*

Construct a 95% confidence interval for the proportion of adults in the United States who say that their favorite sport to watch is football.

Solution   From Example 1, $\hat{p} \approx 0.290402$. So,

$$\hat{q} = 1 - 0.290402 = 0.709598.$$

Using $n = 1219$, you can verify that the sampling distribution of $\hat{p}$ can be approximated by the normal distribution.

$$n\hat{p} \approx 1219 \cdot 0.290402 \approx 354 > 5$$

and

$$n\hat{p} \approx 1219 \cdot 0.709598 \approx 865 > 5$$

Using $z_c = 1.96$, the margin of error is

$$E = z_c \sqrt{\frac{\hat{p}\hat{q}}{n}} \approx 1.96 \sqrt{\frac{(0.290402)(0.709598)}{1219}} \approx 0.025.$$

The 95% confidence interval is as follows.

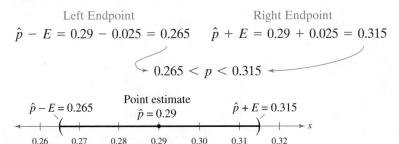

Left Endpoint   Right Endpoint

$$\hat{p} - E = 0.29 - 0.025 = 0.265 \qquad \hat{p} + E = 0.29 + 0.025 = 0.315$$

$$0.265 < p < 0.315$$

$\hat{p} - E = 0.265$ Point estimate $\hat{p} + E = 0.315$
$\hat{p} = 0.29$

0.26   0.27   0.28   0.29   0.30   0.31   0.32

Interpretation   With 95% confidence, you can say that the proportion of adults who say football is their favorite sport is between 26.5% and 31.5%.

▶ Try It Yourself 2

Use the data given in Try It Yourself 1 to construct a 90% confidence interval for the proportion of adults who say that Abraham Lincoln was the greatest president.

a. *Find* $\hat{p}$ and $\hat{q}$.
b. *Verify* that the sampling distribution of $\hat{p}$ can be approximated by the normal distribution.
c. *Find* z_c and E.
d. *Use* $\hat{p}$ and E to find the left and right endpoints.
e. *Specify* the 90% confidence interval for the proportion of adults who say that Abraham Lincoln was the greatest president.

Answer: Page A42

The confidence level of 95% used in Example 2 is typical of opinion polls. The result, however, is usually not stated as a confidence interval. Instead, the result of Example 2 would be stated as "29% with a margin of error of ±2.5%."

EXAMPLE 3

Constructing a Confidence Interval for p

The graph shown at the right is from a survey of 900 U.S. adults. Construct a 99% confidence interval for the proportion of adults who think that teenagers are the more dangerous drivers. *(Adapted from The Gallup Organization)*

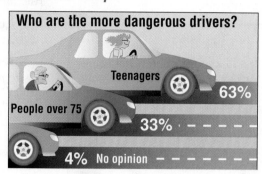

Who are the more dangerous drivers?

Teenagers 63%

People over 75 33%

4% No opinion

Solution   From the graph, $\hat{p} = 0.63$. So,

$$\hat{q} = 1 - 0.63$$

$$= 0.37.$$

Using these values and the values $n = 900$ and $z_c = 2.575$, the margin of error is

$$E = z_c \sqrt{\frac{\hat{p}\hat{q}}{n}}$$

$$\approx 2.575 \sqrt{\frac{(0.63)(0.37)}{900}} \quad \text{Use Table 4 in Appendix B to estimate that } z_c \text{ is halfway between 2.57 and 2.58.}$$

$$\approx 0.041.$$

The 99% confidence interval is as follows.

Left Endpoint

$$\hat{p} - E = 0.63 - 0.041 = 0.589$$

Right Endpoint

$$\hat{p} + E = 0.63 + 0.041 = 0.671$$

$$0.589 < p < 0.671$$

Interpretation   With 99% confidence, you can say that the proportion of adults who think that teenagers are the more dangerous drivers is between 58.9% and 67.1%.

▸ Try It Yourself 3

Use the survey information in Example 3 to construct a 99% confidence interval for the proportion of adults who think that people over 75 are the more dangerous drivers.

a. *Identify* n and $\hat{p}$.
b. *Use* $\hat{p}$ to find $\hat{q}$.
c. *Verify* that the sampling distribution of $\hat{p}$ is approximately normal.
d. *Identify* the critical value z_c that corresponds to the given level of confidence.
e. *Find* the left and right endpoints of the confidence interval.
f. *Specify* the 99% confidence interval for the proportion of adults who think that people over 75 are the more dangerous drivers.

Answer: Page A42

Insight

In Example 3, note that $np \geq 5$ and $nq \geq 5$. So, the sampling distribution of $\hat{p}$ is approximately normal.

To explore this topic further, see Activity 6.3 on page 343.

▸ **Increasing Sample Size to Increase Precision**

One way to increase the precision of the confidence interval without decreasing the level of confidence is to increase the sample size.

FINDING A MINIMUM SAMPLE SIZE TO ESTIMATE p

Given a c-confidence level and a margin of error E, the minimum sample size n needed to estimate p is

$$n = \hat{p}\hat{q}\left(\frac{z_c}{E}\right)^2.$$

This formula assumes that you have a preliminary estimate for $\hat{p}$ and $\hat{q}$. If not, use $\hat{p} = 0.5$ and $\hat{q} = 0.5$.

EXAMPLE 4

Determining a Minimum Sample Size

You are running a political campaign and wish to estimate, with 95% confidence, the proportion of registered voters who will vote for your candidate. Your estimate must be accurate within 3% of the true population. Find the minimum sample size needed if (1) no preliminary estimate is available and (2) a preliminary estimate gives $\hat{p} = 0.31$. Compare your results.

Solution

1. Because you do not have a preliminary estimate for $\hat{p}$, use $\hat{p} = 0.5$ and $\hat{q} = 0.5$. Using $z_c = 1.96$ and $E = 0.03$, you can solve for n.

$$n = \hat{p}\hat{q}\left(\frac{z_c}{E}\right)^2 = (0.5)(0.5)\left(\frac{1.96}{0.03}\right)^2 \approx 1067.11$$

Because n is a decimal, round up to the nearest whole number, 1068.

2. You have a preliminary estimate of $\hat{p} = 0.31$. So, $\hat{q} = 0.69$. Using $z_c = 1.96$ and $E = 0.03$, you can solve for n.

$$n = \hat{p}\hat{q}\left(\frac{z_c}{E}\right)^2 = (0.31)(0.69)\left(\frac{1.96}{0.03}\right)^2 \approx 913.02$$

Because n is a decimal, round up to the nearest whole number, 914.

Interpretation   With no preliminary estimate, the minimum sample size should be at least 1068 voters. With a preliminary estimate of $\hat{p} = 0.31$, the sample size should be at least 914 voters. So, you would need a larger sample size if no preliminary estimate is available.

▸ **Try It Yourself 4**

You wish to estimate, with 90% confidence and within 2% of the true population, the proportion of males age 20 to 34 who have high blood pressure. Find the minimum sample size needed if (1) no preliminary estimate is available and (2) a previous survey found that 6.4% of males in this age group had high blood pressure. *(Source: National Center for Health Statistics)*

a. *Identify* $\hat{p}$, $\hat{q}$, z_c, and E. If $\hat{p}$ is unknown, use 0.5.
b. *Use* $\hat{p}$, $\hat{q}$, z_c, and E to *find* the minimum sample size n.
c. *Determine* how many males should be included in the sample.

Answer: Page A42

6.3 EXERCISES

■ Building Basic Skills and Vocabulary

True or False?   *In Exercises 1 and 2, determine whether the statement is true or false. If it is false, rewrite it as a true statement.*

1. To estimate the value of p, the population proportion of successes, use the point estimate x.

2. The point estimate for the proportion of failures is $1 - \hat{p}$.

Finding $\hat{p}$ and $\hat{q}$ *In Exercises 3–12, let p be the population proportion for the given condition. Find point estimates for p and q.*

3. **Recycling**   In a survey of 1002 U.S. adults, 752 say they recycle. *(Adapted from ABC News Poll)*

4. **Charity**   In a survey of 2939 U.S. adults, 2439 say they have contributed to a charity in the past 12 months. *(Adapted from Harris Interactive)*

5. **Obese or Overweight?**   A study of 4431 U.S. adults found that 2938 were obese or overweight. *(Adapted from National Health and Nutrition Examination Survey)*

6. **Eating Meat**   Of 458 U.S. adults surveyed, 224 eat meat daily. *(Adapted from Greenfield Online)*

7. **Planning for the Future**   Of 848 children surveyed, 144 plan to join a volunteer group in the future. *(Adapted from National Geographic Kids)*

8. **Vacation**   In a survey of 1003 U.S. adults, 110 say they would go on vacation to Europe if cost did not matter. *(Adapted from The Gallup Poll)*

9. **Quitting Smoking?**   In a survey of 284 smokers, 204 smokers reported that they wanted to quit smoking. *(Adapted from American Lung Association)*

10. **Happy at Work?**   In a survey of 1003 U.S. adults, 662 would be happy spending the rest of their career with their current employer. *(Adapted from Maritz Poll)*

11. **Tax Audit**   In a survey of 1000 U.S. adults, 230 said they were somewhat concerned or very concerned about their taxes being audited. *(Adapted from Rasmussen Reports)*

12. **Stressful Travel**   In a survey of 3224 U.S. adults, 1515 said flying is the most stressful form of travel. *(Adapted from Travelocity)*

■ Using and Interpreting Concepts

13. **Election Poll**   An election poll reported that a candidate had an approval rating of 48% with a margin of error E of 3%. Construct a confidence interval for the proportion of adults who approve of the candidate.

14. **Direct Mail**   A survey shows that 51% of adults prefer to receive advertisements through the mail. The margin of error E is 5.2%. Construct a confidence interval for the proportion of adults who prefer to receive advertisements through the mail. *(Source: Cable & Telecommunications Association for Marketing)*

Constructing a Confidence Interval *In Exercises 15–20, construct the 95% and 99% confidence intervals for the population proportion p using the indicated sample statistics. Which interval is wider? If convenient, use technology to construct the confidence intervals.*

15. Use the statistics in Exercise 3. **16.** Use the statistics in Exercise 4.

17. Use the statistics in Exercise 5. **18.** Use the statistics in Exercise 6.

19. Use the statistics in Exercise 7. **20.** Use the statistics in Exercise 8.

21. Travel Plans You are a travel agent and wish to estimate, with 95% confidence, the proportion of vacationers who plan to travel outside the United States in the next 12 months. Your estimate must be accurate within 3% of the true proportion.

(a) No preliminary estimate is available. Find the minimum sample size needed.

(b) Find the minimum sample size needed, using a prior study that found that 26% of the respondents said they planned to travel outside the United States in the next 12 months. *(Source: Wirthlin Worldwide)*

(c) Compare the results from parts (a) and (b).

22. Online Service Usage You are a travel agent and wish to estimate, with 98% confidence, the proportion of vacationers who use an online service or the Internet to make travel reservations. Your estimate must be accurate within 4% of the population proportion.

(a) No preliminary estimate is available. Find the minimum sample size needed.

(b) Find the minimum sample size needed, using a prior study that found that 30% of the respondents said they used an online service or the Internet to make travel reservations. *(Source: Travel Industry Association of America)*

(c) Compare the results from parts (a) and (b).

23. Camcorder Repairs You wish to estimate, with 96% confidence, the proportion of camcorders that need repairs or have problems by the time the product is five years old. Your estimate must be accurate within 2.5% of the true proportion.

(a) No preliminary estimate is available. Find the minimum sample size needed.

(b) Find the minimum sample size needed, using a prior study that found that 25% of camcorders needed repairs or had problems by the time the product was five years old. *(Source: Consumer Reports)*

(c) Compare the results from parts (a) and (b).

24. Computer Repairs You wish to estimate, with 97% confidence and within 3.5% of the true population, the proportion of computers that need repairs or have problems by the time the product is three years old.

(a) No preliminary estimate is available. Find the minimum sample size needed.

(b) Find the minimum sample size needed, using a prior study that found that 19% of computers needed repairs or had problems by the time the product was three years old. *(Source: Consumer Reports)*

(c) Compare the results from parts (a) and (b).

Constructing Confidence Intervals *In Exercises 25 and 26, use the following information. The table shows the results of a survey in which 400 adults from the East, 400 adults from the South, 400 adults from the Midwest, and 400 adults from the West were asked if traffic congestion is a serious problem in their community.* (Adapted from The Harris Poll)

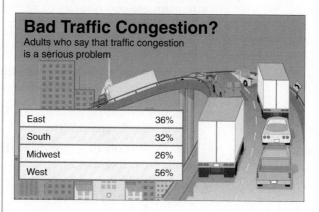

Bad Traffic Congestion?
Adults who say that traffic congestion
is a serious problem

East	36%
South	32%
Midwest	26%
West	56%

25. **East and South**   Construct a 99% confidence interval for

   (a) the proportion of adults from the East who say traffic congestion is a serious problem.

   (b) the proportion of adults from the South who say traffic congestion is a serious problem. Is it possible that these two proportions are equal? Explain your reasoning.

26. **Midwest and West**   Construct a 99% confidence interval for

   (a) the proportion of adults from the Midwest who say traffic congestion is a serious problem.

   (b) the proportion of adults from the West who say traffic congestion is a serious problem. Is it possible that these two proportions are equal? Explain your reasoning.

Constructing Confidence Intervals *In Exercises 27 and 28, use the following information. The graph shows the results of a survey in which 2563 adults from the United States, 1125 adults from France, and 1086 adults from Germany were asked if they believed that the activities of humans are contributing to an increase in global temperatures.* (Source: The Harris Poll)

Are humans contributing to global warming?

United States France Germany
65% 88% 92%

27. Global Warming Construct a 99% confidence interval for

(a) the proportion of adults from the United States who say that the activities of humans are contributing to an increase in global temperatures.

(b) the proportion of adults from France who say that the activities of humans are contributing to an increase in global temperatures.

(c) the proportion of adults from Germany who say that the activities of humans are contributing to an increase in global temperatures.

28. Global Warming Determine whether it is possible that the following proportions are equal and explain your reasoning.

(a) The proportion of adults from Exercise 27(a) and the proportion of adults from Exercise 27(b).

(b) The proportion of adults from Exercise 27(b) and the proportion of adults from Exercise 27(c).

(c) The proportion of adults from Exercise 27(a) and the proportion of adults from Exercise 27(c).

■ Extending Concepts

Newspaper Surveys *In Exercises 29 and 30, translate the newspaper excerpt into a confidence interval for p. Approximate the value of the level of confidence, c.*

29. In a survey of 8451 U.S. adults, 31.4% said they were taking vitamin E as a supplement. The survey's margin of error is plus or minus 1%. *(Source: Decision Analyst, Inc.)*

30. In a survey of 1001 U.S. adults, 27% said they had smoked a cigarette in the past week. The survey's margin of error is plus or minus 3%. *(Source: The Gallup Organization)*

31. Why Check It? Why is it necessary to check that $n\hat{p} \geq 5$ and $n\hat{q} \geq 5$?

32. Sample Size The equation for determining the sample size $n = \hat{p}\hat{q}[(z_c)/E]^2$ can be obtained by solving the equation for the margin of error $E = z_c \sqrt{(\hat{p}\hat{q})/n}$ for n. Show that this is true and justify each step.

33. Maximum Value of $\hat{p}\hat{q}$ Complete the tables for different values of $\hat{p}$ and $\hat{q} = 1 - \hat{p}$. From the table, which value of $\hat{p}$ appears to give the maximum value of the product $\hat{p}\hat{q}$?

$\hat{p}$	$\hat{q} = 1 - \hat{p}$	$\hat{p}\hat{q}$
0.0	1.0	0.00
0.1	0.9	0.09
0.2	0.8	
0.3		
0.4		
0.5		
0.6		
0.7		
0.8		
0.9		
1.0		

$\hat{p}$	$\hat{q} = 1 - \hat{p}$	$\hat{p}\hat{q}$
0.45		
0.46		
0.47		
0.48		
0.49		
0.50		
0.51		
0.52		
0.53		
0.54		
0.55		

APPLET

The *confidence intervals for a proportion* applet allows you to visually investigate confidence intervals for a proportion. You can specify the sample size n and the true proportion p. When you click SIMULATE, 100 separate samples of size n will be selected from a population with a proportion of successes equal to p. For each of the 100 samples, a 95% confidence interval (in green) and a 99% confidence interval (in blue) are displayed in the plot to the right. Each of these intervals is computed using the standard normal approximation. If an interval does not contain the true proportion, it is displayed in red. Note that the 99% confidence interval is always wider than the 95% confidence interval. Additional simulations can be carried out by clicking SIMULATE multiple times. The cumulative number of times that each type of interval contains the true proportion is also shown. Press CLEAR to clear existing results and start a new simulation.

n: 100

p: 0.5

Simulate

Cumulative results:

	95% CI	99% CI
Contained p		
Did not contain p		
Prop. contained		

Clear

■ Explore

Step 1 Specify a value for n.

Step 2 Specify a value for p.

Step 5 Click SIMULATE to generate the confidence intervals.

■ Draw Conclusions

APPLET

1. Run the simulation for $p = 0.6$ and $n = 10, 20, 40,$ and 100. Clear the results after each trial. What proportion of the confidence intervals for each confidence level contains the population proportion? What happens to the proportion of confidence intervals that contains the population proportion for each confidence level as the sample size increases?

2. Run the simulation for $p = 0.4$ and $n = 100$ so that at least 1000 confidence intervals are generated. Compare the proportion of confidence intervals that contains the population proportion for each confidence level. Is this what you would expect? Explain.

6.4 Confidence Intervals for Variance and Standard Deviation

The Chi-Square Distribution • Confidence Intervals for σ^2 and σ

▸ The Chi-Square Distribution

In manufacturing, it is necessary to control the amount that a process varies. For instance, an automobile part manufacturer must produce thousands of parts to be used in the manufacturing process. It is important that the parts vary little or not at all. How can you measure, and consequently control, the amount of variation in the parts? You can start with a point estimate.

DEFINITION

The **point estimate for σ^2** is s^2 and the **point estimate for σ** is s. s^2 is the most unbiased estimate for σ^2.

You can use a *chi-square distribution* to construct a confidence interval for the variance and standard deviation.

DEFINITION

If the random variable x has a normal distribution, then the distribution of

$$\chi^2 = \frac{(n-1)s^2}{\sigma^2}$$

forms a **chi-square distribution** for samples of any size $n > 1$. Four properties of the chi-square distribution are as follows.

1. All chi-square values χ^2 are greater than or equal to zero.
2. The chi-square distribution is a family of curves, each determined by the degrees of freedom. To form a confidence interval for σ^2, use the χ^2-distribution with degrees of freedom equal to one less than the sample size.

   $$\text{d.f.} = n - 1 \qquad \text{Degrees of freedom}$$

3. The area under each curve of the chi-square distribution equals one.
4. Chi-square distributions are positively skewed.

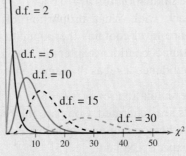

Chi-square distributions

Study Tip

The Greek letter χ is pronounced "$k\bar{i}$," which rhymes with the more familiar Greek letter π.

There are two critical values for each level of confidence. The value χ_R^2 represents the right-tail critical value and χ_L^2 represents the left-tail critical value. Table 6 in Appendix B lists critical values of χ^2 for various degrees of freedom and areas. Each area in the table represents the region under the chi-square curve to the *right* of the critical value.

Study Tip

For chi-square critical values with a *c*-confidence level, the following values are what you look up in Table 6 in Appendix B.

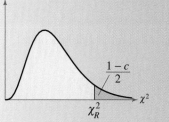

Area to the right of χ_R^2

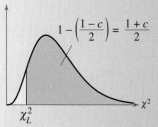

Area to the right of χ_L^2

The result is that you can conclude that the area between the left and right critical values is *c*.

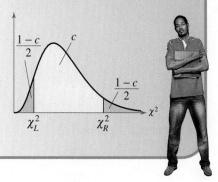

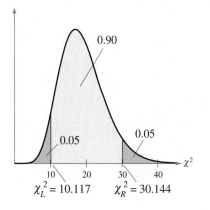

$\chi_L^2 = 10.117$ $\chi_R^2 = 30.144$

EXAMPLE 1

Finding Critical Values for χ^2

Find the critical values χ_R^2 and χ_L^2 for a 90% confidence interval when the sample size is 20.

Solution

Because the sample size is 20, there are

d.f. $= n - 1 = 20 - 1 = 19$ degrees of freedom.

The areas to the right of χ_R^2 and χ_L^2 are

$$\text{Area to right of } \chi_R^2 = \frac{1 - c}{2} = \frac{1 - 0.90}{2} = 0.05$$

and

$$\text{Area to right of } \chi_L^2 = \frac{1 + c}{2} = \frac{1 + 0.90}{2} = 0.95.$$

Part of Table 6 is shown. Using d.f. $= 19$ and the areas 0.95 and 0.05, you can find the critical values, as shown by the highlighted areas in the table.

Degrees of freedom	α						
	0.995	**0.99**	**0.975**	**0.95**	**0.90**	**0.10**	**0.05**
1	—	—	0.001	0.004	0.016	2.706	3.841
2	0.010	0.020	0.051	0.103	0.211	4.605	5.991
3	0.072	0.115	0.216	0.352	0.584	6.251	7.815
15	4.601	5.229	6.262	7.261	8.547	22.307	24.996
16	5.142	5.812	6.908	7.962	9.312	23.542	26.296
17	5.697	6.408	7.564	8.672	10.085	24.769	27.587
18	6.265	7.015	8.231	9.390	10.865	25.989	28.869
19	6.844	7.633	8.907	10.117	11.651	27.204	30.144
20	7.434	8.260	9.591	10.851	12.443	28.412	31.410

χ_L^2 χ_R^2

From the table, you can see that $\chi_R^2 = 30.144$ and $\chi_L^2 = 10.117$.

Interpretation   So, 90% of the area under the curve lies between 10.117 and 30.144.

▶ **Try It Yourself 1**

Find the critical values χ_R^2 and χ_L^2 for a 95% confidence interval when the sample size is 25.

a. *Identify* the degrees of freedom and the level of confidence.
b. *Find* the area to the right of χ_R^2 and χ_L^2.
c. *Use* Table 6 of Appendix B to find χ_R^2 and χ_L^2.   *Answer: Page A42*

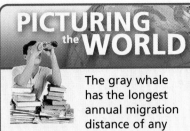

PICTURING the WORLD

The gray whale has the longest annual migration distance of any mammal. Gray whales leave from Baja, California and western Mexico in the spring, migrating to the Bering and Chukchi seas for the summer months. Tracking a sample of 51 whales for a year provided a mean migration distance of 11,064 miles with a standard deviation of 860 miles. (Adapted from National Marine Fisheries Services)

Construct a 90% confidence interval for the standard deviation for the migration distance of gray whales. Assume that the population of migration distances has a normal distribution.

▶ Confidence Intervals for σ^2 and σ

You can use the critical values χ_R^2 and χ_L^2 to construct confidence intervals for a population variance and standard deviation. As you would expect, the best point estimate for the variance is s^2 and the best point estimate for the standard deviation is s.

DEFINITION

A c-confidence interval for a population variance and standard deviation is as follows.

Confidence Interval for σ^2:

$$\frac{(n-1)s^2}{\chi_R^2} < \sigma^2 < \frac{(n-1)s^2}{\chi_L^2}$$

Confidence Interval for σ:

$$\sqrt{\frac{(n-1)s^2}{\chi_R^2}} < \sigma < \sqrt{\frac{(n-1)s^2}{\chi_L^2}}$$

The probability that the confidence intervals contain σ^2 or σ is c.

GUIDELINES

Constructing a Confidence Interval for a Variance and Standard Deviation

In Words	*In Symbols*
1. Verify that the population has a normal distribution.	
2. Identify the sample statistic n and the degrees of freedom.	d.f. $= n - 1$
3. Find the point estimate s^2.	$s^2 = \dfrac{\sum(x - \bar{x})^2}{n - 1}$
4. Find the critical values χ_R^2 and χ_L^2 that correspond to the given level of confidence c.	Use Table 6 in Appendix B.

Left Endpoint   Right Endpoint

5. Find the left and right endpoints and form the confidence interval for the population variance.

$$\frac{(n-1)s^2}{\chi_R^2} < \sigma^2 < \frac{(n-1)s^2}{\chi_L^2}$$

6. Find the confidence interval for the population standard deviation by taking the square root of each endpoint.

$$\sqrt{\frac{(n-1)s^2}{\chi_R^2}} < \sigma < \sqrt{\frac{(n-1)s^2}{\chi_L^2}}$$

EXAMPLE 2

Constructing a Confidence Interval

You randomly select and weigh 30 samples of an allergy medicine. The sample standard deviation is 1.20 milligrams. Assuming the weights are normally distributed, construct 99% confidence intervals for the population variance and standard deviation.

Solution

The areas to the right of χ_R^2 and χ_L^2 are

$$\text{Area to right of } \chi_R^2 = \frac{1 - c}{2} = \frac{1 - 0.99}{2} = 0.005$$

and

$$\text{Area to right of } \chi_L^2 = \frac{1 + c}{2} = \frac{1 + 0.99}{2} = 0.995.$$

Using the values $n = 30$, d.f. $= 29$, and $c = 0.99$, the critical values χ_R^2 and χ_L^2 are

$$\chi_R^2 = 52.336 \qquad \text{and} \qquad \chi_L^2 = 13.121.$$

Using these critical values and $s = 1.20$, the confidence interval for σ^2 is as follows.

Left Endpoint

$$\frac{(n - 1)s^2}{\chi_R^2} = \frac{(30 - 1)(1.20)^2}{52.336} \approx 0.80$$

Right Endpoint

$$\frac{(n - 1)s^2}{\chi_L^2} = \frac{(30 - 1)(1.20)^2}{13.121} \approx 3.18$$

$$0.80 < \sigma^2 < 3.18$$

The confidence interval for σ is

$$\sqrt{\frac{(30 - 1)(1.20)^2}{52.336}} < \sigma < \sqrt{\frac{(30 - 1)(1.20)^2}{13.121}}$$

$$0.89 < \sigma < 1.78.$$

Interpretation With 99% confidence, you can say that the population variance is between 0.80 and 3.18. The population standard deviation is between 0.89 and 1.78 milligrams.

▶ Try It Yourself 2

Find the 90% and 95% confidence intervals for the population variance and standard deviation of the medicine weights.

a. *Find* the critical values χ_R^2 and χ_L^2 for each confidence interval.
b. *Use* n, s, χ_R^2, and χ_L^2 to find the left and right endpoints for each confidence interval for the variance.
c. *Find* the square roots of the endpoints of each confidence interval.
d. *Specify* the 90% and 95% confidence intervals for the population variance and standard deviation.

Answer: Page A42

Study Tip

When a confidence interval for a population variance or standard deviation is computed, the general *round-off rule* is to round off to the same number of decimal places given for the sample variance or standard deviation.

6.4 EXERCISES

■ Building Basic Skills and Vocabulary

In Exercises 1–6, find the critical values χ_R^2 and χ_L^2 for the given confidence level c and sample size n.

1. $c = 0.90$, $n = 10$

2. $c = 0.99$, $n = 13$

3. $c = 0.95$, $n = 22$

4. $c = 0.98$, $n = 26$

5. $c = 0.99$, $n = 30$

6. $c = 0.80$, $n = 29$

■ Using and Interpreting Concepts

Constructing Confidence Intervals *In Exercises 7–20, assume each sample is taken from a normally distributed population and construct the indicated confidence intervals for (a) the population variance σ^2 and (b) the population standard deviation σ.*

7. Vitamins To analyze the variation of vitamin supplement tablets, you randomly select and weigh 14 tablets. The results (in milligrams) are shown. Use a 90% level of confidence.

500.000	499.995	500.010	499.997	500.015
499.988	500.000	499.996	500.020	500.002
499.998	499.996	500.003	500.000	

8. Cough Syrup You randomly select and measure the contents of 15 bottles of cough syrup. The results (in fluid ounces) are shown. Use a 90% level of confidence.

4.211	4.246	4.269	4.241	4.260
4.293	4.189	4.248	4.220	4.239
4.253	4.209	4.300	4.256	4.290

9. Car Batteries The number of hours of reserve capacity of 18 randomly selected automotive batteries is shown. Use a 99% level of confidence. *(Adapted from Consumer Reports)*

1.70	1.60	1.94	1.58	1.74	1.60
1.86	1.72	1.38	1.46	1.64	1.49
1.55	1.70	1.75	0.88	1.77	2.07

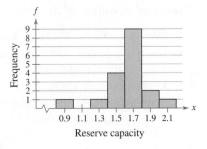

10. Bolts   You randomly select and measure the lengths of 17 bolts. The results (in inches) are shown. Use a 95% level of confidence.

1.286   1.138   1.240   1.132   1.381   1.137
1.300   1.167   1.240   1.401   1.241   1.171
1.217   1.360   1.302   1.331   1.383

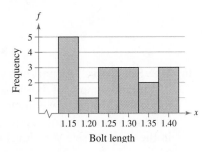

11. Lawn Mower   A lawn mower manufacturer is trying to determine the standard deviation of the life of one of its lawn mower models. To do this, it randomly selects 12 lawn mowers that were sold several years ago and finds that the sample standard deviation is 3.25 years. Use a 99% level of confidence. *(Adapted from Consumer Reports)*

12. Home Theater Systems   A magazine includes a report on the prices of home theater systems. The article states that 14 randomly selected home theater systems had a sample standard deviation of $123. Use a 95% level of confidence. *(Adapted from Consumer Reports)*

13. Hotels   As part of your vacation planning, you randomly contact 10 hotels in your destination area and record the room rate of each. The results are shown in the stem-and-leaf plot. Use a 90% level of confidence.

```
 6 | 0  3      Key: 8|3 = 83
 7 |
 8 | 3
 9 | 0
10 | 2  8
11 | 3  8
12 | 2
13 |
14 | 1
```

14. Pulse Rates   The pulse rates of a random sample of 16 adults are shown in the stem-and-leaf plot. Use a 95% level of confidence.

```
 6 | 2          Key: 6|2 = 62
 6 | 5  8  9
 7 | 0  1  4  4
 7 | 6  6  7  9  9
 8 | 0  0
 8 | 7
```

15. Water Quality   As part of a water quality survey, you test the water hardness in several randomly selected streams. The results are shown in the figure. Use a 95% level of confidence.

Water quality survey

$n = 19$
$s = 15$ grains/gallon

16. Web Site Costs   As part of a survey, you ask a random sample of business owners how much they would be willing to pay for a Web site for their company. The results are shown in the figure. Use a 90% level of confidence.

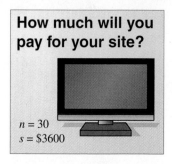

How much will you pay for your site?

$n = 30$
$s = \$3600$

17. Monthly Income   The monthly incomes of 14 randomly selected individuals who have recently graduated with a bachelor's degree in economics have a sample standard deviation of $342. Use a 95% level of confidence. *(Adapted from U.S. Bureau of Labor Statistics)*

18. Annual Precipitation   The average annual precipitation (in inches) of a random sample of 30 years in Anchorage, Alaska has a sample standard deviation of 2.46 inches. Use a 99% level of confidence. *(Source: Alaska Climate Research Center)*

19. Waiting Times   The waiting times (in minutes) of a random sample of 22 people at a bank have a sample standard deviation of 3.6 minutes. Use a 98% level of confidence.

20. Motorcycles   The prices of a random sample of 20 new motorcycles have a sample standard deviation of $3900. Use a 90% level of confidence.

■ Extending Concepts

21. Vitamin Tablet Weights   You are analyzing the sample of vitamin supplement tablets in Exercise 7. The population standard deviation of the tablets' weights should be less than 0.015 milligram. Does the confidence interval you constructed for σ suggest that the variation in the tablets' weights is at an acceptable level? Explain your reasoning.

22. Cough Syrup Bottle Contents   You are analyzing the sample of cough syrup bottles in Exercise 8. The population standard deviation of the bottles' contents should be less than 0.025 fluid ounce. Does the confidence interval you constructed for σ suggest that the variation in the bottles' contents is at an acceptable level? Explain your reasoning.

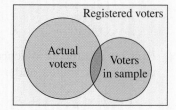

Statistics in the Real World

Uses

By now, you know that complete information about population parameters is often not available. The techniques of this chapter can be used to make interval estimates of these parameters so that you can make informed decisions.

From what you learned in this chapter, you know that point estimates (sample statistics) of population parameters are usually close but rarely equal to the actual value of the parameter they are estimating. Remembering this can help you make good decisions in your career and in everyday life. For instance, suppose the results of a survey tell you that 52% of the population plans to vote in favor of the rezoning of a portion of a town from residential to commercial use. You know that this is only a point estimate of the actual proportion that will vote in favor of rezoning. If the interval estimate is $0.49 < p < 0.55$, then you know this means it is possible that the item will not receive a majority vote.

Abuses

Unrepresentative Samples There are many ways that surveys can result in incorrect predictions. When you read the results of a survey, remember to question the sample size, the sampling technique, and the questions asked. For example, suppose you want to know the proportion of people who will vote in favor of rezoning. From the diagram at the right, you can see that even if your sample is large enough, it may not consist of actual voters.

Using a small sample might be the only way to make an estimate but be aware that a change in one data value may completely change the results. Generally, the larger the sample size, the more accurate the results will be.

Biased Survey Questions In surveys, it is also important to analyze the wording of the questions. For example, the question about rezoning might be presented as: "Knowing that rezoning will result in more businesses contributing to school taxes, would you support the rezoning?"

■ EXERCISES

1. ***Unrepresentative Samples*** Find an example of a survey that is reported in a newspaper or magazine. Describe different ways that the sample could have been unrepresentative of the population.

2. ***Biased Survey Questions*** Find an example of a survey that is reported in a newspaper or magazine. Describe different ways that the survey questions could have been biased.

6 CHAPTER SUMMARY

What did you **learn?**	EXAMPLE(S)	REVIEW EXERCISES
Section 6.1		
■ How to find a point estimate and a margin of error $$E = z_c \frac{\sigma}{\sqrt{n}}$$	*1, 2*	*1, 2*
■ How to construct and interpret confidence intervals for the population mean $$\bar{x} - E < \mu < \bar{x} + E$$	*3–5*	*3, 4*
■ How to determine the minimum sample size required when estimating μ $$n = \left(\frac{z_c \sigma}{E} \right)^2$$	*6*	*5–8*
Section 6.2		
■ How to interpret the *t*-distribution and use a *t*-distribution table $$t = \frac{(\bar{x} - \mu)}{(s/\sqrt{n})}$$	*1*	*9–12*
■ How to construct confidence intervals when $n < 30$, the population is normally distributed, and σ is unknown. $$\bar{x} - E < \mu < \bar{x} + E, \quad E = t_c \frac{s}{\sqrt{n}}$$	*2–4*	*13–22*
Section 6.3		
■ How to find a point estimate for the population proportion $$\hat{p} = \frac{x}{n}$$	*1*	*23–30*
■ How to construct a confidence interval for a population proportion $$\hat{p} - E < p < \hat{p} + E, \quad E = z_c \sqrt{\frac{\hat{p}\hat{q}}{n}}$$	*2, 3*	*31–38*
■ How to determine the minimum sample size required when estimating a population proportion $$n = \hat{p}\hat{q} \left(\frac{z_c}{E} \right)^2$$	*4*	*39, 40*
Section 6.4		
■ How to interpret the chi-square distribution and use a chi-square distribution table $$\chi^2 = \frac{(n-1)s^2}{\sigma^2}$$	*1*	*41–44*
■ How to use the chi-square distribution to construct a confidence interval for the variance and standard deviation $$\frac{(n-1)s^2}{\chi_R^2} < \sigma^2 < \frac{(n-1)s^2}{\chi_L^2}, \quad \sqrt{\frac{(n-1)s^2}{\chi_R^2}} < \sigma < \sqrt{\frac{(n-1)s^2}{\chi_L^2}}$$	*2*	*45–48*

6 REVIEW EXERCISES

Section 6.1

In Exercises 1 and 2, find (a) the point estimate of the population mean and (b) the margin of error for a 90% confidence interval.

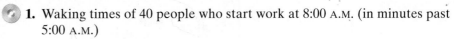

 1. Waking times of 40 people who start work at 8:00 A.M. (in minutes past 5:00 A.M.)

135	145	95	140	135	95	110	50
90	165	110	125	80	125	130	110
25	75	65	100	60	125	115	135
95	90	140	40	75	50	130	85
100	160	135	45	135	115	75	130

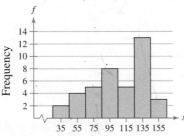

Waking times (in minutes past 5 A.M.)

 2. Length of work commute of 32 people (in miles)

12	9	7	2	8	7	3	27
21	10	13	3	7	2	30	7
6	13	6	14	4	1	10	3
13	6	2	9	2	12	16	18

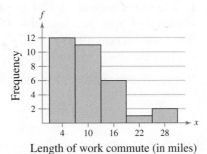

Length of work commute (in miles)

In Exercises 3 and 4, construct the indicated confidence interval for the population mean μ. If convenient, use technology to construct the confidence interval.

3. $c = 0.95, \bar{x} = 10.3, s = 0.277, n = 100$

4. $c = 0.90, \bar{x} = 0.0925, s = 0.0013, n = 45$

In Exercises 5–8, determine the minimum sample size to estimate μ.

5. Use the results from Exercise 1. Determine the minimum survey size that is necessary to be 95% confident that the sample mean waking time is within 10 minutes of the actual mean waking time.

6. Use the results from Exercise 1. Now suppose you want 99% confidence with a maximum error of 2 minutes. How many people would you need to survey?

7. Use the results from Exercise 2. Determine the minimum survey size that is necessary to be 95% confident that the sample mean length of work commute is within 2 miles of the actual mean length of work commute.

8. Use the results from Exercise 2. Now suppose you want 98% confidence with a maximum error of 0.5 mile. How many people would you need to survey?

Section 6.2

In Exercises 9–12, find the critical value t_c for the given confidence level c and sample size n.

9. $c = 0.95, n = 8$

10. $c = 0.90, n = 22$

11. $c = 0.98, n = 15$

12. $c = 0.99, n = 30$

In Exercises 13–16, find the margin of error for μ.

13. $c = 0.90, s = 25.6, n = 16, \bar{x} = 72.1$

14. $c = 0.95, s = 1.1, n = 25, \bar{x} = 3.5$

15. $c = 0.98, s = 0.9, n = 12, \bar{x} = 6.8$

16. $c = 0.99, s = 16.5, n = 20, \bar{x} = 25.2$

In Exercises 17–20, construct the confidence interval for μ using the statistics from the given exercise. If convenient, use technology to construct the confidence interval.

17. Exercise 13   18. Exercise 14

19. Exercise 15   20. Exercise 16

21. In a random sample of 15 CD players brought in for repair, the average repair cost was $80 and the standard deviation was $14. Construct a 90% confidence interval for μ. Assume the repair costs are normally distributed. *(Adapted from Consumer Reports)*

22. Repeat Exercise 21 using a 99% confidence interval.

Section 6.3

In Exercises 23–30, let p be the proportion of the population who respond yes. Use the given information to find $\hat{p}$ and $\hat{q}$.

23. In a survey of 2000 U.S. adults, 560 pay their bills online. *(Adapted from Pew Research Center)*

24. In a survey of 500 U.S. adults, 425 said they would trust doctors to tell the truth. *(Adapted from The Harris Poll)*

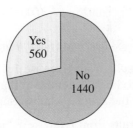

25. In a survey of 2010 U.S. adults, 442 said that in the past 3 years an organization notified them of lost, stolen, or improperly disclosed personal information. *(Adapted from The Harris Poll)*

26. In a survey of 800 U.S. adults, 90 are making the minimum payment(s) on their credit card(s). *(Adapted from Cambridge Consumer Credit Index)*

27. In a survey of 644 U.S. teens, 116 said they think their business leaders are ethical. *(Source: USA TODAY)*

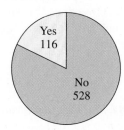

28. In a survey of 1007 U.S. adults, 594 said they approve of labor unions. *(Adapted from The Gallup Organization)*

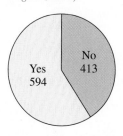

29. In a survey of 4813 U.S. adult Internet users, 2021 said that they have high-speed Internet access in their homes. *(Adapted from Pew Internet and American Life Project)*

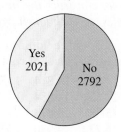

30. In a survey of 2365 U.S. adults, 1230 said they worry most about missing deductions when filing their taxes. *(Adapted from USA TODAY)*

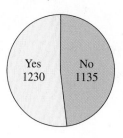

In Exercises 31–38, construct the indicated confidence interval for the population proportion p. If convenient, use technology to construct the confidence interval.

31. Use the sample in Exercise 23 with $c = 0.95$.

32. Use the sample in Exercise 24 with $c = 0.99$.

33. Use the sample in Exercise 25 with $c = 0.90$.

34. Use the sample in Exercise 26 with $c = 0.98$.

35. Use the sample in Exercise 27 with $c = 0.99$.

36. Use the sample in Exercise 28 with $c = 0.90$.

37. Use the sample in Exercise 29 with $c = 0.95$.

38. Use the sample in Exercise 30 with $c = 0.98$.

39. You wish to estimate, with 95% confidence and within 5% of the true population, the proportion of U.S. adults that think they should be saving more money.

    (a) No preliminary estimate is available. Find the minimum sample size needed.

    (b) Find the minimum sample size needed, using a prior study that found that 63% of U.S. adults think that they should be saving more money. *(Source: Pew Research Center)*

    (c) Compare the results from parts (a) and (b).

40. Repeat Exercise 39 part (b), using a 99% confidence level and a margin of error of 2.5%. How does this sample size compare with your answer from Exercise 39 part (b)?

Section 6.4

In Exercises 41–44, find the critical values x_R^2 and x_L^2 for the given confidence level c and sample size n.

41. $c = 0.95, n = 13$

42. $c = 0.98, n = 25$

43. $c = 0.90, n = 8$

44. $c = 0.99, n = 10$

In Exercises 45–48, construct the indicated confidence intervals for σ^2 and σ. Assume the samples are each taken from a normally distributed population.

45. A random sample of the liquid content (in fluid ounces) of 16 beverage cans is shown. Use a 95% level of confidence.

14.816	14.863	14.814	14.998
14.965	14.824	14.884	14.838
14.916	15.021	14.874	14.856
14.860	14.772	14.980	14.919

46. Repeat Exercise 45 using a 99% level of confidence.

47. A random sample of the sodium content (in milligrams) of 24 boxes of corn flakes cereal is shown. Use a 90% level of confidence.

290.8	292.5	288.0	291.9	290.3
291.4	290.0	290.3	289.9	289.3
291.2	290.6	289.8	289.7	291.1
292.9	288.7	290.9	289.9	290.6
291.4	289.7	290.0	291.3	

48. Repeat Exercise 47 using a 95% level of confidence.

6 CHAPTER QUIZ

Take this quiz as you would take a quiz in class. After you are done, check your work against the answers given in the back of the book.

1. The following data set represents the repair costs (in dollars) for a random sample of 30 dishwashers. *(Adapted from Consumer Reports)*

41.82	52.81	57.80	68.16	73.48	78.88	88.13	88.79
90.07	90.35	91.68	91.72	93.01	95.21	95.34	96.50
100.05	101.32	103.59	104.19	105.62	111.32	117.14	118.42
118.77	119.01	120.70	140.52	141.84	147.06		

   (a) Find the point estimate of the population mean.

   (b) Find the margin of error for a 95% level of confidence.

   (c) Construct a 95% confidence interval for the population mean and interpret the results.

2. You want to estimate the mean repair cost for dishwashers. The estimate must be within $10 of the population mean. Determine the required sample size to construct a 99% confidence interval for the population mean. Assume the population standard deviation is $22.50. *(Adapted from Consumer Reports)*

3. The following data set represents the average yards per catch for a random sample of wide receivers in a recent season. *(Source: National Football League)*

   11.1   14.4   12.8   12.0   15.2   13.9   11.7   13.2   11.6   13.7

   (a) Find the sample mean.

   (b) Find the sample standard deviation.

   (c) Use the *t*-distribution to construct a 90% confidence interval for the population mean and interpret the results. Assume the population of the data set is normally distributed.

   (d) Repeat part (c), assuming $\sigma = 2.63$ yards. Compare the results.

4. In a random sample of seven aerospace engineers, the mean monthly income was $6824 and the standard deviation was $340. Assume the monthly incomes are normally distributed and use a *t*-distribution to construct a 95% confidence interval for the population mean monthly income for aerospace engineers. *(Adapted from U.S. Bureau of Labor Statistics)*

5. In a survey of 1037 adults from the United States age 65 and over, 643 were concerned about getting the flu. *(Source: Harvard School for Public Health)*

   (a) Find a point estimate for the population proportion p of those concerned about getting the flu.

   (b) Construct a 90% confidence interval for the population proportion.

   (c) Find the minimum sample size needed to estimate the population proportion at the 99% confidence level in order to ensure that the estimate is accurate within 4% of the population proportion.

6. Refer to the data set in Exercise 1. Assume the population of dishwasher repair costs is normally distributed.

   (a) Construct a 95% confidence interval for the population variance.

   (b) Construct a 95% confidence interval for the population standard deviation.

Putting It All Together

REAL Statistics — Real Decisions

As part of the U.S. Environmental Protection Agency's (EPA) efforts to "protect human health and safeguard the natural environment," the EPA conducts the Urban Air Toxics Monitoring Program (UATMP). The program has gathered thousands of air samples and analyzed them for concentrations of more than 50 different organic compounds, such as formaldehyde (used as a preservative in vaccinations, to store biological specimens, and in the production of permanent adhesives and insulation). Formaldehyde is also found in the smoke from forest fires, automobile exhaust, and tobacco smoke. The results from UATMP are used to gain insight into the effects of air pollution and determine if efforts to clean up the air are working.

For instance, using air samples from a major city, the EPA can analyze the results and estimate the mean concentration of formaldehyde in the air using a 95% confidence interval. They can then compare the interval with previous years' results to see if there are any trends and if there has been a significant change in the amount of formaldehyde in the air.

You work for the EPA and are asked to interpret the results shown in the graph at the right. The graph shows the point estimate for the population mean concentration and the 95% confidence interval for μ for formaldehyde over a three-year period. The data are based on air samples taken at one city.

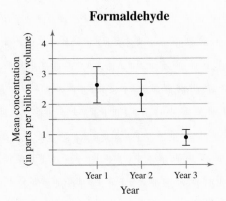

■ Exercises

1. *Interpreting the Results*

Consider the graph of the mean concentration levels of formaldehyde. For the following years, decide if there has been a change in the mean concentration level of formaldehyde. Explain your reasoning.

(a) From Year 1 to Year 2

(b) From Year 2 to Year 3

(c) From Year 1 to Year 3

2. *What Can You Conclude?*

Using the results of Exercise 1, what can you conclude about the efforts to reduce the concentration of formaldehyde in the air?

3. *How Do You Think They Did It?*

How do you think the EPA constructed the 95% confidence interval for the population mean concentration of the organic compounds in the air? Do the following to answer the question (you do not need to make any calculations).

(a) What sampling distribution do you think they used? Why?

(b) Do you think they used the population standard deviation in calculating the margin of error? Why or why not? If not, what could they have used?

THE GALLUP ORGANIZATION

MOST ADMIRED POLLS

Since 1948, the Gallup Organization has conducted a "most admired" poll. The methodology for the 2006 poll is described at the right.

> ### Survey Question
> *What man* that you have heard or read about, living today in any part of the world, do you admire most? And who is your second choice?*

*Survey respondents are asked an identical question about most admired woman.

WWW.GALLUPPOLL.COM

"These results are based on telephone interviews with a randomly selected national sample of 1010 adults, aged 18 and over, conducted December 11–14, 2006. For results based on this sample, one can say with 95 percent confidence that the maximum error attributable to sampling and other random effects is ±3 percentage points. In addition to sampling error, question wording and practical difficulties in conducting surveys can introduce error or bias into the findings of public opinion polls."

■ EXERCISES

1. In 2006, the most named man was George W. Bush at 13%. Use a technology tool to find a 95% confidence interval for the proportion that would have chosen George W. Bush.

2. Does the confidence interval you obtained in Exercise 1 agree with the statement issued by the Gallup Organization that the proportion is 13% plus or minus 3%? Explain.

3. In 2006, the most named woman was Hillary Clinton. The second named woman was Oprah Winfrey, who was named by 9% of the people in the sample. Use a technology tool to find a 95% confidence interval for the proportion of the population that would have chosen Oprah Winfrey.

4. Use a technology tool to simulate a most admired poll. Assume that the actual population proportion who most admire Oprah Winfrey is 12%. Run the simulation several times using $n = 1010$.

(a) What was the least value you obtained for $\hat{p}$?

(b) What was the greatest value you obtained for $\hat{p}$?

MINITAB

Generate ⟨200⟩ rows of data

Store in column(s): ⟨C1⟩

Number of trials: ⟨1010⟩

Probability of success: ⟨.12⟩

5. Is it possible that the actual proportion of the population that most admired Oprah Winfrey was 12% or greater? Explain your reasoning.

Extended solutions are given in the *Technology Supplement*. Technical instruction is provided for MINITAB, Excel, and the TI-83/84.

6 USING TECHNOLOGY TO CONSTRUCT CONFIDENCE INTERVALS

Here are some MINITAB and TI-83/84 printouts for some examples in this chapter. To duplicate the MINITAB results, you need the original data. For the TI-83/84, you can simply enter the descriptive statistics. Answers may be slightly different because of rounding.

(See Example 3, page 313.)

9	20	18	16	9	9	11	13	22	16	5	18	6	6	5	12	25
17	23	7	10	9	10	10	5	11	18	18	9	9	17	13	11	7
14	6	11	12	11	6	12	14	11	9	18	12	12	17	11	20	

Display Descriptive Statistics...
Store Descriptive Statistics...

1-Sample Z...
1-Sample t...
2-Sample t...
Paired t...

1 Proportion...
2 Proportions...

MINITAB

Z Confidence Intervals

The assumed sigma = 5

Variable	N	Mean	StDev	SE Mean	95.0 % CI
C1	50	12.4	5.010	0.707	(11.014, 13.786)

(See Example 2, page 327.)

159°F	173°F	162°F	151°F	173°F	162°F	148°F	172°F
167°F	170°F	151°F	153°F	172°F	143°F	166°F	170°F

Display Descriptive Statistics...
Store Descriptive Statistics...

1-Sample Z...
1-Sample t...
2-Sample t...
Paired t...

1 Proportion...
2 Proportions...

MINITAB

T Confidence Intervals

Variable	N	Mean	StDev	SE Mean	95.0 % CI
C3	16	162.00	10.00	2.50	(156.67, 167.33)

(See Example 2, page 336.)

Display Descriptive Statistics...
Store Descriptive Statistics...

1-Sample Z...
1-Sample t...
2-Sample t...
Paired t...

1 Proportion...
2 Proportions...

MINITAB

Test and Confidence Interval for One Proportion

Test of p = 0.29 vs p not = 0.29

Sample	X	N	Sample p	95.0 % CI	Z-Value	P-Value
1	354	1219	0.290402	(0.264919, 0.315885)	0.03	0.975

(See Example 5, page 315.)

TI-83/84

EDIT CALC **TESTS**
1: Z–Test…
2: T–Test…
3: 2–SampZTest…
4: 2–SampTTest…
5: 1–PropZTest…
6: 2–PropZTest…
7↓ ZInterval…

↓

TI-83/84

ZInterval
  Inpt: Data **Stats**
  s: 1.5
  x̄: 22.9
  n: 20
  C–Level: .9
  Calculate

↓

TI-83/84

ZInterval
  (22.348, 23.452)
  x̄= 22.9
  n= 20

(See Example 3, page 328.)

TI-83/84

EDIT CALC **TESTS**
2↑ T–Test…
3: 2–SampZTest…
4: 2–SampTTest…
5: 1–PropZTest…
6: 2–PropZTest…
7: ZInterval…
8↓ TInterval…

↓

TI-83/84

TInterval
  Inpt: Data **Stats**
  x̄: 6.22
  Sx: .42
  n: 20
  C–Level: .99
  Calculate

↓

TI-83/84

TInterval
  (5.9513, 6.4887)
  x̄= 6.22
  Sx= .42
  n= 20

(See Example 2, page 336.)

TI-83/84

EDIT CALC **TESTS**
5↑ 1–PropZTest…
6: 2–PropZTest…
7: ZInterval…
8: TInterval…
9: 2–SampZInt…
0: 2–SampTInt…
A↓ 1–PropZInt…

↓

TI-83/84

1–PropZInt
  x: 354
  n: 1219
  C–Level: .95
  Calculate

↓

TI-83/84

1–PropZInt
  (.26492, .31589)
  p̂= .2904019688
  n= 1219

CHAPTER

7

Hypothesis Testing with One Sample

7.1 Introduction to Hypothesis Testing

7.2 Hypothesis Testing for the Mean (Large Samples)

　■ ACTIVITY

　■ CASE STUDY

7.3 Hypothesis Testing for the Mean (Small Samples)

7.4 Hypothesis Testing for Proportions

　■ ACTIVITY

7.5 Hypothesis Testing for Variance and Standard Deviation

　■ USES AND ABUSES

　■ REAL STATISTICS–
　　REAL DECISIONS

　■ TECHNOLOGY

Computer software is protected by federal copyright laws. Each year, software companies lose billions of dollars because of pirated software. Federal criminal penalties for software piracy can include fines of up to $250,000 and jail terms of up to five years.

In Chapter 6, you began your study of inferential statistics. There, you learned how to form a confidence interval estimate about a population parameter, such as the proportion of people in the United States who agree with a certain statement. For instance, in a nationwide poll conducted by *Harris Interactive* on behalf of the Business Software Alliance (BSA), U.S. students ages 8 to 18 years were asked several questions about their attitudes toward copyright law and Internet behavior. Here are some of the results.

Survey Question	Number Surveyed	Number Who Said Yes
Have you ever downloaded music from the Internet without paying for it?	1644	526
Have you not downloaded without paying for it because you do not want to get in trouble with the law?	1644	690
Is downloading music without paying for it always wrong?	1644	986
Have you ever downloaded software from the Internet without paying for it?	1644	230

WHERE YOU'RE GOING ➡

In this chapter, you will continue your study of inferential statistics. But now, instead of making an estimate about a population parameter, you will learn how to test a claim about a parameter.

For instance, suppose that you work for *Harris Interactive* and are asked to test a claim that the proportion of U.S. students ages 8 to 18 who download music without paying for it is $p = 0.25$. To test the claim, you take a random sample of $n = 1644$ students and find that 526 of them download music without paying for it. Your sample statistic is $\hat{p} \approx 0.320$.

Is your sample statistic different enough from the claim ($p = 0.25$) to decide that the claim is false? The answer lies in the sampling distribution of sample proportions taken from a population in which $p = 0.25$. The graph below shows that your sample statistic is over 6 standard errors from the claim value. If the claim is true, the probability of the sample statistic's being 6 standard errors or more from the claimed value

is extremely small. Something is wrong! If your sample was truly random, then you can conclude that the actual proportion of the student population is not 0.25. In other words, you tested the original claim (hypothesis), and you decided to reject it.

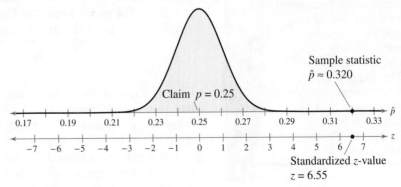

Sampling distribution

7.1 Introduction to Hypothesis Testing

What You SHOULD LEARN

▸ A practical introduction to hypothesis tests

▸ How to state a null hypothesis and an alternative hypothesis

▸ How to identify type I and type II errors and interpret the level of significance

▸ How to know whether to use a one-tailed or two-tailed statistical test and finding a *P*-value

▸ How to make and interpret a decision based on the results of a statistical test

▸ How to write a claim for a hypothesis test

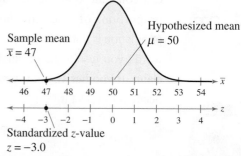

Hypothesis Tests ▸ Stating a Hypothesis ▸ Types of Errors and Level of Significance ▸ Statistical Tests and *P*-values ▸ Making a Decision and Interpreting the Decision ▸ Strategies for Hypothesis Testing

▸ Hypothesis Tests

Throughout the remainder of this course, you will study an important technique in inferential statistics called hypothesis testing. A **hypothesis test** is a process that uses sample statistics to test a claim about the value of a population parameter. Researchers in fields such as medicine, psychology, and business rely on hypothesis testing to make informed decisions about new medicines, treatments, and marketing strategies.

For instance, suppose an automobile manufacturer advertises that its new hybrid car has a mean mileage of 50 miles per gallon. If you suspect that the mean mileage is not 50 miles per gallon, how could you show that the advertisement is false?

Obviously, you cannot test *all* the vehicles, but you can still make a reasonable decision about the mean mileage by taking a random sample from the population of vehicles and measuring the mileage of each. If the sample mean differs enough from the advertisement's mean, you can decide that the advertisement is wrong.

For instance, to test that the mean mileage of all hybrid vehicles of this type is $\mu = 50$ miles per gallon, you could take a random sample of $n = 30$ vehicles and measure the mileage of each. Suppose you obtain a sample mean of $\bar{x} = 47$ miles per gallon with a sample standard deviation of $s = 5.5$ miles per gallon. Does this indicate that the manufacturer's advertisement is false?

To decide, you do something unusual—*you assume the advertisement is correct!* That is, you assume that $\mu = 50$. Then, you examine the sampling distribution of sample means (with $n = 30$) taken from a population in which $\mu = 50$ and $\sigma = 5.5$. From the Central Limit Theorem, you know this sampling distribution is normal with a mean of 50 and standard error of

$$\frac{5.5}{\sqrt{30}} \approx 1.$$

Insight

As you study this chapter, don't get confused regarding concepts of certainty and importance. For instance, even if you were very certain that the mean mileage of a type of hybrid vehicle is not 50 miles per gallon, the actual mean mileage might be very close to this value and the difference might not be important.

In the graph at the right, notice that your sample mean of $\bar{x} = 47$ miles per gallon is highly unlikely—it is about 3 standard errors from the claimed mean! Using the techniques you studied in Chapter 5, you can determine that if the advertisement is true, the probability of obtaining a sample

Sampling Distribution of $\bar{x}$

Sample mean $\bar{x} = 47$

Hypothesized mean $\mu = 50$

Standardized *z*-value $z = -3.0$

mean of 47 or less is about 0.0013. This is an unusual event! Your assumption that the company's advertisement is correct has led you to an improbable result. So, either you had a very unusual sample, or the advertisement is probably false. The logical conclusion is that the advertisement is probably false.

▶ Stating a Hypothesis

A statement about a population parameter is called a **statistical hypothesis.** To test a population parameter, you should carefully state a pair of hypotheses—one that represents the claim and the other, its complement. When one of these hypotheses is false, the other must be true. Either hypothesis—the *null hypothesis* or the *alternative hypothesis*—may represent the original claim.

Insight

The term *null hypothesis* was introduced by Ronald Fisher (see page 35). If the statement in the null hypothesis is not true, then the alternative hypothesis must be true.

PICTURING the WORLD

A sample of 25 randomly selected patients with early-stage high blood pressure underwent a special chiropractic adjustment to help lower their blood pressure. After eight weeks, the mean drop in the patients' systolic blood pressure was 14 millimeters of mercury. So, it is claimed that the mean drop in systolic blood pressure of all patients who undergo this special chiropractic adjustment is 14 millimeters of mercury. (Adapted from: the Journal of Human Hypertension)

Determine a null hypothesis and alternative hypothesis for this claim.

DEFINITION

1. A **null hypothesis** H_0 is a statistical hypothesis that contains a statement of equality, such as $\leq$, $=$, or $\geq$.
2. The **alternative hypothesis** H_a is the complement of the null hypothesis. It is a statement that must be true if H_0 is false and it contains a statement of strict inequality, such as $>$, $\neq$, or $<$.

H_0 is read as "H subzero" or "H naught" and H_a is read as "H sub-a."

To write the null and alternative hypotheses, translate the claim made about the population parameter from a verbal statement to a mathematical statement. Then, write its complement. For instance, if the claim value is k and the population parameter is μ, then some possible pairs of null and alternative hypotheses are

$$\begin{cases} H_0\colon \mu \leq k \\ H_a\colon \mu > k \end{cases} \qquad \begin{cases} H_0\colon \mu \geq k \\ H_a\colon \mu < k \end{cases} \qquad \begin{cases} H_0\colon \mu = k \\ H_a\colon \mu \neq k \end{cases}$$

Regardless of which of the three pairs of hypotheses you use, you always assume $\mu = k$ and examine the sampling distribution on the basis of this assumption. Within this sampling distribution, you will determine whether or not a sample statistic is unusual.

The following table shows the relationship between possible verbal statements about the parameter μ and the corresponding null and alternative hypotheses. Similar statements can be made to test other population parameters, such as p, σ, or σ^2.

Verbal Statement H_0 The mean is ...	Mathematical Statements	Verbal Statement H_a The mean is ...
... greater than or equal to k. ... at least k. ... not less than k.	$\begin{cases} H_0\colon \mu \geq k \\ H_a\colon \mu < k \end{cases}$	... less than k. ... below k. ... fewer than k.
... less than or equal to k. ... at most k. ... not more than k.	$\begin{cases} H_0\colon \mu \leq k \\ H_a\colon \mu > k \end{cases}$	... greater than k. ... above k. ... more than k.
... equal to k. ... k. ... exactly k.	$\begin{cases} H_0\colon \mu = k \\ H_a\colon \mu \neq k \end{cases}$	... not equal to k. ... different from k. ... not k.

EXAMPLE 1

Stating the Null and Alternative Hypotheses

Write the claim as a mathematical sentence. State the null and alternative hypotheses, and identify which represents the claim.

1. A university publicizes that the proportion of its students who graduate in 4 years is 82%.
2. A water faucet manufacturer announces that the mean flow rate of a certain type of faucet is less than 2.5 gallons per minute.
3. A cereal company advertises that the mean weight of the contents of its 20-ounce size cereal boxes is more than 20 ounces.

Solution

1. The claim "the proportion … is 82%" can be written as $p = 0.82$. Its complement is $p \neq 0.82$. Because $p = 0.82$ contains the statement of equality, it becomes the null hypothesis. In this case, the null hypothesis represents the claim.

   $H_0: p = 0.82$ (Claim)

   $H_a: p \neq 0.82$

2. The claim "the mean … is less than 2.5 gallons per minute" can be written as $\mu < 2.5$. Its complement is $\mu \geq 2.5$. Because $\mu \geq 2.5$ contains the statement of equality, it becomes the null hypothesis. In this case, the alternative hypothesis represents the claim.

   $H_0: \mu \geq 2.5$ gallons per minute

   $H_a: \mu < 2.5$ gallons per minute (Claim)

3. The claim "the mean … is more than 20 ounces" can be written as $\mu > 20$. Its complement is $\mu \leq 20$. Because $\mu \leq 20$ contains the statement of equality, it becomes the null hypothesis. In this case, the alternative hypothesis represents the claim.

   $H_0: \mu \leq 20$ ounces

   $H_a: \mu > 20$ ounces (Claim)

▶ **Try It Yourself 1**

Write the claim as a mathematical sentence. State the null and alternative hypotheses, and identify which represents the claim.

1. A consumer analyst reports that the mean life of a certain type of automobile battery is not 74 months.
2. A television manufacturer publishes that the variance of the life of a certain type of television is less than or equal to 3.5.
3. A radio station publicizes that its proportion of the local listening audience is greater than 39%.

a. *Identify* the verbal claim and *write* it as a mathematical statement.
b. *Write* the complement of the claim.
c. *Identify* the null and alternative hypotheses and *determine* which one represents the claim.

Answer: Page A43

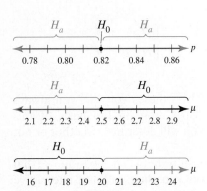

In each of these graphs, notice that each point on the number line is in H_0 or H_a, but no point is in both.

▶ Types of Errors and Level of Significance

No matter which hypothesis represents the claim, you always begin a hypothesis test by assuming that the equality condition in the null hypothesis is true. So, when you perform a hypothesis test, you make one of two decisions:

1. reject the null hypothesis or
2. fail to reject the null hypothesis.

Because your decision is based on a sample rather than the entire population, there is always the possibility you will make the wrong decision.

For instance, suppose you claim that a certain coin is not fair. To test your claim, you flip the coin 100 times and get 49 heads and 51 tails. You would probably agree that you do not have enough evidence to support your claim. Even so, it is possible that the coin is actually not fair and you had an unusual sample.

But what if you flip the coin 100 times and get 21 heads and 79 tails? It would be a rare occurrence to get only 21 heads out of 100 tosses with a fair coin. So, you probably have sufficient evidence to support your claim that the coin is not fair. However, you can't be 100% sure. It is possible that the coin is fair and you had an unusual sample.

If p represents the proportion of heads, the claim that "the coin is not fair" can be written as the mathematical statement $p \neq 0.5$. Its complement, "the coin is fair," is written as $p = 0.5$. So, your null hypothesis and alternative hypothesis are

$$H_0: p = 0.5$$

and

$$H_a: p \neq 0.5. \text{ (Claim)}$$

Remember, the only way to be absolutely certain of whether H_0 is true or false is to test the entire population. Because your decision—to reject H_0 or to fail to reject H_0—is based on a sample, you must accept the fact that your decision might be incorrect. You might reject a null hypothesis when it is actually true. Or, you might fail to reject a null hypothesis when it is actually false.

DEFINITION

A **type I error** occurs if the null hypothesis is rejected when it is true.

A **type II error** occurs if the null hypothesis is not rejected when it is false.

The following table shows the four possible outcomes of a hypothesis test.

Decision	Truth of H_0	
	H_0 is true.	H_0 is false.
Do not reject H_0.	Correct decision	Type II error
Reject H_0.	Type I error	Correct decision

	Truth About Defendant	
Verdict	Innocent	Guilty
Not guilty	Justice	Type II error
Guilty	Type I error	Justice

Hypothesis testing is sometimes compared to the legal system used in the United States. Under this system, the following steps are used.

1. A carefully worded accusation is written.

2. The defendant is assumed innocent (H_0) until proven guilty. The burden of proof lies with the prosecution. If the evidence is not strong enough, there is no conviction. A "not guilty" verdict does not prove that a defendant is innocent.

3. The evidence needs to be conclusive beyond a reasonable doubt. The system assumes that more harm is done by convicting the innocent (type I error) than by not convicting the guilty (type II error).

EXAMPLE 2

Identifying Type I and Type II Errors

The USDA limit for salmonella contamination for chicken is 20%. A meat inspector reports that the chicken produced by a company exceeds the USDA limit. You perform a hypothesis test to determine whether the meat inspector's claim is true. When will a type I or type II error occur? Which is more serious? *(Source: United States Department of Agriculture)*

Solution Let p represent the proportion of the chicken that is contaminated. The meat inspector's claim is "more than 20% is contaminated." You can write the null and alternative hypotheses as follows.

H_0: $p \leq 0.2$ The proportion is less than or equal to 20%.

H_a: $p > 0.2$ (Claim)   The proportion is greater than 20%.

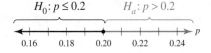

A type I error will occur if the actual proportion of contaminated chicken is less than or equal to 0.2, but you decide to reject H_0. A type II error will occur if the actual proportion of contaminated chicken is greater than 0.2, but you do not reject H_0. With a type I error, you might create a health scare and hurt the sales of chicken producers who were actually meeting the USDA limits. With a type II error, you could be allowing chicken that exceeded the USDA contamination limit to be sold to consumers. A type II error could result in sickness or even death.

▶ Try It Yourself 2

A company specializing in parachute assembly states that its main parachute failure rate is not more than 1%. You perform a hypothesis test to determine whether the company's claim is false. When will a type I or type II error occur? Which is more serious?

a. *State* the null and alternative hypotheses.
b. *Write* the possible type I and type II errors.
c. *Determine* which error is more serious.   *Answer: Page A43*

You will reject the null hypothesis when the sample statistic from the sampling distribution is unusual. You have already identified unusual events to be those that occur with a probability of 0.05 or less. When using statistical tests, an unusual event is sometimes required to have a probability of 0.10 or less, 0.05 or less, or 0.01 or less. Because there is variation from sample to sample, there is always a possibility that you will reject a null hypothesis when it is actually true. In other words, although the null hypothesis is true, your sample statistic is determined to be an unusual event in the sampling distribution. You can decrease the probability of doing so by lowering the *level of significance.*

Insight

When you decrease α (the maximum allowable probability of making a type I error), you are likely to be increasing β. The value $1 - \beta$ is called the **power of the test.** It represents the probability of rejecting the null hypothesis when the alternative hypothesis is true. The value of the power is difficult (and sometimes impossible) to find in most cases.

DEFINITION

In a hypothesis test, the **level of significance** is your maximum allowable probability of making a type I error. It is denoted by α, the lowercase Greek letter alpha.

The probability of a type II error is denoted by β, the lowercase Greek letter beta.

By setting the level of significance at a small value, you are saying that you want the probability of rejecting a true null hypothesis to be small. Three commonly used levels of significance are $\alpha = 0.10$, $\alpha = 0.05$, and $\alpha = 0.01$.

▶ Statistical Tests and *P*-values

After stating the null and alternative hypotheses and specifying the level of significance, the next step in a hypothesis test is to obtain a random sample from the population and calculate sample statistics such as the mean and the standard deviation. The statistic that is compared with the parameter in the null hypothesis is called the **test statistic.** The type of test used and the sampling distribution are based on the test statistic.

In this chapter, you will learn about several one-sample statistical tests. The following table shows the relationships between population parameters and their corresponding test statistics and standardized test statistics.

Population parameter	Test statistic	Standardized test statistic
μ	$\overline{x}$	z (Section 7.2, $n \geq 30$), t (Section 7.3, $n < 30$)
p	$\hat{p}$	z (Section 7.4)
σ^2	s^2	χ^2 (Section 7.5)

One way to decide whether to reject the null hypothesis is to determine whether the probability of obtaining the standardized test statistic (or one that is more extreme) is less than the level of significance.

DEFINITION

If the null hypothesis is true, a ***P*-value** (or **probability value**) of a hypothesis test is the probability of obtaining a sample statistic with a value as extreme or more extreme than the one determined from the sample data.

The *P*-value of a hypothesis test depends on the nature of the test. There are three types of hypothesis tests—a left-, right-, or two-tailed test. The type of test depends on the location of the region of the sampling distribution that favors a rejection of H_0. This region is indicated by the alternative hypothesis.

DEFINITION

1. If the alternative hypothesis H_a contains the less-than inequality symbol ($<$), the hypothesis test is a **left-tailed test.**

$H_0: \mu \geq k$
$H_a: \mu < k$

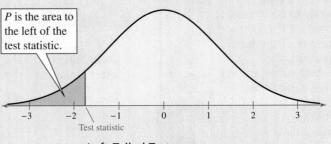

P is the area to the left of the test statistic.

Test statistic

Left-Tailed Test

2. If the alternative hypothesis H_a contains the greater-than inequality symbol ($>$), the hypothesis test is a **right-tailed test.**

$H_0: \mu \leq k$
$H_a: \mu > k$

P is the area to the right of the test statistic.

Test statistic

Right-Tailed Test

3. If the alternative hypothesis H_a contains the not-equal-to symbol ($\neq$), the hypothesis test is a **two-tailed test.** In a two-tailed test, each tail has an area of $\frac{1}{2}P$.

$H_0: \mu = k$
$H_a: \mu \neq k$

P is twice the area to the left of the negative test statistic.

P is twice the area to the right of the positive test statistic.

Test statistic   Test statistic

Two-Tailed Test

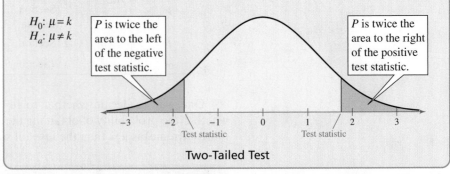

Study Tip

The third type of test is called a two-tailed test because evidence that would support the alternative hypothesis could lie in either tail of the sampling distribution.

The smaller the *P*-value of the test, the more evidence there is to reject the null hypothesis. A very small *P*-value indicates an unusual event. Remember, however, that even a very low *P*-value does not constitute proof that the null hypothesis is false, only that it is probably false.

E X A M P L E   3

Identifying the Nature of a Hypothesis Test

For each claim, state H_0 and H_a in words and in symbols. Then determine whether the hypothesis test is a left-tailed test, right-tailed test, or two-tailed test. Sketch a normal sampling distribution and shade the area for the P-value.

1. A university publicizes that the proportion of its students who graduate in 4 years is 82%.

2. A water faucet manufacturer announces that the mean flow rate of a certain type of faucet is less than 2.5 gallons per minute (gpm).

3. A cereal company advertises that the mean weight of the contents of its 20-ounce size cereal boxes is more than 20 ounces.

Solution

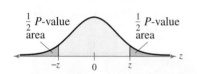

In Symbols	*In Words*
1. H_0: $p = 0.82$	The proportion of students who graduate in 4 years is 82%.
H_a: $p \neq 0.82$	The proportion of students who graduate in 4 years is not 82%.

Because H_a contains the $\neq$ symbol, the test is a two-tailed hypothesis test. The graph of the normal sampling distribution at the left shows the shaded area for the P-value.

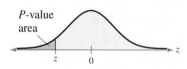

2. H_0: $\mu \geq 2.5$ gpm	The mean flow rate of a certain type of faucet is greater than or equal to 2.5 gallons per minute.
H_a: $\mu < 2.5$ gpm	The mean flow rate of a certain type of faucet is less than 2.5 gallons per minute.

Because H_a contains the $<$ symbol, the test is a left-tailed hypothesis test. The graph of the normal sampling distribution at the left shows the shaded area for the P-value.

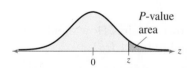

3. H_0: $\mu \leq 20$ oz	The mean weight of the contents of the cereal boxes is less than or equal to 20 ounces.
H_a: $\mu > 20$ oz	The mean weight of the contents of the cereal boxes is greater than 20 ounces.

Because H_a contains the $>$ symbol, the test is a right-tailed hypothesis test. The graph of the normal sampling distribution at the left shows the shaded area for the P-value.

Try It Yourself 3

For each claim, determine whether the hypothesis test is a left-, right-, or two-tailed test. Sketch a normal sampling distribution and shade the area for the P-value.

1. A consumer analyst reports that the mean life of a certain type of automobile battery is 74 months.
2. A radio station publicizes that its proportion of the local listening audience is greater than 39%.

a. *Write* H_0 and H_a.
b. *Determine* whether the test is left-tailed, right-tailed, or two-tailed.
c. *Sketch* the sampling distribution and shade the area for the P-value.

Answer: Page A43

▶ **Making a Decision and Interpreting the Decision**

To conclude a hypothesis test, you make a decision and interpret that decision. There are only two possible outcomes to a hypothesis test: (1) reject the null hypothesis, and (2) fail to reject the null hypothesis.

DECISION RULE BASED ON *P*-VALUE

To use a P-value to make a conclusion in a hypothesis test, compare the P-value with α.

1. If $P \leq \alpha$, then reject H_0.
2. If $P > \alpha$, then fail to reject H_0.

Failing to reject the null hypothesis does not mean that you have accepted the null hypothesis as true. It simply means that there is not enough evidence to reject the null hypothesis. If you want to support a claim, state it so that it becomes the alternative hypothesis. If you want to disprove a claim, state it so that it becomes the null hypothesis. The following table will help you interpret your decision.

Decision	Claim	
	Claim is H_0.	Claim is H_a.
Reject H_0.	There is enough evidence to reject the claim.	There is enough evidence to support the claim.
Fail to reject H_0.	There is not enough evidence to reject the claim.	There is not enough evidence to support the claim.

EXAMPLE 4

Interpreting a Decision

You perform a hypothesis test for each of the following claims. How should you interpret your decision if you reject H_0? If you fail to reject H_0?

1. H_0 (Claim): A university publicizes that the proportion of its students who graduate in 4 years is 82%.

2. H_a (Claim): *Consumer Reports* states that the mean stopping distance (on a dry surface) for a Honda Civic is less than 136 feet.

Solution

1. The claim is represented by H_0 so if you reject H_0, then you should conclude "there is sufficient evidence to indicate that the university's claim is false." If you fail to reject H_0, then you should conclude "there is insufficient evidence to indicate that the university's claim (of a four-year graduation rate of 82%) is false."

2. The claim is represented by H_a so the null hypothesis is "the mean stopping distance ... is greater than or equal to 136 feet." If you reject H_0, then you should conclude "there is enough evidence to support *Consumer Reports'* claim that the stopping distance for a Honda Civic is less than 136 feet." If you fail to reject H_0, then you should conclude "there is not enough evidence to support *Consumer Reports'* claim that the stopping distance for a Honda Civic is less than 136 feet."

▶ **Try It Yourself 4**

You perform a hypothesis test for the following claim. How should you interpret your decision if you reject H_0? If you fail to reject H_0?

  H_a (Claim): A radio station publicizes that its proportion of the local listening audience is greater than 39%.

a. Interpret your decision if you reject the null hypothesis.
b. Interpret your decision if you fail to reject the null hypothesis.

Answer: Page A43

The general steps for a hypothesis test are summarized below.

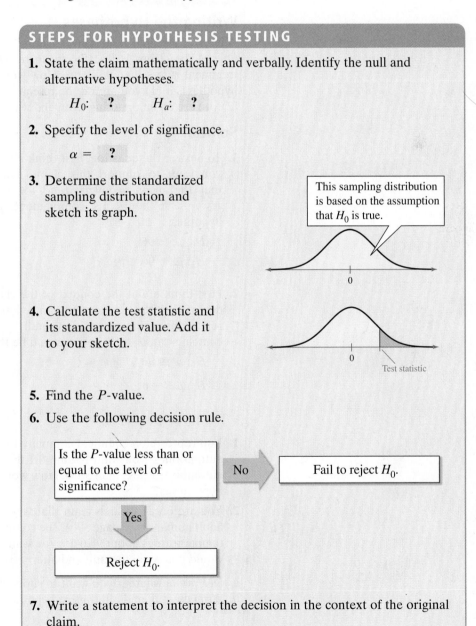

STEPS FOR HYPOTHESIS TESTING

1. State the claim mathematically and verbally. Identify the null and alternative hypotheses.

  H_0: **?** H_a: **?**

2. Specify the level of significance.

  $\alpha =$ **?**

3. Determine the standardized sampling distribution and sketch its graph.

> This sampling distribution is based on the assumption that H_0 is true.

0

4. Calculate the test statistic and its standardized value. Add it to your sketch.

0

Test statistic

5. Find the *P*-value.

6. Use the following decision rule.

Is the *P*-value less than or equal to the level of significance?

No → Fail to reject H_0.

Yes ↓

Reject H_0.

7. Write a statement to interpret the decision in the context of the original claim.

In the steps above, the graphs show a right-tailed test. However, the same basic steps also apply to left-tailed and two-tailed tests.

▶ Strategies for Hypothesis Testing

In a courtroom, the strategy used by an attorney depends on whether the attorney is representing the defense or the prosecution. In a similar way, the strategy that you will use in hypothesis testing should depend on whether you are trying to support or reject a claim. Remember that you cannot use a hypothesis test to support your claim if your claim is the null hypothesis. So, as a researcher, if you want a conclusion that supports your claim, word your claim so it is the alternative hypothesis. If you want to reject a claim, word it so it is the null hypothesis.

EXAMPLE 5

Writing the Hypotheses

A medical research team is investigating the benefits of a new surgical treatment. One of the claims is that the mean recovery time for patients after the new treatment is less than 96 hours. How would you write the null and alternative hypotheses if (1) you are on the research team and want to support the claim? (2) you are on an opposing team and want to reject the claim?

Solution

1. To answer the question, first think about the context of the claim. Because you want to support this claim, make the alternative hypothesis state that the mean recovery time for patients is less than 96 hours. So, $H_a: \mu < 96$ hours. Its complement, $\mu \geq 96$ hours, would be the null hypothesis.

   $H_0: \mu \geq 96$

   $H_a: \mu < 96$ (Claim)

2. First think about the context of the claim. As an opposing researcher, you do not want the recovery time to be less than 96 hours. Because you want to reject this claim, make it the null hypothesis. So, $H_0: \mu \leq 96$ hours. Its complement, $\mu > 96$ hours, would be the alternative hypothesis.

   $H_0: \mu \leq 96$ (Claim)

   $H_a: \mu > 96$

▶ Try It Yourself 5

1. You represent a chemical company that is being sued for paint damage to automobiles. You want to support the claim that the mean repair cost per automobile is less than $650. How would you write the null and alternative hypotheses?

2. You are on a research team that is investigating the mean temperature of adult humans (see page 396). The commonly accepted claim is that the mean temperature is about 98.6°F. You want to show that this claim is false. How would you write the null and alternative hypotheses?

   a. *Determine* whether you want to support or reject the claim.
   b. *Write* the null and alternative hypotheses. *Answer: Page A43*

7.1 EXERCISES

■ Building Basic Skills and Vocabulary

1. What are the two types of hypotheses used in a hypothesis test? How are they related?

2. Describe the two types of error possible in a hypothesis test decision.

True or False?   *In Exercises 3–8, determine whether the statement is true or false. If it is false, rewrite it as a true statement.*

3. In a hypothesis test, you assume the alternative hypothesis is true.

4. A statistical hypothesis is a statement about a sample.

5. If you decide to reject the null hypothesis, you can support the alternative hypothesis.

6. The level of significance is the maximum probability you allow for rejecting a null hypothesis when it is actually true.

7. A large *P*-value in a test will favor a rejection of the null hypothesis.

8. If you want to support a claim, write it as your null hypothesis.

Stating Hypotheses   *In Exercises 9–14, use the given statement to represent a claim. Write its complement and state which is H_0 and which is H_a.*

9. $\mu \leq 645$ **10.** $\mu < 128$

11. $\sigma \neq 5$ **12.** $\sigma^2 \geq 1.2$

13. $p < 0.45$ **14.** $p = 0.21$

Graphical Analysis   *In Exercises 15–18, match the alternative hypothesis with its graph. Then state the null hypothesis and sketch its graph.*

15. $H_a: \mu > 3$ (a)

16. $H_a: \mu < 3$ (b)

17. $H_a: \mu \neq 3$ (c)

18. $H_a: \mu > 2$ (d)

Identifying Tests   *In Exercises 19–22, determine whether the hypothesis test with the given null and alternative hypotheses is left-tailed, right-tailed, or two-tailed.*

19. $H_0: \mu \leq 8.0$
    $H_a: \mu > 8.0$

20. $H_0: \sigma \geq 5.2$
    $H_a: \sigma < 5.2$

21. $H_0: \sigma^2 = 142$
    $H_a: \sigma^2 \neq 142$

22. $H_0: p = 0.25$
    $H_a: p \neq 0.25$

■ **Using and Interpreting Concepts**

Stating the Hypotheses   *In Exercises 23–28, state the claim mathematically. Write the null and alternative hypotheses. Identify which is the claim.*

23. **Light Bulbs**   A light bulb manufacturer claims that the mean life of a certain type of light bulb is more than 750 hours.

24. **Shipping Errors**   As stated by a company's shipping department, the number of shipping errors per million shipments has a standard deviation that is less than 3.

25. **Base Price of an ATV**   The standard deviation of the base price of a certain type of all-terrain vehicle is no more than $320.

26. **College Students**   A research organization reports that 28% of the residents in Ann Arbor, Michigan are college students. *(Adapted from U.S. Census Bureau)*

27. **Seat Belts**   The results of a recent study show that the proportion of people in the United States who use seat belts when riding in a car or truck is 81%. *(Source: National Center for Statistics and Analysis)*

28. **Drying Time**   A company claims that its brands of paint have a mean drying time of less than 45 minutes.

Identifying Errors   *In Exercises 29–34, write sentences describing type I and type II errors for a hypothesis test of the indicated claim.*

29. **Repeat Buyers**   A furniture store claims that at least 60% of its new customers will return to buy their next piece of furniture.

30. **Literary Skills**   A study claims that the proportion of adults in the United States that are illiterate in English is 5%. *(Source: National Center for Education Statistics)*

31. **Chess**   A local chess club claims that the length of time to play a game has a standard deviation of more than 12 minutes.

32. **Diabetes Gene**   According to a recent study, 50% of all Americans carry a variant of a gene that increases the risk of diabetes. *(Adapted from American Journal of Clinical Nutrition)*

33. **Computers**   According to a recent survey, 88% of college students own a computer. *(Source: Harris Poll)*

34. **Satellite Television**   According to a recent study, 30% of U.S. households subscribe to satellite television. *(Source: J.D. Power and Associates)*

Identifying Tests   *In Exercises 35–40, determine whether the hypothesis test for each claim is left-tailed, right-tailed, or two-tailed. Explain your reasoning.*

35. **Security Alarms**   At least 14% of all homeowners have a home security alarm.

36. **Clocks**   A manufacturer of grandfather clocks claims that the mean time its clocks lose is no more than 0.02 second per day.

37. **Lung Cancer**   A government report claims that the proportion of lung cancer cases that are due to smoking is 87%. *(Source: LungCancer.org)*

38. **Tires**   The mean life of a certain tire is no less than 80,000 miles. *(Adapted from Goodyear)*

39. Return Rate A financial analyst claims that the return rate of a 15-year U.S. bond has a standard deviation of 5.3%.

40. Dreams A research institute claims that the mean length of most dreams is greater than 10 minutes. *(Adapted from The Lucidity Institute)*

Interpreting a Decision *In Exercises 41–46, consider each claim. If a hypothesis test is performed, how should you interpret a decision that*

(a) rejects the null hypothesis?

(b) fails to reject the null hypothesis?

41. Pictures Developed A film company claims that the mean number of pictures developed for a single-use camera with 24 exposures is more than 22.

42. Shipment Weights A government worker claims that the standard deviation of the mean weight of all U.S. Postal Service shipments is 0.40 pound.

43. Hourly Wages The U.S. Department of Labor claims that the proportion of hourly workers earning over $11.55 per hour is greater than 75%. *(Adapted from U.S. Bureau of Labor Statistics)*

44. Gas Mileage An automotive manufacturer claims the standard deviation for the gas mileage of its models is 3.9 miles per gallon.

45. SUV Prices An automotive manufacturer claims the mean price of a small SUV is less than $26,860. *(Adapted from Consumer Reports)*

46. Calories A sports drink maker claims the mean calorie content of its beverages is 72 calories per serving.

47. Writing Hypotheses: Medicine Your medical research team is investigating the mean cost of a 30-day supply of a certain heart medication. A pharmaceutical company thinks that the mean cost is less than $60. You want to support this claim. How would you write the null and alternative hypotheses?

48. Writing Hypotheses: Taxicab Company A taxicab company claims that the mean travel time between two destinations is about 21 minutes. You work for the bus company and want to reject this claim. How would you write the null and alternative hypotheses?

49. Writing Hypotheses: Refrigerator Manufacturer A refrigerator manufacturer claims that the mean life of its competitor's refrigerators is less than 15 years. You are asked to perform a hypothesis test to test this claim. How would you write the null and alternative hypotheses if

(a) you represent the manufacturer and want to support the claim?

(b) you represent the competitor and want to reject the claim?

50. Writing Hypotheses: Internet Provider An Internet provider is trying to gain advertising deals and claims that the mean time a customer spends online per day is greater than 28 minutes. You are asked to test this claim. How would you write the null and alternative hypotheses if

(a) you represent the Internet provider and want to support the claim?

(b) you represent a competing advertiser and want to reject the claim?

■ Extending Concepts

51. Getting at the Concept   Why can decreasing the probability of a type I error cause an increase in the probability of a type II error?

52. Getting at the Concept   Why not use a level of significance of $\alpha = 0$?

Graphical Analysis   *In Exercises 53–56, you are given a null hypothesis and three confidence intervals that represent three samplings. Decide whether each confidence interval indicates that you should reject H_0. Explain your reasoning.*

53. H_0: $\mu \geq 70$

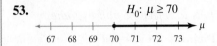

(a) $67 < \mu < 71$

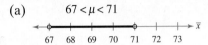

(b) $67 < \mu < 69$

(c) $69.5 < \mu < 72.5$

54. H_0: $\mu \leq 54$

(a) $53.5 < \mu < 56.5$

(b) $51.5 < \mu < 54.5$

(c) $54.5 < \mu < 55.5$

55. H_0: $p \leq 0.20$

(a) $0.21 < p < 0.23$

(b) $0.19 < p < 0.23$

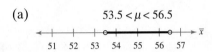

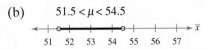

(c) $0.175 < p < 0.205$

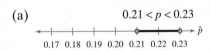

56. H_0: $p \geq 0.73$

(a) $0.73 < p < 0.75$

(b) $0.715 < p < 0.725$

(c) $0.695 < p < 0.745$

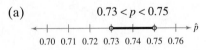

7.2 Hypothesis Testing for the Mean (Large Samples)

What You SHOULD LEARN

▸ How to find *P*-values and use them to test a mean μ

▸ How to use *P*-values for a *z*-test

▸ How to find critical values and rejection regions in a normal distribution

▸ How to use rejection regions for a *z*-test

Using *P*-values to Make Decisions ▸ Using *P*-values for a *z*-Test ▸ Rejection Regions and Critical Values ▸ Using Rejection Regions for a *z*-Test

▸ Using *P*-values to Make Decisions

In Chapter 5, you learned that when the sample size is at least 30, the sampling distribution for $\bar{x}$ (the sample mean) is normal. In Section 7.1, you learned that a way to reach a conclusion in a hypothesis test is to use a *P*-value for the sample statistic, such as $\bar{x}$. Recall that when you assume the null hypothesis is true, a *P*-value (or probability value) of a hypothesis test is the probability of obtaining a sample statistic with a value as extreme or more extreme than the one determined from the sample data. The decision rule for a hypothesis test based on a *P*-value is as follows.

DECISION RULE BASED ON *P*-VALUE

To use a *P*-value to make a conclusion in a hypothesis test, compare the *P*-value with α.

1. If $P \leq \alpha$, then reject H_0.
2. If $P > \alpha$, then fail to reject H_0.

EXAMPLE 1

Interpreting a *P*-value

The *P*-value for a hypothesis test is $P = 0.0237$. What is your decision if the level of significance is (1) $\alpha = 0.05$ and (2) $\alpha = 0.01$?

Solution

1. Because $0.0237 < 0.05$, you should reject the null hypothesis.
2. Because $0.0237 > 0.01$, you should fail to reject the null hypothesis.

▸ Try It Yourself 1

The *P*-value for a hypothesis test is $P = 0.0347$. What is your decision if the level of significance is (1) $\alpha = 0.01$ and (2) $\alpha = 0.05$?

a. *Compare* the *P*-value with the level of significance.
b. *Make* your decision. *Answer: Page A43*

Insight

The lower the *P*-value, the more evidence there is in favor of rejecting H_0. The *P*-value gives you the lowest level of significance for which the sample statistic allows you to reject the null hypothesis. In Example 1, you would reject H_0 at any level of significance greater than or equal to 0.0237.

FINDING THE *P*-VALUE FOR A HYPOTHESIS TEST

After determining the hypothesis test's standardized test statistic and the test statistic's corresponding area, do one of the following to find the *P*-value.

a. For a left-tailed test, $P = $ (Area in left tail).
b. For a right-tailed test, $P = $ (Area in right tail).
c. For a two-tailed test, $P = 2$(Area in tail of test statistic).

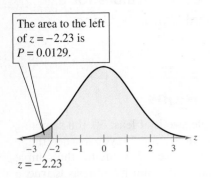

The area to the left of $z = -2.23$ is $P = 0.0129$.

$z = -2.23$

Left-Tailed Test

Finding a *P*-value for a Left-Tailed Test

Find the *P*-value for a left-tailed hypothesis test with a test statistic of $z = -2.23$. Decide whether to reject H_0 if the level of significance is $\alpha = 0.01$.

Solution

The graph shows a standard normal curve with a shaded area to the left of $z = -2.23$. For a left-tailed test,

$$P = (\text{Area in left tail}).$$

From Table 4 in Appendix B, the area corresponding to $z = -2.23$ is 0.0129, which is the area in the left tail. So, the *P*-value for a left-tailed hypothesis test with a test statistic of $z = -2.23$ is $P = 0.0129$.

Interpretation   Because the *P*-value of 0.0129 is greater than 0.01, you should fail to reject H_0.

▶ Try It Yourself 2

Find the *P*-value for a left-tailed hypothesis test with a test statistic of $z = -1.62$. Decide whether to reject H_0 if the level of significance is $\alpha = 0.05$.

a. *Use* Table 4 in Appendix B to locate the area that corresponds to $z = -1.62$.
b. *Calculate* the *P*-value for a left-tailed test, the area in the left tail.
c. *Compare* the *P*-value with α and *decide* whether to reject H_0.

Answer: Page A43

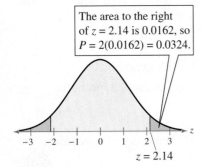

The area to the right of $z = 2.14$ is 0.0162, so $P = 2(0.0162) = 0.0324$.

$z = 2.14$

Two-Tailed Test

Finding a *P*-value for a Two-Tailed Test

Find the *P*-value for a two-tailed hypothesis test with a test statistic of $z = 2.14$. Decide whether to reject H_0 if the level of significance is $\alpha = 0.05$.

Solution

The graph shows a standard normal curve with shaded areas to the left of $z = -2.14$ and to the right of $z = 2.14$. For a two-tailed test,

$$P = 2(\text{Area in tail of test statistic}).$$

From Table 4, the area corresponding to $z = 2.14$ is 0.9838. The area in the right tail is $1 - 0.9838 = 0.0162$. So, the *P*-value for a two-tailed hypothesis test with a test statistic of $z = 2.14$ is $P = 2(0.0162) = 0.0324$.

Interpretation   Because the *P*-value of 0.0324 is less than 0.05, you should reject H_0.

▶ Try It Yourself 3

Find the *P*-value for a two-tailed hypothesis test with a test statistic of $z = 2.31$. Decide whether to reject H_0 if the level of significance is $\alpha = 0.01$.

a. *Use* Table 4 to locate the area that corresponds to $z = 2.31$.
b. *Calculate* the *P*-value for a two-tailed test, twice the area in the tail of the test statistic.
c. *Compare* the *P*-value with α and *decide* whether to reject H_0.

Answer: Page A43

▸ Using *P*-values for a *z*-Test

The *z*-test for the mean is used in populations for which the sampling distribution of sample means is normal. To use the *z*-test, you need to find the standardized value for your test statistic $\bar{x}$.

$$z = \frac{(\text{Sample mean}) - (\text{Hypothesized mean})}{\text{Standard error}}$$

Study Tip

With all hypothesis tests, it is helpful to sketch the sampling distribution. Your sketch should include the standardized test statistic.

z-TEST FOR A MEAN μ

The **z-test for a mean** is a statistical test for a population mean. The *z*-test can be used when the population is normal and σ is known, or for any population when the sample size *n* is at least 30. The **test statistic** is the sample mean $\bar{x}$ and the **standardized test statistic** is *z*.

$$z = \frac{\bar{x} - \mu}{\sigma/\sqrt{n}}$$

Recall that $\dfrac{\sigma}{\sqrt{n}}$ = standard error = $\sigma_{\bar{x}}$.

When $n \geq 30$, you can use the sample standard deviation *s* in place of σ.

Insight

When the sample size is at least 30, you know the following about the sampling distribution of sample means.

(1) The shape is normal.

(2) The mean is the hypothesized mean.

(3) The standard error is $s/\sqrt{n}$, where *s* can be used in place of σ.

GUIDELINES

Using *P*-values for a *z*-Test for Mean μ

In Words	*In Symbols*
1. State the claim mathematically and verbally. Identify the null and alternative hypotheses.	State H_0 and H_a.
2. Specify the level of significance.	Identify α.
3. Determine the standardized test statistic.	$z = \dfrac{\bar{x} - \mu}{\sigma/\sqrt{n}}$ or if $n \geq 30$, use $\sigma \approx s$.
4. Find the area that corresponds to *z*.	Use Table 4 in Appendix B.
5. Find the *P*-value. **a.** For a left-tailed test, *P* = (Area in left tail). **b.** For a right-tailed test, *P* = (Area in right tail). **c.** For a two-tailed test, *P* = 2(Area in tail of test statistic).	
6. Make a decision to reject or fail to reject the null hypothesis.	Reject H_0 if *P*-value is less than or equal to α. Otherwise, fail to reject H_0.
7. Interpret the decision in the context of the original claim.	

EXAMPLE 4

Hypothesis Testing Using *P*-values

In an advertisement, a pizza shop claims that its mean delivery time is less than 30 minutes. A random selection of 36 delivery times has a sample mean of 28.5 minutes and a standard deviation of 3.5 minutes. Is there enough evidence to support the claim at $\alpha = 0.01$? Use a *P*-value.

Solution   The claim is "the mean delivery time is less than 30 minutes." So, the null and alternative hypotheses are

$$H_0: \mu \geq 30 \text{ minutes} \quad \text{and} \quad H_a: \mu < 30 \text{ minutes.} \text{ (Claim)}$$

The level of significance is $\alpha = 0.01$. The standardized test statistic is

$$z = \frac{\bar{x} - \mu}{\sigma/\sqrt{n}}$$ Because $n \geq 30$, use the *z*-test.

$$= \frac{28.5 - 30}{3.5/\sqrt{36}}$$ Because $n \geq 30$, use $\sigma \approx s = 3.5$. Assume $\mu = 30$.

$$\approx -2.57.$$

In Table 4 of Appendix B, the area corresponding to $z = -2.57$ is 0.0051. Because this test is a left-tailed test, the *P*-value is equal to the area to the left of $z = -2.57$. So, $P = 0.0051$. Because the *P*-value is less than $\alpha = 0.01$, you should decide to reject the null hypothesis.

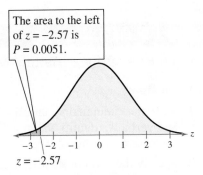

The area to the left of $z = -2.57$ is $P = 0.0051$.

$z = -2.57$

Left-Tailed Test

Interpretation   At the 1% level of significance, you have sufficient evidence to conclude that the mean delivery time is less than 30 minutes.

▶ Try It Yourself 4

Homeowners claim that the mean speed of automobiles traveling on their street is greater than the speed limit of 35 miles per hour. A random sample of 100 automobiles has a mean speed of 36 miles per hour and a standard deviation of 4 miles per hour. Is there enough evidence to support the claim at $\alpha = 0.05$? Use a *P*-value.

a. *Identify* the claim. Then *state* the null and alternative hypotheses.
b. *Identify* the level of significance.
c. *Find* the standardized test statistic *z*.
d. *Find* the *P*-value.
e. *Decide* whether to reject the null hypothesis.
f. *Interpret* the decision in the context of the original claim.   *Answer: Page A43*

EXAMPLE 5

Hypothesis Testing Using *P*-values

See MINITAB steps on page 434.

You think that the average franchise investment information shown in the graph is incorrect, so you randomly select 30 franchises and determine the necessary investment for each. The sample mean investment is $135,000 with a standard deviation of $30,000. Is there enough evidence to support your claim at $\alpha = 0.05$? Use a *P*-value.

Franchise Investment

Average investment is $143,260.

Solution   The claim is "the mean is different from $143,260." So, the null and alternative hypotheses are

$$H_0: \mu = \$143,260 \quad \text{and} \quad H_a: \mu \neq \$143,260. \text{ (Claim)}$$

The level of significance is $\alpha = 0.05$. The standardized test statistic is

$$z = \frac{\bar{x} - \mu}{\sigma/\sqrt{n}}$$

Because $n \geq 30$, use the *z*-test.

$$= \frac{135,000 - 143,260}{30,000/\sqrt{30}}$$

Because $n \geq 30$, use $\sigma \approx s = 30,000$.
Assume $\mu = 143,260$.

$$\approx -1.51.$$

In Table 4, the area corresponding to $z = -1.51$ is 0.0655. Because the test is a two-tailed test, the *P*-value is equal to twice the area to the left of $z = -1.51$. So,

$$P = 2(0.0655) = 0.1310.$$

Because the *P*-value is greater than α, you should fail to reject the null hypothesis.

Interpretation   There is not enough evidence at the 5% level of significance to conclude that the mean franchise investment is different from $143,260.

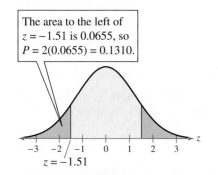

The area to the left of $z = -1.51$ is 0.0655, so $P = 2(0.0655) = 0.1310$.

$z = -1.51$

Two-Tailed Test

▶ Try It Yourself 5

One of your distributors reports an average of 150 sales per day for the distributorship. You suspect that this average is not accurate, so you randomly select 35 days and determine the number of sales each day. The sample mean is 143 daily sales with a standard deviation of 15 sales. At $\alpha = 0.01$, is there enough evidence to doubt the distributor's reported average? Use a *P*-value.

a. *Identify* the claim. Then *state* the null and alternative hypotheses.
b. *Identify* the level of significance.
c. *Find* the standardized test statistic *z*.
d. *Find* the *P*-value.
e. *Decide* whether to reject the null hypothesis.
f. *Interpret* the decision in the context of the original claim.

Answer: Page A43

EXAMPLE 6

Using a Technology Tool to Find a *P*-value

What decision should you make for the following TI-83/84 displays, using a level of significance of $\alpha = 0.05$?

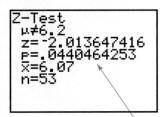

TI-83/84

```
Z-Test
 Inpt:Data Stats
 μ0:6.2
 σ:.47
 x̄:6.07
 n:53
 μ:≠μ0 <μ0 >μ0
Calculate Draw
```

TI-83/84

```
Z-Test
 μ≠6.2
 z=-2.013647416
 p=.0440464253
 x̄=6.07
 n=53
```

Solution The *P*-value for this test is given as 0.0440464253. Because the *P*-value is less than 0.05, you should reject the null hypothesis.

▶ **Try It Yourself 6**

For the TI-83/84 hypothesis test shown in Example 6, make a decision at the $\alpha = 0.01$ level of significance.

a. *Compare* the *P*-value with the level of significance.
b. *Make* your decision.

Answer: Page A43

▶ Rejection Regions and Critical Values

Another method to decide whether to reject the null hypothesis is to determine whether the standardized test statistic falls within a range of values called the rejection region of the sampling distribution.

DEFINITION

A **rejection region** (or **critical region**) of the sampling distribution is the range of values for which the null hypothesis is not probable. If a test statistic falls in this region, the null hypothesis is rejected. A **critical value** z_0 separates the rejection region from the nonrejection region.

GUIDELINES

Finding Critical Values in a Normal Distribution
1. Specify the level of significance α.
2. Decide whether the test is left-tailed, right-tailed, or two-tailed.
3. Find the critical value(s) z_0. If the hypothesis test is
    a. *left-tailed*, find the *z*-score that corresponds to an area of α.
    b. *right-tailed*, find the *z*-score that corresponds to an area of $1 - \alpha$.
    c. *two-tailed*, find the *z*-scores that correspond to $\frac{1}{2}\alpha$ and $1 - \frac{1}{2}\alpha$.
4. Sketch the standard normal distribution. Draw a vertical line at each critical value and shade the rejection region(s).

EXAMPLE 7

Finding a Critical Value for a Left-Tailed Test

Find the critical value and rejection region for a left-tailed test with $\alpha = 0.01$.

Solution   The graph at the right shows a standard normal curve with a shaded area of 0.01 in the left tail. In Table 4, the z-score that corresponds to an area of 0.01 is -2.33. So, the critical value is $z_0 = -2.33$. The rejection region is to the left of this critical value.

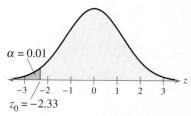

1% Level of Significance

▶ **Try It Yourself 7**

Find the critical value and rejection region for a left-tailed test with $\alpha = 0.10$.

a. *Draw* a graph of the standard normal curve with an area of α in the left tail.
b. *Use* Table 4 to locate the area that is closest to α.
c. *Find* the z-score that corresponds to this area.
d. *Identify* the rejection region.

Answer: Page A43

If you cannot find the exact area in Table 4, use the area that is closest. For instance, in Example 7, the area closest to 0.01 is 0.0099. When the area is exactly midway between two areas in the table, use the z-score midway between the corresponding z-scores.

EXAMPLE 8

Finding Critical Values for a Two-Tailed Test

Find the critical values and rejection regions for a two-tailed test with $\alpha = 0.05$.

Solution   The graph at the right shows a standard normal curve with shaded areas of $\frac{1}{2}\alpha = 0.025$ in each tail. The area to the left of $-z_0$ is $\frac{1}{2}\alpha = 0.025$, and the area to the left of z_0 is $1 - \frac{1}{2}\alpha = 0.975$. In Table 4, the z-scores that correspond to the areas 0.025 and 0.975 are -1.96 and 1.96, respectively. So, the critical values are $-z_0 = -1.96$ and $z_0 = 1.96$. The rejection regions are to the left of $-z_0$ and to the right of z_0.

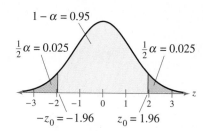

5% Level of Significance

▶ **Try It Yourself 8**

Find the critical values and rejection regions for a two-tailed test with $\alpha = 0.08$.

a. *Draw* a graph of the standard normal curve with an area of $\frac{1}{2}\alpha$ in each tail.

b. *Use* Table 4 to locate the areas that are closest to $\frac{1}{2}\alpha$ and $1 - \frac{1}{2}\alpha$.
c. *Find* the z-scores that correspond to these areas.
d. *Identify* the rejection regions.

Answer: Page A43

▶ Using Rejection Regions for a *z*-Test

To conclude a hypothesis test using rejection region(s), you make a decision and interpret the decision as follows.

DECISION RULE BASED ON REJECTION REGION

To use a rejection region to conduct a hypothesis test, calculate the standardized test statistic z. If the standardized test statistic

1. is in the rejection region, then reject H_0.
2. is *not* in the rejection region, then fail to reject H_0.

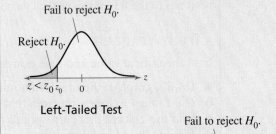

Left-Tailed Test

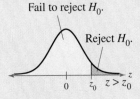

Right-Tailed Test

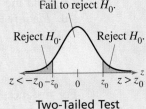

Two-Tailed Test

Failing to reject the null hypothesis does not mean that you have accepted the null hypothesis as true. It simply means that there is not enough evidence to reject the null hypothesis.

GUIDELINES

Using Rejection Regions for a *z*-Test for a Mean μ

In Words	*In Symbols*
1. State the claim mathematically and verbally. Identify the null and alternative hypotheses.	State H_0 and H_a.
2. Specify the level of significance.	Identify α.
3. Sketch the sampling distribution.	
4. Determine the critical value(s).	Use Table 4 in Appendix B.
5. Determine the rejection region(s).	
6. Find the standardized test statistic.	$z = \dfrac{\overline{x} - \mu}{\sigma/\sqrt{n}}$, or if $n \geq 30$ use $\sigma \approx s$.
7. Make a decision to reject or fail to reject the null hypothesis.	If z is in the rejection region, reject H_0. Otherwise, fail to reject H_0.
8. Interpret the decision in the context of the original claim.	

EXAMPLE 9

Testing μ with a Large Sample

See TI-83/84 steps on page 435.

Employees in a large accounting firm claim that the mean salary of the firm's accountants is less than that of its competitor's, which is \$45,000. A random sample of 30 of the firm's accountants has a mean salary of \$43,500 with a standard deviation of \$5200. At $\alpha = 0.05$, test the employees' claim.

Solution   The claim is "the mean salary is less than \$45,000." So, the null and alternative hypotheses can be written as

$$H_0: \mu \geq \$45,000 \quad \text{and} \quad H_a: \mu < \$45,000. \text{ (Claim)}$$

Because the test is a left-tailed test and the level of significance is $\alpha = 0.05$, the critical value is $z_0 = -1.645$ and the rejection region is $z < -1.645$. The standardized test statistic is

$$z = \frac{\bar{x} - \mu}{\sigma/\sqrt{n}} \qquad \text{Because } n \geq 30, \text{ use the } z\text{-test.}$$

$$= \frac{43,500 - 45,000}{5200/\sqrt{30}} \qquad \begin{array}{l}\text{Because } n \geq 30, \text{ use } \sigma \approx s = 5200. \\ \text{Assume } \mu = 45,000.\end{array}$$

$$\approx -1.58.$$

The graph shows the location of the rejection region and the standardized test statistic z. Because z is not in the rejection region, you fail to reject the null hypothesis.

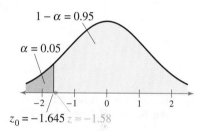

5% Level of Significance

Interpretation   There is not enough evidence at the 5% level of significance to support the employees' claim that the mean salary is less than \$45,000.

Be sure you understand the decision made in this example. Even though your sample has a mean of \$43,500, you cannot (at a 5% level of significance) support the claim that the mean of all the accountants' salaries is less than \$45,000. The difference between your test statistic and the hypothesized mean is probably due to sampling error.

▶ Try It Yourself 9

The CEO of the firm claims that the mean work day of the firm's accountants is less than 8.5 hours. A random sample of 35 of the firm's accountants has a mean work day of 8.2 hours with a standard deviation of 0.5 hour. At $\alpha = 0.01$, test the CEO's claim.

a. *Identify* the claim and state H_0 and H_a.
b. *Identify* the level of significance α.
c. *Find* the critical value z_0 and identify the rejection region.
d. *Find* the standardized test statistic z.
e. *Sketch* a graph. *Decide* whether to reject the null hypothesis.
f. *Interpret* the decision in the context of the original claim.

Answer: Page A43

PICTURING the WORLD

Each year, the Environmental Protection Agency (EPA) publishes reports of gas mileage for all makes and models of passenger vehicles. In a recent year, the compact car with an automatic transmission that posted the best mileage was the Honda Civic Hybrid. It had a mean mileage of 49 miles per gallon (city) and 51 miles per gallon (highway). Suppose that Honda believes a Civic Hybrid exceeds 51 miles per gallon on the highway. To support its claim, it tests 34 cars on highway driving and obtains a sample mean of 52.1 miles per gallon with a standard deviation of 2.3 miles per gallon. (Source: EPA)

Is the evidence strong enough to support the claim that the Civic's highway miles per gallon exceeds the EPA estimate? Use a z-test with $\alpha = 0.01$.

EXAMPLE 10

Testing μ with a Large Sample

The U.S. Department of Agriculture reports that the mean cost of raising a child from birth to age 2 in a rural area is $10,460. You believe this value is incorrect, so you select a random sample of 900 children (age 2) and find that the mean cost is $10,345 with a standard deviation of $1540. At $\alpha = 0.05$, is there enough evidence to conclude that the mean cost is different from $10,460? *(Adapted from U.S. Department of Agriculture Center for Nutrition Policy and Promotion)*

Solution You want to support the claim that "the mean cost is different from $10,460." So, the null and alternative hypotheses are

$$H_0: \mu = \$10,460$$

and

$$H_a: \mu \neq \$10,460. \text{ (Claim)}$$

Because the test is a two-tailed test and the level of significance is $\alpha = 0.05$, the critical values are $-z_0 = -1.96$ and $z_0 = 1.96$. The rejection regions are $z < -1.96$ and $z > 1.96$. The standardized test statistic is

$$z = \frac{\overline{x} - \mu}{\sigma/\sqrt{n}} \qquad \text{Because } n \geq 30, \text{ use the } z\text{-test.}$$

$$= \frac{10,345 - 10,460}{1540/\sqrt{900}} \qquad \begin{array}{l} \text{Because } n \geq 30, \text{ use } \sigma \approx s = 1540. \\ \text{Assume } \mu = \$10,460. \end{array}$$

$$\approx -2.24.$$

The graph shows the location of the rejection regions and the standardized test statistic z. Because z is in the rejection region, you should reject the null hypothesis.

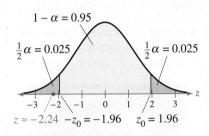

5% Level of Significance

Interpretation You have enough evidence to conclude that the mean cost of raising a child from birth to age 2 in a rural area is significantly different from $10,460 at the 5% level of significance.

▶ Try It Yourself 10

Using the information and results of Example 10, determine whether there is enough evidence to support the claim that the mean cost of raising a child from birth to age 2 in a rural area is different from $10,460. Use $\alpha = 0.01$.

a. *Identify* the level of significance α.
b. *Find* the critical values $\pm z_0$ and identify the rejection regions.
c. Sketch a graph. *Decide* whether to reject the null hypothesis.
d. *Interpret* the decision in the context of the original claim.

Answer: Page A43

Z-Test
$\mu \neq 10460$
$z=-2.24025974$
$P=.025073983$
$\overline{x}=10345$
$n=900$

Using a TI-83/84, you can find the standardized test statistic automatically.

To explore this topic further, see Activity 7.2 on page 395.

7.2 EXERCISES

■ Building Basic Skills and Vocabulary

In Exercises 1–6, find the P-value for the indicated hypothesis test with the given standardized test statistic z. Decide whether to reject H_0 for the given level of significance α.

1. Left-tailed test, $z = -1.20$,
   $\alpha = 0.10$

2. Left-tailed test, $z = -1.69$,
   $\alpha = 0.05$

3. Right-tailed test, $z = 2.34$,
   $\alpha = 0.01$

4. Right-tailed test, $z = 1.23$,
   $\alpha = 0.10$

5. Two-tailed test, $z = -1.56$,
   $\alpha = 0.05$

6. Two-tailed test, $z = 2.30$,
   $\alpha = 0.01$

Graphical Analysis   *In Exercises 7–12, match each P-value with the graph that displays its area. The graphs are labeled (a)–(f).*

7. $P = 0.0089$

8. $P = 0.0132$

9. $P = 0.3050$

10. $P = 0.0688$

11. $P = 0.0233$

12. $P = 0.0287$

(a)
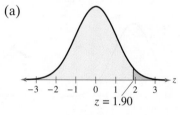
$z = 1.90$

(b)
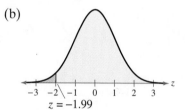
$z = -1.99$

(c)
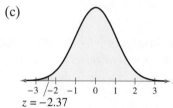
$z = -2.37$

(d)
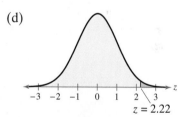
$z = 2.22$

(e)
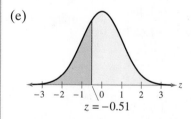
$z = -0.51$

(f)
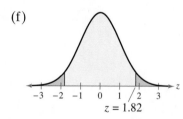
$z = 1.82$

13. Given $H_0: \mu = 100$, $H_a: \mu \neq 100$, and $P = 0.0461$.

   (a) Do you reject or fail to reject H_0 at the 0.01 level of significance?

   (b) Do you reject or fail to reject H_0 at the 0.05 level of significance?

14. Given $H_0: \mu \geq 8.5$, $H_a: \mu < 8.5$, and $P = 0.0691$.

    (a) Do you reject or fail to reject H_0 at the 0.01 level of significance?

    (b) Do you reject or fail to reject H_0 at the 0.05 level of significance?

Finding Critical Values *In Exercises 15–20, find the critical value(s) for the indicated type of test and level of significance* α.

15. Right-tailed test, $\alpha = 0.05$ **16.** Right-tailed test, $\alpha = 0.08$

17. Left-tailed test, $\alpha = 0.03$ **18.** Left-tailed test, $\alpha = 0.09$

19. Two-tailed test, $\alpha = 0.02$ **20.** Two-tailed test, $\alpha = 0.10$

Graphical Analysis *In Exercises 21–24,*

(a) state whether the graph shows a left-tailed, right-tailed, or two-tailed test.

(b) state whether $\alpha = 0.01$, 0.05, *or* 0.10.

21.

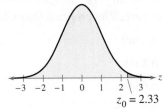

22.

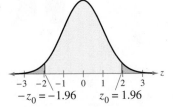

23.

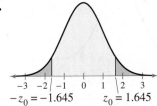

24.

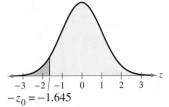

Graphical Analysis *In Exercises 25–28, state whether each standardized test statistic z allows you to reject the null hypothesis. Explain your reasoning.*

25. (a) $z = 1.631$

    (b) $z = 1.723$

    (c) $z = -1.464$

    (d) $z = -1.655$

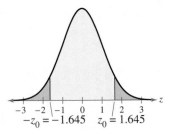

26. (a) $z = 1.98$

    (b) $z = -1.89$

    (c) $z = 1.65$

    (d) $z = -1.99$

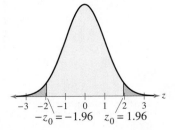

27. (a) $z = -1.301$

(b) $z = 1.203$

(c) $z = 1.280$

(d) $z = 1.286$

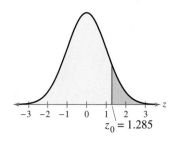

28. (a) $z = 2.557$

(b) $z = -2.755$

(c) $z = 2.585$

(d) $z = -2.475$

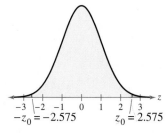

In Exercises 29–32, test the claim about the population mean μ at the given level of significance using the given sample statistics.

29. Claim: $\mu = 40$; $\alpha = 0.05$. Sample statistics: $\bar{x} = 39.2$, $s = 3.23$, $n = 75$

30. Claim: $\mu > 1030$; $\alpha = 0.05$. Sample statistics: $\bar{x} = 1035$, $s = 23$, $n = 50$

31. Claim: $\mu \neq 6000$; $\alpha = 0.01$. Sample statistics: $\bar{x} = 5800$, $s = 350$, $n = 35$

32. Claim: $\mu \leq 22{,}500$; $\alpha = 0.01$. Sample statistics: $\bar{x} = 23{,}250$, $s = 1200$, $n = 45$

■ Using and Interpreting Concepts

Testing Claims Using *P*-values   *In Exercises 33–38,*

(a) write the claim mathematically and identify H_0 and H_a.

(b) find the standardized test statistic z and its corresponding area. If convenient, use technology.

(c) find the P-value. If convenient, use technology.

(d) decide whether to reject or fail to reject the null hypothesis.

(e) interpret the decision in the context of the original claim.

33. Mathematics Assessment Tests   In Illinois, a random sample of 85 eighth grade students has a mean score of 282 with a standard deviation of 35 on a national mathematics assessment test. This test result prompts a state school administrator to declare that the mean score for the state's eighth graders on the examination is more than 275. At $\alpha = 0.04$, is there enough evidence to support the administrator's claim? *(Adapted from National Center for Education Statistics)*

34. Sprinkler System   A manufacturer of sprinkler systems designed for fire protection claims that the average activating temperature is at least 135°F. To test this claim, you randomly select a sample of 32 systems and find the mean activation temperature to be 133°F with a standard deviation of 3.3°F. At $\alpha = 0.10$, do you have enough evidence to support the manufacturer's claim?

35. Tea Drinkers A tea drinker's society estimates that the mean consumption of tea by a person in the United States is more than 8 gallons per year. In a random sample of 100 people, you find that the mean consumption of tea is 7.9 gallons per year with a standard deviation of 2.67 gallons. At $\alpha = 0.07$, can you support the society's claim? *(Adapted from U.S. Department of Agriculture)*

36. Tuna Consumption A nutritionist claims that the mean tuna consumption by a person in the United States is 3.1 pounds per year. A random sample of 60 people in the United States shows that the mean tuna consumption by a person is 2.9 pounds per year with a standard deviation of 0.94 pound. At $\alpha = 0.08$, can you reject the nutritionist's claim? *(Adapted from U.S. Department of Agriculture)*

37. Quitting Smoking The number of years it took a random sample of 32 former smokers to quit smoking permanently is listed. At $\alpha = 0.05$, is there enough evidence to reject the claim that the mean time it takes smokers to quit smoking permanently is 15 years? *(Adapted from The Gallup Organization)*

15.7 13.2 22.6 13.0 10.7 18.1 14.7   7.0 17.3   7.5 21.8
12.3 19.8 13.8 16.0 15.5 13.1 20.7 15.5   9.8 11.9 16.9
 7.0 19.3 13.2 14.6 20.9 15.4 13.3 11.6 10.9 21.6

38. Salaries An Alabama politician claims that the mean annual salary for engineering managers in Alabama is more than the national mean, $100,800. The annual salaries (in dollars) for a random sample of 34 engineering managers in Alabama are listed. At $\alpha = 0.03$, is there enough evidence to support the politician's claim? *(Adapted from America's Career InfoNet)*

92,860	94,975	88,714	82,917	98,117	102,415
96,216	98,234	86,719	79,821	94,556	97,612
99,963	101,415	89,714	90,648	96,159	99,176
101,519	94,161	97,178	98,736	100,317	94,932
89,714	93,198	95,117	97,482	99,632	100,589
93,613	92,144	91,716	96,031		

Testing Claims *In Exercises 39–46, (a) write the claim mathematically and identify H_0 and H_a, (b) find the critical values and identify the rejection regions, (c) find the standardized test statistic, (d) decide whether to reject or fail to reject the null hypothesis, and (e) interpret the decision in the context of the original claim.*

39. Caffeine Content in Colas A company that makes cola drinks states that the mean caffeine content per one 12-ounce bottle of cola is 40 milligrams. You want to test this claim. During your tests, you find that a random sample of thirty 12-ounce bottles of cola has a mean caffeine content of 39.2 milligrams with a standard deviation of 7.5 milligrams. At $\alpha = 0.01$, can you reject the company's claim? *(Adapted from American Beverage Association)*

40. Caffeine Content in Coffee A coffee shop claims that its fresh-brewed drinks have a mean caffeine content of 140 milligrams per 8 ounces. You want to test this claim. You find that a random sample of 42 eight-ounce servings has a mean caffeine content of 146 milligrams and a standard deviation of 22 milligrams. At $\alpha = 0.05$, do you have enough evidence to reject the shop's claim? *(Adapted from American Beverage Association)*

41. Light Bulbs   A light bulb manufacturer guarantees that the mean life of a certain type of light bulb is at least 750 hours. A random sample of 36 light bulbs has a mean life of 745 hours with a standard deviation of 60 hours. At $\alpha = 0.02$, do you have enough evidence to reject the manufacturer's claim?

42. Sodium Content in Cereal   In your work for a national health organization, you are asked to monitor the amount of sodium in a certain brand of cereal. You find that a random sample of 52 cereal servings has a mean sodium content of 232 milligrams with a standard deviation of 10 milligrams. At $\alpha = 0.04$, can you conclude that the mean sodium content per serving of cereal is greater than 230 milligrams?

43. Nitrogen Dioxide Levels   A scientist estimates that the mean nitrogen dioxide level in Calgary is greater than 32 parts per billion. You want to test this estimate. To do so, you determine the nitrogen dioxide levels for 34 randomly selected days. The results (in parts per billion) are listed below. At $\alpha = 0.06$, can you support the scientist's estimate? *(Adapted from Clean Air Strategic Alliance)*

24	36	44	35	44	34	29	40	39	43	41	32
33	29	29	43	25	39	25	42	29	22	22	25
14	15	14	29	25	27	22	24	18	17

44. Fluorescent Lamps   A fluorescent lamp manufacturer guarantees that the mean life of a certain type of lamp is at least 10,000 hours. You want to test this guarantee. To do so, you record the life of a random sample of 32 fluorescent lamps. The results (in hours) are shown below. At $\alpha = 0.09$, do you have enough evidence to reject the manufacturer's claim?

8,800	9,155	13,001	10,250	10,002	11,413	8,234	10,402
10,016	8,015	6,110	11,005	11,555	9,254	6,991	12,006
10,420	8,302	8,151	10,980	10,186	10,003	8,814	11,445
6,277	8,632	7,265	10,584	9,397	11,987	7,556	10,380

45. Weight Loss   A weight loss program claims that program participants have a mean weight loss of at least 10 pounds after 1 month. You work for a medical association and are asked to test this claim. A random sample of 30 program participants and their weight losses (in pounds) after 1 month is listed in the stem-and-leaf plot below. At $\alpha = 0.03$, do you have enough evidence to reject the program's claim?

Weight Loss (in pounds)
after One Month

```
 5 | 7 7        Key: 5|7 = 5.7
 6 | 6 7
 7 | 0 1 9
 8 | 2 2 7 9
 9 | 0 3 5 6 8
10 | 2 5 6 6
11 | 1 2 5 7 8
12 | 0 7 8
13 | 8
14 |
15 | 0
```

46. Fire Drill   An engineering company claims that the mean time it takes an employee to evacuate a building during a fire drill is less than 60 seconds. You want to test this claim. A random sample of 50 employees and their evacuation times (in seconds) is listed in the stem-and-leaf plot below. At $\alpha = 0.01$, can you support the company's claim?

Evacuation Time (in seconds)

```
 0 | 7 9      Key: 0|7 = 7
 1 | 1 9 9
 2 | 2 6 7 9 9
 3 | 1 1 6 7 7 9 9
 4 | 1 1 3 3 3 4 6 6 7
 5 | 2 3 4 5 7 8 8 8 9 9
 6 | 1 3 3 4 6 6 7
 7 | 4 6 9
 8 | 4 6
 9 | 4
10 | 2
```

■ Extending Concepts

47. Electric Usage   You believe the mean annual kilowatt hour usage of U.S. residential customers is less than 11,500. You do some research and find that a random sample of 30 residential customers has a mean kilowatt hour usage of 11,400 with a standard deviation of 320 kilowatt hours. You conduct a statistical experiment where $H_0: \mu \geq 11,500$ and $H_a: \mu < 11,500$. At $\alpha = 0.01$, explain why you cannot reject H_0. *(Adapted from Edison Electric Institute)*

48. Vehicle Miles of Travel   You believe the annual mean vehicle miles of travel (VMT) per U.S. household is greater than 22,000 miles. You do some research and find that a random sample of 36 U.S. households has a mean annual VMT of 22,200 miles with a standard deviation of 775 miles. You conduct a statistical experiment where $H_0: \mu \leq 22,000$ and $H_a: \mu > 22,000$. At $\alpha = 0.05$, explain why you cannot reject H_0. *(Adapted from U.S. Federal Highway Administration)*

49. Using Different Values of α and n   In Exercise 47, you believe that H_0 is not valid. Which of the following allows you to reject H_0?

(a) Use the same values but increase α from 0.01 to 0.02.

(b) Use the same values but increase α from 0.01 to 0.05.

(c) Use the same values but increase n from 30 to 50.

(d) Use the same values but increase n from 30 to 100.

50. Using Different Values of α and n   In Exercise 48, you believe that H_0 is not valid. Which of the following allows you to reject H_0?

(a) Use the same values but increase α from 0.05 to 0.06.

(b) Use the same values but increase α from 0.05 to 0.07.

(c) Use the same values but increase n from 36 to 40.

(d) Use the same values but increase n from 36 to 80.

51. Writing   Explain the difference between the classical z-test for μ and the z-test for μ using a P-value.

ACTIVITY 7.2

APPLET

The *hypothesis test for a mean* applet allows you to visually investigate hypothesis tests for a mean. You can specify the sample size, n, the shape of the distribution (Normal or Right skewed), the true population mean (Mean), the true population standard deviation (Std. Dev.), the null value for the mean (Null mean), and the alternative for the test (Alternative). When you click SIMULATE, 100 separate samples of size n will be selected from a population with these population parameters. For each of the 100 samples, a hypothesis test based on the Z statistic is performed, and the results from each test are displayed in the plots to the right. The test statistic for each test is shown in the top plot and the P-value is shown in the bottom plot. The green and blue lines represent the cutoffs for rejecting the null hypothesis with the 0.05 and 0.01 level tests, respectively. Additional simulations can be carried out by clicking SIMULATE multiple times. The cumulative number of times that each test rejects the null hypothesis is also shown. Press CLEAR to clear existing results and start a new simulation.

■ Explore

Step 1 Specify a value for n.
Step 2 Specify a distribution.
Step 3 Specify a value for the mean.
Step 4 Specify a value for the standard deviation.
Step 5 Specify a value for the null mean.
Step 6 Specify an alternative hypothesis.
Step 7 Click SIMULATE to generate the hypothesis tests.

n:	100
Distribution:	Normal
Mean:	50
Std. Dev.:	10
Null mean:	50
Alternative:	<

Simulate

Cumulative results:

	0.05 level	0.01 level
Reject null		
Fail to reject null		
Prop. rejected		

Clear

■ Draw Conclusions

APPLET

1. Set $n = 30$, Mean = 40, Std. Dev. = 5, Null mean = 40, alternative hypothesis to "not equal," and the distribution to "normal." Run the simulation so that at least 1000 hypothesis tests are run. Compare the proportion of null hypothesis rejections for the 0.05 level and the 0.01 level. Is this what you would expect? Explain.

2. Suppose a null hypothesis is rejected at the 0.01 level. Will it be rejected at the 0.05 level? Explain. Suppose a null hypothesis is rejected at the 0.05 level. Will it be rejected at the 0.01 level? Explain.

3. Set $n = 50$, Mean = 25, Std. Dev. = 3, Null mean = 27, alternative hypothesis to "<," and the distribution to "normal." What is the null hypothesis? Run the simulation so that at least 1000 hypothesis tests are run. Compare the proportion of null hypothesis rejections for the 0.05 level and the 0.01 level. Is this what you would expect? Explain.

CASE STUDY

Human Body Temperature: What's Normal?

In an article in the *Journal of Statistics Education* (vol. 4, no. 2), Allen Shoemaker describes a study that was reported in the Journal of the American Medical Association (JAMA).* It is generally accepted that the mean body temperature of an adult human is 98.6°F. In his article, Shoemaker uses the data from the JAMA article to test this hypothesis. Here is a summary of his test.

Claim: The body temperature of adults is 98.6°F.

$$H_0: \mu = 98.6°F \text{ (Claim)} \qquad H_a: \mu \neq 98.6°F$$

Sample Size: $n = 130$

Population: Adult human temperatures (Fahrenheit)

Distribution: Approximately normal

Test Statistics: $\bar{x} = 98.25$, $s = 0.73$

* Data for the JAMA article were collected from healthy men and women, ages 18 to 40, at the University of Maryland Center for Vaccine Development, Baltimore.

Men's Temperatures (in degrees Fahrenheit)

```
96 | 3
96 | 7 9
97 | 0 1 1 1 2 3 4 4 4 4
97 | 5 5 6 6 6 7 8 8 8 8 9 9
98 | 0 0 0 0 0 0 1 1 2 2 2 2 3 3 4 4 4 4
98 | 5 5 6 6 6 6 6 6 7 7 8 8 8 9
99 | 0 0 0 1 2 3 4
99 | 5
100 |
100 |          Key: 96|3 = 96.3
```

Women's Temperatures (in degrees Fahrenheit)

```
96 | 4
96 | 7 8
97 | 2 2 4
97 | 6 7 7 8 8 8 9 9 9
98 | 0 0 0 0 0 1 2 2 2 2 2 2 3 3 3 4 4 4 4 4
98 | 5 6 6 6 6 7 7 7 7 7 7 8 8 8 8 8 8 8 9
99 | 0 0 1 1 2 2 3 4
99 | 9
100 | 0
100 | 8      Key: 96|4 = 96.4
```

■ Exercises

1. Complete the hypothesis test for all adults (men and women) by performing the following steps. Use a level of significance of $\alpha = 0.05$.

   (a) Sketch the sampling distribution.

   (b) Determine the critical values and add them to your sketch.

   (c) Determine the rejection regions and shade them in your sketch.

   (d) Find the standardized test statistic. Add it to your sketch.

   (e) Make a decision to reject or fail to reject the null hypothesis.

   (f) Interpret the decision in the context of the original claim.

2. If you lower the level of significance to $\alpha = 0.01$, does your decision change? Explain your reasoning.

3. Test the hypothesis that the mean temperature of men is 98.6°F. What can you conclude at a level of significance of $\alpha = 0.01$?

4. Test the hypothesis that the mean temperature of women is 98.6°F. What can you conclude at a level of significance of $\alpha = 0.01$?

5. Use the sample of 130 temperatures to form a 99% confidence interval for the mean body temperature of adult humans.

6. The conventional "normal" body temperature was established by Carl Wunderlich over 100 years ago. What, in Wunderlich's sampling procedure, do you think might have led him to an incorrect conclusion?

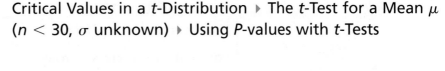

7.3 Hypothesis Testing for the Mean (Small Samples)

What You SHOULD LEARN

▸ How to find critical values in a *t*-distribution

▸ How to use the *t*-test to test a mean μ

▸ How to use technology to find *P*-values and use them with a *t*-test to test a mean μ

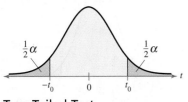

Critical Values in a *t*-Distribution ▸ The *t*-Test for a Mean μ ($n < 30$, σ unknown) ▸ Using *P*-values with *t*-Tests

▸ Critical Values in a *t*-Distribution

In Section 7.2, you learned how to perform a hypothesis test for a population mean when the sample size was at least 30. In real life, it is often not practical to collect samples of size 30 or more. However, if the population has a normal, or nearly normal, distribution, you can still test the population mean μ. To do so, you can use the *t*-sampling distribution with $n - 1$ degrees of freedom.

GUIDELINES

Finding Critical Values in a *t*-Distribution

1. Identify the level of significance α.
2. Identify the degrees of freedom d.f. $= n - 1$.
3. Find the critical value(s) using Table 5 in Appendix B in the row with $n - 1$ degrees of freedom. If the hypothesis test is
   a. *left-tailed,* use "One Tail, α" column with a negative sign.
   b. *right-tailed,* use "One Tail, α" column with a positive sign.
   c. *two-tailed,* use "Two Tails, α" column with a negative and a positive sign.

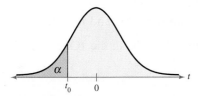

Left-Tailed Test

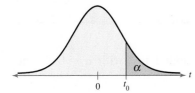

Right-Tailed Test

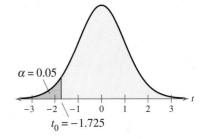

Two-Tailed Test

EXAMPLE 1

Finding Critical Values for *t*

Find the critical value t_0 for a left-tailed test given $\alpha = 0.05$ and $n = 21$.

Solution   The degrees of freedom are

$$\text{d.f.} = n - 1 = 21 - 1 = 20.$$

To find the critical value, use Table 5 in Appendix B with d.f. $= 20$ and 0.05 in the "One Tail, α" column. Because the test is a left-tailed test, the critical value is negative. So,

$$t_0 = -1.725.$$

$\alpha = 0.05$

$t_0 = -1.725$

▸ Try It Yourself 1

Find the critical value t_0 for a left-tailed test with $\alpha = 0.01$ and $n = 14$.

a. *Find* the *t*-value in Table 5 in Appendix B. Use d.f. $= 13$ and $\alpha = 0.01$ in the "One Tail, α" column.
b. *Use* a negative sign.

Answer: Page A44

EXAMPLE 2

Finding Critical Values for *t*

Find the critical value t_0 for a right-tailed test with $\alpha = 0.01$ and $n = 17$.

Solution The degrees of freedom are

d.f. $= n - 1$

$= 17 - 1$

$= 16.$

To find the critical value, use Table 5 with d.f. $= 16$ and $\alpha = 0.01$ in the "One tail, α" column. Because the test is right tailed, the critical value is positive. So,

$t_0 = 2.583.$

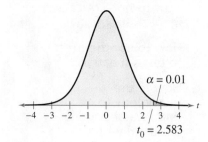

▶ **Try It Yourself 2**

Find the critical value t_0 for a right-tailed test with $\alpha = 0.05$ and $n = 9$.

a. *Find* the *t*-value in Table 5 using d.f. $= 8$ and $\alpha = 0.05$ in the "One tail, α" column.
b. *Use* a positive sign.

Answer: Page A44

Insight

To learn how to determine if a random sample is taken from a normal distribution, see Appendix C.

EXAMPLE 3

Finding Critical Values for *t*

Find the critical values t_0 and $-t_0$ for a two-tailed test with $\alpha = 0.05$ and $n = 26$.

Solution The degrees of freedom are

d.f. $= n - 1$

$= 26 - 1$

$= 25.$

To find the critical value, use Table 5 with d.f. $= 25$ and $\alpha = 0.05$ in the "Two tail, α" column. Because the test is two-tailed, one critical value is negative and one is positive. So,

$-t_0 = -2.060$ and $t_0 = 2.060.$

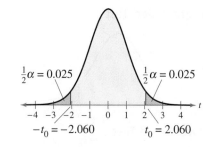

▶ **Try It Yourself 3**

Find the critical values $\pm t_0$ for a two-tailed test with $\alpha = 0.01$ and $n = 16$.

a. *Find* the *t*-value in Table 5 using d.f. $= 15$ and $\alpha = 0.01$ in the "Two tail, α" column.
b. *Use* a negative and a positive sign.

Answer: Page A44

▶ The *t*-Test for a Mean μ ($n < 30$, σ unknown)

To test a claim about a mean μ using a small sample ($n < 30$) from a normal, or nearly normal, distribution when σ is unknown, you can use a *t*-sampling distribution.

$$t = \frac{(\text{Sample mean}) - (\text{Hypothesized mean})}{\text{Standard error}}$$

t-TEST FOR A MEAN μ

The **t-test for a mean** is a statistical test for a population mean. The *t*-test can be used when the population is normal or nearly normal, σ is unknown, and $n < 30$. The **test statistic** is $\bar{x}$ and the **standardized test statistic** is t.

$$t = \frac{\bar{x} - \mu}{s/\sqrt{n}}$$

The degrees of freedom are

d.f. = $n - 1$.

GUIDELINES

Using the *t*-Test for a Mean μ (Small Sample)

In Words	*In Symbols*
1. State the claim mathematically and verbally. Identify the null and alternative hypotheses.	State H_0 and H_a.
2. Specify the level of significance.	Identify α.
3. Identify the degrees of freedom and sketch the sampling distribution.	d.f. = $n - 1$
4. Determine any critical values.	Use Table 5 in Appendix B.
5. Determine any rejection regions.	
6. Find the standardized test statistic.	$t = \dfrac{\bar{x} - \mu}{s/\sqrt{n}}$
7. Make a decision to reject or fail to reject the null hypothesis.	If t is in the rejection region, reject H_0. Otherwise, fail to reject H_0.
8. Interpret the decision in the context of the original claim.	

Remember that when you make a decision, the possibility of a type I or a type II error exists.

If you prefer using *P*-values, turn to page 402 to learn how to use *P*-values for a *t*-test for a mean μ (small sample).

On the basis of a *t*-test, a decision was made whether to send truckloads of waste contaminated with cadmium to a sanitary landfill or a hazardous waste landfill. The trucks were sampled to determine if the mean level of cadmium exceeded the allowable amount of 1 milligram per liter for a sanitary landfill. In the study, the null hypothesis was $\mu \leq 1$. (Source: Pacific Northwest National Laboratory)

	H_0 True	H_0 False
Fail to reject H_0.		
Reject H_0.		

Describe the possible type I and type II errors of this situation.

EXAMPLE 4

Testing μ with a Small Sample

See MINITAB steps on page 434.

A used car dealer says that the mean price of a 2005 Honda Pilot LX is at least $23,900. You suspect this claim is incorrect and find that a random sample of 14 similar vehicles has a mean price of $23,000 and a standard deviation of $1113. Is there enough evidence to reject the dealer's claim at $\alpha = 0.05$? Assume the population is normally distributed. *(Adapted from Kelley Blue Book)*

Solution

The claim is "the mean price is at least $23,900." So, the null and alternative hypotheses are

$$H_0: \mu \geq \$23,900 \text{ (Claim)}$$

and

$$H_a: \mu < \$23,900.$$

The test is a left-tailed test, the level of significance is $\alpha = 0.05$, and there are d.f. = 14 − 1 = 13 degrees of freedom. So, the critical value is $t_0 = -1.771$. The rejection region is $t < -1.771$. The standardized test statistic is

$$t = \frac{\bar{x} - \mu}{s/\sqrt{n}} \qquad \text{Because } n < 30, \text{ use the } t\text{-test.}$$

$$= \frac{23,000 - 23,900}{1113/\sqrt{14}} \qquad \text{Assume } \mu = 23,900.$$

$$\approx -3.026.$$

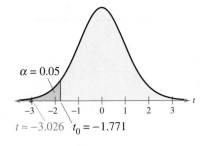

$\alpha = 0.05$

$t \approx -3.026 \quad t_0 = -1.771$

The graph shows the location of the rejection region and the standardized test statistic t. Because t is in the rejection region, you should decide to reject the null hypothesis.

Interpretation There is enough evidence at the 5% level of significance to reject the claim that the mean price of a 2005 Honda Pilot LX is at least $23,900.

▶ Try It Yourself 4

An insurance agent says that the mean cost of insuring a 2005 Honda Pilot LX is at least $1350. A random sample of 9 similar insurance quotes has a mean cost of $1290 and a standard deviation of $70. Is there enough evidence to reject the agent's claim at $\alpha = 0.01$? Assume the population is normally distributed.

a. *Identify* the claim and state H_0 and H_a.
b. *Identify* the level of significance α and the degrees of freedom d.f.
c. *Find* the critical value t_0 and identify the rejection region.
d. *Use* the t-test to find the standardized test statistic t.
e. *Sketch* a graph. *Decide* whether to reject the null hypothesis.
f. *Interpret* the decision in the context of the original claim.

Answer: Page A44

EXAMPLE 5

Testing μ with a Small Sample

See TI-83/84 steps on page 435.

An industrial company claims that the mean pH level of the water in a nearby river is 6.8. You randomly select 19 water samples and measure the pH of each. The sample mean and standard deviation are 6.7 and 0.24, respectively. Is there enough evidence to reject the company's claim at $\alpha = 0.05$? Assume the population is normally distributed.

Solution   The claim is "the mean pH level is 6.8." So, the null and alternative hypotheses are

$$H_0: \mu = 6.8 \text{ (Claim)}$$

and

$$H_a: \mu \neq 6.8.$$

The test is a two-tailed test, the level of significance is $\alpha = 0.05$, and there are d.f. $= 19 - 1 = 18$ degrees of freedom. So, the critical values are $-t_0 = -2.101$ and $t_0 = 2.101$. The rejection regions are $t < -2.101$ and $t > 2.101$. The standardized test statistic is

$$t = \frac{\bar{x} - \mu}{s/\sqrt{n}} \qquad \text{Because } n < 30, \text{ use the } t\text{-test.}$$

$$= \frac{6.7 - 6.8}{0.24/\sqrt{19}} \qquad \text{Assume } \mu = 6.8.$$

$$\approx -1.816.$$

The graph shows the location of the rejection region and the standardized test statistic t. Because t is not in the rejection region, you should decide not to reject the null hypothesis.

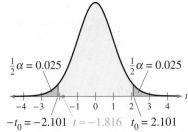

$\frac{1}{2}\alpha = 0.025$ $\frac{1}{2}\alpha = 0.025$

$-t_0 = -2.101$ $t \approx -1.816$ $t_0 = 2.101$

5% Level of Significance

Interpretation   There is not enough evidence at the 5% level of significance to reject the claim that the mean pH is 6.8.

▶ Try It Yourself 5

The company also claims that the mean conductivity of the river is 1890 milligrams per liter. The conductivity of a water sample is a measure of the total dissolved solids in the sample. You randomly select 19 water samples and measure the conductivity of each. The sample mean and standard deviation are 2500 milligrams per liter and 700 milligrams per liter, respectively. Is there enough evidence to reject the company's claim at $\alpha = 0.01$? Assume the population is normally distributed.

a. *Identify* the claim and state H_0 and H_a.
b. *Identify* the level of significance α and the degrees of freedom d.f.
c. *Find* the critical values $\pm t_0$ and identify the rejection regions.
d. *Use* the t-test to find the standardized test statistic t.
e. *Sketch* a graph. *Decide* whether to reject the null hypothesis.
f. *Interpret* the decision in the context of the original claim.

Answer: Page A44

▶ Using *P*-values with *t*-Tests

Suppose you wanted to find a *P*-value given $t = 1.98$, 15 degrees of freedom, and a right-tailed test. Using Table 5 in Appendix B, you can determine that P falls between $\alpha = 0.025$ and $\alpha = 0.05$, but you cannot determine an exact value for P. In such cases, you can use technology to perform a hypothesis test and find exact *P*-values.

EXAMPLE 6

Using *P*-values with a *t*-Test

The American Automobile Association claims that the mean daily meal cost for a family of four traveling on vacation in Florida is $118. A random sample of 11 such families has a mean daily meal cost of $128 with a standard deviation of $20. Is there enough evidence to reject the claim at $\alpha = 0.10$? Assume the population is normally distributed. *(Adapted from American Automobile Association)*

Solution The TI-83/84 display at the far left shows how to set up the hypothesis test. The two displays on the right show the possible results, depending on whether you select "Calculate" or "Draw."

TI-83/84

T–Test
Inpt:Data **Stats**
μ_0:118
x̄:128
Sx:20
n:11
μ: **≠μ_0** <μ_0 >μ_0
Calculate Draw

TI-83/84

T–Test
$\mu \neq 118$
t=1.658312395
p=.1282459922
x̄=128
Sx=20
n=11

TI-83/84

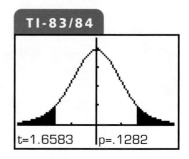

t=1.6583   p=.1282

From the displays, you can see that $P \approx 0.1282$. Because $P > 0.10$, you should fail to reject the null hypothesis. In other words, there is not enough evidence to reject the claim at the 10% level of significance.

▶ Try It Yourself 6

The American Automobile Association claims that the mean nightly lodging rate for a family of four traveling on vacation in Florida is at least $185. A random sample of 6 such families has a mean nightly lodging rate of $172 with a standard deviation of $15. Is there enough evidence to reject the claim at $\alpha = 0.05$? Assume the population is normally distributed. *(Adapted from American Automobile Association)*

a. *Use* a TI-83/84 to find the *P*-value.
b. *Compare* the *P*-value with the level of significance α.
c. *Make* a decision.
d. *Interpret* the decision in the context of the original claim.

Answer: Page A44

Study Tip

Note that the TI-83/84 display on the far right in Example 6 also displays the standardized test statistic $t \approx 1.6583$.

If you are using the TI-83/84 and have the original data from a sample, remember that you can enter it into a list and use the Data input option instead of the Stats input option. To use MINITAB to perform a one-sample *t*-test, you must have the original data.

7.3 EXERCISES

■ Building Basic Skills and Vocabulary

1. Explain how to find critical values for a *t*-sampling distribution.

2. Explain how to use a *t*-test to test a hypothesized mean μ given a small sample ($n < 30$). What assumption about the population is necessary?

In Exercises 3–14, find the critical value(s) for the indicated t-test, level of significance α, and sample size n.

3. Right-tailed test, $\alpha = 0.05$, $n = 23$

4. Right-tailed test, $\alpha = 0.01$, $n = 11$

5. Left-tailed test, $\alpha = 0.025$, $n = 19$

6. Left-tailed test, $\alpha = 0.05$, $n = 14$

7. Two-tailed test, $\alpha = 0.01$, $n = 27$

8. Two-tailed test, $\alpha = 0.05$, $n = 10$

9. Right-tailed test, $\alpha = 0.10$, $n = 20$

10. Right-tailed test, $\alpha = 0.05$, $n = 8$

11. Left-tailed test, $\alpha = 0.01$, $n = 28$

12. Left-tailed test, $\alpha = 0.005$, $n = 12$

13. Two-tailed test, $\alpha = 0.02$, $n = 5$

14. Two-tailed test, $\alpha = 0.10$, $n = 22$

Graphical Analysis *In Exercises 15–18, state whether the standardized test statistic t indicates that you should reject the null hypothesis. Explain.*

15. (a) $t = 2.091$
    (b) $t = 0$
    (c) $t = -1.08$
    (d) $t = -2.096$

16. (a) $t = 1.308$
    (b) $t = -1.389$
    (c) $t = 1.650$
    (d) $t = -0.998$

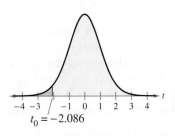

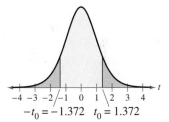

17. (a) $t = -2.502$
    (b) $t = 2.203$
    (c) $t = 2.680$
    (d) $t = -2.703$

18. (a) $t = 1.705$
    (b) $t = -1.755$
    (c) $t = -1.585$
    (d) $t = 1.745$

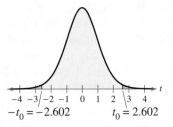

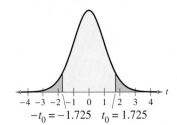

In Exercises 19–22, use a t-test to test the claim about the population mean μ at the given level of significance α using the given sample statistics. For each claim, assume the population is normally distributed.

19. Claim: $\mu = 15$; $\alpha = 0.01$.
Sample statistics: $\bar{x} = 13.9$, $s = 3.23$, $n = 6$

20. Claim: $\mu > 25$; $\alpha = 0.05$.
Sample statistics: $\bar{x} = 26.2$, $s = 2.32$, $n = 17$

21. Claim: $\mu \geq 8000$; $\alpha = 0.01$.
Sample statistics: $\bar{x} = 7700$, $s = 450$, $n = 25$

22. Claim: $\mu \neq 52{,}200$; $\alpha = 0.05$.
Sample statistics: $\bar{x} = 53{,}220$, $s = 1200$, $n = 4$

■ Using and Interpreting Concepts

Testing Claims   *In Exercises 23–28,*

(a) write the claim mathematically and identify H_0 and H_a.

(b) find the critical value(s) and identify the rejection region(s).

(c) find the standardized test statistic. If convenient, use technology.

(d) decide whether to reject or fail to reject the null hypothesis.

(e) interpret the decision in the context of the original claim.

For each claim, assume the population is normally distributed.

23. Microwave Repair Costs   A microwave oven repairer says that the mean repair cost for damaged microwave ovens is less than $100. You work for the repairer and want to test this claim. You find that a random sample of 5 microwave ovens has a mean repair cost of $75 and a standard deviation of $12.50. At $\alpha = 0.01$, do you have enough evidence to support the repairer's claim? *(Adapted from Consumer Reports)*

24. Computer Repair Costs   A computer repairer believes that the mean repair cost for damaged computers is more than $95. To test this claim, you determine the repair costs for 7 randomly selected computers and find that the mean repair cost is $100 per computer with a standard deviation of $42.50. At $\alpha = 0.01$, do you have enough evidence to support the repairer's claim? *(Adapted from Consumer Reports)*

25. Waste Recycled   An environmentalist estimates that the mean waste recycled by adults in the United States is more than 1 pound per person per day. You want to test this claim. You find that the mean waste recycled per person per day for a random sample of 12 adults in the United States is 1.46 pounds and the standard deviation is 0.28 pound. At $\alpha = 0.05$, can you support the claim? *(Adapted from U.S. Environmental Protection Agency)*

26. Waste Generated   As part of your work for an environmental awareness group, you want to test a claim that the mean waste generated by adults in the United States is more than 4 pounds per day. In a random sample of 10 adults in the United States, you find that the mean waste generated per person per day is 4.54 pounds with a standard deviation of 1.21 pounds. At $\alpha = 0.05$, can you support the claim? *(Adapted from U.S. Environmental Protection Agency)*

27. Annual Pay   An employment information service claims the mean annual pay for full-time male workers over age 25 and without a high school diploma is $25,000. The annual pay for a random sample of 10 full-time male workers without a high school diploma is listed. At $\alpha = 0.05$, test the claim that the mean salary is $25,000. *(Adapted from U.S. Bureau of Labor Statistics)*

26,185   23,814   22,374   25,189   26,318
20,767   30,782   29,541   24,597   28,955

28. Annual Pay   An employment information service claims the mean annual pay for full-time female workers over age 25 and without a high school diploma is $19,100. The annual pay for a random sample of 12 full-time female workers without a high school diploma is listed. At $\alpha = 0.05$, test the claim that the mean salary is $19,100. *(Adapted from U.S. Bureau of Labor Statistics)*

18,165   16,012   18,794   18,803   19,864   19,177
17,328   21,445   20,354   19,143   18,316   19,237

Testing Claims Using *P*-values   *In Exercises 29–34, (a) write the claim mathematically and identify H_0 and H_a, (b) use technology to find the P-value, (c) decide whether to reject or fail to reject the null hypothesis, and (d) interpret the decision in the context of the original claim. Assume the population is normally distributed.*

29. Soda Consumption   For your study on the food consumption habits of teenage males, you randomly select 20 teenage males and ask each how many 12-ounce servings of soda he drinks each day. The results are listed below. At $\alpha = 0.05$, is there enough evidence to support the claim that teenage males drink fewer than three 12-ounce servings of soda per day? *(Adapted from Center for Science in the Public Interest)*

2.1   2.3   2.4   1.2   0.8   2.1   2.0   2.2   2.5   2.1
1.6   2.1   1.8   2.2   2.0   2.8   3.2   0.5   1.4   1.2

30. School Supplies   A company that manufactures school supplies says that teachers spend a mean of more than $550 of their own money on school supplies in a year. A random sample of the amounts (in dollars) that 24 teachers spent on school supplies in a recent year is listed below. At $\alpha = 0.05$, is there enough evidence to support the company's claim? *(Adapted from National School Supply and Equipment Association)*

715   623   582   721   602   621   462   320   532   566   686   532
603   420   684   713   531   888   482   361   560   910   546   860

31. Class Size   You receive a brochure from a large university. The brochure indicates that the mean class size for full-time faculty is fewer than 32 students. You want to test this claim. You randomly select 18 classes taught by full-time faculty and determine the class size of each. The results are listed below. At $\alpha = 0.01$, can you support the university's claim? *(Adapted from National Center for Education Statistics)*

35   28   29   33   32   40   26   25   29   28   30   36   33   29   27   30   28   25

32. Faculty Classroom Hours   The dean of a university estimates that the mean number of classroom hours per week for full-time faculty is 11.0. As a member of the student council, you want to test this claim. A random sample of the number of classroom hours for eight full-time faculty for one week is listed below. At $\alpha = 0.01$, can you reject the dean's claim? *(Adapted from National Center for Education Statistics)*

11.8   8.6   12.6   7.9   6.4   10.4   13.6   9.1

33. Eating Out A restaurant association says the typical household in the United States spends a mean of $2634 per year on food away from home. You are a consumer reporter for a national publication and want to test this claim. You randomly select 12 U.S. households and find out how much each spent on food away from home per year. Can you reject the restaurant association's claim at $\alpha = 0.02$? *(Adapted from U.S. Bureau of Labor Statistics)*

3013 1724 1949 3516 2475 2767 2231 4512 2926 3148 2188 2978

34. Lodging Costs A travel association says the daily lodging costs for a family in the United States is $152. You work for a tourist publication and want to test this claim. You randomly select 10 U.S. families and find out how much each spent on lodging for one overnight trip. At $\alpha = 0.02$, can you reject the travel association's claim? *(Adapted from the American Automobile Association)*

164 137 142 155 119 104 74 204 148 181

■ Extending Concepts

35. Credit Card Balances To test the claim that the mean credit card balance among families that have a balance is greater than $2328, you do some research and find that a random sample of 6 cardholders has a mean credit card balance of $2528 with a standard deviation of $325. You conduct a statistical experiment where $H_0: \mu \leq \$2328$ and $H_a: \mu > \$2328$. At $\alpha = 0.01$, explain why you cannot reject H_0. Assume the population is normally distributed. *(Adapted from Myvesta)*

36. Using Different Values of α and n In Exercise 35, you believe that H_0 is not valid. Which of the following allows you to reject H_0? (a) Use the same values but increase α from 0.01 to 0.05. (b) Use the same values but increase α from 0.01 to 0.10. (c) Use the same values but increase n from 6 to 12. (d) Use the same values but increase n from 6 to 24.

Deciding on a Distribution *In Exercises 37 and 38, decide whether you should use a normal sampling distribution or a t-sampling distribution to perform the hypothesis test. Justify your decision. Then use the distribution to test the claim. Write a short paragraph about the results of the test and what you can conclude about the claim.*

37. Gas Mileage A car company says that the mean gas mileage for its luxury sedan is at least 23 miles per gallon (mpg). You believe the claim is incorrect and find that a random sample of 5 cars has a mean gas mileage of 22 mpg and a standard deviation of 4 mpg. Assume the gas mileage of all of the company's luxury sedans is normally distributed. At $\alpha = 0.05$, test the company's claim. *(Adapted from Consumer Reports)*

38. Master's Degree An education publication claims that the average price for 1 year of graduate school for a full-time student in a master's degree program at a public institution is less than $23,000. A random sample of 50 graduate schools has a mean price of $21,856 and a standard deviation of $3163 for 1 year. At $\alpha = 0.01$, test the publication's claim. *(Adapted from National Center for Education Statistics)*

7.4 Hypothesis Testing for Proportions

What You
SHOULD LEARN

▶ How to use the z-test to test a population proportion p

Hypothesis Test for Proportions

▶ Hypothesis Test for Proportions

In Sections 7.2 and 7.3, you learned how to perform a hypothesis test for a population mean. In this section, you will learn how to test a population proportion p.

Hypothesis tests for proportions occur when a politician wants to know the proportion of his or her constituents who favor a certain bill or when a quality assurance engineer tests the proportion of parts that are defective.

If $np \geq 5$ and $nq \geq 5$ for a binomial distribution, then the sampling distribution for $\hat{p}$ is normal with

$$\mu_{\hat{p}} = p \quad \text{and} \quad \sigma_{\hat{p}} = \sqrt{pq/n}.$$

Z-TEST FOR A PROPORTION P

The **z-test for a proportion** is a statistical test for a population proportion p. The z-test can be used when a binomial distribution is given such that $np \geq 5$ and $nq \geq 5$. The **test statistic** is the sample proportion $\hat{p}$ and the **standardized test statistic** is z.

$$z = \frac{\hat{p} - \mu_{\hat{p}}}{\sigma_{\hat{p}}} = \frac{\hat{p} - p}{\sqrt{pq/n}}$$

GUIDELINES

Using a z-Test for a Proportion p
Verify that $np \geq 5$ and $nq \geq 5$.

In Words	*In Symbols*
1. State the claim mathematically and verbally. Identify the null and alternative hypotheses.	State H_0 and H_a.
2. Specify the level of significance.	Identify α.
3. Sketch the sampling distribution.	
4. Determine any critical values.	Use Table 4 in Appendix B.
5. Determine any rejection regions.	
6. Find the standardized test statistic.	$z = \dfrac{\hat{p} - p}{\sqrt{pq/n}}$
7. Make a decision to reject or fail to reject the null hypothesis.	If z is in the rejection region, reject H_0. Otherwise, fail to reject H_0.
8. Interpret the decision in the context of the original claim.	

Insight

A hypothesis test for a proportion p can also be performed using P-values. Use the guidelines on page 381 for using P-values for a z-test for a mean μ, but in Step 3 find the standardized test statistic by using the formula

$$z = \frac{\hat{p} - p}{\sqrt{pq/n}}.$$

The other steps in the test are the same.

EXAMPLE 1

Hypothesis Test for a Proportion

See TI-83/84 steps on page 435.

A research center claims that less than 20% of Internet users in the United States have a wireless network in their home. In a random sample of 100 adults, 15% say they have a wireless network in their home. At $\alpha = 0.01$, is there enough evidence to support the researcher's claim? *(Adapted from Pew Research Center)*

Solution   The products $np = 100(0.20) = 20$ and $nq = 100(0.80) = 80$ are both greater than 5. So, you can use a z-test. The claim is "less than 20% have a wireless network in their home." So, the null and alternative hypotheses are

$$H_0: p \geq 0.2 \quad \text{and} \quad H_a: p < 0.2. \; (\text{Claim})$$

Because the test is a left-tailed test and the level of significance is $\alpha = 0.01$, the critical value is $z_0 = -2.33$ and the rejection region is $z < -2.33$. The standardized test statistic is

$$z = \frac{\hat{p} - p}{\sqrt{pq/n}}$$ Because $np \geq 5$ and $nq \geq 5$, you can use the z-test.

$$= \frac{0.15 - 0.2}{\sqrt{(0.2)(0.8)/100}}$$ Assume $p = 0.2$.

$$= -1.25.$$

The graph shows the location of the rejection region and the standardized test statistic z. Because z is not in the rejection region, you should fail to reject the null hypothesis.

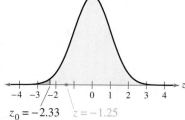

$z_0 = -2.33 \quad z = -1.25$

Interpretation   At the 1% significance level, there is not enough evidence to support the claim that less than 20% of Internet users in the United States have a wireless network in their home.

▶ Try It Yourself 1

A research center claims that less than 30% of cellular phone users whose phone can connect to the Internet have done so while at home. In a random sample of 86 adults, 20% say they have used their cellular phone to connect to the Internet while at home. At $\alpha = 0.05$, is there enough evidence to support the researcher's claim? *(Adapted from Pew Research Center)*

a. *Verify* that $np \geq 5$ and $nq \geq 5$.
b. *Identify* the claim and state H_0 and H_a.
c. *Identify* the level of significance α.
d. *Find* the critical value z_0 and *identify* the rejection region.
e. *Use* the z-test to find the standardized test statistic z.
f. *Decide* whether to reject the null hypothesis. Use a graph if necessary.
g. *Interpret* the decision in the context of the original claim.   *Answer: Page A44*

To use a P-value to perform the hypothesis test in Example 1, use Table 4 to find the area corresponding to $z = -1.25$. The area is 0.1056. Because this is a left-tailed test, the P-value is equal to the area to the left of $z = -1.25$. So, $P = 0.1056$. Because the P-value is greater than $\alpha = 0.01$, you should fail to reject the null hypothesis. Note that this is the same result obtained in Example 1.

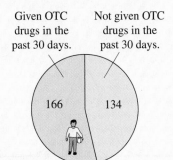

EXAMPLE 2

Hypothesis Test for a Proportion

> See MINITAB steps on page 434.

Zogby International claims that 45% of people in the United States support making cigarettes illegal within the next 5 to 10 years. You decide to test this claim and ask a random sample of 200 people in the United States whether they support making cigarettes illegal within the next 5 to 10 years. Of the 200 people, 49% support this law. At $\alpha = 0.05$, is there enough evidence to reject the claim?

Solution The products $np = 200(0.45) = 90$ and $nq = 200(0.55) = 110$ are both greater than 5. So, you can use a z-test. The claim is "45% of people in the United States support making cigarettes illegal within the next 5 to 10 years." So, the null and alternative hypotheses are

$$H_0: p = 0.45 \text{ (Claim)} \quad \text{and} \quad H_a: p \neq 0.45.$$

Because the test is a two-tailed test and the level of significance is $\alpha = 0.05$, the critical values are $-z_0 = -1.96$ and $z_0 = 1.96$. The rejection regions are $z < -1.96$ and $z > 1.96$. The standardized test statistic is

$$z = \frac{\hat{p} - p}{\sqrt{pq/n}}$$

   Because $np \geq 5$ and $nq \geq 5$, you can use the z-test.

$$= \frac{0.49 - 0.45}{\sqrt{(0.45)(0.55)/200}}$$

   Assume $p = 0.45$.

$$\approx 1.14.$$

The graph shows the location of the rejection regions and the standardized test statistic z. Because z is not in the rejection region, you should fail to reject the null hypothesis.

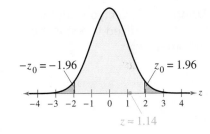

$-z_0 = -1.96$ $z_0 = 1.96$

$z \approx 1.14$

Interpretation At the 5% significance level, there is not enough evidence to reject the claim that 45% of people in the United States support making cigarettes illegal within the next 5 to 10 years.

▶ Try It Yourself 2

A Roper Poll claims that 5% of U.S. adults have had vivid dreams about UFOs. You decide to test this claim and ask a random sample of 250 U.S. adults whether they have had vivid dreams about UFOs. Of those surveyed, 8% reply yes. At $\alpha = 0.01$, is there enough evidence to reject the claim?

a. *Verify* that $np \geq 5$ and $nq \geq 5$.
b. *Identify* the claim and state H_0 and H_a.
c. *Identify* the level of significance α.
d. *Find* the critical values $-z_0$ and z_0 and *identify* the rejection regions.
e. *Use* the z-test to find the standardized test statistic z.
f. *Decide* whether to reject the null hypothesis. Use a graph if necessary.
g. *Interpret* the decision in the context of the original claim.

Answer: Page A44

EXAMPLE 3

Hypothesis Test for a Proportion

The Pew Research Center claims that more than 55% of U.S. adults regularly watch their local television news. You decide to test this claim and ask a random sample of 425 adults in the United States whether they regularly watch their local television news. Of the 425 adults, 255 respond yes. At $\alpha = 0.05$, is there enough evidence to support the claim?

Solution The products $np = 425(0.55) \approx 234$ and $nq = 425(0.45) \approx 191$ are both greater than 5. So, you can use a z-test. The claim is "more than 55% of U.S. adults watch their local television news." So, the null and alternative hypotheses are

$$H_0: p \le 0.55 \quad \text{and} \quad H_a: p > 0.55. \text{ (Claim)}$$

Because the test is a right-tailed test and the level of significance is $\alpha = 0.05$, the critical value is $z_0 = 1.645$ and the rejection region is $z > 1.645$. The standardized test statistic is

$$z = \frac{\hat{p} - p}{\sqrt{pq/n}} \qquad \text{Because } np \ge 5 \text{ and } nq \ge 5, \text{ you can use the } z\text{-test.}$$

$$= \frac{(x/n) - p}{\sqrt{pq/n}} \qquad \hat{p} = x/n.$$

$$= \frac{(255/425) - 0.55}{\sqrt{(0.55)(0.45)/425}} \qquad \text{Assume } p = 0.55.$$

$$\approx 2.07.$$

The graph shows the location of the rejection region and the standardized test statistic z. Because z is in the rejection region, you should decide to reject the null hypothesis.

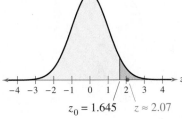

$z_0 = 1.645 \qquad z \approx 2.07$

Interpretation There is enough evidence at the 5% level of significance to support the claim that more than 55% of U.S. adults regularly watch their local television news.

```
1-PropZTest
 prop>.55
 z=2.071938535
 p=.0191355209
 p̂=.6
 n=425
```

Using a TI-83/84, you can find the standardized test statistic automatically.

To explore this topic further, see Activity 7.4 on page 413.

▶ Try It Yourself 3

The Pew Research Center claims that more than 30% of U.S. adults regularly watch the Weather Channel. You decide to test this claim and ask a random sample of 75 adults whether they regularly watch the Weather Channel. Of the 75 adults, 27 respond yes. At $\alpha = 0.01$, is there enough evidence to support the claim?

a. *Verify* that $np \ge 5$ and $nq \ge 5$.
b. *Identify* the claim and state H_0 and H_a.
c. *Identify* the level of significance α.
d. *Find* the critical value z_0 and *identify* the rejection region.
e. *Use* the z-test to find the standardized test statistic z.
f. *Decide* whether to reject the null hypothesis. Use a graph if necessary.
g. *Interpret* the decision in the context of the original claim.

Answer: Page A44

7.4 EXERCISES

For Extra Help

MyStatLab

■ Building Basic Skills and Vocabulary

1. Explain how to test a population proportion p.

2. Explain how to decide when a normal distribution can be used to approximate a binomial distribution.

In Exercises 3–8, decide whether the normal sampling distribution can be used. If it can be used, test the claim about the population proportion p at the given level of significance α using the given sample statistics.

3. Claim: $p \neq 0.25$; $\alpha = 0.05$. Sample statistics: $\hat{p} = 0.239$, $n = 105$

4. Claim: $p \leq 0.30$; $\alpha = 0.05$. Sample statistics: $\hat{p} = 0.35$, $n = 500$

5. Claim: $p < 0.12$; $\alpha = 0.01$. Sample statistics: $\hat{p} = 0.10$, $n = 20$

6. Claim: $p > 0.125$; $\alpha = 0.01$. Sample statistics: $\hat{p} = 0.2325$, $n = 45$

7. Claim: $p \geq 0.48$; $\alpha = 0.10$. Sample statistics: $\hat{p} = 0.40$, $n = 70$

8. Claim: $p = 0.80$; $\alpha = 0.10$. Sample statistics: $\hat{p} = 0.875$, $n = 16$

■ Using and Interpreting Concepts

Testing Claims *In Exercises 9–14, (a) write the claim mathematically and identify H_0 and H_a, (b) find the critical value(s) and identify the rejection region(s), (c) find the standardized test statistic, (d) decide whether to reject or fail to reject the null hypothesis, and (e) interpret the decision in the context of the original claim. If convenient, use technology to find the standardized test statistic.*

9. **Smokers** A medical researcher says that at least 20% of U.S. adults are smokers. In a random sample of 200 U.S. adults, 18.5% say that they are smokers. At $\alpha = 0.01$, is there enough evidence to reject the researcher's claim? *(Adapted from U.S. National Center for Health Statistics)*

10. **Do You Eat Breakfast?** A research center estimates that no more than 40% of U.S. adults eat breakfast every day. In a random sample of 250 U.S. adults, 41.6% say they eat breakfast every day. At $\alpha = 0.01$, is there enough evidence to reject the researcher's claim? *(Adapted from Harris Interactive)*

11. **Environmentally Conscious Consumers** You are employed by an environmental conservation agency that recently claimed that more than 30% of U.S. consumers have stopped buying a certain product because the manufacturing of the product pollutes the environment. You want to test this claim. You randomly select 1050 U.S. consumers and find that 32% have stopped buying this product because of pollution concerns. At $\alpha = 0.03$, can you support the agency's claim? *(Adapted from Wirthlin Worldwide)*

12. **Genetically Modified Foods** An environmentalist claims that more than 60% of British consumers are concerned about the use of genetic modification in food production and want to avoid genetically modified foods. You want to test this claim. You find that in a random sample of 100 British consumers, 65% say that they are concerned about the use of genetic modification in food production and want to avoid genetically modified foods. At $\alpha = 0.10$, can you support the environmentalist's claim? *(Adapted from Consumers' Association)*

13. **Finding a Real Estate Agent**   In your work for a real estate company, you find that in a sample of 1762 home buyers, 722 found their real estate agent through a friend. At $\alpha = 0.02$, can you reject the claim that 44% of home buyers find their real estate agent through a friend? *(Adapted from USA TODAY)*

14. **Do You Like to Fly?**   A researcher claims that 24% of adults in the United States are afraid to fly. You want to test this claim. You find that in a random sample of 1075 adults in the United States, 292 are afraid to fly. At $\alpha = 0.05$, can you reject the researcher's claim? *(Source: Marist Institute for Public Opinion)*

Free Samples   *In Exercises 15 and 16, use the graph, which shows what adults think about the effectiveness of free samples.*

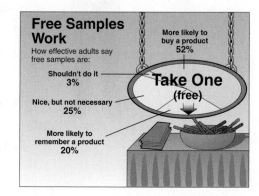

15. **Do Free Samples Work?**   You interview a random sample of 50 adults. The results of the survey show that 48% of the adults said they were more likely to buy a product when there are free samples. At $\alpha = 0.05$, can you reject the claim that at least 52% of the adults are more likely to buy a product when there are free samples?

16. **Should Free Samples Be Used?**   Use your conclusion from Exercise 15 to write a paragraph on the use of free samples. Do you think a company should use free samples to get people to buy a product? Explain.

■ Extending Concepts

Alternative Formula   *In Exercises 17 and 18, use the following information. When you know the number of successes x, the sample size n, and probability p, it can be easier to use the formula*

$$z = \frac{x - np}{\sqrt{npq}}$$

to find the standardized test statistic when using a z-test for a proportion p.

17. Rework Exercise 13 using the alternative formula and compare the results.

18. The alternative formula is derived from the formula

$$z = \frac{\hat{p} - p}{\sqrt{pq/n}} = \frac{(x/n) - p}{\sqrt{pq/n}}.$$

Use this formula to derive the alternative formula. Justify each step.

APPLET

The *hypothesis test for a proportion* applet allows you to visually investigate hypothesis tests for a proportion. You can specify the sample size, n, the true proportion (True p), the null value for the proportion (Null p), and the alternative for the test (Alternative). When you click SIMULATE, 100 separate samples of size n will be selected from a population with a proportion of successes equal to True p. For each of the 100 samples, a hypothesis test based on the Z statistic is performed, and the results from each test are displayed in the plots to the right. The test statistic for each test is shown in the top plot and the P-value is shown in the bottom plot. The green and blue lines represent the cutoffs for rejecting the null hypothesis with the 0.05 and 0.01 level tests, respectively. Additional simulations can be carried out by clicking SIMULATE multiple times. The cumulative number of times that each test rejects the null hypothesis is also shown. Press CLEAR to clear existing results and start a new simulation.

■ Explore

Step 1 Specify a value for n.

Step 2 Specify a value for the true proportion.

Step 3 Specify a value for the null proportion.

Step 4 Specify an alternative hypothesis.

Step 5 Click SIMULATE to generate the hypothesis tests.

■ Draw Conclusions

APPLET

1. Set $n = 25$, True $p = 0.35$, Null $p = 0.35$, and the alternative hypothesis to "not equal." Run the simulation so that at least 1000 hypothesis tests are run. Compare the proportion of null hypothesis rejections for the 0.05 level and the 0.01 level. Is this what you would expect? Explain.

2. Set $n = 50$, True $p = 0.6$, Null $p = 0.4$, and the alternative hypothesis to "$<$." What is the null hypothesis? Run the simulation so that at least 1000 hypothesis tests are run. Compare the proportion of null hypothesis rejections for the 0.05 level and the 0.01 level. Perform a hypothesis test for each level. Use the results of the hypothesis tests to explain the results of the simulation.

7.5 Hypothesis Testing for Variance and Standard Deviation

What You SHOULD LEARN

▸ How to find critical values for a χ^2-test

▸ How to use the χ^2-test to test a variance or a standard deviation

▸ Critical Values for a χ^2-Test

In real life, it is often important to produce consistent predictable results. For instance, consider a company that manufactures golf balls. The manufacturer must produce millions of golf balls, each having the same size and the same weight. There is a very low tolerance for variation. If the population is normal, you can test the variance and standard deviation of the process using the chi-square distribution with $n - 1$ degrees of freedom.

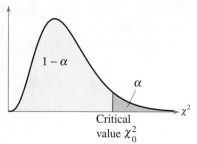

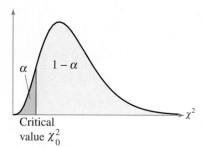

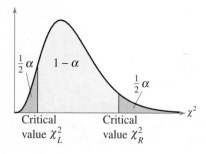

> ## GUIDELINES
>
> Finding Critical Values for the χ^2-Test
> 1. Specify the level of significance α.
> 2. Determine the degrees of freedom d.f. $= n - 1$.
> 3. The critical values for the χ^2-distribution are found in Table 6 of Appendix B. To find the critical value(s) for a
>   a. *right-tailed test*, use the value that corresponds to d.f. and α.
>   b. *left-tailed test*, use the value that corresponds to d.f. and $1 - \alpha$.
>   c. *two-tailed test*, use the values that correspond to d.f. and $\frac{1}{2}\alpha$ and d.f. and $1 - \frac{1}{2}\alpha$.

EXAMPLE 1

Finding Critical Values for χ^2

Find the critical χ^2-value for a right-tailed test when $n = 26$ and $\alpha = 0.10$.

Solution   The degrees of freedom are

   d.f. $= n - 1 = 26 - 1 = 25$.

The graph at the right shows a χ^2-distribution with 25 degrees of freedom and a shaded area of $\alpha = 0.10$ in the right tail. In Table 6 in Appendix B with d.f. $= 25$ and $\alpha = 0.10$, the critical value is

   $\chi_0^2 = 34.382$.

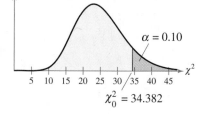

$\chi_0^2 = 34.382$

▸Try It Yourself 1

Find the critical χ^2-value for a right-tailed test when $n = 18$ and $\alpha = 0.01$.

Find the value using Table 6 in Appendix B with d.f. $= n - 1$ and the area α.

Answer: Page A44

EXAMPLE 2

Finding Critical Values for χ^2

Find the critical χ^2-value for a left-tailed test when $n = 11$ and $\alpha = 0.01$.

Solution The degrees of freedom are d.f. $= n - 1 = 11 - 1 = 10$. The graph at the right shows a χ^2-distribution with 10 degrees of freedom and a shaded area of $\alpha = 0.01$ in the left tail. The area to the right of the critical value is

$$1 - \alpha = 1 - 0.01 = 0.99.$$

In Table 6 with d.f. $= 10$ and the area $1 - \alpha = 0.99$, the critical value is $\chi_0^2 = 2.558$.

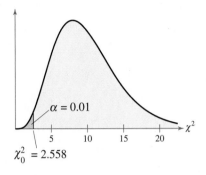

▶ Try It Yourself 2

Find the critical χ^2-value for a left-tailed test when $n = 30$ and $\alpha = 0.05$.

Find the value using Table 6 with d.f. $= n - 1$ and the area $1 - \alpha$.

Answer: Page A44

EXAMPLE 3

Finding Critical Values for χ^2

Find the critical χ^2-values for a two-tailed test when $n = 13$ and $\alpha = 0.01$.

Solution The degrees of freedom are d.f. $= n - 1 = 13 - 1 = 12$. The graph at the right shows a χ^2-distribution with 12 degrees of freedom and a shaded area of $\frac{1}{2}\alpha = 0.005$ in each tail. The areas to the right of the critical values are

$$\frac{1}{2}\alpha = 0.005$$

and

$$1 - \frac{1}{2}\alpha = 0.995.$$

In Table 6 with d.f. $= 12$ and the areas 0.005 and 0.995, the critical values are $\chi_L^2 = 3.074$ and $\chi_R^2 = 28.299$.

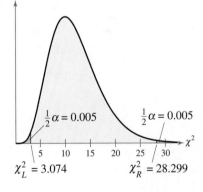

▶ Try It Yourself 3

Find the critical χ^2-values for a two-tailed test when $n = 19$ and $\alpha = 0.05$.

a. *Find* the first critical value χ_R^2 using Table 6 with d.f. $= n - 1$ and the area $\frac{1}{2}\alpha$.

b. *Find* the second critical value χ_L^2 using Table 6 with d.f. $= n - 1$ and the area $1 - \frac{1}{2}\alpha$.

Answer: Page A44

Note that because chi-square distributions are not symmetric (like normal or t-distributions), in a two-tailed test the two critical values are not opposites. Each critical value must be calculated separately.

▶ The Chi-Square Test

To test a variance σ^2 or a standard deviation σ of a population that is normally distributed, you can use the χ^2-test. The χ^2-test for a variance or standard deviation is not as robust as the tests for the population mean μ or the population proportion p. So, it is essential in performing a χ^2-test for a variance or standard deviation that the population be normally distributed. The results can be misleading if the population is not normal.

χ^2-TEST FOR A VARIANCE σ^2 OR STANDARD DEVIATION σ

The **χ^2-test for a variance or standard deviation** is a statistical test for a population variance or standard deviation. The χ^2-test can be used when the population is normal. The **test statistic** is s^2 and the **standardized test statistic**

$$\chi^2 = \frac{(n - 1)s^2}{\sigma^2}$$

follows a chi-square distribution with degrees of freedom

d.f. $= n - 1$.

GUIDELINES

Using the χ^2-Test for a Variance or Standard Deviation

In Words	*In Symbols*
1. State the claim mathematically and verbally. Identify the null and alternative hypotheses.	State H_0 and H_a.
2. Specify the level of significance.	Identify α.
3. Determine the degrees of freedom and sketch the sampling distribution.	d.f. $= n - 1$
4. Determine any critical values.	Use Table 6 in Appendix B.
5. Determine any rejection regions.	
6. Find the standardized test statistic.	$\chi^2 = \dfrac{(n - 1)s^2}{\sigma^2}$
7. Make a decision to reject or fail to reject the null hypothesis.	If χ^2 is in the rejection region, reject H_0. Otherwise, fail to reject H_0.
8. Interpret the decision in the context of the original claim.	

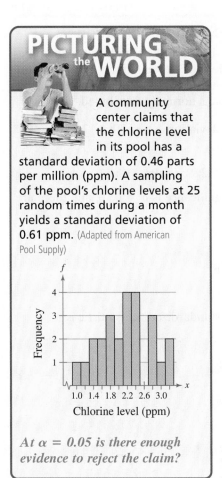

EXAMPLE 4

Using a Hypothesis Test for the Population Variance

A dairy processing company claims that the variance of the amount of fat in the whole milk processed by the company is no more than 0.25. You suspect this is wrong and find that a random sample of 41 milk containers has a variance of 0.27. At $\alpha = 0.05$, is there enough evidence to reject the company's claim? Assume the population is normally distributed.

Solution   The claim is "the variance is no more than 0.25." So, the null and alternative hypotheses are

$$H_0: \sigma^2 \le 0.25 \ \text{(Claim)} \quad \text{and} \quad H_a: \sigma^2 > 0.25.$$

The test is a right-tailed test, the level of significance is $\alpha = 0.05$, and there are d.f. $= 41 - 1 = 40$ degrees of freedom. So, the critical value is

$$\chi_0^2 = 55.758.$$

The rejection region is $\chi^2 > 55.758$. The standardized test statistic is

$$\chi^2 = \frac{(n-1)s^2}{\sigma^2} \qquad \text{Use the chi-square test.}$$

$$= \frac{(41-1)(0.27)}{0.25} \qquad \text{Assume } \sigma^2 = 0.25.$$

$$= 43.2.$$

The graph shows the location of the rejection region and the standardized test statistic χ^2. Because χ^2 is not in the rejection region, you should fail to reject the null hypothesis.

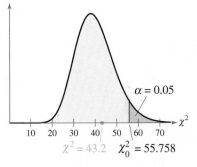

$\chi^2 = 43.2 \quad \chi_0^2 = 55.758$

Interpretation   You don't have enough evidence at the 5% level of significance to reject the company's claim that the variance of the amount of fat in the whole milk is no more than 0.25.

▶ Try It Yourself 4

A bottling company claims that the variance of the amount of sports drink in a 12-ounce bottle is no more than 0.40. A random sample of 31 bottles has a variance of 0.75. At $\alpha = 0.01$, is there enough evidence to reject the company's claim? Assume the population is normally distributed.

a. *Identify* the claim and state H_0 and H_a.
b. *Identify* the level of significance α and the degrees of freedom d.f.
c. *Find* the critical value and *identify* the rejection region.
d. *Use* the χ^2-test to find the standardized test statistic χ^2.
e. *Decide* whether to reject the null hypothesis. Use a graph if necessary.
f. *Interpret* the decision in the context of the original claim.

Answer: Page A44

EXAMPLE 5

Using a Hypothesis Test for the Standard Deviation

A restaurant claims that the standard deviation in the length of serving times is less than 2.9 minutes. A random sample of 23 serving times has a standard deviation of 2.1 minutes. At $\alpha = 0.10$, is there enough evidence to support the restaurant's claim? Assume the population is normally distributed.

Solution The claim is "the standard deviation is less than 2.9 minutes." So, the null and alternative hypotheses are

$$H_0: \sigma \geq 2.9 \text{ minutes} \quad \text{and} \quad H_a: \sigma < 2.9 \text{ minutes. (Claim)}$$

The test is a left-tailed test, the level of significance is $\alpha = 0.10$, and there are

$$\text{d.f.} = 23 - 1$$
$$= 22$$

degrees of freedom. So, the critical value is

$$\chi_0^2 = 14.042.$$

The rejection region is $\chi^2 < 14.042$. The standardized test statistic is

$$\chi^2 = \frac{(n-1)s^2}{\sigma^2} \qquad \text{Use the chi-square test.}$$

$$= \frac{(23-1)(2.1)^2}{2.9^2} \qquad \text{Assume } \sigma = 2.9.$$

$$\approx 11.536.$$

The graph shows the location of the rejection region and the standardized test statistic χ^2. Because χ^2 is in the rejection region, you should reject the null hypothesis.

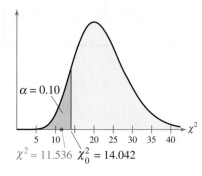

$\chi^2 \approx 11.536 \quad \chi_0^2 = 14.042$

Interpretation There is enough evidence at the 10% level of significance to support the claim that the standard deviation for the length of serving times is less than 2.9 minutes.

▶ **Try It Yourself 5**

A police chief claims that the standard deviation in the length of response times is less than 3.7 minutes. A random sample of 9 response times has a standard deviation of 3.0 minutes. At $\alpha = 0.05$, is there enough evidence to support the police chief's claim? Assume the population is normally distributed.

a. *Identify* the claim and state H_0 and H_a.
b. *Identify* the level of significance α and the degrees of freedom d.f.
c. *Find* the critical value and *identify* the rejection region.
d. *Use* the χ^2-test to find the standardized test statistic χ^2.
e. *Decide* whether to reject the null hypothesis. Use a graph if necessary.
f. *Interpret* the decision in the context of the original claim.

Answer: Page A44

EXAMPLE 6

Using a Hypothesis Test for the Population Variance

A sporting goods manufacturer claims that the variance of the strength in a certain fishing line is 15.9. A random sample of 15 fishing line spools has a variance of 21.8. At $\alpha = 0.05$, is there enough evidence to reject the manufacturer's claim? Assume the population is normally distributed.

Solution   The claim is "the variance is 15.9." So, the null and alternative hypotheses are

$$H_0: \sigma^2 = 15.9 \text{ (Claim)} \quad \text{and} \quad H_a: \sigma^2 \neq 15.9.$$

The test is a two-tailed test, the level of significance is $\alpha = 0.05$, and there are

$$\text{d.f.} = 15 - 1$$
$$= 14$$

degrees of freedom. So, the critical values are $\chi^2_L = 5.629$ and $\chi^2_R = 26.119$. The rejection regions are $\chi^2 < 5.629$ and $\chi^2 > 26.119$. The standardized test statistic is

$$\chi^2 = \frac{(n-1)s^2}{\sigma^2} \qquad \text{Use the chi-square test.}$$

$$= \frac{(15-1)(21.8)}{15.9} \qquad \text{Assume } \sigma^2 = 15.9.$$

$$\approx 19.195.$$

The graph shows the location of the rejection regions and the standardized test statistic χ^2. Because χ^2 is not in the rejection regions, you should fail to reject the null hypothesis.

Interpretation   At the 5% level of significance, there is not enough evidence to reject the claim that the variance in the strength of the fishing line is 15.9.

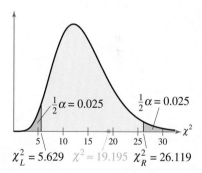

$$\chi^2_L = 5.629 \quad \chi^2 \approx 19.195 \quad \chi^2_R = 26.119$$

▶ Try It Yourself 6

A tire manufacturer claims that the variance of the diameters in a certain tire model is 8.6. A random sample of 10 tires has a variance of 4.3. At $\alpha = 0.01$, is there enough evidence to reject the manufacturer's claim? Assume the population is normally distributed.

a. _Identify_ the claim and state H_0 and H_a.
b. _Identify_ the level of significance α and the degrees of freedom d.f.
c. _Find_ the critical values and _identify_ the rejection regions.
d. _Use_ the χ^2-test to find the standardized test statistic χ^2.
e. _Decide_ whether to reject the null hypothesis. Use a graph if necessary.
f. _Interpret_ the decision in the context of the original claim.

Answer: Page A44

7.5 EXERCISES

■ Building Basic Skills and Vocabulary

1. Explain how to find critical values in a χ^2 sampling distribution.

2. Explain how to test a population variance or a population standard deviation.

In Exercises 3–8, find the critical value(s) for the indicated test for a population variance, sample size n, and level of significance α.

3. Right-tailed test,
   $n = 27, \alpha = 0.05$

4. Right-tailed test,
   $n = 10, \alpha = 0.10$

5. Left-tailed test,
   $n = 7, \alpha = 0.01$

6. Left-tailed test,
   $n = 24, \alpha = 0.05$

7. Two-tailed test,
   $n = 16, \alpha = 0.10$

8. Two-tailed test,
   $n = 29, \alpha = 0.01$

Graphical Analysis *In Exercises 9–12, state whether the standardized test statistic χ^2 allows you to reject the null hypothesis.*

9. (a) $\chi^2 = 2.091$
   (b) $\chi^2 = 0$
   (c) $\chi^2 = 1.086$
   (d) $\chi^2 = 6.3471$

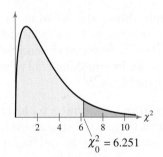

$\chi_0^2 = 6.251$

10. (a) $\chi^2 = 0.771$
    (b) $\chi^2 = 9.486$
    (c) $\chi^2 = 0.701$
    (d) $\chi^2 = 9.508$

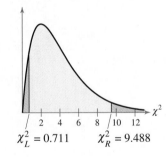

$\chi_L^2 = 0.711$ $\chi_R^2 = 9.488$

11. (a) $\chi^2 = 22.302$
    (b) $\chi^2 = 23.309$
    (c) $\chi^2 = 8.457$
    (d) $\chi^2 = 8.577$

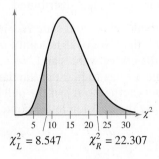

$\chi_L^2 = 8.547$ $\chi_R^2 = 22.307$

12. (a) $\chi^2 = 10.065$
    (b) $\chi^2 = 10.075$
    (c) $\chi^2 = 10.585$
    (d) $\chi^2 = 10.745$

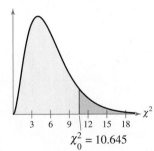

$\chi_0^2 = 10.645$

In Exercises 13 and 14, use a χ^2-test to test the claim about the population variance σ^2 or standard deviation σ at the given level of significance α using the given sample statistics. Assume the population is normally distributed.

13. Claim: $\sigma^2 = 0.52$; $\alpha = 0.05$. Sample statistics: $s^2 = 0.508$, $n = 18$

14. Claim: $\sigma < 40$; $\alpha = 0.01$. Sample statistics: $s = 40.8$, $n = 12$

■ Using and Interpreting Concepts

Testing Claims   *In Exercises 15–24, (a) write the claim mathematically and identify H_0 and H_a, (b) find the critical value(s) and identify the rejection region(s), (c) use the χ^2-test to find the standardized test statistic, (d) decide whether to reject or fail to reject the null hypothesis, and (e) interpret the decision in the context of the original claim. For each claim, assume the population is normally distributed.*

15. Life of Appliances   A large appliance company estimates that the variance of the life of its appliances is 3. You work for a consumer advocacy group and are asked to test this claim. You find that a random sample of the lives of 27 of the company's appliances has a variance of 2.8. At $\alpha = 0.05$, do you have enough evidence to reject the company's claim? *(Adapted from Consumer Reports)*

16. Hybrid Vehicle Gas Mileage   An automotive manufacturer believes that the variance of the gas mileage for its hybrid vehicles is 6. You work for an energy conservation agency and want to test this claim. You find that a random sample of the miles per gallon of 28 of the manufacturer's hybrid vehicles has a variance of 4.25. At $\alpha = 0.05$, do you have enough evidence to reject the manufacturer's claim? *(Adapted from Green Hybrid)*

17. Science Assessment Tests   On a science assessment test, the scores of a random sample of 22 eighth grade students have a standard deviation of 33.4 points. This result prompts a test administrator to claim that the standard deviation for eighth graders on the examination is less than 36 points. At $\alpha = 0.10$, is there enough evidence to support the administrator's claim? *(Adapted from National Center for Educational Statistics)*

18. U.S. History Assessment Tests   A state school administrator says that the standard deviation of test scores for eighth grade students who took a U.S. history assessment test is less than 30 points. You work for the administrator and are asked to test this claim. You randomly select 18 tests and find that the tests have a standard deviation of 33.6 points. At $\alpha = 0.01$, is there enough evidence to support the administrator's claim? *(Adapted from National Center for Educational Statistics)*

19. Hospital Waiting Times   A hospital spokesperson claims that the standard deviation of the waiting times experienced by patients in its minor emergency department is no more than 0.5 minute. A random sample of 25 waiting times has a standard deviation of 0.7 minute. At $\alpha = 0.10$, can you reject the spokesperson's claim?

20. Length of Stay   A doctor says the standard deviation of the lengths of stay for patients involved in a crash in which the vehicle struck a tree is 6.14 days. A random sample of 20 lengths of stay for patients involved in this type of crash has a standard deviation of 6.5 days. At $\alpha = 0.05$, can you reject the doctor's claim? *(Adapted from National Highway Traffic Safety Administration)*

21. **Total Charge**   An insurance agent says the standard deviation of the total hospital charge for patients involved in a crash in which the vehicle struck a construction barricade is less than \$3500. A random sample of 28 total hospital charges for patients involved in this type of crash has a standard deviation of \$4100. At $\alpha = 0.10$, can you support the agent's claim? *(Adapted from National Highway Traffic Safety Administration)*

22. **Hotel Room Rates**   A travel agency estimates that the standard deviation of the room rates of hotels in a certain city is no more than \$30. You work for a consumer advocacy group and are asked to test this claim. You find that a random sample of 21 hotels has a standard deviation of \$35.25. At $\alpha = 0.01$, do you have enough evidence to reject the agency's claim?

23. **Salaries**   The annual salaries of 16 randomly chosen actuaries are listed below. At $\alpha = 0.05$, can you conclude that the standard deviation of the annual salaries is greater than \$20,000? *(Adapted from America's Career InfoNet)*

68,146	57,529	108,761	68,433	64,600	99,548	71,286	60,516
84,014	119,920	120,975	91,345	62,865	76,852	88,522	95,794

24. **Salaries**   An employment information service says that the standard deviation of the annual salaries for public relations managers is at least \$14,500. The annual salaries for 18 randomly chosen public relations managers are listed. At $\alpha = 0.10$, can you reject the claim? *(Adapted from America's Career InfoNet)*

62,514	75,721	54,649	76,764	94,224	85,077
74,595	75,362	87,399	87,742	90,140	74,416
59,813	80,567	76,310	105,438	59,581	56,805

■ **Extending Concepts**

P-values   *You can calculate the P-value for a χ^2-test using technology. After calculating the χ^2-test value, you can use the cumulative density function (CDF) to calculate the area under the curve. From Example 4 on page 417, $\chi^2 = 43.2$. Using a TI-83/84 (choose 7 from the DISTR menu), enter 0 for the lower bound, 43.2 for the upper bound, and 40 for the degrees of freedom as shown.*

TI-83/84

χ^2 cdf (0, 43.2, 40)
.6637768667

The P-value is approximately $1 - 0.6638 = 0.3362$. Because $P > \alpha = 0.05$, the conclusion is to fail to reject H_0.

In Exercises 25–28, use the P-value method to perform the hypothesis test for the indicated exercise.

25. Exercise 21   26. Exercise 22

27. Exercise 23   28. Exercise 24

Uses & Abuses

Uses

Hypothesis Testing Hypothesis testing is important in many different fields because it gives a scientific procedure for assessing the validity of a claim about a population. Some of the concepts in hypothesis testing are intuitive, but some are not. For example, the *American Journal of Clinical Nutrition* suggests that eating dark chocolate can help prevent heart disease. A random sample of healthy volunteers were assigned to eat 3.5 ounces of dark chocolate each day for 15 days. After 15 days, the mean systolic blood pressure of the volunteers was 6.4 millimeters of mercury lower. A hypothesis test could show if this drop in systolic blood pressure is significant or simply due to sampling error.

Careful inferences must be made concerning the results. In another part of the study, it was found that white chocolate did not result in similar benefits. So, the inference of health benefits cannot be extended to all types of chocolate. You also would not infer that you should eat large quantities of chocolate because the benefits must be weighed against known risks, such as weight gain, acne, and acid reflux.

Abuses

Not Using a Random Sample The entire theory of hypothesis testing is based on the fact that the sample is randomly selected. If the sample is not random, then you cannot use it to infer anything about a population parameter.

Attempting to Prove the Null Hypothesis If the *P*-value for a hypothesis test is greater than the level of significance, you have not proven the null hypothesis is true—only that there is not enough evidence to reject it. For example, with a *P*-value higher than the level of significance, a researcher could not prove that there is no benefit to eating dark chocolate—only that there is not enough evidence to support the claim that there is a benefit.

Making Type I or Type II Errors Remember that a type I error is rejecting a null hypothesis that is true and a type II error is failing to reject a null hypothesis that is false. You can decrease the probability of a type I error by lowering the level of significance. Generally, if you decrease the probability of making a type I error, you increase the probability of making a type II error. You can decrease the chance of making both types of errors by increasing the sample size.

■ EXERCISES

Would You Consider Puchasing a Hybrid Car?

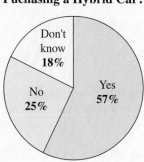

In Exercises 1–4, assume that you work in a market research department. You are asked to write a report about the claim that 57% of all new car buyers would seriously consider purchasing a hybrid car.

1. ***Not Using a Random Sample*** How could you choose a random sample to test this hypothesis?

2. ***Attempting to Prove the Null Hypothesis*** What is the null hypothesis in this situation? Describe how your report could be incorrect by trying to prove the null hypothesis.

3. ***Making a Type I Error*** Describe how your report could make a type I error.

4. ***Making a Type II Error*** Describe how your report could make a type II error.

7 A SUMMARY OF HYPOTHESIS TESTING

With hypothesis testing, perhaps more than any other area of statistics, it can be difficult to see the forest for all the trees. To help you see the forest—the overall picture—a summary of what you studied in this chapter is provided.

Writing the Hypotheses

- You are given a claim about a population parameter μ, p, σ^2, or σ.

- Rewrite the claim and its complement using $\underbrace{\le, \ge, =}_{H_0}$ and $\underbrace{>, <, \ne}_{H_a}$.

- Identify the claim. Is it H_0 or H_a?

Specifying a Level of Significance

- Specify α, the maximum acceptable probability of rejecting a valid H_0 (a type I error).

Insight

Large sample sizes will usually increase the cost and effort of testing a hypothesis, but they also tend to make your decision more reliable.

Specifying the Sample Size

- Specify your sample size n.

Choosing the Test ■ Any population ■ Normally distributed population

- Mean: H_0 describes a hypothesized population mean μ.

  - Use a **z-test** for *any* population if $n \ge 30$.

  - Use a **z-test** if the population is normal and σ is known for any n.

  - Use a **t-test** if the population is normal and $n < 30$, but σ is unknown.

- **Proportion:** H_0 describes a hypothesized population proportion p.

  - Use a **z-test** for *any* population if $np \ge 5$ and $nq \ge 5$.

- **Variance or Standard Deviation:** H_0 describes a hypothesized population variance σ^2 or standard deviation σ.

  - Use a **χ^2-test** if the population is normal.

Sketching the Sampling Distribution

- Use H_a to decide if the test is left-tailed, right-tailed, or two-tailed.

Finding the Standardized Test Statistic

- Take a random sample of size n from the population.

- Compute the test statistic $\bar{x}$, $\hat{p}$, or s^2.

- Find the standardized test statistic z, t, or χ^2.

Making a Decision

Option 1. Decision based on rejection region

- Use α to find the critical value(s) z_0, t_0, or χ_0^2 and rejection region(s).

- **Decision Rule:**

  Reject H_0 if the standardized test statistic is in the rejection region.
  Fail to reject H_0 if the standardized test statistic is not in the rejection region.

Option 2. Decision based on P-value

- Use the standardized test statistic or a technology tool to find the P-value.

- **Decision Rule:**

  Reject H_0 if $P \le \alpha$.
  Fail to reject H_0 if $P > \alpha$.

z-Test for a Hypothesized Mean μ *(Section 7.2)*

Test Statistic: $\overline{x}$

Critical value: z_0 (Use Table 4.)

If $n \geq 30$, *s* can be used in place of σ. Sampling distribution of sample means is a normal distribution.

Standardized Test Statistic: z

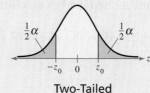

$$z = \frac{\overline{x} - \mu}{\sigma/\sqrt{n}}$$

Sample mean — Hypothesized mean
Population standard deviation — Sample size

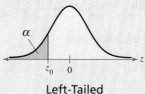
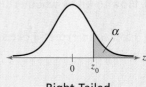

Left-Tailed   Two-Tailed   Right-Tailed

z-Test for a Hypothesized Proportion p *(Section 7.4)*

Test Statistic: $\hat{p}$

Critical value: z_0 (Use Table 4.)

Sampling distribution of sample proportions is a normal distribution.

Standardized Test Statistic: z

Sample proportion — Hypothesized proportion

$$z = \frac{\hat{p} - p}{\sqrt{pq/n}}$$

$q = 1 - p$ —— Sample size

t-Test for a Hypothesized Mean μ *(Section 7.3)*

Test Statistic: $\overline{x}$

Critical value: t_0 (Use Table 5.)

Sampling distribution of sample means is approximated by a *t*-distribution with d.f. $= n - 1$.

Standardized Test Statistic: t

Sample mean — Hypothesized mean

$$t = \frac{\overline{x} - \mu}{s/\sqrt{n}}$$

Sample standard deviation — Sample size

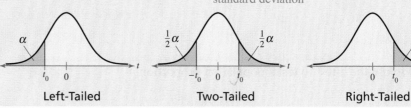

Left-Tailed   Two-Tailed   Right-Tailed

χ^2-Test for a Hypothesized Variance σ^2 or Standard Deviation σ *(Section 7.5)*

Test Statistic: s^2

Critical value: χ_0^2 (Use Table 6.)

Sampling distribution is approximated by a chi-square distribution with d.f. $= n - 1$.

Standardized Test Statistic: χ^2

Sample size — Sample variance

$$\chi^2 = \frac{(n-1)s^2}{\sigma^2}$$

Hypothesized variance

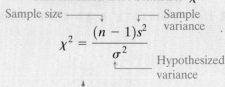
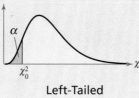
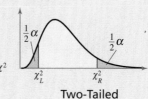
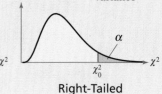

Left-Tailed   Two-Tailed   Right-Tailed

7 CHAPTER SUMMARY

What did you learn?

	EXAMPLE(S)	REVIEW EXERCISES
Section 7.1		
■ How to state a null hypothesis and an alternative hypothesis	*1*	*1–6*
■ How to identify type I and type II errors	*2*	*7–10*
■ How to know whether to use a one-tailed or a two-tailed statistical test	*3*	*7–10*
■ How to interpret a decision based on the results of a statistical test	*4*	*7–10*
Section 7.2		
■ How to find critical values for a z-test	*7, 8*	*11–14*
■ How to use rejection regions for a z-test	*9, 10*	*15–18, 21, 22*
■ How to find P-values and use them to test a mean μ	*1–6*	*19–22*
Section 7.3		
■ How to find critical values in a t-distribution	*1–3*	*23–26*
■ How to use the t-test to test a mean μ	*4, 5*	*27–34*
■ How to use technology to find P-values and use them with a t-test to test a mean μ	*6*	*35, 36*
Section 7.4		
■ How to use the z-test to test a population proportion p	*1–3*	*37–46*
Section 7.5		
■ How to find critical values for a χ^2-test	*1–3*	*47–50*
■ How to use the χ^2-test to test a variance or a standard deviation	*4–6*	*51–56*

7 REVIEW EXERCISES

Section 7.1

In Exercises 1–6, use the given claim to state a null hypothesis and an alternative hypothesis. Identify which hypothesis represents the claim.

1. Claim: $\mu \leq 1479$

2. Claim: $\mu = 95$

3. Claim: $p < 0.205$

4. Claim: $\mu \neq 150{,}020$

5. Claim: $\sigma > 6.2$

6. Claim: $p \geq 0.78$

In Exercises 7–10, do the following.

(a) State the null and alternative hypotheses.

(b) Determine when a type I or type II error occurs for a hypothesis test of the claim.

(c) Determine whether the hypothesis test is left-tailed, right-tailed, or two-tailed. Explain your reasoning.

(d) How should you interpret a decision that rejects the null hypothesis?

(e) How should you interpret a decision that fails to reject the null hypothesis?

7. A research center believes that the proportion of college students that occasionally or frequently come late to class is 63%. *(Adapted from Higher Education Research Institute at UCLA)*

8. A tire manufacturer guarantees that the mean life of a certain type of tire is at least 30,000 miles.

9. A soup maker says that the standard deviation of the sodium content in one serving of a certain soup is no more than 50 milligrams. *(Adapted from Consumer Reports)*

10. An energy bar maker claims that the mean number of grams of carbohydrates in one bar is less than 25.

Section 7.2

In Exercises 11–14, find the critical value(s) for the indicated z-test and level of significance α.

11. Left-tailed test, $\alpha = 0.02$

12. Two-tailed test, $\alpha = 0.005$

13. Right-tailed test, $\alpha = 0.025$

14. Two-tailed test, $\alpha = 0.08$

In Exercises 15–18, use a z-test to test the claim about the population mean μ at the given level of significance α using the given sample statistics. If convenient, use technology.

15. Claim: $\mu \leq 45$; $\alpha = 0.05$. Sample statistics: $\bar{x} = 47.2$, $s = 6.7$, $n = 42$

16. Claim: $\mu \neq 0$; $\alpha = 0.05$. Sample statistics: $\bar{x} = -0.69$, $s = 2.62$, $n = 60$

17. Claim: $\mu < 5.500$; $\alpha = 0.01$. Sample statistics: $\bar{x} = 5.497$, $s = 0.011$, $n = 36$

18. Claim: $\mu = 7450$; $\alpha = 0.05$. Sample statistics: $\bar{x} = 7512$, $s = 243$, $n = 57$

In Exercises 19 and 20, use a P-value to test the claim about the population mean μ using the given sample statistics. State your decision for $\alpha = 0.10$, $\alpha = 0.05$, and $\alpha = 0.01$ levels of significance. If convenient, use technology.

19. Claim: $\mu \leq 0.05$; Sample statistics: $\bar{x} = 0.057$, $s = 0.018$, $n = 32$

20. Claim: $\mu \neq 230$; Sample statistics: $\bar{x} = 216.5$, $s = 17.3$, $n = 48$

In Exercises 21 and 22, test the claim about the population mean μ using rejection region(s) or a P-value. If convenient, use technology.

21. A tourist agency in New York claims the mean daily cost of meals and lodging for a family of 4 traveling in New York is $326. You work for a consumer protection advocate and want to test this claim. In a random sample of 50 families of 4 traveling in New York, the mean daily cost of meals and lodging is $318 and the standard deviation is $25. At $\alpha = 0.05$, do you have enough evidence to reject the agency's claim? *(Adapted from American Automobile Association)*

22. A tourist agency in Hawaii claims the mean daily cost of meals and lodging for a family of 4 traveling in Hawaii is at most $650. You work for a consumer protection advocate and want to test this claim. In a random sample of 45 families of 4 traveling in Hawaii, the mean daily cost of meals and lodging is $657 with a standard deviation of $40. At $\alpha = 0.05$, do you have enough evidence to reject the tourist agency's claim? *(Adapted from American Automobile Association)*

Section 7.3

In Exercises 23–26, find the critical value(s) for the indicated t-test, level of significance α, and sample size n.

23. Two-tailed test, $\alpha = 0.05$, $n = 20$

24. Right-tailed test, $\alpha = 0.01$, $n = 8$

25. Left-tailed test, $\alpha = 0.10$, $n = 15$

26. Two-tailed test, $\alpha = 0.05$, $n = 12$

In Exercises 27–32, use a t-test to test the claim about the population mean μ at the given level of significance α using the given sample statistics. For each claim, assume the population is normally distributed. If convenient, use technology.

27. Claim: $\mu \neq 95$; $\alpha = 0.05$. Sample statistics: $\bar{x} = 94.1$, $s = 1.53$, $n = 12$

28. Claim: $\mu > 12,700$; $\alpha = 0.05$. Sample statistics: $\bar{x} = 12,804$, $s = 248$, $n = 21$

29. Claim: $\mu \geq 0$; $\alpha = 0.10$. Sample statistics: $\bar{x} = -0.45$, $s = 1.38$, $n = 16$

30. Claim: $\mu = 4.20$; $\alpha = 0.02$. Sample statistics: $\bar{x} = 4.41$, $s = 0.26$, $n = 9$

31. Claim: $\mu \leq 48$; $\alpha = 0.01$. Sample statistics: $\bar{x} = 52$, $s = 2.5$, $n = 7$

32. Claim: $\mu < 850$; $\alpha = 0.025$. Sample statistics: $\bar{x} = 875$, $s = 25$, $n = 14$

In Exercises 33 and 34, use a t-test to investigate the claim. For each claim, assume each population is normally distributed. If convenient, use technology.

33. A fitness magazine advertises that the mean monthly cost of joining a health club is $25. You work for a consumer advocacy group and are asked to test this claim. You find that a random sample of 18 clubs has a mean monthly cost of $26.25 and a standard deviation of $3.23. At $\alpha = 0.10$, do you have enough evidence to reject the advertisement's claim?

34. A restaurant claims that its hamburgers have no more than 10 grams of fat. You work for a nutritional health agency and are asked to test this claim. You find that a random sample of 9 hamburgers has a mean fat content of 13.5 grams and a standard deviation of 5.8 grams. At $\alpha = 0.10$, do you have enough evidence to reject the restaurant's claim?

In Exercises 35 and 36, use a t-statistic and its P-value to test the claim about the population mean μ using the given data. Assume the population is normally distributed. If convenient, use technology.

35. An education publication claims that the mean expenditure per student in public elementary and secondary schools is at least $10,200. You want to test this claim. You randomly select 16 school districts and find the average expenditure per student. The results are listed below. At $\alpha = 0.01$, can you reject the publication's claim? *(Adapted from National Center for Education Statistics)*

9,242	10,857	10,377	8,935	9,545	9,974
9,847	10,641	9,364	10,157	9,784	9,962
10,065	9,851	9,763	9,969		

36. A large university says the mean number of classroom hours per week for full-time faculty is more than 9. A random sample of the number of classroom hours for 11 full-time faculty for one week is listed. At $\alpha = 0.05$, test the university's claim. *(Adapted from National Center for Education Statistics)*

| 10.7 | 9.8 | 11.6 | 9.7 | 7.6 | 11.3 |
| 14.1 | 8.1 | 11.5 | 8.5 | 6.9 | |

Section 7.4

In Exercises 37–44, decide whether the normal sampling distribution can be used to approximate the binomial distribution. If it can, use the z-test to test the claim about the population proportion p at the given level of significance α using the given sample statistics. If convenient, use technology.

37. Claim: $p = 0.15$; $\alpha = 0.05$. Sample statistics: $\hat{p} = 0.09$, $n = 40$

38. Claim: $p < 0.70$; $\alpha = 0.01$. Sample statistics: $\hat{p} = 0.50$, $n = 68$

39. Claim: $p < 0.08$; $\alpha = 0.05$. Sample statistics: $\hat{p} = 0.03$, $n = 45$

40. Claim: $p = 0.50$; $\alpha = 0.10$. Sample statistics: $\hat{p} = 0.71$, $n = 129$

41. Claim: $p \geq 0.04$; $\alpha = 0.10$. Sample statistics: $\hat{p} = 0.03$, $n = 30$

42. Claim: $p \neq 0.34$; $\alpha = 0.01$. Sample statistics: $\hat{p} = 0.29$, $n = 60$

43. Claim: $p \neq 0.20$; $\alpha = 0.01$. Sample statistics: $\hat{p} = 0.23$, $n = 56$

44. Claim: $p \leq 0.80$; $\alpha = 0.10$. Sample statistics: $\hat{p} = 0.85$, $n = 43$

In Exercises 45 and 46, test the claim about the population proportion p. If convenient, use technology.

45. A polling agency claims that over 40% of adults shop for a gift within a week of an event. In a random survey of 2730 people in the United States, 1130 said they shop for a gift within a week of an event. Test the agency's claim at the $\alpha = 0.10$ level. What can you conclude? *(Adapted from Harris Interactive)*

46. The Western blot assay is a blood test for the presence of HIV. It has been found that this test sometimes gives false positive results for HIV. A medical researcher claims that the rate of false positives 2%. A recent study of 300 randomly selected U.S. blood donors who do not have HIV found that 3 received a false positive test result. Test the researcher's claim of a 2% false positive rate at the $\alpha = 0.05$ level. What can you conclude? *(Adapted from Centers for Disease Control and Prevention)*

Section 7.5

In Exercises 47–50, find the critical value(s) for the indicated χ^2-test for a population variance, sample size n, and level of significance α.

47. Right-tailed test, $n = 20$, $\alpha = 0.05$ **48.** Two-tailed test, $n = 14$, $\alpha = 0.01$

49. Right-tailed test, $n = 25$, $\alpha = 0.10$ **50.** Left-tailed test, $n = 6$, $\alpha = 0.05$

In Exercises 51–54, use a χ^2-test to test the claim about the population variance σ^2 or standard deviation σ at the given level of significance α and using the given sample statistics. Assume the population is normally distributed.

51. Claim: $\sigma^2 > 2$; $\alpha = 0.10$. Sample statistics: $s^2 = 2.95$, $n = 18$

52. Claim: $\sigma^2 \leq 60$; $\alpha = 0.025$. Sample statistics: $s^2 = 72.7$, $n = 15$

53. Claim: $\sigma = 1.25$; $\alpha = 0.05$. Sample statistics: $s = 1.03$, $n = 6$

54. Claim: $\sigma \neq 0.035$; $\alpha = 0.01$. Sample statistics: $s = 0.026$, $n = 16$

In Exercises 55 and 56, test the claim about the population variance or standard deviation. For each claim, assume the population is normally distributed.

55. A bolt manufacturer makes a type of bolt to be used in airtight containers. The manufacturer needs to be sure that all of its bolts are very similar in width, so it sets an upper tolerance limit for the variance of bolt width at 0.01. A random sample of the widths of 28 bolts has a variance of 0.064. Test the manufacturer's claim that the variance is at most 0.01 at the $\alpha = 0.005$ level. What can you conclude?

56. A bottler needs to be sure that its liquid dispensers are set properly. The standard deviation of liquid dispensed must be no more than 0.0025 liter. A random sample of 14 bottles has a standard deviation of 0.0031 liter. Test the bottler's claim that the standard deviation is no more than 0.0025 liter at the $\alpha = 0.01$ level. What can you conclude?

7 CHAPTER QUIZ

Take this quiz as you would take a quiz in class. After you are done, check your work against the answers given in the back of the book. If convenient, use technology.

For this quiz, do the following. If convenient, use technology.

(a) Write the claim mathematically. Identify H_0 and H_a.

(b) Determine whether the hypothesis test is one-tailed or two-tailed and whether to use a z-test, a t-test, or a χ^2-test. Explain your reasoning.

(c) If necessary, find the critical value(s) and identify the rejection region(s).

(d) Find the appropriate test statistic. If necessary, find the P-value.

(e) Decide whether to reject or fail to reject the null hypothesis. Then interpret the decision in the context of the original claim.

1. A citrus grower's association believes that the mean utilization of fresh citrus fruits by people in the United States is at least 22 pounds per year. A random sample of 103 people in the United States has a mean utilization of fresh citrus fruits of 21.6 pounds per year and a standard deviation of 7 pounds. At $\alpha = 0.02$, can you reject the association's claim that the mean utilization of fresh citrus fruits by people in the United States is at least 22 pounds per year? *(Adapted from U.S. Department of Agriculture)*

2. An auto maker estimates that the mean gas mileage of its sports utility vehicle is at least 20 miles per gallon. A random sample of 8 such vehicles had a mean of 18 miles per gallon and a standard deviation of 5 miles per gallon. At $\alpha = 0.05$, can you reject the auto maker's claim that the mean gas mileage of its sports utility vehicle is at least 20 miles per gallon? Assume the population is normally distributed. *(Adapted from Consumer Reports)*

3. A maker of microwave ovens advertises that no more than 10% of its microwaves need repair during the first 5 years of use. In a random sample of 57 microwaves that are 5 years old, 13% needed repairs. At $\alpha = 0.04$, can you reject the maker's claim that no more than 10% of its microwaves need repair during the first five years of use? *(Adapted from Consumer Reports)*

4. A state school administrator says that the standard deviation of SAT critical reading test scores is 113. A random sample of 14 SAT critical reading test scores has a standard deviation of 108. At $\alpha = 0.01$, test the administrator's claim. What can you conclude? Assume the population is normally distributed. *(Adapted from College Board Online)*

5. An employment information service reports that the mean annual salary for full-time male workers ages 25 to 34 with a bachelor's degree is $48,718. In a random sample of 12 full-time male workers ages 25 to 34 with a bachelor's degree, the mean annual salary is $47,164 and the standard deviation is $6500. Can you reject the service's claim? Use a *P*-value and $\alpha = 0.05$. Assume the population is normally distributed. *(Adapted from U.S. Census Bureau)*

6. A tourist agency in Kansas claims the mean daily cost of meals and lodging for a family of 4 traveling in the state is $201. You work for a consumer protection advocate and want to test this claim. In a random sample of 35 families of 4 traveling in Kansas, the mean daily cost of meals and lodging is $216 and the standard deviation is $30. Do you have enough evidence to reject the agency's claim? Use a *P*-value and $\alpha = 0.05$. *(Adapted from American Automobile Association)*

REAL Statistics — Real Decisions

You work for the public relations department of the Social Security Administration. In an effort to design better advertising campaigns, your department decides to conduct a survey to find out the opinions people in the United States have about the Social Security system. One of the questions asked and the results of each response and the respondent's age are shown in the table.

Your department believes that less than 40% of people in the United States expect that Social Security will be able to pay all the benefits they are entitled to under current law. Also, your department believes that the mean age of people in the United States who would say yes to this question is 60 years or older. As the department's research analyst, you must work with the data and determine if these claims can be supported or rejected.

■ **Exercises**

1. **How Would You Do It?**

   (a) What sampling technique would you use to select the sample for the study? Why? What sampling technique would you use if you wanted to select samples from four age groups: 18–34, 35–44, 45–54, and 55 and over?

   (b) Which technique in part (a) will give you a sample that is representative of the population?

   (c) Identify possible flaws or biases in your study.

2. **Testing a Proportion**

   Test the claim that less than 40% of people in the United States expect that Social Security will be able to pay all the benefits they are entitled to under current law. Use $\alpha = 0.10$. Write a paragraph that interprets the test's decision. Does the decision support your department's claim?

3. **Testing a Mean**

   Test the claim that the mean age of people in the United States who would say yes to the survey question shown in the table is 60 years or older. Use $\alpha = 0.10$ and assume that the population is normally distributed. Write a paragraph that interprets the test's decision. Is there enough evidence to reject your department's claim?

4. **Your Conclusions**

   On the basis of your analysis of the responses to this survey question, what would you tell your department?

WWW.SOCIALSECURITY.GOV

When you retire, do you expect that Social Security will be able to pay all the benefits you are entitled to under current law, or not?

Age	Response
83	Yes
37	No
49	No
27	Yes
27	No
59	Yes
44	Yes
46	No
25	No
30	No
72	Yes
66	No
47	No
47	No
50	Yes
76	Yes
51	Yes
58	No
79	Yes
69	Yes
66	No
35	Yes
47	No
29	Yes
76	No
31	Yes
40	No
61	Yes
30	Yes
71	No
64	No
18	No

(Adapted from *Newsweek*)

TECHNOLOGY   MINITAB   EXCEL   T1-83/84

THE CASE OF THE VANISHING WOMEN

53% ➡ 29% ➡ 9% ➡ 0%

From 1966 to 1968, Dr. Benjamin Spock and others were tried for conspiracy to violate the Selective Service Act by encouraging resistance to the Vietnam War. By a series of three selections, no women ended up being on the jury. In 1969, Hans Zeisel wrote an article in *The University of Chicago Law Review* using statistics and hypothesis testing to argue that the jury selection was biased against Dr. Spock. Dr. Spock was a well-known pediatrician and author of books about raising children. Millions of mothers had read his books and followed his advice. Zeisel argued that, by keeping women off the jury, the court prejudiced the verdict.

The jury selection process for Dr. Spock's trial is shown at the right.

Stage 1. The clerk of the Federal District Court selected 350 people "at random" from the Boston City Directory. The directory contained several hundred names, 53% of whom were women. However, only 102 of the 350 people selected were women.

Stage 2. The trial judge, Judge Ford, selected 100 people "at random" from the 350 people. This group was called a venire and it contained only nine women.

Stage 3. The court clerk assigned numbers to the members of the venire and, one by one, they were interrogated by the attorneys for the prosecution and defense until 12 members of the jury were chosen. At this stage, only one potential female juror was questioned, and she was eliminated by the prosecutor under his quota of peremptory challenges (for which he did not have to give a reason).

■ EXERCISES

1. The MINITAB display below shows a hypothesis test for a claim that the proportion of women in the city directory is $p = 0.53$. In the test, $n = 350$ and $\hat{p} = 0.2914$. Should you reject the claim? What is the level of significance? Explain.

2. In Exercise 1, you rejected the claim that $p = 0.53$. But this claim was true. What type of error is this?

3. If you reject a true claim with a level of significance that is virtually zero, what can you infer about the randomness of your sampling process?

4. Describe a hypothesis test for Judge Ford's "random" selection of the venire. Use a claim of

$$p = \frac{102}{350} \approx 0.2914.$$

   (a) Write the null and alternative hypotheses.
   (b) Use a technology tool to perform the test.
   (c) Make a decision.
   (d) Interpret the decision in the context of the original claim. Could Judge Ford's selection of 100 venire members have been random?

MINITAB

Test and Confidence Interval for One Proportion

Test of p = 0.53 vs p not = 0.53

Sample	X	N	Sample p	99.0 % CI	Z-Value	P-Value
1	102	350	0.291429	(0.228862, 0.353995)	-8.94	0.000

Extended solutions are given in the *Technology Supplement*. Technical instruction is provided for MINITAB, Excel, and the TI-83/84.

7 USING TECHNOLOGY TO PERFORM HYPOTHESIS TESTS

Here are some MINITAB and TI-83/84 printouts for some of the examples in this chapter. To duplicate the MINITAB results, you need the original data. For the TI-83/84, you can simply enter the descriptive statistics.

(See Example 5, page 383.)

Data for Investments for 30 Franchises

$70,700	$69,400	$90,600	$85,500	$97,100	$100,800
$114,700	$119,600	$123,600	$127,200	$131,200	$132,000
$134,400	$136,700	$138,500	$140,900	$143,300	$143,900
$151,100	$151,700	$157,200	$159,800	$163,000	$163,500
$169,300	$167,400	$168,800	$168,800	$159,100	$170,200

Display Descriptive Statistics...
Store Descriptive Statistics...

1-Sample Z...
1-Sample t...
2-Sample t...
Paired t...

1 Proportion...
2 Proportions...

MINITAB

Z-Test of the Mean

Test of mu = 143260 vs mu not = 143260
The assumed sigma = 30000

Variable	N	Mean	StDev	SE Mean	Z	P
C1	30	135000	30000	5477	−1.51	0.13

(See Example 4, page 400.)

Data for prices of 14 Honda Pilot LXs

$21,200	$21,500	$21,700	$22,000	$22,500
$22,700	$22,900	$23,200	$23,500	$23,700
$24,000	$24,100	$24,300	$24,700	

Display Descriptive Statistics...
Store Descriptive Statistics...

1-Sample Z...
1-Sample t...
2-Sample t...
Paired t...

1 Proportion...
2 Proportions...

MINITAB

T-Test of the Mean

Test of mu = 23900 vs mu < 23900

Variable	N	Mean	StDev	SE Mean	T	P
C1	14	23000	1113	297	−3.03	0.005

(See Example 2, page 409.)

Display Descriptive Statistics...
Store Descriptive Statistics...

1-Sample Z...
1-Sample t...
2-Sample t...
Paired t...

1 Proportion...
2 Proportions...

MINITAB

Test and Confidence Interval for One Proportion

Test of p = 0.45 vs p not = 0.45

Sample	X	N	Sample p	95.0 % CI	Z-Value	P-Value
1	98	200	0.490000	(0.420719, 0.559281)	1.14	0.256

(See Example 9, page 387.)   (See Example 5, page 401.)   (See Example 1, page 408.)

TI-83/84

EDIT CALC **TESTS**

1: Z-Test…
2: T-Test…
3: 2-SampZTest…
4: 2-SampTTest…
5: 1-PropZTest…
6: 2-PropZTest…
7↓ZInterval…

TI-83/84

EDIT CALC **TESTS**

1: Z-Test…
2: T-Test…
3: 2-SampZTest…
4: 2-SampTTest…
5: 1-PropZTest…
6: 2-PropZTest…
7↓ZInterval…

TI-83/84

EDIT CALC **TESTS**

1: Z-Test…
2: T-Test…
3: 2-SampZTest…
4: 2-SampTTest…
5: 1-PropZTest…
6: 2-PropZTest…
7↓ZInterval…

↓

TI-83/84

Z-Test

Inpt:Data **Stats**
μ_0: 45000
σ: 5200
$\bar{x}$: 43500
n: 30
μ: $\neq \mu_0$ **$< \mu_0$** $> \mu_0$
Calculate Draw

TI-83/84

T-Test

Inpt:Data **Stats**
μ_0: 6.8
$\bar{x}$: 6.7
Sx: .24
n: 19
μ: **$\neq \mu_0$** $< \mu_0$ $> \mu_0$
Calculate Draw

TI-83/84

1-PropZTest

p_0: .2
x: 15
n: 100
prop$\neq p_0$ **$< p_0$** $> p_0$
Calculate Draw

↓

TI-83/84

Z-Test
 $\mu < 45000$
 z= −1.579968916
 p= .0570569964
 $\bar{x}$= 43500
 n= 30

TI-83/84

T-Test
 $\mu \neq 6.8$
 t= −1.816207893
 p= .0860316039
 $\bar{x}$= 6.7
 Sx= .24
 n= 19

TI-83/84

1-PropZTest
 prop< .2
 z= −1.25
 p= .105649839
 $\hat{p}$= .15
 n= 100

↓

TI-83/84

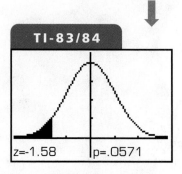

z=-1.58 | p=.0571

TI-83/84

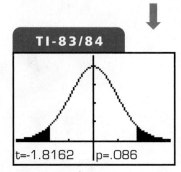

t=-1.8162 | p=.086

TI-83/84

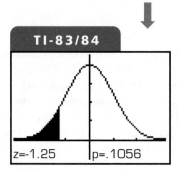

z=-1.25 | p=.1056

CHAPTER 8

Hypothesis Testing with Two Samples

8.1 Testing the Difference Between Means (Large Independent Samples)

■ CASE STUDY

8.2 Testing the Difference Between Means (Small Independent Samples)

8.3 Testing the Difference Between Means (Dependent Samples)

8.4 Testing the Difference Between Proportions

■ USES AND ABUSES

■ REAL STATISTICS– REAL DECISIONS

■ TECHNOLOGY

The *National Youth Tobacco Survey (NYTS)*, a report published by the Centers for Disease Control and Prevention, provides information on the most widely used tobacco products among U.S. students. One of the national health objectives for 2010 is to reduce current cigarette use among high school students to 16% or less.

← WHERE YOU'VE BEEN

In Chapter 6, you were introduced to inferential statistics and you learned how to form confidence intervals to estimate a parameter. Then, in Chapter 7, you learned how to test a claim about a population parameter, basing your decision on sample statistics and their distributions.

The *National Youth Tobacco Survey (NYTS)* is a study conducted by the Centers for Disease Control and Prevention to provide information about student use of tobacco products. As part of this study in a recent year, a random sample of 6869 U.S. male high school students was surveyed. The following proportions were found.

Male High School Students   ($n = 6869$)

Characteristic	Frequency	Proportion
Smoke cigarettes (at least one in the last 30 days)	1484	0.216
Smoke cigars (at least one in the last 30 days)	1264	0.184
Use smokeless tobacco (at least once in the last 30 days)	680	0.099

WHERE YOU'RE GOING →

In this chapter, you will continue your study of inferential statistics and hypothesis testing. Now, however, instead of testing a hypothesis about a single population, you will learn how to test a hypothesis that compares two populations.

For instance, in the *NYTS* study a random sample of 6869 U.S. high school female students was also surveyed. Here are the study's findings for this second group.

Female High School Students   ($n = 6869$)

Characteristic	Frequency	Proportion
Smoke cigarettes (at least one in the last 30 days)	1497	0.218
Smoke cigars (at least one in the last 30 days)	522	0.076
Use smokeless tobacco (at least once in the last 30 days)	82	0.012

From these two samples, can you conclude that there is a significantly greater proportion of high school students who smoke cigarettes, smoke cigars, or use smokeless tobacco among males than among females? Or, might the differences in the proportions be due to chance?

In this chapter, you will learn that you can answer these questions by testing the hypothesis that the two proportions are equal. For the proportions of students who use smokeless tobacco, for instance, the *P*-value for the hypothesis that $p_1 = p_2$ is about 0.0000. So, it is almost impossible that the two groups experienced the same proportion that use smokeless tobacco.

8.1 Testing the Difference Between Means (Large Independent Samples)

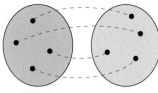

What You SHOULD LEARN

▸ How to decide whether two samples are independent or dependent

▸ An introduction to two-sample hypothesis testing for the difference between two population parameters

▸ How to perform a two-sample z-test for the difference between two means μ_1 and μ_2 using large independent samples

Independent Samples

Sample 1   Sample 2

Dependent Samples

Sample 1   Sample 2

Insight

Dependent samples often involve identical twins, before and after results for the same person or object, or results of individuals matched for specific characteristics.

Independent and Dependent Samples ▸ An Overview of Two-Sample Hypothesis Testing ▸ Two-Sample z-Test for the Difference Between Means

▸ Independent and Dependent Samples

In Chapter 7, you studied methods for testing a claim about the value of a population parameter. In this chapter, you will learn how to test a claim comparing parameters from two populations. When you compare the means of two different populations, the method you use to sample as well as the sample sizes will determine the type of test you will use.

DEFINITION

Two samples are **independent** if the sample selected from one population is not related to the sample selected from the second population. Two samples are **dependent** if each member of one sample corresponds to a member of the other sample. Dependent samples are also called **paired samples** or **matched samples.**

EXAMPLE 1

Independent and Dependent Samples

Classify each pair of samples as independent or dependent and justify your answer.

1. Sample 1: Resting heart rates of 35 individuals before drinking coffee
   Sample 2: Resting heart rates of the same individuals after drinking two cups of coffee
2. Sample 1: Test scores for 35 statistics students
   Sample 2: Test scores for 42 biology students who do not study statistics

Solution

1. These samples are dependent. Because the resting heart rates of the same individuals are taken, the samples are related. The samples can be paired with respect to each individual.
2. These samples are independent. It is not possible to form a pairing between the members of samples; the sample sizes are different, and the data represent test scores for different individuals.

▸ Try It Yourself 1

Classify each pair of samples as independent or dependent.

1. Sample 1: Heights of 27 adult females
   Sample 2: Heights of 27 adult males
2. Sample 1: Midterm exam scores of 14 chemistry students
   Sample 2: Final exam scores of the same 14 chemistry students

Determine whether the samples are independent or dependent.

Answer: Page A45

▶ An Overview of Two-Sample Hypothesis Testing

In this section you will learn how to test a claim comparing the means of two different populations using independent samples.

For instance, suppose you are developing a marketing plan for an Internet service provider and want to determine whether there is a difference in the amount of time male and female college students spend online each day. The only way you can conclude with certainty that there is a difference is to take a census of all college students, calculate the mean daily times male students and female students spend online, and find the difference. Of course, it is not practical to take such a census. However, you can still determine with some degree of certainty whether such a difference exists.

You can begin by assuming that there is no difference in the mean times of the two populations. That is, $\mu_1 - \mu_2 = 0$. Then by taking a random sample from each population, and using the resulting two-sample test statistic $\bar{x}_1 - \bar{x}_2$, you can perform a two-sample hypothesis test. Suppose you obtain the following results:

Insight

The members in the two samples are not matched or paired, so the samples are independent.

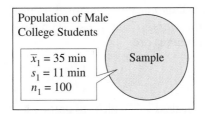

Population of Male College Students

$\bar{x}_1 = 35$ min
$s_1 = 11$ min
$n_1 = 100$

Sample

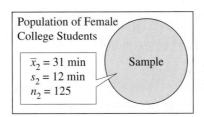

Population of Female College Students

$\bar{x}_2 = 31$ min
$s_2 = 12$ min
$n_2 = 125$

Sample

The graph below shows the sampling distribution of $\bar{x}_1 - \bar{x}_2$ for many similar samples taken from each population, under the assumption that $\mu_1 - \mu_2 = 0$. From the graph, you can see that it is quite unlikely to obtain sample means that differ by 4 minutes if the actual difference is 0. The difference of the sample means would be more than 2.5 standard errors from the hypothesized difference of 0! So, you can conclude that there is a significant difference in the amount of time male college students and female college students spend online each day.

Sampling Distribution

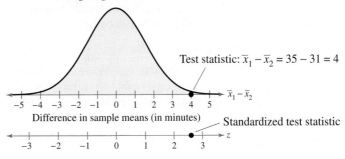

Test statistic: $\bar{x}_1 - \bar{x}_2 = 35 - 31 = 4$

Difference in sample means (in minutes)

Standardized test statistic

It is important to remember that when you perform a two-sample hypothesis test using independent samples, you are testing a claim concerning the difference between the parameters in two populations, not the values of the parameters themselves.

DEFINITION

For a two-sample hypothesis test with independent samples,

1. the **null hypothesis H_0** is a statistical hypothesis that usually states there is no difference between the parameters of two populations. The null hypothesis always contains the symbol $\le$, $=$, or $\ge$.

2. the **alternative hypothesis H_a** is a statistical hypothesis that is true when H_0 is false. The alternative hypothesis contains the symbol $>$, $\ne$, or $<$.

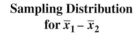

Study Tip

You can also write the null and alternative hypotheses as follows.

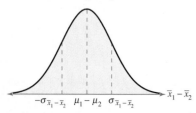

$$\begin{cases} H_0: \mu_1 - \mu_2 = 0 \\ H_a: \mu_1 - \mu_2 \ne 0 \end{cases}$$

$$\begin{cases} H_0: \mu_1 - \mu_2 \le 0 \\ H_a: \mu_1 - \mu_2 > 0 \end{cases}$$

$$\begin{cases} H_0: \mu_1 - \mu_2 \ge 0 \\ H_a: \mu_1 - \mu_2 < 0 \end{cases}$$

To write a null and an alternative hypothesis for a two-sample hypothesis test with independent samples, translate the claim made about the population parameters from a verbal statement to a mathematical statement. Then, write its complementary statement. For instance, if the claim is about two population parameters μ_1 and μ_2, then some possible pairs of null and alternative hypotheses are

$$\begin{cases} H_0: \mu_1 = \mu_2 \\ H_a: \mu_1 \ne \mu_2 \end{cases}, \quad \begin{cases} H_0: \mu_1 \le \mu_2 \\ H_a: \mu_1 > \mu_2 \end{cases}, \quad \text{and} \quad \begin{cases} H_0: \mu_1 \ge \mu_2 \\ H_a: \mu_1 < \mu_2 \end{cases}.$$

Regardless of which hypotheses you use, you always assume there is no difference between the population means, or $\mu_1 = \mu_2$.

▶ Two-Sample *z*-Test for the Difference Between Means

In the remainder of this section, you will learn how to perform a *z*-test for the difference between two population means μ_1 and μ_2. Three conditions are necessary to perform such a test.

1. The samples must be randomly selected.
2. The samples must be independent.
3. Each sample size must be at least 30 or, if not, each population must have a normal distribution with a known standard deviation.

If these requirements are met, then the **sampling distribution for $\bar{x}_1 - \bar{x}_2$ (the difference of the sample means)** is a normal distribution with mean and standard error as follows.

Sampling Distribution for $\bar{x}_1 - \bar{x}_2$

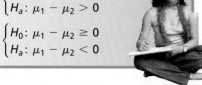

In Words	In Symbols
The mean of the difference of the sample means is the assumed difference between the two population means. When no difference is assumed, the mean is 0.	Mean $= \mu_{\bar{x}_1 - \bar{x}_2}$ $= \mu_{\bar{x}_1} - \mu_{\bar{x}_2}$ $= \mu_1 - \mu_2$
The variance of the sampling distribution is the sum of the variances of the individual sampling distributions for $\bar{x}_1$ and $\bar{x}_2$. The standard error is the square root of the sum of the variances.	Standard error $= \sigma_{\bar{x}_1 - \bar{x}_2}$ $= \sqrt{\sigma_{\bar{x}_1}^2 + \sigma_{\bar{x}_2}^2}$ $= \sqrt{\dfrac{\sigma_1^2}{n_1} + \dfrac{\sigma_2^2}{n_2}}$

Because the sampling distribution for $\bar{x}_1 - \bar{x}_2$ is a normal distribution, you can use the z-test to test the difference between two population means μ_1 and μ_2. Notice that the standardized test statistic takes the form of

$$z = \frac{(\text{Observed difference}) - (\text{Hypothesized difference})}{\text{Standard error}}.$$

TWO-SAMPLE z-TEST FOR THE DIFFERENCE BETWEEN MEANS

A **two-sample z-test** can be used to test the difference between two population means μ_1 and μ_2 when a large sample (at least 30) is randomly selected from each population and the samples are *independent*. The **test statistic** is $\bar{x}_1 - \bar{x}_2$, and the **standardized test statistic** is

$$z = \frac{(\bar{x}_1 - \bar{x}_2) - (\mu_1 - \mu_2)}{\sigma_{\bar{x}_1 - \bar{x}_2}} \quad \text{where} \quad \sigma_{\bar{x}_1 - \bar{x}_2} = \sqrt{\frac{\sigma_1^2}{n_1} + \frac{\sigma_2^2}{n_2}}.$$

When the samples are large, you can use s_1 and s_2 in place of σ_1 and σ_2. If the samples are not large, you can still use a two-sample z-test, provided the populations are normally distributed and the population standard deviations are known.

If the null hypothesis states $\mu_1 = \mu_2$, $\mu_1 \leq \mu_2$, or $\mu_1 \geq \mu_2$, then $\mu_1 = \mu_2$ is assumed and the expression $\mu_1 - \mu_2$ is equal to 0 in the preceding test.

GUIDELINES

Using a Two-Sample z-Test for the Difference Between Means (Large Independent Samples)

In Words	*In Symbols*
1. State the claim mathematically. Identify the null and alternative hypotheses.	State H_0 and H_a.
2. Specify the level of significance.	Identify α.
3. Sketch the sampling distribution.	
4. Determine the critical value(s).	Use Table 4 in Appendix B.
5. Determine the rejection region(s).	
6. Find the standardized test statistic.	$z = \dfrac{(\bar{x}_1 - \bar{x}_2) - (\mu_1 - \mu_2)}{\sigma_{\bar{x}_1 - \bar{x}_2}}$
7. Make a decision to reject or fail to reject the null hypothesis.	If z is in the rejection region, reject H_0. Otherwise, fail to reject H_0.
8. Interpret the decision in the context of the original claim.	

A hypothesis test for the difference between means can also be performed using P-values. Use the same guidelines above, skipping Steps 4 and 5. After finding the standardized test statistic, use the Standard Normal Table to calculate the P-value. Then make a decision to reject or fail to reject the null hypothesis. If P is less than or equal to α, reject H_0. Otherwise, fail to reject H_0.

PICTURING the WORLD

There are about 23,600 civilian federal employees working in Michigan and about 25,100 in Massachusetts. In a survey, 200 federal employees in each state were asked to report their salary. The results were as follows.
(Adapted from United States Office of Personnel Management)

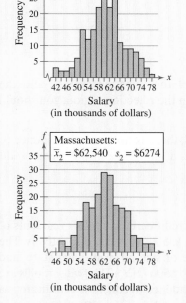

Is there enough evidence to conclude that there is a difference in the mean incomes of civilian federal employees in Michigan and Massachusetts using $\alpha = 0.05$?

Sample Statistics for Credit Card Debt

Females	Males
$\bar{x}_1 = \$2290$	$\bar{x}_2 = \$2370$
$s_1 = \$750$	$s_2 = \$800$
$n_1 = 200$	$n_2 = 200$

EXAMPLE 2

A Two-Sample *z*-Test for the Difference Between Means

See TI-83/84 steps on page 489.

A consumer education organization claims that there is a difference in the mean credit card debt of males and females in the United States. The results of a random survey of 200 individuals from each group are shown at the left. The two samples are independent. Do the results support the organization's claim? Use $\alpha = 0.05$. *(Adapted from Myvesta)*

Solution You want to test the claim that there is a difference in the mean credit card debts of males and females in the United States. So, the null and alternative hypotheses are

$$H_0: \mu_1 = \mu_2 \quad \text{and} \quad H_a: \mu_1 \neq \mu_2. \text{ (Claim)}$$

Because the test is a two-tailed test and the level of significance is $\alpha = 0.05$, the critical values are $-z_0 = -1.96$ and $z_0 = 1.96$. The rejection regions are $z < -1.96$ and $z > 1.96$. Because both samples are large, s_1 and s_2 are used in place of σ_1 and σ_2 to calculate the standard error.

$$\sigma_{\bar{x}_1 - \bar{x}_2} = \sqrt{\frac{s_1^2}{n_1} + \frac{s_2^2}{n_2}} = \sqrt{\frac{750^2}{200} + \frac{800^2}{200}} \approx 77.5403$$

The standardized test statistic is

$$z = \frac{(\bar{x}_1 - \bar{x}_2) - (\mu_1 - \mu_2)}{\sigma_{\bar{x}_1 - \bar{x}_2}} \qquad \text{Use the } z\text{-test.}$$

$$\approx \frac{(2290 - 2370) - 0}{77.5403} \qquad \text{Assume } \mu_1 = \mu_2, \text{ so } \mu_1 - \mu_2 = 0.$$

$$\approx -1.03.$$

The graph at the left shows the location of the rejection regions and the standardized test statistic z. Because z is not in the rejection region, you should fail to reject the null hypothesis.

Interpretation At the 5% significance level, there is not enough evidence to support the organization's claim that there is a difference in the mean credit card debt of males and females.

▶ Try It Yourself 2

A survey indicates that the mean per capita credit card charge for residents of New Hampshire and New York is $3900 and $3500 per year, respectively. The survey included a randomly selected sample of size 50 from each state, and sample standard deviations are $900 (NH) and $500 (NY). The two samples are independent. At $\alpha = 0.01$, is there enough evidence to conclude that there is a difference in the mean credit card charges? *(Adapted from Card Management Information Services and the U.S. Census Bureau)*

a. *Identify* the claim and state H_0 and H_a.
b. *Specify* the level of significance α.
c. *Find* the critical values and identify the rejection regions.
d. *Use* the z-test to find the standardized test statistic z.
e. *Decide* whether to reject the null hypothesis. Use a graph if necessary.
f. *Interpret* the decision in the context of the original claim.

Answer: Page A45

Study Tip

In Example 2, you can also use a *P*-value to perform the hypothesis test. For instance, the test is a two-tailed test, so the *P*-value is equal to twice the area to the left of $z = -1.03$, or

$$2(0.1515) = 0.303.$$

Because $0.303 > 0.05$, you should fail to reject H_0.

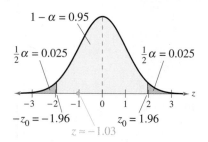

$1 - \alpha = 0.95$

$\frac{1}{2}\alpha = 0.025$ $\frac{1}{2}\alpha = 0.025$

$-z_0 = -1.96$ $z_0 = 1.96$

$z \approx -1.03$

**Sample Statistics for Daily
Cost of Meals and Lodging
for a Family of Four**

Texas	Virginia
$\bar{x}_1 = \$248$	$\bar{x}_2 = \$252$
$s_1 = \$15$	$s_2 = \$22$
$n_1 = 50$	$n_2 = 35$

EXAMPLE 3

Using Technology to Perform a Two-Sample z-Test

The American Automobile Association claims that the average daily cost for meals and lodging for vacationing in Texas is less than the same average costs for vacationing in Virginia. The table at the left shows the results of a random survey of vacationers in each state. The two samples are independent. At $\alpha = 0.01$, is there enough evidence to support the claim? [$H_0: \mu_1 \geq \mu_2$ and $H_a: \mu_1 < \mu_2$ (claim)]

Solution   The top two displays show how to set up the hypothesis test using a TI-83/84. The remaining displays show the possible results, depending on whether you select *Calculate* or *Draw*.

Study Tip

Note that the TI-83/84 displays $P \approx 0.1751$. Because $P > \alpha$, you should fail to reject the null hypothesis.

To use MINITAB to perform a two-sample z-test, you must use raw data.

TI-83/84

```
2-SampZTest
 Inpt:Data Stats
 σ1:15
 σ2:22
 x̄1:248
 n1:50
 x̄2:252
↓n2:35
```

TI-83/84

```
2-SampZTest
↑σ2:22
 x̄1:248
 n1:50
 x̄2:252
 n2:35
 μ1:≠μ2  <μ2  >μ2
 Calculate Draw
```

TI-83/84

```
2-SampZTest
 μ1<μ2
 z=−.9343200811
 p=.1750693839
 x̄1:248
 x̄2:252
↓n1:50
```

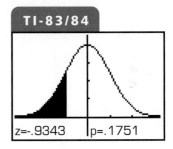

Because the test is a left-tailed test and $\alpha = 0.01$, the rejection region is $z < -2.33$. The standardized test statistic $z \approx -0.93$ is not in the rejection region, so you should fail to reject the null hypothesis.

Interpretation   At the 1% significance level, there is not enough evidence to support the American Automobile Association's claim.

▸ Try It Yourself 3

The American Automobile Association claims that the average daily meal and lodging costs for vacationing in Maryland are greater than the same average costs for vacationing in Colorado. The table at the left shows the results of a random survey of vacationers in each state. The two samples are independent. At $\alpha = 0.05$, is there enough evidence to support the claim?

a. *Use* a TI-83/84 to find the test statistic or the *P*-value.
b. *Make* a decision and *interpret*.   *Answer: Page A45*

**Sample Statistics for Daily
Cost of Meals and Lodging
for a Family of Four**

Maryland	Colorado
$\bar{x}_1 = \$293$	$\bar{x}_2 = \$286$
$s_1 = \$22$	$s_2 = \$18$
$n_1 = 150$	$n_2 = 200$

8.1 EXERCISES

For Extra Help

MyStatLab

■ Building Basic Skills and Vocabulary

1. What is the difference between two samples that are dependent and two samples that are independent? Give an example of two dependent samples and two independent samples.

2. Explain how to perform a two-sample z-test for the difference between the means of two populations using large independent samples.

3. Describe another way you can perform a hypothesis test for the difference between the means of two populations using large independent samples.

4. What conditions are necessary in order to use the z-test to test the difference between two population means?

In Exercises 5–12, classify the two given samples as independent or dependent. Explain your reasoning.

5. Sample 1: The SAT scores for 35 high school students who did not take an SAT preparation course

   Sample 2: The SAT scores for 40 high school students who did take an SAT preparation course

6. Sample 1: The SAT scores for 44 high school students

   Sample 2: The SAT scores for the same 44 high school students after taking an SAT preparation course

7. Sample 1: The weights of 51 adults

   Sample 2: The weights of the same 51 adults after participating in a diet and exercise program for one month

8. Sample 1: The weights of 40 females

   Sample 2: The weights of 40 males

9. Sample 1: The average speed of 23 powerboats using an old hull design

   Sample 2: The average speed of 14 powerboats using a new hull design

10. Sample 1: The fuel mileage of 10 cars

    Sample 2: The fuel mileage of the same 10 cars using an alternative fuel

11. The table shows the braking distances (in feet) for each of four different sets of tires with the car's antilock braking system (ABS) on and with ABS off. The tests were done on ice with cars traveling at 15 miles per hour. *(Source: Consumer Reports)*

Tire Set	1	2	3	4
Braking distance with ABS	42	55	43	61
Braking distance without ABS	58	67	59	75

12. The table shows the heart rates (in beats per minute) of five people before exercising and after.

Person	1	2	3	4	5
Heart rate before exercising	65	72	85	78	93
Heart rate after exercising	127	135	140	136	150

In Exercises 13–16, (a) find the test statistic, (b) find the standardized test statistic, (c) decide whether the standardized test statistic is in the rejection region, and (d) decide whether you should reject or fail to reject the null hypothesis. The samples are random and independent.

13. Claim: $\mu_1 = \mu_2$, $\alpha = 0.05$. Sample statistics: $\bar{x}_1 = 16$, $s_1 = 1.1$, $n_1 = 50$ and $\bar{x}_2 = 14$, $s_2 = 1.5$, $n_2 = 50$

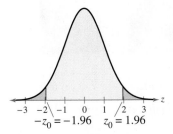

FIGURE FOR EXERCISE 13

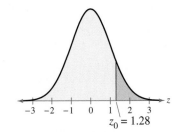

FIGURE FOR EXERCISE 14

14. Claim: $\mu_1 > \mu_2$, $\alpha = 0.10$. Sample statistics: $\bar{x}_1 = 500$, $s_1 = 30$, $n_1 = 100$ and $\bar{x}_2 = 510$, $s_2 = 15$, $n_2 = 75$

15. Claim: $\mu_1 < \mu_2$, $\alpha = 0.01$. Sample statistics: $\bar{x}_1 = 1225$, $s_1 = 75$, $n_1 = 35$ and $\bar{x}_2 = 1195$, $s_2 = 105$, $n_2 = 105$

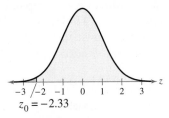

FIGURE FOR EXERCISE 15

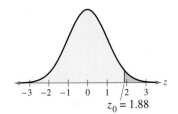

FIGURE FOR EXERCISE 16

16. Claim: $\mu_1 \leq \mu_2$, $\alpha = 0.03$. Sample statistics: $\bar{x}_1 = 5004$, $s_1 = 136$, $n_1 = 144$ and $\bar{x}_2 = 4895$, $s_2 = 215$, $n_2 = 156$

In Exercises 17 and 18, use the given sample statistics to test the claim about the difference between two population means μ_1 and μ_2 at the given level of significance α.

17. Claim: $\mu_1 > \mu_2$, $\alpha = 0.01$. Statistics: $\bar{x}_1 = 5.2$, $s_1 = 0.2$, $n_1 = 45$ and $\bar{x}_2 = 5.5$, $s_2 = 0.3$, $n_2 = 37$

18. Claim: $\mu_1 \neq \mu_2$, $\alpha = 0.05$. Statistics: $\bar{x}_1 = 52$, $s_1 = 2.5$, $n_1 = 70$ and $\bar{x}_2 = 45$, $s_2 = 5.5$, $n_2 = 60$

■ Using and Interpreting Concepts

Testing the Difference Between Two Means *In Exercises 19–32, (a) identify the claim and state H_0 and H_a, (b) use Table 4 in Appendix B to find the critical value(s) and identify the rejection region(s), (c) find the standardized test statistic z. (d) decide whether to reject or fail to reject the null hypothesis, and (e) interpret the decision in the context of the original claim. If convenient, use technology to solve the problem. In each exercise, assume the samples are randomly selected and that the samples are independent.*

19. Braking Distances A safety engineer records the braking distances of two types of tires. Each randomly selected sample has 35 tires. The results of the tests are shown in the figure. At $\alpha = 0.10$, can the engineer support the claim that the mean braking distance is different for the two types of tires? *(Adapted from Consumer Reports)*

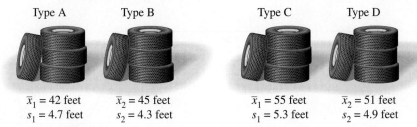

Type A	Type B	Type C	Type D

$\bar{x}_1 = 42$ feet $\bar{x}_2 = 45$ feet $\bar{x}_1 = 55$ feet $\bar{x}_2 = 51$ feet
$s_1 = 4.7$ feet $s_2 = 4.3$ feet $s_1 = 5.3$ feet $s_2 = 4.9$ feet

FIGURE FOR EXERCISE 19   **FIGURE FOR EXERCISE 20**

20. Braking Distances To compare the braking distances for two types of tires, a safety engineer conducts 50 braking tests for each of the two types of tires. The results of the tests are shown in the figure. At $\alpha = 0.10$, can the engineer support the claim that the mean braking distance for Type C is greater than the mean braking distance for Type D? *(Adapted from Consumer Reports)*

21. Repair Costs: Microwave Ovens You want to buy a microwave oven and will choose Model A if its repair costs are lower than Model B's. You research the repair costs of 47 Model A ovens and 55 Model B ovens. The results of your research are shown in the figure. At $\alpha = 0.01$, would you buy Model A? *(Adapted from Consumer Reports)*

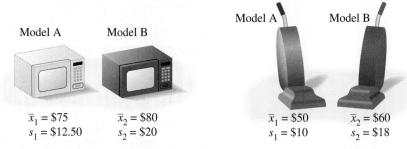

Model A	Model B	Model A	Model B

$\bar{x}_1 = \$75$ $\bar{x}_2 = \$80$ $\bar{x}_1 = \$50$ $\bar{x}_2 = \$60$
$s_1 = \$12.50$ $s_2 = \$20$ $s_1 = \$10$ $s_2 = \$18$

FIGURE FOR EXERCISE 21   **FIGURE FOR EXERCISE 22**

22. Repair Costs: Vacuum Cleaners You want to buy a vacuum cleaner, and a salesperson tells you the repair costs for Model A and Model B are equal. You research the repair costs of 34 Model A vacuum cleaners and 46 Model B vacuum cleaners. The results of your research are shown in the figure. At $\alpha = 0.01$, can you reject the salesperson's claim? *(Adapted from Consumer Reports)*

23. ACT Scores The mean ACT score for 43 male high school students is 21.1 and the standard deviation is 5.0. The mean ACT score for 56 female high school students is 20.9 and the standard deviation is 4.7. At $\alpha = 0.01$, can you reject the claim that male and female high school students have equal ACT scores? *(Adapted from ACT Inc.)*

24. **ACT Scores**   A guidance counselor claims that high school students in a college prep program have higher ACT scores than those in a general program. The mean ACT score for 49 high school students who are in a college prep program is 22.2 and the standard deviation is 4.8. The mean ACT score for 44 high school students who are in a general program is 20.0 and the standard deviation is 5.4. At $\alpha = 0.10$, can you support the guidance counselor's claim? *(Adapted from ACT Inc.)*

25. **Lodging Costs**   A travel association says that the mean daily lodging cost for a family traveling in North Carolina is the same as in South Carolina. The mean daily lodging cost for 35 families traveling in North Carolina is $131 and the standard deviation is $26. The mean daily lodging cost for 35 families traveling in South Carolina is $136 and the standard deviation is $19. At $\alpha = 0.10$, is there enough evidence to reject the travel association's claim? *(Adapted from the American Automobile Association)*

26. **Money Spent Eating Out**   A restaurant association says that households in the United States headed by people under the age of 25 spend less on food away from home than households headed by people ages 55–64. The mean amount spent by 30 households headed by people under the age of 25 is $2015 and the standard deviation is $113. The mean amount spent by 30 households headed by people ages 55–64 is $2715 and the standard deviation is $97. At $\alpha = 0.05$, can you support the restaurant association's claim? *(Adapted from Bureau of Labor Statistics)*

27. **Lodging Costs**   Refer to Exercise 25. Two more samples are taken, one from North Carolina and one from South Carolina. For 50 families traveling in North Carolina, $\bar{x}_1 = \$145$ and $s_1 = \$28$. For 50 families traveling in South Carolina, $\bar{x}_2 = \$138$ and $s_2 = \$24$. Use $\alpha = 0.10$. Do the new samples lead to a different conclusion?

28. **Money Spent Eating Out**   Refer to Exercise 26. Two more samples are taken, one from each age group. For 40 households headed by people under the age of 25, $\bar{x}_1 = \$2130$ and $s_1 = \$124$. For 40 households headed by people ages 55–64, $\bar{x}_2 = \$2655$ and $s_2 = \$116$. Use $\alpha = 0.05$. Do the new samples lead to a different conclusion?

29. **Watching More TV?**   A sociologist claims that children ages 6–17 spent more time watching television in 1981 than children ages 6–17 do today. A study was conducted in 1981 to find the time that children ages 6–17 watched television on weekdays. The results (in hours per weekday) are shown below.

2.0	2.5	2.1	2.3	2.1	1.6	2.6	2.1	2.1	2.4
2.1	2.1	1.5	1.7	2.1	2.3	2.5	3.3	2.2	2.9
1.5	1.9	2.4	2.2	1.2	3.0	1.0	2.1	1.9	2.2

Recently, a similar study was conducted. The results are shown below.

2.9	1.8	0.9	1.6	2.0	1.7	2.5	1.1	1.6	2.0
1.4	1.7	1.7	1.9	1.6	1.7	1.2	2.0	2.6	1.6
1.5	2.5	1.6	2.1	1.7	1.8	1.1	1.4	1.2	2.3

At $\alpha = 0.025$, can you support the sociologist's claim? *(Adapted from University of Michigan's Institute for Social Research)*

30. Spending More Time Studying? A sociologist thinks that middle school boys spent less time studying in 1981 than middle school boys do today. A study was conducted in 1981 to find the time that middle school boys spent studying on weekdays. The results (in minutes per weekday) are shown below.

31.9	35.4	28.0	39.1	30.5	31.9	33.0	29.6	35.7	30.2
38.8	35.9	37.1	36.2	32.6	36.9	24.2	28.5	28.7	41.1
33.8	32.1	28.7	35.4	36.6	34.3	35.5	34.2	33.8	25.3
27.7	21.9	30.0	36.8	26.9					

Recently, a similar study was conducted. The results are shown below.

44.7	54.6	41.1	46.7	43.0	46.6	42.9	48.7	50.0	47.9
47.2	58.0	51.0	41.1	49.6	51.3	39.0	45.6	49.8	54.4
47.1	45.5	52.8	49.4	47.2	54.8	40.2	45.4	48.6	50.0
51.5	55.0	44.7	42.2	52.0					

At $\alpha = 0.03$, can you support the sociologist's claim? *(Adapted from University of Michigan's Institute for Social Research)*

31. Washer Diameters A production engineer claims that there is no difference in the mean washer diameter manufactured by two different methods. The first method produces washers with the following diameters (in inches).

0.861	0.864	0.882	0.887	0.858	0.879	0.887	0.876	0.870
0.894	0.884	0.882	0.869	0.859	0.887	0.875	0.863	0.887
0.882	0.862	0.906	0.880	0.877	0.864	0.873	0.860	0.866
0.869	0.877	0.863	0.875	0.883	0.872	0.879	0.861	

The second method produces washers with these diameters (in inches).

0.705	0.703	0.715	0.711	0.690	0.720	0.702	0.686	0.704
0.712	0.718	0.695	0.708	0.695	0.699	0.715	0.691	0.696
0.680	0.703	0.697	0.694	0.714	0.694	0.672	0.688	0.700
0.715	0.709	0.698	0.696	0.700	0.706	0.695	0.715	

At $\alpha = 0.01$, can you reject the production engineer's claim?

32. Nut Diameters A production engineer claims that there is no difference in the mean nut diameter manufactured by two different methods. The first method produces nuts with the following diameters (in centimeters).

3.330	3.337	3.329	3.354	3.325	3.343	3.333	3.347	3.332
3.358	3.353	3.335	3.341	3.331	3.327	3.326	3.337	3.336
3.323	3.347	3.329	3.345	3.329	3.338	3.353	3.339	3.338
3.338	3.350	3.320	3.364	3.340	3.348	3.339	3.336	3.321
3.316	3.352	3.320	3.336					

The second method produces nuts with these diameters (in centimeters).

3.513	3.490	3.498	3.504	3.483	3.512	3.494	3.514	3.495
3.489	3.493	3.499	3.497	3.495	3.496	3.485	3.506	3.517
3.484	3.498	3.522	3.505	3.501	3.491	3.500	3.499	3.475
3.486	3.501	3.496	3.504	3.513	3.511	3.501	3.487	3.508
3.515	3.505	3.496	3.505					

At $\alpha = 0.04$, can you reject the production engineer's claim?

33. Getting at the Concept Explain why the null hypothesis $H_0: \mu_1 = \mu_2$ is equivalent to the null hypothesis $H_0: \mu_1 - \mu_2 = 0$.

34. Getting at the Concept   Explain why the null hypothesis H_0: $\mu_1 \geq \mu_2$ is equivalent to the null hypothesis H_0: $\mu_1 - \mu_2 \geq 0$.

■ Extending Concepts

Testing a Difference Other Than Zero   *Sometimes a researcher is interested in testing a difference in means other than zero. For instance, you may want to determine if children today spend an average of 9 hours a week more in day care (or preschool) than children did 20 years ago. In Exercises 35–38, you will test the difference between two means using a null hypothesis of H_0: $\mu_1 - \mu_2 = k$, H_0: $\mu_1 - \mu_2 \geq k$, or H_0: $\mu_1 - \mu_2 \leq k$. The formula for the z-test is still*

$$z = \frac{(\bar{x}_1 - \bar{x}_2) - (\mu_1 - \mu_2)}{\sigma_{\bar{x}_1 - \bar{x}_2}} \quad where \quad \sigma_{\bar{x}_1 - \bar{x}_2} = \sqrt{\frac{\sigma_1^2}{n_1} + \frac{\sigma^2}{n_2}}.$$

35. Time in Day Care or Preschool   In 1981, a study of 70 randomly selected children (under 3 years old) found that the mean length of time spent in day care or preschool per week was 11.5 hours with a standard deviation of 3.8 hours. A recent study of 65 randomly selected children (under 3 years old) found that the mean length of time spent in day care or preschool per week was 20 hours and the standard deviation was 6.7 hours. At $\alpha = 0.01$, test the claim that children spend 9 hours a week more in day care or preschool today than they did in 1981. *(Adapted from University of Michigan's Institute for Social Research)*

36. Time Watching TV   A recent study of 48 randomly selected children (ages 6–8) found that the mean length of time spent watching television each week was 12.95 hours and the standard deviation was 4.31 hours. The mean time 56 randomly selected children (ages 9–11) watched television each week was 15.02 hours and the standard deviation was 4.99 hours. At $\alpha = 0.05$, test the claim that the mean time per week children ages 6–8 watch television is 2 hours less than that of children ages 9–11. *(Adapted from University of Michigan's Institute for Social Research)*

37. Statistician Salaries   Is the difference between the mean annual salaries of statisticians in Massachusetts and North Carolina more than $6000? To decide, you select a random sample of statisticians from each state. The results of each survey are shown in the figure. At $\alpha = 0.10$, what should you conclude? *(Adapted from America's Career InfoNet)*

Statisticians in Massachusetts

$\bar{x}_1 = \$67,900$
$s_1 = \$8875$
$n_1 = 45$

Statisticians in North Carolina

$\bar{x}_2 = \$64,000$
$s_2 = \$9175$
$n_2 = 42$

38. Photographer and Computer Programmer Salaries   At $\alpha = 0.05$, test the claim that the difference between the mean salary for computer programmers and the mean salary for photographers in Wisconsin is greater than $30,000. The results of a survey of randomly selected computer programmers and photographers in Wisconsin are shown in the figure. *(Adapted from America's Career InfoNet)*

Computer Programmers in Wisconsin

$\bar{x}_1 = \$54,900$
$s_1 = \$8250$
$n_1 = 31$

Photographers in Wisconsin

$\bar{x}_2 = \$27,200$
$s_2 = \$3200$
$n_2 = 33$

Constructing Confidence Intervals for $\mu_1 - \mu_2$ *You can construct a confidence interval for the difference between two population means $\mu_1 - \mu_2$ by using the following if $n_1 \geq 30$ and $n_2 \geq 30$, or both populations are normally distributed. Also, the samples must be randomly selected and independent.*

$$(\bar{x}_1 - \bar{x}_2) - z_c\sqrt{\frac{\sigma_1^2}{n_1} + \frac{\sigma_2^2}{n_2}} < \mu_1 - \mu_2 < (\bar{x}_1 - \bar{x}_2) + z_c\sqrt{\frac{\sigma_1^2}{n_1} + \frac{\sigma_2^2}{n_2}}$$

In Exercises 39 and 40, construct the indicated confidence interval for $\mu_1 - \mu_2$.

39. DASH Diet and Systolic Blood Pressure A study was conducted to see if a specific diet and exercise program called the DASH (Dietary Approaches to Stop Hypertension) program, which emphasizes the consumption of fruits, vegetables, and low-fat dairy products, can reduce systolic blood pressure more than a traditional diet and exercise program does. After 6 months, 269 people using the DASH diet had a mean systolic blood pressure of 123.1 mm Hg and a standard deviation of 9.9 mm Hg. After the same time period, 268 people using a traditional diet and exercise program had a mean systolic blood pressure of 125 mm Hg and a standard deviation of 10.1 mm Hg. Before the study, each group had the same mean systolic blood pressure. Construct a 95% confidence interval for $\mu_1 - \mu_2$ where μ_1 is the mean systolic blood pressure for the group using the DASH diet and exercise program and μ_2 is the mean systolic blood pressure for the group using the traditional diet and exercise program. *(Source: The Journal of the American Medical Association)*

40. Comparing Cancer Drugs Two groups of patients with colorectal cancer are treated with a different drug. Group A's 140 patients are treated using the drug Irinotecan and Group B's 127 patients are treated using the drug Fluorouracil. The mean number of months that Group A reported no cancer-related pain was 10.3 and the standard deviation was 1.2. The mean number of months that Group B reported no cancer-related pain was 8.5 and the standard deviation was 1.5. Construct a 95% confidence interval for $\mu_1 - \mu_2$, where μ_1 is the mean number of months that Group A reported no cancer-related pain and μ_2 is the mean number of months that Group B reported no cancer-related pain. *(Adapted from The Lancet)*

41. Make a Decision Refer to the study in Exercise 39. At $\alpha = 0.05$, test the claim that the mean systolic blood pressure for the group using the DASH diet and exercise program is less than the mean systolic blood pressure for the group using the traditional diet and exercise program. Would you recommend using the DASH diet and exercise program over using the traditional diet and exercise program? Explain your reasoning.

42. Make a Decision Refer to the study in Exercise 40. At $\alpha = 0.05$, test the claim that the mean number of months of cancer-related pain relief obtained with Irinotecan is greater than the mean number of months of cancer-related pain relief obtained with Fluorouracil. Would you recommend using Irinotecan over Fluorouracil to relieve cancer-related pain? Explain your reasoning.

43. Getting at the Concept Compare the confidence interval you constructed in Exercise 39 with the hypothesis test result in Exercise 41. Explain why you would reject the null hypothesis if the confidence interval contains only negative numbers.

44. Getting at the Concept Compare the confidence interval you constructed in Exercise 40 with the hypothesis test result in Exercise 42. Explain why you would reject the null hypothesis if the confidence interval contains only positive numbers.

Diets and Weight Loss

A study in *The Journal of the American Medical Association* describes the effects of diets on weight control. In the study, 311 women were randomly divided into four groups. The first group followed the Atkins diet, which is based on very low carbohydrate intake. The second group followed the LEARN (lifestyle, exercise, attitudes, relationships, nutrition) diet, which is based on low fat and high carbohydrate intake. The third group followed the Ornish diet, which is based on very high carbohydrate intake. The fourth group followed the Zone diet, which is based on low carbohydrate intake.

Each group received weekly instruction for two months, and there was a follow-up one year from the beginning of the study. The mean weight losses of each group after one year on the diet are shown in the table below.

	Atkins $n_1 = 77$	LEARN $n_2 = 79$	Ornish $n_3 = 76$	Zone $n_4 = 79$
Weight Loss (in pounds)	$\bar{x}_1 = 10.36$ $s_1 = 15.79$	$\bar{x}_2 = 5.73$ $s_2 = 12.50$	$\bar{x}_3 = 4.85$ $s_3 = 13.73$	$\bar{x}_4 = 3.53$ $s_4 = 12.00$

■ Exercises

In Exercises 1–4, perform a two-sample z-test to determine whether the mean weight losses of the two indicated groups are different. For each exercise, write your conclusion as a sentence. Use a = 0.05.

1. Test the weight losses of people in the Atkins group against those in the LEARN group.

2. Test the weight losses of people in the Ornish group against those in the Zone group.

3. Test the weight losses of people in the LEARN group against those in the Zone group.

4. Test the weight losses of people in the Atkins group against those in the Ornish group.

5. Suppose that in another study, 42 people used an herbal supplement and a high-fiber, low-calorie diet to lose weight. The mean weight loss of this group was 7.05 pounds and the standard deviation was 7.28 pounds.

   (a) Test the mean weight loss of this group with the Atkins group described previously. Use a = 0.01.

   (b) Test the mean weight loss of this group with the Zone group described previously. Use a = 0.01.

6. In which comparisons in Exercises 1–5 did you find a difference in weight losses? Write a summary of your findings.

8.2 Testing the Difference Between Means (Small Independent Samples)

▸ How to perform a *t*-test for the difference between two population means μ_1 and μ_2 using small independent samples

The Two-Sample *t*-Test for the Difference Between Means

▸ The Two-Sample *t*-Test for the Difference Between Means

As you have learned, in real life, it is often not practical to collect samples of size 30 or more from each of two populations. However, if both populations have a normal distribution, you can still test the difference between their means. In this section, you will learn how to use a *t*-test to test the difference between two population means μ_1 and μ_2 using independent samples from each population. The following conditions are necessary to use a *t*-test for small independent samples.

1. The samples must be randomly selected.
2. The samples must be independent. Recall that two samples are *independent* if the sample selected from one population is not related to the sample selected from the second population.
3. Each population must have a normal distribution.

When these conditions are met, the sampling distribution for the difference between the sample means $\overline{x}_1 - \overline{x}_2$ is approximated by a *t*-distribution with mean $\mu_1 - \mu_2$. So, you can use a two-sample *t*-test to test the difference between the two population means μ_1 and μ_2. The standard error and the degrees of freedom of the sampling distribution depend on whether the population variances σ_1^2 and σ_2^2 are equal.

Study Tip

You will learn to test for differences in variances in two populations in Chapter 10. In this chapter, each example and exercise will state whether the variances are equal.

TWO-SAMPLE *t*-TEST FOR THE DIFFERENCE BETWEEN MEANS

A **two-sample *t*-test** is used to test the difference between two population means μ_1 and μ_2 when a sample is randomly selected from each population. Performing this test requires each population to be normally distributed, and the samples should be independent. The standardized test statistic is

$$t = \frac{(\overline{x}_1 - \overline{x}_2) - (\mu_1 - \mu_2)}{\sigma_{\overline{x}_1 - \overline{x}_2}}.$$

Variances are equal: If the population variances are equal, then information from the two samples is combined to calculate a **pooled estimate of the standard deviation** $\hat{\sigma}$.

$$\hat{\sigma} = \sqrt{\frac{(n_1 - 1)s_1^2 + (n_2 - 1)s_2^2}{n_1 + n_2 - 2}}$$

The standard error for the sampling distribution of $\overline{x}_1 - \overline{x}_2$ is

$$\sigma_{\overline{x}_1 - \overline{x}_2} = \hat{\sigma} \cdot \sqrt{\frac{1}{n_1} + \frac{1}{n_2}} \quad \text{Variances equal}$$

and d.f. $= n_1 + n_2 - 2$.

Variances are not equal: If the population variances are not equal, then the standard error is

$$\sigma_{\overline{x}_1 - \overline{x}_2} = \sqrt{\frac{s_1^2}{n_1} + \frac{s_2^2}{n_2}} \quad \text{Variances not equal}$$

and d.f. $=$ smaller of $n_1 - 1$ or $n_2 - 1$.

PICTURING the WORLD

A study published by the American Psychological Association in the journal *Neuropsychology* reported that children with musical training showed better verbal memory than children with no musical training. The study also showed that the longer the musical training, the better the verbal memory. Suppose you tried to duplicate the results as follows. A verbal memory test with a possible 100 points was administered to 90 children. Half had musical training, while the other half acted as the control group and had no musical training. The 45 children with training had an average score of 83.12 with a standard deviation of 5.7. The 45 students in the control group had an average score of 79.9 with a standard deviation of 6.2.

At $\alpha = 0.05$, is there enough evidence to support the claim that musical training increases verbal memory test scores? Assume the populations are normally distributed and the population variances are equal.

The requirements for the z-test described in Section 8.1 and the t-test described in this section are shown in the flowchart below.

Two-Sample Tests for Independent Samples

Are both sample sizes at least 30? → **Yes** → Use the z-test.

↓ **No**

Are both populations normal? → **No** → You cannot use the z-test or the t-test.

↓ **Yes**

Are both population standard deviations known? → **No** → Are the population variances equal? → **Yes** → Use the t-test with $\sigma_{\bar{x}_1 - \bar{x}_2} = \hat{\sigma}\sqrt{\dfrac{1}{n_1} + \dfrac{1}{n_2}}$ and d.f. $= n_1 + n_2 - 2$.

↓ **Yes**

Use the z-test.

(Are the population variances equal?) ↓ **No**

Use the t-test with $\sigma_{\bar{x}_1 - \bar{x}_2} = \sqrt{\dfrac{s_1^2}{n_1} + \dfrac{s_2^2}{n_2}}$ and d.f. $=$ smaller of $n_1 - 1$ or $n_2 - 1$.

GUIDELINES

Using a Two-Sample t-Test for the Difference Between Means (Small Independent Samples)

In Words	*In Symbols*
1. State the claim. Identify the null and alternative hypotheses.	State H_0 and H_a.
2. Specify the level of significance.	Identify α.
3. Identify the degrees of freedom and sketch the sampling distribution.	d.f. $= n_1 + n_2 - 2$ or d.f. $=$ smaller of $n_1 - 1$ or $n_2 - 1$
4. Determine the critical value(s).	Use Table 5 in Appendix B. If $n > 29$, use the last row (∞) in the t-distribution table.
5. Determine the rejection region(s).	
6. Find the standardized test statistic.	$t = \dfrac{(\bar{x}_1 - \bar{x}_2) - (\mu_1 - \mu_2)}{\sigma_{\bar{x}_1 - \bar{x}_2}}$
7. Make a decision to reject or fail to reject the null hypothesis.	If t is in the rejection region, reject H_0. Otherwise, fail to reject H_0.
8. Interpret the decision in the context of the original claim.	

Sample Statistics for Braking Distance on Dry Pavement

GTI	Focus
$\overline{x}_1 = 134$ ft	$\overline{x}_2 = 143$ ft
$s_1 = 6.9$ ft	$s_2 = 2.6$ ft
$n_1 = 8$	$n_2 = 10$

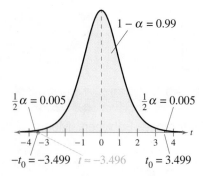

$1 - \alpha = 0.99$

$\frac{1}{2}\alpha = 0.005$ $\frac{1}{2}\alpha = 0.005$

$-t_0 = -3.499$ $t \approx -3.496$ $t_0 = 3.499$

Sample Statistics for Braking Distance on Wet Pavement

GTI	Focus
$\overline{x}_1 = 141$ ft	$\overline{x}_2 = 151$ ft
$s_1 = 7.0$ ft	$s_2 = 3.1$ ft
$n_1 = 8$	$n_2 = 10$

EXAMPLE 1

A Two-Sample *t*-Test for the Difference Between Means

See MINITAB steps on page 488.

The braking distances of 8 Volkswagen GTIs and 10 Ford Focuses were tested when traveling at 60 miles per hour on dry pavement. The results are shown at the left. Can you conclude that there is a difference in the mean braking distances of the two types of cars? Use $\alpha = 0.01$. Assume the populations are normally distributed and the population variances are not equal. *(Adapted from Consumer Reports)*

Solution You want to test whether the mean stopping distances are different. So, the null and alternative hypotheses are

$$H_0: \mu_1 = \mu_2 \quad \text{and} \quad H_a: \mu_1 \neq \mu_2. \text{ (Claim)}$$

Because the variances are not equal and the smaller sample size is 8, use d.f. $= 8 - 1 = 7$. Because the test is a two-tailed test with d.f. $= 7$ and $\alpha = 0.01$, the critical values are $-t_0 = -3.499$ and $t_0 = 3.499$. The rejection regions are $t < -3.499$ and $t > 3.499$. The standard error is

$$\sigma_{\overline{x}_1 - \overline{x}_2} = \sqrt{\frac{s_1^2}{n_1} + \frac{s_2^2}{n_2}} = \sqrt{\frac{6.9^2}{8} + \frac{2.6^2}{10}} \approx 2.5743.$$

The standardized test statistic is

$$t = \frac{(\overline{x}_1 - \overline{x}_2) - (\mu_1 - \mu_2)}{\sigma_{\overline{x}_1 - \overline{x}_2}} \qquad \text{Use the } t\text{-test.}$$

$$\approx \frac{(134 - 143) - 0}{2.5743} \qquad \text{Assume } \mu_1 = \mu_2, \text{ so } \mu_1 - \mu_2 = 0.$$

$$\approx -3.496.$$

The graph at the left shows the location of the rejection regions and the standardized test statistic *t*. Because *t* is not in the rejection region, you should fail to reject the null hypothesis.

Interpretation At the 1% significance level, there is not enough evidence to conclude that the mean braking distances of the cars are different.

▶ Try It Yourself 1

The braking distances (in feet) of the same cars from Example 1 were tested when traveling on wet pavement at 60 miles per hour. The results are shown at the left. Can you conclude that the mean braking distances are different? Use $\alpha = 0.05$. Assume the populations are normally distributed and the population variances are not equal. *(Adapted from Consumer Reports)*

a. *Identify* the claim and state H_0 and H_a.
b. *Specify* the level of significance α.
c. *Determine* the degrees of freedom.
d. *Find* the critical values and *identify* the rejection regions.
e. *Use* the *t*-test to find the standardized test statistic *t*.
f. *Decide* whether to reject the null hypothesis. Use a graph if necessary.
g. *Interpret* the decision in the context of the original claim.

Answer: Page A45

**Sample Statistics for
Calling Range**

Manufacturer	Competition
$\bar{x}_1 = 1275$ ft	$\bar{x}_2 = 1250$ ft
$s_1 = 45$ ft	$s_2 = 30$ ft
$n_1 = 14$	$n_2 = 16$

EXAMPLE 2

A Two-Sample *t*-Test for the Difference Between Means

See TI-83/84 steps on page 489.

A manufacturer claims that the calling range (in feet) of its 2.4-GHz cordless telephone is greater than that of its leading competitor. You perform a study using 14 randomly selected phones from the manufacturer and 16 randomly selected similar phones from its competitor. The results are shown at the left. At $\alpha = 0.05$, can you support the manufacturer's claim? Assume the populations are normally distributed and the population variances are equal.

Solution   The claim is "the mean range of the manufacturer's cordless phone is greater than the mean range of the manufacturer's leading competitor." So, the null and alternative hypotheses are

$$H_0: \mu_1 \le \mu_2 \quad \text{and} \quad H_a: \mu_1 > \mu_2. \text{ (Claim)}$$

Because the variances are equal, d.f. $= n_1 + n_2 - 2 = 14 + 16 - 2 = 28$. Because the test is a right-tailed test, d.f. $= 28$, and $\alpha = 0.05$, the critical value is $t_0 = 1.701$. The rejection region is $t > 1.701$. The standard error is

$$\sigma_{\bar{x}_1 - \bar{x}_2} = \sqrt{\frac{(n_1 - 1)s_1^2 + (n_2 - 1)s_2^2}{n_1 + n_2 - 2}} \cdot \sqrt{\frac{1}{n_1} + \frac{1}{n_2}}$$

$$= \sqrt{\frac{(13)(45^2) + (15)(30^2)}{14 + 16 - 2}} \cdot \sqrt{\frac{1}{14} + \frac{1}{16}} \approx 13.8018.$$

The standardized test statistic is

$$t = \frac{(\bar{x}_1 - \bar{x}_2) - (\mu_1 - \mu_2)}{\sigma_{\bar{x}_1 - \bar{x}_2}} \qquad \text{Use the } t\text{-test.}$$

$$\approx \frac{(1275 - 1250) - 0}{13.8018} \qquad \text{Assume } \mu_1 = \mu_2, \text{ so } \mu_1 - \mu_2 = 0.$$

$$\approx 1.811.$$

Study Tip

It is important to note that when using a TI-83/84 for the two-sample *t*-test, select the *Pooled: Yes* input option when the variances are equal.

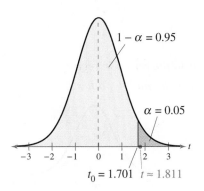

$1 - \alpha = 0.95$

$\alpha = 0.05$

$t_0 = 1.701 \quad t \approx 1.811$

The graph at the left shows the location of the rejection region and the standardized test statistic *t*. Because *t* is in the rejection region, you should decide to reject the null hypothesis.

Interpretation   At the 5% significance level, there is enough evidence to support the manufacturer's claim that its phone has a greater calling range than its competitor's.

▶ Try It Yourself 2

A manufacturer claims that the watt usage of its 17-inch flat panel monitors is less than that of its leading competitor. You perform a study and obtain the results shown at the left. At $\alpha = 0.10$, is there enough evidence to support the manufacturer's claim? Assume the populations are normally distributed and the population variances are equal.

a. *Identify* the claim and state H_0 and H_a.
b. *Specify* the level of significance α.
c. *Determine* the degrees of freedom.
d. *Find* the critical value and *identify* the rejection region.
e. *Use* the *t*-test to find the standardized test statistic *t*.
f. *Decide* whether to reject the null hypothesis. Use a graph if necessary.
g. *Interpret* the decision in the context of the original claim.

Answer: Page A45

Sample Statistics for Watt Usage

Manufacturer	Competition
$\bar{x}_1 = 32$	$\bar{x}_2 = 35$
$s_1 = 2.1$	$s_2 = 1.8$
$n_1 = 12$	$n_2 = 15$

8.2 EXERCISES

■ Building Basic Skills and Vocabulary

1. Explain how to perform a two-sample t-test for the difference between the means of two populations.

2. What conditions are necessary in order to use a t-test to test the difference between two population means?

In Exercises 3–10, use Table 5 in Appendix B to find the critical value(s) for the indicated alternative hypothesis, level of significance α, and sample sizes n_1 and n_2. Assume that the samples are independent, normal, and random and that the population variances are (a) equal and (b) not equal.

3. $H_a: \mu_1 \neq \mu_2, \alpha = 0.10, n_1 = 11, n_2 = 14$

4. $H_a: \mu_1 > \mu_2, \alpha = 0.01, n_1 = 12, n_2 = 15$

5. $H_a: \mu_1 < \mu_2, \alpha = 0.025, n_1 = 15, n_2 = 9$

6. $H_a: \mu_1 \neq \mu_2, \alpha = 0.05, n_1 = 19, n_2 = 22$

7. $H_a: \mu_1 > \mu_2, \alpha = 0.05, n_1 = 13, n_2 = 8$

8. $H_a: \mu_1 < \mu_2, \alpha = 0.10, n_1 = 9, n_2 = 4$

9. $H_a: \mu_1 \neq \mu_2, \alpha = 0.01, n_1 = 12, n_2 = 17$

10. $H_a: \mu_1 > \mu_2, \alpha = 0.005, n_1 = 7, n_2 = 11$

In Exercises 11–14,

(a) find the test statistic.

(b) find the standardized test statistic.

(c) decide whether the standardized test statistic is in the rejection region.

(d) decide whether you should reject or fail to reject the null hypothesis.

11. $H_0: \mu_1 = \mu_2, \alpha = 0.01$
    Sample statistics: $\bar{x}_1 = 33.7, s_1 = 3.5,$
    $n_1 = 10$ and $\bar{x}_2 = 35.5, s_2 = 2.2, n_2 = 7$
    Assume $\sigma_1^2 = \sigma_2^2$.

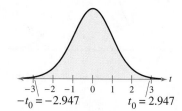

12. $H_0: \mu_1 \geq \mu_2, \alpha = 0.10$
    Sample statistics: $\bar{x}_1 = 0.515, s_1 = 0.305,$
    $n_1 = 11$ and $\bar{x}_2 = 0.475, s_2 = 0.215, n_2 = 9$
    Assume $\sigma_1^2 = \sigma_2^2$.

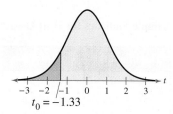

13. $H_0: \mu_1 \leq \mu_2, \alpha = 0.05$
    Sample statistics: $\bar{x}_1 = 2250, s_1 = 175,$
    $n_1 = 13$ and $\bar{x}_2 = 2305, s_2 = 52, n_2 = 10$
    Assume $\sigma_1^2 \neq \sigma_2^2$.

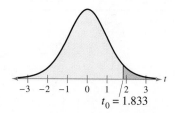

14. H_0: $\mu_1 \leq \mu_2$, $\alpha = 0.01$
Sample statistics: $\bar{x}_1 = 45$, $s_1 = 4.8$,
$n_1 = 16$ and $\bar{x}_2 = 50$, $s_2 = 1.2$, $n_2 = 14$
Assume $\sigma_1^2 \neq \sigma_2^2$.

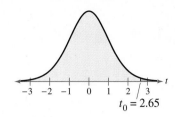

$t_0 = 2.65$

■ Using and Interpreting Concepts

Testing the Difference Between Two Means *In Exercises 15–24, (a) identify the claim and state H_0 and H_a, (b) find the critical value(s) and identify the rejection region(s), (c) find the standardized test statistic, (d) decide whether to reject or fail to reject the null hypothesis, and (e) interpret the decision in the context of the original claim. If convenient, use technology to solve the problem. In each exercise, assume the populations have approximately normal distributions.*

15. Footwell Intrusion   An insurance actuary claims that the mean footwell intrusions for small and midsize cars are equal. Crash tests at 40 miles per hour were performed on 12 randomly selected small cars and 17 randomly selected midsize cars. The amount that the footwell intruded on the driver's legs was measured. The mean footwell intrusion for the small cars was 10.1 centimeters with a standard deviation of 4.11 centimeters. The mean footwell intrusion for the midsize cars was 8.3 centimeters with a standard deviation of 4.02 centimeters. At $\alpha = 0.10$, can you reject the insurance actuary's claim? Assume the population variances are equal. *(Adapted from Insurance Institute for Highway Safety)*

16. Footwell Intrusion   The footwell intrusions for small pickups and small sport utility vehicles in several crash tests at 40 miles per hour were compared. For the 5 randomly selected pickups that were crashed, the mean footwell intrusion was 11.0 centimeters with a standard deviation of 4.07 centimeters. For the 8 randomly selected small sport utility vehicles that were crashed, the mean footwell intrusion was 10.6 centimeters with a standard deviation of 6.62 centimeters. At $\alpha = 0.05$, can you reject the claim that the mean footwell intrusions for these vehicle types are equal? Assume the population variances are equal. *(Adapted from Insurance Institute for Highway Safety)*

17. Repair Costs: Bumpers   In crash tests at 5 miles per hour, the mean bumper repair cost for 14 randomly selected small cars is $473 with a standard deviation of $190. In similar tests of 23 randomly selected midsize cars, the mean bumper repair cost is $741 with a standard deviation of $205. At $\alpha = 0.10$, can you conclude that the mean bumper repair cost is less for small cars than it is for midsize cars? Assume that the population variances are equal. *(Adapted from Insurance Institute for Highway Safety)*

18. Repair Costs: Bumpers   Crash tests at 5 miles per hour were performed on 5 randomly selected small pickups and 8 randomly selected small sport utility vehicles. For the small pickups, the mean bumper repair cost was $1090 and the standard deviation was $403. For the small sport utility vehicles, the mean bumper repair cost was $485 and the standard deviation was $382. At $\alpha = 0.10$, can you conclude that the mean bumper repair cost is greater for small pickups than for small sport utility vehicles? Assume the population variances are equal. *(Adapted from Insurance Institute for Highway Safety)*

19. **Annual Wages**   A personnel director from Pennsylvania claims that the mean annual income is greater in Allegheny County than it is in Erie County. In Allegheny County, a random sample of 19 residents has a mean annual income of $42,200 and a standard deviation of $8600. In Erie County, a random sample of 15 residents has a mean annual income of $37,900 and a standard deviation of $5500. At $\alpha = 0.10$, can you support the personnel director's claim? Assume the population variances are not equal. *(Adapted from U.S. Census Bureau)*

20. **Annual Wages**   A random sample of 17 residents of Escambia County in Florida has a mean annual income of $36,700 and a standard deviation of $7800. In Miami-Dade County in Florida, a random sample of 18 residents has a mean annual income of $34,700 and a standard deviation of $7375. Test the claim at $\alpha = 0.01$ that the mean annual incomes in Escambia and Miami-Dade Counties are not the same. Assume the population variances are equal. *(Adapted from U.S. Census Bureau)*

21. **Tensile Strength**   The tensile strength of a metal is a measure of its ability to resist tearing when it is pulled lengthwise. A new experimental type of treatment produced steel bars with the following tensile strengths (in newtons per square millimeter).

Experimental Method:

> 363 355 305 350 340
> 373 311 348 338 320

The old method produced steel bars with the following tensile strengths (in newtons per square millimeter).

Old Method:

> 362 382 368 398 381 391 400
> 410 396 411 385 385 395

At $\alpha = 0.01$, does the new treatment make a difference in the tensile strength of steel bars? Assume the population variances are equal and the samples are random.

22. **Tensile Strength**   An engineer wants to compare the tensile strengths of steel bars that are produced using a conventional method and an experimental method. (The tensile strength of a metal is a measure of its ability to resist tearing when pulled lengthwise.) To do so, the engineer randomly selects steel bars that are manufactured using each method and records the following tensile strengths (in newtons per square millimeter).

Experimental Method:

> 395 389 421 394 407 411 389 402 422
> 416 402 408 400 386 411 405 389

Conventional Method:

> 362 352 380 382 413 384 400
> 378 419 379 384 388 372 383

At $\alpha = 0.10$, can the engineer claim that the experimental method produces steel with greater mean tensile strength? Should the engineer recommend using the experimental method? Assume the population variances are not equal.

23. Teaching Methods   A new method of teaching reading is being tested on third grade students. A group of randomly selected third grade students is taught using the new curriculum. A control group of randomly selected third grade students is taught using the old curriculum. The reading test scores of the two groups are shown in the stem-and-leaf plot.

Old Curriculum   **New Curriculum**

9	3		Key:
9 9	4	3	9|4 = 49 (old curriculum)
9 8 8 4 3 3 2 1	5	2 4	4|3 = 43 (new curriculum)
7 6 4 2 2 1 0 0	6	0 1 1 4 7 7 7 7 7 8 9 9	
	7	0 1 1 2 3 3 4 9	
	8	2 4	

At $\alpha = 0.10$, is there enough evidence to conclude that the new method of teaching reading produces higher reading test scores than the old method does? Would you recommend changing to the new method does? Assume the population variances are equal.

24. Teaching Methods   Two teaching methods and their effects on science test scores are being reviewed. A randomly selected group of students is taught in traditional lab sessions. A second randomly selected group of students is taught using interactive simulation software. The science test scores of the two groups are shown in the stem-and-leaf plot.

Traditional Lab   **Interactive Simulation Software**

	4	6	Key:
9 9 8 8 7 6 6 3 2 1 0	7	0 4 5 5 7 7 8	0|9 = 90 (traditional)
9 8 5 1 1 1 0 0	8	0 0 3 4 7 8 8 9 9	9|1 = 91 (interactive)
2 0	9	1 3 9	

At $\alpha = 0.05$, can you support the claim that the mean science test score is lower for students taught using the traditional lab method than it is for students taught using the interactive simulation software? Assume the population variances are equal.

■ **Extending Concepts**

Constructing Confidence Intervals for $\mu_1 - \mu_2$ *If the sampling distribution for $\bar{x}_1 - \bar{x}_2$ is approximated by a t-distribution and the populations have equal variances, you can construct a confidence interval for $\mu_1 - \mu_2$ by using the following.*

$$(\bar{x}_1 - \bar{x}_2) - t_c \hat{\sigma} \sqrt{\frac{1}{n_1} + \frac{1}{n_2}} < \mu_1 - \mu_2 < (\bar{x}_1 - \bar{x}_2) + t_c \hat{\sigma} \sqrt{\frac{1}{n_1} + \frac{1}{n_2}}$$

where $\hat{\sigma} = \sqrt{\dfrac{(n_1 - 1)s_1^2 + (n_2 - 1)s_2^2}{n_1 + n_2 - 2}}$ *and d.f.* $= n_1 + n_2 - 2$

In Exercises 25 and 26, construct a confidence interval for $\mu_1 - \mu_2$. Assume the populations are approximately normal with equal variances.

25. Calories In a study of various fast foods, you find that the mean calorie content of 15 grilled chicken sandwiches from Burger King is $\bar{x}_1 = 450$ calories with a standard deviation of $s_1 = 6.2$ calories. You also find that the mean calorie content of 12 similar grilled chicken sandwiches from McDonald's is $\bar{x}_2 = 420$ calories with a standard deviation of $s_2 = 8.1$ calories. Construct a 95% confidence interval for the difference in mean calorie content of grilled chicken sandwiches. (*Adapted from Burger King Brands, Inc. and McDonald's Corporation*)

26. Protein A nutritionist wants to compare the mean protein content of grilled chicken sandwiches from Burger King and McDonald's. To do so, she randomly selects several grilled chicken sandwiches from each restaurant and measures the protein content (in grams) of each. The results are listed below. Construct a 95% confidence interval for the difference in mean protein content of grilled chicken sandwiches. (*Adapted from Burger King Brands, Inc. and McDonald's Corporation*)

Restaurant	Mean protein content	Standard deviation	Sample size
Burger King	$\bar{x}_1 = 37$ grams	$s_1 = 2.1$ grams	$n_1 = 15$
McDonald's	$\bar{x}_2 = 32$ grams	$s_2 = 1.8$ grams	$n_2 = 12$

Constructing Confidence Intervals for $\mu_1 - \mu_2$ *If the sampling distribution for $\bar{x}_1 - \bar{x}_2$ is approximated by a t-distribution and the population variances are not equal, you can construct a confidence interval for $\mu_1 - \mu_2$ by using the following.*

$$(\bar{x}_1 - \bar{x}_2) - t_c\sqrt{\frac{s_1^2}{n_1} + \frac{s_2^2}{n_2}} < \mu_1 - \mu_2 < (\bar{x}_1 - \bar{x}_2) + t_c\sqrt{\frac{s_1^2}{n_1} + \frac{s_2^2}{n_2}}$$

and d.f. is the smaller of $n_1 - 1$ or $n_2 - 1$.

In Exercises 27 and 28, construct the indicated confidence interval for $\mu_1 - \mu_2$. Assume the populations are approximately normal with unequal variances.

27. Cholesterol To compare the mean cholesterol content (in milligrams) of grilled chicken sandwiches from from Burger King and McDonald's, you randomly select several grilled chicken sandwiches from each restaurant and measure their cholesterol contents. The results are listed below. Construct a 90% confidence interval for the difference in mean cholesterol content of grilled chicken sandwiches. (*Adapted from Burger King Brands, Inc. and McDonald's Corporation*)

Restaurant	Mean cholesterol content	Standard deviation	Sample size
Burger King	$\bar{x}_1 = 75$ mg	$s_1 = 3.64$ mg	$n_1 = 16$
McDonald's	$\bar{x}_2 = 70$ mg	$s_2 = 2.12$ mg	$n_2 = 14$

28. Carbohydrates A study of fast food finds that the mean carbohydrate content of 16 grilled chicken sandwiches from Burger King is $\bar{x}_1 = 53$ grams with a standard deviation of $s_1 = 2.57$ grams. The study also finds that the mean carbohydrate content of 14 grilled chicken sandwiches from McDonald's is $\bar{x}_2 = 51$ grams with a standard deviation of $s_2 = 1.53$ grams. Construct a 90% confidence interval for the difference in mean carbohydrate content. (*Adapted from Burger King Brands, Inc. and McDonald's Corporation*)

8.3 Testing the Difference Between Means (Dependent Samples)

The *t*-Test for the Difference Between Means

▸ **The *t*-Test for the Difference Between Means**

In Sections 8.1 and 8.2, you performed two-sample hypothesis tests with independent samples using the test statistic $\bar{x}_1 - \bar{x}_2$ (the difference between the means of the two samples). To perform a two-sample hypothesis test with dependent samples, you will use a different technique. You will first find the difference d for each data pair:

$$d = x_1 - x_2. \qquad \text{Difference between entries for a data pair}$$

The test statistic is the mean $\bar{d}$ of these differences

$$\bar{d} = \frac{\Sigma d}{n}. \qquad \text{Mean of the differences between paired data entries in the dependent samples}$$

The following conditions are required to conduct the test.

1. The samples must be randomly selected.

2. The samples must be dependent (paired).

3. Both populations must be normally distributed.

If these requirements are met, then the sampling distribution for $\bar{d}$, the mean of the differences of the paired data entries in the dependent samples, is approximated by a *t*-distribution with $n - 1$ degrees of freedom, where n is the number of data pairs.

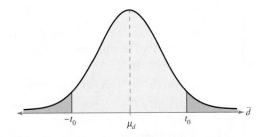

The following symbols are used for the *t*-test for μ_d. Although formulas are given for the mean and standard deviation of differences, you should use a technology tool to calculate these statistics.

Study Tip

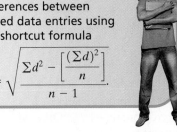

You can also calculate the standard deviation of the differences between paired data entries using the shortcut formula

$$s_d = \sqrt{\frac{\Sigma d^2 - \left[\frac{(\Sigma d)^2}{n}\right]}{n - 1}}.$$

Symbol	Description
n	The number of pairs of data
d	The difference between entries for a data pair, $d = x_1 - x_2$
μ_d	The hypothesized mean of the differences of paired data in the population
$\bar{d}$	The mean of the differences between the paired data entries in the dependent samples $$\bar{d} = \frac{\Sigma d}{n}$$
s_d	The standard deviation of the differences between the paired data entries in the dependent samples $$s_d = \sqrt{\frac{\Sigma (d - \bar{d})^2}{n - 1}}$$

When you use a t-distribution to approximate the sampling distribution for $\overline{d}$, the mean of the differences between paired data entries, you can use a t-test to test a claim about the mean of the differences for a population of paired data.

t-TEST FOR THE DIFFERENCE BETWEEN MEANS

A t-test can be used to test the difference of two population means when a sample is randomly selected from each population. The requirements for performing the test are that each population must be normal and each member of the first sample must be paired with a member of the second sample. The **test statistic** is

$$\overline{d} = \frac{\sum d}{n}$$

and the **standardized test statistic** is

$$t = \frac{\overline{d} - \mu_d}{s_d / \sqrt{n}}$$

The degrees of freedom are

$$\text{d.f.} = n - 1.$$

PICTURING the WORLD

The manufacturer of an appetite suppressant claims that when its product is taken while following a low-fat diet with regular exercise for 4 months, the average weight loss is 20 pounds. To test this claim, you studied 12 randomly selected dieters taking an appetite suppressant for 4 months. The dieters followed a low-fat diet with regular exercise all 4 months. The results are shown in the following table.

(Adapted from NetHealth, Inc.)

Weights (in pounds) of 12 dieters

	Original weight	4th month
1	185	168
2	194	177
3	213	196
4	198	180
5	244	229
6	162	144
7	211	197
8	273	252
9	178	161
10	192	178
11	181	161
12	209	193

Does your study provide sufficient evidence to reject the manufacturer's claim at a level of significance of $\alpha = 0.10$? Assume the weights are normally distributed.

GUIDELINES

Using the t-Test for the Difference Between Means (Dependent Samples)

In Words	*In Symbols*
1. State the claim mathematically. Identify the null and alternative hypotheses.	State H_0 and H_a.
2. Specify the level of significance.	Identify α.
3. Identify the degrees of freedom and sketch the sampling distribution.	$\text{d.f.} = n - 1$
4. Determine the critical value(s).	Use Table 5 in Appendix B. If $n > 29$, use the last row (∞) in the t-distribution table.
5. Determine the rejection region(s).	
6. Calculate $\overline{d}$ and s_d.	$\overline{d} = \dfrac{\sum d}{n}$ $s_d = \sqrt{\dfrac{\sum (d - \overline{d})^2}{n - 1}}$
7. Find the standardized test statistic.	$t = \dfrac{\overline{d} - \mu_d}{s_d / \sqrt{n}}$
8. Make a decision to reject or fail to reject the null hypothesis.	If t is in the rejection region, reject H_0. Otherwise, fail to reject H_0.
9. Interpret the decision in the context of the original claim.	

Old	New	d	d^2
89	83	6	36
84	83	1	1
96	92	4	16
82	84	−2	4
74	76	−2	4
92	91	1	1
85	80	5	25
91	91	0	0
		$\Sigma = 13$	$\Sigma = 87$

EXAMPLE 1

The t-Test for the Difference Between Means

> See MINITAB steps on page 488.

A golf club manufacturer claims that golfers can lower their scores by using the manufacturer's newly designed golf clubs. Eight golfers are randomly selected, and each is asked to give his or her most recent score. After using the new clubs for one month, the golfers are again asked to give their most recent score. The scores for each golfer are shown in the table. Assuming the golf scores are normally distributed, is there enough evidence to support the manufacturer's claim at $\alpha = 0.10$?

Golfer	1	2	3	4	5	6	7	8
Score (old design)	89	84	96	82	74	92	85	91
Score (new design)	83	83	92	84	76	91	80	91

Solution   The claim is that "golfers can lower their scores." In other words, the manufacturer claims that the score using the old clubs will be greater than the score using the new clubs. Each difference is given by

$$d = (\text{old score}) - (\text{new score}).$$

The null and alternative hypotheses are

$$H_0: \mu_d \leq 0 \qquad \text{and} \qquad H_a: \mu_d > 0. \text{ (Claim)}$$

Because the test is a right-tailed test, $\alpha = 0.10$, and d.f. $= 8 - 1 = 7$, the critical value is $t_0 = 1.415$. The rejection region is $t > 1.415$. Using the table at the left, you can calculate $\overline{d}$ and s_d as follows. Notice that the shortcut formula is used to calculate the standard deviation.

$$\overline{d} = \frac{\Sigma d}{n} = \frac{13}{8} = 1.625$$

$$s_d = \sqrt{\frac{\Sigma d^2 - \left[\frac{(\Sigma d)^2}{n}\right]}{n - 1}} = \sqrt{\frac{87 - \frac{13^2}{8}}{8 - 1}} \approx 3.0677$$

The standardized test statistic is

$$t = \frac{\overline{d} - \mu_d}{s_d/\sqrt{n}} \qquad \text{Use the } t\text{-test.}$$

$$\approx \frac{1.625 - 0}{3.0677/\sqrt{8}} \qquad \text{Assume } \mu_d = 0.$$

$$\approx 1.498.$$

The graph at the right shows the location of the rejection region and the standardized test statistic t. Because t is in the rejection region, you should decide to reject the null hypothesis. There is enough evidence to support the golf club manufacturer's claim.

Interpretation   At the 10% significance level, the results of this test indicate that after the golfers used the new clubs, their scores were significantly lower.

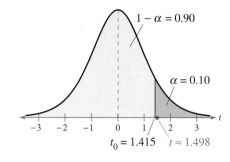

Before	After
72	73
81	80
76	79
74	76
75	76
80	80
68	74
75	77
78	75
76	74
74	76
77	78

▶ **Try It Yourself 1**

A physician claims that an experimental medication increases an individual's heart rate. Twelve test subjects are randomly selected, and the heart rate of each is measured. The subjects are then injected with the medication and, after 1 hour, the heart rate of each is measured again. The results are listed at the left. Assuming the heart rates are normally distributed, is there enough evidence to support the physician's claim at $\alpha = 0.05$?

a. *Identify* the claim and state H_0 and H_a.
b. *Specify* the level of significance α and the degrees of freedom d.f.
c. *Find* the critical value t_0 and *identify* the rejection region.
d. *Calculate* $\bar{d}$ and s_d.
e. *Use* the t-test to find the standardized test statistic t.
f. *Decide* whether to reject the null hypothesis. Use a graph if necessary.
g. *Interpret* the decision in the context of the original claim.

Answer: Page A45

EXAMPLE 2

The *t*-Test for the Difference Between Means

A state legislator wants to determine whether her performance rating (0–100) has changed from last year to this year. The following table shows the legislator's performance rating from the same 16 randomly selected voters for last year and this year. At $\alpha = 0.01$, is there enough evidence to conclude that the legislator's performance rating has changed? Assume the performance ratings are normally distributed.

Voter	1	2	3	4	5	6	7	8
Rating (last year)	60	54	78	84	91	25	50	65
Rating (this year)	56	48	70	60	85	40	40	55

Voter	9	10	11	12	13	14	15	16
Rating (last year)	68	81	75	45	62	79	58	63
Rating (this year)	80	75	78	50	50	85	53	60

Study Tip

If you prefer to use a technology tool for this type of test, enter the data in two columns and form a third column in which you calculate the difference for each pair. You can now perform a one-sample *t*-test on the difference column as shown in Chapter 7.

Solution If there is a change in the legislator's rating, there will be a difference between "this year's" ratings and "last year's" ratings. Because the legislator wants to see if there is a difference, the null and alternative hypotheses are

$$H_0: \mu_d = 0$$

and

$$H_a: \mu_d \neq 0. \text{ (Claim)}$$

Because the test is a two-tailed test, $\alpha = 0.01$, and d.f. $= 16 - 1 = 15$, the critical values are $-t_0 = -2.947$ and $t_0 = 2.947$. The rejection regions are $t < -2.947$ and $t > 2.947$.

Before	After	d	d^2
60	56	4	16
54	48	6	36
78	70	8	64
84	60	24	576
91	85	6	36
25	40	−15	225
50	40	10	100
65	55	10	100
68	80	−12	144
81	75	6	36
75	78	−3	9
45	50	−5	25
62	50	12	144
79	85	−6	36
58	53	5	25
63	60	3	9
		$\Sigma = 53$	$\Sigma = 1581$

Using the table at the left, you can calculate $\bar{d}$ and s_d as shown below.

$$\bar{d} = \frac{\Sigma d}{n} = \frac{53}{16} = 3.3125$$

$$s_d = \sqrt{\frac{\Sigma d^2 - \left[\frac{(\Sigma d)^2}{n}\right]}{n-1}} = \sqrt{\frac{1581 - \frac{53^2}{16}}{16-1}} \approx 9.6797$$

The standardized test statistic is

$$t = \frac{\bar{d} - \mu_d}{s_d/\sqrt{n}} \qquad \text{Use the } t\text{-test.}$$

$$\approx \frac{3.3125 - 0}{9.6797/\sqrt{16}} \qquad \text{Assume } \mu_d = 0.$$

$$\approx 1.369.$$

The graph at the right shows the location of the rejection region and the standardized test statistic t. Because t is not in the rejection region, you should fail to reject the null hypothesis.

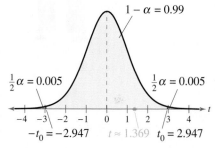

Interpretation   At the 1% significance level, there is not enough evidence to conclude that the legislator's performance rating has changed.

▶ Try It Yourself 2

A medical researcher wants to determine whether a drug changes the body's temperature. Seven test subjects are randomly selected, and the body temperature (in degrees Fahrenheit) of each is measured. The subjects are then given the drug and, after 20 minutes, the body temperature of each is measured again. The results are listed below. At $\alpha = 0.05$, is there enough evidence to conclude that the drug changes the body's temperature? Assume the body temperatures are normally distributed.

Subject	1	2	3	4	5	6	7
Initial Temperature	101.8	98.5	98.1	99.4	98.9	100.2	97.9
Second Temperature	99.2	98.4	98.2	99	98.6	99.7	97.8

a. *Identify* the claim and state H_0 and H_a.
b. *Specify* the level of significance α and the degrees of freedom d.f.
c. *Find* the critical values and the rejection regions.
d. *Calculate* $\bar{d}$ and s_d.
e. *Use* the t-test to find the standardized test statistic t.
f. *Decide* whether to reject the null hypothesis. Use a graph if necessary.
g. *Interpret* the decision in the context of the original claim.

Answer: Page A45

8.3 EXERCISES

■ Building Basic Skills and Vocabulary

1. What conditions are necessary in order to use the dependent samples t-test for the mean of the difference of two populations?

2. Explain what the symbols $\overline{d}$ and s_d represent.

In Exercises 3–8, test the claim about the mean of the difference of two populations. Use a t-test for dependent, random samples at the given level of significance with the given statistics. Is the test right-tailed, left-tailed, or two-tailed? Assume the populations are normally distributed.

3. Claim: $\mu_d < 0, \alpha = 0.05$. Statistics: $\overline{d} = 1.5, s_d = 3.2, n = 14$

4. Claim: $\mu_d = 0, \alpha = 0.01$. Statistics: $\overline{d} = 3.2, s_d = 8.45, n = 8$

5. Claim: $\mu_d \leq 0, \alpha = 0.10$. Statistics: $\overline{d} = 6.5, s_d = 9.54, n = 16$

6. Claim: $\mu_d > 0, \alpha = 0.05$. Statistics: $\overline{d} = 0.55, s_d = 0.99, n = 28$

7. Claim: $\mu_d \geq 0, \alpha = 0.01$. Statistics: $\overline{d} = -2.3, s_d = 1.2, n = 15$

8. Claim: $\mu_d \neq 0, \alpha = 0.10$. Statistics: $\overline{d} = -1, s_d = 2.75, n = 20$

■ Using and Interpreting Concepts

Testing the Difference Between Two Means *In Exercises 9–20, (a) identify the claim and state H_0 and H_a, (b) find the critical value(s) and identify the rejection region(s), (c) calculate $\overline{d}$ and s_d, (d) use the t-test to find the standardized test statistic t, (e) decide whether to reject or fail to reject the null hypothesis, and (f) interpret the decision in the context of the original claim. If convenient, use technology to solve the problem. For each randomly selected sample, assume the distribution of the population is normal.*

 9. **SAT Scores** The table shows the critical reading scores for 14 students the first two times they took the SAT. At $\alpha = 0.01$, is there enough evidence to conclude that the students' critical reading SAT scores improved the second time they took the SAT?

Student	1	2	3	4	5	6	7
Score on first SAT	445	510	429	452	629	433	551
Score on second SAT	446	571	517	478	610	453	516

Student	8	9	10	11	12	13	14
Score on first SAT	358	477	325	513	636	571	442
Score on second SAT	478	532	399	531	648	603	461

 10. **SAT Scores** An SAT prep course claims to improve the test scores of students. The table shows the critical reading scores for 10 students the first two times they took the SAT. Before taking the SAT for the second time, each student took a course to try to improve his or her critical reading SAT scores. Test the claim at $\alpha = 0.01$.

Student	1	2	3	4	5	6	7
Score on first SAT	308	456	352	433	306	471	422
Score on second SAT	400	524	409	491	348	583	451

Student	8	9	10
Score on first SAT	370	320	418
Score on second SAT	408	391	450

11. Gas Mileage   The table shows the gas mileages (in miles per gallon) of eight cars with and without using a fuel additive. At $\alpha = 0.10$, is there enough evidence to conclude that the fuel additive improved gas mileage?

Car	1	2	3	4	5	6	7	8
Gas mileage without additive	23.1	25.4	21.9	24.3	19.9	21.2	25.9	24.8
Gas mileage with fuel additive	23.6	27.7	23.6	26.8	22.1	22.4	26.3	26.6

12. Gas Mileage   To test whether a fuel additive improves gas mileage, investigators measured the gas mileage (in miles per gallon) of nine cars with and without the fuel additive. The results are shown below. At $\alpha = 0.10$, can you conclude that the fuel additive improved gas mileage?

Car	1	2	3	4	5	6	7	8	9
Gas mileage without additive	17.8	20.3	28.7	23.1	16.9	18.7	21.7	18.6	29.2
Gas mileage with fuel additive	19.7	22.1	30.4	23.4	17.8	21.6	23.5	20.5	30.1

13. Losing Weight   A nutritionist claims that a particular exercise program will help participants lose weight after one month. The table shows the weights of 12 adults before participating in the exercise program and 1 month after participating in the exercise program. At $\alpha = 0.10$, can you conclude that the exercise program helps participants lose weight?

Participant	1	2	3	4	5	6
Weight before exercise program	157	185	120	212	230	165
Weight after exercise program	150	181	121	206	215	169

Participant	7	8	9	10	11	12
Weight before exercise program	207	251	196	140	137	172
Weight after exercise program	210	232	188	138	145	172

14. Losing Weight The table shows the weights of 14 adults before a dieting program and 2 weeks after the dieting program. At $\alpha = 0.10$, is there enough evidence to conclude that the program helped adults lose weight?

Participant	1	2	3	4	5	6	7
Weight before dieting program	194	234	265	188	170	212	139
Weight after dieting program	190	235	255	187	175	209	139

Participant	8	9	10	11	12	13	14
Weight before dieting program	280	291	210	190	155	166	198
Weight after dieting program	277	285	212	194	152	167	196

15. Headaches A physical therapist suggests that soft tissue therapy and spinal manipulation help to reduce the length of time patients suffer from headaches. The table shows the number of hours per day 11 patients suffered from headaches before and after 7 weeks of receiving soft tissue therapy and spinal manipulation. At $\alpha = 0.01$, is there enough evidence to support the therapist's claim? *(Adapted from The Journal of the American Medical Association)*

Patient	1	2	3	4	5	6
Daily headache hours (before)	2.8	2.4	2.8	2.6	2.7	2.9
Daily headache hours (after)	1.6	1.3	1.6	1.4	1.5	1.6

Patient	7	8	9	10	11
Daily headache hours (before)	3.2	2.9	4.1	1.6	2.5
Daily headache hours (after)	1.7	1.6	1.8	1.2	1.4

16. Grip Strength A physical therapist suggests that one 600-mg dose of Vitamin C will increase muscular endurance. The table shows the number of repetitions 15 males made on a hand dynamometer (measures grip strength) until the grip strength of three consecutive trials is 50% of their maximum grip strength. At $\alpha = 0.05$, test the claim that Vitamin C will increase muscular endurance. *(Adapted from Journal of Sports Medicine and Physical Fitness)*

Participant	1	2	3	4	5	6	7	8
Repetitions using placebo	417	279	678	636	170	699	372	582
Repetitions using Vitamin C	145	185	387	593	248	245	349	902

Participant	9	10	11	12	13	14	15
Repetitions using placebo	363	258	288	526	180	172	278
Repetitions using Vitamin C	159	122	264	1052	218	117	185

17. Blood Pressure A pharmaceutical company guarantees that its new drug reduces systolic blood pressure. The table shows the systolic blood pressures (in millimeters of mercury) of eight patients before taking the new drug and two hours after taking the drug. At $\alpha = 0.05$, can you conclude that the new drug reduces systolic blood pressure?

Patient	1	2	3	4	5	6	7	8
Systolic blood pressure (before)	201	171	186	162	165	167	175	148
Systolic blood pressure (after)	192	165	167	155	148	144	152	134

18. Blood Pressure The diastolic blood pressures (in millimeters of mercury) of nine patients before taking a new drug and two hours after taking the drug are shown in the table below. At $\alpha = 0.05$, can you conclude that the new drug reduces diastolic blood pressure?

Patient	1	2	3	4	5	6	7	8	9
Diastolic blood pressure (before)	103	122	106	112	125	97	107	118	112
Diastolic blood pressure (after)	98	121	107	105	108	89	102	114	101

19. Product Ratings A company wants to determine whether its consumer product ratings (0–10) have changed from last year to this year. The table shows the company's product ratings from the same eight consumers for last year and this year. At $\alpha = 0.05$, is there enough evidence to conclude that the product ratings have changed?

Consumer	1	2	3	4	5	6	7	8
Rating (last year)	5	7	2	3	9	10	8	7
Rating (this year)	5	9	4	6	9	9	9	8

20. Performance Ratings A manufacturing plant wants to determine whether its manager performance ratings (0–100) have changed from last month to this month. The table shows the plant's performance ratings from the same six managers for last month and this month. At $\alpha = 0.05$, is there enough evidence to conclude that the plant's performance ratings have changed?

Manager	1	2	3	4	5	6
Rating (last month)	85	96	70	76	81	78
Rating (this month)	88	85	89	86	92	89

■ **Extending Concepts**

Constructing Confidence Intervals for μ_d   *To construct a confidence interval for μ_d, use the following inequality.*

$$\overline{d} - t_c \frac{s_d}{\sqrt{n}} < \mu_d < \overline{d} + t_c \frac{s_d}{\sqrt{n}}$$

In Exercises 21 and 22, construct the indicated confidence interval for μ_d. Assume the populations are normally distributed.

21. Drug Testing   A sleep disorder specialist wants to test the effectiveness of a new drug that is reported to increase the number of hours of sleep patients get during the night. To do so, the specialist randomly selects 16 patients and records the number of hours of sleep each gets with and without the new drug. The results of the two-night study are listed below. Construct a 90% confidence interval for μ_d.

Patient	1	2	3	4	5	6	7	8	9
Hours of sleep without the drug	1.8	2.0	3.4	3.5	3.7	3.8	3.9	3.9	4.0
Hours of sleep using the drug	3.0	3.6	4.0	4.4	4.5	5.2	5.5	5.7	6.2

Patient	10	11	12	13	14	15	16
Hours of sleep without the drug	4.9	5.1	5.2	5.0	4.5	4.2	4.7
Hours of sleep using the drug	6.3	6.6	7.8	7.2	6.5	5.6	5.9

22. Herbal Medicine Testing   An herbal medicine is tested on 14 randomly selected patients with sleeping disorders. The table shows the number of hours of sleep patients got during one night without using the herbal medicine and the number of hours of sleep the patients got on another night after the herbal medicine was administered. Construct a 95% confidence interval for μ_d.

Patient	1	2	3	4	5	6	7
Hours of sleep without medicine	1.0	1.4	3.4	3.7	5.1	5.1	5.2
Hours of sleep using the herbal medicine	2.9	3.3	3.5	4.4	5.0	5.0	5.2

Patient	8	9	10	11	12	13	14
Hours of sleep without medicine	5.3	5.5	5.8	4.2	4.8	2.9	4.5
Hours of sleep using the herbal medicine	5.3	6.0	6.5	4.4	4.7	3.1	4.7

8.4 Testing the Difference Between Proportions

Two-Sample z-Test for the Difference Between Proportions

▸ **Two-Sample z-Test for the Difference Between Proportions**

In this section, you will learn how to use a z-test to test the difference between two population proportions p_1 and p_2 using a sample proportion from each population. If a claim is about two population parameters p_1 and p_2, then some possible pairs of null and alternative hypotheses are

$$\begin{cases} H_0: p_1 = p_2 \\ H_a: p_1 \neq p_2 \end{cases}, \quad \begin{cases} H_0: p_1 \leq p_2 \\ H_a: p_1 > p_2 \end{cases}, \quad \text{and} \quad \begin{cases} H_0: p_1 \geq p_2 \\ H_a: p_1 < p_2 \end{cases}.$$

Regardless of which hypotheses you use, you always assume there is no difference between the population proportions, or $p_1 = p_2$.

For instance, suppose you want to determine whether the proportion of female college students who earn a bachelor's degree in four years is different from the proportion of male college students who earn a bachelor's degree in four years. The following conditions are necessary to use a z-test to test such a difference.

1. The samples must be randomly selected.
2. The samples must be independent.
3. The samples must be large enough to use a normal sampling distribution.
   That is, $n_1 p_1 \geq 5$, $n_1 q_1 \geq 5$, $n_2 p_2 \geq 5$, and $n_2 q_2 \geq 5$.

If these conditions are met, then the **sampling distribution for $\hat{p}_1 - \hat{p}_2$, the difference between the sample proportions,** is a normal distribution with mean

$$\mu_{\hat{p}_1 - \hat{p}_2} = p_1 - p_2$$

and standard error

$$\sigma_{\hat{p}_1 - \hat{p}_2} = \sqrt{\frac{p_1 q_1}{n_1} + \frac{p_2 q_2}{n_2}}.$$

Notice that you need to know the population proportions to calculate the standard error. Because a hypothesis test for $p_1 - p_2$ is based on the assumption that $p_1 = p_2$, you can calculate a weighted estimate of p_1 and p_2 using

$$\bar{p} = \frac{x_1 + x_2}{n_1 + n_2}, \text{ where } x_1 = n_1 \hat{p}_1 \text{ and } x_2 = n_2 \hat{p}_2.$$

With the weighted estimate $\bar{p}$, the standard error of the sampling distribution for $\hat{p}_1 - \hat{p}_2$ is

$$\sigma_{\hat{p}_1 - \hat{p}_2} = \sqrt{\bar{p}\,\bar{q}\left(\frac{1}{n_1} + \frac{1}{n_2}\right)}, \text{ where } \bar{q} = 1 - \bar{p}.$$

Also observe that you need to know the population proportions in verifying that the samples are large enough to be approximated by the normal distribution. But when determining whether the z-test can be used for the difference between proportions for a binomial experiment, you should use $\bar{p}$ in place of p_1 and p_2 and use $\bar{q}$ in place of q_1 and q_2.

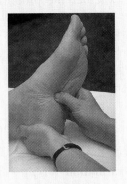
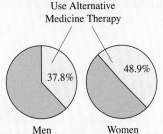
If the sampling distribution for $\hat{p}_1 - \hat{p}_2$ is normal, you can use a two-sample z-test to test the difference between two population proportions p_1 and p_2.

TWO-SAMPLE z-TEST FOR THE DIFFERENCE BETWEEN PROPORTIONS

A two-sample z-test is used to test the difference between two population proportions p_1 and p_2 when a sample is randomly selected from each population. The **test statistic** is

$$\hat{p}_1 - \hat{p}_2$$

and the **standardized test statistic** is

$$z = \frac{(\hat{p}_1 - \hat{p}_2) - (p_1 - p_2)}{\sqrt{\overline{p}\,\overline{q}\left(\dfrac{1}{n_1} + \dfrac{1}{n_2}\right)}}$$

where

$$\overline{p} = \frac{x_1 + x_2}{n_1 + n_2} \quad \text{and} \quad \overline{q} = 1 - \overline{p}.$$

Note: $n_1\overline{p}$, $n_1\overline{q}$, $n_2\overline{p}$, and $n_2\overline{q}$ must be at least 5.

If the null hypothesis states $p_1 = p_2$, $p_1 \leq p_2$, or $p_1 \geq p_2$, then $p_1 = p_2$ is assumed and the expression $p_1 - p_2$ is equal to 0 in the preceding test.

GUIDELINES

Using a Two-Sample z-Test for the Difference Between Proportions

In Words	*In Symbols*
1. State the claim. Identify the null and alternative hypotheses.	State H_0 and H_a.
2. Specify the level of significance.	Identify α.
3. Determine the critical value(s).	Use Table 4 in Appendix B.
4. Determine the rejection region(s).	
5. Find the weighted estimate of p_1 and p_2.	$\overline{p} = \dfrac{x_1 + x_2}{n_1 + n_2}$
6. Find the standardized test statistic.	$z = \dfrac{(\hat{p}_1 - \hat{p}_2) - (p_1 - p_2)}{\sqrt{\overline{p}\,\overline{q}\left(\dfrac{1}{n_1} + \dfrac{1}{n_2}\right)}}$
7. Make a decision to reject or fail to reject the null hypothesis.	If z is in the rejection region, reject H_0. Otherwise, fail to reject H_0.
8. Interpret the decision in the context of the original claim.	

To use P-values in a test for the difference between proportions, use the same guidelines as above, skipping Steps 3 and 4. After finding the standardized test statistic, use the Standard Normal Table to calculate the P-value. Then make a decision to reject or fail to reject the null hypothesis. If P is less than or equal to α, reject H_0. Otherwise fail to reject H_0.

**Sample Statistics for
Internet Users**

Females	Males
$n_1 = 200$	$n_2 = 250$
$\hat{p}_1 = 0.30$	$\hat{p}_2 = 0.38$
$n_1\hat{p}_1 = 60$	$n_2\hat{p}_2 = 95$

Study Tip

To find x_1 and x_2, use

$x_1 = n_1\hat{p}_1$ and

$x_2 = n_2\hat{p}_2$.

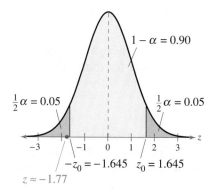

$1 - \alpha = 0.90$

$\frac{1}{2}\alpha = 0.05$ $\frac{1}{2}\alpha = 0.05$

$-z_0 = -1.645$ $z_0 = 1.645$

$z \approx -1.77$

EXAMPLE 1

A Two-Sample *z*-Test for the Difference Between Proportions

> See TI-83/84 steps on page 489.

In a study of 200 randomly selected adult female and 250 randomly selected adult male Internet users, 30% of the females and 38% of the males said that they plan to shop online at least once during the next month. At $\alpha = 0.10$, test the claim that there is a difference between the proportion of female and the proportion of male Internet users who plan to shop online.

Solution   You want to determine whether there is a difference between the proportions. So, the null and alternative hypotheses are

$$H_0: p_1 = p_2 \quad \text{and} \quad H_a: p_1 \neq p_2. \text{ (Claim)}$$

Because the test is two-tailed and the level of significance is $\alpha = 0.10$, the critical values are $-z_0 = -1.645$ and $z_0 = 1.645$. The rejection regions are $z < -1.645$ and $z > 1.645$. The weighted estimate of the population proportions is

$$\overline{p} = \frac{x_1 + x_2}{n_1 + n_2} = \frac{60 + 95}{200 + 250} = \frac{155}{450} \approx 0.3444$$

and

$$\overline{q} = 1 - \overline{p} = 1 - 0.3444 = 0.6556.$$

Because $200(0.3444)$, $200(0.6556)$, $250(0.3444)$, and $250(0.6556)$ are at least 5, you can use a two-sample z-test. The standardized test statistic is

$$z = \frac{(\hat{p}_1 - \hat{p}_2) - (p_1 - p_2)}{\sqrt{\overline{p}\,\overline{q}\left(\dfrac{1}{n_1} + \dfrac{1}{n_2}\right)}} \approx \frac{(0.30 - 0.38) - 0}{\sqrt{(0.3444)(0.6556)\left(\dfrac{1}{200} + \dfrac{1}{250}\right)}} \approx -1.77.$$

The graph at the left shows the location of the rejection regions and the standardized test statistic. Because z is in the rejection region, you should decide to reject the null hypothesis.

Interpretation   You have enough evidence at the 10% significance level to conclude that there is a difference between the proportion of female and the proportion of male Internet users who plan to shop online.

▶ Try It Yourself 1

Consider the results of the *NYTS* study discussed in the Chapter Opener. At $\alpha = 0.05$, is there a difference between the proportion of male high school students who smoke cigarettes and the proportion of female high school students who smoke cigarettes?

a. *Identify* the claim and state H_0 and H_a.
b. *Specify* the level of significance α.
c. *Find* the critical values and *identify* the rejection regions.
d. *Find* $\overline{p}$ and $\overline{q}$.
e. *Verify* that $n_1\overline{p}$, $n_1\overline{q}$, $n_2\overline{p}$, and $n_2\overline{q}$ are at least five.
f. *Use* the two-sample z-test to find the standardized test statistic z.
g. *Decide* whether to reject the null hypothesis.
h. *Interpret* the decision in the context of the original claim.

Answer: Page A45

Sample Statistics for Cholesterol-Reducing Medication

Received medication	Received placebo
$n_1 = 4700$	$n_2 = 4300$
$x_1 = 301$	$x_2 = 357$
$\hat{p}_1 = 0.064$	$\hat{p}_2 = 0.083$

Study Tip

To find $\hat{p}_1$ and $\hat{p}_2$ use

$$\hat{p}_1 = \frac{x_1}{n_1} \text{ and }$$

$$\hat{p}_2 = \frac{x_2}{n_2}.$$

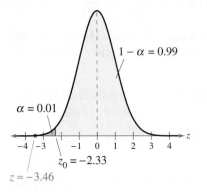

$1 - \alpha = 0.99$

$\alpha = 0.01$

$z_0 = -2.33$

$z \approx -3.46$

EXAMPLE 2

A Two-Sample z-Test for the Difference Between Proportions

A medical research team conducted a study to test the effect of a cholesterol-reducing medication. At the end of the study, the researchers found that of the 4700 randomly selected subjects who took the medication, 301 died of heart disease. Of the 4300 randomly selected subjects who took a placebo, 357 died of heart disease. At $\alpha = 0.01$, can you conclude that the death rate due to heart disease is lower for those who took the medication than for those who took the placebo? *(Adapted from New England Journal of Medicine)*

Solution You want to determine whether the death rate due to heart disease is lower for those who took the medication than for those who took the placebo. So, the null and alternative hypotheses are

$$H_0: p_1 \geq p_2 \quad \text{and} \quad H_a: p_1 < p_2. \text{ (Claim)}$$

Because the test is left-tailed and the level of significance is $\alpha = 0.01$, the critical value is $z_0 = -2.33$. The rejection region is $z < -2.33$. The weighted estimate of p_1 and p_2 is

$$\overline{p} = \frac{x_1 + x_2}{n_1 + n_2} = \frac{301 + 357}{4700 + 4300} = \frac{658}{9000} \approx 0.0731$$

and $\overline{q} = 1 - \overline{p} = 1 - 0.0731 = 0.9269$. Because $4700(0.0731)$, $4700(0.9269)$, $4300(0.0731)$, and $4300(0.9269)$ are at least 5, you can use a two-sample z-test.

$$z = \frac{(\hat{p}_1 - \hat{p}_2) - (p_1 - p_2)}{\sqrt{\overline{p}\,\overline{q}\left(\frac{1}{n_1} + \frac{1}{n_2}\right)}} \approx \frac{(0.064 - 0.083) - 0}{\sqrt{(0.0731)(0.9269)\left(\frac{1}{4700} + \frac{1}{4300}\right)}} \approx -3.46$$

The graph at the left shows the location of the rejection region and the standardized test statistic. Because z is in the rejection region, you should decide to reject the null hypothesis.

Interpretation At the 1% significance level, there is enough evidence to conclude that the death rate due to heart disease is lower for those who took the medication than for those who took the placebo.

▶ Try It Yourself 2

Consider the results of the *NYTS* study discussed in the Chapter Opener. At $\alpha = 0.05$, can you conclude that the proportion of male high school students who smoke cigars is greater than the proportion of female high school students who smoke cigars?

a. *Identify* the claim and state H_0 and H_a.
b. *Specify* the level of significance α.
c. *Find* the critical value and *identify* the rejection region.
d. *Find* $\overline{p}$ and $\overline{q}$.
e. *Verify* that $n_1\overline{p}$, $n_1\overline{q}$, $n_2\overline{p}$, and $n_2\overline{q}$ are at least five.
f. *Use* the two-sample z-test to find the standardized test statistic z.
g. *Decide* whether to reject the null hypothesis.
h. *Interpret* the decision in the context of the original claim.

Answer: Page A45

8.4 EXERCISES

■ Building Basic Skills and Vocabulary

1. Explain how to perform a two-sample z-test for the difference between two population proportions.

2. What conditions are necessary in order to use the z-test to test the difference between two population proportions?

In Exercises 3–6, test the claim about the difference between two population proportions p_1 and p_2 for the given level of significance α and the given sample statistics. Is the test right-tailed, left-tailed, or two-tailed? Assume the sample statistics are from independent random samples.

3. Claim: $p_1 \neq p_2$, $\alpha = 0.01$.
Sample statistics: $x_1 = 35$, $n_1 = 70$ and $x_2 = 36$, $n_2 = 60$

4. Claim: $p_1 < p_2$, $\alpha = 0.05$.
Sample statistics: $x_1 = 471$, $n_1 = 785$ and $x_2 = 372$, $n_2 = 465$

5. Claim: $p_1 \leq p_2$, $\alpha = 0.10$.
Sample statistics: $x_1 = 344$, $n_1 = 860$ and $x_2 = 304$, $n_2 = 800$

6. Claim: $p_1 = p_2$, $\alpha = 0.05$.
Sample statistics: $x_1 = 29$, $n_1 = 45$ and $x_2 = 25$, $n_2 = 30$

■ Using and Interpreting Concepts

Testing the Difference Between Two Proportions *In Exercises 7–16, (a) identify the claim and state H_0 and H_a, (b) find the critical value(s) and identify the rejection region(s), (c) find the standardized test statistic, (d) decide whether to reject or fail to reject the null hypothesis, and (e) interpret the decision in the context of the original claim. If convenient, use technology to solve the problem. Assume the random samples are independent.*

7. Alternative Medicine Use In a 1991 study of 1539 adults, 520 said they had used alternative medicines (for example, folk remedies and homeopathy) in the previous year. In a more recent study of 2055 adults, 865 said they had used alternative medicines in the previous year. At $\alpha = 0.05$, can you reject the claim that the proportion of adults using alternative medicines has not changed since 1991? *(Source: The Journal of the American Medical Association)*

Have You Used Alternative Medicines in the Past Year?

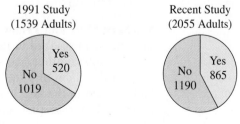

1991 Study
(1539 Adults)

No 1019 / Yes 520

Recent Study
(2055 Adults)

No 1190 / Yes 865

8. **Antidepressants** A medical research team studied patients using an antidepressant drug to recover from chronic depression. Of 77 patients who used the drug for 2 years, 5 suffered a new bout of depression. Of 84 patients who used the drug for 7 months, 19 suffered a new bout of depression. At $\alpha = 0.10$, can you reject the claim that the proportions of patients suffering new bouts of depression are the same for the two groups? *(Adapted from The Journal of the American Medical Association)*

Have You Suffered a New Bout of Depression?

Used Antidepressant   Used Antidepressant
for 2 Years (77 Patients)   for 7 Months (84 Patients)

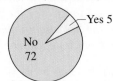

9. **Recommended Servings of Vegetables** In a survey of 5240 male senior citizens, 2201 said they eat the daily recommended number of servings of vegetables. In a survey of 6180 female senior citizens, 2348 said they eat the daily recommended number of servings of vegetables. At $\alpha = 0.10$, can you reject the claim that the proportions of senior citizens who said they eat the daily recommended number of servings of vegetables are the same for the two groups? *(Adapted from USDA Economic Research Service)*

10. **Recommended Servings of Fruit** In a survey of 1245 male senior citizens, 361 said they eat the daily recommended number of servings of fruit. In a survey of 1065 female senior citizens, 341 said they eat the daily recommended number of servings of fruit. At $\alpha = 0.01$, can you support the claim that the proportion of senior citizens who said they eat the daily recommended number of servings of fruit is lower for males than for females? *(Adapted from USDA Economic Research Service)*

11. **Smokers in Alabama and Missouri** A state-by-state survey found that the proportions of adults who are smokers in Alabama and Missouri were 24.8% and 23.4%, respectively. (Suppose the number of respondents from each state was 2000.) At $\alpha = 0.01$, can you support the claim that the proportion of adults who are smokers is greater in Alabama than in Missouri? *(Adapted from The Centers for Disease Control and Prevention)*

12. **Smokers in California and Oregon** In a random survey of 1500 adults in California and 1000 adults in Oregon, you find that the percentages of smokers are 15.2% and 18.5%, respectively. At $\alpha = 0.05$, is there enough evidence to conclude that the proportion of adults who are smokers is lower in California than in Oregon? *(Adapted from The Centers for Disease Control and Prevention)*

13. **Smokers: Male and Female** In a survey of 9300 twelfth grade males, 2083 said they had smoked in the last 30 days. In a survey of 4900 twelfth grade females, 985 said they had smoked in the last 30 days. At $\alpha = 0.01$, can you support the claim that the proportion of twelfth grade males who said they had smoked in the last 30 days is less than the proportion of twelfth grade females who said they had smoked in the last 30 days? *(Adapted from Monitoring the Future Study, University of Michigan)*

14. **Smokers: Then and Now**   In a survey of 12,900 twelfth grade students, 3444 said they had smoked in the last 30 days. In another survey of 14,200 twelfth grade students taken four years later, 3067 said they had smoked in the last 30 days. At $\alpha = 0.10$, can you reject the claim that the proportion of twelfth grade students who said they had smoked in the last 30 days has not changed? *(Adapted from the Monitoring the Future Study, University of Michigan)*

15. **Internet Users**   In a survey of 1150 adult males, 805 said they use the Internet. In a survey of 1050 females, 746 said they use the Internet. At $\alpha = 0.05$, can you reject the claim that the proportions of Internet users are the same for the two groups? *(Adapted from Pew Internet and American Life Project)*

16. **Internet Users**   In a survey of 485 adults who live in an urban area, 354 said they use the Internet. In a survey of 315 adults who live in a rural area, 189 said they use the Internet. At $\alpha = 0.05$, can you support the claim that the proportion of adults who use the Internet is greater for adults who live in an urban area than for adults who live in a rural area? *(Adapted from Pew Internet and American Life Project)*

Teen TV Time   *In Exercises 17–20, refer to the figure. Assume the survey included 700 boys and 500 girls, and assume the samples are random and independent.*

17. **Less Than One Hour of TV**   At $\alpha = 0.01$, can you support the claim that the proportion of teens who watch less than 1 hour of TV per week is greater for girls than for boys?

18. **Ten to Twenty Hours of TV**   A television marketing representative believes that the proportion of teens who watch 10 to 20 hours of TV per week is greater for boys than for girls. If the representative's belief is based on the results of the survey, is there enough evidence to support the representative's belief? Use $\alpha = 0.01$.

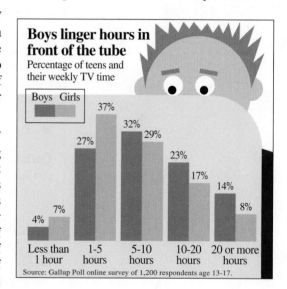

Boys linger hours in front of the tube
Percentage of teens and their weekly TV time

Boys Girls

Less than 1 hour: 4%, 7%
1-5 hours: 27%, 37%
5-10 hours: 32%, 29%
10-20 hours: 23%, 17%
20 or more hours: 14%, 8%

Source: Gallup Poll online survey of 1,200 respondents age 13-17.

19. **One to Five Hours of TV**   On the basis of the survey, an educational organization reports that the proportion of teens who watch 1 to 5 hours of TV per week is greater for girls than for boys. Using $\alpha = 0.05$, can you support the organization's claim?

20. **Five to Ten Hours of TV**   At $\alpha = 0.05$, can you reject the claim that the proportion of teens who watch 5 to 10 hours of TV per week is the same for boys and for girls?

Moving Out *In Exercises 21–24, refer to the figure. Assume the survey included 13,300 men and 13,200 women in 2000 and 14,100 men and 13,800 women in 2006, and assume the samples are random and independent. (Adapted from U.S. Census Bureau)*

21. **Men: Then and Now** At $\alpha = 0.05$, can you support the claim that the proportion of men ages 18 to 24 living in parents' homes was greater in 2000 than in 2006?

22. **Women: Then and Now** At $\alpha = 0.05$, can you support the claim that the proportion of women ages 18 to 24 living in parents' homes was greater in 2000 than in 2006?

23. **Then: Men and Women** At $\alpha = 0.01$, can you reject the claim that the proportion of 18- to 24-year-olds living in parents' homes in 2000 was the same for men and women?

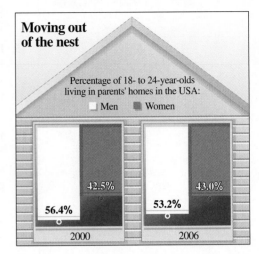

Moving out of the nest

Percentage of 18- to 24-year-olds living in parents' homes in the USA:

Men   Women

42.5%   43.0%

56.4%   53.2%

2000   2006

24. **Now: Men and Women** At $\alpha = 0.01$, can you reject the claim that the proportion of 18- to 24-year-olds living in parents' homes in 2006 was the same for men and women?

■ Extending Concepts

Constructing Confidence Intervals for $p_1 - p_2$ *You can construct a confidence interval for the difference between two population proportions $p_1 - p_2$ by using the following inequality.*

$$(\hat{p}_1 - \hat{p}_2) - z_c\sqrt{\frac{\hat{p}_1\hat{q}_1}{n_1} + \frac{\hat{p}_2\hat{q}_2}{n_2}} < p_1 - p_2 < (\hat{p}_1 - \hat{p}_2) + z_c\sqrt{\frac{\hat{p}_1\hat{q}_1}{n_1} + \frac{\hat{p}_2\hat{q}_2}{n_2}}$$

In Exercises 25 and 26, construct the indicated confidence interval for $p_1 - p_2$. Assume the samples are random and independent.

25. **Students Planning to Study Engineering** Several years ago, a survey of 1,068,000 students taking the SAT revealed that 8.8% of the students were planning to study engineering in college. In a recent survey of 1,476,000 students taking the SAT, 8.3% of the students were planning to study engineering. Construct a 95% confidence interval for the difference between proportions $p_1 - p_2$. *(Source: College Board)*

26. **Students Planning to Study Social Science** In a certain year, the percent of students taking the SAT who said they intended to study social science in college was 11.6%. Ten years later, 9.2% said they intended to study social science in college. Construct a 95% confidence interval for the difference between proportions $p_1 - p_2$. Assume 1,068,000 students were surveyed the first year and 1,476,000 students were surveyed 10 years later. *(Source: College Board)*

Uses

Hypothesis Testing with Two Samples Hypothesis testing enables you to decide whether differences in samples indicate actual differences in populations or are merely due to sampling error. For example, a study conducted on 2 groups of 4-year-olds compared the behavior of the children who attended preschool with those who stayed home with a parent. Aggressive behavior such as stealing toys, pushing other children, and starting fights was measured in both groups. The study showed that children who attended preschool were three times more likely to be aggressive than those who stayed home. These statistics were used to persuade parents to keep their children at home until they start school at age 5.

Abuses

Study Funding The study did not mention that it is normal for 4-year-olds to display aggressive behavior. Parents who keep their children at home but take them to play groups also observe their children being aggressive. Psychologists have suggested that this is the way children learn to interact with each other. The children who stayed home were less aggressive, but their behavior was considered abnormal. A follow-up study performed by a different group demonstrated that the children who stayed home before attending school ended up being more aggressive at a later age than those who had attended preschool.

The first study was funded by a mother support group who used the statistics to promote their own predetermined agenda. When dealing with statistics, always know who is paying for a study. *(Source: British Broadcasting Corporation)*

Using Nonrepresentative Samples In comparisons of data collected from two different samples, care should be taken to ensure that there are no confounding variables. For instance, suppose you are examining a claim that a new arthritis medication lessens joint pain.

If the group that is given a medication is over 60 years old and the group given the placebo is under 40, variables other than the medication might affect the outcome of the study. When you look for other abuses in a study, consider how the claim in the study was determined. What were the sample sizes? Were the samples random? Were they independent? Was the sampling conducted by an unbiased researcher?

■ EXERCISES

1. ***Using Nonrepresentative Samples*** Assume that you work for the Food and Drug Administration (*www.fda.gov*). A pharmaceutical company has applied for approval to market a new arthritis medication. The research involved a test group that was given the medication and another test group that was given a placebo. Describe some ways that the test groups might not have been representative of the entire population of people with arthritis.

2. Medical research often involves blind and double-blind testing. Explain what these two terms mean.

8 CHAPTER SUMMARY

What did you **learn?**	EXAMPLE(S)	REVIEW EXERCISES

Section 8.1

■ How to decide whether two samples are independent or dependent

1   *1, 2*

■ How to perform a two-sample z-test for the difference between two means μ_1 and μ_2 using large independent samples

2, 3   *3–8*

$$z = \frac{(\overline{x}_1 - \overline{x}_2) - (\mu_1 - \mu_2)}{\sigma_{\overline{x}_1 - \overline{x}_2}}$$

Section 8.2

■ How to perform a t-test for the difference between two population means μ_1 and μ_2 using small independent samples

1, 2   *9–16*

$$t = \frac{(\overline{x}_1 - \overline{x}_2) - (\mu_1 - \mu_2)}{\sigma_{\overline{x}_1 - \overline{x}_2}}$$

Section 8.3

■ How to perform a t-test to test the mean of the differences for a population of paired data

1, 2   *17–22*

$$t = \frac{\overline{d} - \mu_d}{s_d / \sqrt{n}}$$

Two-Sample Hypothesis Testing for Population Means

Are the samples independent?	No →	Are both populations normal?	No →	Cannot use hypothesis tests discussed in this chapter.

Yes ↓ (populations normal) → Use t-test for dependent samples (Section 8.3).

Yes ↓ (samples independent)

Are both samples large?	No →	Are both populations normal?	No →	Cannot use hypothesis tests discussed in this chapter.

Yes ↓ → Use z-test for large independent samples (Section 8.1).

Yes ↓ → Are both standard deviations known? | No → Use t-test for small independent samples (Section 8.2).

Yes ↓ → Use z-test (Section 8.1).

Section 8.4

■ How to perform a z-test for the difference between two population proportions p_1 and p_2

1, 2   *23–28*

$$z = \frac{(\hat{p}_1 - \hat{p}_2) - (p_1 - p_2)}{\sqrt{\overline{p}\,\overline{q}\left(\dfrac{1}{n_1} + \dfrac{1}{n_2}\right)}}$$

8 REVIEW EXERCISES

Section 8.1

In Exercises 1 and 2, classify the two given samples as independent or dependent. Explain your reasoning.

1. Sample 1: Maze completion times for 14 standard laboratory mice

   Sample 2: Maze completion times for 14 laboratory mice bred for higher metabolic rate

2. Sample 1: Maze completion times for 43 mice

   Sample 2: Maze completion times for those 43 mice after two weeks of maze practice

In Exercises 3–6, use the given sample statistics (independent samples) to test the claim about the difference between two population means μ_1 and μ_2 at the given level of significance α.

3. Claim: $\mu_1 \geq \mu_2$, $\alpha = 0.05$. Sample statistics: $\bar{x}_1 = 1.28$, $s_1 = 0.30$, $n_1 = 96$ and $\bar{x}_2 = 1.34$, $s_2 = 0.23$, $n_2 = 85$

4. Claim: $\mu_1 = \mu_2$, $\alpha = 0.01$. Sample statistics: $\bar{x}_1 = 5595$, $s_1 = 52$, $n_1 = 156$ and $\bar{x}_2 = 5575$, $s_2 = 68$, $n_2 = 216$

5. Claim: $\mu_1 < \mu_2$, $\alpha = 0.10$. Sample statistics: $\bar{x}_1 = 0.28$, $s_1 = 0.11$, $n_1 = 41$ and $\bar{x}_2 = 0.33$, $s_2 = 0.10$, $n_2 = 34$

6. Claim: $\mu_1 \neq \mu_2$, $\alpha = 0.05$. Sample statistics: $\bar{x}_1 = 87$, $s_1 = 14$, $n_1 = 410$ and $\bar{x}_2 = 85$, $s_2 = 15$, $n_2 = 340$

In Exercises 7 and 8, (a) identify the claim and state H_0 and H_a, (b) find the critical value(s) and identify the rejection region(s), (c) find the standardized test statistic z, (d) decide whether to reject or fail to reject the null hypothesis, and (e) interpret the decision in the context of the original claim. If convenient, use technology to solve the problem.

7. In a fast-food study, a nutritionist finds that the mean calorie content of 36 randomly selected Wendy's fish sandwiches is 480 calories with a standard deviation of 32 calories. The mean calorie content of 41 randomly selected Long John Silver's fish sandwiches is 470 calories with a standard deviation of 54 calories. At $\alpha = 0.05$, is there enough evidence for the nutritionist to conclude that the Long John Silver's sandwich has fewer calories than the Wendy's sandwich? *(Adapted from Wendy's International Inc. and Long John Silver's)*

8. A study of fast-food nutrition compared the caloric content of french fries. Thirty-eight randomly selected servings of Burger King medium french fries had a mean of 360 calories and a standard deviation of 50 calories, and 35 randomly selected servings of McDonald's medium french fries had a mean of 380 calories and a standard deviation of 45 calories. At $\alpha = 0.10$, can you support the claim that the caloric contents of the two types of french fries are different? *(Adapted from Burger King Brands, Inc. and McDonald's Corporation)*

Section 8.2

In Exercises 9–14, use the given sample statistics to test the claim about the difference between two population means μ_1 and μ_2 at the given level of significance α. Assume that the samples are random and independent and that the populations are approximately normally distributed.

9. Claim: $\mu_1 = \mu_2$, $\alpha = 0.05$. Sample statistics: $\overline{x}_1 = 300$, $s_1 = 26$, $n_1 = 19$ and $\overline{x}_2 = 290$, $s_2 = 22$, $n_2 = 12$. Assume equal variances.

10. Claim: $\mu_1 = \mu_2$, $\alpha = 0.10$. Sample statistics: $\overline{x}_1 = 0.015$, $s_1 = 0.011$, $n_1 = 8$ and $\overline{x}_2 = 0.019$, $s_2 = 0.004$, $n_2 = 6$. Assume variances are not equal.

11. Claim: $\mu_1 \leq \mu_2$, $\alpha = 0.05$. Sample statistics: $\overline{x}_1 = 183.5$, $s_1 = 1.3$, $n_1 = 25$ and $\overline{x}_2 = 184.7$, $s_2 = 3.9$, $n_2 = 25$. Assume variances are not equal.

12. Claim: $\mu_1 \geq \mu_2$, $\alpha = 0.01$. Sample statistics: $\overline{x}_1 = 24.5$, $s_1 = 2.95$, $n_1 = 19$ and $\overline{x}_2 = 26.4$, $s_2 = 2.15$, $n_2 = 20$. Assume equal variances.

13. Claim: $\mu_1 \neq \mu_2$, $\alpha = 0.01$. Sample statistics: $\overline{x}_1 = 61$, $s_1 = 3.3$, $n_1 = 5$ and $\overline{x}_2 = 55$, $s_2 = 1.2$, $n_2 = 7$. Assume equal variances.

14. Claim: $\mu_1 \geq \mu_2$, $\alpha = 0.10$. Sample statistics: $\overline{x}_1 = 520$, $s_1 = 25$, $n_1 = 7$ and $\overline{x}_2 = 500$, $s_2 = 55$, $n_2 = 6$. Assume variances are not equal.

In Exercises 15 and 16, (a) identify the claim and state H_0 and H_a, (b) find the critical value(s) and identify the rejection region(s), (c) find the standardized test statistic, (d) decide whether to reject or fail to reject the null hypothesis, and (e) interpret the decision in the context of the original claim. If convenient, use technology to solve the problem.

 15. A study of methods for teaching reading in the third grade was conducted. One classroom of 21 students participated in directed reading activities for eight weeks. Another classroom of 23 students followed the same curriculum without the activities. Students in both classrooms then took the same reading test.

The following are reading scores for the first (treated) classroom.

24	43	58	71	43	49
61	44	67	49	53	56
59	52	62	54	57	33
46	43	57			

The following are reading scores for the second (control) classroom.

42	43	55	26	62	37
33	41	19	54	20	85
46	10	17	60	53	42
37	42	55	28	48	

Diagnostics suggest that the data are sampled from a normal population and the population variances are equal. Test the claim that third graders taught with the directed reading activities scored higher than those taught without the activities. Use $\alpha = 0.05$. *(Source: StatLib/Schmitt, Maribeth C., The Effects of an Elaborated Directed Reading Activity on the Metacomprehension Skills of Third Graders)*

16. A real estate agent claims that there is no difference between the mean household incomes of two neighborhoods. The mean income of 12 randomly selected households from the first neighborhood was $32,750 with a standard deviation of $1900. In the second neighborhood, 10 randomly selected households had a mean income of $31,200 with a standard deviation of $1825. Assume normal distributions and equal population variances. Test the claim at $\alpha = 0.05$.

Section 8.3

In Exercises 17–20, using a test for dependent, random samples, test the claim about the mean of the difference of the two populations at the given level of significance α using the given statistics. Is the test right-tailed, left-tailed, or two-tailed? Assume the populations are normally distributed.

17. Claim: $\mu_d = 0$, $\alpha = 0.05$. Statistics: $\bar{d} = 10$, $s_d = 12.4$, $n = 100$

18. Claim: $\mu_d < 0$, $\alpha = 0.01$. Statistics: $\bar{d} = 3.2$, $s_d = 1.38$, $n = 25$

19. Claim: $\mu_d \leq 6$, $\alpha = 0.10$. Statistics: $\bar{d} = 10.3$, $s_d = 1.24$, $n = 33$

20. Claim: $\mu_d \neq 15$, $\alpha = 0.05$. Statistics: $\bar{d} = 17.5$, $s_d = 4.05$, $n = 37$

In Exercises 21 and 22, (a) identify the claim and state H_0 and H_a, (b) find the critical value(s) and identify the rejection region(s), (c) calculate $\bar{d}$ and s_d, (d) use the t-test to find the standardized test statistic t, (e) decide whether to reject or fail to reject the null hypothesis, and (f) interpret the decision in the context of the original claim. If convenient, use technology to solve the problem. For each sample, assume the distribution of the population is normal.

21. A medical researcher wants to test the effects of calcium supplements on men's systolic blood pressure. In part of the study, 10 randomly selected men are given a calcium supplement for 12 weeks. The researcher measures the men's systolic blood pressure at the beginning and at the end of the 12-week study and records the results shown below. At $\alpha = 0.10$, can the researcher claim that the men's systolic blood pressure decreased? *(Source: The Journal of the American Medical Association)*

Patient	1	2	3	4	5	6	7	8	9	10
Before	107	110	123	129	112	111	107	112	136	102
After	100	114	105	112	115	116	106	102	125	104

22. In a study testing the effects of an herbal supplement on systolic blood pressure in men, 11 randomly selected men were given an herbal supplement for 15 weeks. The following measurements are for each subject's systolic blood pressure taken before and after the 15-week treatment period. At $\alpha = 0.10$, can you support the claim that systolic blood pressure was lowered? *(Adapted from The Journal of the American Medical Association)*

Patient	1	2	3	4	5	6	7	8	9	10	11
Before	123	109	112	102	98	114	119	112	110	117	130
After	124	97	113	105	95	119	114	114	121	118	133

Section 8.4

In Exercises 23–26, test the claim about the difference between two population proportions p_1 and p_2 at the given level of significance α using the given sample statistics. Is the test right-tailed, left-tailed, or two-tailed? Assume the sample statistics are from independent random samples.

23. Claim: $p_1 = p_2$, $\alpha = 0.05$. Sample statistics: $x_1 = 425$, $n_1 = 840$ and $x_2 = 410$, $n_2 = 760$

24. Claim: $p_1 \le p_2$, $\alpha = 0.01$. Sample statistics: $x_1 = 36$, $n_1 = 100$ and $x_2 = 46$, $n_2 = 200$

25. Claim: $p_1 > p_2$, $\alpha = 0.10$. Sample statistics: $x_1 = 261$, $n_1 = 556$ and $x_2 = 207$, $n_2 = 483$

26. Claim: $p_1 < p_2$, $\alpha = 0.05$. Sample statistics: $x_1 = 86$, $n_1 = 900$ and $x_2 = 107$, $n_2 = 1200$

In Exercises 27 and 28, (a) identify the claim and state H_0 and H_a, (b) find the critical value(s) and identify the rejection region(s), (c) find the standardized test statistic, (d) decide whether to reject or fail to reject the null hypothesis, and (e) interpret the decision in the context of the original claim. If convenient, use technology to solve the problem. Assume the samples are independent.

27. In a random sample of 800 U.S. adults in 2003, 398 considered the amount of federal income tax they had to pay to be too high. In a recent year, in a random sample of 1000 U.S. adults, 530 considered the amount too high. At $\alpha = 0.10$, can you reject the claim that the proportions of U.S. adults who considered the amount of federal income tax they had to pay to be too high were the same for the two years? *(Adapted from Gallup Poll)*

Study Done in 2003
(800 U.S. Adults)

Study Done Recently
(1000 U.S. Adults)

28. In a random sample of 6164 students taking the SAT reasoning test who were planning to major in military sciences, 986 were female. In a random sample of 42,890 students planning to major in computer or information sciences, 5576 were female. At $\alpha = 0.05$, test the claim that the proportion of females with intended military sciences majors was greater than the proportion of females with intended computer or information sciences majors. *(Adapted from College Board)*

Planning to Major in
Military Sciences

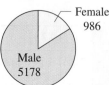

Planning to Major in
Computer or Information Sciences

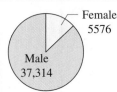

8 CHAPTER QUIZ

Take this quiz as you would take a quiz in class. After you are done, check your work against the answers given in the back of the book.

For this quiz, do the following.

(a) *Write the claim mathematically and identify H_0 and H_a.*

(b) *Determine whether the hypothesis test is a one-tailed test or a two-tailed test and whether to use a z-test or a t-test. Explain your reasoning.*

(c) *Find the critical value(s) and identify the rejection region(s).*

(d) *Use the appropriate test to find the appropriate standardized test statistic. If convenient, use technology.*

(e) *Decide whether to reject or fail to reject the null hypothesis.*

(f) *Interpret the decision in the context of the original claim.*

1. The mean score on a science assessment for 49 randomly selected male high school students was 149 with a standard deviation of 35. The mean score on the same test for 50 randomly selected female high school students was 145 with a standard deviation of 33. At $\alpha = 0.05$, can you support the claim that the mean score on the science assessment for the male high school students was higher than for the female high school students? *(Adapted from National Center for Education Statistics)*

2. A science teacher claims that the mean scores on a science assessment test for fourth grade boys and girls are equal. The mean score for 13 randomly selected boys is 153 with a standard deviation of 32 and the mean score for 15 randomly selected girls is 149 with a standard deviation of 30. At $\alpha = 0.01$, can you reject the teacher's claim? Assume the populations are normally distributed and the variances are equal. *(Adapted from National Center for Education Statistics)*

3. In a random sample of 6382 drivers ages 21 to 24 involved in fatal crashes, 32% had a blood alcohol concentration of 0.08% or greater. In a random sample of 11,179 drivers ages 25 to 34 involved in fatal crashes, 27% had a blood alcohol concentration of 0.08% or greater. At $\alpha = 0.10$, can you support the claim that the proportion of drivers involved in fatal crashes with a blood alcohol concentration of 0.08% or greater is higher for drivers ages 21 to 24 than for the drivers ages 25 to 34? *(Source: U.S. National Highway Safety Traffic Administration)*

4. The table shows the mathematics scores for 12 randomly selected students the first and second times they took the SAT. At $\alpha = 0.05$, is there enough evidence to conclude that the students' SAT scores improved on the second test? Assume the populations are normally distributed.

Student	1	2	3	4	5	6
First score	457	419	343	539	394	413
Second score	532	523	427	607	444	490

Student	7	8	9	10	11	12
First score	392	421	439	340	493	339
Second score	428	524	532	397	550	357

REAL Statistics — Real Decisions

You work for the statistics department of the National Center for Health Statistics. In an effort to determine if the mean length of hospital stays for patients diagnosed with pneumonia is different today from what it was 9 years ago, your department decides to analyze data from a random selection of hospital records. The results for several patients ages 17 and younger are shown in the histograms for 9 years ago and this year.

Your department believes that there is a difference in the mean length of hospital stays for patients (ages 17 and younger) diagnosed with pneumonia. As the department's research analyst, it is your job to work with the data and determine if this claim can be supported.

■ Exercises

1. How Would You Do It?

(a) What sampling technique would you use to select the sample for the study? Why? What sampling technique would you use if you divided hospital records according to four geographic regions (northeast, south, midwest, and west), randomly selected one region, and obtained records from each hospital in that region?

(b) Which technique in part (a) would be easiest to implement? Why?

(c) Identify possible flaws or biases in your study.

2. Choosing a Test

To test the claim that there is a difference in the mean length of hospital stays for patients (ages 17 and younger) diagnosed with pneumonia, should you use a z-test or a t-test? Are the samples independent or dependent? Do you need to know what each population's distribution is? Do you need to know anything about the population variances?

3. Testing a Mean

Test the claim that there is a difference in the mean length of hospital stays for patients (ages 17 and younger) diagnosed with pneumonia. Assume the populations are normal and the population variances are not equal. Use $\alpha = 0.05$. Write a paragraph that interprets the test's decision. Does the decision support your department's claim?

Patients 17 and Younger with Pneumonia (9 Years Ago)

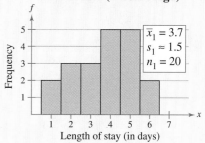

$\bar{x}_1 = 3.7$
$s_1 \approx 1.5$
$n_1 = 20$

Patients 17 and Younger with Pneumonia (This Year)

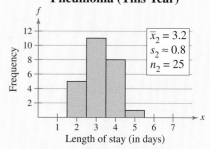

$\bar{x}_2 = 3.2$
$s_2 \approx 0.8$
$n_2 = 25$

TECHNOLOGY   MINITAB   EXCEL   T1-83/84

TAILS OVER HEADS

In the article "Tails over Heads" in the *Washington Post* (Oct. 13, 1996), journalist William Casey describes one of his hobbies—keeping track of every coin he finds on the street! From January 1, 1985 until the article was written, Casey found 11,902 coins.

As each coin is found, Casey records the time, date, location, value, mint location, and whether the coin is lying heads up or tails up. In the article, Casey notes that 6130 coins were found tails up and 5772 were found heads up. Of the 11,902 coins found, 43 were minted in San Francisco, 7133 were minted in Philadelphia, and 4726 were minted in Denver.

A simulation of Casey's experiment can be done in MINITAB as shown below. A frequency histogram of one simulation's results is shown at the right.

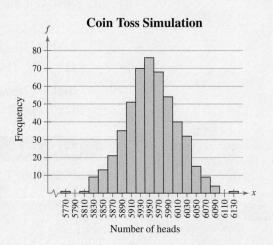

Coin Toss Simulation

MINITAB

Generate ⟨500⟩ rows of data   Number of trials: ⟨11902⟩

Store in column(s)   Probability of success: ⟨.5⟩

⟨   C1⟩

CALC, RANDOM DATA, BINOMIAL DISTRIBUTION

■ EXERCISES

1. Use a technology tool to perform a one-sample *z*-test to test the hypothesis that the probability that a "found coin" will be lying heads up is 0.5. Use $\alpha = 0.01$. Use Casey's data as your sample and write your conclusion as a sentence.

2. Do Casey's data differ significantly from chance? If so, what might be the reason?

3. In the simulation shown above, what percent of the trials had heads less than or equal to the number of heads in Casey's data? Use a technology tool to repeat the simulation. Are your results comparable?

In Exercises 4 and 5, use a technology tool to perform a two-sample z-test to decide whether there is a difference in the mint dates and in the values of coins found on a street from 1985 through 1996. Write your conclusion as a sentence. Use $\alpha = 0.05$.

4. Mint dates of coins (years)

Philadelphia:	Denver:
$\bar{x}_1 = 1984.8$	$\bar{x}_2 = 1983.4$
$s_1 = 8.6$	$s_2 = 8.4$

5. Value of coins (dollars)

Philadelphia:	Denver:
$\bar{x}_1 = \$0.034$	$\bar{x}_2 = \$0.033$
$s_1 = \$0.054$	$s_2 = \$0.052$

Extended solutions are given in the *Technology Supplement.* Technical instruction is provided for MINITAB, Excel, and the TI-83/84.

8 USING TECHNOLOGY TO PERFORM TWO-SAMPLE HYPOTHESIS TESTS

Here are some MINITAB and TI-83/84 printouts for several examples in this chapter. To duplicate the MINITAB results, you need the original data. For the TI-83/84, you can simply enter the descriptive statistics.

(See Example 1, page 454.)

Braking Distances (in feet) for 8 Volkswagen GTIs

127   132   143   127   132   141   142   128

Braking Distances (in feet) for 10 Ford Focuses

141   140   147   141   140   143   145   145   146   142

Display Descriptive Statistics...
Store Descriptive Statistics...

1-Sample Z...
1-Sample t...
2-Sample t...
Paired t...

1 Proportion...
2 Proportions...

MINITAB

Two-Sample T-Test and Confidence Interval

Two-sample T for C1 vs C2

	N	Mean	StDev	SE Mean
C1	8	134	6.93	2.4
C2	10	143	2.58	0.82

99% CI for difference: (–17.66, –0.336)
T-Test of difference = 0 (vs not =): T-Value = –3.49
P-Value = 0.008   DF = 8
Difference = mu C1 – mu C2
Estimate for difference: –9.00

(See Example 1, page 463.)

Golf Scores, Old and New Club Design

Golfer	1	2	3	4	5	6	7	8
Score (old design)	89	84	96	82	74	92	85	91
Score (new design)	83	83	92	84	76	91	80	91

Display Descriptive Statistics...
Store Descriptive Statistics...

1-Sample Z...
1-Sample t...
2-Sample t...
Paired t...

1 Proportion...
2 Proportions...

MINITAB

Paired T-Test

Paired T for C1 – C2

	N	Mean	StDev	SE Mean
C1	8	86.63	6.89	2.43
C2	8	85.00	5.81	2.05
Difference	8	1.63	3.07	1.08

T-Test of mean difference = 0 (vs>0): T-Value = 1.50   P-Value = 0.089

(See Example 2, page 442.)

(See Example 2, page 455.)

(See Example 1, page 473.)

TI-83/84

EDIT CALC
1: Z–Test…
2: T–Test…
 2–SampZTest…
4: 2–SampTTest…
5: 1–PropZTest…
6: 2–PropZTest…
7↓ZInterval…

TI-83/84

EDIT CALC **TESTS**
1: Z–Test…
2: T–Test…
3: 2–SampZTest…
4: 2–SampTTest…
5: 1–PropZTest…
6: 2–PropZTest…
7↓ZInterval…

TI-83/84

EDIT CALC **TESTS**
1: Z–Test…
2: T–Test…
3: 2–SampZTest…
4: 2–SampTTest…
5: 1–PropZTest…
6: 2–PropZTest…
7↓ZInterval…

TI-83/84

2–SampZTest
  Inpt:Data
  σ1: 750
  σ2: 800
  $\bar{x}$1: 2290
  n1: 200
  $\bar{x}$2: 2370
↓n2: 200

TI-83/84

2–SampTTest
  Inpt:Data
  $\bar{x}$1: 1275
  Sx1: 45
  n1: 14
  $\bar{x}$2: 1250
  Sx2: 30
↓n2: 16

TI-83/84

2–PropZTest
  x1: 60
  n1: 200
  x2: 95
  n2: 250

  p1: $\neq$ **p2** < p2 > p2
  Calculate Draw

TI-83/84

2–SampZTest
↑σ2: 800
  $\bar{x}$1: 2290
  n1: 200
  $\bar{x}$2: 2370
  n2: 200
  μ1: **$\neq \mu$2** < μ2 > μ2
  Calculate Draw

TI-83/84

2–SampTTest
↑n1: 14
  $\bar{x}$2: 1250
  Sx2: 30
  n2: 16
  μ1: $\neq \mu$2 < μ2 **> μ2**

  Pooled: No **Yes**
  Calculate Draw

TI-83/84

2–PropZTest
  p1 $\neq$ p2
  z= −1.774615984
  p= .0759612188
  $\hat{p}$1= .3
  $\hat{p}$2= .38
↓$\hat{p}$= .3444444444

TI-83/84

2–SampZTest
  μ1 $\neq$ μ2
  z= −1.031721408
  p= .3022026809
  $\bar{x}$1= 2290
  $\bar{x}$2= 2370
↓n1= 200

TI-83/84

2–SampTTest
  μ1 > μ2
  t= 1.811358919
  p= .0404131295
  df= 28
  $\bar{x}$1= 1275
↓$\bar{x}$2= 1250

Cumulative Review

CHAPTERS 6 – 8

1. In a survey of 1000 adults, 570 say it is somewhat or very likely that life exists on other planets. *(Adapted from Rasmussen Reports)*

   (a) Construct a 95% confidence interval for the proportion of adults who say it is somewhat or very likely that life exists on other planets.

   (b) A researcher claims that more than 60% of adults believe it is somewhat or very likely that life exists on other planets. At $\alpha = 0.05$, can you support the researcher's claim? Interpret the decision in the context of the original claim.

2. A pulmonologist suggests that a smoking ban in bars will reduce the amount of nitric oxide exhaled by asthmatic bar workers. The table shows the nitric oxide levels (in parts per billion) of a sample of 12 asthmatic bar workers before the smoking ban and one month after the smoking ban. At $\alpha = 0.05$, test the claim that a smoking ban in bars will reduce the amount of nitric oxide exhaled by asthmatic bar workers. Assume the population is normally distributed. Interpret the decision in the context of the original claim. *(Adapted from The Journal of the American Medical Association)*

Worker	1	2	3	4	5	6	7	8	9	10	11	12
Exhaled nitric oxide before ban	34	37	41	29	36	35	38	30	33	31	33	35
Exhaled nitric oxide after ban	24	31	35	21	29	37	26	21	25	28	23	30

In Exercises 3–6, construct the indicated confidence interval for the population mean μ. Which distribution did you use to create the confidence interval?

3. $c = 0.95, \bar{x} = 26.97, s = 3.4, n = 42$

4. $c = 0.90, \bar{x} = 3.46, s = 1.63, n = 16$

5. $c = 0.99, \bar{x} = 12.1, s = 2.64, n = 26$

6. $c = 0.95, \bar{x} = 8.21, s = 0.62, n = 8$

7. A pediatrician claims that the mean birth weight for a single-birth baby is greater than the mean birth weight of a baby that has a twin. The mean birth weight of a random sample of 85 single-birth babies is 3086 grams with a standard deviation of 563 grams. The mean birth weight of a random sample of 68 babies that have a twin is 2263 grams with a standard deviation of 624 grams. At $\alpha = 0.10$, can you support the pediatrician's claim? Interpret the decision in the context of the original claim.

In Exercises 8–11, use the given claim to state a null hypothesis and an alternative hypothesis. Identify which hypothesis represents the claim.

8. Claim: $\mu < 33$

9. Claim: $p \geq 0.19$

10. Claim: $\sigma = 0.63$

11. Claim: $\mu \neq 2.28$

12. The mean number of chronic medications taken by a random sample of 26 elderly adults in a community has a sample standard deviation of 3.1 medications. Assume the population is normally distributed. *(Adapted from The Journal of the American Medical Association)*

    (a) Construct a 99% confidence interval for the population variance.

    (b) Construct a 99% confidence interval for the population standard deviation.

    (c) A pharmacist believes that the standard deviation of the mean number of chronic medications taken by elderly adults in the community is less than 2.5 medications. At $\alpha = 0.01$, can you support the pharmacist's claim? Interpret the decision in the context of the original claim.

13. A tennis instructor claims that the string tension of racquets used for power is less than the string tension of racquets used for control. The mean string tension of a random sample of 15 power racquets is 57.9 pounds with a standard deviation of 0.8 pound. The mean string tension of a random sample of 15 control racquets is 61.1 pounds with a standard deviation of 0.6 pound. At $\alpha = 0.05$, can you support the tennis instructor's claim? Interpret the decision in the context of the original claim. Assume the populations are normally distributed and the variances are equal.

14. After cardiac surgery, a six-minute walking test is performed upon admission to a rehabilitation program. The number of meters walked for a random sample of 26 adults is listed. Assume the population is normally distributed. *(Adapted from CHEST: The Cardiopulmonary and Critical Care Journal)*

347	186	331	98	508	133	302	391	246
319	274	212	435	168	89	116	416	424
316	374	288	335	367	298	380	349	

    (a) Construct a 95% confidence interval for the population mean distance walked.

    (b) A physical therapist claims that the mean distance walked is less than 280 meters. At $\alpha = 0.10$, can you support the claim? Interpret the decision in the context of the original claim.

15. A medical research team studied the number of head and neck injuries sustained by hockey players. Of the 319 players who wore a full-face shield, 195 sustained an injury. Of the 323 players who wore a half-face shield, 204 sustained an injury. At $\alpha = 0.10$, can you reject the claim that the proportions of players sustaining head and neck injuries are the same for the two groups? Interpret the decision in the context of the original claim. *(Source: The Journal of the American Medical Association)*

16. On a national mathematics assessment test, a random sample of 120 twelfth grade students has a mean score of 150 with a standard deviation of 34. *(Adapted from National Center for Education Statistics)*

    (a) Construct a 90% confidence interval for the population mean test score.

    (b) This test result prompts a school administrator to claim that the mean score for all twelfth grade students who took the test is at least 145. At $\alpha = 0.05$, can you reject the administrator's claim? Interpret the decision in the context of the original claim.

4

PART FOUR

More Statistical Inference

CHAPTER 9   Correlation and Regression

CHAPTER 10   Chi-Square Tests and the *F*-Distribution

CHAPTER 11   Nonparametric Tests

Correlation and Regression

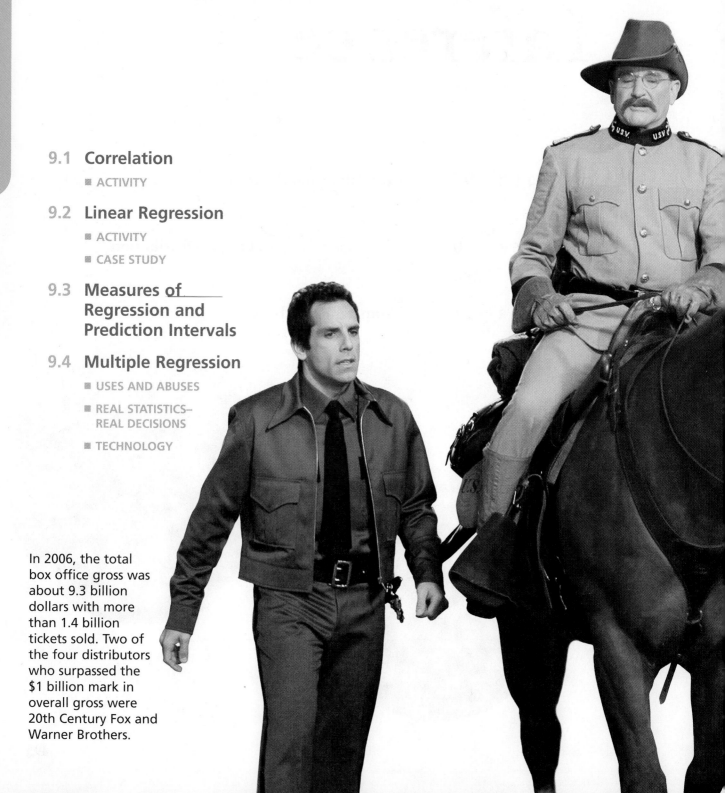

9.1 Correlation
- ACTIVITY

9.2 Linear Regression
- ACTIVITY
- CASE STUDY

9.3 Measures of Regression and Prediction Intervals

9.4 Multiple Regression
- USES AND ABUSES
- REAL STATISTICS– REAL DECISIONS
- TECHNOLOGY

In 2006, the total box office gross was about 9.3 billion dollars with more than 1.4 billion tickets sold. Two of the four distributors who surpassed the $1 billion mark in overall gross were 20th Century Fox and Warner Brothers.

In Chapters 1–8, you studied descriptive statistics, probability, and inferential statistics. One of the techniques you learned in descriptive statistics was graphing paired data with a scatter plot (Section 2.2). For instance, the budgets and worldwide grosses of 25 of the most expensive movies distributed by 20th Century Fox are shown in tabular form at the right and in graphical form below.

25 of the Most Expensive 20th Century Fox Movies

Budget (in millions of dollars)	Worldwide Gross (in millions of dollars)
200	1835.4
150	459.4
125	406.4
125	542.7
115	924.3
115	656.7
115	848.5
110	571.1
110	211.4
110	150.5
105	348.8
102	358.8
100	365.3
100	359.1
100	249.0
90	365.0
87.5	329.5
85	427.2
80	260.7
80	179.1
78	179.3
75	34
75	36.8
72	176.1
65	56.4

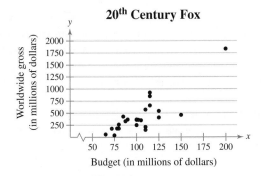

20th Century Fox

WHERE YOU'RE GOING →

In this chapter, you will study how to describe and test the significance of relationships between two variables when data are presented as ordered pairs. For instance, in the scatter plot for the 20th Century Fox movies, it appears that higher grosses tend to correspond to higher budgets and lower grosses tend to correspond to lower budgets. This relationship is described by saying that the worldwide grosses are positively correlated to the movies' budgets. Graphically, the relationship can be described by drawing a line, called a regression line, that fits the points as closely as possible. The second scatter plot below shows 25 of the most expensive movies distributed by Warner Brothers. From the scatter plot, it appears that there is no linear correlation between the worldwide grosses and the movies' budgets.

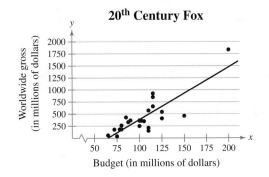

20th Century Fox

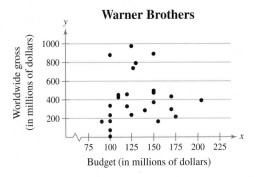

Warner Brothers

9.1 Correlation

What You SHOULD LEARN

▸ An introduction to linear correlation, independent and dependent variables, and the types of correlation

▸ How to find a correlation coefficient

▸ How to test a population correlation coefficient ρ using a table

▸ How to perform a hypothesis test for a population correlation coefficient ρ

▸ How to distinguish between correlation and causation

An Overview of Correlation ▸ Correlation Coefficient ▸ Using a Table to Test a Population Correlation Coefficient ρ ▸ Hypothesis Testing for a Population Correlation Coefficient ρ ▸ Correlation and Causation

▸ An Overview of Correlation

Suppose a safety inspector wants to determine whether a relationship exists between the number of hours of training for an employee and the number of accidents involving that employee. Or suppose a psychologist wants to know whether a relationship exists between the number of hours a person sleeps each night and that person's reaction time. How would he or she determine if any relationship exists?

In this section, you will study how to describe what type of relationship, or correlation, exists between two quantitative variables and how to determine whether the correlation is significant.

> **DEFINITION**
>
> A **correlation** is a relationship between two variables. The data can be represented by the ordered pairs (x, y) where x is the **independent** (or **explanatory**) **variable** and y is the **dependent** (or **response**) **variable.**

In Section 2.2, you learned that the graph of ordered pairs (x, y) is called a **scatter plot.** In a scatter plot, the ordered pairs (x, y) are graphed as points in a coordinate plane. The independent (explanatory) variable x is measured by the horizontal axis, and the dependent (response) variable y is measured by the vertical axis. A scatter plot can be used to determine whether a linear (straight line) correlation exists between two variables. The following scatter plots show several types of correlation.

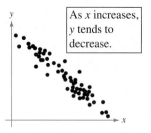

As x increases, y tends to decrease.

Negative Linear Correlation

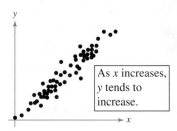

As x increases, y tends to increase.

Positive Linear Correlation

No Correlation

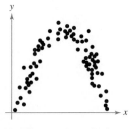

Nonlinear Correlation

Advertising expenses (1000s of $), x	Company sales (1000s of $), y
2.4	225
1.6	184
2.0	220
2.6	240
1.4	180
1.6	184
2.0	186
2.2	215

EXAMPLE 1

Constructing a Scatter Plot

A marketing manager conducted a study to determine whether there is a linear relationship between money spent on advertising and company sales. The data are shown in the table at the left. Display the data in a scatter plot and determine whether there appears to be a positive or negative linear correlation or no linear correlation.

Solution The scatter plot is shown at the right. From the scatter plot, it appears that there is a positive linear correlation between the variables.

Interpretation Reading from left to right, as the advertising expenses increase, the sales tend to increase.

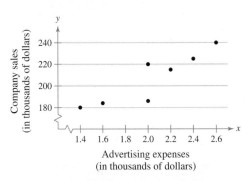

▶ Try It Yourself 1

A sociologist conducted a study to determine whether there is a linear relationship between family income level and percent of income donated to charities. The data are shown in the table at the left. Display the data in a scatter plot and determine the type of correlation.

a. *Draw* and *label* the x- and y-axes.
b. *Plot* each ordered pair.
c. Does there appear to be a linear correlation? If so, *interpret* the correlation in the context of the data.

Answer: Page A46

Income level (1000s of $), x	Donating percent, y
50	8
65	6
48	10
42	9
59	5
72	3

EXAMPLE 2

Constructing a Scatter Plot

A student nurse conducts a study to determine whether there is a linear relationship between an individual's weight (in pounds) and daily water consumption (in ounces). The data are shown in the following table. Organize the data in a scatter plot and describe the type of correlation.

Weight, x	142	201	119	102	141	124	220	154
Water, y	54	86	32	50	64	82	39	21

Solution The scatter plot is shown at the right. From the scatter plot, it appears that there is no linear correlation between the variables.

Interpretation A person's weight does not appear to be related to the amount of water that person consumes.

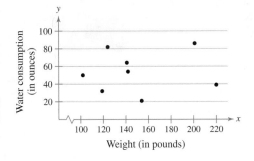

▶**Try It Yourself 2**

A marketing manager conducts a study to determine whether there is a linear relationship between a person's age and the number of magazines to which that person subscribes. The data are shown in the following table. Display the data in a scatter plot and determine the type of correlation.

Age, x	55	48	26	21	33	50	64	35
Subscriptions, y	2	3	0	4	3	0	6	1

a. *Draw* and *label* the x- and y-axes.
b. *Plot* each ordered pair.
c. Does there appear to be a linear correlation? If so, *interpret* the correlation in the context of the data.

Answer: Page A46

Duration, x	Time, y	Duration, x	Time, y
1.80	56	3.78	79
1.82	58	3.83	85
1.90	62	3.88	80
1.93	56	4.10	89
1.98	57	4.27	90
2.05	57	4.30	89
2.13	60	4.43	89
2.30	57	4.47	86
2.37	61	4.53	89
2.82	73	4.55	86
3.13	76	4.60	92
3.27	77	4.63	91
3.65	77		

EXAMPLE 3

Constructing a Scatter Plot Using Technology

Old Faithful, located in Yellowstone National Park, is the world's most famous geyser. The duration (in minutes) of several of Old Faithful's eruptions and the times (in minutes) until the next eruption are shown in the table at the left. Using a TI-83/84, display the data in a scatter plot. Determine the type of correlation.

Solution Begin by entering the x-values into List 1 and the y-values into List 2. Use *Stat Plot* to construct the scatter plot. The plot should look similar to the one shown below. From the scatter plot, it appears that the variables have a positive linear correlation.

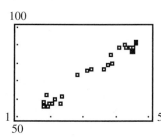

Interpretation You can conclude that the longer the duration of the eruption, the longer the time before the next eruption begins.

▶**Try It Yourself 3**

Consider the data from the Chapter Opener on page 495 on 25 of the most expensive 20th Century Fox movies. Use a technology tool to display the data in a scatter plot. Determine the type of correlation.

a. *Enter* the data into List 1 and List 2.
b. *Construct* the scatter plot.
c. Does there appear to be a linear correlation? If so, *interpret* the correlation in the context of the data.

Answer: Page A46

▶ Correlation Coefficient

Interpreting correlation using a scatter plot can be subjective. A more precise way to measure the type and strength of a linear correlation between two variables is to calculate the correlation coefficient. Although a formula for the sample correlation coefficient is given, it is more convenient to use a technology tool to calculate this value.

DEFINITION

The **correlation coefficient** is a measure of the strength and the direction of a linear relationship between two variables. The symbol r represents the sample correlation coefficient. A formula for r is

$$r = \frac{n\sum xy - (\sum x)(\sum y)}{\sqrt{n\sum x^2 - (\sum x)^2}\sqrt{n\sum y^2 - (\sum y)^2}}$$

where n is the number of pairs of data.

The population correlation coefficient is represented by ρ (the lowercase Greek letter rho, pronounced "row").

The range of the correlation coefficient is -1 to 1. If x and y have a strong positive linear correlation, r is close to 1. If x and y have a strong negative linear correlation, r is close to -1. If there is no linear correlation or a weak linear correlation, r is close to 0. It is important to remember that if r is close to 0, it does not mean that there is no relation between x and y, just that there is no *linear* relation. Several examples are shown below.

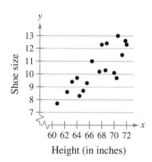

Strong positive correlation
$r = 0.81$

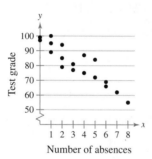

Strong negative correlation
$r = -0.92$

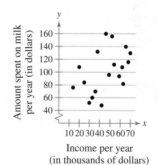

Weak positive correlation
$r = 0.45$

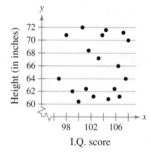

No correlation
$r = 0.04$

GUIDELINES

Calculating a Correlation Coefficient

In Words	*In Symbols*
1. Find the sum of the x-values.	$\sum x$
2. Find the sum of the y-values.	$\sum y$
3. Multiply each x-value by its corresponding y-value and find the sum.	$\sum xy$
4. Square each x-value and find the sum.	$\sum x^2$
5. Square each y-value and find the sum.	$\sum y^2$
6. Use these five sums to calculate the correlation coefficient.	$r = \dfrac{n\sum xy - (\sum x)(\sum y)}{\sqrt{n\sum x^2 - (\sum x)^2}\sqrt{n\sum y^2 - (\sum y)^2}}$

E X A M P L E 4

Finding the Correlation Coefficient

Calculate the correlation coefficient for the advertising expenditures and company sales data given in Example 1. What can you conclude?

Solution   Use a table to help calculate the correlation coefficient.

Advertising expenses (1000s of $), x	Company sales (1000s of $), y	xy	x^2	y^2
2.4	225	540	5.76	50,625
1.6	184	294.4	2.56	33,856
2.0	220	440	4	48,400
2.6	240	624	6.76	57,600
1.4	180	252	1.96	32,400
1.6	184	294.4	2.56	33,856
2.0	186	372	4	34,596
2.2	215	473	4.84	46,225
$\Sigma x = 15.8$	$\Sigma y = 1634$	$\Sigma xy = 3289.8$	$\Sigma x^2 = 32.44$	$\Sigma y^2 = 337{,}558$

With these sums and $n = 8$, the correlation coefficient is

$$r = \frac{n\Sigma xy - (\Sigma x)(\Sigma y)}{\sqrt{n\Sigma x^2 - (\Sigma x)^2}\sqrt{n\Sigma y^2 - (\Sigma y)^2}}$$

$$= \frac{8(3289.8) - (15.8)(1634)}{\sqrt{8(32.44) - 15.8^2}\sqrt{8(337{,}558) - 1634^2}}$$

$$= \frac{501.2}{\sqrt{9.88}\sqrt{30{,}508}} \approx 0.9129.$$

The result $r \approx 0.913$ suggests a strong positive linear correlation.

Interpretation   As the amount spent on advertising increases, the company sales also increase.

▶ Try It Yourself 4

Calculate the correlation coefficient for the income level and donating percent data given in Try It Yourself 1. What can you conclude?

Income level (1000s of $), x	Donating percent, y
50	8
65	6
48	10
42	9
59	5
72	3

a. *Identify n.*
b. *Use a table to calculate* Σx, Σy, Σxy, Σx^2, *and* Σy^2.
c. *Use the resulting sums and n to calculate* r.
d. What can you conclude?   *Answer: Page A46*

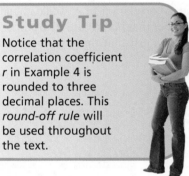

Study Tip

Notice that the correlation coefficient *r* in Example 4 is rounded to three decimal places. This *round-off rule* will be used throughout the text.

EXAMPLE 5

Using Technology to Find a Correlation Coefficient

Use a technology tool to calculate the correlation coefficient for the Old Faithful data given in Example 3. What can you conclude?

Solution   MINITAB, Excel, and the TI-83/84 each have features that allow you to calculate a correlation coefficient for paired data sets. Try using this technology to find r. You should obtain results similar to the following.

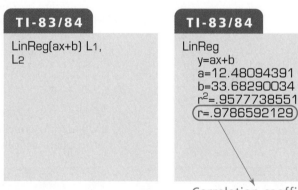

MINITAB

Correlations: C1, C2

Pearson correlation of C1 and C2 = 0.979

EXCEL

	A	B	C
26	CORREL(A1:A25,B1:B25)		
27			0.978659

To explore this topic further, see Activity 9.1 on page 512.

Before using the TI-83/84 to calculate r, you must enter the Diagnostic On command. To do so, enter the following keystrokes:

[2nd] [0]

cursor to *DiagnosticOn*

[ENTER] [ENTER] .

The following screens describe how to find r using a TI-83/84 with the data stored in List 1 and List 2. To begin, use the STAT keystroke.

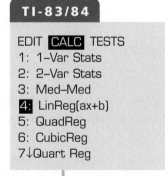

TI-83/84

EDIT **CALC** TESTS
1: 1–Var Stats
2: 2–Var Stats
3: Med–Med
4: LinReg(ax+b)
5: QuadReg
6: CubicReg
7↓Quart Reg

TI-83/84

LinReg(ax+b) L₁, L₂

TI-83/84

LinReg
  y=ax+b
  a=12.48094391
  b=33.68290034
  r²=.9577738551
  r=.9786592129

Correlation coefficient

The result, $r \approx 0.979$, suggests a strong positive linear correlation.

▶ Try It Yourself 5

Calculate the correlation coefficient for the data from the Chapter Opener on page 495 on 25 of the most expensive 20th Century Fox movies. What can you conclude?

a. *Enter* the data.
b. Use the appropriate feature to *calculate r*.
c. What can you conclude?

Answer: Page A46

▶ Using a Table to Test a Population Correlation Coefficient ρ

Once you have calculated r, the sample correlation coefficient, you will want to determine whether there is enough evidence to decide that the population correlation coefficient ρ is significant. In other words, based on a few pairs of data, can you make an inference about the population of all such data pairs? Remember that you are using sample data to make a decision about population data, so it is always possible that your inference may be wrong. In correlation studies, the small percentage of times when you decide that the correlation is significant when it is really not is called the *level of significance*. It is typically set at $\alpha = 0.01$ or 0.05. When $\alpha = 0.05$, you will probably decide that the population correlation coefficient is significant when it is really not 5% of the time. (Of course, 95% of the time, you will correctly determine that a correlation coefficient is significant.) When $\alpha = 0.01$, you will make this type of error only 1% of the time. When using a lower level of significance, however, you may fail to identify some significant correlations.

In order for a correlation coefficient to be significant, its absolute value must be close to 1. To determine whether the population correlation coefficient ρ is significant, use the critical values given in Table 11 in Appendix B. A portion of the table is shown below. If $|r|$ is greater than the critical value, there is enough evidence to decide that the correlation is significant. Otherwise, there is *not* enough evidence to say that the correlation is significant. For instance, to determine whether ρ is significant for five pairs of data ($n = 5$) at a level of significance of $\alpha = 0.01$, you need to compare $|r|$ with a critical value of 0.959, as shown in the table.

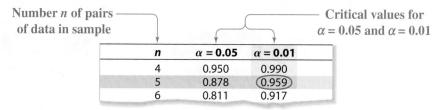

| Number n of pairs of data in sample | | Critical values for $\alpha = 0.05$ and $\alpha = 0.01$ |

n	$\alpha = 0.05$	$\alpha = 0.01$
4	0.950	0.990
5	0.878	0.959
6	0.811	0.917

If $|r| > 0.959$, the correlation is significant. Otherwise, there is *not* enough evidence to conclude that the correlation is significant. The guidelines for this process are as follows.

GUIDELINES

Using Table 11 for the Correlation Coefficient ρ

In Words	*In Symbols*
1. Determine the number of pairs of data in the sample.	Determine n.
2. Specify the level of significance.	Specify α.
3. Find the critical value.	Use Table 11 in Appendix B.
4. Decide if the correlation is significant.	If $|r| >$ critical value, the correlation is significant. Otherwise, there is *not* enough evidence to conclude that the correlation is significant.
5. Interpret the decision in the context of the original claim.	

EXAMPLE 6

Using Table 11 for a Correlation Coefficient

In Example 5, you used 25 pairs of data to find $r \approx 0.979$. Is the correlation coefficient significant? Use $\alpha = 0.05$.

Solution

The number of pairs of data is 25, so $n = 25$. The level of significance is $\alpha = 0.05$. Using Table 11, find the critical value in the $\alpha = 0.05$ column that corresponds to the row with $n = 25$. The number in that column and row is 0.396.

n	$\alpha = 0.05$	$\alpha = 0.01$
4	0.950	0.990
5	0.878	0.959
6	0.811	0.917
7	0.754	0.875
8	0.707	0.834
9	0.666	0.798
10	0.632	0.765
11	0.602	0.735
12	0.576	0.708
13	0.553	0.684
14	0.532	0.661
19	0.456	0.575
20	0.444	0.561
21	0.433	0.549
22	0.423	0.537
23	0.413	0.526
24	0.404	0.515
25	0.396	0.505
26	0.388	0.496
27	0.381	0.487
28	0.374	0.479
29	0.367	0.471

> ## Insight
> Notice that the fewer data points in your study, the stronger the evidence has to be to conclude that the correlation coefficient is significant.

Because $|r| \approx 0.979 > 0.396$, you can decide that the population correlation is significant.

Interpretation At the 5% significance level, there is enough evidence to conclude that there is a significant linear correlation between the duration of Old Faithful's eruptions and the time between eruptions.

▶ Try It Yourself 6

In Try It Yourself 4, you calculated the correlation of the income level and donating percent data to be $r \approx -0.916$. Is the correlation coefficient significant? Use $\alpha = 0.01$.

a. *Determine* the number of pairs of data in the sample.
b. *Specify* the level of significance.
c. *Find* the critical value. Use Table 11 in Appendix B.
d. *Compare* $|r|$ with the critical value and *decide* if the correlation is significant.
e. *Interpret* the decision in the context of the original claim.

Answer: Page A46

▶ Hypothesis Testing for a Population Correlation Coefficient ρ

You can also use a hypothesis test to determine whether the sample correlation coefficient r provides enough evidence to conclude that the population correlation coefficient ρ is significant. A hypothesis test for ρ can be one-tailed or two-tailed. The null and alternative hypotheses for these tests are as follows.

$$\begin{cases} H_0: \rho \geq 0 \ (\text{no significant negative correlation}) \\ H_a: \rho < 0 \ (\text{significant negative correlation}) \end{cases} \quad \textbf{Left-tailed test}$$

$$\begin{cases} H_0: \rho \leq 0 \ (\text{no significant positive correlation}) \\ H_a: \rho > 0 \ (\text{significant positive correlation}) \end{cases} \quad \textbf{Right-tailed test}$$

$$\begin{cases} H_0: \rho = 0 \ (\text{no significant correlation}) \\ H_a: \rho \neq 0 \ (\text{significant correlation}) \end{cases} \quad \textbf{Two-tailed test}$$

In this text, you will consider only two-tailed hypothesis tests for ρs.

THE t-TEST FOR THE CORRELATION COEFFICIENT

A **t-test** can be used to test whether the correlation between two variables is significant. The **test statistic** is r and the **standardized test statistic**

$$t = \frac{r}{\sigma_r} = \frac{r}{\sqrt{\dfrac{1 - r^2}{n - 2}}}$$

follows a t-distribution with $n - 2$ degrees of freedom.

GUIDELINES

Using the t-Test for the Correlation Coefficient ρ

In Words	*In Symbols*
1. Identify the null and alternative hypotheses.	State H_0 and H_a.
2. Specify the level of significance.	Identify α.
3. Identify the degrees of freedom.	d.f. $= n - 2$
4. Determine the critical value(s) and the rejection region(s).	Use Table 5 in Appendix B.
5. Find the standardized test statistic.	$t = \dfrac{r}{\sqrt{\dfrac{1 - r^2}{n - 2}}}$
6. Make a decision to reject or fail to reject the null hypothesis.	If t is in the rejection region, reject H_0. Otherwise, fail to reject H_0.
7. Interpret the decision in the context of the original claim.	

The *t*-Test for a Correlation Coefficient

In Example 4, you used eight pairs of data to find $r \approx 0.9129$. Test the significance of this correlation coefficient. Use $\alpha = 0.05$.

Solution   The null and alternative hypotheses are

$$H_0: \rho = 0 \ (\text{no correlation}) \quad \text{and} \quad H_a: \rho \neq 0 \ (\text{significant correlation}).$$

Because there are eight pairs of data in the sample, there are $8 - 2 = 6$ degrees of freedom. Because the test is a two-tailed test, $\alpha = 0.05$, and d.f. = 6, the critical values are $-t_0 = -2.447$ and $t_0 = 2.447$. The rejection regions are $t < -2.447$ and $t > 2.447$. Using the *t*-test, the standardized test statistic is

$$t = \frac{r}{\sqrt{\dfrac{1 - r^2}{n - 2}}}$$

$$= \frac{0.9129}{\sqrt{\dfrac{1 - (0.9129)^2}{8 - 2}}} \approx 5.478.$$

The following graph shows the location of the rejection regions and the standardized test statistic.

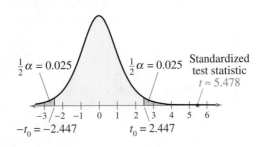

Because t is in the rejection region, you should decide to reject the null hypothesis.

Interpretation   At the 5% significance level, there is enough evidence to conclude that there is a significant linear correlation between advertising expenses and company sales.

▶ **Try It Yourself 7**

In Try It Yourself 5, you calculated the correlation coefficient of 25 of the most expensive 20th Century Fox movies to be $r \approx 0.83773$. Test the significance of this correlation coefficient. Use $\alpha = 0.01$.

a. *State* the null and alternative hypotheses.
b. *Specify* the level of significance.
c. *Identify* the degrees of freedom.
d. *Determine* the critical values and the rejection regions.
e. *Find* the standardized test statistic.
f. *Make a decision* to reject or fail to reject the null hypothesis.
g. *Interpret* the decision in the context of the original claim.

Answer: Page A46

Insight

In Example 7, you can use Table 11 in Appendix B to test the population correlation coefficient ρ. Given $n = 8$ and $\alpha = 0.05$, the critical value from Table 11 is 0.707. Because

$$|r| \approx 0.913 > 0.707,$$

the correlation is significant. Note that this is the same result you obtained using a *t*-test for the population correlation coefficient ρ.

Study Tip

Be sure you see in Example 7 that rejecting the null hypothesis means that there is sufficient evidence that the correlation is significant.

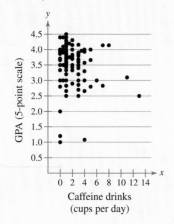

The following scatter plot shows the results of a survey conducted as a group project by students in a high school statistics class in the San Francisco area. In the survey, 125 high school students were asked their grade point average (GPA) and the number of caffeine drinks they consumed each day.

What type of correlation, if any, does the scatter plot show between caffeine consumption and GPA?

▶ Correlation and Causation

The fact that two variables are strongly correlated does not in itself imply a cause-and-effect relationship between the variables. More in-depth study is usually needed to determine whether there is a causal relationship between the variables.

If there is a significant correlation between two variables, a researcher should consider the following possibilities.

1. Is there a direct cause-and-effect relationship between the variables?

That is, does x cause y? For instance, consider the relationship between advertising expenses and company sales that has been discussed throughout this section. It is reasonable to conclude that spending more money on advertising will result in more sales.

2. Is there a reverse cause-and-effect relationship between the variables?

That is, does y cause x? For instance, consider the Old Faithful data that have been discussed throughout this section. These variables have a positive linear correlation, and it is possible to conclude that the duration of an eruption affects the time before the next eruption. However, it is also possible that the time between eruptions affects the duration of the next eruption.

3. Is it possible that the relationship between the variables can be caused by a third variable or perhaps a combination of several other variables?

For instance, consider the budgets and worldwide grosses of 25 of the most expensive movies distributed by 20th Century Fox listed in the Chapter Opener. Although these variables have a positive linear correlation, it is doubtful that just because the budgets decrease, the worldwide grosses will also decrease. The relationship is probably due to several other variables, such as advertising, the actors/actresses in the movies, and other movies that open in theaters at the same time.

4. Is it possible that the relationship between two variables may be a coincidence?

For instance, although it may be possible to find a significant correlation between the number of animal species living in certain regions and the number of people who own more than two cars in those regions, it is highly unlikely that the variables are directly related. The relationship is probably due to coincidence.

Determining which of the above cases is valid for a data set can be difficult. For instance, consider the following example. Suppose a person breaks out in a rash each time he eats shrimp at a certain restaurant. The natural conclusion is that the person is allergic to shrimp. However, upon further study by an allergist, it is found that the person is not allergic to shrimp, but to a type of seasoning the chef is putting into the shrimp.

9.1 EXERCISES

■ Building Basic Skills and Vocabulary

1. Which value of r indicates a stronger correlation: $r = 0.834$ or $r = -0.925$? Explain your reasoning.

2. Which of the following values could not represent a correlation coefficient? Explain why.

(a) $r = -0.902$ (b) $r = 0.887$ (c) $r = -1.045$ (d) $r = 0.023$

3. Explain how to decide whether a sample correlation coefficient indicates that the population correlation coefficient is significant.

4. Discuss the difference between r and ρ.

Graphical Analysis   *In Exercises 5–8, the scatter plots of paired data sets are shown. Determine whether there is a positive linear correlation, negative linear correlation, or no linear correlation between the variables.*

5.

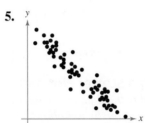

6.

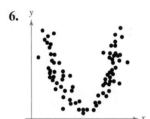

7.

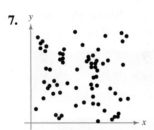

8.

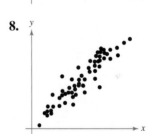

Graphical Analysis   *In Exercises 9–12, the scatter plots show the results of a survey of 20 randomly selected males ages 24–35. Using age as the explanatory variable, match each scatter plot to the appropriate description. Explain your reasoning.*

(a) Age and body temperature

(b) Age and balance on student loans

(c) Age and income

(d) Age and height

9.

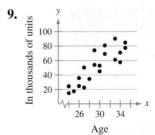

10.

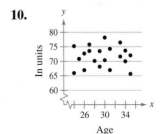

11.

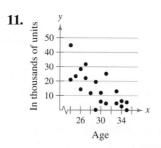

12.

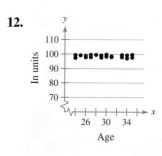

In Exercises 13 and 14, identify the explanatory variable and the response variable.

13. A nutritionist wants to determine if the amount of water consumed each day by persons of the same weight and on the same diet can be used to predict individual weight loss.

14. An insurance company hires an actuary to determine whether the number of hours of safety driving classes can be used to predict the number of driving accidents for each driver.

■ Using and Interpreting Concepts

Constructing a Scatter Plot and Determining Correlation   *In Exercises 15–22, (a) display the data in a scatter plot, (b) calculate the correlation coefficient r, and (c) make a conclusion about the type of correlation.*

15. Age and Blood Pressure   The ages (in years) of 10 men and their systolic blood pressures

Age, x	16	25	39	45	49
Systolic blood pressure, y	109	122	143	132	199

Age, x	64	70	29	57	22
Systolic blood pressure, y	185	199	130	175	118

16. Age and Vocabulary   The ages (in years) of 11 children and the number of words in their vocabulary

Age, x	1	2	3	4	5	6
Vocabulary size, y	3	440	1200	1500	2100	2600

Age, x	3	5	2	4	6
Vocabulary size, y	1100	2000	500	1525	2500

17. Hours Studying and Test Scores   The number of hours 13 students spent studying for a test and their scores on that test

Hours spent studying, x	0	1	2	4	4	5	5	5	6	6	7	7	8
Test score, y	40	41	51	48	64	69	73	75	68	93	84	90	95

18. Hours Online and Test Scores   The number of hours 12 students spent online during the weekend and the scores of each student who took a test the following Monday

Hours spent online, x	0	1	2	3	3	5
Test score, y	96	85	82	74	95	68

Hours spent online, x	5	5	6	7	7	10
Test score, y	76	84	58	65	75	50

19. Movie Budgets and Grosses   The budget (in millions of dollars) and worldwide gross (in million of dollars) for eight of the most expensive movies ever made *(Adapted from The Numbers)*

Budget, x	207	204	200	200	180	175	175	170
Gross, y	553	391	1835	784	749	218	255	433

20. Speed of Sound   The altitude (in thousands of feet) and speed of sound (in feet per second)

Altitude, x	0	5	10	15	20	25
Speed of sound, y	1116.3	1096.9	1077.3	1057.2	1036.8	1015.8

Altitude, x	30	35	40	45	50
Speed of sound, y	994.5	969.0	967.7	967.7	967.7

21. Earnings and Dividends   The earnings per share and dividends per share for 10 telecommunications services companies in a recent year *(Source: The Value Line Investment Survey)*

Earnings per share, x	2.34	1.96	1.39	3.07	0.65
Dividends per share, y	1.33	1.07	1.15	0.25	1.00

Earnings per share, x	5.21	0.88	3.23	2.54	1.03
Dividends per share, y	1.00	1.59	1.20	1.62	0.20

22. Crimes and Arrests   The number of crimes reported (in millions) and the number of arrests reported (in millions) by the U.S. Department of Justice for 14 years *(Adapted from the National Crime Victimization Survey and Uniform Crime Reports)*

Crimes, x	1.66	1.65	1.60	1.55	1.44	1.40	1.32
Arrests, y	0.72	0.72	0.78	0.80	0.73	0.72	0.68

Crimes, x	1.23	1.22	1.23	1.22	1.18	1.16	1.19
Arrests, y	0.64	0.63	0.63	0.62	0.60	0.59	0.60

Testing Claims *In Exercises 23–28, use Table 11 in Appendix B as shown in Example 6 or perform a hypothesis test using Table 5 in Appendix B as shown in Example 7 to make a conclusion about the indicated correlation coefficient. If convenient, use technology to solve the problem.*

23. **Braking Distances: Dry Surface**   The weights (in pounds) of eight vehicles and the variability of their braking distances (in feet) when stopping on a dry surface are shown in the table. Can you conclude that there is a significant linear correlation between vehicle weight and variability in braking distance on a dry surface? Use $\alpha = 0.01$. *(Adapted from National Highway Traffic Safety Administration)*

Weight, x	5940	5340	6500	5100	5850	4800	5600	5890
Variability in braking distance, y	1.78	1.93	1.91	1.59	1.66	1.50	1.61	1.70

24. **Braking Distances: Wet Surface**   The weights (in pounds) of eight vehicles and the variability of their braking distances (in feet) when stopping on a wet surface are shown in the table. At $\alpha = 0.05$, can you conclude that there is a significant linear correlation between vehicle weight and variability in braking distance on a wet surface? *(Adapted from National Highway Traffic Safety Administration)*

Weight, x	5890	5340	6500	4800	5940	5600	5100	5850
Variability in braking distance, y	2.92	2.40	4.09	1.72	2.88	2.53	2.32	2.78

25. **Hours Studying and Test Scores**   The number of hours 13 students spent studying for a test and their scores on that test are shown in the table. Is there enough evidence to conclude that there is a significant linear correlation between the data? Use $\alpha = 0.01$. (Use the value of r found in Exercise 17.)

Hours spent studying, x	0	1	2	4	4	5	5	5	6	6	7	7	8
Test score, y	40	41	51	48	64	69	73	75	68	93	84	90	95

26. **Hours Online and Test Scores**   An instructor wants to show students that there is a linear correlation between the number of hours they spend online during a weekend and their scores on a test taken the following Monday. The number of hours spent online and the test scores for 12 randomly selected students are shown in the table. At $\alpha = 0.05$, is there enough evidence for the instructor to conclude that there is a significant linear correlation between the data? (Use the value of r found in Exercise 18.)

Hours spent online, x	0	1	2	3	3	5	5	5	6	7	7	10
Test score, y	96	85	82	74	95	68	76	84	58	65	75	50

27. Earnings and Dividends The following table shows the earnings per share and dividends per share for 10 telecommunications services companies in a recent year. At $\alpha = 0.01$, can you conclude that there is a significant linear correlation between earnings per share and dividends per share? (Use the value of r found in Exercise 21.) *(Source: The Value Line Investment Survey)*

Earnings per share, x	2.34	1.96	1.39	3.07	0.65
Dividends per share, y	1.33	1.07	1.15	0.25	1.00

Earnings per share, x	5.21	0.88	3.23	2.54	1.03
Dividends per share, y	1.00	1.59	1.20	1.62	0.20

28. Crimes and Arrests The following table shows the number of crimes reported (in millions) and the number of arrests reported (in millions) by the U.S. Department of Justice for 14 years. At $\alpha = 0.05$, can you conclude that there is a significant linear correlation between the number of crimes and the number of arrests? (Use the value of r found in Exercise 22.) *(Adapted from the National Crime Victimization Survey and Uniform Crime Reports)*

Crimes, x	1.66	1.65	1.60	1.55	1.44	1.40	1.32
Arrests, y	0.72	0.72	0.78	0.80	0.73	0.72	0.68

Crimes, x	1.23	1.22	1.23	1.22	1.18	1.16	1.19
Arrests, y	0.64	0.63	0.63	0.62	0.60	0.59	0.60

■ Extending Concepts

Interchanging *x* and *y* *In Exercises 29 and 30, calculate the correlation coefficient r, letting Row 1 represent the x-values and Row 2 the y-values. Then calculate the correlation coefficient r, letting Row 2 represent the x-values and Row 1 the y-values. What effect does switching the explanatory and response variables have on the correlation coefficient?*

29.

Row 1	16	25	39	45	49	64	70
Row 2	109	122	143	132	199	185	199

30.

Row 1	0	1	2	3	3	5	5	5	6	7
Row 2	96	85	82	74	95	68	76	84	58	65

31. Writing Use your school's library, the Internet, or some other reference source to find a real-life data set with the indicated cause-and-effect relationship. Write a paragraph describing each variable and explain why you think the variables have the indicated cause-and-effect relationship.

(a) *Direct Cause-and-Effect:* Changes in one variable cause changes in the other variable.

(b) *Other Factors:* The relationship between the variables is caused by a third variable.

(c) *Coincidence:* The relationship between the variables is a coincidence.

ACTIVITY

APPLET

The *correlation by eye* applet allows you to guess the sample correlation coefficient, r, for a data set. When the applet loads, a data set consisting of 20 points is displayed. Points can be added to the plot by clicking the mouse. Points on the plot can be removed by clicking on the point and then dragging the point into the trash can. All of the points on the plot can be removed by simply clicking inside the trash can. You can enter your guess for r in the "Guess" field, and then click SHOW R! to see if you are within 0.1 of the true value. When you click NEW DATA, a new data set is generated.

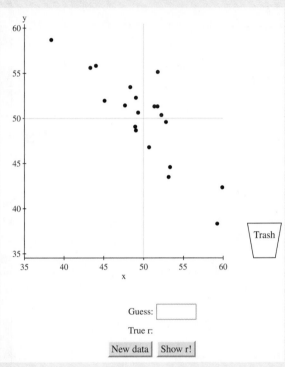

■ Explore

Step 1 Add five points to the plot.
Step 2 Enter a guess for r.
Step 3 Click SHOW R!
Step 4 Click NEW DATA.
Step 5 Remove five points from the plot.
Step 6 Enter a guess for r.
Step 7 Click SHOW R!

■ Draw Conclusions

APPLET

1. Generate a new data set. Using your knowledge of correlation, try to guess the value of r for the data set. Repeat this 10 times. How many times were you correct? Describe how you chose each r value.

2. Describe how to create a data set with a value of r that is approximately 1.

3. Describe how to create a data set with a value of r that is approximately 0.

4. Try to create a data set with a value of r that is approximately -0.9. Then try to create a data set with a value of r that is approximately 0.9. What did you do differently to create the two data sets?

9.2 Linear Regression

What You SHOULD LEARN

▸ How to find the equation of a regression line

▸ How to predict *y*-values using a regression equation

Regression Lines ▸ Applications of Regression Lines

▸ Regression Lines

After verifying that the linear correlation between two variables is significant, the next step is to determine the equation of the line that best models the data. This line is called a regression line, and its equation can be used to predict the value of *y* for a given value of *x*. Although many lines can be drawn through a set of points, a regression line is determined by specific criteria.

Consider the scatter plot and the line shown below. For each data point, d_i represents the difference between the observed *y*-value and the predicted *y*-value for a given *x*-value on the line. These differences are called **residuals** and can be positive, negative, or zero. When the point is above the line, d_i is positive. When the point is below the line, d_i is negative. If the observed *y*-value equals the predicted *y*-value, $d_i = 0$. Of all possible lines that can be drawn through a set of points, the regression line is the line for which the sum of the squares of all the residuals

$$\sum d_i^2$$

is a minimum.

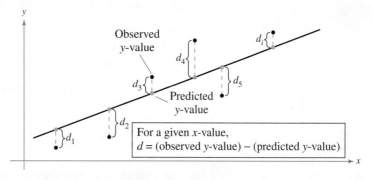

For a given *x*-value,
$d =$ (observed *y*-value) − (predicted *y*-value)

DEFINITION

A **regression line,** also called a **line of best fit,** is the line for which the sum of the squares of the residuals is a minimum.

Study Tip

When determining the equation of a regression line, it is helpful to construct a scatter plot of the data to check for outliers, which can greatly influence a regression line. You should also check for gaps and clusters in the data.

In algebra, you learned that you can write an equation of a line by finding its slope *m* and *y*-intercept *b*. The equation has the form

$$y = mx + b.$$

Recall that the slope of a line is the ratio of its rise over its run and the *y*-intercept is the *y*-value of the point at which the line crosses the *y*-axis. It is the *y*-value when $x = 0$.

In algebra, you used two points to determine the equation of a line. In statistics, you will use every point in the data set to determine the equation of the regression line.

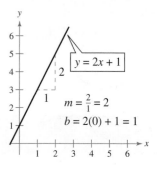

$y = 2x + 1$

$m = \dfrac{2}{1} = 2$

$b = 2(0) + 1 = 1$

The equation of a regression line allows you to use the independent (explanatory) variable x to make predictions for the dependent (response) variable y.

Study Tip

Notice that both the slope m and the y-intercept b in Example 1 are rounded to three decimal places. This *round-off rule* will be used throughout the text.

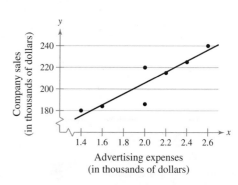

THE EQUATION OF A REGRESSION LINE

The equation of a regression line for an independent variable x and a dependent variable y is

$$\hat{y} = mx + b$$

where $\hat{y}$ is the predicted y-value for a given x-value. The slope m and y-intercept b are given by

$$m = \frac{n\sum xy - (\sum x)(\sum y)}{n\sum x^2 - (\sum x)^2} \quad \text{and} \quad b = \bar{y} - m\bar{x} = \frac{\sum y}{n} - m\frac{\sum x}{n}$$

where $\bar{y}$ is the mean of the y-values in the data set and $\bar{x}$ is the mean of the x-values. The regression line always passes through the point $(\bar{x}, \bar{y})$.

Advertising expenses (1000s of \$), x	Company sales (1000s of \$), y
2.4	225
1.6	184
2.0	220
2.6	240
1.4	180
1.6	184
2.0	186
2.2	215

EXAMPLE 1

Finding the Equation of a Regression Line

Find the equation of the regression line for the advertising expenditures and company sales data used in Section 9.1.

Solution In Example 4 of Section 9.1, you found that $n = 8$, $\sum x = 15.8$, $\sum y = 1634$, $\sum xy = 3289.8$, and $\sum x^2 = 32.44$. You can use these values to calculate the slope and y-intercept of the regression line as shown.

$$m = \frac{n\sum xy - (\sum x)(\sum y)}{n\sum x^2 - (\sum x)^2} = \frac{8(3289.8) - (15.8)(1634)}{8(32.44) - 15.8^2} = \frac{501.2}{9.88} \approx 50.72874$$

$$b = \bar{y} - m\bar{x} = \frac{1634}{8} - (50.72874)\frac{15.8}{8} = 204.25 - (50.72874)(1.975) \approx 104.0607$$

So, the equation of the regression line is

$$\hat{y} = 50.729x + 104.061.$$

To sketch the regression line, use any two x-values within the range of data and calculate their corresponding y-values from the regression line. Then draw a line through the two points. The regression line and scatter plot of the data are shown at the right. If you plot the point $(\bar{x}, \bar{y}) = (1.975, 204.25)$, you will notice that the line passes through this point.

▶ **Try It Yourself 1**

Find the equation of the regression line for the income level and donating percent data used in Section 9.1.

a. *Identify* n, $\sum x$, $\sum y$, $\sum xy$, and $\sum x^2$ from Try It Yourself 4 of Section 9.1.
b. *Calculate* the slope m.
c. *Calculate* the y-intercept b.
d. *Write* the equation of the regression line. *Answer: Page A46*

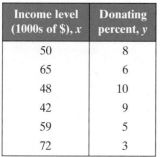

Income level (1000s of \$), x	Donating percent, y
50	8
65	6
48	10
42	9
59	5
72	3

Duration, x	Time, y	Duration, x	Time, y
1.80	56	3.78	79
1.82	58	3.83	85
1.90	62	3.88	80
1.93	56	4.10	89
1.98	57	4.27	90
2.05	57	4.30	89
2.13	60	4.43	89
2.30	57	4.47	86
2.37	61	4.53	89
2.82	73	4.55	86
3.13	76	4.60	92
3.27	77	4.63	91
3.65	77		

To explore this topic further, see Activity 9.2 on page 523.

EXAMPLE 2

Using Technology to Find a Regression Equation

Use a technology tool to find the equation of the regression line for the Old Faithful data used in Section 9.1.

Solution   MINITAB, Excel, and the TI-83/84 each have features that automatically calculate a regression equation. Try using this technology to find the regression equation. You should obtain results similar to the following.

MINITAB

Regression Analysis: C2 versus C1

The regression equation is
C2 = 33.7 + 12.5 C1

Predictor	Coef	SE Coef	T	P
Constant	33.683	1.894	17.79	0.000
C1	12.4809	0.5464	22.84	0.000

S = 2.88153   R-Sq = 95.8%   R-Sq(adj) = 95.6%

EXCEL

	A	B	C	D
1	Slope:			
2	INDEX(LINEST(known_y's,known_x's),1)			
3				12.48094
4				
5	Y-intercept:			
6	INDEX(LINEST(known_y's,known_x's),2)			
7				33.6829

TI-83/84

LinReg
y=ax+b
a=12.48094391
b=33.68290034
r²=.9577738551
r=.9786592129

From the displays, you can see that the regression equation is

$$\hat{y} = 12.481x + 33.683.$$

The TI-83/84 display at the right shows the regression line and a scatter plot of the data in the same viewing window. To do this, use *Stat Plot* to construct the scatter plot and enter the regression equation as y_1.

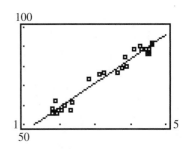

▶ Try It Yourself 2

Use a technology tool to find the equation of the regression line for the budgets and worldwide grosses of 25 of the most expensive 20th Century Fox movies given in the Chapter Opener on page 495.

a. *Enter* the data.
b. *Perform the necessary steps* to calculate the slope and y-intercept.
c. *Specify* the regression equation.

Answer: Page A46

PICTURING the WORLD

The following scatter plot shows the relationship between the number of motor vehicles in a state and the number of motor vehicle-caused deaths. (Adapted from U.S. Federal Highway Administration and U.S. National Highway Traffic Safety Administration)

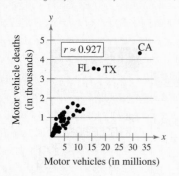

Describe the correlation between these two variables in words. Use the scatter plot to predict the number of motor vehicle-caused deaths in a state that has 16 million motor vehicles. The regression line for this scatter plot is $\hat{y} = 0.148x + 0.155$. Use this equation to make a prediction. (Assume x and y have a significant linear correlation.) How does your algebraic prediction compare with your graphical one?

▶ ## Applications of Regression Lines

After finding the equation of a regression line, you can use the equation to predict y-values over the range of the data *if the correlation between x and y is significant*. For example, an advertising executive could forecast company sales on the basis of advertising expenditures. To predict y-values, substitute the given x-value into the regression equation, then calculate $\hat{y}$, the predicted y-value.

EXAMPLE 3

Predicting *y*-Values Using Regression Equations

The regression equation for the advertising expenses (in thousands of dollars) and company sales (in thousands of dollars) data is

$$\hat{y} = 50.729x + 104.061.$$

Use this equation to predict the *expected* company sales for the following advertising expenses. (Recall from Section 9.1, Example 7 that x and y have a significant linear correlation.)

1. 1.5 thousand dollars   **2.** 1.8 thousand dollars   **3.** 2.5 thousand dollars

Solution   To predict the expected company sales, substitute each advertising expenditure for x in the regression equation. Then calculate $\hat{y}$.

1. $\hat{y} = 50.729x + 104.061$
   $= 50.729(1.5) + 104.061$
   ≈ 180.155

Interpretation   When the advertising expenses are $1500, the company sales are about $180,155.

2. $\hat{y} = 50.729x + 104.061$
   $= 50.729(1.8) + 104.061$
   ≈ 195.373

Interpretation   When the advertising expenses are $1800, the company sales are about $195,373.

3. $\hat{y} = 50.729x + 104.061$
   $= 50.729(2.5) + 104.061$
   ≈ 230.884

Interpretation   When the advertising expenses are $2500, the company sales are about $230,884.

Prediction values are meaningful only for x-values in (or close to) the range of the data. The x-values in the original data set range from 1.4 to 2.6. So, it would not be appropriate to use the regression line $\hat{y} = 50.729x + 104.061$ to predict company sales for advertising expenditures such as 0.5 ($500) or 5.0 ($5000).

▶ ### Try It Yourself 3

The regression equation for the Old Faithful data is $\hat{y} = 12.481x + 33.683$. Use this to predict the time until the next eruption for each of the following eruption durations. (Recall from Section 9.1, Example 6 that x and y have a significant linear correlation.)

1. 2 minutes
2. 3.32 minutes

a. *Substitute* each value for x into the regression equation.
b. *Calculate* $\hat{y}$.
c. *Specify* the predicted time until the next eruption for each eruption duration.

Answer: Page A46

9.2 EXERCISES

■ **Building Basic Skills and Vocabulary**

In Exercises 1–8, match the description in the left column with a description in the right column.

1. Regression line

2. Residual

3. The *y*-value of a data point corresponding to x_i

4. The *y*-value for a point on the regression line corresponding to x_i

5. Slope

6. *y*-intercept

7. The mean of the *y*-values

8. The point a regression line always passes through

a. The difference between the observed *y*-value of a data point and the predicted *y*-value on the line for the same data point

b. $\hat{y}_i$

c. The line of best fit

d. y_i

e. *b*

f. $(\overline{x}, \overline{y})$

g. *m*

h. $\overline{y}$

Graphical Analysis *In Exercises 9–12, match the regression equation with the appropriate graph. (Note that the x- and y-axes are broken.)*

9. $\hat{y} = -1.04x + 50.3$

10. $\hat{y} = 1.662x + 83.34$

11. $\hat{y} = 0.00114x + 2.53$

12. $\hat{y} = -0.667x + 52.6$

a.

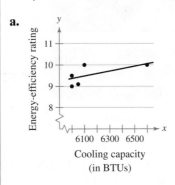

Cooling capacity
(in BTUs)

b.

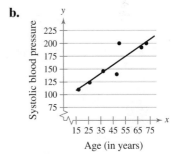

Age (in years)

c.

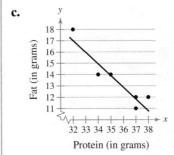

Protein (in grams)

d.

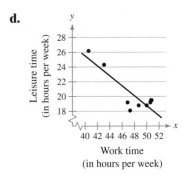

Work time
(in hours per week)

■ Using and Interpreting Concepts

Finding the Equation of a Regression Line   *In Exercises 13–22, find the equation of the regression line for the given data. Then construct a scatter plot of the data and draw the regression line. (Each pair of variables has a significant correlation.) Then use the regression equation to predict the value of y for each of the given x-values, if meaningful. If the x-value is not meaningful to predict the value of y, explain why not. If convenient, use technology to solve the problem.*

13. Miami Building Heights   The heights (in feet) and the number of stories of nine notable buildings in Miami *(Source: Emporis Buildings)*

Height, x	764	625	520	510	492	484	450	430	410
Stories, y	55	47	51	28	39	34	33	31	40

(a) $x = 500$ feet (b) $x = 650$ feet
(c) $x = 310$ feet (d) $x = 725$ feet

14. Age and Vocabulary   The ages (in years) of seven children and the number of words in their vocabulary

Age, x	3	4	4	5	6	2	3
Vocabulary size, y	1100	1300	1500	2100	2600	460	1200

(a) $x = 2$ years (b) $x = 3$ years
(c) $x = 6$ years (d) $x = 12$ years

15. Hours Studying and Test Scores   The number of hours 13 students spent studying for a test and their scores on that test

Hours spent studying, x	0	1	2	4	4	5	5
Test score, y	40	41	51	48	64	69	73

Hours spent studying, x	5	6	6	7	7	8
Test score, y	75	68	93	84	90	95

(a) $x = 3$ hours (b) $x = 6.5$ hours
(c) $x = 13$ hours (d) $x = 4.5$ hours

16. Hours Online   The number of hours 12 students spent online during the weekend and the scores of each student who took a test the following Monday

Hours spent online, x	0	1	2	3	3	5
Test score, y	96	85	82	74	95	68

Hours spent online, x	5	5	6	7	7	10
Test score, y	76	84	58	65	75	50

(a) $x = 4$ hours (b) $x = 8$ hours
(c) $x = 9$ hours (d) $x = 15$ hours

17. Hot Dogs: Caloric and Sodium Content   The caloric content and the sodium content (in milligrams) for 10 beef hot dogs *(Source: Consumer Reports)*

Calories, x	150	170	120	120	90
Sodium, y	420	470	350	360	270

Calories, x	180	170	140	90	110
Sodium, y	550	530	460	380	330

(a) $x = 170$ calories (b) $x = 100$ calories
(c) $x = 140$ calories (d) $x = 210$ calories

18. Trees: Heights and Diameters   The height (in feet) and trunk diameters (in inches) of 11 trees

Height, x	70	72	75	76	71	73
Trunk diameter, y	8.3	10.5	11.0	11.4	9.2	10.9

Height, x	85	78	77	80	82
Trunk diameter, y	14.9	14.0	16.3	18.0	15.8

(a) $x = 74$ feet (b) $x = 81$ feet
(c) $x = 95$ feet (d) $x = 79$ feet

19. Shoe Size and Height   The shoe sizes and heights (in inches) for 14 men

Shoe size, x	8.5	9.0	9.0	9.5	10.0	10.0	10.5
Height, y	66.0	68.5	67.5	70.0	70.0	72.0	71.5

Shoe size, x	10.5	11.0	11.0	11.0	12.0	12.0	12.5
Height, y	69.5	71.5	72.0	73.0	73.5	74.0	74.0

(a) $x = $ size 11.5 (b) $x = $ size 8.0
(c) $x = $ size 15.5 (d) $x = $ size 10.0

20. Age and Hours Slept   The age (in years) and the number of hours slept in a day by 10 infants

Age, x	0.1	0.2	0.4	0.7	0.6	0.9
Hours slept, y	14.9	14.5	13.9	14.1	13.9	13.7

Age, x	0.1	0.2	0.4	0.9
Hours slept, y	14.3	13.9	14.0	14.1

(a) $x = 0.3$ year (b) $x = 3.9$ years
(c) $x = 0.6$ year (d) $x = 0.8$ year

Weight, x	Variability in braking distance, y
5720	2.19
4050	1.36
6130	2.58
5000	1.74
5010	1.78
4270	1.69
5500	1.80
5550	1.87

TABLE FOR EXERCISE 21

21. **Braking Distances: Dry Surface**   The weights (in pounds) of eight vehicles and the variability of their braking distances (in feet) when stopping on a dry surface *(Adapted from National Highway Traffic Safety Administration)*

(a) $x = 4500$ pounds   (b) $x = 6000$ pounds
(c) $x = 7500$ pounds   (d) $x = 5750$ pounds

22. **Braking Distances: Wet Surface**   The weights (in pounds) of eight vehicles and the variability of their braking distances (in feet) when stopping on a wet surface *(Adapted from National Highway Traffic Safety Administration)*

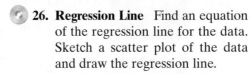

Weight, x	5720	4050	6130	5000	5010	4270	5500	5550
Variability in braking distance, y	3.78	2.43	4.63	2.88	3.25	2.76	3.42	3.51

(a) $x = 4800$ pounds   (b) $x = 5850$ pounds
(c) $x = 4075$ pounds   (d) $x = 3000$ pounds

23. **Writing**   Explain how to predict y-values using the equation of a regression line.

24. **Writing**   Given a set of data and a corresponding regression line, describe all values of x that provide meaningful predictions for y.

Electrical Engineer Salary   *In Exercises 25–29, use the following information. You work for a salary analyst and gather the data shown in the table. The table shows the ages of 13 electrical engineers and their annual salaries. (Adapted from Payscale, Inc.)*

Age (in years), x	Annual Salary (in thousands), y
22	53.5
25	56.3
29	59.8
34	63.1
39	65.9
43	69.7
48	73.6
53	75.8
56	78.1
61	80.3
64	79.4
67	76.3
69	72.4

25. **Correlation**   Using the scatter plot of the electrical engineer salary data shown, what type of correlation, if any, do you think the data have? Explain.

26. **Regression Line**   Find an equation of the regression line for the data. Sketch a scatter plot of the data and draw the regression line.

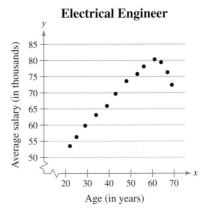

27. **Using the Regression Line**   The analyst used the regression line you found in Exercise 26 to predict the annual salary for an electrical engineer that is $x = 74$ years old. Is this a valid prediction? Explain your reasoning.

28. **Significant Correlation?**   The analyst claims that the population has a significant correlation for $\alpha = 0.01$. Verify this claim.

29. **Cause and Effect**   Write a paragraph describing the cause-and-effect relationship between the age and the annual salary of electrical engineers.

■ **Extending Concepts**

Interchanging x and y   *In Exercises 30 and 31, do the following.*

(a) Find the equation of the regression line for the given data, letting Row 1 represent the x-values and Row 2 the y-values. Sketch a scatter plot of the data and draw the regression line.

(b) Find the equation of the regression line for the given data, letting Row 2 represent the x-values and Row 1 the y-values. Sketch a scatter plot of the data and draw the regression line.

(c) What effect does switching the explanatory and response variables have on the regression line?

30.

Row 1	16	25	39	45	49	64	70
Row 2	109	122	143	132	199	185	199

31.

Row 1	0	1	2	3	3	5	5	5	6	7
Row 2	96	85	82	74	95	68	76	84	58	65

Residual Plots   *A **residual plot** allows you to assess correlation data and check for possible problems with a regression model. To construct a residual plot, make a scatter plot of $(x, y - \hat{y})$, where $y - \hat{y}$ is the residual of each y-value. If the resulting plot shows any type of pattern, the regression line is not a good representation of the relationship between the two variables. If it does not show a pattern, that is, the residuals fluctuate about 0, then the regression line is a good representation. Be aware that if a point on the residual plot appears to be outside the pattern of the other points, then it may be an outlier.*

In Exercises 32 and 33, (a) find the equation of the regression line, (b) construct a scatter plot of the data and draw the regression line, (c) construct a residual plot, and (d) determine if there are any patterns in the residual plot and explain what they suggest about the relationship between the variables.

32.

x	8	4	15	7	6	3	12	10	5
y	18	11	29	18	14	8	25	20	12

33.

x	38	34	40	46	43	48	60	55	52
y	24	22	27	32	30	31	27	26	28

Influential Points   *An **influential point** is a point in a data set that can greatly affect the graph of a regression line. An outlier may or may not be an influential point. To determine if a point is influential, find two regression lines: one including all the points in the data set, and the other excluding the possible influential point. If the slope or y-intercept of the regression line shows significant changes, the point can be considered influential. An influential point can be removed from a data set only if there is proper justification.*

In Exercises 34 and 35, (a) construct a scatter plot of the data, (b) identify any possible outliers, and (c) determine if the point is influential. Explain your reasoning.

34.

x	1	3	6	8	12	14
y	4	7	10	9	15	3

35.

x	5	6	9	10	14	17	19	44
y	32	33	28	26	25	23	23	8

36. Chapter Opener   Consider the data from the Chapter Opener on page 495 on 25 of the most expensive movies distributed by 20th Century Fox. Is the data point (200, 1835.4) an outlier? If so, is it influential? Explain.

Transformations to Achieve Linearity   *When a linear model is not appropriate to represent data, other models can be used. In some cases, the values of x or y must be transformed to find an appropriate model. In a **logarithmic transformation,** the logarithms of the variables are used instead of using the original variables when creating a scatter plot and calculating the regression line.*

In Exercises 37–40, use the data shown in the table that shows the number of bacteria present after a certain number of hours.

Number of hours, x	Number of bacteria, y
1	165
2	280
3	468
4	780
5	1310
6	1920
7	4900

37. Find the equation of the regression line for the data. Then construct a scatter plot of (x, y) and sketch the regression line with it.

38. Replace each y-value in the table with its logarithm, $\log y$. Find the equation of the regression line for the transformed data. Then construct a scatter plot of $(x, \log y)$ and sketch the regression line with it. What do you notice?

39. An **exponential equation** is a nonlinear regression equation of the form $y = ab^x$. Use a technology tool to find the exponential equation for the original data. Note that you can also find this model by solving the equation $\log y = mx + b$ from Exercise 38 for y.

40. Compare your results in Exercise 39 with the equation of the regression line and its graph in Exercise 37. Which equation is a better model for the data? Explain.

In Exercises 41–44, use the data shown in the table.

x	y
1	695
2	410
3	256
4	110
5	80
6	75
7	68
8	74

41. Find the equation of the regression line for the data. Then construct a scatter plot of (x, y) and sketch the regression line with it.

42. Replace each x-value and y-value in the table with its logarithm. Find the equation of the regression line for the transformed data. Then construct a scatter plot of $(\log x, \log y)$ and sketch the regression line with it. What do you notice?

43. A **power equation** is a nonlinear regression equation of the form $y = ax^b$. Use a technology tool to find the power equation for the original data. Note that you can also find this model by solving the equation $\log y = m(\log x) + b$ from Exercise 42 for y.

44. Compare your results in Exercise 43 with the equation of the regression line and its graph in Exercise 41. Which equation is a better model for the data? Explain.

Logarithmic Equation   *In Exercises 45–48, use the following information and a technology tool. The **logarithmic equation** is a nonlinear regression equation of the form $y = a + b \ln x$.*

45. Find and graph the logarithmic equation for the data given in Exercise 19.

46. Find and graph the logarithmic equation for the data given in Exercise 20.

47. Compare your results in Exercise 45 with the equation of the regression line and its graph. Which equation is a better model for the data? Explain.

48. Compare your results in Exercise 46 with the equation of the regression line and its graph. Which equation is a better model for the data? Explain.

ACTIVITY 9.2

APPLET

The *regression by eye* applet allows you to interactively estimate the regression line for a data set. When the applet loads, a data set consisting of 20 points is displayed. Points on the plot can be added to the plot by clicking the mouse. Points on the plot can be removed by clicking on the point and then dragging the point into the trash can. All of the points on the plot can be removed by simply clicking inside the trash can. You can move the green line on the plot by clicking and dragging the endpoints. You should try to move the line in order to minimize the sum of the squares of the residuals, also known as the sum of square error (SSE). Note that the regression line minimizes SSE. The SSE for the green line and for the regression line are given below the plot. The equations of each line are given above the plot. Click SHOW REGRESSION LINE! to see the regression line in the plot. Click NEW DATA to generate a new data set.

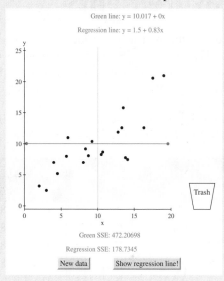

■ Explore

Step 1 Move the endpoints of the green line to try to approximate the regression line.

Step 2 Click SHOW REGRESSION LINE!

■ Draw Conclusions

APPLET

1. Click NEW DATA to generate a new data set. Try to move the green line to where the regression line should be. Then click SHOW REGRESSION LINE!. Repeat this five times. Describe how you moved each green line.

2. On a blank plot, place 10 points so that they have a strong positive correlation. Record the equation of the regression line. Then, add a point in the upper left corner of the plot and record the equation of the regression line. How does the regression line change?

3. Remove the point from the upper-left corner of the plot. Add 10 more points so that there is still a strong positive correlation. Record the equation of the regression line. Add a point in the upper-left corner of the plot and record the equation of the regression line. How does the regression line change?

4. Use the results of Exercises 2 and 3 to describe what happens to the slope of the regression line when an outlier is added as the sample size increases.

CASE STUDY

Correlation of Body Measurements

In a study published in *Medicine and Science in Sports and Exercise* (volume 17, no. 2, page 189) the measurements of 252 men (ages 22–81) are given. Of the 14 measurements taken of each man, some have significant correlations and others don't. For instance, the scatter plot at the right shows that the hip and abdomen circumferences of the men have a strong linear correlation ($r = 0.85$). The partial table shown here lists only the first nine rows of the data.

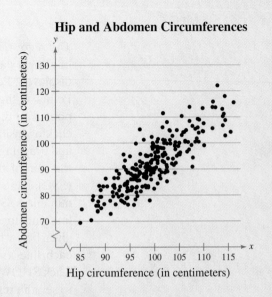

Hip and Abdomen Circumferences

Age (yr)	Weight (lb)	Height (in.)	Neck (cm)	Chest (cm)	Abdom. (cm)	Hip (cm)	Thigh (cm)	Knee (cm)	Ankle (cm)	Bicep (cm)	Forearm (cm)	Wrist (cm)	Body fat %
22	173.25	72.25	38.5	93.6	83.0	98.7	58.7	37.3	23.4	30.5	28.9	18.2	6.1
22	154.00	66.25	34.0	95.8	87.9	99.2	59.6	38.9	24.0	28.8	25.2	16.6	25.3
23	154.25	67.75	36.2	93.1	85.2	94.5	59.0	37.3	21.9	32.0	27.4	17.1	12.3
23	198.25	73.50	42.1	99.6	88.6	104.1	63.1	41.7	25.0	35.6	30.0	19.2	11.7
23	159.75	72.25	35.5	92.1	77.1	93.9	56.1	36.1	22.7	30.5	27.2	18.2	9.4
23	188.15	77.50	38.0	96.6	85.3	102.5	59.1	37.6	23.2	31.8	29.7	18.3	10.3
24	184.25	71.25	34.4	97.3	100.0	101.9	63.2	42.2	24.0	32.2	27.7	17.7	28.7
24	210.25	74.75	39.0	104.5	94.4	107.8	66.0	42.0	25.6	35.7	30.6	18.8	20.9
24	156.00	70.75	35.7	92.7	81.9	95.3	56.4	36.5	22.0	33.5	28.3	17.3	14.2

■ Exercises

1. Using your intuition, classify the following (x, y) pairs as having a weak correlation $(0 < r < 0.5)$, a moderate correlation $(0.5 < r < 0.8)$, or a strong correlation $(0.8 < r < 1.0)$.

   (a) (weight, neck)   (b) (weight, height)
   (c) (age, body fat)   (d) (chest, hip)
   (e) (age, wrist)   (f) (ankle, wrist)
   (g) (forearm, height) (h) (bicep, forearm)
   (i) (weight, body fat) (j) (knee, thigh)
   (k) (hip, abdomen)   (l) (abdomen, hip)

2. Now, use a technology tool to find the correlation coefficient for each pair in Exercise 1. Compare your results with those obtained by intuition.

3. Use a technology tool to find the regression line for each pair in Exercise 1 that has a strong correlation.

4. Use the results of Exercise 3 to predict the following.

   (a) The neck circumference of a man whose weight is 180 pounds

   (b) The abdomen circumference of a man whose hip circumference is 100 centimeters

5. Are there pairs of measurements that have stronger correlation coefficients than 0.85? Use a technology tool and intuition to reach a conclusion.

9.3 Measures of Regression and Prediction Intervals

What You SHOULD LEARN

▸ How to interpret the three types of variation about a regression line

▸ How to find and interpret the coefficient of determination

▸ How to find and interpret the standard error of estimate for a regression line

▸ How to construct and interpret a prediction interval for y

Variation about a Regression Line ▸ The Coefficient of Determination ▸ The Standard Error of Estimate ▸ Prediction Intervals

▸ Variation about a Regression Line

In this section, you will study two measures used in correlation and regression studies—the coefficient of determination and the standard error of estimate. You will also learn how to construct a prediction interval for y using a regression line and a given value of x. Before studying these concepts, you need to understand the three types of variation about a regression line.

To find the total variation, the explained variation, and the unexplained variation about a regression line, you must first calculate the **total deviation,** the **explained deviation,** and the **unexplained deviation** for each ordered pair (x_i, y_i) in a data set. These deviations are shown in the graph.

$$\text{Total deviation} = y_i - \overline{y}$$
$$\text{Explained deviation} = \hat{y}_i - \overline{y}$$
$$\text{Unexplained deviation} = y_i - \hat{y}_i$$

After calculating the deviations for each data point (x_i, y_i), you can find the total variation, the explained variation, and the unexplained variation.

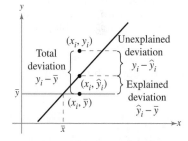

Study Tip

Consider the advertising and sales data used throughout this chapter with a regression line of

$$\hat{y} = 50.729x + 104.061.$$

Using the data point $(2.0, 220)$, you can find the total, explained, and unexplained deviations as follows.

Total deviation:

$$y_i - \overline{y} = 220 - 204.25$$
$$= 15.75$$

Explained deviation:

$$\hat{y}_i - \overline{y} = 205.519 - 204.25$$
$$= 1.269$$

Unexplained deviation:

$$y_i - \hat{y}_i = 220 - 205.519$$
$$= 14.481$$

DEFINITION

The **total variation** about a regression line is the sum of the squares of the differences between the y-value of each ordered pair and the mean of y.

$$\text{Total variation} = \sum (y_i - \overline{y})^2$$

The **explained variation** is the sum of the squares of the differences between each predicted y-value and the mean of y.

$$\text{Explained variation} = \sum (\hat{y}_i - \overline{y})^2$$

The **unexplained variation** is the sum of the squares of the differences between the y-value of each ordered pair and each corresponding predicted y-value.

$$\text{Unexplained variation} = \sum (y_i - \hat{y}_i)^2$$

The sum of the explained and unexplained variations is equal to the total variation.

$$\text{Total variation} = \text{Explained variation} + \text{Unexplained variation}$$

As its name implies, the *explained variation* can be explained by the relationship between x and y. The *unexplained variation* cannot be explained by the relationship between x and y and is due to chance or other variables.

▶ The Coefficient of Determination

You already know how to calculate the correlation coefficient r. The square of this coefficient is called the coefficient of determination. It can be shown that the coefficient of determination is equal to the ratio of the explained variation to the total variation.

DEFINITION

The **coefficient of determination** r^2 is the ratio of the explained variation to the total variation. That is,

$$r^2 = \frac{\text{Explained variation}}{\text{Total variation}}.$$

It is important that you interpret the coefficient of determination correctly. For instance, if the correlation coefficient is $r = 0.90$, then the coefficient of determination is

$$r^2 = 0.90^2$$
$$= 0.81.$$

This means that 81% of the variation of y can be explained by the relationship between x and y. The remaining 19% of the variation is unexplained and is due to other factors or to sampling error.

EXAMPLE 1

Finding the Coefficient of Determination

The correlation coefficient for the advertising expenses and company sales data as calculated in Example 4 of Section 9.1 is $r \approx 0.913$. Find the coefficient of determination. What does this tell you about the explained variation of the data about the regression line? About the unexplained variation?

Solution The coefficient of determination is

$$r^2 = (0.913)^2$$
$$\approx 0.834.$$

Interpretation About 83.4% of the variation in the company sales can be explained by the variation in the advertising expenditures. About 16.6% of the variation is unexplained and is due to chance or other variables.

▶ Try It Yourself 1

The correlation coefficient for the Old Faithful data as calculated in Example 5 of Section 9.1 is $r \approx 0.979$. Find the coefficient of determination. What does this tell you about the explained variation of the data about the regression line? About the unexplained variation?

a. *Identify* the correlation coefficient r.
b. *Calculate* the coefficient of determination r^2.
c. What percent of the variation in the times is explained? What percent is unexplained? *Answer: Page A46*

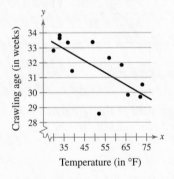

▸ The Standard Error of Estimate

When a $\hat{y}$-value is predicted from an x-value, the prediction is a point estimate. You can construct an interval estimate for $\hat{y}$, but first you need to calculate the standard error of estimate.

DEFINITION

The **standard error of estimate** s_e is the standard deviation of the observed y_i-values about the predicted $\hat{y}$-value for a given x_i-value. It is given by

$$s_e = \sqrt{\frac{\sum(y_i - \hat{y}_i)^2}{n - 2}}$$

where n is the number of ordered pairs in the data set.

From this formula, you can see that the standard error of estimate is the square root of the unexplained variation divided by $n - 2$. So, the closer the observed y-values are to the predicted y-values, the smaller the standard error of estimate will be.

GUIDELINES

Finding the Standard Error of Estimate s_e

In Words	*In Symbols*
1. Make a table that includes the column headings shown at the right.	$x_i,\ y_i,\ \hat{y}_i,\ (y_i - \hat{y}_i),$ $(y_i - \hat{y}_i)^2$
2. Use the regression equation to calculate the predicted y-values.	$\hat{y}_i = mx_i + b$
3. Calculate the sum of the squares of the differences between each observed y-value and the corresponding predicted y-value.	$\sum (y_i - \hat{y}_i)^2$
4. Find the standard error of estimate.	$s_e = \sqrt{\dfrac{\sum(y_i - \hat{y}_i)^2}{n - 2}}$

You can also find the standard error of estimate using the following formula.

$$s_e = \sqrt{\frac{\sum y^2 - b\sum y - m\sum xy}{n - 2}}$$

This formula is easy to use if you have already calculated the slope m, the y-intercept b, and several of the sums. For instance, the regression line for the data set given at the left is $\hat{y} = 1.84247x + 51.77413$, and the values of the sums are $\sum y^2 = 80{,}877.5$, $\sum y = 1137$, and $\sum xy = 11{,}940.25$. When the alternative formula is used, the standard error of estimate is

$$s_e = \sqrt{\frac{\sum y^2 - b\sum y - m\sum xy}{n - 2}}$$

$$= \sqrt{\frac{80{,}877.5 - 51.77413(1137) - 1.84247(11{,}940.25)}{16 - 2}} \approx 0.877.$$

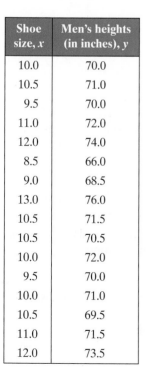

Shoe size, x	Men's heights (in inches), y
10.0	70.0
10.5	71.0
9.5	70.0
11.0	72.0
12.0	74.0
8.5	66.0
9.0	68.5
13.0	76.0
10.5	71.5
10.5	70.5
10.0	72.0
9.5	70.0
10.0	71.0
10.5	69.5
11.0	71.5
12.0	73.5

EXAMPLE 2

Finding the Standard Error of Estimate

The regression equation for the advertising expenses and company sales data as calculated in Example 1 of Section 9.2 is

$$\hat{y} = 50.729x + 104.061.$$

Find the standard error of estimate.

Solution   Use a table to calculate the sum of the squared differences of each observed y-value and the corresponding predicted y-value.

x_i	y_i	$\hat{y}_i$	$(y_i - \hat{y}_i)^2$
2.4	225	225.81	0.6561
1.6	184	185.23	1.5129
2.0	220	205.52	209.6704
2.6	240	235.96	16.3216
1.4	180	175.08	24.2064
1.6	184	185.23	1.5129
2.0	186	205.52	381.0304
2.2	215	215.66	0.4356
			$\Sigma = 635.3463$

Unexplained variation

When $n = 8$ and $\sum(y_i - \hat{y}_i)^2 = 635.3463$ are used, the standard error of estimate is

$$s_e = \sqrt{\frac{\sum(y_i - \hat{y}_i)^2}{n - 2}}$$

$$= \sqrt{\frac{635.3463}{8 - 2}}$$

$$\approx 10.290.$$

Interpretation   The standard error of estimate of the company sales for a specific advertising expense is about $10,290.

▶ Try It Yourself 2

A researcher collects the data shown at the left and concludes that there is a significant relationship between the amount of radio advertising time (in minutes per week) and the weekly sales of a product (in hundreds of dollars). Find the standard error of estimate. Use the regression equation

$$\hat{y} = 1.405x + 7.311.$$

a. *Use a table* to calculate the sum of the squared differences of each observed y-value and the corresponding predicted y-value.
b. *Identify* the number n of ordered pairs in the data set.
c. *Calculate* s_e.
d. *Interpret* the results.   *Answer: Page A46*

Radio ad time	Weekly sales
15	26
20	32
20	38
30	56
40	54
45	78
50	80
60	88

Bivariate Normal Distribution

▶ Prediction Intervals

Two variables have a **bivariate normal distribution** if for any fixed values of x, the corresponding values of y are normally distributed and for any fixed values of y, the corresponding values of x are normally distributed. Because regression equations are determined using sample data and because x and y are assumed to have a bivariate normal distribution, you can construct a prediction interval for the true value of y. To construct the prediction interval, use a t-distribution with $n - 2$ degrees of freedom.

DEFINITION

Given a linear regression equation $\hat{y} = mx + b$ and x_0, a specific value of x, a **c-prediction interval** for y is

$$\hat{y} - E < y < \hat{y} + E$$

where

$$E = t_c s_e \sqrt{1 + \frac{1}{n} + \frac{n(x_0 - \overline{x})^2}{n\sum x^2 - (\sum x)^2}}.$$

The point estimate is $\hat{y}$ and the margin of error is E. The probability that the prediction interval contains y is c.

GUIDELINES

Construct a Prediction Interval for y for a Specific Value of x

In Words	*In Symbols*
1. Identify the number of ordered pairs in the data set n and the degrees of freedom.	$d.f. = n - 2$
2. Use the regression equation and the given x-value to find the point estimate $\hat{y}$.	$\hat{y}_i = mx_i + b$
3. Find the critical value t_c that corresponds to the given level of confidence c.	Use Table 5 in Appendix B.
4. Find the standard error of estimate s_e.	$s_e = \sqrt{\dfrac{\sum (y_i - \hat{y}_i)^2}{n - 2}}$
5. Find the margin of error E.	$E = t_c s_e \sqrt{1 + \dfrac{1}{n} + \dfrac{n(x_0 - \overline{x})^2}{n\sum x^2 - (\sum x)^2}}$
6. Find the left and right endpoints and form the prediction interval.	Left endpoint: $\hat{y} - E$ Right endpoint: $\hat{y} + E$ Interval: $\hat{y} - E < y < \hat{y} + E$

Study Tip

The formulas for s_e and E use the quantities $\sum(y_i - \hat{y}_i)^2$, $(\sum x)^2$, and $\sum x^2$. Use a table to calculate these quantities.

EXAMPLE 3

Constructing a Prediction Interval

Using the results of Example 2, construct a 95% prediction interval for the company sales when the advertising expenses are $2100. What can you conclude?

Solution Because $n = 8$, there are

$$8 - 2 = 6$$

degrees of freedom. Using the regression equation

$$\hat{y} = 50.729x + 104.061$$

and

$$x = 2.1$$

the point estimate is

$$\hat{y} = 50.729x + 104.061$$

$$= 50.729(2.1) + 104.061$$

$$\approx 210.592.$$

From Table 5, the critical value is $t_c = 2.447$ and from Example 2, $s_e \approx 10.290$. Using these values, the margin of error is

$$E = t_c s_e \sqrt{1 + \frac{1}{n} + \frac{n(x_0 - \overline{x})^2}{n(\sum x^2) - (\sum x)^2}}$$

$$= (2.447)(10.290)\sqrt{1 + \frac{1}{8} + \frac{8(2.1 - 1.975)^2}{8(32.44) - (15.8)^2}}$$

$$\approx 26.857.$$

Using $\hat{y} = 210.592$ and $E = 26.857$, the prediction interval is

Left Endpoint	Right Endpoint
$210.592 - 26.857 = 183.735$	$210.592 + 26.857 = 237.449$

$$183.735 < y < 237.449.$$

Interpretation You can be 95% confident that when advertising expenses are $2100, the company sales will be between $183,735 and $237,449.

▶ Try It Yourself 3

Construct a 95% prediction interval for the company sales when the advertising expenses are $2500. What can you conclude?

a. *Specify* n, d.f., t_c, s_e.
b. *Calculate* $\hat{y}$ when $x = 2.5$.
c. *Calculate* the margin of error E.
d. *Construct* the prediction interval.
e. *Interpret* the results. *Answer: Page A46*

Answer: Page A46

Insight

The greater the difference between x and $\overline{x}$, the wider the prediction interval is. For instance, in Example 3 the 95% prediction intervals for $1.4 < x < 2.6$ are shown below.

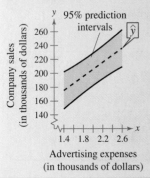

Company sales (in thousands of dollars)

Advertising expenses (in thousands of dollars)

9.3 EXERCISES

■ Building Basic Skills and Vocabulary

Graphical Analysis   *In Exercises 1–3, use the graph to answer the question.*

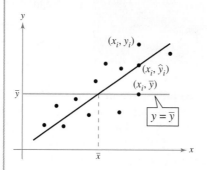

1. Describe the total variation about a regression line in words and in symbols.

2. Describe the explained variation about a regression line in words and in symbols.

3. Describe the unexplained variation about a regression line in words and in symbols.

4. The coefficient of determination is the ratio of which two types of variations? What does the coefficient of determination measure?

In Exercises 5–8, use the value of the linear correlation coefficient to calculate the coefficient of determination. What does this tell you about the explained variation of the data about the regression line? About the unexplained variation?

5. $r = 0.350$

6. $r = -0.275$

7. $r = -0.891$

8. $r = 0.964$

■ Using and Interpreting Concepts

Finding Types of Variations and the Coefficient of Determination
In Exercises 9–16, use the data to find the (a) coefficient of determination and interpret the result, and (b) standard error of estimate s_e and interpret the result.

 9. Stock Offerings   The number of initial public offerings of stock issued in a recent 12-year period and the total proceeds of these offerings (in millions of U.S. dollars) are shown in the table. The equation of the regression line is $\hat{y} = 40.049x + 21{,}843.09$. *(Source: Securities Data Co.)*

Number of issues, x	412	461	687	483	317	487
Proceeds, y	17,784	28,745	42,572	32,478	34,585	65,069

Number of issues, x	385	81	70	68	186	169
Proceeds, y	65,627	34,368	22,136	10,122	32,380	28,677

10. Cigarettes The table shows the number of cigarettes consumed (in billions) in the United States and the number of cigarettes exported (in billions) from the United States for seven years. The equation of the regression line is $\hat{y} = 0.671x - 136.771$. *(Adapted from Alcohol and Tobacco Tax and Trade Bureau)*

Cigarettes consumed in U.S., x	435	430	425	415	400	388	376
Cigarettes exported by U.S., y	166	154	145	130	127	122	124

11. Retail Space and Sales The table shows the total square footage (in billions) of retailing space at shopping centers and their sales (in billions of U.S. dollars) for 11 years. The equation of the regression line is $\hat{y} = 549.448x - 1881.694$. *(Adapted from International Council of Shopping Centers)*

Total square footage, x	5.0	5.1	5.2	5.3	5.5	5.6
Sales, y	893.8	933.9	980.0	1032.4	1105.3	1181.1

Total square footage, x	5.7	5.8	5.9	6.0	6.1
Sales, y	1221.7	1277.2	1339.2	1432.6	1530.4

12. Work and Leisure Time The median number of work hours per week and the median number of leisure hours per week for people in the United States for 10 recent years are shown in the table. The equation of the regression line is $\hat{y} = -0.646x + 50.734$. *(Source: Louis Harris & Associates)*

Median no. of work hrs. per week, x	40.6	43.1	46.9	47.3	46.8
Median no. of leisure hrs. per week, y	26.2	24.3	19.2	18.1	16.6

Median no. of work hrs. per week, x	48.7	50.0	50.7	50.6	50.8
Median no. of leisure hrs. per week, y	18.8	18.8	19.5	19.2	19.5

13. Earnings of Men and Women The table shows median weekly earnings (in U.S. dollars) of full-time male and female workers for five years. The equation of the regression line is $\hat{y} = 1.369x - 402.687$. *(Source: U.S. Bureau of Labor Statistics)*

Median weekly earnings of male workers, x	670	679	695	713	722
Median weekly earnings of female workers, y	512	529	552	573	585

14. Voter Turnout   The U.S. voting age population (in millions) and the turnout of the voting age population (in millions) for federal elections for eight nonpresidential election years are shown in the table. The data can be modeled by the regression equation $\hat{y} = 0.342x + 5.990$. *(Adapted from Federal Election Commission)*

Voting age population, x	146.3	158.4	169.9	178.6
Turnout in federal elections, y	55.9	58.9	67.6	65.0

Voting age population, x	185.8	193.7	200.9	215.5
Turnout in federal elections, y	67.9	75.1	73.1	79.8

15. Campaign Money   The money raised and spent (both in millions of U.S. dollars) by all congressional campaigns for 8 recent 2-year periods are shown in the table. The data can be modeled by the regression equation $\hat{y} = 0.943x + 21.541$. *(Source: Federal Election Commission)*

Money raised, x	471.7	659.3	740.5	790.5	781.3	1047.3	969.5	1206.1
Money spent, y	446.3	680.2	725.2	765.3	740.4	1005.6	936.3	1156.8

16. Fund Assets   The table shows the total assets (in billions of U.S. dollars) of individual retirement accounts (IRAs) and federal pension plans for nine years. The equation of the regression line is $\hat{y} = 0.21x + 288.18$. *(Source: Investment Company Institute)*

IRAs, x	1467	1728	2150	2651	2629
Federal pension plans, y	606	659	716	774	797

IRAs, x	2619	2533	3080	3475
Federal pension plans, y	860	894	959	1024

Constructing and Interpreting Prediction Intervals   *In Exercises 17–24, construct the indicated prediction interval and interpret the results.*

17. Proceeds   Construct a 95% prediction interval for the proceeds from initial public offerings in Exercise 9 when the number of issues is 712.

18. Cigarettes Consumed   Construct a 95% prediction interval for the cigarettes exported by the United States in Exercise 10 when the number of cigarettes consumed in the United States is 450 billion.

19. Retail Sales   Using the results of Exercise 11, construct a 90% prediction interval for shopping center sales when the total square footage of shopping centers is 4.5 billion.

20. Leisure Hours   Using the results of Exercise 12, construct a 90% prediction interval for the median number of leisure hours per week when the median number of work hours per week is 45.1.

21. Earnings of Female Workers When the median weekly earnings of male workers is $650, find a 99% prediction interval for the median weekly earnings of female workers. Use the results of Exercise 13.

22. Predicting Voter Turnout When the voting age population is 210 million, construct a 99% prediction interval for the voter turnout in federal elections. Use the results of Exercise 14.

23. Campaign Spending A total of $775.8 million is raised in one 2-year period for congressional campaigns. Construct a prediction interval for the money spent by the campaigns. Use the results of Exercise 15 and $c = 0.95$.

24. Total Assets The total assets in IRAs is $2500 billion. Construct a prediction interval for the total assets in federal pension plans. Use the results of Exercise 16 and $c = 0.90$.

■ Extending Concepts

Old Vehicles *In Exercises 25–31, use the information shown at the right.*

25. Scatter Plot Construct a scatter plot of the data. Show $\bar{y}$ and $\bar{x}$ on the graph.

26. Regression Line Find and graph the regression line.

27. Deviation Calculate the explained deviation, the unexplained deviation, and the total deviation for each data point.

Keeping cars longer.
The median age of vehicles on U.S. roads for seven different years:

Cars, x	Trucks, y
9.2	6.9
9.0	6.8
8.4	6.8
8.3	6.9
6.5	6.5
6.0	6.3
4.9	5.9

(Source: Polk Co.)

28. Variation Find the (a) explained variation, (b) unexplained variation, and (c) total variation.

29. Coefficient of Determination Find the coefficient of determination. What can you conclude?

30. Error of Estimate Find the standard error of estimate s_e and interpret the results.

31. Prediction Interval Construct a 95% prediction interval for the median age of trucks in use when the median age of cars in use is 8.6 years.

32. Correlation Coefficient and Slope Recall that the formula for the correlation coefficient r is

$$r = \frac{n\Sigma xy - (\Sigma x)(\Sigma y)}{\sqrt{n\Sigma x^2 - (\Sigma x)^2}\sqrt{n\Sigma y^2 - (\Sigma y)^2}}$$

and the formula for the slope m of a regression line is

$$m = \frac{n\Sigma xy - (\Sigma x)(\Sigma y)}{n\Sigma x^2 - (\Sigma x)^2}.$$

Given a set of data, why must the slope m of the data's regression line always have the same sign as the data's correlation coefficient r?

Hypothesis Testing for Slope   *In Exercises 33 and 34, use the following information.*

When testing the slope M of the regression line for the population, you usually test that the slope is zero, or $H_0: M = 0$. A slope of zero indicates that there is no linear relationship between x and y. To perform the t-test for the slope M, use the standardized test statistic

$$t = \frac{m}{s_e}\sqrt{\sum x^2 - \frac{(\sum x)^2}{n}}$$

with n − 2 degrees of freedom. Then, using the critical values found in Table 5 in Appendix B, make a decision whether to reject or fail to reject the null hypothesis. You can also use the LinRegTTest feature on a TI-83/84 to calculate the standardized test statistic as well as the corresponding P-value. If $P \le \alpha$, then reject the null hypothesis. If $P > \alpha$, then do not reject H_0.

33. The following table shows the weights (in pounds) and the number of hours slept in a day by a random sample of infants. Test the claim that $M \ne 0$. Use $\alpha = 0.01$. Then interpret the results in the context of the problem. If convenient, use technology to solve the problem.

Weight, x	8.1	10.2	9.9	7.2	6.9	11.2	11	15
Hours slept, y	14.8	14.6	14.1	14.2	13.8	13.2	13.9	12.5

34. The following table shows the ages (in years) and salaries (in thousands of dollars) for a random sample of engineers at a company. Test the claim that $M \ne 0$. Use $\alpha = 0.05$. Then interpret the results in the context of the problem. If convenient, use technology to solve the problem.

Age, x	25	34	29	30	42	38	49	52	35	40
Salary, y	57.5	61.2	59.9	58.7	87.5	67.4	89.2	85.3	69.5	75.1

Confidence Intervals for *y*-Intercept and Slope   *You can construct confidence intervals for the y-intercept B and slope M of the regression line $y = Mx + B$ for the population by using the following inequalities.*

***y*-intercept B:** $b - E < B < b + E$

$$\text{where } E = t_c s_e \sqrt{\frac{1}{n} + \frac{\bar{x}^2}{\sum x^2 - \frac{(\sum x)^2}{n}}} \quad \text{and}$$

slope M: $m - E < M < m + E$

$$\text{where } E = \frac{t_c s_e}{\sqrt{\sum x^2 - \frac{(\sum x)^2}{n}}}$$

The values of m and b are obtained from the sample data, and the critical value t_c is found using Table 5 in Appendix B with n − 2 degrees of freedom.

In Exercises 35 and 36, construct the indicated confidence interval.

35. Construct the 95% confidence interval for *B* and *M* using the advertising expenses and company sales data found in Example 2.

36. Construct the 99% confidence interval for *B* and *M* using the advertising expenses and company sales data found in Example 2.

9.4 Multiple Regression

What You
SHOULD LEARN

▸ How to use technology to find a multiple regression equation, the standard error of estimate, and the coefficient of determination

▸ How to use a multiple regression equation to predict y-values

Finding a Multiple Regression Equation ▸ Predicting y-Values

▸ Finding a Multiple Regression Equation

In many instances, a better prediction model can be found for a dependent (response) variable by using more than one independent (explanatory) variable. For example, a more accurate prediction for the company sales discussed in previous sections might be made by considering the number of employees on the sales staff as well as the advertising expenses. Models that contain more than one independent variable are multiple regression models.

DEFINITION

A **multiple regression equation** has the form

$$\hat{y} = b + m_1x_1 + m_2x_2 + m_3x_3 + \cdots + m_kx_k$$

where $x_1, x_2, x_3, \ldots, x_k$ are the independent variables, b is the y-intercept, and y is the dependent variable.

The y-intercept b is the value of y when all x_i are 0. Each coefficient m_i is the amount of change in y when the independent variable x_i is changed by one unit and all other independent variables are held constant.

Insight

Because the mathematics associated with multiple regression is complicated, this section focuses on how to use technology to find a multiple regression equation and how to interpret the results.

EXAMPLE 1

Finding a Multiple Regression Equation

A researcher wants to determine how employee salaries at a certain company are related to the length of employment, previous experience, and education. The researcher selects eight employees from the company and obtains the following data.

Employee	Salary, y	Employment (in years), x_1	Experience (in years), x_2	Education (in years), x_3
A	57,310	10	2	16
B	57,380	5	6	16
C	54,135	3	1	12
D	56,985	6	5	14
E	58,715	8	8	16
F	60,620	20	0	12
G	59,200	8	4	18
H	60,320	14	6	17

Use MINITAB to find a multiple regression equation that models the data.

Solution   Enter the y-values in C1 and the x_1-, x_2-, and x_3-values in C2, C3, and C4, respectively. Select "Regression▶Regression . . ." from the *Stat* menu. Using the salaries as the response variable and the remaining data as the predictors, you should obtain results similar to the following.

<table>
<tr><td colspan="5">**MINITAB**</td></tr>
<tr><td colspan="5">**Regression Analysis: Salary, y versus x1, x2, x3**</td></tr>
<tr><td colspan="5">The regression equation is
Salary, y = 49764 + 364 x1 + 228 x2 + 267 x3</td></tr>
<tr><td>Predictor</td><td>Coef</td><td>SE Coef</td><td>T</td><td>P</td></tr>
<tr><td>Constant</td><td>49764 — b</td><td>1981</td><td>25.12</td><td>0.000</td></tr>
<tr><td>x1</td><td>364.41 — m₁</td><td>48.32</td><td>7.54</td><td>0.002</td></tr>
<tr><td>x2</td><td>227.6 — m₂</td><td>123.8</td><td>1.84</td><td>0.140</td></tr>
<tr><td>x3</td><td>266.9 — m₃</td><td>147.4</td><td>1.81</td><td>0.144</td></tr>
<tr><td colspan="5">S = 659.490   R-Sq = 94.4%   R-Sq(adj) = 90.2%</td></tr>
</table>

The regression equation is $\hat{y} = 49{,}764 + 364x_1 + 228x_2 + 267x_3$.

▶ **Try It Yourself 1**

A statistics professor wants to determine how students' final grades are related to the midterm exam grades and number of classes missed. The professor selects 10 students from her class and obtains the following data.

Student	Final grade, y	Midterm exam, x_1	Classes missed, x_2
1	81	75	1
2	90	80	0
3	86	91	2
4	76	80	3
5	51	62	6
6	75	90	4
7	44	60	7
8	81	82	2
9	94	88	0
10	93	96	1

Use technology to find a multiple regression equation that models the data.

a. *Enter* the data.
b. *Calculate* the regression line.   *Answer: Page A47*

MINITAB displays much more than the regression equation and the coefficients of the independent variables. For example, it also displays the standard error of estimate, denoted by S, and the coefficient of determination, denoted by R-Sq. In Example 1, $S = 659.490$ and R-$Sq = 94.4\%$. So, the standard error of estimate is \$659.49. The coefficient of determination tells you that 94.4% of the variation in y can be explained by the multiple regression model. The remaining 5.6% is unexplained and is due to other factors or chance.

Study Tip

In Example 1, it is important that you interpret the coefficients m_1, m_2, and m_3 correctly. For instance, if x_2 and x_3 are held constant and x_1 increases by 1, then y increases by \$364. Similarly, if x_1 and x_3 are held constant and x_2 increases by 1, then y increases by \$228. If x_1 and x_2 are held constant and x_3 increases by 1, then y increases by \$267.

PICTURING the WORLD

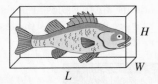

In a lake in Finland, 159 fish of 7 species were caught and measured for weight *G*, length *L*, height *H*, and width *W* (*H* and *W* are percents of *L*). The regression equation for *G* and *L* is

$$G = -488 + 28.5L,$$
$$r = 0.925.$$

When all four variables are used, the regression equation is

$$G = -711 + 28.2L +$$
$$1.46H + 13.4W,$$
$$r = 0.931.$$

Predict the weight of a fish with the following measurements: L = 40, H = 17, and W = 11. How do your predictions vary when you use a single variable versus many variables? Which do you think is more accurate?

▸ Predicting *y*-Values

After finding the equation of the multiple regression line, you can use the equation to predict *y*-values over the range of the data. To predict *y*-values, substitute the given value for each independent variable into the equation, then calculate $\hat{y}$.

EXAMPLE 2

Predicting *y*-Values Using Multiple Regression Equations

Use the regression equation found in Example 1 to predict an employee's salary given the following conditions.

1. 12 years of current employment, 5 years of experience, and 16 years of education
2. 4 years of current employment, 2 years of experience, and 12 years of education
3. 8 years of current employment, 7 years of experience, and 17 years of education

Solution   To predict each employee's salary, substitute the values for x_1, x_2, and x_3 into the regression equation. Then calculate $\hat{y}$.

1. $\hat{y} = 49{,}764 + 364x_1 + 228x_2 + 267x_3$

   $\qquad = 49{,}764 + 364(12) + 228(5) + 267(16)$

   $\qquad = 59{,}544$

   The employee's predicted salary is $59,544.

2. $\hat{y} = 49{,}764 + 364x_1 + 228x_2 + 267x_3$

   $\qquad = 49{,}764 + 364(4) + 228(2) + 267(12)$

   $\qquad = 54{,}880$

   The employee's predicted salary is $54,880.

3. $\hat{y} = 49{,}764 + 364x_1 + 228x_2 + 267x_3$

   $\qquad = 49{,}764 + 364(8) + 228(7) + 267(17)$

   $\qquad = 58{,}811$

   The employee's predicted salary is $58,811.

▸ Try It Yourself 2

Use the regression equation found in Try It Yourself 1 to predict a student's final grade given the following conditions.

1. A student has a midterm exam score of 89 and misses 1 class.
2. A student has a midterm exam score of 78 and misses 3 classes.
3. A student has a midterm exam score of 83 and misses 2 classes.

a. *Substitute* the midterm score for x_1 into the regression equation.
b. *Substitute* the corresponding number of missed classes for x_2 into the regression equation.
c. *Calculate* $\hat{y}$.
d. What is each student's final grade?

Answer: Page A47

9.4 EXERCISES

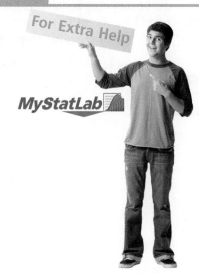

For Extra Help

MyStatLab

■ Building Basic Skills and Vocabulary

Predicting y-Values   *In Exercises 1–4, use the multiple regression equation to predict the y-values for the given values of the independent variables.*

1. **Cotton Yield**   The equation used to predict cotton yield (in pounds) is

$$\hat{y} = 640 - 0.105x_1 + 0.124x_2$$

where x_1 is the number of acres planted (in thousands) and x_2 is the number of acres harvested (in thousands). *(Source: U.S. National Agricultural Statistics Service)*

(a) $x_1 = 13,500$, $x_2 = 12,000$ (b) $x_1 = 15,000$, $x_2 = 13,500$
(c) $x_1 = 14,000$, $x_2 = 13,500$ (d) $x_1 = 14,500$, $x_2 = 13,000$

2. **Wheat Yield**   To predict the annual wheat yield (in bushels per acre), use the equation

$$\hat{y} = 17 - 0.000642x_1 + 0.00125x_2$$

where x_1 is the number of acres planted (in thousands) and x_2 is the number of acres harvested (in thousands). *(Source: U.S. National Agricultural Statistics Service)*

(a) $x_1 = 60,000$, $x_2 = 45,000$ (b) $x_1 = 62,500$, $x_2 = 53,000$
(c) $x_1 = 57,500$, $x_2 = 50,000$ (d) $x_1 = 59,000$, $x_2 = 48,500$

3. **Black Cherry Tree Volume**   The volume (in cubic feet) of black cherry trees can be modeled by the equation

$$\hat{y} = -52.2 + 0.3x_1 + 4.5x_2$$

where x_1 is the tree's height (in feet) and x_2 is the tree's diameter (in inches). *(Source: Journal of the Royal Statistical Society)*

(a) $x_1 = 70$, $x_2 = 8.6$ (b) $x_1 = 65$, $x_2 = 11.0$
(c) $x_1 = 83$, $x_2 = 17.6$ (d) $x_1 = 87$, $x_2 = 19.6$

4. **Earnings per Share**   The earnings per share (in dollars) for McDonald's Corporation are given by the equation

$$\hat{y} = -0.415 + 0.0009x_1 + 0.168x_2$$

where x_1 represents total revenue (in billions of dollars) and x_2 represents shareholders' equity (in billions of dollars). *(Source: McDonald's Corporation)*

(a) $x_1 = 15.2$, $x_2 = 10.3$ (b) $x_1 = 19.8$, $x_2 = 14.5$
(c) $x_1 = 12.1$, $x_2 = 9.1$ (d) $x_1 = 21.5$, $x_2 = 15.8$

■ Using and Interpreting Concepts

Finding a Multiple Regression Equation   *In Exercises 5 and 6, use technology to find the multiple regression equation for the data shown in the table. Then answer the following.*

(a) *What is the standard error of estimate?*

(b) *What is the coefficient of determination?*

(c) *Interpret the results of (a) and (b).*

5. Sales The total square footage (in billions) of retailing space at shopping centers, the number (in thousands) of shopping centers, and the sales (in billions of dollars) for shopping centers for a recent 11-year period are shown in the table. *(Adapted from International Council of Shopping Centers)*

Sales, y	Total square footage, x_1	Number of shopping centers, x_2
893.8	5.0	41.2
933.9	5.1	42.1
980.0	5.2	43.0
1032.4	5.3	43.7
1105.3	5.5	44.4
1181.1	5.6	45.1
1221.7	5.7	45.8
1277.2	5.8	46.4
1339.2	5.9	47.1
1432.6	6.0	47.8
1530.4	6.1	48.7

6. Shareholder's Equity The following table shows the net sales (in billions of dollars), total assets (in billions of dollars), and shareholder's equity (in billions of dollars) for Wal-Mart for a recent six-year period. *(Adapted from Wal-Mart Stores, Inc.)*

Shareholder's equity, y	Net sales, x_1	Total assets, x_2
35.2	201.2	79.3
39.5	226.5	90.2
43.6	252.8	102.5
49.4	281.5	117.1
53.2	308.9	135.6
61.6	345.0	151.2

■ Extending Concepts

Adjusted r^2 *The calculation of r^2, the coefficient of determination, depends on the number of data pairs and the number of independent variables. An adjusted value of r^2 can be calculated, based on the number of degrees of freedom, as follows.*

$$r_{adj}^2 = 1 - \left[\frac{(1 - r^2)(n - 1)}{n - k - 1} \right]$$

where n is the number of data pairs and k is the number of independent variables.

In Exercises 7 and 8, after calculating r_{adj}^2, determine the percentage of the variation in y that can be explained by the relationships between variables according to r_{adj}^2. Compare this result with the one obtained using r^2.

7. Calculate r_{adj}^2 for the data in Exercise 5.

8. Calculate r_{adj}^2 for the data in Exercise 6.

Uses & Abuses

Statistics in the Real World

Uses

Correlation and Regression   Correlation and regression analysis can be used to determine whether there is a significant relationship between two variables. If there is, you can use one of the variables to predict the value of the other variable. For example, educators have used correlation and regression analysis to determine that there is a significant correlation between a student's SAT score and the grade point average from a student's freshman year at college. Consequently, many colleges and universities use SAT scores of high school applicants as a predictor of the applicant's initial success at college.

Abuses

Confusing Correlation and Causation   The most common abuse of correlation in studies is to confuse the concepts of correlation with those of causation (see page 506). Good SAT scores do not cause good college grades. Rather, there are other variables, such as good study habits and motivation, that contribute to both. When a strong correlation is found between two variables, look for other variables that are correlated with both.

Considering Only Linear Correlation   The correlation studied in this chapter is linear correlation. When the correlation coefficient is close to 1 or close to -1, the data points can be modeled by a straight line. It is possible that a correlation coefficient is close to zero but there is still a strong correlation of a different type. Consider the data listed in the table at the left. The value of the correlation coefficient is 0; however, the data are perfectly correlated with the equation $x^2 + y^2 = 1$ as shown in the graph.

Ethics   When data are collected, all of the data should be used when calculating statistics. In this chapter, you learned that before finding the equation of a regression line, it is helpful to construct a scatter plot of the data to check for outliers, gaps, and clusters in the data. A researcher cannot use only those data points that fit his or her hypothesis or those that show a significant correlation. Although eliminating outliers may help a data set coincide with predicted patterns or fit a regression line, it is unethical to amend data in such a way. An outlier or any other point that influences a regression model can be removed only if it is properly justified.

In most cases, the best and sometimes safest approach for presenting statistical measurements is with and without an outlier being included. By doing this, the decision as to whether or not to recognize the outlier is left to the reader.

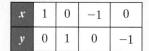

x	1	0	−1	0
y	0	1	0	−1

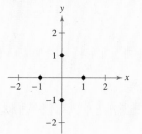

■ EXERCISES

1. ***Confusing Correlation and Causation***   Find an example of an article in a newspaper or magazine that confuses correlation and causation. Discuss other variables that could contribute to the relationship between the variables.

2. ***Considering Only Linear Correlation***   Find an example of two real-life variables that have a nonlinear correlation.

9 CHAPTER SUMMARY

What did you **learn?**	EXAMPLE(S)	REVIEW EXERCISES

Section 9.1

■ How to construct a scatter plot

1–3 | *1–4*

■ How to find a correlation coefficient

$$r = \frac{n\sum xy - (\sum x)(\sum y)}{\sqrt{n\sum x^2 - (\sum x)^2}\sqrt{n\sum y^2 - (\sum y)^2}}$$

4, 5 | *1–4*

■ How to perform a hypothesis test for a population correlation coefficient ρ

$$t = \frac{r}{\sqrt{\dfrac{1 - r^2}{n - 2}}}$$

7 | *5–10*

Section 9.2

■ How to find the equation of a regression line, $\hat{y} = mx + b$

$$m = \frac{n\sum xy - (\sum x)(\sum y)}{n\sum x^2 - (\sum x)^2}$$
$$b = \bar{y} - m\bar{x}$$
$$= \frac{\sum y}{n} - m\frac{\sum x}{n}$$

1, 2 | *11–14*

■ How to predict y-values using a regression equation

3 | *15–18*

Section 9.3

■ How to find and interpret the coefficient of determination r^2

1 | *19–24*

■ How to find and interpret the standard error of estimate for a regression line

$$s_e = \sqrt{\frac{\sum(y_i - \hat{y}_i)^2}{n - 2}} = \sqrt{\frac{\sum y^2 - b\sum y - m\sum xy}{n - 2}}$$

2 | *23, 24*

■ How to construct and interpret a prediction interval for y, $\hat{y} - E < y < \hat{y} + E$

$$E = t_c s_e \sqrt{1 + \frac{1}{n} + \frac{n(x_0 - \bar{x})^2}{n\sum x^2 - (\sum x)^2}}$$

3 | *25–30*

Section 9.4

■ How to use technology to find a multiple regression equation, the standard error of estimate, and the coefficient of determination

1 | *31, 32*

■ How to use a multiple regression equation to predict y-values

$$\hat{y} = b + m_1 x_1 + m_2 x_2 + m_3 x_3 + \cdots + m_k x_k$$

2 | *33, 34*

9 REVIEW EXERCISES

Section 9.1

In Exercises 1–4, display the data in a scatter plot. Then find the sample correlation coefficient r. Determine whether there is a positive linear correlation, a negative linear correlation, or no linear correlation between the variables. What can you conclude?

1. The ages of eight cows (in years) and their milk production (in gallons) per week

Age, x	4	4	6	7	7	8	10	11
Milk production, y	37.0	35.4	33.3	33.1	32.3	33.7	30.2	29.6

2. The number of convertibles sold at a car dealership in a month and the average monthly temperature (in degrees Fahrenheit)

Convertibles sold, x	0	3	6	5	7	8
Average monthly temperature, y	42	50	58	62	75	77

3. The IQ and brain size, as measured by the total pixel count (in thousands) from an MRI scan, for nine female college students *(Adapted from Intelligence)*

IQ, x	138	140	96	83	101	135	85	77	88
Pixel count, y	991	856	879	865	808	791	799	794	894

4. The annual per capita sugar consumption (in kilograms) and the average number of cavities of 11- and 12-year-old children in seven countries

Sugar consumption, x	2.1	5.0	6.3	6.5	7.7	8.7	11.6
Cavities, y	0.59	1.51	1.55	1.70	2.18	2.10	2.73

In Exercises 5 and 6, use the given sample statistics to test the claim about the population correlation coefficient ρ at the indicated level of significance α.

5. Claim: $\rho \neq 0, \alpha = 0.01$. Sample statistics: $r = 0.24, n = 26$

6. Claim: $\rho \neq 0, \alpha = 0.05$. Sample statistics: $r = -0.55, n = 22$

In Exercises 7–10, test the claim about the population correlation coefficient ρ at the indicated level of significance α. Then interpret the decision in the context of the original claim.

7. Refer to the data in Exercise 1. At $\alpha = 0.05$, test the claim that there is a linear correlation between a cow's age and milk production.

8. Refer to the data in Exercise 2. Is there enough evidence to conclude that there is a linear correlation between the number of convertibles sold and the average monthly temperature? Use $\alpha = 0.05$.

9. Refer to the data in Exercise 3. At $\alpha = 0.01$, test the claim that there is a linear correlation between a female college student's IQ and brain size.

10. Refer to the data in Exercise 4. Is there enough evidence to conclude that there is a linear correlation between sugar consumption and tooth decay? Use $\alpha = 0.01$.

Section 9.2

In Exercises 11–14, find the equation of the regression line for the given data. Then construct a scatter plot of the data and draw the regression line. Can you make a guess about the sign and magnitude of r? Calculate r and check your guess. If convenient, use technology to solve the problem.

11. The heights (in inches) of adult brothers and sisters from 11 families

Sister, x	65	62	63	68	63	67	64	60	67	65	68
Brother, y	70	69	66	74	72	74	70	67	68	72	74

12. The number of households (in millions) with multiple television sets and the average time (in minutes) per day spent watching television per household for nine years *(Adapted from Nielsen Media Research)*

Households, x	72.4	73.9	76.2	76.8	78.4	80.3	82.8	86.6	89.5
Time, y	435	446	455	460	464	478	481	491	494

13. The ages (in years) and the number of hours of sleep in one night of seven adults

Age, x	35	20	59	42	68	38	75
Hours of sleep, y	7	9	5	6	5	8	4

14. The engine displacement (in cubic inches) and the fuel efficiency (in miles per gallon) of seven automobiles

Displacement, x	170	134	220	305	109	256	322
Fuel efficiency, y	29.5	34.5	23.0	17.0	33.5	23.0	15.5

In Exercises 15–18, use the regression equations found in Exercises 11–14 to predict the value of y for each value of x, if meaningful. If not, explain why not. (Correlation between x and y in Exercises 11–14 is significant for $\alpha = 0.05$.)

15. Refer to Exercise 11. What height would you predict for a male whose sister is (a) 61 inches? (b) 66 inches? (c) 75 inches? (d) 50 inches?

16. Refer to Exercise 12. What average time per day spent watching television per household would you predict for (a) 60 million households with multiple television sets? (b) 85 million households with multiple television sets? (c) 75 million households with multiple television sets? (d) 97 million households with multiple television sets?

17. Refer to Exercise 13. How many hours of sleep would you predict for an adult of age (a) 18 years? (b) 25 years? (c) 85 years? (d) 50 years?

18. Refer to Exercise 14. What fuel efficiency rating would you predict for a car with an engine displacement of (a) 86 cubic inches? (b) 198 cubic inches? (c) 289 cubic inches? (d) 407 cubic inches?

Section 9.3

In Exercises 19–22, use the value of the linear correlation coefficient r to find the coefficient of determination. Interpret the result.

19. $r = -0.553$

20. $r = -0.962$

21. $r = 0.181$

22. $r = 0.740$

In Exercises 23 and 24, use the data to find the (a) coefficient of determination r^2 and interpret the result, and (b) standard error of estimate s_e and interpret the result.

23. The table shows the area of eight living spaces (in square feet) and the cooling capacity (in Btu per hour) of the air conditioners used in those spaces. The regression equation is $\hat{y} = 9.468x + 3002.991$. *(Adapted from Consumer Reports)*

Living area, x	730	485	205	420	550	590	385	630
Cooling capacity, y	10,200	7000	5300	6800	7250	9000	6900	9400

24. The table shows the cooking areas (in square inches) of 18 gas grills and their prices (in dollars). The regression equation is $\hat{y} = 1.454x - 532.053$. *(Source: Lowe's)*

Area, x	780	530	942	660	600	732	660	640	869
Price, y	359	98	547	299	449	799	699	199	1049

Area, x	860	700	942	890	733	732	464	869	600
Price, y	499	248	597	999	428	849	99	999	399

In Exercises 25–30, construct the indicated prediction interval and interpret the results.

25. Construct a 90% prediction interval for the height of a male in Exercise 11 whose sister is 64 inches tall.

26. Construct a 90% prediction interval for the average time per day spent watching television per household in Exercise 12 when 74 million households have multiple television sets..

27. Construct a 95% prediction interval for the number of hours of sleep for an adult in Exercise 13 who is 45 years old.

28. Construct a 95% prediction interval for the fuel efficiency of an automobile in Exercise 14 that has an engine displacement of 265 cubic inches.

29. Construct a 99% prediction interval for the cooling capacity of an air conditioner in Exercise 23 that is used in a living area of 720 square feet.

30. Construct a 99% prediction interval for the price of a gas grill in Exercise 24 with a usable cooking area of 900 square inches.

Section 9.4

In Exercises 31 and 32, use the data in the table, which shows the carbon monoxide, tar, and nicotine content, all in milligrams, of 14 brands of U.S. cigarettes. (*Source: Federal Trade Commission*)

Carbon monoxide, y	Tar, x_1	Nicotine, x_2
15	16	1.1
17	16	1.0
11	10	0.8
12	11	0.9
14	13	0.8
16	14	0.8
14	16	1.2
16	16	1.2
10	10	0.8
18	19	1.4
17	17	1.2
11	12	1.0
10	9	0.7
14	15	1.2

31. Use technology to find the multiple regression equation from the data.

32. Find the standard error of estimate s_e and the coefficient of determination r^2. What percentage of the variation of y can be explained by the regression equation?

In Exercises 33 and 34, use the multiple regression equation to predict the y-values for the given values of the independent variables.

33. An equation that can be used to predict fuel economy (in miles per gallon) for automobiles is $\hat{y} = 41.3 - 0.004x_1 - 0.0049x_2$, where x_1 is the engine displacement (in cubic inches) and x_2 is the vehicle weight (in pounds).

    (a) $x_1 = 305, x_2 = 3750$

    (b) $x_1 = 225, x_2 = 3100$

    (c) $x_1 = 105, x_2 = 2200$

    (d) $x_1 = 185, x_2 = 3000$

34. Use the regression equation found in Exercise 31.

    (a) $x_1 = 10, x_2 = 0.7$

    (b) $x_1 = 15, x_2 = 1.1$

    (c) $x_1 = 13, x_2 = 0.8$

    (d) $x_1 = 9, x_2 = 0.8$

9 CHAPTER QUIZ

Take this quiz as you would take a quiz in class. After you are done, check your work against the answers given in the back of the book.

For Exercises 1–8, use the data in the table, which shows the personal income and outlays (both in trillions of dollars) for Americans for 11 recent years. (*Adapted from U.S. Commerce Department, Bureau of Economic Analysis*)

Personal income, x	Personal outlays, y
6.5	5.5
6.9	5.8
7.4	6.1
7.8	6.5
8.4	7.0
8.7	7.4
8.9	7.6
9.2	8.0
9.7	8.5
10.2	9.1
10.9	9.6

1. Construct a scatter plot for the data. Do the data appear to have a positive linear correlation, a negative linear correlation, or no linear correlation? Explain.

2. Calculate the correlation coefficient r. What can you conclude?

3. Test the level of significance of the correlation coefficient r. Use $\alpha = 0.05$.

4. Find the equation of the regression line for the data. Draw the regression line on the scatter plot.

5. Use the regression equation to predict the personal outlays when the personal income is 6.2 trillion dollars.

6. Find the coefficient of determination r^2 and interpret the results.

7. Find the standard error of estimate s_e and interpret the results.

8. Construct a 95% prediction interval for personal outlays when personal income is 7.6 trillion dollars. Interpret the results.

9. The equation used to predict sunflower yield (in pounds) is

$$\hat{y} = 924 - 0.604x_1 + 0.813x_2$$

where x_1 is the number of acres planted (in thousands) and x_2 is the number of acres harvested (in thousands). Use the regression equation to predict the y-values for the given values of the independent variables listed below. Then determine which variable has a greater influence on the value of y. (*Source: U.S. National Agricultural Statistics Service*)

(a) $x_1 = 2643$, $x_2 = 2518$ (b) $x_1 = 3506$, $x_2 = 3383$

(c) $x_1 = 1894$, $x_2 = 1726$ (d) $x_1 = 2344$, $x_2 = 2197$

Putting It All Together

REAL Statistics — Real Decisions

The Center for Infant Development, part of the Department of Psychology at the University of Denver, is a research center that focuses on perceptual and cognitive development in infants from two months to three years of age. Graduate students, postdoctoral fellows, and members of the research staff can perform studies to see how infants think and behave under particular circumstances.

You are a member of the research staff at the Center for Infant Development at the University of Denver. You are interested in determining whether babies take longer to learn how to crawl during the cold winter months than during the warmer summer months. You decide to record the age (in weeks) of each child when the child is able to crawl and the temperature (in degrees Fahrenheit) when the child crawls. You want to determine if there is a significant correlation between the mean crawling age and the mean temperature.

UNIVERSITY OF
DENVER
1864
www.du.edu

Mean monthly temperature, x	Mean crawling age, y
33	33.64
30	32.82
33	33.83
37	33.35
48	33.38
57	32.32
66	29.84
73	30.52
72	29.70
63	31.84
52	28.58
39	31.44

(Source: Janette Benson
Infant Behavior and Development)

■ Exercises

1. Analyzing the Data

(a) The data in the table at the right show the mean temperature (in degrees Fahrenheit) for each month and the mean age (in weeks) of the infants that began to crawl during that month. Construct a scatter plot of the data. Use the graph to determine whether there is a positive linear correlation, a negative linear correlation, or no linear correlation between the mean crawling age and the mean monthly temperature.

(b) Calculate the correlation coefficient r and verify your conclusion in part (a).

(c) Test the significance of the correlation coefficient found in part (b). Use $\alpha = 0.05$.

(d) Find the equation of the regression line for the temperature and the mean crawling age. Add the graph of the regression line to your scatter plot in part (a). Does the regression line appear to be a good fit?

(e) Can you use the equation of the regression line to predict the mean crawling age given the temperature? Why or why not?

(f) Find the coefficient of determination r^2 and the standard error of estimate s_e and interpret the results.

2. What Do You Think?

According to your analysis, would you agree or disagree with the following? Why or why not?

Because there is a significant linear correlation between mean monthly temperature and the mean crawling age, parents can consider the temperature when determining when their baby will crawl.

TECHNOLOGY

MINITAB   **EXCEL**   **T1-83/84**

U.S. Food and Drug
Administration

NUTRIENTS IN BREAKFAST CEREALS

The U.S. Food and Drug Administration (FDA) requires nutrition labeling for most foods. Under FDA regulations, manufacturers are required to list the amounts of certain nutrients in their foods, such as calories, sugar, fat, and carbohydrates. This nutritional information is displayed in the "Nutrition Facts" panel on the food's package.

The table shows the following nutritional content for one cup of each of 21 different breakfast cereals.

C = calories
S = sugar in grams
F = fat in grams
R = carbohydrates in grams

Cereal	C	S	F	R
Apple Jacks	120	15	0.5	28
Berry Burst Cheerios	100	8	1	22
Cheerios	100	1	2	20
Cocoa Puffs	110	12	1.5	23
Cookie Crisp	100	11	1	22
Corn Chex	120	3	0.5	26
Corn Flakes	100	2	0	24
Corn Pops	120	14	0	28
Count Chocula	110	12	1	23
Crispix	110	3	0	25
Froot Loops	120	13	1	26
Frosted Flakes	110	11	0	27
Honey Nut Cheerios	110	9	1.5	22
Lucky Charms	110	11	1	22
Multi Grain Cheerios	110	6	1	23
Product 19	100	4	0	25
Raisin Bran	190	19	1.5	45
Rice Krispies	120	3	0	29
Special K	120	4	0.5	22
Trix	120	13	1.5	28
Wheaties	100	4	0.5	22

■ EXERCISES

1. Use a technology tool to draw a scatter plot of the following (x, y) pairs in the data set.

   (a) (calories, sugar)

   (b) (calories, fat)

   (c) (calories, carbohydrates)

   (d) (sugar, fat)

   (e) (sugar, carbohydrates)

   (f) (fat, carbohydrates)

2. From the scatter plots in Exercise 1, which pairs of variables appear to have a strong linear correlation?

3. Use a technology tool to find the correlation coefficient for each pair of variables in Exercise 1. Which has the strongest linear correlation?

4. Use a technology tool to find an equation of a regression line for the following variables.

   (a) (calories, sugar)

   (b) (calories, carbohydrates)

5. Use the results of Exercise 4 to predict the following.

   (a) The sugar content of one cup of cereal that has a caloric content of 120 calories

   (b) The carbohydrate content of one cup of cereal that has a caloric content of 120 calories

6. Use a technology tool to find the multiple regression equations of the following forms.

   (a) $C = b + m_1 S + m_2 F + m_3 R$

   (b) $C = b + m_1 S + m_2 R$

7. Use the results of Exercise 6 to predict the caloric content of 1 cup of cereal that has 10 grams of sugar and 25 grams of carbohydrates.

Extended solutions are given in the *Technology Supplement*. Technical instruction is provided for MINITAB, Excel, and the TI-83/84.

CHAPTER 10

Chi Square Tests and the *F*-Distribution

10.1 Goodness of Fit

10.2 Independence

- CASE STUDY

10.3 Comparing Two Variances

10.4 Analysis of Variance

- USES AND ABUSES
- REAL STATISTICS– REAL DECISIONS
- TECHNOLOGY

Crash tests performed by the Insurance Institute for Highway Safety demonstrate how a vehicle will react when in a realistic collision. Tests are performed on the front, side, and rear of the vehicles. Results of these tests are classified using the ratings *good*, *acceptable*, *marginal*, and *poor*.

The Insurance Institute for Highway Safety buys new vehicles each year and crashes them into a barrier at 40 miles per hour to compare how different vehicles protect drivers in a frontal offset crash. In this test, 40% of the total width of the vehicle strikes the barrier on the driver side. The forces and impacts that occur during a crash test are measured by equipping dummies with special instruments and placing them in the car. The crash test results include data on head, chest, and leg injuries. For a low crash test number, the injury potential is low. If the crash test number is high, then the injury potential is high. Using the techniques of Chapter 8, you can determine if the mean chest injury potential is the same for pickups and minivans. (Assume the population variances are equal.) The sample statistics are as follows. *(Source: Insurance Institute for Highway Safety)*

Vehicle	Number	Mean chest injury	Standard deviation
Minivans	$n_1 = 25$	$\bar{x}_1 = 33.0$	$s_1 = 6.75$
Pickups	$n_2 = 20$	$\bar{x}_2 = 29.6$	$s_2 = 4.60$

For the means of chest injury, the P-value for the hypothesis that $\mu_1 = \mu_2$ is about 0.061. At $\alpha = 0.05$, you fail to reject the null hypothesis. So, you do not have enough evidence to conclude that there is a significant difference in the means of the chest injury potential in a 40-mile per hour frontal offset crash for minivans and pickups.

WHERE YOU'RE GOING

In Chapter 8, you learned how to test a hypothesis that compares two populations by basing your decisions on sample statistics and their distributions. In this chapter, you will learn how to test a hypothesis that compares three or more populations.

For instance, in addition to the crash tests for minivans and pickups, a third group of vehicles was also tested. The results for all three types of vehicles are as follows.

Vehicle	Number	Mean chest injury	Standard deviation
Minivans	$n_1 = 25$	$\bar{x}_1 = 33.0$	$s_1 = 6.75$
Pickups	$n_2 = 20$	$\bar{x}_2 = 29.6$	$s_2 = 4.60$
Midsize SUVs	$n_3 = 43$	$\bar{x}_3 = 35.0$	$s_3 = 5.33$

From these three samples, is there evidence of a difference in chest injury potential among minivans, pickups, and midsize SUVs in a 40 mile-per-hour frontal offset crash?

In this chapter, you will learn that you can answer this question by testing the hypothesis that the three means are equal. For the means of chest injury, the P-value for the hypothesis that $\mu_1 = \mu_2 = \mu_3$ is about 0.003. At $\alpha = 0.05$, you can reject the null hypothesis. So, you can conclude that for the three types of vehicles tested, at least one of the means of the chest injury potential in a 40 mile-per-hour frontal offset crash is different from the others.

10.1 Goodness of Fit

The Chi-Square Goodness-of-Fit Test

▸ The Chi-Square Goodness-of-Fit Test

Suppose a marketing executive is planning a new advertising campaign and wants to determine the proportions of radio music listeners in a specific broadcast region who prefer each of six types of music. To determine these proportions, the executive can perform a multinomial experiment. A **multinomial experiment** is a probability experiment consisting of a fixed number of trials in which there are more than two possible outcomes for each independent trial. The probability for each outcome is fixed, and each outcome is classified into **categories.** (Remember from Section 4.2 that a **binomial** experiment has only two possible outcomes.)

Now, suppose the marketing executive wants to test a radio station's claim concerning the distribution of proportions of music preferences. To do so, the executive could compare the distribution of proportions obtained in the multinomial experiment with the radio station's specified distribution. How can the executive compare the distributions? The answer is, perform a chi-square goodness-of-fit test.

> ### DEFINITION
>
> A **chi-square goodness-of-fit test** is used to test whether a frequency distribution fits an expected distribution.

To begin a goodness-of-fit test, you must first state a null and an alternative hypothesis. Generally, the null hypothesis states that the frequency distribution fits the specified distribution and the alternative hypothesis states that the frequency distribution does not fit the specified distribution.

For example, suppose the radio station claims that the distribution of music preferences for listeners in the broadcast region is as shown below.

Distribution of music preferences			
Classical	4%	Oldies	2%
Country	36%	Pop	18%
Gospel	11%	Rock	29%

To test the radio station's claim, the executive can perform a chi-square goodness-of-fit test using the following null and alternative hypotheses.

H_0: The distribution of music preferences in the broadcast region is 4% classical, 36% country, 11% gospel, 2% oldies, 18% pop, and 29% rock. (Claim)

H_a: The distribution of music preferences differs from the claimed or expected distribution.

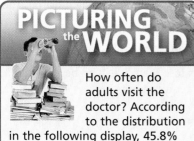

PICTURING the WORLD

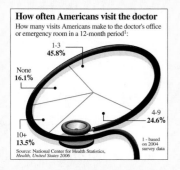

How often do adults visit the doctor? According to the distribution in the following display, 45.8% of all U.S. adults visit the doctor one to three times in a year.

How often Americans visit the doctor
How many visits Americans make to the doctor's office or emergency room in a 12-month period[1]:

1-3
45.8%

None
16.1%

4-9
24.6%

10+
13.5%

1 - based on 2004 survey data

Source: National Center for Health Statistics, *Health, United States 2006*

A sample of 274 adults is asked how many visits they make to the doctor in a year: 1–3, 4–9, 10 or more, or none. What is the expected frequency for each response?

To calculate the test statistic for the chi-square goodness-of-fit test, you can use observed frequencies and expected frequencies. To calculate the expected frequencies, you must assume the null hypothesis is true.

DEFINITION

The **observed frequency** *O* of a category is the frequency for the category observed in the sample data.

The **expected frequency** *E* of a category is the *calculated* frequency for the category. Expected frequencies are obtained assuming the specified (or hypothesized) distribution. The expected frequency for the *i*th category is

$$E_i = np_i$$

where *n* is the number of trials (the sample size) and p_i is the assumed probability of the *i*th category.

EXAMPLE 1

Finding Observed Frequencies and Expected Frequencies

A marketing executive randomly selects 500 radio music listeners from the broadcast region and asks each whether he or she prefers classical, country, gospel, oldies, pop, or rock music. The results are shown at the right. Find the observed frequencies and the expected frequencies for each type of music.

Survey results ($n = 500$)	
Classical	8
Country	210
Gospel	72
Oldies	10
Pop	75
Rock	125

Solution The observed frequency for each type of music is the number of radio music listeners naming a particular type of music. The expected frequency for each type of music is the product of the number of listeners in the survey and the probability that a listener will name a particular type of music. The observed frequencies and expected frequencies are shown in the following table.

Type of music	% of listeners	Observed frequency	Expected frequency
Classical	4%	8	$500(0.04) = 20$
Country	36%	210	$500(0.36) = 180$
Gospel	11%	72	$500(0.11) = 55$
Oldies	2%	10	$500(0.02) = 10$
Pop	18%	75	$500(0.18) = 90$
Rock	29%	125	$500(0.29) = 145$

▸ **Try It Yourself 1**

Suppose the executive randomly selects 300 radio music listeners in the listening region. Find the expected frequencies for each type of music.

Multiply 300 by the probability that a listener will name each particular type of music.

Answer: Page A47

Insight

The sum of the expected frequencies always equals the sum of the observed frequencies. For instance, in Example 1 the sum of the observed frequencies and the sum of the expected frequencies are both 500.

For the chi-square goodness-of-fit test to be used, the following must be true.

1. The observed frequencies must be obtained using a random sample.
2. Each expected frequency must be greater than or equal to 5.

If the expected frequency of a category is less than 5, it may be possible to combine it with another category to meet the requirements.

THE CHI-SQUARE GOODNESS-OF-FIT TEST

If the conditions listed above are satisfied, then the sampling distribution for the goodness-of-fit test is approximated by a chi-square distribution with $k - 1$ degrees of freedom, where k is the number of categories. The test statistic for the chi-square goodness-of-fit test is

$$\chi^2 = \Sigma \frac{(O - E)^2}{E}$$

where O represents the observed frequency of each category and E represents the expected frequency of each category.

When the observed frequencies closely match the expected frequencies, the differences between O and E will be small and the chi-square test statistic will be close to 0. As such, the null hypothesis is unlikely to be rejected. However, when there are large discrepancies between the observed frequencies and the expected frequencies, the differences between O and E will be large, resulting in a large chi-square test statistic. A large chi-square test statistic is evidence for rejecting the null hypothesis. So, the chi-square goodness-of-fit test is always a right-tailed test.

GUIDELINES

Performing a Chi-Square Goodness-of-Fit Test

In Words	*In Symbols*
1. Identify the claim. State the null and alternative hypotheses.	State H_0 and H_a.
2. Specify the level of significance.	Identify α.
3. Identify the degrees of freedom.	d.f. $= k - 1$
4. Determine the critical value.	Use Table 6 in Appendix B.
5. Determine the rejection region.	
6. Calculate the test statistic.	$\chi^2 = \Sigma \dfrac{(O - E)^2}{E}$
7. Make a decision to reject or fail to reject the null hypothesis.	If χ^2 is in the rejection region, reject H_0. Otherwise, fail to reject H_0.
8. Interpret the decision in the context of the original claim.	

Performing a Chi-Square Goodness-of-Fit Test

The music preferences of the listeners in a radio station's broadcast region are distributed as shown in the table at the left below. You randomly select 500 radio music listeners from the broadcast region and ask each whether he or she prefers classical, country, gospel, oldies, pop, or rock music. The survey results are shown in the table at the right below. Using $\alpha = 0.01$, perform a chi-square goodness-of-fit test to test whether the distributions are different.

Distribution of music preferences			
Classical	4%	Oldies	2%
Country	36%	Pop	18%
Gospel	11%	Rock	29%

Survey results ($n = 500$)			
Classical	8	Oldies	10
Country	210	Pop	75
Gospel	72	Rock	125

Type of music	Observed frequency	Expected frequency
Classical	8	20
Country	210	180
Gospel	72	55
Oldies	10	10
Pop	75	90
Rock	125	145

Solution The observed and expected frequencies are shown in the table at the left. The expected frequencies were calculated in Example 1. Because the observed frequencies were obtained using a random sample and each expected frequency is at least 5, you can use the chi-square goodness-of-fit test to test the proposed distribution. The null and alternative hypotheses are as follows.

H_0: The distribution of music preferences in the broadcast region is 4% classical, 36% country, 11% gospel, 2% oldies, 18% pop, and 29% rock.

H_a: The distribution of music preferences differs from the claimed or expected distribution. (Claim)

Because there are 6 categories, the chi-square distribution has $k - 1 = 6 - 1 = 5$ degrees of freedom. With d.f. $= 5$ and $\alpha = 0.01$, the critical value is $\chi_0^2 = 15.086$. With the observed and expected frequencies, the chi-square test statistic is

$$\chi^2 = \Sigma \frac{(O - E)^2}{E}$$

$$= \frac{(8 - 20)^2}{20} + \frac{(210 - 180)^2}{180} + \frac{(72 - 55)^2}{55} + \frac{(10 - 10)^2}{10}$$

$$+ \frac{(75 - 90)^2}{90} + \frac{(125 - 145)^2}{145}$$

$$\approx 22.713.$$

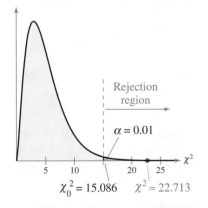

Rejection region

$\alpha = 0.01$

$\chi_0^2 = 15.086$ $\chi^2 \approx 22.713$

The graph shows the location of the rejection region and the chi-square test statistic. Because χ^2 is in the rejection region, you should decide to reject the null hypothesis.

Interpretation At the 1% significance level, there is enough evidence to conclude that the distribution of music preferences differs from the radio station's claimed or expected distribution.

Ages	Previous age distribution	Survey results
0–9	16%	76
10–19	20%	84
20–29	8%	30
30–39	14%	60
40–49	15%	54
50–59	12%	40
60–69	10%	42
70+	5%	14

▶ Try It Yourself 2

A sociologist claims that the age distribution for the residents of a certain city is different than it was 10 years ago. The distribution of ages 10 years ago is shown in the table at the left. You randomly select 400 residents and record the age of each. The survey results are shown in the table. At $\alpha = 0.05$, perform a chi-square goodness-of-fit test to determine whether the distribution has changed.

a. *Verify* that the expected frequency is at least 5 for each category.
b. *Identify* the claimed distribution and state H_0 and H_a.
c. *Specify* the level of significance α.
d. *Identify* the degrees of freedom.
e. *Determine* the critical value and the rejection region.
f. *Calculate* the chi-square test statistic.
g. *Decide* whether to reject the null hypothesis. Use a graph if necessary.
h. *Interpret* the decision in the context of the original claim.   *Answer: Page A47*

EXAMPLE 3

Performing a Chi-Square Goodness-of-Fit Test

The display at the right shows two distributions describing opinions on what is more important to save for. You work for a financial services company and want to test the distribution describing men's opinions. To test the distribution, you randomly select 400 men and ask each which is more important— saving for retirement or saving for children's college education. The results are shown in the table at the left. At $\alpha = 0.05$, test the claimed or expected distribution.

Men's survey results ($n = 400$)	
Retirement	186
Children's college education	143
Not sure	71

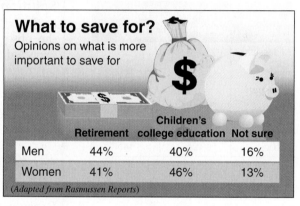

What to save for?
Opinions on what is more important to save for

	Retirement	Children's college education	Not sure
Men	44%	40%	16%
Women	41%	46%	13%

(Adapted from Rasmussen Reports)

Solution The observed frequencies and the expected frequencies are shown in the following table. Because the men were randomly selected, and each expected frequency is at least 5, you can use the chi-square goodness-of-fit test to test the claimed distribution.

Response	Observed frequency	Expected frequency
Retirement	186	400(0.44) = 176
Children's college education	143	400(0.40) = 160
Not sure	71	400(0.16) = 64

The null and alternative hypotheses are as follows.

H_0: The distribution of men's opinions on saving is 44% retirement, 40% children's college education, and 16% not sure. (Claim)

H_a: The distribution of men's opinions on saving differs from the claimed or expected distribution.

Because there are 3 categories, the chi-square distribution has $k - 1 = 3 - 1 = 2$ degrees of freedom. Using d.f. $= 2$ and $\alpha = 0.05$, the critical value is $\chi_0^2 = 5.991$. With the observed and expected frequencies, the chi-square test statistic is as shown in the following table.

O	E	$O - E$	$(O - E)^2$	$\dfrac{(O - E)^2}{E}$
186	176	10	100	0.568182
143	160	-17	289	1.80625
71	64	7	49	0.765625
				$\chi^2 = \Sigma \dfrac{(O - E)^2}{E} \approx 3.140$

Study Tip

Another way to calculate the chi-square test statistic is to organize the calculations in a table as shown in Example 3.

The graph shows the location of the rejection region and the chi-square test statistic. Because χ^2 is not in the rejection region, you should decide not to reject the null hypothesis.

Interpretation   At the 5% significance level, there is not enough evidence to dispute the claimed or expected distribution of men's opinions.

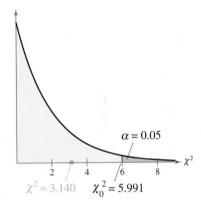

$\chi^2 \approx 3.140$ $\chi_0^2 = 5.991$

▶ **Try It Yourself 3**

You also want to test the distribution describing women's opinions. To test the distribution, you randomly select 300 women and ask each which is more important—saving for retirement or saving for children's college education. The results are shown in the table at the left. At $\alpha = 0.01$, test the claimed or expected distribution. What can you conclude?

Women's survey results ($n = 300$)	
Retirement	129
Children's college education	149
Not sure	22

a. *Verify* that the expected frequency is at least 5 for each category.
b. *Identify* the claimed distribution and state H_0 and H_a.
c. *Specify* the level of significance α.
d. *Identify* the degrees of freedom.
e. *Determine* the critical value and the rejection region.
f. Use the observed and expected frequencies to *calculate the chi-square test statistic.*
g. *Decide* whether to reject the null hypothesis. Use a graph if necessary.
h. *Interpret* the decision in the context of the original claim.

Answer: Page A47

The chi-square goodness-of-fit test is often used to determine whether a distribution is uniform. For such tests, the expected frequencies of the categories are equal. When testing a uniform distribution, you can find the expected frequency of each category by dividing the sample size by the number of categories. For example, suppose a company believes that the number of sales made by its sales force is uniform throughout the five-day work week. If the sample consists of 1000 sales, then the expected value of the sales for each day will be $1000/5 = 200$.

EXAMPLE 4

Performing a Chi-Square Goodness-of-Fit Test

The manufacturer of M&M's candies claims that the number of different-colored candies in bags of dark chocolate M&M's is uniformly distributed. To test this claim, you randomly select a bag that contains 500 dark chocolate M&M's. The results are shown in the table. Using $\alpha = 0.10$, perform a chi-square goodness-of-fit test to test the claimed or expected distribution. What can you conclude? *(Adapted from Mars Incorporated)*

Color	Frequency, f
Brown	80
Yellow	95
Red	88
Blue	83
Orange	76
Green	78

Solution

The claim is that the distribution is uniform, so the expected frequencies of the colors are equal. To find each expected frequency, divide the sample size by the number of colors. So, for each color, $E = 500/6 \approx 83.33$. Because each expected frequency is at least 5 and the M&M's were randomly selected, you can use the chi-square goodness-of-fit test to test the claimed distribution. The null and alternative hypotheses are as follows.

H_0: The distribution of the different-colored candies in bags of dark chocolate M&M's is uniform. (Claim)

H_a: The distribution of the different-colored candies in bags of dark chocolate M&M's is not uniform.

Because there are 6 categories, the chi-square distribution has $k - 1 = 6 - 1 = 5$ degrees of freedom. Using d.f. $= 5$ and $\alpha = 0.10$, the critical value is $\chi_0^2 = 9.236$. With the observed and expected frequencies, the chi-square test statistic is shown in the following table.

O	E	$O - E$	$(O - E)^2$	$\dfrac{(O - E)^2}{E}$
80	83.3	−3.33	11.09	0.1330853234
95	83.3	11.67	136.19	1.634345374
88	83.3	4.67	21.81	0.2617304692
83	83.3	−0.33	0.11	0.0013200528
76	83.3	−7.33	53.73	0.6447857914
78	83.3	−5.33	28.41	0.3409336373
				$\chi^2 = \Sigma \dfrac{(O - E)^2}{E} \approx 3.016$

The graph shows the location of the rejection region and the chi-square test statistic. Because χ^2 is not in the rejection region, you should decide not to reject the null hypothesis.

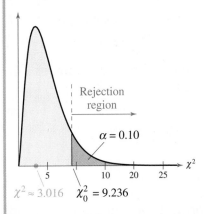

$\chi^2 \approx 3.016$ $\chi_0^2 = 9.236$

Interpretation   At the 10% significance level, there is not enough evidence to dispute the claim that the distribution of the different-colored candies in bags of dark chocolate M&M's is uniform.

▶ Try It Yourself 4

The manufacturer of M&M's candies claims that the number of different-colored candies in bags of peanut M&M's is uniformly distributed. To test this claim, you randomly select a bag that contains 180 peanut M&M's. The results are shown in the table. Using $\alpha = 0.05$, perform a chi-square goodness-of-fit test to test the claimed or expected distribution. What can you conclude? *(Adapted from Mars Incorporated)*

Color	Frequency, f
Brown	22
Yellow	27
Red	22
Blue	41
Orange	41
Green	27

a. *Verify* that the expected frequency is at least 5 for each category.
b. *Identify* the claimed distribution and state H_0 and H_a.
c. *Specify* the level of significance α.
d. *Identify* the degrees of freedom.
e. *Determine* the critical value and the rejection region.
f. Calculate the chi-square test statistic.
g. *Decide* whether to reject the null hypothesis. Use a graph if necessary.
h. *Interpret* the decision in the context of the original claim.

Answer: Page A47

10.1 EXERCISES

■ Building Basic Skills and Vocabulary

1. What is a multinomial experiment?

2. What conditions are necessary to use the chi-square goodness-of-fit test?

Finding Expected Frequencies *In Exercises 3–6, find the expected frequency for the given values of n and p_i.*

3. $n = 150$, $p_i = 0.3$

4. $n = 500$, $p_i = 0.9$

5. $n = 230$, $p_i = 0.25$

6. $n = 415$, $p_i = 0.08$

■ Using and Interpreting Concepts

Performing a Chi-Square Goodness-of-Fit Test *In Exercises 7–18, (a) identify the claim and state H_0 and H_a, (b) determine the critical value and the rejection region, (c) calculate the test statistic χ^2, and (d) decide whether to reject or fail to reject the null hypothesis. Then interpret the decision in the context of the original claim.*

7. Credit Card Use Results from a survey two years ago asking college students what their top motivations are for using a credit card are shown in the graph. To determine whether this distribution has changed, you randomly select 425 college students and ask each what the top motivation is for using a credit card. The results are shown in the table. Can you conclude that there has been a change in the claimed or expected distribution? Use $\alpha = 0.05$.

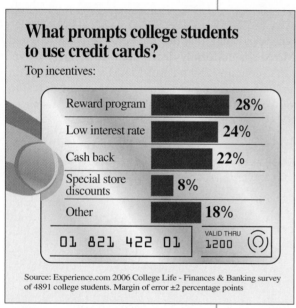

What prompts college students to use credit cards?

Top incentives:

Reward program	28%
Low interest rate	24%
Cash back	22%
Special store discounts	8%
Other	18%

01 821 422 01   VALID THRU 1200

Source: Experience.com 2006 College Life - Finances & Banking survey of 4891 college students. Margin of error ±2 percentage points

FIGURE FOR EXERCISE 7

Survey results	
Response	**Frequency, f**
Reward program	112
Low interest rate	98
Cash back	107
Special store discounts	46
Other	62

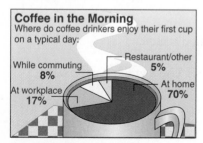

Coffee in the Morning
Where do coffee drinkers enjoy their first cup on a typical day:

While commuting 8%
Restaurant/other 5%
At workplace 17%
At home 70%

FIGURE FOR EXERCISE 8

8. Coffee Results from a survey five years ago asking where coffee drinkers typically drink their first cup of coffee are shown in the graph. To determine whether this distribution has changed, you randomly select 581 coffee drinkers and ask each where they typically drink their first cup of coffee. The results are shown in the table. Can you conclude that there has been a change in the claimed or expected distribution? Use $\alpha = 0.05$. *(Source: TeleNation)*

Survey results	
Response	**Frequency, f**
At home	389
At workplace	110
While commuting	55
Restaurant/other	27

9. **Tax Cuts or Entitlements** An economist believes that the distribution of the opinions of U.S. adults on whether tax cuts or entitlements are more important is different from the one shown in the graph. The economist randomly selects 600 adults and asks each which is more important—keeping Medicare, Social Security and Medicaid or cutting taxes. The results are shown in the table. At $\alpha = 0.01$, are the distributions different?

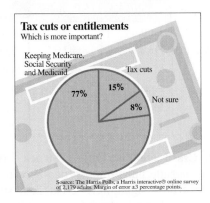

Tax cuts or entitlements
Which is more important?

Keeping Medicare, Social Security and Medicaid — 77%
Tax cuts — 15%
Not sure — 8%

Source: The Harris Polls, a Harris interactive® online survey of 2,179 adults. Margin of error ±3 percentage points.

Survey results	
Response	**Frequency, f**
Keeping Medicare, Social Security and Medicaid	431
Tax cuts	107
Not sure	62

10. **Reasons Workers Leave** A personnel director believes that the distribution of the reasons workers leave their jobs is different from the one shown in the graph. The director randomly selects 200 workers who recently left their jobs and asks each his or her reason for doing so. The results are shown in the table. At $\alpha = 0.01$, are the distributions different? *(Source: Robert Half International, Inc.)*

Why workers leave
Reasons given for good employees quitting their jobs:
41% Limited advancement potential
25% Lack of recognition
15% Low salary/benefits
10% Unhappy with management
9% Bored/don't know

Survey results	
Response	**Frequency, f**
Limited advancement potential	78
Lack of recognition	52
Low salary/benefits	30
Unhappy with mgmt.	25
Bored/don't know	15

11. **Bicycle Accidents: Day of Week** A bicycle safety organization claims that fatal bicycle accidents are uniformly distributed throughout the week. The table shows the day of the week for which 782 randomly selected fatal bicycle accidents occurred. At $\alpha = 0.10$, can you reject the claim that the distribution is uniform? *(Source: National Highway Traffic Safety Administration)*

Day	Frequency, f	Day	Frequency, f
Sunday	108	Thursday	123
Monday	112	Friday	105
Tuesday	105	Saturday	118
Wednesday	111		

12. Bicycle Accidents: Month of Year A bicycle safety organization conducted a study of 783 randomly selected fatal bicycle accidents. The table shows the number of accidents that occurred in each month. At $\alpha = 0.10$, can you conclude that fatal bicycle accidents are not uniformly distributed by month? *(Source: National Highway Traffic Safety Administration)*

Month	Frequency, *f*	Month	Frequency, *f*
January	37	July	66
February	42	August	86
March	43	September	81
April	62	October	94
May	79	November	57
June	93	December	43

13. Crash Deaths: Object Struck The pie chart shows the distribution of roadside hazard crash deaths with respect to the object hit. After highway warning signs were erected, a study of 691 randomly selected roadside hazard crash deaths was conducted to see if there was a change in the distribution. The results are shown in the table. Can you conclude that there is a change in the distribution? Use $\alpha = 0.01$. *(Adapted from Insurance Institute for Highway Safety)*

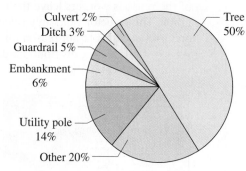

Survey results	
Object Struck	**Frequency, *f***
Tree	375
Utility pole	86
Embankment	53
Guardrail	42
Ditch	27
Culvert	18
Other	90

14. Crash Deaths: Time of Day The pie chart shows the distribution of the time of day of roadside hazard crash deaths for a previous year. The results of a recent study of 627 randomly selected roadside hazard crash deaths are shown in the table. At $\alpha = 0.01$, has the distribution changed? *(Adapted from Insurance Institute for Highway Safety)*

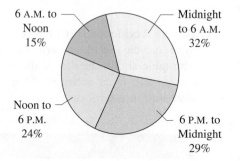

Survey results	
Time of day	**Frequency, *f***
Midnight to 6 A.M.	224
6 A.M. to Noon	128
Noon to 6 P.M.	115
6 P.M. to Midnight	160

15. Educational Attainment   A social service organization reports that the level of educational attainment of mothers receiving food stamps is uniformly distributed. To test this claim, you randomly select 99 mothers who currently receive food stamps and record the educational attainment of each. The results are shown in the following table. At $\alpha = 0.025$, can you reject the claim that the distribution is uniform? *(Adapted from U.S. Census Bureau)*

Response	Frequency, f
Not a high school graduate	37
High school graduate	40
College (1 year or more)	22

16. Births by Season   A doctor believes that the number of births by season is uniformly distributed. To test this claim, you randomly select 2247 births and record the season in which each takes place. The results are shown below. At $\alpha = 0.01$, can you reject the claim that the distribution is uniform? *(Adapted from National Center for Health Statistics)*

Season	Frequency, f
Spring	564
Summer	603
Fall	555
Winter	525

17. Fatal Work Injuries   The pie chart shows the national distribution of fatal work injuries in the United States. You believe that the distribution of fatal work injuries is different in the western United States and randomly select 6231 fatal work injuries occurring in that region and record how each occurred. The results are shown in the table. At $\alpha = 0.05$, can you conclude that the distribution of fatal work injuries in the western United States is different from the national distribution? *(Adapted from U.S. Bureau of Labor Statistics)*

Study results: Western U.S.	
Cause	**Frequency, f**
Transportation accidents	2891
Contacts with objects and equipment	1159
Assaults/violent acts	804
Falls	754
Exposure to harmful substances or environments	531
Fires and explosions	92

18. **Hours Worked by College Students** An education council says that 22% of undergraduates do not work, 26% work 1 to 20 hours per week, 18% work 21 to 34 hours per week, and 34% work 35 or more hours per week. You randomly select 120 college students and gather the results shown in the table. At $\alpha = 0.01$, can you reject the council's claim? *(Adapted from American Council on Education)*

Response	Frequency, f
Did not work	29
Work 1 to 20 hours	26
Work 21 to 34 hours	25
Work 35 or more hours	40

■ Extending Concepts

Testing for Normality *Using a chi-square goodness-of-fit test, you can decide, with some degree of certainty, whether a variable is normally distributed. In all chi-square tests for normality, the null and alternative hypotheses are as follows.*

H_0: The variable has a normal distribution.

H_a: The variable does not have a normal distribution.

To determine the expected frequencies when performing a chi-square test for normality, first find the mean and standard deviation of the frequency distribution. Then use the mean and standard deviation to compute the z-score for each class boundary. Then use the z-scores to calculate the area under the standard normal curve for each class. Multiplying the resulting class areas by the sample size yields the expected frequency for each class.

In Exercises 19 and 20, (a) find the expected frequencies, (b) determine the critical value and the rejection region, (c) calculate the test statistic χ^2, and (d) decide whether to reject or fail to reject the null hypothesis. Then interpret the decision in the context of the original claim.

19. **Test Scores** The frequency distribution shows the results of 200 test scores. Are the test scores normally distributed? Use $\alpha = 0.01$.

Class boundaries	49.5–58.5	58.5–67.5	67.5–76.5
Frequency, f	19	61	82

Class boundaries	76.5–85.5	85.5–94.5
Frequency, f	34	4

20. **Test Scores** At $\alpha = 0.05$, test the claim that the 400 test scores shown in the frequency distribution are normally distributed.

Class boundaries	50.5–60.5	60.5–70.5	70.5–80.5
Frequency, f	28	106	151

Class boundaries	80.5–90.5	90.5–100.5
Frequency, f	97	18

10.2 Independence

Contingency Tables ▸ The Chi-Square Test for Independence

▸ Contingency Tables

In Section 3.2, you learned that two events are **independent** if the occurrence of one event does not affect the probability of the occurrence of the other event. For instance, the outcomes of a roll of a die and a toss of a coin are independent. But, suppose a medical researcher wants to determine if there is a relationship between caffeine consumption and heart attack risk. Are these variables independent or are they dependent? In this section, you will learn how to use the chi-square test for independence to answer such a question. To perform a chi-square test for independence, you will use sample data that are organized in a contingency table.

> ### DEFINITION
>
> An **$r \times c$ contingency table** shows the observed frequencies for two variables. The observed frequencies are arranged in r rows and c columns. The intersection of a row and a column is called a **cell.**

For example, the following table is a 2 × 5 contingency table. It has two rows and five columns and shows the results of a random sample of 550 company CEOs classified by age and size of company. From the table, you can see that 108 of the CEOs between the ages of 50 and 59 direct small or midsize companies, and 85 of the CEOs in this age group direct large companies.

Study Tip

In a contingency table, the notation $E_{r,\,c}$ represents the expected frequency for the cell in row r, column c. For instance, in the table at the right, $E_{1,\,4}$ represents the expected frequency for the cell in row 1, column 4.

Company size	Age				
	39 and under	**40–49**	**50–59**	**60–69**	**70 and over**
Small/midsize	42	69	108	60	21
Large	5	18	85	120	22

(Adapted from Grant Thornton LLP, The Segal Company)

Assuming the two variables of study in a contingency table are independent, you can use the contingency table to find the expected frequency for each cell. The formula for calculating the expected frequency for each cell is given below.

> ### FINDING THE EXPECTED FREQUENCY FOR CONTINGENCY TABLE CELLS
>
> The expected frequency for a cell $E_{r,\,c}$ in a contingency table is
>
> $$\text{Expected frequency } E_{r,\,c} = \frac{(\text{Sum of row } r) \times (\text{Sum of column } c)}{\text{Sample size}}.$$

When you find the sum of each row and column in a contingency table, you are calculating the **marginal frequencies.** A marginal frequency is the frequency that an entire category of one of the variables occurs. For instance, in the table above, the marginal frequency for CEOs between the ages of 40 and 49 is 69 + 18 = 87. The observed frequencies in the interior of a contingency table are called **joint frequencies.** The marginal frequencies for the contingency table in Example 1 have already been calculated.

Insight

In Example 1, once the expected frequency for $E_{1,1}$ has been calculated to be 25.64, you can determine the expected frequency for $E_{2,1}$ to be $47 - 25.64 = 21.36$. That is, the expected frequency for the last cell in each row or column can be found by subtracting from the total.

EXAMPLE 1

Finding Expected Frequencies

Find the expected frequency for each cell in the contingency table. Assume that the variables, age and company size, are independent.

Company size	Age					Total
	39 and under	40–49	50–59	60–69	70 and over	
Small/midsize	42	69	108	60	21	300
Large	5	18	85	120	22	250
Total	47	87	193	180	43	550

Solution   After calculating the marginal frequencies, you can use the formula

$$\text{Expected frequency } E_{r,c} = \frac{(\text{Sum of row } r) \times (\text{Sum of column } c)}{\text{Sample size}}$$

to find each expected frequency as shown.

$$E_{1,1} = \frac{300 \cdot 47}{550} \approx 25.64 \quad E_{1,2} = \frac{300 \cdot 87}{550} \approx 47.45 \quad E_{1,3} = \frac{300 \cdot 193}{550} \approx 105.27$$

$$E_{1,4} = \frac{300 \cdot 180}{550} \approx 98.18 \quad E_{1,5} = \frac{300 \cdot 43}{550} \approx 23.45 \quad E_{2,1} = \frac{250 \cdot 47}{550} \approx 21.36$$

$$E_{2,2} = \frac{250 \cdot 87}{550} \approx 39.55 \quad E_{2,3} = \frac{250 \cdot 193}{550} \approx 87.73 \quad E_{2,4} = \frac{250 \cdot 180}{550} \approx 81.82$$

$$E_{2,5} = \frac{250 \cdot 43}{550} \approx 19.55$$

▶ Try It Yourself 1

The marketing consultant for a travel agency wants to determine whether certain travel concerns are related to travel purpose. A random sample of 300 travelers is selected and each is asked his or her primary travel concern. The results are classified as shown in the contingency table. Assuming that the variables travel concern and travel purpose are independent, find the expected frequency for each cell. *(Adapted from NPD Group for Embassy Suites)*

Travel purpose	Travel concern			
	Hotel room	Leg room on plane	Rental car size	Other
Business	36	108	14	22
Leisure	38	54	14	14

a. *Calculate* the marginal frequencies.
b. *Determine* the sample size.
c. *Use the formula* to find the expected frequency for each cell.

Answer: Page A47

▶ The Chi-Square Test for Independence

After finding the expected frequencies, you can test whether the variables are independent using a chi-square independence test.

DEFINITION

A **chi-square independence test** is used to test the independence of two variables. Using a chi-square test, you can determine whether the occurrence of one variable affects the probability of the occurrence of the other variable.

For the chi-square independence test to be used, the following conditions must be true.

1. The observed frequencies must be obtained using a random sample.

2. Each expected frequency must be greater than or equal to 5.

THE CHI-SQUARE INDEPENDENCE TEST

If the conditions listed above are satisfied, then the sampling distribution for the chi-square independence test is approximated by a chi-square distribution with

$$(r - 1)(c - 1)$$

degrees of freedom, where r and c are the number of rows and columns, respectively, of a contingency table. The test statistic for the chi-square independence test is

$$\chi^2 = \Sigma \frac{(O - E)^2}{E}$$

where O represents the observed frequencies and E represents the expected frequencies.

To begin the independence test, you must first state a null hypothesis and an alternative hypothesis. For a chi-square independence test, the null and alternative hypotheses are always some variation of the following statements.

H_0: The variables are independent.

H_a: The variables are dependent.

The expected frequencies are calculated on the assumption that the two variables are independent. If the variables are independent, then you can expect little difference between the observed frequencies and the expected frequencies. When the observed frequencies closely match the expected frequencies, the differences between O and E will be small and the chi-square test statistic will be close to 0. As such, the null hypothesis is unlikely to be rejected.

However, if the variables are dependent, there will be large discrepancies between the observed frequencies and the expected frequencies. When the differences between O and E are large, the chi-square test statistic is also large. A large chi-square test statistic is evidence for rejecting the null hypothesis. So, the chi-square independence test is always a right-tailed test.

PICTURING the WORLD

A researcher wishes to determine if a relationship exists between job status (full- or part-time) and two different work arrangements. The results of a random sample of 884 workers are shown in the contingency table. (Adapted from the U.S. Bureau of Labor Statistics)

	Work arrangement	
Status	**Contract**	**Traditional**
Full-time	12	720
Part-time	4	148

Can the researcher use this sample to test for independence using a chi-square independence test? Why or why not?

GUIDELINES

Performing a Chi-Square Test for Independence

In Words	*In Symbols*
1. Identify the claim. State the null and alternative hypotheses.	State H_0 and H_a.
2. Specify the level of significance.	Identify α.
3. Identify the degrees of freedom.	d.f. $= (r-1)(c-1)$
4. Determine the critical value.	Use Table 6 in Appendix B.
5. Determine the rejection region.	
6. Calculate the test statistic.	$\chi^2 = \Sigma \dfrac{(O-E)^2}{E}$
7. Make a decision to reject or fail to reject the null hypothesis.	If χ^2 is in the rejection region, reject H_0. Otherwise, fail to reject H_0.
8. Interpret the decision in the context of the original claim.	

EXAMPLE 2

Performing a Chi-Square Independence Test

The contingency table shows the results of a random sample of 550 company CEOs classified by age and size of company. The expected frequencies are displayed in parentheses. At $\alpha = 0.01$, can you conclude that the CEOs' ages are related to company size?

Company size	Age of CEOs					Total
	39 and under	40–49	50–59	60–69	70 and over	
Small/midsize	42 (25.64)	69 (47.45)	108 (105.27)	60 (98.18)	21 (23.45)	300
Large	5 (21.36)	18 (39.55)	85 (87.73)	120 (81.82)	22 (19.55)	250
Total	47	87	193	180	43	550

Solution The expected frequencies were calculated in Example 1. Because each expected frequency is at least 5 and the CEOs were randomly selected, you can use the chi-square independence test to test whether the variables are independent. The null and alternative hypotheses are as follows.

H_0: The CEOs' ages are independent of the company size.

H_a: The CEOs' ages are dependent on the company size. (Claim)

Because the contingency table has two rows and five columns, the chi-square distribution has $(r-1)(c-1) = (2-1)(5-1) = 4$ degrees of freedom. Because d.f. = 4 and $\alpha = 0.01$, the critical value is $\chi_0^2 = 13.277$. With the observed and expected frequencies, the chi-square test statistic is as shown.

O	E	$O - E$	$(O - E)^2$	$\dfrac{(O - E)^2}{E}$
42	25.64	16.36	267.6496	10.4388
69	47.45	21.55	464.4025	9.7872
108	105.27	2.73	7.4529	0.0708
60	98.18	−38.18	1457.7124	14.8473
21	23.45	−2.45	6.0025	0.2560
5	21.36	−16.36	267.6496	12.5304
18	39.55	−21.55	464.4025	11.7422
85	87.73	−2.73	7.4529	0.0850
120	81.82	38.18	1457.7124	17.8161
22	19.55	2.45	6.0025	0.3070
			$\chi^2 = \Sigma\dfrac{(O - E)^2}{E} \approx 77.881$	

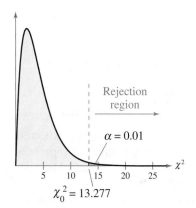

Rejection region

$\alpha = 0.01$

$\chi_0^2 = 13.277$

The graph shows the location of the rejection region. Because $\chi^2 \approx 77.881$ is in the rejection region, you should decide to reject the null hypothesis.

Interpretation   There is enough evidence at the 1% significance level to conclude that the CEOs' ages and the company size are dependent.

▶ Try It Yourself 2

The marketing consultant for a travel agency wants to determine whether travel concerns are related to travel purpose. A random sample of 300 travelers is selected and each is asked his or her primary travel concern. The results are classified as shown in the contingency table. At $\alpha = 0.01$, can the consultant conclude that the travel concerns depend on the purpose of travel? (The expected frequencies are displayed in parentheses.) *(Adapted from NPD Group for Embassy Suites)*

Travel purpose	Travel concern				Total
	Hotel room	Leg room on plane	Rental car size	Other	
Business	36 (44.4)	108 (97.2)	14 (16.8)	22 (21.6)	180
Leisure	38 (29.6)	54 (64.8)	14 (11.2)	14 (14.4)	120
Total	74	162	28	36	300

a. *Identify* the claim and state H_0 and H_a.
b. *Specify* the level of significance α.
c. *Determine* the degrees of freedom.
d. *Determine* the critical value and the rejection region.
e. Use the observed and expected frequencies to *calculate the chi-square test statistic.*
f. *Decide* whether to reject the null hypothesis. Use a graph if necessary.
g. *Interpret* the decision in the context of the original claim.   *Answer: Page A47*

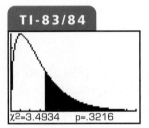
EXAMPLE 3

Using Technology for a Chi-Square Independence Test

A health club manager wants to determine whether the number of days per week that college students spend exercising is related to gender. A random sample of 275 college students is selected and the results are classified as shown in the table. At $\alpha = 0.05$, is there enough evidence to conclude that the number of days spent exercising per week is related to gender?

Gender	Days per week spent exercising				
	0–1	2–3	4–5	6–7	Total
Male	40	53	26	6	125
Female	34	68	37	11	150
Total	74	121	63	17	275

Solution The null and alternative hypotheses can be stated as follows.

H_0: The number of days spent exercising per week is independent of gender.

H_a: The number of days spent exercising per week depends on gender. (Claim)

Using a TI-83/84, enter the observed frequencies into Matrix A and the expected frequencies into Matrix B making sure that each expected frequency is greater than or equal to 5. Choose the TESTS menu and select C: $\chi^2 - Test$. Then set up the chi-square test as shown in the top-left screen.

The other displays at the left show the results of selecting *Calculate* or *Draw*. Because d.f. = 3 and $\alpha = 0.05$, the critical value is $\chi^2_0 = 7.815$. So, the rejection region is $\chi^2 > 7.815$. The test statistic $\chi^2 \approx 3.493$ is not in the rejection region, so you should fail to reject the null hypothesis.

Interpretation There is not enough evidence to conclude that the number of days spent exercising per week is related to gender.

▶ Try It Yourself 3

A researcher wants to determine whether the number of minutes adults spend online per day is related to gender. A random sample of 450 adults is selected and the results are classified as shown in the table. At $\alpha = 0.05$, is there enough evidence to conclude that the number of minutes spent online per day is related to gender?

Gender	Minutes spent online per day					
	0–15	15–30	30–45	45–60	60 and over	Total
Male	19	36	75	90	55	275
Female	21	72	45	19	18	175
Total	40	108	120	109	73	450

a. *Identify* the claim and state H_0 and H_a.
b. *Use* a technology tool to enter the observed and expected frequencies into matrices.
c. *Determine* the critical value and the rejection region.
d. *Use* the technology tool to find the chi-square test statistic.
e. *Decide* whether to reject the null hypothesis. Use a graph if necessary.
f. *Interpret* the decision in the context of the original claim. *Answer: Page A48*

Study Tip

You can also use a *P*-value to perform a chi-square test for independence. For instance, in Example 3, note that the TI-83/84 displays $P = .321624691$. Because $P > \alpha$, you should fail to reject the null hypothesis.

■ Building Basic Skills and Vocabulary

1. Explain how to find the expected frequency for a cell in a contingency table.

2. Explain why the chi-square independence test is always a right-tailed test.

True or False? *In Exercises 3–6, determine whether the statement is true or false. If it is false, rewrite it as a true statement.*

3. In order to use the chi-square independence test, each observed frequency must be greater than or equal to 5.

4. A contingency table with two rows and five columns will have $(2)(5) = 10$ degrees of freedom.

5. If the two variables of the chi-square test for independence are dependent, then you can expect little difference between the observed frequencies and the expected frequencies.

6. If the test statistic for the chi-square independence test is large, you will, in most cases, reject the null hypothesis.

Finding Expected Frequencies *In Exercises 7–12, (a) calculate the marginal frequencies, and (b) find the expected frequency for each cell in the contingency table. Assume that the variables are independent.*

7.

Result	Athlete has	
	Stretched	**Not stretched**
Injury	18	22
No injury	211	189

8.

Result	Treatment	
	Flu shot	**No flu shot**
Got the flu	54	157
Did not get the flu	196	103

9.

Result	Treatment		
	Brand-name	**Generic**	**Placebo**
Improvement	24	21	10
No change	12	13	45

10.

Size of restaurant	Rating		
	Excellent	**Fair**	**Poor**
Seats 100 or fewer	182	203	165
Seats over 100	180	311	159

11.

Gender	Type of car			
	Compact	Full-size	SUV	Truck/van
Male	28	39	21	22
Female	24	32	20	14

12.

Result	Age			
	18–30	31–42	43–61	62 and older
Willing to buy a hybrid	72	66	73	69
Not willing to buy a hybrid	14	21	19	21

■ Using and Interpreting Concepts

Performing a Chi-Square Test for Independence *In Exercises 13–24, perform the indicated chi-square test for independence by doing the following.*

(a) Identify the claim and state the null and alternative hypotheses.

(b) Determine the degrees of freedom, find the critical value, and identify the rejection region.

(c) Calculate the test statistic. If convenient, use technology.

(d) Decide to reject or fail to reject the null hypothesis. Then interpret the decision in the context of the original claim.

13. Achievement and School Location Is achieving a basic skill level in a subject related to the location of the school? The results of a random sample of students by the location of school and the number of those students achieving basic skill levels in three subjects is shown in the contingency table. At $\alpha = 0.01$, test the hypothesis that the variables are independent. *(Adapted from USA TODAY)*

Location of school	Subject		
	Reading	Math	Science
Urban	43	42	38
Suburban	63	66	65

14. Attitudes about Safety The results of a random sample of students by type of school and their attitudes on safety steps taken by the school staff are shown in the contingency table. At $\alpha = 0.01$, can you conclude that attitudes about the safety steps taken by the school staff are related to the type of school? *(Adapted from USA TODAY)*

Type of school	School staff has	
	Taken all steps necessary for student safety	Taken some steps toward student safety
Public	40	51
Private	64	34

15. Grades for Our Leaders   The contingency table shows how a random sample of college freshmen graded the leaders of three types of institutions. At $\alpha = 0.05$, can you conclude that the grades are related to the institution? *(Adapted from Louis Harris for Northwestern Mutual Life Insurance)*

Institution	Grade				
	A	B	C	D	F
Military	25	46	19	5	3
Religious	18	44	24	7	5
Media/press	5	23	37	21	12

16. Rating Public Schools   The contingency table shows how a random sample of adults rated their local public schools and how they rated public schools nationally. At $\alpha = 0.05$, can you conclude that the adults' ratings are related to the type of school? *(Adapted from USA TODAY)*

Type of school	Rating			
	Excellent	Good	Fair	Poor
Local	120	405	263	151
National	41	238	481	179

17. Obsessive-Compulsive Disorder   The results of a random sample of patients with obsessive-compulsive disorder treated with a drug or with a placebo are shown in the contingency table. At $\alpha = 0.10$, can you conclude that the treatment is related to the result? On the basis of these results, would you recommend using the drug as part of a treatment for obsessive-compulsive disorder? *(Adapted from The Journal of the American Medical Association)*

Result	Treatment	
	Drug	Placebo
Improvement	39	25
No change	54	70

18. Chronic Fatigue Syndrome   The contingency table shows the results of a random sample of patients with chronic fatigue syndrome treated with a drug or with a placebo. At $\alpha = 0.10$, can you conclude that the treatment and result are dependent? On the basis of these results, would you recommend using the drug as part of a treatment for chronic fatigue syndrome? *(Adapted from The Journal of the American Medical Association)*

Result	Treatment	
	Drug	Placebo
Improvement	20	19
No change	10	16

19. Continuing Education You work for a college's continuing education department and want to determine whether the reasons given by workers for continuing their education is related to job type. In your study, you randomly collect the data shown in the contingency table. At $\alpha = 0.01$, can you conclude that the reason and type of worker are dependent? How could you use this information in your marketing efforts? *(Adapted from USA TODAY)*

Type of worker	Reason		
	Professional	Personal	Professional and personal
Technical	30	36	41
Other	47	25	30

20. Ages and Goals You are investigating the relationship between the ages of U.S. adults and what aspect of career development they consider to be the most important. You randomly collect the data shown in the contingency table. At $\alpha = 0.01$, is there enough evidence to conclude that age is related to what aspect of career development is considered to be most important? *(Adapted from Harris Interactive)*

Age	Career development aspect		
	Learning new skills	Pay increases	Career path
18–26 years	31	22	21
27–41 years	27	31	33
42–61 years	19	14	8

21. Vehicles and Crashes You work for an insurance company and are studying the relationship between types of crashes and the vehicles involved. As part of your study, you randomly select 3059 vehicle crashes and organize the resulting data as shown in the contingency table. At $\alpha = 0.05$, can you conclude that the type of crash depends on the type of vehicle? *(Adapted from Insurance Institute for Highway Safety)*

Type of crash	Vehicle		
	Car	Pickup	Sport utility
Single-vehicle	832	365	300
Multiple-vehicle	1149	237	176

22. Alcohol-Related Accidents The contingency table shows the results of a random sample of fatally injured passenger vehicle drivers (with blood alcohol concentrations greater than or equal to 0.08) by age and gender. At $\alpha = 0.05$, can you conclude that age is related to gender in such alcohol-related accidents? *(Adapted from Insurance Institute for Highway Safety)*

Gender	Age					
	16–20	21–30	31–40	41–50	51–60	61 and older
Male	31	108	61	52	27	17
Female	6	18	15	14	5	3

23. **Coauthored Articles**   The contingency table shows a random sample of engineering, psychology, and biology articles and if and how they were coauthored. At $\alpha = 0.10$, can you conclude that the subject matter and coauthorship are related? *(Adapted from CHI Research, Inc.)*

	Subject matter		
Coauthorship	**Engineering**	**Psychology**	**Biology**
Coauthored	47	44	50
Internationally coauthored	17	9	16
Not coauthored	36	47	34

24. **Library Internet Access Speed**   The contingency table shows a random sample of urban, suburban, and rural libraries and the speed of their Internet access. In the table, kbps represents kilobits per second and mbps represents megabits per second. At $\alpha = 0.01$, can you conclude that the metropolitan status of libraries and Internet access speed are related? *(Adapted from Information Use Management and Policy Institute)*

	Metropolitan status		
Access speed	**Urban**	**Suburban**	**Rural**
128 kbps or less	6	7	19
129 kpbs–1.5 mbps	52	46	43
Greater than 1.5 mbps	33	26	13

■ **Extending Concepts**

Homogeneity of Proportions Test   *Another chi-square test that involves a contingency table is the **homogeneity of proportions test**. This test is used to determine if several proportions are equal when samples are taken from different populations. Before the populations are sampled and the contingency table is made, the sample sizes are determined. After randomly sampling different populations, you can test whether the proportion of elements in a category is the same for each population using the same guidelines in performing a chi-square independence test. The null and alternative hypotheses are always some variation of the following statements.*

H_0: The proportions are equal.

H_a: At least one of the proportions is different from the others.

Performing a homogeneity of proportions test requires that the observed frequencies be obtained using a random sample, and each expected frequency must be greater than or equal to 5.

25. **Motor Vehicle Crash Deaths** The contingency table shows the results of a random sample of motor vehicle crash deaths by age and gender. At $\alpha = 0.05$, perform a homogeneity of proportions test on the claim that the proportions of motor vehicle crash deaths involving males or females are the same for each age group. *(Adapted from Insurance Institute for Highway Safety)*

Gender	Age			
	16–24	25–34	35–44	45–54
Male	101	73	64	60
Female	38	23	24	23

Gender	Age			
	55–64	65–74	75–84	85 and older
Male	38	24	20	8
Female	18	14	15	6

26. **Obsessive-Compulsive Disorder** The contingency table shows the results of a random sample of patients with obsessive-compulsive disorder after being treated with a drug or with a placebo. At $\alpha = 0.10$, perform a homogeneity of proportions test on the claim that the proportions of the results for drug and placebo treatment are the same. *(Adapted from The Journal of the American Medical Association)*

Result	Treatment	
	Drug	Placebo
Improvement	39	25
No change	54	70

Contingency Tables and Relative Frequencies *In Exercises 27–33, use the following information.*

The frequencies in a contingency table can easily be written as relative frequencies by dividing each frequency by the sample size. The contingency table below shows the number of U.S. adults (in millions) ages 25 and over by employment status and educational attainment. *(Adapted from U.S. Census Bureau)*

Status	Educational Attainment			
	Not a high school graduate	High school graduate	Some college, no degree	Associate's, bachelor's, or advanced degree
Employed	11.5	35.9	21.3	51.4
Unemployed	1.1	2.1	1.0	1.4
Not in the labor force	15.4	22.7	9.4	15.4

27. Rewrite the contingency table using relative frequencies.

28. What percent of U.S. adults ages 25 and over have some college education, but no degree, and are employed?

29. What percent of U.S. adults ages 25 and over have a degree and are not in the labor force?

30. What percent of U.S. adults ages 25 and over are employed and not high school graduates?

31. What percent of U.S. adults ages 25 and over are employed?

32. What percent of U.S. adults ages 25 and over are not high school graduates?

33. Explain why you cannot perform the chi-square independence test on these data.

Conditional Relative Frequencies *In Exercises 34–41, use the contingency table from Exercises 27–33 and the following information.*

Relative frequencies can also be calculated based on the row totals (by dividing each row entry by the row's total) or the column totals (by dividing each column entry by the column's total). These frequencies are **conditional relative frequencies** and can be used to determine if an association exists between two categories in a contingency table.

34. Calculate the conditional relative frequencies in the contingency table based on the row totals.

35. What percent of U.S. adults ages 25 and over who are employed are high school graduates only?

36. What percent of U.S. adults ages 25 and over who are not in the labor force have some college education, but no degree?

37. Calculate the conditional relative frequencies in the contingency table based on the column totals.

38. What percent of U.S. adults ages 25 and over who have a degree are not in the labor force?

39. What percent of U.S. adults ages 25 and over who are not high school graduates are unemployed?

40. Use your results from Exercise 37 to construct a bar graph that shows the percentages of U.S. adults ages 25 and over based on employment status. Each category of employment status will have four bars, representing the four levels of educational attainment mentioned in the contingency table.

41. What conclusions can you make from the bar graph you constructed in Exercise 40?

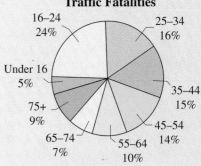

U.S. Distribution of Traffic Fatalities

16–24 24%
25–34 16%
Under 16 5%
35–44 15%
75+ 9%
45–54 14%
65–74 7%
55–64 10%

Traffic Safety Facts

Each year, the National Highway Traffic Safety Administration (NHTSA) together with the National Center for Statistics and Analysis (NCSA) publishes *Traffic Safety Facts,* which summarizes the motor vehicle traffic crash experience for the United States. *Traffic Safety Facts 2005* includes trend data, crash data, vehicle data, and people data. Also, the NHTSA and NCSA publish a report summarizing the motor vehicle crash data of the 32 states in the NHTSA's State Data System.

In 2005, there were 43,443 fatalities in the United States as a result of motor vehicle crashes. The pie chart at the right shows the national distribution of traffic fatalities with respect to age group. For example, 16% of all motor vehicle fatalities were adults ages 25–34. Using the data from the 32 states in the NHTSA's State Data System as a sample, the contingency table shows the number of motor vehicle fatalities according to age and geographic location within the United States.

Motor Vehicle Fatalities

| Age | Region | | |
	Eastern U.S.	Central U.S.	Western U.S.
Under 16	651	841	414
16–24	3309	3478	1655
25–34	2255	2346	1154
35–44	2132	2163	1021
45–54	1977	1994	955
55–64	1359	1361	668
65–74	941	939	386
75+	1354	1190	498

■ Exercises

1. In 2005, how many people in the United States ages 16–24 died as a result of a motor vehicle crash?

2. Assuming the variables region and age are independent, in which region did the number of motor vehicle fatalities for the 16–24 age group exceed the expected number of fatalities?

3. Assuming the variables region and age are independent, in which region did the number of motor vehicle fatalities for the 25–34 age group exceed the expected number of fatalities?

4. At $\alpha = 0.05$, perform a chi-square independence test to determine whether the variables region and age are independent. What can you conclude?

In Exercises 5–7, perform a chi-square goodness-of-fit test to compare the national distribution of motor vehicle fatalities with the distribution of each region of the United States. Use the national distribution as the claimed distribution. Use $\alpha = 0.05$.

5. Compare the distribution of the sample of motor vehicle fatalities from the eastern United States with the national distribution. What can you conclude?

6. Compare the distribution of the sample of motor vehicle fatalities from the central United States with the national distribution. What can you conclude?

7. Compare the distribution of the sample of motor vehicle fatalities from the western United States with the national distribution. What can you conclude?

8. In addition to the variables used in this case study, what other variables do you think are important considerations when studying the distribution of motor vehicle fatalities?

10.3 Comparing Two Variances

The F-Distribution ▸

▸ The F-Distributio

In Chapter 8, you learned how
means and population proport
difference between two popula
variances are equal. To determin
can perform a two-sample F-test.

In this section, you will lear
F-distribution to compare two va

DEFINITION

Let s_1^2 and s_2^2 represent the sample   ...ces of two different populations. If both populations are normal and the population variances σ_1^2 and σ_2^2 are equal, then the sampling distribution of

$$F = \frac{s_1^2}{s_2^2}$$

is called an **F-distribution.** Several properties of the F-distribution are as follows.

1. The F-distribution is a family of curves each of which is determined by two types of degrees of freedom: the degrees of freedom corresponding to the variance in the numerator, denoted by **d.f.$_N$**, and the degrees of freedom corresponding to the variance in the denominator, denoted by **d.f.$_D$**.
2. F-distributions are positively skewed.
3. The total area under each curve of an F-distribution is equal to 1.
4. F-values are always greater than or equal to zero.
5. For all F-distributions, the mean value of F is approximately equal to 1.

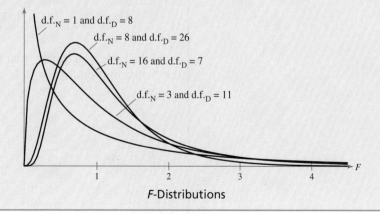

F-Distributions

Table 7 in Appendix B lists the critical values for the *F*-distribution for selected levels of significance α and degrees of freedom, d.f.$_N$ and d.f.$_D$.

GUIDELINES

Finding Critical Values for the *F*-Distribution

1. Specify the level of significance α.
2. Determine the degrees of freedom for the numerator, d.f.$_N$.
3. Determine the degrees of freedom for the denominator, d.f.$_D$.
4. Use Table 7 in Appendix B to find the critical value. If the hypothesis test is
   a. one tailed, use the α *F*-table.
   b. two tailed, use the $\frac{1}{2}\alpha$ *F*-table.

EXAMPLE 1

Finding Critical *F*-Values for a Right-Tailed Test

Find the critical *F*-value for a right-tailed test when $\alpha = 0.05$, d.f.$_N = 6$, and d.f.$_D = 29$.

Solution

A portion of Table 7 is shown below. Using the $\alpha = 0.05$ *F*-table with d.f.$_N = 6$ and d.f.$_D = 29$, you can find the critical value as shown by the highlighted areas in the table.

d.f.$_D$: Degrees of freedom, denominator	$\alpha = 0.05$							
	d.f.$_N$: Degrees of freedom, numerator							
	1	2	3	4	5	6	7	8
1	161.4	199.5	215.7	224.6	230.2	234.0	236.8	238.9
2	18.51	19.00	19.16	19.25	19.30	19.33	19.35	19.37
26	4.23	3.37	2.98	2.74	2.59	2.47	2.39	2.32
27	4.21	3.35	2.96	2.73	2.57	2.46	2.37	2.31
28	4.20	3.34	2.95	2.71	2.56	2.45	2.36	2.29
29	4.18	3.33	2.93	2.70	2.55	(2.43)	2.35	2.28
30	4.17	3.32	2.92	2.69	2.53	2.42	2.33	2.27

From the table, you can see that the critical value is $F_0 = 2.43$. The graph shows the *F*-distribution for $\alpha = 0.05$, d.f.$_N = 6$, d.f.$_D = 29$, and $F_0 = 2.43$.

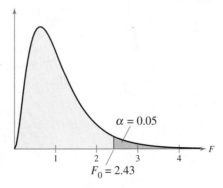

$\alpha = 0.05$

$F_0 = 2.43$

▶**Try It Yourself 1**

Find the critical F-value for a right-tailed test when $\alpha = 0.01$, d.f.$_N = 3$, and d.f.$_D = 15$.

a. *Specify* the level of significance α.
b. *Use* Table 7 in Appendix B to find the critical value.   *Answer: Page A48*

When performing a two-tailed hypothesis test using the F-distribution, you need only to find the right-tailed critical value. You must, however, remember to use the $\frac{1}{2}\alpha$ F-table.

EXAMPLE 2

Finding Critical F-Values for a Two-Tailed Test

Find the critical F-value for a two-tailed test when $\alpha = 0.05$, d.f.$_N = 4$, and d.f.$_D = 8$.

Solution

A portion of Table 7 is shown below. Using the

$$\frac{1}{2}\alpha = \frac{1}{2}(0.05) = 0.025$$

F-table with d.f.$_N = 4$, and d.f.$_D = 8$, you can find the critical value as shown by the highlighted areas in the table.

d.f.$_D$: Degrees of freedom, denominator	$\alpha = 0.025$							
	d.f.$_N$: Degrees of freedom, numerator							
	1	2	3	4	5	6	7	8
1	647.8	799.5	864.2	899.6	921.8	937.1	948.2	956.7
2	38.51	39.00	39.17	39.25	39.30	39.33	39.36	39.37
3	17.44	16.04	15.44	15.10	14.88	14.73	14.62	14.54
4	12.22	10.65	9.98	9.60	9.36	9.20	9.07	8.98
5	10.01	8.43	7.76	7.39	7.15	6.98	6.85	6.76
6	8.81	7.26	6.60	6.23	5.99	5.82	5.70	5.60
7	8.07	6.54	5.89	5.52	5.29	5.12	4.99	4.90
8	7.57	6.06	5.42	(5.05)	4.82	4.65	4.53	4.43
9	7.21	5.71	5.08	4.72	4.48	4.32	4.20	4.10

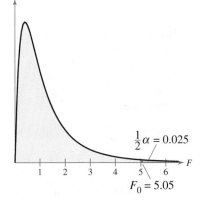

$$\tfrac{1}{2}\alpha = 0.025$$

$$F_0 = 5.05$$

From the table, the critical value is $F_0 = 5.05$. The graph shows the F-distribution for $\frac{1}{2}\alpha = 0.025$, d.f.$_N = 4$, d.f.$_D = 8$, and $F_0 = 5.05$.

▶**Try It Yourself 2**

Find the critical F-value for a two-tailed test when $\alpha = 0.01$, d.f.$_N = 2$, and d.f.$_D = 5$.

a. *Specify* the level of significance α.
b. *Use* Table 7 in Appendix B with $\frac{1}{2}\alpha$ to find the critical value.

Answer: Page A48

▶ The Two-Sample *F*-Test for Variances

In the remainder of this section, you will learn how to perform a two-sample *F*-test for comparing two population variances using a sample from each population. Such a test has three conditions that must be met.

1. The samples must be randomly selected.
2. The samples must be independent.
3. Each population must have a normal distribution.

If these requirements are met, you can use the *F*-test to compare the population variances σ_1^2 and σ_2^2.

TWO-SAMPLE *F*-TEST FOR VARIANCES

A two-sample *F*-test is used to compare two population variances σ_1^2 and σ_2^2 when a sample is randomly selected from each population. The populations must be independent and normally distributed. The test statistic is

$$F = \frac{s_1^2}{s_2^2}$$

where s_1^2 and s_2^2 represent the sample variances with $s_1^2 \geq s_2^2$. The degrees of freedom for the numerator is d.f.$_N = n_1 - 1$ and the degrees of freedom for the denominator is d.f.$_D = n_2 - 1$, where n_1 is the size of the sample having variance s_1^2 and n_2 is the size of the sample having variance s_2^2.

GUIDELINES

Using a Two-Sample *F*-Test to Compare σ_1^2 and σ_2^2

In Words	*In Symbols*
1. Identify the claim. State the null and alternative hypotheses.	State H_0 and H_a.
2. Specify the level of significance.	Identify α.
3. Identify the degrees of freedom.	d.f.$_N = n_1 - 1$ d.f.$_D = n_2 - 1$
4. Determine the critical value.	Use Table 7 in Appendix B.
5. Determine the rejection region.	
6. Calculate the test statistic.	$F = \dfrac{s_1^2}{s_2^2}$
7. Make a decision to reject or fail to reject the null hypothesis.	If F is in the rejection region, reject H_0. Otherwise, fail to reject H_0.
8. Interpret the decision in the context of the original claim.	

Does location have an effect on the variance of real estate selling prices? A random sample of selling prices (in thousands of dollars) of condominiums sold in south Florida is shown in the table. The first column represents the selling prices of condominiums in Miami, and the second column lists the selling prices of condominiums in Fort Lauderdale. (Adapted from Florida Association of Realtors and the University of Florida Real Estate Research Center)

Miami	Fort Lauderdale
265.0	199.0
272.0	215.9
271.0	210.2
255.9	198.6
250.5	195.0
315.0	195.0
295.0	185.7
275.0	190.0
260.0	197.0
258.9	201.0

Assuming the population of selling prices is normally distributed, is it possible to use a two-sample F-test to compare the population variances?

Normal solution	Treated solution
$n = 25$	$n = 20$
$s^2 = 180$	$s^2 = 56$

EXAMPLE 3

Performing a Two-Sample *F*-Test

A restaurant manager is designing a system that is intended to decrease the variance of the time customers wait before their meals are served. Under the old system, a random sample of 10 customers had a variance of 400. Under the new system, a random sample of 21 customers had a variance of 256. At $\alpha = 0.10$, is there enough evidence to convince the manager to switch to the new system? Assume both populations are normally distributed.

Solution   Because $400 > 256$, $s_1^2 = 400$, and $s_2^2 = 256$. Therefore, s_1^2 and σ_1^2 represent the sample and population variances for the old system, respectively. With the claim "the variance of the waiting times under the new system is less than the variance of the waiting times under the old system," the null and alternative hypotheses are

$$H_0: \sigma_1^2 \leq \sigma_2^2 \quad \text{and} \quad H_a: \sigma_1^2 > \sigma_2^2. \text{ (Claim)}$$

Because the test is a right-tailed test with $\alpha = 0.10$, d.f.$_N = n_1 - 1 = 10 - 1 = 9$, and d.f.$_D = n_2 - 1 = 21 - 1 = 20$, the critical value is $F_0 = 1.96$. With the F-test, the test statistic is

$$F = \frac{s_1^2}{s_2^2} = \frac{400}{256} \approx 1.56.$$

The graph shows the location of the rejection region and the test statistic. Because F is not in the rejection region, you should fail to reject the null hypothesis.

Interpretation   There is not enough evidence to convince the manager to switch to the new system.

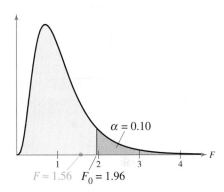

$F \approx 1.56 \quad F_0 = 1.96$

▶ Try It Yourself 3

A medical researcher claims that a specially treated intravenous solution decreases the variance of the time required for nutrients to enter the bloodstream. Independent samples from each type of solution are randomly selected, and the results are shown in the table at the left. At $\alpha = 0.01$, is there enough evidence to support the researcher's claim? Assume the populations are normally distributed.

a. *Identify* the claim and state H_0 and H_a.
b. *Specify* the level of significance α.
c. *Identify* the degrees of freedom for the numerator and for the denominator.
d. *Determine* the critical value and the rejection region.
e. Use the F-test to *calculate the test statistic F.*
f. *Decide* whether to reject the null hypothesis. Use a graph if necessary.
g. *Interpret* the decision in the context of the original claim.

Answer: Page A48

Stock A	Stock B
$n_2 = 30$	$n_1 = 31$
$s_2 = 3.5$	$s_1 = 5.7$

```
2-SampFTest
 σ1≠σ2
 F=2.652244898
 p=.0102172459
 Sx1=5.7
 Sx2=3.5
↓n1=31
```

Using a TI-83/84, you can find the test statistic *F* in Example 4 automatically. Notice that you can also use the *P*-value shown to perform the two-sample *F*-test. The *P*-value above is about 0.0102. Because 0.0102 < 0.05, you should decide to reject the null hypothesis.

Location A	Location B
$n = 16$	$n = 22$
$s = 0.95$	$s = 0.78$

Performing a Two-Sample *F*-Test

You want to purchase stock in a company and are deciding between two different stocks. Because a stock's risk can be associated with the standard deviation of its daily closing prices, you randomly select samples of the daily closing prices for each stock to obtain the results shown at the left. At $\alpha = 0.05$, can you conclude that one of the two stocks is a riskier investment? Assume the stock closing prices are normally distributed.

Solution Because $5.7^2 > 3.5^2$, $s_1^2 = 5.7^2$, and $s_2^2 = 3.5^2$. Therefore, s_1^2 and σ_1^2 represent the sample and population variances for Stock B, respectively. With the claim "one of the stocks is a riskier investment," the null and alternative hypotheses are

$$H_0: \sigma_1^2 = \sigma_2^2 \quad \text{and} \quad H_a: \sigma_1^2 \neq \sigma_2^2. \text{ (Claim)}$$

Because the test is a two-tailed test with $\frac{1}{2}\alpha = \frac{1}{2}(0.05) = 0.025$, d.f.$_N = n_1 - 1 = 31 - 1 = 30$, and d.f.$_D = n_2 - 1 = 30 - 1 = 29$, the critical value is $F_0 = 2.09$. With the *F*-test, the test statistic is

$$F = \frac{s_1^2}{s_2^2}$$

$$= \frac{5.7^2}{3.5^2} \quad \text{Square sample standard deviations to obtain sample variances.}$$

$$\approx 2.65.$$

The graph shows the location of the rejection region and the test statistic. Because *F* is in the rejection region, you should reject the null hypothesis.

Interpretation There is enough evidence to support the claim that one of the two stocks is a riskier investment.

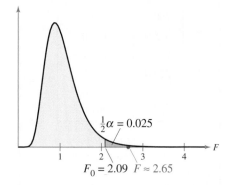

▶ Try It Yourself 4

A biologist claims that the pH levels of the soil in two geographic locations have equal standard deviations. Independent samples from each location are randomly selected, and the results are shown at the left. At $\alpha = 0.01$, is there enough evidence to reject the biologist's claim? Assume the pH levels are normally distributed.

a. *Identify* the claim and state H_0 and H_a.
b. *Specify* the level of significance α.
c. *Identify* the degrees of freedom for the numerator and for the denominator.
d. *Determine* the critical value and the rejection region.
e. Use the *F*-test to *calculate the test statistic F*.
f. *Decide* whether to reject the null hypothesis. Use a graph if necessary.
g. *Interpret* the decision in the context of the original claim.

Answer: Page A48

10.3 EXERCISES

■ Building Basic Skills and Vocabulary

1. Explain how to find the critical value for an *F*-test.

2. List five properties of the *F*-distribution.

3. List the three conditions that must be met in order to use a two-sample *F*-test.

4. Explain how to determine the values of d.f.$_N$ and d.f.$_D$ when performing a two-sample *F*-test.

In Exercises 5–10, find the critical F-value for a right-tailed test using the indicated level of significance α and degrees of freedom d.f.$_N$ and d.f.$_D$.

5. $\alpha = 0.05$, d.f.$_N = 9$, d.f.$_D = 16$

6. $\alpha = 0.01$, d.f.$_N = 2$, d.f.$_D = 24$

7. $\alpha = 0.01$, d.f.$_N = 5$, d.f.$_D = 13$

8. $\alpha = 0.05$, d.f.$_N = 6$, d.f.$_D = 19$

9. $\alpha = 0.10$, d.f.$_N = 10$, d.f.$_D = 15$

10. $\alpha = 0.025$, d.f.$_N = 7$, d.f.$_D = 3$

In Exercises 11–16, test the claim about the differences between two population variances σ_1^2 and σ_2^2 at the given level of significance α using the given sample statistics. Assume the sample statistics are from independent samples that are randomly selected and each population has a normal distribution.

11. Claim: $\sigma_1^2 > \sigma_2^2$, $\alpha = 0.10$.
Sample statistics: $s_1^2 = 773$,
$n_1 = 5$; $s_2^2 = 765$, $n_2 = 6$

12. Claim: $\sigma_1^2 = \sigma_2^2$, $\alpha = 0.05$.
Sample statistics: $s_1^2 = 310$,
$n_1 = 7$; $s_2^2 = 297$, $n_2 = 8$

13. Claim: $\sigma_1^2 \leq \sigma_2^2$, $\alpha = 0.01$.
Sample statistics: $s_1^2 = 842$,
$n_1 = 11$; $s_2^2 = 836$, $n_2 = 10$

14. Claim: $\sigma_1^2 \neq \sigma_2^2$, $\alpha = 0.05$.
Sample statistics: $s_1^2 = 245$,
$n_1 = 31$; $s_2^2 = 112$, $n_2 = 28$

15. Claim: $\sigma_1^2 = \sigma_2^2$, $\alpha = 0.01$.
Sample statistics: $s_1^2 = 9.8$,
$n_1 = 13$; $s_2^2 = 2.5$, $n_2 = 20$

16. Claim: $\sigma_1^2 > \sigma_2^2$, $\alpha = 0.05$.
Sample statistics: $s_1^2 = 44.6$,
$n_1 = 16$; $s_2^2 = 39.3$, $n_2 = 12$

■ Using and Interpreting Concepts

Comparing Two Variances *In Exercises 17–24, (a) identify the claim and state H_0 and H_a, (b) determine the critical value and the rejection region, (c) calculate the test statistic, (d) decide whether to reject or fail to reject the null hypothesis, and (e) interpret the decision in the context of the original claim. If convenient, use technology to solve the problem. In each exercise, assume the samples are independent and each population has a normal distribution.*

17. Life of Appliances Company A claims that the variance of the life of its appliances is less than the variance of the life of Company B's appliances. A random sample of the lives of 20 of Company A's appliances has a variance of 2.6. A random sample of the lives of 25 of Company B's appliances has a variance of 2.8. At $\alpha = 0.05$, can you support Company A's claim?

18. Fuel Consumption An automobile manufacturer claims that the variance of the fuel consumption for its hybrid vehicles is less than the variance of the fuel consumption for the hybrid vehicles of a top competitor. A random sample of the fuel consumption of 19 of the manufacturer's hybrids has a variance of 16.2. A random sample of the fuel consumption of 21 of its competitor's hybrids has a variance of 32.5. At $\alpha = 0.05$, can you support the manufacturer's claim? *(Adapted from GreenHybrid)*

19. Science Assessment Tests In a recent interview, a state school administrator stated that the standard deviations of science assessment test scores for eighth grade students are the same in Districts 1 and 2. A random sample of 12 test scores from District 1 has a standard deviation of 36.8 points and a random sample of 14 test scores from District 2 has a standard deviation of 32.5 points. Can you reject the administrator's claim? Use $\alpha = 0.10$. *(Adapted from National Center for Educational Statistics)*

20. U.S. History Assessment Tests A school administrator reports that the standard deviations of U.S. history assessment test scores for eighth grade students are the same in Districts 1 and 2. As proof, the administrator gives the results of a study of test scores in each district. The study shows that a random sample of 10 test scores from District 1 has a standard deviation of 33.9 points and a random sample of 13 test scores from District 2 has a standard deviation of 30.2 points. At $\alpha = 0.01$, can you reject the administrator's claim? *(Adapted from National Center for Educational Statistics)*

21. Waiting Times A random sample of 25 waiting times (in minutes) before patients saw a medical professional in a hospital's minor emergency department had a standard deviation of 0.7 minute. After a new admissions procedure was implemented, a random sample of 21 waiting times had a standard deviation of 0.5 minute. At $\alpha = 0.10$, can you support the hospital's claim that the standard deviation of the waiting times has decreased?

22. Room Rates A travel agency's marketing brochure indicates that the standard deviations of hotel room rates for two cities are the same. A random sample of 31 hotel room rates in one city has a standard deviation of $39.50 and a random sample of 28 hotel room rates in the other city has a standard deviation of $23.75. Can you reject the agency's claim? Use $\alpha = 0.01$.

23. Annual Salaries The annual salaries for a random sample of 16 actuaries working in New York have a standard deviation of $14,900. The annual salaries for a random sample of 17 actuaries working in California have a standard deviation of $9600. Using this information, can you conclude that the standard deviation of the annual salaries for actuaries is greater in New York than in California? Use $\alpha = 0.05$. *(Adapted from America's Career InfoNet)*

Actuaries in New York	Actuaries in California	Public relations managers in Florida	Public relations managers in Louisiana
$s_1 = \$14,900$	$s_2 = \$9600$	$s_1 = \$10,100$	$s_2 = \$6400$
$n_1 = 16$	$n_2 = 17$	$n_1 = 28$	$n_2 = 24$

FIGURE FOR EXERCISE 23   FIGURE FOR EXERCISE 24

24. Annual Salaries An employment information service claims the standard deviation of the annual salaries for public relations managers is greater in Florida than in Louisiana. The annual salaries for a random sample of 28 public relations managers in Florida have a standard deviation of $10,100. The annual salaries for a random sample of 24 public relations managers in Louisiana have a standard deviation of $6400. At $\alpha = 0.05$, can you support the service's claim? *(Adapted from America's Career InfoNet)*

■ Extending Concepts

Finding Left-Tailed Critical *F*-values   *In this section you learned that if s_1^2 is larger than s_2^2, then you only need to calculate the right-tailed critical F-value for a two-tailed test. For other applications of the F-distribution, you will need to calculate the left-tailed critical F-value. To calculate the left-tailed critical F-value, do the following.*

(1) Interchange the values for $d.f._N$ and $d.f._D$.

(2) Find the corresponding F-value in Table 7.

(3) Calculate the reciprocal of the F-value to obtain the left-tailed critical F-value.

In Exercises 25 and 26, find the right- and left-tailed critical F-values for a two-tailed test with the given values of α, $d.f._N$, and $d.f._D$.

25. $\alpha = 0.05$, d.f.$_N$ = 6, d.f.$_D$ = 3   **26.** $\alpha = 0.10$, d.f.$_N$ = 20, d.f.$_D$ = 15

Confidence Interval for σ_1^2/σ_2^2   *When s_1^2 and s_2^2 are the variances of randomly selected, independent samples from normally distributed populations, then a confidence interval for σ_1^2/σ_2^2 is*

$$\frac{s_1^2}{s_2^2}F_L < \frac{\sigma_1^2}{\sigma_1^2} < \frac{s_1^2}{s_2^2}F_R$$

where F_L is the left-tailed critical F-value and F_R is the right-tailed critical F-value.

In Exercises 27 and 28, construct the indicated confidence interval for σ_1^2/σ_2^2. Assume the samples are independent and each population has a normal distribution.

27. Cholesterol Content   In a recent study of the cholesterol content in grilled chicken sandwiches served at fast-food restaurants, a nutritionist found that a random sample of sandwiches from Burger King and from McDonald's had the sample statistics shown in the table. Construct a 95% confidence interval for σ_1^2/σ_2^2, where σ_1^2 and σ_2^2 are the variances of the cholesterol content of grilled chicken sandwiches from Burger King and McDonald's, respectively. *(Adapted from Burger King Brands, Inc. and McDonald's Corporation)*

Cholesterol content for grilled chicken sandwiches		
Restaurant	Burger King	McDonald's
Sample variance	$s_1^2 = 10.89$	$s_2^2 = 9.61$
Sample size	$n_1 = 16$	$n_2 = 12$

Table for Exercise 27

Carbohydrate content for grilled chicken sandwiches		
Restaurant	Burger King	McDonald's
Sample variance	$s_1^2 = 5.29$	$s_2^2 = 3.61$
Sample size	$n_1 = 16$	$n_2 = 12$

Table for Exercise 28

28. Carbohyrate Content   A fast-food study found that the carbohydrate content of 15 randomly selected grilled chicken sandwiches from Burger King had a variance of 5.29. The study also found that the carbohydrate content of 12 randomly selected grilled chicken sandwiches from McDonald's had a variance of 3.61. Construct a 95% confidence interval for σ_1^2/σ_2^2, where σ_1^2 and σ_2^2 are the variances of the carbohydrate content of grilled chicken sandwiches from Burger King and McDonald's, respectively. *(Adapted from Burger King Brands, Inc. and McDonald's Corporation)*

10.4 Analysis of Variance

What You SHOULD LEARN

▸ How to use one-way analysis of variance to test claims involving three or more means

▸ An introduction to two-way analysis of variance

One-Way ANOVA ▸ Two-Way ANOVA

▸ One-Way ANOVA

Suppose a medical researcher is analyzing the effectiveness of three types of pain relievers and wants to determine whether there is a difference in the mean length of the time it takes each medication to provide relief. To determine whether such a difference exists, the researcher can use the *F*-distribution together with a technique called *analysis of variance*. Because one independent variable is being studied, the process is called *one-way analysis of variance*.

DEFINITION

One-way analysis of variance is a hypothesis-testing technique that is used to compare means from three or more populations. Analysis of variance is usually abbreviated as **ANOVA.**

To begin a one-way analysis of variance test, you should first state a null and an alternative hypothesis. For a one-way ANOVA test, the null and alternative hypotheses are always similar to the following statements.

H_0: $\mu_1 = \mu_2 = \mu_3 = \cdots = \mu_k$ (All population means are equal.)

H_a: At least one of the means is different from the others.

When you reject the null hypothesis in an ANOVA test, you can conclude that at least one of the means is different from the others. Without performing more statistical tests, however, you cannot determine which of the means is different.

In a one-way ANOVA test, the following conditions must be true.

1. Each sample must be randomly selected from a normal, or approximately normal, population.
2. The samples must be independent of each other.
3. Each population must have the same variance.

The test statistic for a one-way ANOVA test is the ratio of two variances: the variance between samples and the variance within samples.

$$\text{Test statistic} = \frac{\text{Variance between samples}}{\text{Variance within samples}}$$

1. The variance between samples MS_B measures the differences related to the treatment given to each sample and is sometimes called the **mean square between.**
2. The variance within samples MS_W measures the differences related to entries within the same sample. This variance, sometimes called the **mean square within,** is usually due to sampling error.

ONE-WAY ANALYSIS OF VARIANCE TEST

If the conditions for a one-way analysis of variance test are satisfied, then the sampling distribution for the test is approximated by the F-distribution. The test statistic is

$$F = \frac{MS_B}{MS_W}.$$

The degrees of freedom for the F-test are

$$\text{d.f.}_N = k - 1$$

and

$$\text{d.f.}_D = N - k$$

where k is the number of samples and N is the sum of the sample sizes.

If there is little or no difference between the means, then MS_B will be approximately equal to MS_W and the test statistic will be approximately 1. Values of F close to 1 suggest that you should fail to reject the null hypothesis. However, if one of the means differs significantly from the others, MS_B will be greater than MS_W and the test statistic will be greater than 1. Values of F significantly greater than 1 suggest that you reject the null hypothesis. As such, all one-way ANOVA tests are right-tailed tests. That is, if the test statistic is greater than the critical value, H_0 will be rejected.

Study Tip

The notations n_i, $\bar{x}_i$, and s_i^2 represent the sample size, mean, and variance of the ith sample, respectively. $\bar{\bar{x}}$ is sometimes called the grand mean.

GUIDELINES

Finding the Test Statistic for a One-Way ANOVA Test

In Words	*In Symbols*
1. Find the mean and variance of each sample.	$\bar{x} = \dfrac{\sum x}{n} \quad s^2 = \dfrac{\sum (x - \bar{x})^2}{n - 1}$
2. Find the mean of all entries in all samples (the grand mean).	$\bar{\bar{x}} = \dfrac{\sum x}{N}$
3. Find the sum of squares between the samples.	$SS_B = \sum n_i \left(\bar{x}_i - \bar{\bar{x}} \right)^2$
4. Find the sum of squares within the samples.	$SS_W = \sum (n_i - 1) s_i^2$
5. Find the variance between the samples.	$MS_B = \dfrac{SS_B}{k - 1} = \dfrac{SS_B}{\text{d.f.}_N}$
6. Find the variance within the samples.	$MS_W = \dfrac{SS_W}{N - k} = \dfrac{SS_W}{\text{d.f.}_D}$
7. Find the test statistic.	$F = \dfrac{MS_B}{MS_W}$

The notation SS_B represents the sum of squares between groups.

$$SS_B = n_1(\overline{x}_1 - \overline{\overline{x}})^2 + n_2(\overline{x}_2 - \overline{\overline{x}})^2 + \cdots + n_k(\overline{x}_k - \overline{\overline{x}})^2$$

$$= \Sigma n_i(\overline{x}_i - \overline{\overline{x}})^2$$

The notation SS_W represents the sum of squares within groups.

$$SS_W = (n_1 - 1)s_1^2 + (n_2 - 1)s_2^2 + \cdots + (n_k - 1)s_k^2$$

$$= \Sigma(n_i - 1)s_i^2$$

GUIDELINES

Performing a One-Way Analysis of Variance Test

In Words	*In Symbols*
1. Identify the claim. State the null and alternative hypotheses.	State H_0 and H_a.
2. Specify the level of significance.	Identify α.
3. Identify the degrees of freedom.	$\text{d.f.}_N = k - 1$ $\text{d.f.}_D = N - k$
4. Determine the critical value.	Use Table 7 in Appendix B.
5. Determine the rejection region.	
6. Calculate the test statistic.	$F = \dfrac{MS_B}{MS_W}$
7. Make a decision to reject or fail to reject the null hypothesis.	If *F* is in the rejection region, reject H_0. Otherwise, fail to reject H_0.
8. Interpret the decision in the context of the original claim.	

Tables are a convenient way to summarize the results of a one-way analysis of variance test. ANOVA summary tables are set up as shown below.

ANOVA Summary Table

Variation	Sum of squares	Degrees of freedom	Mean squares	F
Between	SS_B	d.f._N	$MS_B = \dfrac{SS_B}{\text{d.f.}_N}$	$\dfrac{MS_B}{MS_W}$
Within	SS_W	d.f._D	$MS_W = \dfrac{SS_W}{\text{d.f.}_D}$	

EXAMPLE 1

Performing a One-Way ANOVA Test

A medical researcher wants to determine whether there is a difference in the mean length of time it takes three types of pain relievers to provide relief from headache pain. Several headache sufferers are randomly selected and given one of the three medications. Each headache sufferer records the time (in minutes) it takes the medication to begin working. The results are shown in the table. At $\alpha = 0.01$, can you conclude that the mean times are different? Assume that each population of relief times is normally distributed and that the population variances are equal.

Medication 1	Medication 2	Medication 3
12	16	14
15	14	17
17	21	20
12	15	15
	19	
$\overline{x}_1 = \frac{56}{4} = 14$	$\overline{x}_2 = \frac{85}{5} = 17$	$\overline{x}_3 = \frac{66}{4} = 16.5$
$s_1^2 = 6$	$s_2^2 = 8.5$	$s_3^2 = 7$

Solution   The null and alternative hypotheses are as follows.

H_0: $\mu_1 = \mu_2 = \mu_3$

H_a: At least one mean is different from the others. (Claim)

Because there are $k = 3$ samples, $\text{d.f.}_N = k - 1 = 3 - 1 = 2$. The sum of the sample sizes is $N = n_1 + n_2 + n_3 = 4 + 5 + 4 = 13$. So, $\text{d.f.}_D = N - k = 13 - 3 = 10$. Using $\text{d.f.}_N = 2$, $\text{d.f.}_D = 10$, and $\alpha = 0.01$, the critical value is $F_0 = 7.56$. To find the test statistic, first calculate $\overline{\overline{x}}$, MS_B, and MS_W.

$$\overline{\overline{x}} = \frac{\sum x}{N} = \frac{56 + 85 + 66}{13} \approx 15.92$$

$$MS_B = \frac{SS_B}{\text{d.f.}_N} = \frac{\sum n_i (\overline{x}_i - \overline{\overline{x}})^2}{k - 1}$$

$$\approx \frac{4(14 - 15.92)^2 + 5(17 - 15.92)^2 + 4(16.5 - 15.92)^2}{3 - 1}$$

$$\approx \frac{21.92}{2} = 10.96$$

$$MS_W = \frac{SS_W}{\text{d.f.}_D} = \frac{\sum (n_i - 1)s_i^2}{N - k}$$

$$= \frac{(4 - 1)(6) + (5 - 1)(8.5) + (4 - 1)(7)}{13 - 3} = \frac{73}{10} = 7.3$$

Using $MS_B = 10.96$ and $MS_W = 7.3$, the test statistic is

$$F = \frac{MS_B}{MS_W} = \frac{10.96}{7.3} \approx 1.50.$$

PICTURING the WORLD

Adult common cuckoos do not care for their own eggs. Cuckoos lay their eggs in the nests of other birds, such as sparrows, robins, and wrens. These birds adopt the cuckoo eggs, hatching and caring for the eggs along with their own. A biologist is studying the lengths of cuckoo eggs found in sparrow, robin, and wren nests. The randomly selected egg lengths (in millimeters) are shown in the table.

Host nest		
Sparrow	**Robin**	**Wren**
24.08	22.66	20.89
22.95	22.51	20.97
22.82	21.44	22.31
23.98	22.70	21.54
24.59	22.15	20.19
22.95	22.75	21.38
25.16	23.02	20.50
23.39	21.72	20.99
23.74	21.49	20.83
21.15	22.15	20.74
23.81	22.15	21.40
22.40	22.28	21.90
24.17	22.98	

At $\alpha = 0.05$, can you conclude that the mean length of the cuckoo eggs found in one type of nest is different from the others? Assume that each population of cuckoo egg lengths is normally distributed and that the population variances are equal.

The graph shows the location of the rejection region and the test statistic. Because *F* is not in the rejection region, you should fail to reject the null hypothesis.

Interpretation There is not enough evidence at the 1% significance level to conclude that there is a difference in the mean length of time it takes the three pain relievers to provide relief from headache pain.

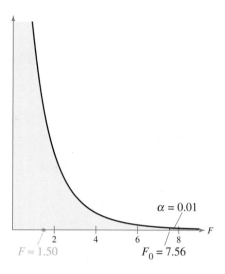

The ANOVA summary table for Example 1 is shown below.

Variation	Sum of squares	Degrees of freedom	Mean squares	F
Between	21.92	2	10.96	1.50
Within	73	10	7.3	

▶ Try It Yourself 1

A sales analyst wants to determine whether there is a difference in the mean monthly sales of a company's four sales regions. Several salespersons from each region are randomly selected and each provides his or her sales amounts (in thousands of dollars) for the previous month. The results are shown in the table. At $\alpha = 0.05$, can the analyst conclude that there is a difference in the mean monthly sales among the sales regions? Assume that each population of sales is normally distributed and that the population variances are equal.

North	East	South	West
34	47	40	21
28	36	30	30
18	30	41	24
24	38	29	37
	44		23
$\bar{x}_1 = 26$	$\bar{x}_2 = 39$	$\bar{x}_3 = 35$	$\bar{x}_4 = 27$
$s_1^2 \approx 45.33$	$s_2^2 = 45$	$s_3^2 \approx 40.67$	$s_4^2 = 42.5$

a. *State* H_0 and H_a.
b. *Specify* the level of significance α.
c. *Identify* the degrees of freedom for the numerator and for the denominator.
d. *Determine* the critical value and the rejection region.
e. *Calculate* the test statistic *F*.
f. *Decide* whether to reject the null hypothesis. Use a graph if necessary.
g. *Interpret* the decision in the context of the original claim.

Answer: Page A48

Using technology greatly simplifies the one-way ANOVA process. When using a technology tool such as Excel, MINITAB, or the TI-83/84 to perform a one-way analysis of variance test, you can use P-values to decide whether to reject the null hypothesis. If the P-value is less than α, you should reject H_0.

Airline 1	Airline 2	Airline 3
122	119	120
135	133	158
126	143	155
131	149	126
125	114	147
116	124	164
120	126	134
108	131	151
142	140	131
113	136	141

EXAMPLE 2

Using Technology to Perform ANOVA Tests

Three airline companies offer flights between Corydon and Lincolnville. Several randomly selected flight times (in minutes) between the towns for each airline are shown at the left. Assume that the populations of flight times are normally distributed, the samples are independent, and the population variances are equal. At $\alpha = 0.01$, can you conclude that there is a difference in the means of the flight times? Use a technology tool.

Solution   The null and alternative hypotheses are as follows.

H_0: $\mu_1 = \mu_2 = \mu_3$

H_a: At least one mean is different from the others. (Claim)

The results obtained by performing the test on a TI-83/84 are shown below. From the results, you can see that $P \approx 0.006$. Because $P < \alpha$, you should reject the null hypothesis.

TI-83/84

```
One-way ANOVA
 F=6.13023478
 p=.0063828069
 Factor
  df=2
  SS=1806.46667
↓ MS=903.233333
```

TI-83/84

```
One-way ANOVA
↑ MS=903.233333
 Error
  df=27
  SS=3978.2
  MS=147.340741
  Sxp=12.1383994
```

Interpretation   There is enough evidence to support the claim. So, you can conclude that there is a difference in the means of the flight times.

▶ Try It Yourself 2

The data shown in the table represent the GPAs of randomly selected freshmen, sophomores, juniors, and seniors. At $\alpha = 0.05$, can you conclude that there is a difference in the means of the GPAs? Assume that the populations of GPAs are normally distributed and that the population variances are equal. Use a technology tool.

Freshmen	2.34	2.38	3.31	2.39	3.40	2.70	2.34			
Sophomores	3.26	2.22	3.26	3.29	2.95	3.01	3.13	3.59	2.84	3.00
Juniors	2.80	2.60	2.49	2.83	2.34	3.23	3.49	3.03	2.87	
Seniors	3.31	2.35	3.27	2.86	2.78	2.75	3.05	3.31		

a. *Enter* the data.
b. *Perform* the ANOVA test.
c. *Compare* the resulting P-value to the given level of significance α.
d. *Interpret* the results.   *Answer: Page A48*

Study Tip

Here are instructions for performing a one-way analysis of variance test on a TI-83/84. Begin by storing the data into List 1, List 2, and so on, depending on the data.

STAT

Choose the TESTS menu.

F: ANOVA(

Then enter L1, L2, and so on, separated by commas.

▶ Two-Way ANOVA

When you want to test the effect of *two* independent variables, or factors, on one dependent variable, you can use a **two-way analysis of variance test.** For example, suppose a medical researcher wants to test the effect of gender *and* type of medication on the mean length of time it takes pain relievers to provide relief. To perform such an experiment, the researcher can use the following two-way ANOVA block design.

A two-way ANOVA test has three null hypotheses—one for each main effect and one for the interaction effect. A **main effect** is the effect of one independent variable on the dependent variable, and the **interaction effect** is the effect of both independent variables on the dependent variable. For example, the hypotheses for the pain reliever experiment are as follows.

Hypotheses for main effects:

H_0: Gender has no effect on the mean length of time it takes a pain reliever to provide relief.

H_a: Gender has an effect on the mean length of time it takes a pain reliever to provide relief.

H_0: The type of medication has no effect on the mean length of time it takes a pain reliever to provide relief.

H_a: The type of medication has an effect on the mean length of time it takes a pain reliever to provide relief.

Hypotheses for interaction effect:

H_0: There is no interaction effect between gender and type of medication on the mean length of time it takes a pain reliever to provide relief.

H_a: There is an interaction effect between gender and type of medication on the mean length of time it takes a pain reliever to provide relief.

To test these hypotheses, you can perform a two-way ANOVA test. Using the *F*-distribution, a two-way ANOVA test calculates an *F*-test statistic for each hypothesis. As a result, it is possible to reject none, one, two, or all of the null hypotheses. The statistics involved with a two-way ANOVA test is beyond the scope of this course. You can, however, use a technology tool such as MINITAB to perform a two-way ANOVA test.

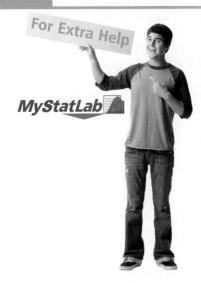

10.4 EXERCISES

■ Building Basic Skills and Vocabulary

1. State a null and alternative hypothesis for a one-way ANOVA test.

2. What conditions are necessary in order to use a one-way ANOVA test?

3. Describe the difference between the variance between samples MS_B and the variance within samples MS_W.

4. Describe the hypotheses for a two-way ANOVA test.

■ Using and Interpreting Concepts

Performing a One-Way ANOVA Test *In Exercises 5–16, perform the indicated one-way ANOVA test by*

(a) identifying the claim and stating H_0 and H_a.

(b) identifying the degrees of freedom for the numerator and for the denominator, determining the critical value, and determining the rejection region.

(c) calculating the test statistic.

(d) deciding to reject or fail to reject the null hypothesis and interpreting the decision in the context of the original claim.

Assume that each sample is drawn from a normal, or approximately normal, population, that the samples are independent of each other, and that the populations have the same variances. If convenient, use technology to solve the problem.

5. **Toothpaste** The table shows the cost per ounce (in dollars) for a random sample of toothpastes exhibiting very good stain removal, good stain removal, and fair stain removal. At $\alpha = 0.05$, can you conclude that the mean costs per ounce are different?
(Source: Consumer Reports)

Very good stain removal	Good stain removal	Fair stain removal
0.47	0.60	0.34
0.49	0.64	0.46
0.33	1.05	1.31
1.52	2.73	0.44
0.64	0.58	0.60
0.36	0.75	
0.41	0.22	
0.37	0.33	
0.48	0.42	
0.50	0.46	
0.51	0.98	
0.35	1.16	

6. **Automobile Batteries** The prices (in dollars) for 17 randomly selected automobile batteries are shown in the table. The prices are classified according to battery type. At $\alpha = 0.05$, is there enough evidence to conclude that at least one of the mean battery prices is different from the others?
(Source: Consumer Reports)

Group size 35	60	60	90	50	80	
Group size 65	80	60	60	90	45	85
Group size 34/78	60	100	90	70	90	60

7. **Exterior Deck Treatments** The table shows the price per gallon (in dollars) for a random sample of exterior deck treatments. At $\alpha = 0.10$, can you reject the claim that the mean price is the same for the three types of treatments? *(Source: Consumer Reports)*

Semitransparent treatments	Lightly tinted treatments	Clear treatments
24	51	13
23	14	13
22	21	10
17	16	12
21		22
17		

8. **Reading Expenditures** The table shows the annual amount spent on reading (in dollars) for a random sample of consumers from four regions of the United States. At $\alpha = 0.10$, can you reject the claim that the mean annual amount is the same in all regions? *(Adapted from U.S. Bureau of Labor Statistics)*

Northeast	Midwest	South	West
228	219	65	163
38	142	105	124
111	219	126	161
79	131	81	209
186	140	61	139
114	49	176	111
263		70	144

9. **Days Spent at a Hospital** In a recent study, a health insurance company investigated the number of days patients spend at a hospital. In part of the study, the company randomly selected patients from various parts of the United States and recorded the number of days each patient spent at a hospital. The results of the study are shown in the table. At $\alpha = 0.01$, can the company reject the claim that the mean number of days patients spend in the hospital is the same for all four regions? *(Adapted from U.S. National Center for Health Statistics)*

Northeast	Midwest	South	West
6	6	3	3
4	6	5	4
7	7	6	6
2	3	6	4
3	5	3	6
4	4	7	6
6	4	4	5
8	3		2
9	2		

10. Building Space   The table shows the square footage (in thousands) for a random sample of buildings from four regions of the United States. At $\alpha = 0.10$, can you conclude that the mean square footage for at least one of the regions is different from the others? *(Adapted from U.S. Energy Information Administration)*

Northeast	Midwest	South	West
16.1	12.3	13.1	14.1
20.2	13.5	15.4	16.1
17.9	7.2	11.6	12.5
13.9	12.7	5.1	11.5
26.8	14.2	15.6	12.6
14.4	16.4	16.0	17.1
20.3	5.7	12.2	6.6
12.2	17.1	7.6	21.1
10.9	20.7	24.5	8.1
19.3	15.5	7.6	3.9
19.6	13.3	11.8	16.4
18.5	9.8	14.4	15.7
21.6	17.1	15.2	12.1
		13.6	12.9

11. Housing Prices   A realtor is comparing the prices of one-family houses in four cities. After randomly selecting one-family houses in the four cities and determining the price for each, the realtor organizes the prices (in thousands of dollars) in a table as shown to the right. At $\alpha = 0.10$, can the realtor reject the claim that the mean price is the same for all four cities? *(Adapted from National Association of Realtors)*

City A	City B	City C	City D
207.0	257.9	253.9	200.9
179.5	215.1	138.9	215.3
224.6	199.3	234.2	285.9
220.3	201.5	198.1	210.7
282.7	221.9	226.7	321.3
240.4	248.8	173.1	202.1
120.8	267.2	190.0	217.4
238.6	158.7	188.9	328.7
208.5	177.9	157.3	257.1
254.0	187.3	237.4	284.0
207.0		128.7	201.3
		239.4	

12. Personal Income   The table shows the salaries of randomly selected individuals from four large metropolitan areas. At $\alpha = 0.05$, can you conclude that the mean salary is different in at least one of the areas? *(Adapted from U.S. Bureau of Economic Analysis)*

Pittsburgh	Dallas	Chicago	Minneapolis
34,300	34,955	36,800	37,720
34,500	38,850	40,600	47,450
32,000	34,700	32,800	42,400
35,650	29,950	43,700	40,250
36,795	39,005	32,045	37,215

13. Mobile Home Prices The table shows the prices (in dollars) for a random sample of new mobile homes from four manufacturers. At $\alpha = 0.05$, can you conclude that at least one of the mean prices is different from the others? *(Adapted from U.S. Census Bureau)*

Manufacturer A	Manufacturer B	Manufacturer C	Manufacturer D
60,424	58,123	62,849	75,876
60,305	59,049	62,531	85,544
59,571	56,625	45,584	75,634
65,204	60,420	52,656	74,385
83,500	55,732	59,335	78,020
58,510	72,117	49,005	87,541
70,549	61,630	59,611	
73,873		56,427	
		51,538	

14. Energy Consumption The table shows the energy consumed (in millions of Btu) in one year for a random sample of households from four regions of the United States. At $\alpha = 0.10$ can you conclude that the mean energy consumption for at least one region is different from the others? *(Adapted from U.S. Energy Information Administration)*

Northeast	Midwest	South	West
85.5	59.7	59.3	24.0
93.5	177.8	71.4	39.2
137.6	64.6	95.4	120.7
113.0	82.3	99.2	54.4
144.3	163.9	59.6	101.4
98.6	182.9	53.9	62.8
69.2	101.6	65.8	37.5
157.0	135.1	53.2	117.8
57.6	92.5	184.6	91.6
	158.5		51.3
	64.9		

15. Sports Team Involvement The table shows the number of female students who played on a sports team in grades 9 through 12 for a random sample of 8 high schools in a state. At $\alpha = 0.01$, can you reject the claim that the mean numbers of female students who played on a sports team are equal for all grades?

Grade 9	82	91	53	133	64	112	63	77
Grade 10	77	87	58	125	51	106	58	72
Grade 11	86	81	46	115	56	87	62	80
Grade 12	65	77	42	102	49	84	65	82

16. Amount Spent on Energy The table shows the amount spent (in dollars) on energy in one year for a random sample of households from four regions of the United States. At $\alpha = 0.01$, can you reject the claim that the mean amounts spent are equal for all regions? *(Adapted from U.S. Energy Information Administration)*

Northeast	Midwest	South	West
2826	1695	1227	840
776	1325	1972	1694
2345	1727	1653	1599
1349	1679	1080	661
1056	1575	1646	1002
1276	1899	1348	856
2396	1074	1750	1491
2343	1410		
1029	1485		
2745			
1004			

■ Extending Concepts

Using Technology to Perform a Two-Way ANOVA Test *In Exercises 17–20, use a technology tool and the given block design to perform a two-way ANOVA test. Use $\alpha = 0.10$. Interpret the results.*

17. Advertising A study was conducted in which a random sample of 20 adults was asked to rate the effectiveness of advertisements. Each adult rated a radio or television advertisement that lasted 30 or 60 seconds. The block design shows these ratings (on a scale of 1 to 5, with 5 being extremely effective).

Advertising medium

Length of ad	Radio	Television
30 sec	2, 3, 5, 1, 3	3, 5, 4, 1, 2
60 sec	1, 4, 2, 2, 5	2, 5, 3, 4, 4

18. Vehicle Sales The owner of a car dealership wants to determine if the gender of a salesperson and the type of vehicle sold affect the number of vehicles sold in a month. The block design shows the number of vehicles, listed by type, sold in a month by a random sample of eight salespeople.

Type of vehicle

Gender	Car	Truck	Van/SUV
Male	6, 5, 4, 5	2, 2, 1, 3	4, 3, 4, 2
Female	5, 7, 8, 7	1, 0, 1, 2	4, 2, 0, 1

19. Grade Point Average A study was conducted in which a random sample of 24 high school students was asked to give their grade point average (GPA). The block design shows the GPAs of male and female students from four different age groups.

Age

Gender	Under 15	15–16	17–18	Over 18
Male	2.5, 2.1, 3.8	4.0, 1.4, 2.0	3.5, 2.2, 2.0	3.1, 0.7, 2.8
Female	4.0, 2.1, 1.9	3.5, 3.0, 2.1	4.0, 2.2, 1.7	1.6, 2.5, 3.6

20. Disk Drive Repairs The manager of a computer repair service wants to determine whether there is a difference in the time it takes four technicians to repair different brands of disk drives. The block design shows the times (in minutes) it took for each technician to repair three disk drives of each brand.

Technician

Brand	Technician 1	Technician 2	Technician 3	Technician 4
Brand A	67, 82, 64	42, 56, 39	69, 47, 38	70, 44, 50
Brand B	44, 62, 55	47, 58, 62	55, 45, 66	47, 29, 40
Brand C	47, 36, 68	39, 74, 51	74, 80, 70	45, 62, 59

The Scheffé Test *If the null hypothesis is rejected in a one-way ANOVA test of three or more means, a **Scheffé Test** can be performed to find which means have a significant difference. In a Scheffé Test, the means are compared two at a time. For example, with three means you would have the following comparisons: $\overline{x}_1$ versus $\overline{x}_2$, $\overline{x}_1$ versus $\overline{x}_3$, and $\overline{x}_2$ versus $\overline{x}_3$. For each comparison, calculate*

$$\frac{(\overline{x}_a - \overline{x}_b)^2}{\dfrac{SS_w}{\Sigma(n_i - 1)}[(1/n_a) + (1/n_b)]}$$

where $\overline{x}_a$ and $\overline{x}_b$ are the means being compared and n_a and n_b are the corresponding sample sizes. Calculate the critical value using the same steps as in a one-way ANOVA test and multiply the result by $k - 1$. Then compare the value that is calculated using the formula above with the critical value. The means have a significant difference if the critical value is less than the value calculated using the formula above.

Use the above information to solve Exercises 21–24.

21. Refer to the data in Exercise 10. At $\alpha = 0.10$, perform a Scheffé Test to determine which means have a significant difference.

22. Refer to the data in Exercise 11. At $\alpha = 0.10$, perform a Scheffé Test to determine which means have a significant difference.

23. Refer to the data in Exercise 13. At $\alpha = 0.05$, perform a Scheffé Test to determine which means have a significant difference.

24. Refer to the data in Exercise 14. At $\alpha = 0.10$, perform a Scheffé Test to determine which means have a significant difference.

Uses & Abuses

Uses

One-Way Analysis of Variance (ANOVA) ANOVA can help you make important decisions about the allocation of resources. For instance, suppose you work for a large manufacturing company and part of your responsibility is to determine the distribution of the company's sales throughout the world and decide where to focus the company's efforts. Because wrong decisions will cost your company money, you want to make sure that you make the right decisions.

Abuses

Preconceived Notions There are several ways that the tests presented in this chapter can be abused. For example, it is easy to allow preconceived notions to affect the results of a chi-square goodness-of-fit test and a test for independence. When testing to see whether a distribution has changed, do not let the existing distribution "cloud" the study results. Similarly, when determining whether two variables are independent, do not let your intuition "get in the way." As with any hypothesis test, you must properly gather appropriate data and perform the corresponding test before you can reach a logical conclusion.

Incorrect Interpretation of Rejection of Null Hypothesis It is important to remember that when you reject the null hypothesis of an ANOVA test, you are simply stating that you have enough evidence to determine that at least one of the population means is different from the others. You are not finding them all to be different. One way to further test which of the population means differs from the others is explained in Extending Concepts of Section 10.4 Exercises.

■ EXERCISES

1. ***Preconceived Notions*** ANOVA depends on having independent variables. Describe an abuse that might occur by having dependent variables. Then describe how the abuse could be avoided.

2. ***Incorrect Interpretation of Rejection of Null Hypothesis*** Find an example of the use of ANOVA. In that use, describe what would be meant by "rejection of the null hypothesis." How should rejection of the null hypothesis be correctly interpreted?

10 CHAPTER SUMMARY

What did you learn?

	EXAMPLE(S)	REVIEW EXERCISES
Section 10.1		
■ How to use the chi-square distribution to test whether a frequency distribution fits a claimed distribution	*1–4*	*1–4*
$$\chi^2 = \sum \frac{(O - E)^2}{E}$$		
Section 10.2		
■ How to use a contingency table to find expected frequencies	*1*	*5–8*
$$E_{r,c} = \frac{(\text{Sum of row } r) \times (\text{Sum of column } c)}{\text{Sample size}}$$		
■ How to use a chi-square distribution to test whether two variables are independent	*2, 3*	*5–8*
Section 10.3		
■ How to interpret the *F*-distribution and use an *F*-table to find critical values	*1, 2*	*9–12*
$$F = \frac{s_1^2}{s_2^2}$$		
■ How to perform a two-sample *F*-test to compare two variances	*3, 4*	*13–18*
Section 10.4		
■ How to use one-way analysis of variance to test claims involving three or more means	*1, 2*	*19, 20*
$$F = \frac{MS_B}{MS_W}$$		

10 REVIEW EXERCISES

Section 10.1

In Exercises 1–4, use a χ^2 goodness-of-fit test to test the claim about the population distribution. Interpret the decision in the context of the original claim.

1. A health care investigator wants to test the following claim: Of all people in the United States, 16% had no health care visits in the previous year, 46% had 1 to 3 health care visits in the previous year, 25% had 4 to 9 health care visits in the previous year, and 13% had 10 or more health care visits in the previous year. A random sample of people in the United States finds that 99 people had no health care visits in the previous year, 376 people had 1 to 3 health care visits in the previous year, 167 people had 4 to 9 health care visits in the previous year, and 92 people had 10 or more health care visits in the previous year. Test the claim at $\alpha = 0.05$. *(Adapted from National Center for Health Statistics)*

2. A golf instructor wants to test the following claim: Of all golf students in the United States, 65% need the most help with short-game shots, 22% need the most help with approach and swing, 9% need the most help with driver shots, and 4% need the most help with putting. A random sample of golf students finds that 276 need the most help with short-game shots, 99 need the most help with approach and swing, 42 need the most help with driver shots, and 18 need the most help with putting. Test the claim at $\alpha = 0.10$. *(Source: PGA of America)*

3. A human resources executive believes that the distribution of the percent of adults who plan to use vacation days during the summer is different from the one shown at the left below. The executive randomly selects 800 adults and asks each how many vacation days they plan to use during the summer. The results are shown at the right below. Test the executive's claim at $\alpha = 0.10$. *(Adapted from Harris Interactive)*

Distribution	
0 days	19%
1–5 days	30%
6–10 days	30%
11–15 days	12%
16–20 days	3%
21 or more days	6%

Survey results	
0 days	165
1–5 days	237
6–10 days	245
11–15 days	88
16–20 days	19
21 or more days	46

4. A legal researcher is studying the age distribution of juries by comparing them with the overall age distribution of available jurors. The researcher claims that the jury distribution is different from the overall distribution; that is, there is a noticeable age bias in jury selection in this area. The table shows the number of jurors at a county court in one year and the percent of persons residing in that county, by age. Test the researcher's claim at $\alpha = 0.01$.

	21–29	30–39	40–49	50–59	60 and above
Jury	45	128	244	224	359
Population	20.5%	21.7%	18.1%	17.3%	22.4%

Section 10.2

In Exercises 5–8, use the given contingency table to

(a) find the expected frequencies of each cell in the table.

(b) perform a chi-square test for independence.

(c) comment on the relationship between the two variables.

Assume the variables are independent. If convenient, use technology to solve the problem.

5. The contingency table shows the educational attainment of a random sample of adults in the United States by age in a recent year. Use $\alpha = 0.10$. *(Adapted from the U.S. Census Bureau)*

	H.S.—did not complete	H.S. completed	College 1–3 years	College 4 or more years
25–44	556	1359	1217	1347
45 and older	964	1941	1389	1488

6. The contingency table shows the results of a random sample of individuals by gender and type of vehicle owned. Use $\alpha = 0.05$.

	Type of vehicle owned			
Gender	**Car**	**Truck**	**SUV**	**Van**
Male	85	96	45	6
Female	110	75	60	3

7. The contingency table shows the age distribution of a random sample of fatally injured male and female passenger vehicle drivers whose blood alcohol content was at least 0.08 in a recent year. Use $\alpha = 0.05$. *(Adapted from Insurance Institute for Highway Safety)*

	Age group					
Gender	**16–20**	**21–30**	**31–40**	**41–50**	**51–60**	**61+**
Male	155	280	265	225	155	50
Female	60	145	145	130	65	15

8. The contingency table shows the distribution of a random sample of fatal pedestrian motor vehicle collisions by the time of day and gender in a recent year. Use $\alpha = 0.10$. *(Adapted from National Highway Traffic Safety Administration)*

	Time of day			
Gender	**12 A.M.–5:59 A.M.**	**6 A.M.–11:59 A.M.**	**12 P.M.–5:59 P.M.**	**6 P.M.–11:59 P.M.**
Male	654	591	909	928
Female	255	365	601	505

Section 10.3

In Exercises 9–12, find the critical F-value for a right-tailed test using the indicated level of significance α and degrees of freedom $d.f._N$ and $d.f._D$.

9. $\alpha = 0.05$, $d.f._N = 6$, $d.f._D = 50$ **10.** $\alpha = 0.01$, $d.f._N = 12$, $d.f._D = 10$

11. $\alpha = 0.10$, $d.f._N = 5$, $d.f._D = 12$ **12.** $\alpha = 0.05$, $d.f._N = 20$, $d.f._D = 25$

In Exercises 13 and 14, test the claim about the differences between two population variances σ_1^2 and σ_2^2 at the indicated level of significance α using the given sample statistics. Assume the sample statistics are from independent samples that are randomly selected and each population has a normal distribution.

13. Claim: $\sigma_1^2 \leq \sigma_2^2$, $\alpha = 0.01$. Sample statistics: $s_1^2 = 653$, $n_1 = 16$ and $s_2^2 = 270$, $n_2 = 21$

14. Claim: $\sigma_1^2 \neq \sigma_2^2$, $\alpha = 0.10$. Sample statistics: $s_1^2 = 112{,}676$, $n_1 = 6$ and $s_2^2 = 49{,}572$, $n_2 = 11$

In Exercises 15–18, test the claim about two population variances at the indicated level of significance α. Interpret the results in the context of the claim. If convenient, use technology to solve the problem. In each exercise, assume the samples are independent and each population has a normal distribution.

15. An agricultural analyst is comparing the wheat production in Oklahoma counties. The analyst claims that the variation in wheat production is greater in Garfield County than in Kay County. A random sample of 21 Garfield County farms yields a standard deviation of 0.76 bushel per acre. A random sample of 16 Kay County farms is found to have a standard deviation of 0.58 bushel per acre. Test the analyst's claim at $\alpha = 0.10$. *(Adapted from Environmental Verification and Analysis Center—University of Oklahoma)*

16. A steel pipe fittings company claims that the yield strength of its nontempered couplings is more variable than that of its tempered couplings. A random sample of 9 tempered couplings has a standard deviation of 13.1 megapascals, and a similar sample of 9 nontempered couplings has a standard deviation of 25.4 megapascals. Test the company's claim at $\alpha = 0.05$.

17. The table shows the SAT verbal test scores for 9 randomly selected female students and 14 randomly selected male students. Assume that SAT verbal test scores are normally distributed. At $\alpha = 0.01$, test the claim that the test score variance for females is different from that for males.

Female	480	610	340	630	520	690	540
Male	560	680	360	530	380	460	630

Female	600	800				
Male	310	730	740	520	560	400

18. A plastics company that produces automobile dashboard inserts has just received a new injection mold that is supposedly more consistent than its current mold. A quality technician wishes to test whether this new mold will produce inserts that are less variable in diameter than those produced with the company's current mold. The table shows independent random samples (of size 12) of insert diameters (in centimeters) for both the current and new molds. At $\alpha = 0.05$, test the claim that the new mold produces inserts that are less variable in diameter than the current mold produces.

New	9.611	9.618	9.594	9.580	9.611	9.597
Current	9.571	9.642	9.650	9.651	9.596	9.636

New	9.638	9.568	9.605	9.603	9.647	9.590
Current	9.570	9.537	9.641	9.625	9.626	9.579

Section 10.4

In Exercises 19 and 20, use the given sample data to perform a one-way ANOVA test using the indicated level of significance α. What can you conclude? Assume that each sample is drawn from a normal, or approximately normal, population, that the samples are independent of each other, and that the populations have the same variances. If convenient, use technology to solve the problem.

19. The table at the right shows the residential electricity cost (in dollars per million Btu) in one year for a random sample of households in four regions of the United States. Use $\alpha = 0.10$ to test for differences among the means for the four regions. *(Adapted from U.S. Energy Information Administration)*

Northeast	Midwest	South	West
40.24	18.40	22.85	35.03
28.18	26.66	29.79	31.51
35.67	28.27	18.93	20.28
34.18	21.38	21.81	28.82
39.03	24.64	25.47	24.07
30.74	20.15	23.64	27.60
32.65	29.77	19.82	29.25
29.98	25.08	28.15	18.57

20. The table at the right shows the annual income (in dollars) for a random sample of families in four regions of the United States. Use $\alpha = 0.05$ to test for differences among the means for the four regions. *(Adapted from U.S. Census Bureau)*

Northeast	Midwest	South	West
66,933	49,216	46,348	63,790
58,198	72,829	70,090	56,198
67,061	70,888	34,393	52,407
43,189	51,643	44,098	50,485
64,020	49,193	32,261	53,962
	64,405	56,798	53,709
	31,119		

10 CHAPTER QUIZ

Take this quiz as you would take a quiz in class. After you are done, check your work against the answers given in the back of the book.

For each exercise,

(a) *state H_0 and H_a.*

(b) *specify the level of significance α.*

(c) *determine the critical value.*

(d) *determine the rejection region.*

(e) *calculate the test statistic.*

(f) *make a decision.*

(g) *interpret the results in the context of the problem.*

If convenient, use technology to solve the problem.

For Exercises 1 and 2, use the following data. The data list the annual wages (in thousands of dollars) for randomly selected individuals from three metropolitan areas. Assume the wages are normally distributed and that the samples are independent. (Adapted from U.S. Bureau of Labor Statistics)

San Jose, CA: 65.2, 78.5, 36.4, 51.8, 42.1, 74.9, 64.0, 65.5, 34.2, 74.3, 97.7, 42.7, 93.4

Dallas, TX: 42.9, 56.4, 29.7, 34.0, 28.4, 35.2, 20.3, 36.9, 30.5, 62.6, 50.7, 34.4, 46.5, 38.0, 45.3, 35.5

Ann Arbor, MI: 31.3, 29.3, 35.4, 32.6, 55.8, 38.1, 37.4, 47.2, 41.6, 31.7, 39.4, 62.1, 31.9, 47.3

1. At $\alpha = 0.01$, is there enough evidence to conclude that the variances in annual wages for San Jose, CA and Dallas, TX are different?

2. Are the mean annual wages equal for all three cities? Use $\alpha = 0.10$. Assume that the population variances are equal.

For Exercises 3 and 4, use the following table. The table lists the distribution of educational achievement for people in the United States ages 25 and older. It also lists the results of a random survey for two additional age categories. (Adapted from U.S. Census Bureau)

	25 and older	35–44	65–74
Not a H.S. graduate	14.8%	35	91
High school graduate	32.2%	95	151
Some college, no degree	16.8%	51	58
Associate's degree	8.6%	30	23
Bachelor's degree	18.1%	61	50
Advanced degree	9.5%	29	33

3. Does the distribution for people in the United States ages 25 and older differ from the distribution for people in the United States ages 35–44? Use $\alpha = 0.01$.

4. Does the distribution for people in the United States ages 25 and older differ from the distribution for people in the United States ages 65–74? Use $\alpha = 0.05$.

Putting It All Together

REAL Statistics — Real Decisions

The National Fraud Information Center (NFIC) was established in 1992 by the National Consumers League (NCL) to combat the growing problem of telemarketing fraud by improving prevention and enforcement. NCL works to protect and promote social and economic justice for consumers and workers in the United States and abroad. The NCL was formed in 1899.

You work for the NFIC as a statistical analyst. You are studying data on telemarketing fraud. Part of your analysis involves testing the goodness of fit, testing for independence, comparing variances, and performing ANOVA.

■ EXERCISES

1. **Goodness of Fit** A claimed distribution for the ages of telemarketing fraud victims is shown in the table at the right. The results of a survey of 1000 randomly selected telemarketing fraud victims are also shown in the table. Using $\alpha = 0.01$, perform a chi-square goodness-of-fit test to test the claimed distribution. What can you conclude? Do you think the claimed distribution is valid? Why or why not?

2. **Independence** The following contingency table shows the results of a random sample of 2000 telemarketing fraud victims classified by age and type of fraud. The frauds were committed using bogus sweepstakes or credit card offers.

   (a) Calculate the expected frequency for each cell in the contingency table. Assume the variables age and type of fraud are independent.

   (b) Can you conclude that the age of the victims is related to the type of fraud? Use $\alpha = 0.01$.

Ages	Claimed distribution	Survey results
Under 20	1%	30
20–29	14%	200
30–39	17%	300
40–49	18%	270
50–59	18%	150
60–69	12%	40
70+	20%	10

TABLE FOR EXERCISE 1

Type of fraud	Age								
	Under 20	20–29	30–39	40–49	50–59	60–69	70–79	80+	Total
Sweepstakes	10	60	70	130	90	160	280	200	1000
Credit cards	20	180	260	240	180	70	30	20	1000
Total	30	240	330	370	270	230	310	220	2000

TECHNOLOGY   MINITAB   EXCEL   T1-83/84

Teacher salaries		
California	Ohio	Wyoming
60,645	45,300	37,300
50,622	46,400	58,022
41,400	42,650	36,800
59,000	58,025	32,440
46,150	64,800	42,250
63,200	41,200	35,600
68,400	44,980	44,600
53,400	50,425	52,935
62,378	47,300	45,500
58,873	45,700	36,160
53,395	44,850	44,200
56,000	65,200	42,260
63,200	37,760	44,185
67,400	52,426	32,450
65,405	53,800	40,200
52,200	50,200	50,786

TEACHER SALARIES

In 1916, the American Federation of Teachers (AFT) was formed by three teacher groups in Chicago, Illinois and locals from Gary, Indiana; New York, New York; Scranton, Pennsylvania; and Washington, D.C. Today, the AFT represents over 1.4 million teachers, higher education faculty and staff, school support staff, state and municipal employees, and health care professionals.

Each year, the AFT publishes the *Survey and Analysis of Teacher Salary Trends*. This report focuses on national trends in teacher salaries, state comparisons, beginning teacher salaries, and salary data and living costs for the nation's 50 largest cities.

The table at the right shows the salaries of a random sample of teachers from California, Ohio, and Wyoming.

■ EXERCISES

In Exercises 1–3, refer to the following samples. Use $\alpha = 0.05$.

(a) *California teachers*

(b) *Ohio teachers*

(c) *Wyoming teachers*

1. Are the samples independent of each other? Explain.

2. Use a technology tool to determine whether each sample is from a normal, or approximately normal, population.

3. Use a technology tool to determine whether the samples were selected from populations having equal variances.

4. Using the results of Exercises 1–3, discuss whether the three conditions for a one-way ANOVA test are satisfied. If so, use a technology tool to test the claim that teachers from California, Ohio, and Wyoming have the same mean salary. Use $\alpha = 0.05$.

5. Repeat Exercises 1–4 using the data in the table below. The table displays the salaries of a random sample of teachers from Alaska, Nevada, and New York.

Teacher salaries		
Alaska	Nevada	New York
62,150	66,120	74,206
53,225	49,550	83,600
69,900	30,600	85,200
52,700	39,356	38,400
34,960	60,600	43,450
46,668	38,674	35,881
60,385	38,605	33,760
53,985	35,252	50,200
52,032	43,478	89,200
48,052	48,259	34,250
47,069	56,884	86,200
37,960	39,265	36,208
40,385	29,499	41,814
51,295	41,305	79,950
48,062	38,802	34,199
80,670	35,187	44,202

Extended solutions are given in the *Technology Supplement*. Technical instruction is provided for MINITAB, Excel, and the TI-83/84.

11

Nonparametric Tests

11.1 The Sign Test

11.2 The Wilcoxon Tests
- CASE STUDY

11.3 The Kruskal-Wallis Test

11.4 Rank Correlation

11.5 The Runs Test
- USES AND ABUSES
- REAL STATISTICS– REAL DECISIONS
- TECHNOLOGY

In a recent year, 27.6% of people ages 25 and older in the United States had a bachelor's degree or more.

Up to this point in the text, you have studied dozens of different statistical formulas and tests that can help you in a decision-making process. Specific conditions had to be satisfied in order to use these formulas and tests.

It is commonly believed that the higher degree of education a person has, the greater the person's income will be. Can this belief be supported by actual data? The data below show the percent of people with a bachelor's degree or higher and the per capita personal income (in thousands of dollars) for the 50 states in a recent year.

Bachelor's degree or higher (%)	19.8	28.7	27.9	17.5	30.4	35.4	36.9	25.6	25.5	26.9	30.6	25.9	29.5	22.5	24.5	30.4	19.0
Per capita personal income (thousands of dollars)	29.1	35.6	30.3	26.9	37.0	37.9	47.8	37.1	33.2	31.1	34.5	28.2	36.1	31.3	32.3	32.8	28.5

Bachelor's degree or higher (%)	19.7	24.2	36.3	36.8	24.6	34.3	21.9	24.9	25.4	25.1	23.5	32.8	36.3	27.2	30.3	25.4	27.2
Per capita personal income (thousands of dollars)	24.8	31.3	41.8	44.3	33.1	37.4	25.3	31.9	29.4	33.6	35.9	38.4	43.8	27.6	40.5	30.6	31.4

Bachelor's degree or higher (%)	22.9	24.0	29.1	25.8	29.2	24.2	25.1	21.6	25.4	29.8	34.4	30.7	30.9	15.1	25.1	22.0
Per capita personal income (thousands of dollars)	32.5	29.3	32.1	34.9	36.2	28.4	31.6	31.1	32.5	28.1	33.3	38.4	35.4	27.2	33.6	36.8

WHERE YOU'RE GOING →

In this chapter, you will study additional statistical tests that do not require the population distribution to meet any specific conditions. Each of these has usefulness in real-life applications.

With the data above, the percent P of people with a bachelor's degree or higher and the per capita personal income I (in thousands of dollars) can be related by the regression equation $I = 0.736P + 13.612$. The correlation coefficient is approximately 0.768. You can determine that the correlation is significant by using Table 11, but the I-values do not pass the normality requirement.

So, although a simple correlation test might indicate a relationship between the percent of people with a bachelor's degree or higher and per capita personal income for each state, one might question the results because the data do not fit the requirements for the test. Similar tests you will study in this chapter, such as Spearman's rank correlation test, will give you additional information. The Spearman's rank correlation coefficient for this data is approximately 0.697. At $\alpha = 0.05$, there is in fact a significant correlation between the percent of people with a bachelor's degree or higher and per capita personal income for each state.

Percent with Bachelor's Degree or Higher and Personal Income for the 50 States

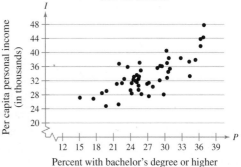

11.1 The Sign Test

▶ How to use the sign test to test a population median

▶ How to use the paired-sample sign test to test the difference between two population medians (dependent samples

The Sign Test for a Population Median ▶ The Paired-Sample Sign Test

▶ The Sign Test for a Population Median

Many of the hypothesis tests studied so far have imposed one or more requirements for a population distribution. For example, some tests require that a population must have a normal distribution, and other tests require that population variances be equal. What if, for a given test, such requirements cannot be met? For these cases, statisticians have developed hypothesis tests that are "distribution free." Such tests are called nonparametric tests.

> **DEFINITION**
>
> A **nonparametric test** is a hypothesis test that does not require any specific conditions concerning the shape of populations or the value of any population parameters.

Nonparametric tests are usually easier to perform than corresponding parametric tests. However, they are usually less efficient than parametric tests. Stronger evidence is required to reject a null hypothesis using the results of a nonparametric test. Consequently, whenever possible, you should use a parametric test. One of the easiest nonparametric tests to perform is the sign test.

Insight

For many nonparametric tests, statisticians test the median instead of the mean.

> **DEFINITION**
>
> The **sign test** is a nonparametric test that can be used to test a population median against a hypothesized value k.

The sign test for a population median can be left-tailed, right-tailed, or two-tailed. The null and alternative hypotheses for each type of test are as follows.

Left-tailed test:
H_0: median $\geq k$ and H_a: median $< k$

Right-tailed test:
H_0: median $\leq k$ and H_a: median $> k$

Two-tailed test:
H_0: median $= k$ and H_a: median $\neq k$

To use the sign test, first compare each entry in the sample with the hypothesized median k. If the entry is below the median, assign it a $-$ sign; if the entry is above the median, assign it a $+$ sign; and if the entry is equal to the median, assign it a 0. Then compare the number of $+$ and $-$ signs. (The 0s are ignored.) If there is a large difference between the number of $+$ signs and the number of $-$ signs, it is likely that the median is different from the hypothesized value and the null hypothesis should be rejected.

Insight

Because the 0s are ignored, there are two possible outcomes when comparing a data entry with a hypothesized median: a + or a − sign. If the median is k, then about half of the values will be above k and half will be below. As such, the probability for each sign is 0.5. Table 8 in Appendix B is constructed using the binomial distribution where $p = 0.5$.

When $n > 25$, you can use the normal approximation (with a correction for continuity) for the binomial. In this case, use $\mu = np = 0.5n$

and $\sigma = \sqrt{npq} = \dfrac{\sqrt{n}}{2}$.

Table 8 in Appendix B lists the critical values for the sign test for selected levels of significance and sample sizes. When the sign test is used, the sample size n is the total number of + and − signs. If the sample size is greater than 25, you can use the standard normal distribution to find the critical values.

TEST STATISTIC FOR THE SIGN TEST

When $n \leq 25$, the test statistic x for the sign test is the smaller number of + or − signs.

When $n > 25$, the test statistic for the sign test is

$$z = \frac{(x + 0.5) - 0.5n}{\dfrac{\sqrt{n}}{2}}$$

where x is the smaller number of + or − signs and n is the sample size, i.e., the total number of + and − signs.

Because x is defined to be the smaller number of + or − signs, the rejection region is always in the left tail. Consequently, the sign test for a population median is always a left-tailed test or a two-tailed test. When the test is two-tailed, use only the left-tailed critical value. (If x is defined to be the larger number of + or − signs, the rejection region is always in the right tail. Right-tailed sign tests are presented in the exercises.)

GUIDELINES

Performing a Sign Test for a Population Median

In Words	*In Symbols*
1. State the claim. Identify the null and alternative hypotheses.	State H_0 and H_a.
2. Specify the level of significance.	Identify α.
3. Determine the sample size n by assigning + signs and − signs to the sample data.	n = total number of + and − signs
4. Determine the critical value.	If $n \leq 25$, use Table 8 in App. B.
	If $n > 25$, use Table 4 in App. B.
5. Calculate the test statistic.	If $n \leq 25$, use x.
	If $n > 25$, use $$z = \frac{(x + 0.5) - 0.5n}{\dfrac{\sqrt{n}}{2}}$$
6. Make a decision to reject or fail to reject the null hypothesis.	If the test statistic is less than or equal to the critical value, reject H_0. Otherwise, fail to reject H_0.
7. Interpret the decision in the context of the original claim.	

EXAMPLE 1

Using the Sign Test

A bank manager claims that the median number of customers per day is no more than 750. A teller doubts the accuracy of this claim. The number of bank customers per day for 16 randomly selected days are listed below. At $\alpha = 0.05$, can the teller reject the bank manager's claim?

775	765	801	742
754	753	739	751
745	750	777	769
756	760	782	789

Solution The teller must disprove the bank manager's claim that "the median number of customers per day is no more than 750." So, the null and alternative hypotheses are

H_0: median ≤ 750 (Claim)   and H_a: median > 750.

The table below shows the results of comparing each data entry with the hypothesized median 750.

+	+	+	−
+	+	−	+
−	0	+	+
+	+	+	+

From the table, you can see that there are 3 − signs and 12 + signs. So, $n = 12 + 3 = 15$. Because $n \leq 25$, use Table 8 to find the critical value. The test is a one-tailed test with $\alpha = 0.05$ and $n = 15$. So, the critical value is 3. Because $n \leq 25$, the test statistic x is the smaller number of + or − signs. So, $x = 3$. Because $x = 3$ is equal to the critical value, the teller should reject the null hypothesis.

Interpretation At the 5% significance level, the teller can reject the bank manager's claim that the median number of customers per day is no more than 750.

▶ Try It Yourself 1

A supermarket manager claims that the median number of customers per day is greater than 2500. A supplier wants to verify the accuracy of this claim. The number of customers per day for 24 randomly selected days is shown below. At $\alpha = 0.025$, can the supplier support the manager's claim?

Number of customers per day for 24 days							
2174	2491	2682	2510	2557	2418	2709	2562
2390	2467	2500	2205	2246	2054	2243	2627
1949	2500	2592	2567	2478	2348	2692	2580

a. *Identify* the claim and *state* H_0 and H_a.
b. *Specify* the level of significance α.
c. *Determine* the sample size n.
d. *Determine* the critical value.
e. *Calculate* the test statistic x.
f. *Decide* whether to reject the null hypothesis.
g. *Interpret* the decision in the context of the original claim.

Answer: Page A48

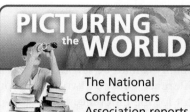
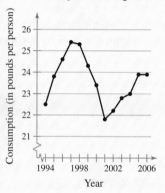
Study Tip

When performing a two-tailed sign test, remember to use only the left-tailed critical value.

EXAMPLE 2

Using the Sign Test

A car dealership claims to give customers a median trade-in offer of at least $6000. A random sample of 103 transactions revealed that the trade-in offer for 60 automobiles was less than $6000 and the trade-in offer for 40 automobiles was more than $6000. At $\alpha = 0.01$, can you reject the dealership's claim?

Solution   To reject the dealership's claim, you must disprove the claim that "the median trade-in offer is at least $6000." The null and alternative hypotheses are

$$H_0: \text{median} \geq 6000 \text{ (Claim)} \quad \text{and} \quad H_a: \text{median} < 6000.$$

Because $n > 25$, use Table 4, the Standard Normal Table, to find the critical value. Because the test is a left-tailed test with $\alpha = 0.01$, the critical value is -2.33. Of the 103 transactions, there are $60 -$ signs and $40 +$ signs. When the zeros are ignored, the sample size is

$$n = 60 + 40 = 100$$

and

$$x = 40.$$

With these values, the test statistic is

$$z = \frac{(40 + 0.5) - 0.5(100)}{\sqrt{100}/2}$$

$$= \frac{-9.5}{5}$$

$$= -1.9.$$

The graph at the right shows the location of the rejection region and the test statistic z. Because z is greater than the critical value, it is not in the rejection region, and you should fail to reject the null hypothesis.

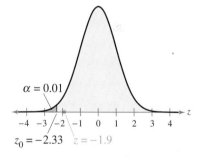

Interpretation   At the 1% significance level, you cannot reject the dealership's claim that the median trade-in offer is at least $6000.

▶ **Try It Yourself 2**

A realtor claims that the median sales price of houses sold in a certain region is $134,500. A random sample of 85 house sales reveals that 30 houses were sold for less than $134,500 and 51 houses were sold for more than $134,500. At $\alpha = 0.10$, can you reject the realtor's claim?

a. *Identify* the claim and *state* H_0 and H_a.
b. *Specify* the level of significance α.
c. *Determine* the sample size n.
d. *Determine* the critical value.
e. *Calculate* the test statistic z.
f. *Decide* whether to reject the null hypothesis.
g. *Interpret* the decision in the context of the original claim.

Answer: Page A48

▸ The Paired-Sample Sign Test

In Section 8.3, you learned how to use a *t*-test for the difference between means of dependent samples. That test required both populations to be normally distributed. If the parametric condition of normality cannot be satisfied, you can use the paired-sample sign test to test the difference between two population medians. To perform the paired-sample sign test for the difference between two population medians, the following conditions must be met.

1. A sample must be randomly selected from each population.

2. The samples must be dependent (paired).

The paired-sample sign test can be left-tailed, right-tailed, or two-tailed. This test is similar to the sign test for a single population median. However, instead of comparing each data entry with a hypothesized median and recording a +, −, or 0, you find the difference between corresponding data entries and record the sign of the difference. Generally, to find the difference, subtract the entry representing the second variable from the entry representing the first variable. Then compare the number of + and − signs. (The 0s are ignored.) If the number of + signs is approximately equal to the number of − signs, the null hypothesis should not be rejected. If, however, there is a significant difference between the number of + signs and the number of − signs, the null hypothesis should be rejected.

GUIDELINES

Performing a Paired-Sample Sign Test

In Words	*In Symbols*
1. State the claim. Identify the null and alternative hypotheses.	State H_0 and H_a.
2. Specify the level of significance.	Identify α.
3. Determine the sample size n by finding the difference for each data pair. Assign a + sign for a positive difference, a − sign for a negative difference, and a 0 for no difference.	n = total number of + and − signs
4. Determine the critical value.	Use Table 8 in Appendix B.
5. Find the test statistic.	x = smaller number of + and − signs
6. Make a decision to reject or fail to reject the null hypothesis.	If the test statistic is less than or equal to the critical value, reject H_0. Otherwise, fail to reject H_0.
7. Interpret the decision in the context of the original claim.	

EXAMPLE 3

Using the Paired-Sample Sign Test

A psychologist claims that the number of repeat offenders will decrease if first-time offenders complete a particular rehabilitation course. You randomly select 10 prisons and record the number of repeat offenders during a two-year period. Then, after first-time offenders complete the course, you record the number of repeat offenders at each prison for another two-year period. The results are shown in the following table. At $\alpha = 0.025$, can you support the psychologist's claim?

Prison	1	2	3	4	5	6	7	8	9	10
Before	21	34	9	45	30	54	37	36	33	40
After	19	22	16	31	21	30	22	18	17	21

Solution   To support the psychologist's claim, you could use the following null and alternative hypotheses.

H_0: The number of repeat offenders will not decrease.

H_a: The number of repeat offenders will decrease. (Claim)

The table below shows the sign of the differences between the "before" and "after" data.

Prison	1	2	3	4	5	6	7	8	9	10
Before	21	34	9	45	30	54	37	36	33	40
After	19	22	16	31	21	30	22	18	17	21
Sign	+	+	−	+	+	+	+	+	+	+

You can see that there is 1 − sign and there are 9 + signs. So, $n = 1 + 9 = 10$. In Table 8 with $\alpha = 0.025$ (one-tailed) and $n = 10$, the critical value is 1. The test statistic x is the smaller number of + or − signs. So, $x = 1$. Because x is equal to the critical value, you should reject the null hypothesis.

Interpretation   At the 2.5% level of significance, you can support the psychologist's claim that the number of repeat offenders will decrease.

▶ Try It Yourself 3

A medical researcher claims that a new vaccine will decrease the number of colds in adults. You randomly select 14 adults and record the number of colds each has in a one-year period. After giving the vaccine to each adult, you again record the number of colds each has in a one-year period. The results are shown in the table at the left. At $\alpha = 0.05$, can you support the researcher's claim?

a. *Identify* the claim and *state* H_0 and H_a.
b. *Specify* the level of significance α.
c. *Determine* the sample size n.
d. *Determine* the critical value.
e. *Find* the test statistic x.
f. *Decide* whether to reject the null hypothesis.
g. *Interpret* the decision in the context of the original claim.

Answer: Page A48

Adult	Before vaccine	After vaccine
1	3	2
2	4	1
3	2	0
4	1	1
5	3	1
6	6	3
7	4	3
8	5	2
9	2	2
10	0	2
11	2	3
12	5	4
13	3	3
14	3	2

11.1 EXERCISES

■ Building Basic Skills and Vocabulary

1. What is a nonparametric test? How does a nonparametric test differ from a parametric test? What are the advantages and disadvantages of using a nonparametric test?

2. Explain how to use the sign test to test a population median.

■ Using and Interpreting Concepts

Performing a Sign Test   *In Exercises 3–18, (a) write the claim mathematically and identify H_0 and H_a, (b) determine the critical value, (c) calculate the test statistic, (d) decide whether to reject or fail to reject the null hypothesis, and (e) interpret the decision in the context of the original claim.*

3. **Credit Card Charges**   In order to estimate the median amount of new credit card charges for the previous month, a financial service accountant randomly selects 12 credit card accounts and records the amount of new charges for each account for the previous month. The amounts are listed below. At $\alpha = 0.01$, can the accountant conclude that the median amount of new credit card charges for the previous month was more than $300? *(Adapted from Board of Governors of the Federal Reserve System)*

   $346.71 $382.59 $255.03 $202.17 $309.80 $265.88
   $299.41 $270.38 $296.54 $318.46 $245.92 $309.47

4. **Temperature**   A meteorologist estimates that the daily median high temperature for the month of July in Pittsburgh is 83° Fahrenheit. The high temperatures (in degrees Fahrenheit) for 15 randomly selected July days in Pittsburgh are listed below. At $\alpha = 0.01$, is there enough evidence to reject the meteorologist's claim? *(Adapted from U.S. National Oceanic and Atmospheric Administration)*

   74   79   81   86   90   79   81   83
   81   74   78   76   84   82   85

5. **Sales Prices of Homes**   A real estate agent believes that the median sales price of new privately owned one-family homes sold in the past year is $210,000 or less. The sales prices of eight randomly selected homes are listed below. At $\alpha = 0.05$, is there enough evidence to reject the agent's claim? *(Adapted from National Association of Realtors)*

   $230,000 $193,250 $149,300 $204,400
   $135,600 $221,000 $209,000 $291,800

6. **Temperature**   During a weather report, a meteorologist states that the daily median high temperature for the month of January in San Diego is 66° Fahrenheit. The high temperatures (in degrees Fahrenheit) for 18 randomly selected January days in San Diego are listed below. At $\alpha = 0.01$, can you reject the meteorologist's claim? *(Adapted from U.S. National Oceanic and Atmospheric Administration)*

   78   74   72   72   70   70   72   78   74
   71   72   72   72   74   77   79   75   73

7. **Credit Card Debt** A financial services institution reports that the median amount of credit card debt for families holding such debts is at least $2200. In a random sample of 104 families holding debt, you see that the debt for 60 families is less than $2200 and the debt for 44 families is greater than $2200. At $\alpha = 0.02$, can you reject the institution's claim? *(Adapted from Board of Governors of the Federal Reserve System)*

8. **Financial Debt** A financial services accountant estimates that the median amount of financial debt for families holding such debts is less than $50,000. In a random sample of 70 families holding debt, the debt for 24 families was less than $50,000 and the debt for 46 families was greater than $50,000. At $\alpha = 0.025$, can you support the accountant's estimate? *(Adapted from Board of Governors of the Federal Reserve System)*

9. **Engineering Doctorates** An engineering association conducted a study to determine the median age of recipients of engineering doctorates. In part of the study, the association randomly selected 20 engineering doctorates and found that 4 were conferred before age 30, 11 were conferred after age 30, and 5 were conferred at age 30. Test the association's claim that the median age of recipients of engineering doctorates is greater than 30 years. Use $\alpha = 0.01$. *(Adapted from U.S. National Science Foundation)*

10. **Biological Science Doctorates** A science association claims that the median age of recipients of biological science doctorates is less than 32 years. In a random sample of 24 biological science doctorates, 5 were conferred before age 32, 13 were conferred after age 32, and 6 were conferred at age 32. At $\alpha = 0.05$, can you support the association's claim? *(Adapted from U.S. National Science Foundation)*

11. **Unit Size** A renters' organization claims that the median number of rooms in renter-occupied units is four. You randomly select 50 renter-occupied units and obtain the results shown below. At $\alpha = 0.05$, can you reject the organization's claim? *(Adapted from U.S. Census Bureau)*

Unit size	Number of units
Fewer than 4 rooms	13
4 rooms	17
More than 4 rooms	20

Data for Exercise 11

Unit size	Number of units
Less than 1000	5
1000	2
More than 1000	15

Data for Exercise 12

12. **Square Footage** A renters' organization believes that the median square footage of renter-occupied units is 1000 square feet. To test this claim, you randomly select 22 renter-occupied units and obtain the results shown above. At $\alpha = 0.10$, can you reject the organization's claim? *(Adapted from U.S. Census Bureau)*

13. **Hourly Earnings** A labor organization estimates that the median hourly earnings of male workers paid hourly rates is $12.16. In a random sample of 41 male workers paid hourly rates, 16 are paid less than $12.16 per hour, 23 are paid more than $12.16 per hour, and 2 are paid $12.16 per hour. At $\alpha = 0.01$, can you reject the organization's claim? *(Adapted from U.S. Bureau of Labor Statistics)*

14. **Hourly Earnings** A labor organization claims that the median hourly earnings of female workers paid hourly rates is at most $10.31. In a random sample of 23 female workers paid hourly rates, 9 are paid less than $10.31 per hour, 11 are paid more than $10.31 per hour, and 3 are paid $10.31 per hour. At $\alpha = 0.05$, can you reject the organization's claim? *(Adapted from U.S. Bureau of Labor Statistics)*

15. **Lower Back Pain** The table shows the lower back pain intensity scores for eight patients before and after receiving acupuncture for eight weeks. At $\alpha = 0.05$, is there enough evidence to conclude that the lower back pain intensity scores decreased after the acupuncture? *(Adapted from Archives of Internal Medicine)*

Patient	1	2	3	4	5	6	7	8
Intensity score (before)	59.2	46.3	65.4	74.0	79.3	81.6	44.4	59.1
Intensity score (after)	12.4	22.5	18.6	59.3	70.1	70.2	13.2	25.9

16. **Lower Back Pain** The table shows the lower back pain intensity scores for 12 patients before and after taking anti-inflammatory drugs for eight weeks. At $\alpha = 0.05$, is there enough evidence to conclude that the lower back pain intensity scores decreased after taking anti-inflammatory drugs? *(Adapted from Archives of Internal Medicine)*

Patient	1	2	3	4	5	6
Intensity score (before)	71.0	42.1	79.1	57.5	64.0	60.4
Intensity score (after)	60.1	23.4	86.2	62.1	44.2	49.7

Patient	7	8	9	10	11	12
Intensity score (before)	68.3	95.2	48.1	78.6	65.4	59.9
Intensity score (after)	58.3	72.6	51.8	82.5	63.2	47.9

17. **Improving SAT Scores** A tutoring agency believes that by completing a special course, students can improve their verbal SAT scores. In part of a study, 12 students take the verbal part of the SAT, complete the special course, then take the verbal part of the SAT again. The students' scores are shown below. At $\alpha = 0.05$, is there enough evidence to conclude that the students' verbal SAT scores improved?

Student	1	2	3	4	5	6
Score on first SAT	308	456	352	433	306	471
Score on second SAT	300	524	409	419	304	483

Student	7	8	9	10	11	12
Score on first SAT	538	207	205	351	360	251
Score on second SAT	708	253	399	350	480	303

18. SAT Scores   Students at a certain school are required to take the SAT twice. The table shows both verbal SAT scores for 12 students. At $\alpha = 0.01$, can you conclude that the students' scores improved the second time they took the SAT?

Student	1	2	3	4	5	6
Score on first SAT	445	510	429	452	629	453
Score on second SAT	446	571	517	478	610	453

Student	7	8	9	10	11	12
Score on first SAT	358	477	325	513	636	571
Score on second SAT	378	532	299	501	648	603

19. Travel Plans   A research organization conducts a survey by randomly selecting adults and asking them whether they prefer unplanned travel activities or planned travel activities. The results are shown in the figure. *(Adapted from Simmons Market Research)*

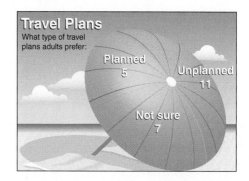

(a) Use a sign test to test the null hypothesis that the proportion of adults who prefer unplanned travel activities is equal to the proportion of adults who prefer planned travel activities. Assign a + sign to an adult who prefers unplanned travel activities, assign a − sign to an adult who prefers planned travel activities, and assign a 0 to an adult who is not sure. Use $\alpha = 0.05$.

(b) What can you conclude?

20. Contacting Parents   A research organization conducts a survey by randomly selecting adults and asking them how frequently they are in contact with their parents by phone. The results are shown in the figure. *(Adapted from Pew Research Center)*

(a) Use a sign test to test the null hypothesis that the proportion of adults who contact their parents by phone weekly is equal to the proportion of adults who contact their parents by phone daily. Assign a + sign to an adult who contacts their parents by phone weekly, assign a − sign to an adult who contacts their parents by phone daily, and assign a 0 to an adult who answered other. Use $\alpha = 0.05$.

(b) What can you conclude?

■ Extending Concepts

More on Sign Tests *When you are using a sign test for $n > 25$ and the test is left-tailed, you know you can reject the null hypothesis if the test statistic*

$$z = \frac{(x + 0.5) - 0.5n}{\frac{\sqrt{n}}{2}}$$

*is less than or equal to the **left-tailed** critical value, where x is the **smaller** number of + and − signs. For a right-tailed test, you can reject the null hypothesis if the test statistic*

$$z = \frac{(x - 0.5) - 0.5n}{\frac{\sqrt{n}}{2}}$$

*is greater than or equal to the **right-tailed** critical value, where x is the **larger** number of + and − signs.*

In Exercises 21–24, (a) write the claim mathematically and identify H_0 and H_a, (b) determine the critical value, (c) calculate the test statistic, (d) decide whether to reject or fail to reject the null hypothesis, and (e) interpret the decision in the context of the original claim.

21. **Weekly Earnings** A labor organization claims that the median weekly earnings of female workers is less than or equal to $585. To test this claim, you randomly select 50 female workers and ask each to provide her weekly earnings. The results are shown in the table. At $\alpha = 0.01$, can you reject the organization's claim? *(Adapted from U.S. Bureau of Labor Statistics)*

Weekly earnings	Number of workers
Less than $585	18
$585	3
More than $585	29

Data for Exercise 21

Weekly earnings	Number of workers
Less than $720	23
$720	2
More than $720	45

Data for Exercise 22

22. **Weekly Earnings** A labor organization states that the median weekly earnings of male workers is greater than $720. To test this claim, you randomly select 70 male workers and ask each to provide his weekly earnings. The results are shown in the table. At $\alpha = 0.01$, can you support the organization's claim? *(Adapted from U.S. Bureau of Labor Statistics)*

23. **Ages of Brides** A marriage counselor estimates that the median age of brides at the time of their first marriage is greater than 25.5 years. In a random sample of 65 brides, 22 are less than 25.5 years old, 38 are more than 25.5 years old, and 5 are 25.5 years old. At $\alpha = 0.05$, can you support the counselor's claim? *(Adapted from U.S. Census Bureau)*

24. **Ages of Grooms** A marriage counselor estimates that the median age of grooms at the time of their first marriage is less than or equal to 27 years. In a random sample of 56 grooms, 23 are less than 27 years old, 33 are more than 27 years old, and none are 27 years old. At $\alpha = 0.05$, is there enough evidence to reject the counselor's claim? *(Adapted from U.S. Census Bureau)*

11.2 The Wilcoxon Tests

What You SHOULD LEARN

▸ How to use the Wilcoxon signed-rank test to determine if two dependent samples are selected from populations having the same distribution

▸ How to use the Wilcoxon rank sum test to determine if two independent samples are selected from populations having the same distribution

The Wilcoxon Signed-Rank Test ▸ The Wilcoxon Rank Sum Test

▸ The Wilcoxon Signed-Rank Test

In this section, you will study the Wilcoxon signed-rank test and the Wilcoxon rank sum test. Unlike the sign test, the strength of these two nonparametric tests is that each considers the magnitude, or size, of the data entries.

In Section 8.3, you used a *t*-test together with dependent samples to determine whether there was a difference between two populations. To use the *t*-test to test such a difference, you must assume (or know) that the dependent samples are randomly selected from populations having a normal distribution. But, what if this assumption cannot be made? Instead of using the two-sample *t*-test, you can use the Wilcoxon signed-rank test.

DEFINITION

The **Wilcoxon signed-rank test** is a nonparametric test that can be used to determine whether two *dependent* samples were selected from populations having the same distribution.

GUIDELINES

Performing a Wilcoxon Signed-Rank Test

In Words	*In Symbols*
1. State the claim. Identify the null and alternative hypotheses.	State H_0 and H_a.
2. Specify the level of significance.	Identify α.
3. Determine the sample size n, which is the number of pairs of data for which the difference is not 0.	
4. Determine the critical value.	Use Table 9 in Appendix B.
5. Calculate the test statistic w_s.	Headers: **Sample 1, Sample 2, Difference, Absolute value, Rank,** and **Signed rank.** Signed rank takes on the same sign as its corresponding difference.
a. Complete a table using the headers listed at the right.	
b. Find the sum of the positive ranks and the sum of the negative ranks.	
c. Select the smaller of absolute values of the sums.	
6. Make a decision to reject or fail to reject the null hypothesis.	If w_s is less than or equal to the critical value, reject H_0. Otherwise, fail to reject H_0.
7. Interpret the decision in the context of the original claim.	

Study Tip

The absolute value of a number is its value, disregarding its sign. A pair of vertical bars, | |, is used to denote absolute value. For example, $|3| = 3$ and $|-7| = 7$.

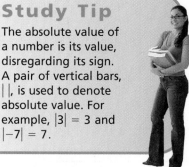

EXAMPLE 1

Performing a Wilcoxon Signed-Rank Test

A sports psychologist believes that listening to music affects the length of athletes' workout sessions. The length of time (in minutes) of 10 athletes' workout sessions, while listening to music and while not listening to music, are shown in the table. At $\alpha = 0.05$, can you support the sports psychologist's claim?

Length of workout session, with music	45	38	28	39	41	47	62	54	33	44
Length of workout session, without music	38	40	33	36	42	41	54	47	28	35

Solution The claim is "Music affects the length of athletes' workout sessions." To test this claim, use the following null and alternative hypotheses.

H_0: There is no difference in the length of the athletes' workout sessions.

H_a: There is a difference in the length of the athletes' workout sessions. (Claim)

This Wilcoxon signed-rank test is a two-tailed test with $\alpha = 0.05$, and because the difference between each data pair is not 0, $n = 10$. From Table 9 in Appendix B, the critical value is 8. To find the test statistic w_s complete a table as shown below.

Study Tip

Do not assign a rank to any differences of zero. In the case of a tie between data entries, use the average of the corresponding ranks. For instance, if two data entries are tied for the fifth rank, use the average of 5 and 6, which is 5.5. If three entries are tied for the fifth rank, use the average of 5, 6, and 7, or 6.

Length of session, with music	Length of session, without music	Difference	Absolute value	Rank	Signed rank
45	38	7	7	7.5	7.5
38	40	−2	2	2	−2
28	33	−5	5	4.5	−4.5
39	36	3	3	3	3
41	42	−1	1	1	−1
47	41	6	6	6	6
62	54	8	8	9	9
54	47	7	7	7.5	7.5
33	28	5	5	4.5	4.5
44	35	9	9	10	10

The sum of the negative ranks is

$$-1 + (-2) + (-4.5) = -7.5.$$

The sum of the positive ranks is

$$(+3) + (+4.5) + (+6) + (+7.5) + (+7.5) + (+9) + (+10) = 47.5.$$

The test statistic is the smaller of the absolute value of these two sums. Because $|-7.5| < |47.5|$, the test statistic is $w_s = 7.5$. Because the test statistic is less than the critical value, that is, $7.5 < 8$, you should decide to reject the null hypothesis.

Interpretation At the 5% level of significance, you have enough evidence to support the claim that music makes a difference in the length of athletes' workout sessions.

PICTURING the WORLD

To help determine when knee arthroscopy patients can resume driving after surgery, the driving reaction times (in milliseconds) of 10 right knee arthroscopy patients were measured before surgery and 4 weeks after surgery using a computer-linked car simulator. The results are shown in the table. (Adapted from Knee Surgery, Sports Traumatology, Arthroscopy Journal)

Patient	Reaction time before surgery	Reaction time 4 weeks after surgery
1	720	730
2	750	645
3	735	745
4	730	640
5	755	660
6	745	670
7	730	650
8	725	730
9	770	675
10	700	705

At $\alpha = 0.05$, can you conclude that the reaction times changed significantly four weeks after surgery?

▶ Try It Yourself 1

A quality control inspector wants to test the claim that a spray-on water repellent is effective. To test this claim, he selects 12 pieces of fabric, sprays water on each, and measures the amount of water repelled (in milliliters). He then applies the water repellent and repeats the experiment. The results are shown in the table. At $\alpha = 0.01$, can he conclude that the water repellent is effective?

No repellent	8	7	7	4	6	10
Repellent applied	15	12	11	6	6	8

No repellent	9	5	9	11	8	4
Repellent applied	8	6	12	8	14	8

a. *Identify* the claim and *state* H_0 and H_a.
b. *Specify* the level of significance α.
c. *Determine* the sample size n.
d. *Determine* the critical value.
e. *Calculate* the test statistic w_s by making a table, finding the sum of the positive ranks and the sum of the negative ranks, and finding the absolute value of each.
f. *Decide* whether to reject the null hypothesis. Use a graph if necessary.
g. *Interpret* the decision in the context of the original claim.

Answer: Page A48

▶ The Wilcoxon Rank Sum Test

In Sections 8.1 and 8.2, you used a z-test or a t-test together with independent samples to determine whether there was a difference between two populations. To use these tests to test such a difference, you had to make several assumptions concerning the distribution of each population. But, what if these assumptions cannot be made? You can still compare the populations using the Wilcoxon rank sum test.

DEFINITION

The **Wilcoxon rank sum test** is a nonparametric test that can be used to determine whether two *independent* samples were selected from populations having the same distribution.

Study Tip

Use the Wilcoxon signed-rank test for dependent samples and the Wilcoxon rank sum test for independent samples.

A requirement for the Wilcoxon rank sum test is that the sample size of both samples must be at least 10. When calculating the test statistic for the Wilcoxon rank sum test, let n_1 represent the sample size of the smaller sample and n_2 represent the sample size of the larger sample. If the two samples have the same size, it does not matter which one is n_1 or n_2.

When calculating the sum of the ranks R, use the ranks for the smaller of the two samples. If the two samples have the same size, you can use the ranks from either sample, but you must use the ranks from the sample you associate with n_1.

TEST STATISTIC FOR THE WILCOXON RANK SUM TEST

Given two independent samples, the test statistic z for the Wilcoxon rank sum test is

$$z = \frac{R - \mu_R}{\sigma_R}$$

where

R = sum of the ranks for the smaller sample,

$$\mu_R = \frac{n_1(n_1 + n_2 + 1)}{2},$$

and

$$\sigma_R = \sqrt{\frac{n_1 n_2(n_1 + n_2 + 1)}{12}}.$$

GUIDELINES

Performing a Wilcoxon Rank Sum Test

In Words	*In Symbols*
1. State the claim. Identify the null and alternative hypotheses.	State H_0 and H_a.
2. Specify the level of significance.	Identify α.
3. Determine the critical value(s).	Use Table 4 in Appendix B.
4. Determine the sample sizes.	$n_1 \leq n_2$
5. Find the sum of the ranks for the smaller sample.	R
a. List the combined data in ascending order.	
b. Rank the combined data.	
c. Add the sum of the ranks for the smaller sample.	
6. Calculate the test statistic.	$z = \dfrac{R - \mu_R}{\sigma_R}$
7. Make a decision to reject or fail to reject the null hypothesis.	If z is in the rejection region, reject H_0. Otherwise, fail to reject H_0.
8. Interpret the decision in the context of the original claim.	

EXAMPLE 2

Performing a Wilcoxon Rank Sum Test

The table shows the earnings (in thousands of dollars) of a random sample of 10 male and 12 female pharmaceutical sales representatives. At $\alpha = 0.10$, can you conclude that there is a difference between the males' and females' earnings?

Male earnings	58	73	94	81	78	74	66	75	97	79		
Female earnings	66	57	81	73	65	78	71	67	64	77	80	70

Solution   The claim is "there is a difference between the males' and females' earnings." The null and alternative hypotheses for this test are as follows.

H_0: There is no difference between the males' and the females' earnings.

H_a: There is a difference between the males' and the females' earnings.
   (Claim)

Because the test is a two-tailed test with $\alpha = 0.10$, the critical values are

$$-z_0 = -1.645 \quad \text{and} \quad z_0 = 1.645.$$

The rejection regions are

$$z \le -1.645 \quad \text{and} \quad z \ge 1.645.$$

Before calculating the test statistic, you must find the values of $R, \mu_R,$ and σ_R. The table shows the combined data listed in ascending order and the corresponding ranks.

Ordered data	Sample	Rank
57	F	1
58	M	2
64	F	3
65	F	4
66	M	5.5
66	F	5.5
67	F	7
70	F	8
71	F	9
73	M	10.5
73	F	10.5

Ordered data	Sample	Rank
74	M	12
75	M	13
77	F	14
78	M	15.5
78	F	15.5
79	M	17
80	F	18
81	M	19.5
81	F	19.5
94	M	21
97	M	22

Because the smaller sample is the sample of males, R is the sum of the male rankings.

$$R = 2 + 5.5 + 10.5 + 12 + 13 + 15.5 + 17 + 19.5 + 21 + 22$$
$$= 138$$

Using $n_1 = 10$ and $n_2 = 12$, you can find μ_R and σ_R as follows.

$$\mu_R = \frac{n_1(n_1 + n_2 + 1)}{2} = \frac{10(10 + 12 + 1)}{2} = \frac{230}{2} = 115$$

$$\sigma_R = \sqrt{\frac{n_1 n_2 (n_1 + n_2 + 1)}{12}}$$

$$= \sqrt{\frac{(10)(12)(10 + 12 + 1)}{12}}$$

$$= \sqrt{\frac{2760}{12}}$$

$$= \sqrt{230}$$

$$\approx 15.17$$

When $R = 138$, $\mu_R = 115$, and $\sigma_R = 15.17$, the test statistic is

$$z = \frac{R - \mu_R}{\sigma_R}$$

$$= \frac{138 - 115}{15.17}$$

$$\approx 1.52.$$

From the graph at the right, you can see that the test statistic z is not in the rejection region. So, you should decide to fail to reject the null hypothesis.

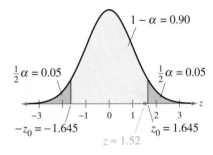

Interpretation At the 10% level of significance, you cannot conclude that there is a difference between the males' and females' earnings.

▶ Try It Yourself 2

You are investigating the automobile insurance claims paid (in thousands of dollars) by two insurance companies. The table shows a random, independent sample of 12 claims paid by two insurance companies. At $\alpha = 0.05$, can you conclude that there is a difference in the claims paid by the companies?

Company A	6.2	10.6	2.5	4.5	6.5	7.4
Company B	7.3	5.6	3.4	1.8	2.2	4.7

Company A	9.9	3.0	5.8	3.9	6.0	6.3
Company B	10.8	4.1	1.7	3.0	4.4	5.3

a. *Identify* the claim and *state* H_0 and H_a.
b. *Specify* the level of significance α.
c. *Determine* the critical value(s).
d. *Determine* the sample sizes n_1 and n_2.
e. *List* the combined data in ascending order, *rank* the data, and *find* the sum of the ranks of the smaller sample.
f. *Calculate* the test statistic.
g. *Decide* whether to reject the null hypothesis. Use a graph if necessary.
h. *Interpret* the decision in the context of the original claim.

Answer: Page A49

11.2 EXERCISES

■ Building Basic Skills and Vocabulary

1. How do you know whether to use a Wilcoxon signed-rank test or a Wilcoxon rank sum test?

2. What is the requirement for the sample size of both samples when using the Wilcoxon rank sum test?

■ Using and Interpreting Concepts

Performing a Wilcoxon Test   *In Exercises 3–8,*

(a) write the claim mathematically and identify H_0 and H_a.

(b) decide whether to use a Wilcoxon signed-rank test or a Wilcoxon rank sum test.

(c) determine the critical value(s).

(d) calculate the test statistic.

(e) decide whether to reject or fail to reject the null hypothesis.

(f) interpret the decision in the context of the original claim.

3. Calcium Supplements and Blood Pressure   In a study testing the effects of calcium supplements on blood pressure in men, 12 men were randomly chosen and given a calcium supplement for 12 weeks. The measurements shown in the table are for each subject's diastolic blood pressure taken before and after the 12-week treatment period. At $\alpha = 0.01$, can you reject the claim that there was no reduction in diastolic blood pressure? *(Adapted from The Journal of American Medicine)*

Patient	1	2	3	4	5	6
Before treatment	108	109	120	129	112	111
After treatment	99	115	105	116	115	117

Patient	7	8	9	10	11	12
Before treatment	117	135	124	118	130	115
After treatment	108	122	120	126	128	106

4. Wholesale Trade and Manufacturing   A private industry analyst claims that there is no difference in the salaries earned by workers in the wholesale trade and manufacturing industries. A random sample of 10 wholesale trade and 10 manufacturing workers and their salaries is shown in the table. At $\alpha = 0.10$, can you reject the analyst's claim? *(Adapted from U.S. Bureau of Economic Analysis)*

Industry	Salary (in thousands of dollars)									
Wholesale trade	56	49	50	64	47	53	58	61	59	56
Manufacturing	56	52	41	59	39	50	61	43	49	37

5. Earnings by Degree A college administrator believes that there is a difference in the earnings of people with bachelor's degrees and those with associate's degrees. The table shows the earnings (in thousands of dollars) of a random sample of 11 people with bachelor's degrees and 10 people with associate's degrees. At $\alpha = 0.05$, is there enough evidence to support the administrator's belief? *(Adapted from U.S. Census Bureau)*

Level of highest degree	Salary (in thousands of dollars)										
Bachelor's	49	45	58	71	65	45	39	51	47	55	47
Associate's	32	35	43	29	34	34	34	37	41	41	

6. Mother's Age and Baby Care A postnatal health care researcher conducts a study of a random selection of mothers under 20 years old and 20–24 years old. The number of weeks each mother breast-fed her baby is shown in the table. At $\alpha = 0.01$, can you reject the researcher's claim that there is no difference in the number of months mothers in these two age groups breast-feed their babies? *(Adapted from U.S. National Center for Health Statistics)*

Age of mother	Duration (in weeks)											
Under 20 years old	21	24	24	30	11	17	10	28	21	12	15	
20–24 years old	25	28	26	23	22	13	28	21	27	32	19	27

7. Teacher Salaries A teacher's union representative claims that there is a difference in the salaries earned by teachers in Massachusetts and Connecticut. A random sample of 12 Massachusetts and 12 Connecticut teachers and their salaries is shown in the table. At $\alpha = 0.05$, is there enough evidence to support the representative's claim? *(Adapted from National Education Association)*

State	Salary (in thousands of dollars)											
Massachusetts	51	59	52	47	51	55	53	51	50	50	64	55
Connecticut	57	61	51	58	53	63	57	63	55	49	54	67

8. Headaches A medical researcher wants to determine whether a new drug affects the number of headache hours experienced by headache sufferers. To do so, the researcher selects seven patients and asks each to give the number of headache hours (per day) each experiences before and after taking the drug. The results are shown in the table. At $\alpha = 0.05$, can the researcher conclude that the new drug affects the number of headache hours?

Patient	1	2	3	4	5	6	7
Headache hours (before)	0.8	2.4	2.8	2.6	2.7	0.9	1.2
Headache hours (after)	1.6	1.3	1.6	1.4	1.5	1.6	1.7

■ Extending Concepts

Wilcoxon Signed-Rank Test for *n* > 30 *If you are performing a Wilcoxon signed-rank test and the sample size n is greater than 30, you can use the Standard Normal Table and the following formula to find the test statistic.*

$$z = \frac{w_s - \dfrac{n(n+1)}{4}}{\sqrt{\dfrac{n(n+1)(2n+1)}{24}}}$$

In Exercises 9 and 10, perform the indicated Wilcoxon signed-rank test using the test statistic for n > 30.

9. Fuel Additive A petroleum engineer wants to know whether a certain fuel additive improves a car's gas mileage. To decide, the engineer records the gas mileage (in miles per gallon) of 33 cars with and without the additive. The results are shown in the table. At $\alpha = 0.10$, can the engineer conclude that the gas mileage is improved?

Car	1	2	3	4	5	6	7	8	9	10	11
Without additive	36.4	36.4	36.6	36.6	36.8	36.9	37.0	37.1	37.2	37.2	36.7
With additive	36.7	36.9	37.0	37.5	38.0	38.1	38.4	38.7	38.8	38.9	36.3

Car	12	13	14	15	16	17	18	19	20	21	22
Without additive	37.5	37.6	37.8	37.9	37.9	38.1	38.4	40.2	40.5	40.9	35.0
With additive	38.9	39.0	39.1	39.4	39.4	39.5	39.8	40.0	40.0	40.1	36.3

Car	23	24	25	26	27	28	29	30	31	32	33
Without additive	32.7	33.6	34.2	35.1	35.2	35.3	35.5	35.9	36.0	36.1	37.2
With additive	32.8	34.2	34.7	34.9	34.9	35.3	35.9	36.4	36.6	36.6	38.3

10. Fuel Additive A petroleum engineer claims that a fuel additive improves gas mileage. The table shows the gas mileage (in miles per gallon) of 32 cars measured with and without the fuel additive. Test the petroleum engineer's claim at $\alpha = 0.05$.

Car	1	2	3	4	5	6	7	8	9	10	11
Without additive	34.0	34.2	34.4	34.4	34.6	34.8	35.6	35.7	30.2	31.6	32.3
With additive	36.6	36.7	37.2	37.2	37.3	37.4	37.6	37.7	34.2	34.9	34.9

Car	12	13	14	15	16	17	18	19	20	21	22
Without additive	33.0	33.1	33.7	33.7	33.8	35.7	36.1	36.1	36.6	36.6	36.8
With additive	34.9	35.7	36.0	36.2	36.5	37.8	38.1	38.2	38.3	38.3	38.7

Car	23	24	25	26	27	28	29	30	31	32
Without additive	37.1	37.1	37.2	37.9	37.9	38.0	38.0	38.4	38.8	42.1
With additive	38.8	38.9	39.1	39.1	39.2	39.4	39.8	40.3	40.8	43.2

CASE STUDY

Earnings by College Degree

Each month, the U.S. Census Bureau conducts the *Current Population Survey* (*CPS*) for the U.S. Bureau of Labor Statistics. The survey provides information about the characteristics of the U.S. workforce, including employment, unemployment, earnings, and hours of work. The survey also provides demographics on characteristics such as age, sex, race, marital status, and educational attainment. This information is essential for interpreting the economic condition of the entire country.

The data from the *CPS* are available in data files and reports issued by the U.S. Census Bureau. One such report discusses the earnings of the U.S. workforce by the type of college degree earned. The table shows the annual earnings (in dollars) by the highest degree earned for randomly selected members of the U.S. workforce in a recent year.

Earnings (in dollars) by Highest Degree			
All persons with a doctorate	Males with a doctorate	All persons with a bachelor's	Females with a bachelor's
103,890	118,363	56,589	41,162
76,554	93,022	64,943	41,165
112,718	74,763	60,523	39,423
75,622	115,783	51,626	21,161
88,569	88,354	54,633	39,196
84,117	100,291	42,097	30,373
101,662	91,342	68,245	51,228
82,322	94,295	32,128	36,078
107,724	75,840	52,349	30,297
93,570	177,225	33,100	39,950

■ Exercises

1. Construct a box-and-whisker plot for each group on the same graph. Do any of the median earnings appear to be the same? Different?

   (a) All persons with a doctorate degree

   (b) Males with a doctorate degree

   (c) All persons with a bachelor's degree

   (d) Females with a bachelor's degree

In Exercises 2–5, use the sign test to test the claim. What can you conclude? Use α = 0.05.

2. The median earnings for all persons with a doctorate degree are less than or equal to $92,000.

3. The median earnings for males with a doctorate degree are $102,500.

4. The median earnings for all persons with a bachelor's degree are greater than or equal to $56,000.

5. The median earnings for females with a bachelor's degree are different from $42,000.

In Exercises 6 and 7, use the Wilcoxon rank sum test to test the claim. Use α = 0.01.

6. There is no difference in the median earnings for all persons with a doctorate degree and the median earnings for males with a doctorate degree.

7. There is a difference in the median earnings for all persons with a bachelor's degree and the median earnings for females with a bachelor's degree.

11.3 The Kruskal-Wallis Test

The Kruskal-Wallis Test

▶ The Kruskal-Wallis Test

In Section 10.4, you learned how to use one-way ANOVA techniques to compare the means of three or more populations. When using one-way ANOVA, you should verify that each independent sample is selected from a population that is normally, or approximately normally, distributed. If, however, you cannot verify that the populations are normal, you can still compare the distributions of three or more populations. To do so, you can use the Kruskal-Wallis test.

> ### DEFINITION
>
> The **Kruskal-Wallis test** is a nonparametric test that can be used to determine whether three or more independent samples were selected from populations having the same distribution.

The null and alternative hypotheses for the Kruskal-Wallis test are as follows.

H_0: There is no difference in the distribution of the populations.

H_a: There is a difference in the distribution of the populations.

Two conditions for using the Kruskal-Wallis test are that each sample must be randomly selected and the size of each sample must be at least 5. If these conditions are met, the sampling distribution for the Kruskal-Wallis test is approximated by a chi-square distribution with $k - 1$ degrees of freedom, where k is the number of samples. You can calculate the Kruskal-Wallis test statistic using the following formula.

> ### TEST STATISTIC FOR THE KRUSKAL-WALLIS TEST
>
> Given three or more independent samples, the test statistic H for the Kruskal-Wallis test is
>
> $$H = \frac{12}{N(N+1)}\left(\frac{R_1^2}{n_1} + \frac{R_2^2}{n_2} + \cdots + \frac{R_k^2}{n_k}\right) - 3(N+1)$$
>
> where
>
> k represents the number of samples,
>
> n_i is the size of the ith sample,
>
> N is the sum of the sample sizes,
>
> and
>
> R_i is the sum of the ranks of the ith sample.

Performing a Kruskal-Wallis test consists of combining and ranking the sample data. The data are then separated according to sample and the sum of the ranks of each sample is calculated.

These sums are then used to calculate the test statistic H, which is an approximation of the variance of the rank sums. If the samples are selected from populations having the same distribution, the sums of the ranks will be approximately equal, H will be small, and the null hypothesis should not be rejected.

If, however, the samples are selected from populations not having the same distribution, the sums of the ranks will be quite different, H will be large, and the null hypothesis should be rejected.

Because the null hypothesis is rejected only when H is significantly large, the Kruskal-Wallis test is always a right-tailed test.

GUIDELINES

Performing a Kruskal-Wallis Test

In Words	*In Symbols*
1. State the claim. Identify the null and alternative hypotheses.	State H_0 and H_a.
2. Specify the level of significance.	Identify α.
3. Identify the degrees of freedom.	d.f. = $k - 1$
4. Determine the critical value and the rejection region.	Use Table 6 in Appendix B.
5. Find the sum of the ranks for each sample. **a.** List the combined data in ascending order. **b.** Rank the combined data.	
6. Calculate the test statistic.	$H = \dfrac{12}{N(N+1)} \cdot \left(\dfrac{R_1^2}{n_1} + \dfrac{R_2^2}{n_2} + \cdots + \dfrac{R_k^2}{n_k} \right) - 3(N+1)$
7. Make a decision to reject or fail to reject the null hypothesis.	If H is in the rejection region, reject H_0. Otherwise, fail to reject H_0.
8. Interpret the decision in the context of the original claim.	

EXAMPLE 1

Performing a Kruskal-Wallis Test

You want to compare the hourly pay rates of actuaries who work in California, Indiana, and Maryland. To do so, you randomly select several actuaries in each state and record their hourly pay rate. The hourly pay rates are shown in the table. At $\alpha = 0.01$, can you conclude that the distributions of actuaries' hourly pay rates in these three states are different? *(Adapted from U.S. Bureau of Labor Statistics)*

Sample Hourly Pay Rates		
CA (Sample 1)	**IN** (Sample 2)	**MD** (Sample 3)
40.50	33.45	49.68
44.98	40.12	44.94
47.78	38.65	48.80
43.20	35.98	49.20
37.10	35.97	40.37
49.88	45.70	48.79
42.05	42.05	53.82
52.94	35.97	45.35
41.70	38.25	53.25
43.85		43.57

Solution You want to test the claim that there is a difference in the hourly pay rates in California, Indiana, and Maryland. The null and alternative hypotheses are as follows.

H_0: There is no difference in the hourly pay rates in the three states.

H_a: There is a difference in the hourly pay rates in the three states. (Claim)

The test is a right-tailed test with $\alpha = 0.01$ and d.f. $= k - 1 = 3 - 1 = 2$. From Table 6, the critical value is $\chi_0^2 = 9.210$. Before calculating the test statistic, you must find the sum of the ranks for each sample. The table shows the combined data listed in ascending order and the corresponding ranks.

Ordered data	Sample	Rank
33.45	IN	1
35.97	IN	2.5
35.97	IN	2.5
35.98	IN	4
37.10	CA	5
38.25	IN	6
38.65	IN	7
40.12	IN	8
40.37	MD	9
40.50	CA	10

Ordered data	Sample	Rank
41.70	CA	11
42.05	IN	12.5
42.05	CA	12.5
43.20	CA	14
43.57	MD	15
43.85	CA	16
44.94	MD	17
44.98	CA	18
45.35	MD	19
45.70	IN	20

Ordered data	Sample	Rank
47.78	CA	21
48.79	MD	22
48.80	MD	23
49.20	MD	24
49.68	MD	25
49.88	CA	26
52.94	CA	27
53.25	MD	28
53.82	MD	29

PICTURING the WORLD

The following randomly collected data were used to compare the water temperature (in degrees Fahrenheit) of cities bordering the Gulf of Mexico. (Adapted from National Oceanographic Data Center)

Cedar Key, FL	Eugene Island, LA	Dauphin Island, AL
62	51	63
69	55	51
77	57	54
59	63	60
60	74	75
75	82	80
83	85	70
65	60	78
79	64	82
86	76	84
82	83	
	86	

At $\alpha = 0.05$, can you conclude that the temperature distributions of the three cities are different?

The sum of the ranks for each sample is as follows.

$$R_1 = 5 + 10 + 11 + 12.5 + 14 + 16 + 18 + 21 + 26 + 27 = 160.5$$
$$R_2 = 1 + 2.5 + 2.5 + 4 + 6 + 7 + 8 + 12.5 + 20 + 63.5$$
$$R_3 = 9 + 15 + 17 + 19 + 22 + 23 + 24 + 25 + 28 + 29 = 211$$

Using these sums and the values $n_1 = 10$, $n_2 = 9$, $n_3 = 10$, and $N = 29$, the test statistic is

$$H = \frac{12}{29(29+1)}\left(\frac{160.5^2}{10} + \frac{63.5^2}{9} + \frac{211^2}{10}\right) - 3(29+1) \approx 13.119.$$

From the graph at the right, you can see that the test statistic H is in the rejection region. So, you should decide to reject the null hypothesis.

Interpretation At the 1% level of significance, you can conclude that there is a difference in actuaries' hourly pay rates in California, Indiana, and Maryland.

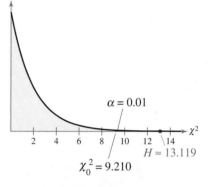

▶ Try It Yourself 1

You want to compare the salaries of pharmacists who work in Colorado, Michigan, and North Carolina. To compare the salaries, you randomly select 10 pharmacists in each state and record their salary. The salaries (in thousands of dollars) are listed in the table. At $\alpha = 0.10$, can you conclude that the distributions of the pharmacists' salaries in these three states are different? *(Adapted from U.S. Bureau of Labor Statistics)*

Sample Salaries		
CO (Sample 1)	MI (Sample 2)	NC (Sample 3)
89.75	93.92	105.77
91.55	106.78	98.34
98.99	98.21	89.92
96.24	93.76	87.25
91.17	89.65	95.36
92.85	94.42	96.02
87.70	95.10	94.72
93.12	86.85	94.75
94.55	94.45	110.99
97.35	96.31	100.27

a. *Identify* the claim and *state* H_0 and H_a.
b. *Specify* the level of significance α.
c. *Identify* the degrees of freedom.
d. *Determine* the critical value and the rejection region.
e. *List* the combined data in ascending order, *rank* the data, and *find* the sum of the ranks of each sample.
f. *Calculate* the test statistic.
g. *Decide* whether to reject the null hypothesis. Use a graph if necessary.
h. *Interpret* the decision in the context of the original claim.

Answer: Page A49

11.3 EXERCISES

■ Building Basic Skills and Vocabulary

1. What are the conditions for using a Kruskal-Wallis test?

2. Explain why the Kruskal-Wallis test is always a right-tailed test.

■ Using and Interpreting Concepts

Performing a Kruskal-Wallis Test *In Exercises 3–6, (a) write the claim mathematically and identify H_0 and H_a, (b) determine the critical value, (c) find the sums of the ranks for each sample and calculate the test statistic, (d) decide whether to reject or fail to reject the null hypothesis, and (e) interpret the decision in the context of the original claim.*

3. Home Insurance The table shows the annual premium for a random sample of home insurance policies in Arizona, Florida, and Louisiana. At $\alpha = 0.05$, can you conclude that the distributions of the annual premiums in these three states are different? *(Adapted from Insurance Information Institute)*

State	Annual Premium (in dollars)						
Arizona	642	750	579	495	836	610	725
Florida	1225	1139	929	897	944	1079	835
Louisiana	1369	1115	1289	920	995	870	1025

4. Home Insurance An independent insurance representative wants to determine whether there is a difference in the annual premiums for home insurance in three states: New Jersey, New York, and Pennsylvania. To do so, the representative randomly selects several homes in each state and records the annual premium for each in the table shown. At $\alpha = 0.05$, can the representative conclude that the distributions of the annual premiums in these states are different? *(Adapted from Insurance Information Institute)*

State	Annual Premium (in dollars)						
New Jersey	639	588	710	799	669	617	625
New York	785	890	807	693	759	975	691
Pennsylvania	593	545	650	718	479	590	

5. Annual Salaries The table shows the annual salaries for a random sample of workers in Georgia, Nevada, Ohio, and Pennsylvania. At $\alpha = 0.10$, can you conclude that the distributions of the annual salaries in these four states are different? *(Adapted from U.S. Census Bureau)*

State	Annual Salary (in thousands of dollars)						
Georgia	31.4	40.5	35.9	24.7	46.9	37.5	42.3
Nevada	52.7	39.1	29.5	34.5	38.8	37.1	46.2
Ohio	27.1	36.4	49.9	55.2	32.9	30.1	33.9
Pennsylvania	37.3	29.5	50.9	49.8	40.2	36.9	37.5

6. Annual Salaries   You are writing an article concerning the annual salaries of workers in four U.S. states: Colorado, Kentucky, Mississippi, and Tennessee. The annual salaries of randomly selected workers from each state are shown in the table. Can you write in your report that the distributions of the annual salaries in these four states are different? Use $\alpha = 0.10$. *(Adapted from U.S. Census Bureau)*

State	Annual Salary (in thousands of dollars)						
Colorado	45.6	43.2	37.9	49.1	40.3	39.9	45.5
Kentucky	33.2	41.9	40.3	33.5	30.7	31.2	32.9
Mississippi	29.1	19.5	30.5	32.9	28.6	34.9	27.2
Tennessee	31.3	34.9	43.5	29.1	36.8	34.9	40.1

■ Extending Concepts

Comparing Two Tests   *In Exercises 7 and 8, perform the indicated test using*

(a) *a Kruskal-Wallis test.*

(b) *a one-way ANOVA test, assuming that each population is normally distributed and the population variances are equal.*

(c) *Compare the results.*

If convenient, use technology to solve the problem.

 7. Hospital Patient Stays   An insurance underwriter reports that the mean number of days patients spend in a hospital differs according to the region of the United States in which the patient lives. The table shows the number of days randomly selected patients spent in a hospital in four U.S. regions. At $\alpha = 0.01$, can you support the underwriter's claim? *(Adapted from U.S. National Center for Health Statistics)*

Region	Number of Days									
Northeast	8	6	6	3	5	11	3	8	1	6
Midwest	5	4	3	9	1	4	6	3	4	7
South	5	8	1	5	8	7	5	1		
West	2	3	6	6	5	4	3	6	5	

 8. Energy Consumption   The table shows the energy consumed (in millions of Btu) in one year for a random sample of households from four U.S. regions. At $\alpha = 0.01$, can you conclude that the mean energy consumptions are different? *(Adapted from U.S. Energy Information Administration)*

Region	Energy Consumed (in millions of Btu)										
Northeast	72	106	151	138	104	108	95	134	100	174	
Midwest	84	183	194	165	120	212	148	129	113	62	97
South	91	40	72	91	147	74	70	67			
West	74	32	78	28	106	39	118	63	70	56	

11.4 Rank Correlation

The Spearman Rank Correlation Coefficient

▸ The Spearman Rank Correlation Coefficient

In Section 9.1, you learned how to measure the strength of the relationship between two variables using the Pearson correlation coefficient r. Two requirements for the Pearson correlation coefficient are that the variables are linearly related and that the population represented by each variable is normally distributed. If these requirements cannot be met, you can examine the relationship between two variables using the nonparametric equivalent to the Pearson correlation coefficient—the Spearman rank correlation coefficient.

The Spearman rank correlation coefficient has several advantages over the Pearson correlation coefficient. For instance, the Spearman rank correlation coefficient can be used to describe the relationship between linear or nonlinear data. The Spearman rank correlation coefficient can be used for data at the ordinal level. And, the Spearman rank correlation coefficient is easier to calculate by hand than the Pearson coefficient.

DEFINITION

The **Spearman rank correlation coefficient r_s** is a measure of the strength of the relationship between two variables. The Spearman rank correlation coefficient is calculated using the ranks of paired sample data entries. The formula for the Spearman rank correlation coefficient is

$$r_s = 1 - \frac{6\sum d^2}{n(n^2 - 1)}$$

where

n is the number of paired data entries

and

d is the difference between the ranks of a paired data entry.

The values of r_s range from -1 to $+1$, inclusive. If the ranks of corresponding data pairs are exactly identical, r_s is equal to $+1$. If the ranks are in "reverse" order, r_s is equal to -1. If the ranks of corresponding data pairs have no relationship, r_s is equal to 0.

After calculating the Spearman rank correlation coefficient, you can determine whether the correlation between the variables is significant. You can make this determination by performing a hypothesis test for the population correlation coefficient ρ_s. The null and alternative hypotheses for this test are as follows.

H_0: $\rho_s = 0$ (There is no correlation between the variables.)

H_a: $\rho_s \neq 0$ (There is a significant correlation between the variables.)

The critical values for the Spearman rank correlation coefficient are listed in Table 10 of Appendix B. Table 10 lists critical values for selected levels of significance and for sample sizes of 30 or less. The test statistic for the hypothesis test is the Spearman rank correlation coefficient r_s.

GUIDELINES

Testing the Significance of the Spearman Rank Correlation Coefficient

In Words	*In Symbols*
1. State the null and alternative hypotheses.	State H_0 and H_a.
2. Specify the level of significance.	Identify α.
3. Determine the critical value.	Use Table 10 in Appendix B.
4. Find the test statistic.	$r_s = 1 - \dfrac{6\sum d^2}{n(n^2 - 1)}$
5. Make a decision to reject or fail to reject the null hypothesis.	If $\lvert r_s \rvert$ is greater than the critical value, reject H_0. Otherwise, fail to reject H_0.
6. Interpret the decision in the context of the original claim.	

EXAMPLE 1

The Spearman Rank Correlation Coefficient

The table shows the prices (in dollars per 100 pounds) received by U.S. farmers for beef and lamb from 1999 to 2005. At $\alpha = 0.05$, can you conclude that there is a correlation between the beef and lamb prices? *(Source: U.S. Department of Agriculture)*

Year	Beef	Lamb
1999	63.4	74.5
2000	68.6	79.8
2001	71.3	66.9
2002	66.5	74.1
2003	79.7	94.4
2004	85.8	101.0
2005	89.7	110.0

Solution   The null and alternative hypotheses are as follows.

H_0: $\rho_s = 0$ (There is no correlation between the beef and lamb prices.)

H_a: $\rho_s \neq 0$ (There is a correlation between the beef and lamb prices.)
(Claim)

PICTURING the WORLD

The table lists the number of men and women (in thousands) who graduated from a U.S. college with a bachelor's degree from 1996 to 2005. (Adapted from National Center for Educational Statistics)

Year	Male	Female
1996	522	642
1997	521	652
1998	520	664
1999	519	682
2000	530	708
2001	532	712
2002	550	742
2003	573	775
2004	595	804
2005	613	826

Does a correlation exist between the number of men and women who graduate with bachelor's degrees each year? Use $\alpha = 0.05$.

Each data set has seven entries. From Table 10 with $\alpha = 0.05$ and $n = 7$, the critical value is 0.786. Before calculating the test statistic, you must find Σd^2, the sum of the squares of the differences of the ranks of the data sets. You can use a table to calculate d^2, as shown below.

Beef prices	Rank	Lamb prices	Rank	d	d^2
63.4	1	74.5	3	−2	4
68.6	3	79.8	4	−1	1
71.3	4	66.9	1	3	9
66.5	2	74.1	2	0	0
79.7	5	94.4	5	0	0
85.8	6	101.0	6	0	0
89.7	7	110.0	7	0	0
					$\Sigma d^2 = 14$

When $n = 7$ and $\Sigma d^2 = 14$, the test statistic is

$$r_s = 1 - \frac{6\Sigma d^2}{n(n^2 - 1)}$$

$$= 1 - \frac{6(14)}{7(7^2 - 1)}$$

$$= 0.75.$$

Because $|0.75| < 0.786$, you should fail to reject the null hypothesis.

Interpretation At the 5% significance level, you cannot conclude that there is a significant correlation between beef and lamb prices between 1999 and 2005.

▶ Try It Yourself 1

The table lists the prices (in dollars per bushel) received by U.S. farmers for oat and wheat from 1998 to 2006. At $\alpha = 0.05$, can you conclude that there is a correlation between the oat and wheat prices? *(Source: U.S. Department of Agriculture)*

Year	1998	1999	2000	2001	2002	2003	2004	2005	2006
Oat	1.10	1.12	1.10	1.59	1.81	1.48	1.48	1.63	1.85
Wheat	2.65	2.48	2.62	2.78	3.56	3.40	3.40	3.42	4.25

a. *State* the null and alternative hypotheses.
b. *Specify* the level of significance α.
c. *Determine* the critical value.
d. *Use a table* to calculate Σd^2.
e. *Find* the standardized test statistic.
f. *Make a decision* to reject or fail to reject the null hypothesis.
g. *Interpret* the decision in the context of the original claim.

Answer: Page A49

Study Tip

Remember that in the case of a tie between data entries, use the average of the corresponding ranks.

11.4 EXERCISES

■ Building Basic Skills and Vocabulary

1. What are some advantages of the Spearman rank correlation coefficient over the Pearson correlation coefficient?

2. What does it mean when r_s is equal to 1? What does it mean when r_s is equal to -1? What does it mean when r_s is equal to 0?

■ Using and Interpreting Concepts

Testing a Claim *In Exercises 3–6, (a) identify the claim and state H_0 and H_a, (b) determine the critical value using Table 10 in Appendix B, (c) find the standardized test statistic r_s, (d) decide whether to reject or fail to reject the null hypothesis, and (e) interpret the decision in the context of the original claim.*

3. Farming: Debt and Income In an agricultural report, a commodities analyst suggests that there is a correlation between debt and income in the farming business. The table shows the total debts and total incomes for farms in seven states for a recent year. At $\alpha = 0.01$, is there enough evidence to support the analyst's claim? *(Adapted from U.S. Department of Agriculture)*

State	Debt (in millions of dollars)	Income (in millions of dollars)
California	19,955	28,926
Illinois	10,480	8,630
Iowa	14,434	12,942
Minnesota	9,982	8,807
Nebraska	10,085	11,028
North Carolina	4,235	7,008
Texas	13,286	15,268

4. Digital Cameras Is the price of a digital camera related to its quality? To answer this question, you randomly select 11 digital cameras and determine the overall score and price of each. The overall score represents the picture quality, weight, and useful features of the camera. The results of the study are shown in the table. At $\alpha = 0.05$, can you conclude that there is a correlation between the overall score and the price? *(Source: Consumer Reports)*

Overall score	Price (in dollars)	Overall score	Price (in dollars)
81	280	73	280
80	330	72	230
79	250	70	200
76	300	67	240
75	230	59	100
74	300		

5. Dishwasher Detergents   The table shows the overall scores and the cost per load for eight dishwasher detergents. The overall score represents the cleaning test results for the dishwasher detergent. At $\alpha = 0.01$, can you conclude that there is a correlation between the overall score and the price? *(Source: Consumer Reports)*

Overall score	87	86	86	84	74	69	67	63
Cost (in cents)	17	17	19	19	10	5	21	14

6. Air Conditioners   The table shows the overall scores and the prices for 12 different models of air conditioners. The overall score represents the comfort, noise, and energy efficiency of the air conditioner. At $\alpha = 0.10$, can you conclude that there is a correlation between the overall score and the price? *(Source: Consumer Reports)*

Overall score	80	76	76	75	74	72
Price (in dollars)	200	150	200	180	170	120

Overall score	72	71	70	69	59	68
Price (in dollars)	210	210	150	140	170	115

Test Scores and GNP   *In Exercises 7–10, use the following table. The table shows the average achievement score of 15-year-olds in science and mathematics along with the gross national product (GNP) of nine countries for a recent year. (The GNP is a measure of a nation's total economic activity.)* *(Adapted from Organization for Economic Cooperation and Development; World Bank)*

Country	Science average	Mathematics average	GNP (in billions of dollars)
Australia	525	524	437
Canada	519	533	774
Czech Republic	523	517	73
France	511	511	1,522
Italy	487	466	1,243
Japan	548	534	4,361
Mexico	405	385	637
Spain	487	485	701
USA	491	483	11,013

7. Science and GNP   At $\alpha = 0.05$, can you conclude that there is a correlation between science achievement scores and GNP?

8. Math and GNP   At $\alpha = 0.05$, can you conclude that there is a correlation between mathematics achievement scores and GNP?

9. Science and Math   At $\alpha = 0.05$, can you conclude that there is a correlation between science and mathematics achievement scores?

10. Writing a Summary   Use the results from Exercises 7–9 to write a summary about the correlation (or lack of correlation) between test scores and GNP.

■ Extending Concepts

Testing the Rank Correlation Coefficient for *n* > 30 *If you are testing the significance of the Spearman rank correlation coefficient and the sample size n is greater than 30, you can use the following formula to find the critical value.*

$$\frac{\pm z}{\sqrt{n-1}}, \ z \text{ corresponds to the level of significance}$$

In Exercises 11 and 12, perform the indicated test.

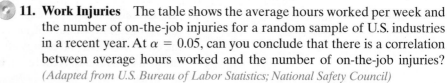

11. Work Injuries The table shows the average hours worked per week and the number of on-the-job injuries for a random sample of U.S. industries in a recent year. At $\alpha = 0.05$, can you conclude that there is a correlation between average hours worked and the number of on-the-job injuries? *(Adapted from U.S. Bureau of Labor Statistics; National Safety Council)*

Hours worked	47.6	44.1	45.6	45.5	44.5	47.3		45.9	45.5	43.7	44.8	42.5
Injuries	16	33	25	33	18	20	21	18	21	28	15	26

Hours worked	46.5	42.3	45.5	41.8	43.1	44.4	44.5	43.7	44.9	47.8	46.6	45.5
Injuries	34	32	26	28	22	19	23	20	28	24	26	29

Hours worked	43.5	42.8	44.8	43.5	47.0	44.5	50.1	46.7	43.1
Injuries	21	28	23	26	24	20	28	26	25

12. Work Injuries in Construction The table shows the average hours worked per week and the number of on-the-job injuries for a random sample of U.S. construction companies in a recent year. At $\alpha = 0.05$, can you conclude that there is a correlation between average hours worked and the number of on-the-job injuries? *(Adapted from U.S. Bureau of Labor Statistics; National Safety Council)*

Hours worked	40.5	38.3	37.8	38.2	38.6	41.2	39.0	41.0	40.6	44.1	39.7	41.2
Injuries	12	13	19	18	22	22	17	13	15	10	18	19

Hours worked	41.1	38.2	42.3	39.2	36.1	36.2	38.7	36.0	37.3	36.5	37.9	38.0
Injuries	13	24	12	12	13	15	18	11	24	16	13	23

Hours worked	36.7	40.1	35.5	38.2	42.3	39.0	39.6	39.1	39.6	39.1
Injuries	14	10	5	14	13	18	15	23	15	23

11.5 The Runs Test

What You
SHOULD LEARN

▸ How to use the runs test to determine whether a data set is random

The Runs Test for Randomness

▸ The Runs Test for Randomness

In obtaining a sample of data, it is important for the data to be selected randomly. But how do you know if the sample data are truly random? One way to test for randomness in a data set is to use a *runs test for randomness*.

Before using a runs test for randomness, you must first know how to determine the number of runs in a data set.

DEFINITION

A **run** is a sequence of data having the same characteristic. Each run is preceded by and followed by data with a different characteristic or by no data at all. The number of data in a run is called the **length** of the run.

EXAMPLE 1

Finding the Number of Runs

A liquid-dispensing machine has been designed to fill one-liter bottles. A quality control inspector decides whether each bottle is filled to an acceptable level and passes inspection (P) or fails inspection (F). Determine the number of runs for each sequence and find the length of each run.

1. $P\ P\ P\ P\ P\ P\ P\ P\ F\ F\ F\ F\ F\ F\ F\ F$
2. $P\ F\ P\ F\ P\ F\ P\ F\ P\ F\ P\ F\ P\ F\ P\ F$
3. $P\ P\ F\ F\ F\ F\ P\ F\ F\ F\ P\ P\ P\ P\ P$

Solution

1. There are two runs. The first 8 Ps form a run of length 8 and the first 8 Fs form another run of length 8, as shown below.

$$\underbrace{P\,P\,P\,P\,P\,P\,P\,P}_{\text{1st run}}\quad\underbrace{F\,F\,F\,F\,F\,F\,F\,F}_{\text{2nd run}}$$

2. There are 16 runs each of length 1, as shown below.

$$\underbrace{P}_{\text{1st run}}\ \underbrace{F}_{\text{2nd run...}}\ P\ F\ P\ F\ P\ F\ P\ F\ P\ F\ P\ F\ P\ \underbrace{F}_{\text{...16th run}}$$

3. There are 5 runs, the first of length 2, the second of length 4, the third of length 1, the fourth of length 3, and the fifth of length 6, as shown below.

$$\underbrace{P\,P}_{\text{1st run}}\ \underbrace{F\,F\,F\,F}_{\text{2nd run}}\ \underbrace{P}_{\text{3rd run}}\ \underbrace{F\,F\,F}_{\text{4th run}}\ \underbrace{P\,P\,P\,P\,P}_{\text{5th run}}$$

▶ **Try It Yourself 1**

A machine produces engine parts. An inspector measures the diameter of each engine part and determines if the part passes inspection (P) or fails inspection (F). The results are shown below. Determine the number of runs in the sequence and find the length of each run.

$$P\ P\ P\ F\ P\ F\ P\ P\ P\ P\ F\ F\ P\ F\ P\ P\ F\ F\ F\ P\ P\ P\ F\ P\ P\ P$$

a. *Separate the data* each time there is a change in the characteristic of the data.
b. *Count the number of groups* to determine the number of runs.
c. *Count the number of data* within each run to determine the length.

Answer: Page A50

When each value in a set of data can be categorized into one of two separate categories, you can use the runs test for randomness to determine whether the data are random.

DEFINITION

The **runs test for randomness** is a nonparametric test that can be used to determine whether a sequence of sample data is random.

The runs test for randomness considers the number of runs in a sequence of sample data in order to test whether a sequence is random. If a sequence has too few or too many runs, it is usually not random. For example, the sequence

$$P\ P\ P\ P\ P\ P\ P\ P\ F\ F\ F\ F\ F\ F\ F\ F$$

from Example 1, Part 1 has too few runs (only 2 runs). The sequence

$$P\ F\ P\ F\ P\ F\ P\ F\ P\ F\ P\ F\ P\ F\ P\ F$$

from Example 1, Part 2 has too many runs (16 runs). So, these sample data are probably not random.

You can use a hypothesis test to determine whether the number of runs in a sequence of sample data is too high or too low. The runs test is a two-tailed test, and the null and alternative hypotheses are as follows.

H_0: The sequence of data is random.

H_a: The sequence of data is not random.

When using the runs test, let n_1 represent the number of data that have one characteristic and let n_2 represent the number of data that have the second characteristic. It does not matter which characteristic you choose to be represented by n_1. Let G represent the number of runs.

n_1 = number of data with one characteristic

n_2 = number of data with other characteristic

G = number of runs

Table 12 in Appendix B lists the critical values for the runs test for selected values of n_1 and n_2 at the $\alpha = 0.05$ level of significance. (In this text, you will use only the $\alpha = 0.05$ level of significance when performing runs tests.) If n_1 or n_2 is greater than 20, you can use the standard normal distribution to find the critical values.

You can calculate the test statistic for the runs test as follows.

TEST STATISTIC FOR THE RUNS TEST

When $n_1 \leq 20$ and $n_2 \leq 20$, the test statistic for the runs test is G, the number of runs.

When $n_1 > 20$ or $n_2 > 20$, the test statistic for the runs test is

$$z = \frac{G - \mu_G}{\sigma_G}$$

where

$$\mu_G = \frac{2n_1 n_2}{n_1 + n_2} + 1 \quad \text{and} \quad \sigma_G = \sqrt{\frac{2n_1 n_2 (2n_1 n_2 - n_1 - n_2)}{(n_1 + n_2)^2 (n_1 + n_2 - 1)}}.$$

GUIDELINES

Performing a Runs Test for Randomness

In Words	*In Symbols*
1. State the claim. Identify the null and alternative hypotheses.	State H_0 and H_a.
2. Specify the level of significance. (Use $\alpha = 0.05$ for the runs test.)	Identify α.
3. Determine the number of data that have each characteristic and the number of runs.	Determine n_1, n_2, and G.
4. Determine the critical values.	If $n_1 \leq 20$ and $n_2 \leq 20$, use Table 12 in Appendix B. If $n_1 > 20$ or $n_2 > 20$, use Table 4 in Appendix B.
5. Calculate the test statistic.	If $n_1 \leq 20$ and $n_2 \leq 20$, use G. If $n_1 > 20$ or $n_2 > 20$, use $$z = \frac{G - \mu_G}{\sigma_G}.$$
6. Make a decision to reject or fail to reject the null hypothesis.	If G is less than or equal to the lower critical value or greater than or equal to the upper critical value, reject H_0. Otherwise, fail to reject H_0. Or, if z is in the rejection region, reject H_0. Otherwise, fail to reject H_0.
7. Interpret the decision in the context of the original claim.	

EXAMPLE 2

Using the Runs Test

A foreman for a construction company records injuries reported by workers during his shift. The following sequence shows whether any injuries were reported during each month in a recent year. *I* represents a month in which at least one injury was reported and *N* represents a month in which no injuries were reported. At $\alpha = 0.05$, can you conclude that the occurrence of injuries each month is not random?

$$I\ I\ N\ N\ N\ I\ N\ I\ I\ N\ N\ N$$

Solution The claim is "The occurrence of injuries is not random." To test this claim, use the following null and alternative hypotheses.

H_0: The occurrence of injuries is random.

H_a: The occurrence of injuries is not random. (Claim)

To find the critical values, first determine n_1, the number of *I*s; n_2, the number of *N*s; and *G*, the number of runs.

$$\underbrace{I\ I}_{}\ \underbrace{N\ N\ N}_{}\ \underbrace{I}_{}\ \underbrace{N}_{}\ \underbrace{I\ I}_{}\ \underbrace{N\ N\ N}_{}$$

| 1st run | 2nd run | 3rd run | 4th run | 5th run | 6th run |

n_1 = number of *I*s = 5

n_2 = number of *N*s = 7

G = number of runs = 6

Because $n_1 \leq 20$, $n_2 \leq 20$, and $\alpha = 0.05$, use Table 12 to find the lower critical value 3 and the upper critical value 11. The test statistic is the number of runs $G = 6$. Because the test statistic *G* is between the critical values 3 and 11, you should fail to reject the null hypothesis.

Interpretation At the 5% significance level, you do not have enough evidence to support the claim that the occurrence of injuries is not random. So, it appears that the injuries reported by workers during the foreman's shift occur randomly.

▶ **Try It Yourself 2**

The genders of 14 students as they enter a classroom are shown below, where *F* represents the females and *M* represents the males. At $\alpha = 0.05$, can you conclude that the sequence of genders is not random?

$$F\ F\ F\ M\ M\ F\ F\ M\ F\ M\ M\ F\ F\ F$$

a. *Identify* the claim and *state* H_0 and H_a.
b. *Specify* the level of significance α.
c. *Determine* n_1, n_2, and *G*.
d. *Determine* the critical values.
e. *Calculate* the test statistic *G*.
f. *Decide* whether to reject the null hypothesis.
g. *Interpret* the decision in the context of the original claim.

Answer: Page A50

EXAMPLE 3

Using the Runs Test

You want to determine whether the selection of recently hired employees in a large company is random with respect to gender. The genders of 36 recently hired employees are shown below. At $\alpha = 0.05$, can you conclude that the selection is not random?

M M F F F F M M M M M M
F F F F F M M M M M M M
F F F M M M M F M M F M

Solution   The claim is "The selection of employees is not random." To test this claim, use the following null and alternative hypotheses.

H_0: The selection of employees is random.

H_a: The selection of employees is not random. (Claim)

To find the critical values, first determine n_1, the number of Fs; n_2, the number of Ms; and G, the number of runs.

$$\underbrace{M\,M}_{\text{1st run}}\ \underbrace{F\,F\,F\,F}_{\text{2nd run}}\ \underbrace{M\,M\,M\,M\,M\,M}_{\text{3rd run}}$$

$$\underbrace{F\,F\,F\,F\,F}_{\text{4th run}}\ \underbrace{M\,M\,M\,M\,M\,M\,M}_{\text{5th run}}$$

$$\underbrace{F\,F\,F}_{\text{6th run}}\ \underbrace{M\,M\,M\,M}_{\text{7th run}}\ \underbrace{F}_{\substack{\text{8th}\\\text{run}}}\ \underbrace{M\,M}_{\substack{\text{9th}\\\text{run}}}\ \underbrace{F}_{\substack{\text{10th}\\\text{run}}}\ \underbrace{M}_{\substack{\text{11th}\\\text{run}}}$$

$n_1 = $ number of Fs $= 14$

$n_2 = $ number of Ms $= 22$

$G = $ number of runs $= 11$

Because $n_2 > 20$, use Table 4 in Appendix B to find that the critical values at the $\alpha = 0.05$ level of significance are

$-z_0 = -1.96$

and

$z_0 = 1.96.$

Before calculating the test statistic, find the values of μ_G and σ_G, as follows.

$$\mu_G = \frac{2n_1 n_2}{n_1 + n_2} + 1$$

$$= \frac{2(14)(22)}{14 + 22} + 1$$

$$= \frac{616}{36} + 1$$

$$\approx 18.11$$

PICTURING the WORLD

The table shows the NFL conference of each winning team from Super Bowl I to Super Bowl XLI, where *A* represents the American Football Conference and *N* represents the National Football Conference. (Source: NFL.com)

Year	Confer-ence	Year	Confer-ence
1967	N	1988	N
1968	N	1989	N
1969	A	1990	N
1970	A	1991	N
1971	A	1992	N
1972	N	1993	N
1973	A	1994	N
1974	A	1995	N
1975	A	1996	N
1976	A	1997	N
1977	A	1998	A
1978	N	1999	A
1979	A	2000	N
1980	A	2001	A
1981	A	2002	A
1982	N	2003	N
1983	N	2004	A
1984	A	2005	A
1985	N	2006	A
1986	N	2007	A
1987	N		

At $\alpha = 0.05$, can you conclude that the sequence is not random?

$$\sigma_G = \sqrt{\frac{2n_1 n_2 (2n_1 n_2 - n_1 - n_2)}{(n_1 + n_2)^2 (n_1 + n_2 - 1)}}$$

$$= \sqrt{\frac{2(14)(22)[2(14)(22) - 14 - 22]}{(14 + 22)^2 (14 + 22 - 1)}}$$

$$\approx 2.81$$

You can find the test statistic as follows.

$$z = \frac{G - \mu_G}{\sigma_G}$$

$$= \frac{11 - 18.11}{2.81}$$

$$\approx -2.53$$

From the graph below, you can see that the test statistic z is in the rejection region. So, you should decide to reject the null hypothesis.

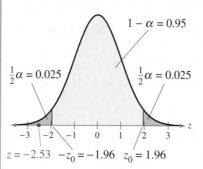

Interpretation You have enough evidence at the 5% level of significance to support the claim that the selection of employees with respect to gender is not random.

▶ Try It Yourself 3

Let S represent a day in a small town in which it snowed and let N represent a day in the same town in which it did not snow. The following are the snowfall results for the entire month of January. At $\alpha = 0.05$, can you conclude that the sequence is not random?

N N N S S N N S N S N N N N S
N S N S N N S N S S N N N N N

a. *Identify* the claim and *state* H_0 and H_a.
b. *Specify* the level of significance α.
c. *Determine* n_1, n_2, and G.
d. *Determine* the critical values.
e. *Calculate* the test statistic z.
f. *Decide* whether to reject the null hypothesis.
g. *Interpret* the decision in the context of the original claim.

Answer: Page A50

When n_1 or n_2 is greater than 20, you can also use a *P*-value to perform a hypothesis test for the randomness of the data. In Example 3, you can calculate the *P*-value to be 0.011. Because $P < \alpha$, you should reject the null hypothesis.

11.5 EXERCISES

■ Building Basic Skills and Vocabulary

Finding the Number of Runs *In Exercises 1–4, determine the number of runs in the given sequence. Then find the length of each run.*

1. *T F T F T T T F F F T F*

2. *U U D D U D U U D D U D U U*

3. *M F M F M F F F F F F M M M F F M M M*

4. *A A A B B B A B B A A A A A A B A A B A B B*

5. Find the values for n_1 and n_2 in Exercise 1.

6. Find the values for n_1 and n_2 in Exercise 2.

7. Find the values for n_1 and n_2 in Exercise 3.

8. Find the values for n_1 and n_2 in Exercise 4.

Finding Critical Values *In Exercises 9–12, use the given sequence and Table 12 in Appendix B to determine the number of runs that are considered too high and the number of runs that are considered too low for the data to be in random order.*

9. *T F T F T F T F T F T F*

10. *M F M M M M M M F F M M*

11. *N S S S N N N N S N S N S S N N N*

12. *X X X X X X X Y Y Y Y Y Y Y Y Y Y Y Y Y Y*

■ Using and Interpreting Concepts

Performing a Runs Test *In Exercises 13–18, use the runs test to*

(a) write the claim mathematically and identify H_0 and H_a.

(b) determine the critical values using Table 4 or Table 12 in Appendix B.

(c) calculate the test statistic.

(d) decide whether to reject or fail to reject the null hypothesis.

(e) interpret the decision in the context of the original claim. Use $\alpha = 0.05$.

13. Coin Toss A coach records the results of the coin toss at the beginning of each football game for a season. The results are shown, where *H* represents heads and *T* represents tails. The coach claimed the tosses were not random. Use the runs test to test the coach's claim.

H T T T H T H H T T T T H T H H

14. Council Members The mayor called on council members at a town meeting in the sequence shown, where *R* represents a Republican council member and *D* represents a Democrat council member. Can you conclude that the selection of members was not random?

R D D D R R D R D D R D D D R R D
R R R D R R R D D D R D R D R R

15. Number Generator A number generator outputs the sequence of digits shown below, where O represents an odd digit and E represents an even digit. Test the claim that the digits were not randomly generated.

O O O E E E E O O O O O E E E
O O E E E E O O O O E E E E O O

16. Dog Identifications A team of veterinarians record, in order, the genders of every dog that is microchipped at their pet hospital in one month. The genders of recently microchipped dogs are shown, where F represents a female and M represents a male. A veterinarian claims that the microchips are random by gender. Do you have enough evidence to reject the doctor's claim?

M M F M F F F F F M M M F F F
M F F F F M F F F M F F F

17. Slot Machines For every spin, a slot machine either pays out (P) or does not pay out (N). The results for a person who plays a slot machine are shown. Can you conclude that the sequence is not random?

N N N N P P N N N N N P N N N N N P
N N N N N N N N P N N N N N N N N
P N N N N P N N P P

18. Golf Tournament A golf tournament official records whether each past winner is American-born (A) or foreign-born (F). The results are shown for every year the tournament has existed. Can you conclude that the sequence is not random?

F F A F F A F F A F F A F F A F F A F F F F F
A F F A F F A F F A F F A F A F F A F F F F F A
F F F F A F F F A

■ Extending Concepts

Runs Test with Quantitative Data *In Exercises 19 and 20, use the following information to perform a runs test. You can also use the runs test for randomness with quantitative data. First, calculate the median. Then assign $+$ to those values above the median and $-$ to those values below the median. Ignore any values that are equal to the median.*

19. Daily High Temperatures The sequence shows the daily high temperatures (in degrees Fahrenheit) for a city during the month of July. Test the claim that the daily high temperatures do not occur randomly. Use $\alpha = 0.05$.

84	87	92	93	95	84	82	83	81	87	92
98	99	93	84	85	86	92	91	95	84	92
83	81	87	92	98	89	93	84	85		

20. Grade Point Averages The sequence shows the grade point averages (GPAs) of students selected from a class. Test the claim that the selection of students' GPAs was not random. Use $\alpha = 0.05$.

3.8	4.0	1.8	1.9	2.5	2.3	3.6	2.4	2.1
1.8	0.7	0.9	1.3	1.8	2.9	3.5	3.9	4.0

21. Use a technology tool to generate a sequence of 30 numbers between 1 and 99. Test the claim that the sequence of numbers is not random.

Uses

Nonparametric Tests   Before you could perform many of the hypothesis tests you learned about in previous chapters, you had to ensure that certain conditions about the population were satisfied. For example, before you could run a *t*-test, you had to verify that the population is normally distributed. One advantage of the nonparametric tests shown in this chapter is that they are distribution free. That is, they do not require any particular information about the population or populations being tested. Another advantage of nonparametric tests is that they are easier to perform than their parametric counterparts. This means that they are easier to understand and quicker to use. Nonparametric tests can often be used when data are at the nominal or ordinal level.

Abuses

Insufficient Evidence   Stronger evidence is needed to reject a null hypothesis in a nonparametric test than it is to reject a null hypothesis in a corresponding parametric test. That is, when you are trying to support a claim represented by the alternative hypothesis, you might need a larger sample when performing a nonparametric test. If the outcome of a nonparametric test results in failing to reject the null hypothesis, you should investigate the sample size used. It may be that a larger sample will produce different results.

Using an Inappropriate Test   In general, when information about the populations (such as the condition of normality) is known, it is more efficient to use a parametric test. However, if information about the population is not known, nonparametric tests can be helpful.

■ EXERCISES

1. ***Insufficient Evidence***   Give an example of a nonparametric test in which there is not enough evidence to reject the null hypothesis.

2. ***Using an Inappropriate Test***   Discuss the nonparametric tests described in this chapter and match each test with its parametric counterpart, which you studied in earlier chapters.

11 CHAPTER SUMMARY

What did you learn?

	EXAMPLE(S)	REVIEW EXERCISES

Section 11.1

■ How to use the sign test to test a population median

$$z = \frac{(x + 0.5) - 0.5n}{\frac{\sqrt{n}}{2}}$$

1, 2 — *1–3, 6*

■ How to use the paired-sample sign to test the difference between two population medians (dependent samples)

3 — *4, 5*

Section 11.2

■ How to use the Wilcoxon signed-rank test and Wilcoxon rank sum test to test the difference between two population distributions

$$z = \frac{R - \mu_R}{\sigma_R}, \quad \mu_R = \frac{n_1(n_1 + n_2 + 1)}{2}, \quad \sigma_R = \sqrt{\frac{n_1 n_2(n_1 + n_2 + 1)}{12}}$$

1, 2 — *7, 8*

Section 11.3

■ How to use the Kruskal-Wallis test to test for differences among three or more population distributions

$$H = \frac{12}{N(N + 1)}\left(\frac{R_1^2}{n_1} + \frac{R_2^2}{n_2} + \cdots + \frac{R_k^2}{n_k}\right) - 3(N + 1)$$

1 — *9, 10*

Section 11.4

■ How to use the Spearman rank correlation coefficient to determine whether the correlation between two variables is significant

$$r_s = 1 - \frac{6\Sigma d^2}{n(n^2 - 1)}$$

1 — *11, 12*

Section 11.5

■ How to use the runs test to determine whether a data set is random

$$G = \text{number of runs}, \quad z = \frac{G - \mu_G}{\sigma_G}, \quad \mu_G = \frac{2n_1 n_2}{n_1 + n_2} + 1, \quad \sigma_G = \sqrt{\frac{2n_1 n_2(2n_1 n_2 - n_1 - n_2)}{(n_1 + n_2)^2(n_1 + n_2 - 1)}}$$

1–3 — *13, 14*

The table summarizes parametric and nonparametric tests. Always use the parametric test if the conditions for that test are satisfied.

Test application	Parametric test	Nonparametric test
One-sample tests	z-test for a population mean t-test for a population mean	Sign test for a population median
Two-sample tests		
Dependent samples	t-test for the difference between means	Paired-sample sign test Wilcoxon signed-rank test
Independent samples	z-test for the difference between means t-test for the difference between means	Wilcoxon rank sum test
Tests involving three or more samples	One-way ANOVA	Kruskal-Wallis test
Correlation	Pearson correlation coefficient	Spearman rank correlation coefficient
Randomness	(No parametric test)	Runs test

11 REVIEW EXERCISES

Section 11.1

In Exercises 1–6, use a sign test to test the claim by doing the following.

(a) *Write the claim mathematically and identify H_0 and H_a.*
(b) *Determine the critical value.*
(c) *Calculate the test statistic.*
(d) *Decide whether to reject or fail to reject the null hypothesis.*
(e) *Interpret the decision in the context of the original claim.*

1. A financial services institution estimates that the median value of stock among families that own stock is $24,300. The stock values (in thousands of dollars) among 17 randomly selected families that own stock are listed below. At $\alpha = 0.01$, can you reject the institution's claim? *(Adapted from Board of Governors of the Federal Reserve System)*

> 14.89 28.89 19.32 30.10 25.27 20.62 23.26 11.75 31.01
> 20.01 20.09 20.74 21.64 19.94 24.87 28.13 24.54

2. A financial services institution claims that the median credit card debt among families that have credit card debt with annual earnings of $25,000 to $49,999 is more than $2000. The credit card debts (in thousands of dollars) among 13 randomly selected families are listed below. At $\alpha = 0.01$, can you support the institution's claim? *(Adapted from Board of Governors of the Federal Reserve System)*

> 2.77 1.90 1.82 1.85 1.78 2.16 2.54
> 2.49 2.28 1.79 2.09 1.72 2.25

3. A mail-order company believes that the median turnover time between receipt of a telephone order and packing of that order is six hours or less. Over a five-day period, 78 orders are randomly selected and their turnover time is recorded in half-hour increments. Eight orders took six hours, 26 orders took less than six hours, and 44 orders took more than six hours. At $\alpha = 0.10$, can you reject the company's claim?

4. In a study testing the effects of calcium supplements on blood pressure in men, 10 randomly selected men were given a calcium supplement for 12 weeks. The following measurements are for each subject's diastolic blood pressure taken before and after the 12-week treatment period. At $\alpha = 0.05$, can you reject the claim that there was no reduction in diastolic blood pressure? *(Adapted from the American Medical Association)*

Patient	1	2	3	4	5	6	7
Before treatment	107	110	123	129	112	111	107
After treatment	100	114	105	112	115	116	106

Patient	8	9	10
Before treatment	112	136	102
After treatment	102	125	104

5. In a study testing the effects of an herbal supplement on blood pressure in men, 11 randomly selected men were given an herbal supplement for 12 weeks. The following measurements are for each subject's diastolic blood pressure taken before and after the 12-week treatment period. At $\alpha = 0.05$, can you reject the claim that there was no reduction in diastolic blood pressure? *(Adapted from The Journal of the American Medical Association)*

Patient	1	2	3	4	5	6	7
Before treatment	123	109	112	102	98	114	119
After treatment	124	97	113	105	95	119	114

Patient	8	9	10	11
Before treatment	112	110	117	130
After treatment	114	121	118	133

6. The career placement office at a large university claims that the median starting salary of graduates with a bachelor's degree in marketing is $40,200. In a random sample of 54 marketing graduates who were currently employed, 21 were paid less than $40,200, and 33 were paid more than $40,200. At $\alpha = 0.05$, can you reject the office's claim? *(Adapted from National Association of Colleges and Employers)*

Section 11.2

In Exercises 7 and 8, use a Wilcoxon test to test the claim by doing the following.

(a) Decide whether the samples are dependent or independent; then choose the appropriate Wilcoxon test.

(b) Write the claim mathematically and identify H_0 and H_a.

(c) Determine the critical value.

(d) Calculate the test statistic.

(e) Decide whether to reject or fail to reject the null hypothesis.

(f) Interpret the decision in the context of the original claim.

7. A career placement advisor estimates that there is a difference in the total time to earn a doctorate degree by female and male graduate students. A random sample of 12 female and 12 male graduate students and their total time to earn a doctorate degree is shown in the table. At $\alpha = 0.01$, can you support the advisor's claim? *(Adapted from National Opinion Research Council)*

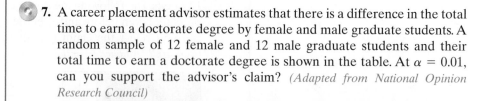

Gender	Total Time (in years)											
Female	13	12	10	13	12	9	11	14	7	7	9	10
Male	11	8	9	11	10	8	8	10	11	9	10	8

8. A medical researcher claims that a new drug affects the number of headache hours experienced by headache sufferers. The number of headache hours (per day) experienced by eight randomly selected patients before and after taking the drug are shown in the table. At $\alpha = 0.05$, can you support the researcher's claim?

Patient	1	2	3	4	5	6	7	8
Headache hours (before)	0.9	2.3	2.7	2.4	2.9	1.9	1.2	3.1
Headache hours (after)	1.4	1.5	1.4	1.8	1.3	0.6	0.7	1.9

Section 11.3

In Exercises 9 and 10, use the Kruskal-Wallis test to test the claim by doing the following.

(a) Write the claim mathematically and identify H_0 and H_a.

(b) Determine the critical value.

(c) Find the sums of the ranks for each sample and calculate the test statistic.

(d) Decide whether to reject or fail to reject the null hypothesis.

(e) Interpret the decision in the context of the original claim.

 9. The table shows the starting salaries for a random sample of college graduates in three fields of study. At $\alpha = 0.05$, can you conclude that the distributions of the starting salaries in these three fields of study are different? *(Adapted from National Association of Colleges and Employers)*

Field of Study	Starting Salary (in thousands of dollars)									
Accounting	44.9	45.8	46.9	46.7	48.9	47.0	46.6	47.1	46.9	46.4
Computer science	53.4	53.6	51.8	53.9	53.2	54.6	53.0	55.8	50.9	53.3
Civil engineering	46.9	48.8	48.6	47.7	46.2	48.5	51.3	48.7	50.2	47.9

10. The table shows the total time to earn a doctorate degree for a random sample of college graduates in three fields of study. At $\alpha = 0.05$, can you conclude that the distributions of the total times in these three fields of study are different? *(Adapted from National Opinion Research Council)*

Field of Study	Total Time (in years)										
Engineering	7	9	8	6	10	8	7	9	8	7	9
Life science	8	8	7	8	7	7	8	6	8	8	7
Social science	10	11	6	9	8	7	11	8	6	9	10

Section 11.4

In Exercises 11 and 12, use the Spearman rank correlation coefficient to test the claim by doing the following.

(a) *Write the claim mathematically and identify H_0 and H_a.*

(b) *Determine the critical value using Table 10 in Appendix B.*

(c) *Find the standardized test statistic r_s.*

(d) *Decide whether to reject the null hypothesis.*

(e) *Interpret the decision in the context of the original claim.*

11. The table shows the overall scores and the prices for eight randomly selected 32-inch LCD televisions. The overall score represents the television's picture quality, sound quality, and ease of use. At $\alpha = 0.01$, can you conclude that there is a correlation between overall score and price? *(Adapted from Consumer Reports)*

Overall score	72	69	67	63	60	58	57	53
Price (in dollars)	1500	900	1000	1100	800	800	1100	950

12. The table shows the overall scores and the prices for nine randomly selected interior paints. The overall score represents how well two coats cover dark colors and resistance to staining, scrubbing, and gloss change. At $\alpha = 0.05$, can you conclude that there is a correlation between overall score and price? *(Adapted from Consumer Reports)*

Overall score	88	86	83	81	78	77	75	73	71
Price (in dollars)	24	19	27	23	15	24	24	20	20

Section 11.5

In Exercises 13 and 14, use the runs test to (a) write the claim mathematically and identify H_0 and H_a, (b) determine the critical values using Table 12 in Appendix B, (c) calculate the test statistic, (d) decide whether to reject or fail to reject the null hypothesis, and (e) interpret the decision in the context of the original claim.

13. A highway patrol officer stops speeding vehicles on an interstate highway. The following shows the gender of the last 25 drivers who were stopped, where F represents a female driver and M represents a male driver. At $\alpha = 0.05$, can you conclude that the stops were not random by gender?

    F M M M F M F M F F F M M
    F F F M M M F M M F F M

14. The following data represent the departure status of the last 18 buses to leave a bus station, where T represents a bus that departed on time and L represents a bus that departed late. At $\alpha = 0.05$, can you conclude that the departure status of the buses is not random?

    T T T T L L L L T
    L L L T T T T T T

11 CHAPTER QUIZ

Take this quiz as you would take a quiz in class. After you are done, check your work against the answers given in the back of the book.

For this quiz, do the following.

(a) *Write the claim mathematically and identify H_0 and H_a.*

(b) *Decide which test to use.*

(c) *Determine the critical value(s).*

(d) *Calculate the test statistic.*

(e) *Decide whether to reject or fail to reject the null hypothesis.*

(f) *Interpret the decision in the context of the original claim.*

1. A women's organization claims that there is a difference in the salaries earned by female and male employees of state and local governments. A random sample of 10 female and 10 male state and local government employees and their salaries is listed in the table. At $\alpha = 0.10$, can you support the organization's claim? *(Adapted from U.S. Equal Employment Opportunity Commission)*

Gender	Salary (in thousands of dollars)									
Female	36.2	35.8	35.4	39.0	30.8	41.3	31.8	32.6	29.8	36.9
Male	53.9	45.3	30.4	41.3	48.8	40.7	41.8	37.3	42.4	46.1

2. A community organization claims that the median number of annual volunteer hours for volunteers is 50 hours. In a random sample of 24 people who volunteered last year, 13 volunteered for less than 50 hours, 9 volunteered for more than 50 hours, and 2 volunteered for 50 hours. At $\alpha = 0.05$, can you reject the organization's claim? *(Adapted from U.S. Bureau of Labor Statistics)*

3. An apartment association wants to determine whether the monthly rent of new apartments differs according to the region of the United States in which the apartment is in. The table shows the monthly rent (in dollars) for a random sample of apartments in four U.S. regions. At $\alpha = 0.05$, can the association conclude that the distributions of the monthly rent prices in these regions are different? *(Adapted from U.S. Census Bureau)*

Region	Monthly Rent (in dollars)						
Northeast	1075	1025	1225	1050	1100	950	950
Midwest	1050	650	750	725	800	800	775
South	1000	1100	950	775	975	900	800
West	1300	875	950	825	1075	1150	1225

4. A meteorologist wants to determine whether days with rain occur randomly in April in his home town. To do so, the meteorologist records whether it rains for each day in April. The results are shown, where R represents a day with rain and N represents a day with no rain. At $\alpha = 0.05$, can the meteorologist conclude that days with rain are not random?

N R N N N N R N R R N R R R
N R R R R N N N N R N R N N R

Putting It All Together

REAL Statistics — Real Decisions

In a recent year, according to the Bureau of Labor Statistics, the median number of years that wage and salary workers had been with their current employer (called employee tenure) was 4.0 years. Information on employee tenure has been gathered since the early 1950s using the *Current Population Survey* (*CPS*), a monthly survey of about 60,000 households that provides information on employment, unemployment, earnings, demographics, and other characteristics of the U.S. population ages 16 and over. With respect to employee tenure, the questions measure how long workers have been with their current employer, not how long they plan to stay with their employer.

stats.bls.gov

■ EXERCISES

1. *How Would You Do It?*

(a) What sampling technique would you use to select the sample for the *CPS*?

(b) Do you think the technique in part (a) will give you a sample that is representative of the U.S. population? Why or why not?

(c) Identify possible flaws or biases in the survey on the basis of the technique you chose in part (a).

2. *Is There a Difference?*

A congressional representative claims that the median tenure for workers from the representative's district is less than the national median tenure of 4.0 years. The claim is based on the representative's data and is shown in the table at the above right. (Assume that the employees were randomly selected.)

(a) Is it possible that the claim is true? What questions should you ask about how the data were collected?

(b) How would you test the representative's claim? Can you use a parametric test, or do you need to use a nonparametric test?

(c) State the null hypothesis and the alternative hypothesis.

(d) Test the claim using $\alpha = 0.05$. What can you conclude?

3. *Comparing Male and Female Employee Tenures*

A congressional representative claims that the median tenure for male workers is greater than the median tenure for female workers. The claim is based on the representative's data and is shown in the table at the right. (Assume that the employees were randomly selected from the representative's district.)

(a) How would you test the representative's claim? Can you use a parametric test, or do you need to use a nonparametric test?

(b) State the null hypothesis and the alternative hypothesis.

(c) Test the claim using $\alpha = 0.05$. What can you conclude?

Employee Tenure of 20 Workers		
4.6	2.6	3.3
2.8	1.5	1.9
4.0	5.0	3.9
5.1	3.7	5.4
3.6	3.9	6.2
1.7	4.6	3.1
4.4	3.6	

TABLE FOR EXERCISE 2

Employee tenure for a sample of male workers	Employee tenure for a sample of female workers
3.9	4.4
4.4	4.9
4.7	5.4
4.3	4.3
4.9	4.0
3.8	1.8
3.6	5.1
4.7	5.1
2.3	3.3
6.5	2.2
0.9	5.2
5.1	3.0
	1.3
	4.0

TABLE FOR EXERCISE 3

TECHNOLOGY   MINITAB   EXCEL   T1-83/84

U.S. INCOME AND ECONOMIC RESEARCH

The National Bureau of Economic Research (NBER) is a private, nonprofit, nonpartisan research organization. The NBER provides information to better understand how the U.S. economy works. Researchers at the NBER concentrate on four types of empirical research: developing new statistical measurements, estimating quantitative models of economic behavior, assessing the effects of public policies on the U.S. economy, and projecting the effects of alternative policy proposals.

One of the NBER's interests is the median income of people in different regions of the United States. The table at the right shows the annual incomes (in dollars) of a random sample of people (15 years and over) in a recent year in four U.S. regions: Northeast, Midwest, South, and West.

Annual Income of People (in dollars)			
Northeast	Midwest	South	West
43,501	26,000	19,755	37,000
31,645	28,200	33,668	31,118
27,997	26,975	32,005	24,934
24,000	33,625	34,534	32,000
25,000	32,189	18,000	34,378
31,900	31,475	23,700	23,500
30,328	30,500	24,000	28,900
29,000	42,000	30,798	40,415
26,450	19,665	35,455	25,228
21,600	40,178	32,500	22,000
39,200	25,370	21,400	28,776
46,450	27,660	25,600	36,564

■ EXERCISES

In Exercises 1–5, refer to the annual income of people in the table. Use $\alpha = 0.05$ for all tests.

1. Construct a box-and-whisker plot for each region. Do the median annual incomes appear to differ between regions?

2. Use a technology tool to perform a sign test to test the claim that the median annual income in the Midwest is greater than $25,000.

3. Use a technology tool to perform a Wilcoxon rank sum test to test the claim that the median annual incomes in the Northeast and South are the same.

4. Use a technology tool to perform a Kruskal-Wallis test to test the claim that the distributions of annual incomes for all four regions are the same.

5. Use a technology tool to perform a one-way ANOVA to test the claim that the average annual incomes for all four regions are the same. Assume that the populations of incomes are normally distributed, the samples are independent, and the population variances are equal. How do your results compare with those in Exercise 4?

6. Repeat Exercises 1, 3, 4, and 5 using the data in the following table. The table shows the annual incomes (in dollars) of a random sample of families in a recent year in four U.S. regions: Northeast, Midwest, South, and West.

Annual Income of Families (in dollars)			
Northeast	Midwest	South	West
51,210	50,420	46,000	53,478
100,665	76,000	48,587	61,795
69,000	31,800	40,200	43,652
103,600	48,000	81,000	59,000
58,980	64,956	46,009	45,500
44,700	44,788	26,000	70,890
39,566	60,500	51,100	52,778
59,950	54,576	29,556	77,800
42,000	57,660	55,421	78,625
66,720	50,000	43,600	33,800
37,995	55,000	68,222	58,320
58,850	52,336	41,885	39,580
51,700	63,250	50,000	54,034
66,000	54,200	35,900	58,550
50,999	70,700	46,362	38,692

Extended solutions are given in the *Technology Supplement*. Technical instruction is provided for MINITAB, Excel, and the TI-83/84.

Cumulative Review

Men, x	Women, y
10.80	12.20
10.30	11.90
10.30	11.50
10.30	11.90
10.40	11.50
10.50	11.50
10.20	11.00
10.00	11.40
9.95	11.08
10.14	11.07
10.06	11.08
10.25	11.06
9.99	10.97
9.92	10.54
9.96	10.82
9.84	10.94
9.87	10.75
9.85	10.93

1. The table at the left shows the winning times (in seconds) for the men's and women's 100-meter run in the Summer Olympics from 1928 to 2004. *(Source: The World Almanac)*

   (a) Display the data in a scatter plot, calculate the correlation coefficient r, and make a conclusion about the type of correlation.

   (b) Test the level of significance of the correlation coefficient r found in part (a). Use $\alpha = 0.05$.

   (c) Find the equation of the regression line for the data. Draw the regression line on the scatter plot.

   (d) Use the regression line to predict the women's 100-meter time when the men's 100-meter time is 9.90 seconds.

2. An employment agency claims that there is a difference in the weekly earnings of workers who are union members and workers who are not union members. A random sample of 10 union members and 10 nonunion members and their weekly earnings is shown in the table. At $\alpha = 0.05$, can you support the agency's claim? *(Adapted from U.S. Bureau of Labor Statistics)*

Worker	Weekly Earnings (in dollars)									
Union member	739	891	576	684	849	768	875	924	788	814
Not a union member	658	591	762	457	500	555	714	652	703	538

3. An investment company claims that the median age of people with mutual funds is 48 years. The ages (in years) of 20 randomly selected mutual fund owners are listed below. At $\alpha = 0.01$, is there enough evidence to reject the company's claim? *(Adapted from Investment Company Institute)*

   46 34 33 27 58 64 54 36 38 42
   26 51 49 44 46 48 39 34 51 63

4. The table at the right shows the residential natural gas expenditures (in dollars) in one year for a random sample of households in four regions of the United States. Assume that the populations are normally distributed, the samples are independent of each other, and the population variances are equal. At $\alpha = 0.10$, can you reject the claim that the mean expenditures are equal for all four regions? *(Adapted from U.S. Energy Information Administration)*

Northeast	Midwest	South	West
1358	319	448	585
529	906	333	498
714	535	701	1005
1053	1083	692	457
893	793	870	265
1445	1263	513	318
535	796	465	509
528	736	1035	593

5. A school administrator reports that the standard deviations of reading test scores for eighth grade students are the same in Colorado and Utah. A random sample of 16 test scores from Colorado has a standard deviation of 34.6 points and a random sample of 15 test scores from Utah has a standard deviation of 33.2 points. At $\alpha = 0.10$, can you reject the administrator's claim? Assume the samples are independent and each population has a normal distribution. *(Adapted from National Center for Education Statistics)*

6. An employment agency representative wants to determine whether there is a difference in the annual household incomes in four regions of the United States. To do so, the representative randomly selects several households in each region and records the annual household income for each in the table. At $\alpha = 0.01$, can the representative conclude that the distributions of the annual household incomes in these regions are different? *(Adapted from U.S. Census Bureau)*

Region	Household Income (in thousands of dollars)						
Northeast	49.7	42.5	51.1	50.2	45.4	47.9	47.0
Midwest	43.7	48.8	39.6	42.9	45.1	46.2	46.4
South	38.9	40.1	43.7	36.0	40.9	43.7	41.5
West	50.1	48.0	44.7	46.8	45.7	47.3	49.2

7. A health care investigator wants to test the following claim: Of all physician practices in the United States, 36% have 1 physician, 32% have 2 to 4 physicians, 20% have 5 to 9 physicians, and 12% have 10 or more physicians. A random sample of physician practices finds that 116 have 1 physician, 84 have 2 to 4 physicians, 66 have 5 to 9 physicians, and 23 have 10 or more physicians. Test the claim at $\alpha = 0.05$. *(Adapted from National Center for Health Statistics)*

8. The table shows the metacarpal bone length (in centimeters) and the height (in centimeters) of nine adults. The equation of the regression line is $\hat{y} = 1.700x + 94.428$. *(Adapted from the American Journal of Physical Anthropology)*

Metacarpal bone length, x	45	51	39	41	48	49	46	43	47
Height, y	171	178	157	163	172	183	173	175	173

(a) Find the coefficient of determination and interpret the results.

(b) Find the standard error of estimate s_e and interpret the results.

(c) Construct a 95% prediction interval for the height of an adult when his or her metacarpal bone length is 50 centimeters. Interpret the results.

9. The table shows the overall scores and the prices for eight different tires. The overall score represents safety-related tests, such as braking, handling, and resistance to hydroplaning. At $\alpha = 0.10$, can you conclude that there is a correlation between the overall score and the price? Use the Spearman rank correlation coefficient. *(Adapted from Consumer Reports)*

Overall score	85	83	83	81	77	72	70	66
Price (in dollars)	81	78	56	77	62	85	62	61

10. The equation used to predict oat yield (in bushels) is $\hat{y} = 91.113 - 0.014x_1 + 0.018x_2$, where x_1 is the number of acres planted (in thousands) and x_2 is the number of acres harvested (in thousands). Use the multiple regression equation to predict the y-values for the given values of the independent variables listed below. *(Source: U.S. National Agricultural Statistics Service)*

(a) $x_1 = 4325$, $x_2 = 1900$ (b) $x_1 = 4900$, $x_2 = 2163$

In this appendix, we use a 0-to-z table as an alternative development of the standard normal distribution. It is intended that this appendix be used after completing the "Properties of a Normal Distribution" subsection of Section 5.1 in the text. If used, this appendix should replace the material in the "Standard Normal Distribution" subsection of Section 5.1 except for the exercises.

Standard Normal Distribution (0-to-z)

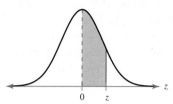

z	.00	.01	.02	.03	.04	.05	.06	.07	.08	.09
0.0	.0000	.0040	.0080	.0120	.0160	.0199	.0239	.0279	.0319	.0359
0.1	.0398	.0438	.0478	.0517	.0557	.0596	.0636	.0675	.0714	.0753
0.2	.0793	.0832	.0871	.0910	.0948	.0987	.1026	.1064	.1103	.1141
0.3	.1179	.1217	.1255	.1293	.1331	.1368	.1406	.1443	.1480	.1517
0.4	.1554	.1591	.1628	.1664	.1700	.1736	.1772	.1808	.1844	.1879
0.5	.1915	.1950	.1985	.2019	.2054	.2088	.2123	.2157	.2190	.2224
0.6	.2257	.2291	.2324	.2357	.2389	.2422	.2454	.2486	.2517	.2549
0.7	.2580	.2611	.2642	.2673	.2704	.2734	.2764	.2794	.2823	.2852
0.8	.2881	.2910	.2939	.2967	.2995	.3023	.3051	.3078	.3106	.3133
0.9	.3159	.3186	.3212	.3238	.3264	.3289	.3315	.3340	.3365	.3389
1.0	.3413	.3438	.3461	.3485	.3508	.3531	.3554	.3577	.3599	.3621
1.1	.3643	.3665	.3686	.3708	.3729	.3749	.3770	.3790	.3810	.3830
1.2	.3849	.3869	.3888	.3907	.3925	.3944	.3962	.3980	.3997	.4015
1.3	.4032	.4049	.4066	.4082	.4099	.4115	.4131	.4147	.4162	.4177
1.4	.4192	.4207	.4222	.4236	.4251	.4265	.4279	.4292	.4306	.4319
1.5	.4332	.4345	.4357	.4370	.4382	.4394	.4406	.4418	.4429	.4441
1.6	.4452	.4463	.4474	.4484	.4495	.4505	.4515	.4525	.4535	.4545
1.7	.4554	.4564	.4573	.4582	.4591	.4599	.4608	.4616	.4625	.4633
1.8	.4641	.4649	.4656	.4664	.4671	.4678	.4686	.4693	.4699	.4706
1.9	.4713	.4719	.4726	.4732	.4738	.4744	.4750	.4756	.4761	.4767
2.0	.4772	.4778	.4783	.4788	.4793	.4798	.4803	.4808	.4812	.4817
2.1	.4821	.4826	.4830	.4834	.4838	.4842	.4846	.4850	.4854	.4857
2.2	.4861	.4864	.4868	.4871	.4875	.4878	.4881	.4884	.4887	.4890
2.3	.4893	.4896	.4898	.4901	.4904	.4906	.4909	.4911	.4913	.4916
2.4	.4918	.4920	.4922	.4925	.4927	.4929	.4931	.4932	.4934	.4936
2.5	.4938	.4940	.4941	.4943	.4945	.4946	.4948	.4949	.4951	.4952
2.6	.4953	.4955	.4956	.4957	.4959	.4960	.4961	.4962	.4963	.4964
2.7	.4965	.4966	.4967	.4968	.4969	.4970	.4971	.4972	.4973	.4974
2.8	.4974	.4975	.4976	.4977	.4977	.4978	.4979	.4979	.4980	.4981
2.9	.4981	.4982	.4982	.4983	.4984	.4984	.4985	.4985	.4986	.4986
3.0	.4987	.4987	.4987	.4988	.4988	.4989	.4989	.4989	.4990	.4990
3.1	.4990	.4991	.4991	.4991	.4992	.4992	.4992	.4992	.4993	.4993
3.2	.4993	.4993	.4994	.4994	.4994	.4994	.4994	.4995	.4995	.4995
3.3	.4995	.4995	.4995	.4996	.4996	.4996	.4996	.4996	.4996	.4997
3.4	.4997	.4997	.4997	.4997	.4997	.4997	.4997	.4997	.4997	.4998

Reprinted with permission of Gale Mosteller, executor of estate of Frederick Mosteller, 3830 13th Street North, Arlington, VA 22201   mosteller.g@ei.com.

A | Alternative Presentation of the Standard Normal Distribution

What You SHOULD LEARN

▸ How to find areas under the standard normal curve

The Standard Normal Distribution

▸ The Standard Normal Distribution

There are infinitely many normal distributions, each with its own mean and standard deviation. The normal distribution with a mean of 0 and a standard deviation of 1 is called the **standard normal distribution.** The horizontal scale of the graph of the standard normal distribution corresponds to z-scores. In Section 2.5, you learned that a z-score is a measure of position that indicates the number of standard deviations a value lies from the mean. Recall that you can transform an x-value to a z-score using the formula

$$z = \frac{\text{value} - \text{mean}}{\text{standard deviation}} = \frac{x - \mu}{\sigma}.$$

Insight

Because every normal distribution can be transformed to the standard normal distribution, you can use z-scores and the standard normal curve to find areas (and therefore probability) under any normal curve.

DEFINITION

The **standard normal distribution** is a normal distribution with a mean of 0 and a standard deviation of 1.

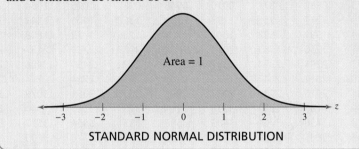

STANDARD NORMAL DISTRIBUTION

If each data value of a normally distributed random variable x is transformed into a z-score, the result will be the standard normal distribution. When this transformation takes place, the area that falls in the interval under the nonstandard normal curve is the *same* as that under the standard normal curve within the corresponding z-boundaries.

In Section 5.1, you learned to approximate areas under a normal curve when values of the random variable x corresponded to -3, -2, -1, 0, 1, 2, or 3 standard deviations from the mean. In this section, you will learn to calculate areas corresponding to other x-values. After you transform an x-value to a z-score, you can use the Standard Normal Table (0-to-z) on page A1. The table lists the area under the standard normal curve between 0 and the given z-score. As you examine the table, notice the following properties.

Study Tip

It is important that you know the difference between x and z. The random variable x is sometimes called a raw score and represents values in a *nonstandard* normal distribution, whereas z represents values in the *standard* normal distribution.

PROPERTIES OF THE STANDARD NORMAL DISTRIBUTION

1. The distribution is symmetric about the mean $(z = 0)$.

2. The area under the standard normal curve to the left of $z = 0$ is 0.5 and the area to the right of $z = 0$ is 0.5.

3. The area under the standard normal curve increases as the distance between 0 and z increases.

At first glance, the table on page A1 appears to give areas for positive *z*-scores only. However, because of the symmetry of the standard normal curve, the table also gives areas for negative *z*-scores (see Example 1).

EXAMPLE 1

Using the Standard Normal Table (0-to-*z*)

1. Find the area under the standard normal curve between $z = 0$ and $z = 1.15$.
2. Find the *z*-scores that correspond to an area of 0.0948.

Solution

1. Find the area that corresponds to $z = 1.15$ by finding 1.1 in the left column and then moving across the row to the column under 0.05. The number in that row and column is 0.3749. So, the area between $z = 0$ and $z = 1.15$ is 0.3749.

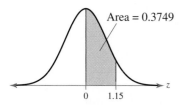

Area = 0.3749

z	.00	.01	.02	.03	.04	.05	.06
0.0	.0000	.0040	.0080	.0120	.0160	.0199	.0239
0.1	.0398	.0438	.0478	.0517	.0557	.0596	.0636
0.2	.0793	.0832	.0871	.0910	.0948	.0987	.1026
0.3	.1179	.1217	.1255	.1293	.1331	.1368	.1406

z	.00	.01	.02	.03	.04	.05	.06
0.9	.3159	.3186	.3212	.3238	.3264	.3289	.3315
1.0	.3413	.3438	.3461	.3485	.3508	.3531	.3554
1.1	.3643	.3665	.3686	.3708	.3729	.3749	.3770
1.2	.3849	.3869	.3888	.3907	.3925	.3944	.3962
1.3	.4032	.4049	.4066	.4082	.4099	.4115	.4131
1.4	.4192	.4207	.4222	.4236	.4251	.4265	.4279

2. Find the *z*-scores that correspond to an area of 0.0948 by locating 0.0948 in the table. The values at the beginning of the corresponding row and at the top of the corresponding column give the *z*-score. For an area of 0.0948, the row value is 0.2 and the column value is 0.04. So, the *z*-scores are $z = -0.24$ and $z = 0.24$.

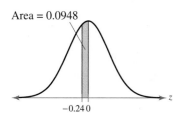

Area = 0.0948

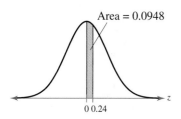

Area = 0.0948

z	.00	.01	.02	.03	.04	.05	.06
0.0	.0000	.0040	.0080	.0120	.0160	.0199	.0239
0.1	.0398	.0438	.0478	.0517	.0557	.0596	.0636
0.2	.0793	.0832	.0871	.0910	.0948	.0987	.1026
0.3	.1179	.1217	.1255	.1293	.1331	.1368	.1406
0.4	.1554	.1591	.1628	.1664	.1700	.1736	.1772
0.5	.1915	.1950	.1985	.2019	.2054	.2088	.2123

▶ Try It Yourself 1

1. Find the area under the standard normal curve between $z = 0$ and $z = 2.19$.

   Locate the given *z*-score and *find the corresponding area* in the Standard Normal Table (0-to-*z*) on page A1.

2. Find the *z*-scores that correspond to an area of 0.4850.

   Locate the given area in the Standard Normal Table (0-to-*z*) on page A1 and *find the corresponding z-score.*   *Answer: Page A50*

Use the following guidelines to find various types of areas under the standard normal curve.

GUIDELINES

Finding Areas under the Standard Normal Curve

1. Sketch the standard normal curve and shade the appropriate area under the curve.
2. Use the Standard Normal Table (0-to-z) on page A1 to find the area that corresponds to the given z-score(s).
3. Find the desired area by following the directions for each case shown.

    a. Area to the left of z

       i. When $z < 0$, *subtract* the area from 0.5.

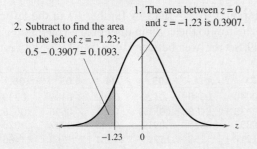

2. Subtract to find the area to the left of $z = -1.23$; $0.5 - 0.3907 = 0.1093$.

1. The area between $z = 0$ and $z = -1.23$ is 0.3907.

       ii. When $z > 0$, *add* 0.5 to the area.

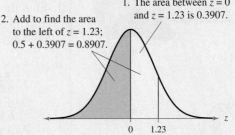

2. Add to find the area to the left of $z = 1.23$; $0.5 + 0.3907 = 0.8907$.

1. The area between $z = 0$ and $z = 1.23$ is 0.3907.

    b. Area to the right of z

       i. When $z < 0$, *add* 0.5 to the area.

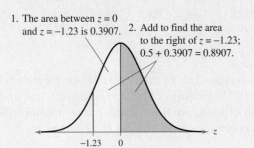

1. The area between $z = 0$ and $z = -1.23$ is 0.3907.

2. Add to find the area to the right of $z = -1.23$; $0.5 + 0.3907 = 0.8907$.

       ii. When $z > 0$, *subtract* the area from 0.5.

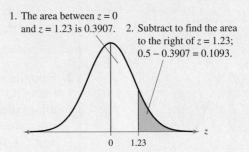

1. The area between $z = 0$ and $z = 1.23$ is 0.3907.

2. Subtract to find the area to the right of $z = 1.23$; $0.5 - 0.3907 = 0.1093$.

    c. Area between two z-scores

       i. When the two z-scores have the same sign (both positive or both negative), *subtract* the smaller area from the larger area.

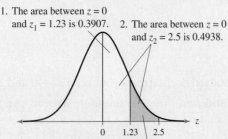

1. The area between $z = 0$ and $z_1 = 1.23$ is 0.3907.

2. The area between $z = 0$ and $z_2 = 2.5$ is 0.4938.

3. Subtract to find the area between $z_1 = 1.23$ and $z_2 = 2.5$; $0.4938 - 0.3907 = 0.1031$.

       ii. When the two z-scores have opposite signs (one negative and one positive), *add* the areas.

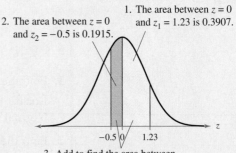

2. The area between $z = 0$ and $z_2 = -0.5$ is 0.1915.

1. The area between $z = 0$ and $z_1 = 1.23$ is 0.3907.

3. Add to find the area between $z_1 = 1.23$ and $z_2 = -0.5$; $0.3907 + 0.1915 = 0.5822$.

Insight

Because the normal distribution is a continuous probability distribution, the area under the standard normal curve to the left of a *z*-score gives the probability that *z* is less than that *z*-score. For instance, in Example 2, the area to the left of $z = -0.99$ is 0.1611. So, $P(z < -0.99) = 0.1611$, which is read as "the probability that *z* is less than -0.99 is 0.1611."

EXAMPLE 2

Finding Area under the Standard Normal Curve

Find the area under the standard normal curve to the left of $z = -0.99$.

Solution   The area under the standard normal curve to the left of $z = -0.99$ is shown.

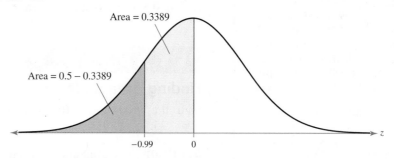

From the Standard Normal Table (0-to-*z*), the area corresponding to $z = -0.99$ is 0.3389. Because the area to the left of $z = 0$ is 0.5, the area to the left of $z = -0.99$ is $0.5 - 0.3389 = 0.1611$.

Interpretation   In other words, 16.11% of the area under the curve falls to the left of $z = -0.99$.

▶ **Try It Yourself 2**

Find the area under the standard normal curve to the left of $z = 2.13$.

a. *Draw* the standard normal curve and shade the area under the curve and to the left of $z = 2.13$.
b. Use the Standard Normal Table (0-to-*z*) on page A1 to *find the area* that corresponds to $z = 2.13$.
c. *Add* 0.5 to the resulting area.   *Answer: Page A50*

EXAMPLE 3

Finding Area under the Standard Normal Curve

Find the area under the standard normal curve to the right of $z = 1.06$.

Solution   The area under the standard normal curve to the right of $z = 1.06$ is shown.

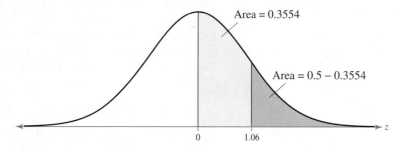

From the Standard Normal Table (0-to-*z*), the area corresponding to $z = 1.06$ is 0.3554. Because the area to the right of $z = 0$ is 0.5, the area to the right of $z = 1.06$ is $0.5 - 0.3554 = 0.1446$.

Interpretation   In other words, 14.46% of the area under the curve falls to the right of $z = 1.06$.

PICTURING the WORLD

According to one publication, the number of births in a recent year was 4,112,052. The weights of the newborns can be approximated by a normal distribution, as shown by the following graph. (Source: National Center for Health Statistics)

Weights of Newborns

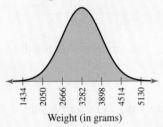

Weight (in grams)

Find the z-scores that correspond to weights of 2000, 3000, and 4000 grams. Are any of these unusually heavy or light?

▶ **Try It Yourself 3**

Find the area under the standard normal curve to the right of $z = -2.16$.

a. *Draw* the standard normal curve and shade the area below the curve and to the right of $z = -2.16$.
b. Use the Standard Normal Table (0-to-z) on page A1 to *find the area* that corresponds to $z = -2.16$.
c. *Add* 0.5 to the resulting area. *Answer: Page A50*

EXAMPLE 4

Finding Area under the Standard Normal Curve

Find the area under the standard normal curve between $z = -1.5$ and $z = 1.25$.

Solution The area under the standard normal curve between $z = -1.5$ and $z = 1.25$ is shown.

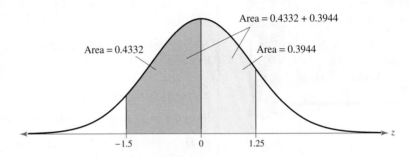

From the Standard Normal Table, the area corresponding to $z = -1.5$ is 0.4332 and the area corresponding to $z = 1.25$ is 0.3944. To find the area between these two z-scores, add the resulting areas.

Area = 0.4332 + 0.3944 = 0.8276

Interpretation In other words, 82.76% of the area under the curve falls between $z = -1.5$ and $z = 1.25$.

▶ **Try It Yourself 4**

Find the area under the standard normal curve between $z = -2.16$ and $z = -1.35$.

a. *Draw* the standard normal curve and shade the area below the curve that is between $z = -2.16$ and $z = -1.35$.
b. Use the Standard Normal Table (0-to-z) on page A1 to *find the areas* that correspond to $z = -2.16$ and to $z = -1.35$.
c. *Subtract* the smaller area from the larger area. *Answer: Page A50*

Recall in Section 2.5 you learned, using the Empirical Rule, that values lying more than two standard deviations from the mean are considered unusual. Values lying more than three standard deviations from the mean are considered *very* unusual. So if a z-score is greater than 2 or less than -2, it is unusual. If a z-score is greater than 3 or less than -3, it is *very* unusual.

Table 1— Random Numbers

92630	78240	19267	95457	53497	23894	37708	79862	76471	66418
79445	78735	71549	44843	26104	67318	00701	34986	66751	99723
59654	71966	27386	50004	05358	94031	29281	18544	52429	06080
31524	49587	76612	39789	13537	48086	59483	60680	84675	53014
06348	76938	90379	51392	55887	71015	09209	79157	24440	30244
28703	51709	94456	48396	73780	06436	86641	69239	57662	80181
68108	89266	94730	95761	75023	48464	65544	96583	18911	16391
99938	90704	93621	66330	33393	95261	95349	51769	91616	33238
91543	73196	34449	63513	83834	99411	58826	40456	69268	48562
42103	02781	73920	56297	72678	12249	25270	36678	21313	75767
17138	27584	25296	28387	51350	61664	37893	05363	44143	42677
28297	14280	54524	21618	95320	38174	60579	08089	94999	78460
09331	56712	51333	06289	75345	08811	82711	57392	25252	30333
31295	04204	93712	51287	05754	79396	87399	51773	33075	97061
36146	15560	27592	42089	99281	59640	15221	96079	09961	05371
29553	18432	13630	05529	02791	81017	49027	79031	50912	09399
23501	22642	63081	08191	89420	67800	55137	54707	32945	64522
57888	85846	67967	07835	11314	01545	48535	17142	08552	67457
55336	71264	88472	04334	63919	36394	11196	92470	70543	29776
10087	10072	55980	64688	68239	20461	89381	93809	00796	95945
34101	81277	66090	88872	37818	72142	67140	50785	21380	16703
53362	44940	60430	22834	14130	96593	23298	56203	92671	15925
82975	66158	84731	19436	55790	69229	28661	13675	99318	76873
54827	84673	22898	08094	14326	87038	42892	21127	30712	48489
25464	59098	27436	89421	80754	89924	19097	67737	80368	08795
67609	60214	41475	84950	40133	02546	09570	45682	50165	15609
44921	70924	61295	51137	47596	86735	35561	76649	18217	63446
33170	30972	98130	95828	49786	13301	36081	80761	33985	68621
84687	85445	06208	17654	51333	02878	35010	67578	61574	20749
71886	56450	36567	09395	96951	35507	17555	35212	69106	01679
00475	02224	74722	14721	40215	21351	08596	45625	83981	63748
25993	38881	68361	59560	41274	69742	40703	37993	03435	18873
92882	53178	99195	93803	56985	53089	15305	50522	55900	43026
25138	26810	07093	15677	60688	04410	24505	37890	67186	62829
84631	71882	12991	83028	82484	90339	91950	74579	03539	90122
34003	92326	12793	61453	48121	74271	28363	66561	75220	35908
53775	45749	05734	86169	42762	70175	97310	73894	88606	19994
59316	97885	72807	54966	60859	11932	35265	71601	55577	67715
20479	66557	50705	26999	09854	52591	14063	30214	19890	19292
86180	84931	25455	26044	02227	52015	21820	50599	51671	65411
21451	68001	72710	40261	61281	13172	63819	48970	51732	54113
98062	68375	80089	24135	72355	95428	11808	29740	81644	86610
01788	64429	14430	94575	75153	94576	61393	96192	03227	32258
62465	04841	43272	68702	01274	05437	22953	18946	99053	41690
94324	31089	84159	92933	99989	89500	91586	02802	69471	68274
05797	43984	21575	09908	70221	19791	51578	36432	33494	79888
10395	14289	52185	09721	25789	38562	54794	04897	59012	89251
35177	56986	25549	59730	64718	52630	31100	62384	49483	11409
25633	89619	75882	98256	02126	72099	57183	55887	09320	73463
16464	48280	94254	45777	45150	68865	11382	11782	22695	41988

Table 2— Binomial Distribution

This table shows the probability of x successes in n independent trials, each with probability of success p.

n	x	.01	.05	.10	.15	.20	.25	.30	.35	.40	.45	.50	.55	.60	.65	.70	.75	.80	.85	.90	.95
2	0	.980	.902	.810	.723	.640	.563	.490	.423	.360	.303	.250	.203	.160	.123	.090	.063	.040	.023	.010	.002
	1	.020	.095	.180	.255	.320	.375	.420	.455	.480	.495	.500	.495	.480	.455	.420	.375	.320	.255	.180	.095
	2	.000	.002	.010	.023	.040	.063	.090	.123	.160	.203	.250	.303	.360	.423	.490	.563	.640	.723	.810	.902
3	0	.970	.857	.729	.614	.512	.422	.343	.275	.216	.166	.125	.091	.064	.043	.027	.016	.008	.003	.001	.000
	1	.029	.135	.243	.325	.384	.422	.441	.444	.432	.408	.375	.334	.288	.239	.189	.141	.096	.057	.027	.007
	2	.000	.007	.027	.057	.096	.141	.189	.239	.288	.334	.375	.408	.432	.444	.441	.422	.384	.325	.243	.135
	3	.000	.000	.001	.003	.008	.016	.027	.043	.064	.091	.125	.166	.216	.275	.343	.422	.512	.614	.729	.857
4	0	.961	.815	.656	.522	.410	.316	.240	.179	.130	.092	.062	.041	.026	.015	.008	.004	.002	.001	.000	.000
	1	.039	.171	.292	.368	.410	.422	.412	.384	.346	.300	.250	.200	.154	.112	.076	.047	.026	.011	.004	.000
	2	.001	.014	.049	.098	.154	.211	.265	.311	.346	.368	.375	.368	.346	.311	.265	.211	.154	.098	.049	.014
	3	.000	.000	.004	.011	.026	.047	.076	.112	.154	.200	.250	.300	.346	.384	.412	.422	.410	.368	.292	.171
	4	.000	.000	.000	.001	.002	.004	.008	.015	.026	.041	.062	.092	.130	.179	.240	.316	.410	.522	.656	.815
5	0	.951	.774	.590	.444	.328	.237	.168	.116	.078	.050	.031	.019	.010	.005	.002	.001	.000	.000	.000	.000
	1	.048	.204	.328	.392	.410	.396	.360	.312	.259	.206	.156	.113	.077	.049	.028	.015	.006	.002	.000	.000
	2	.001	.021	.073	.138	.205	.264	.309	.336	.346	.337	.312	.276	.230	.181	.132	.088	.051	.024	.008	.001
	3	.000	.001	.008	.024	.051	.088	.132	.181	.230	.276	.312	.337	.346	.336	.309	.264	.205	.138	.073	.021
	4	.000	.000	.000	.002	.006	.015	.028	.049	.077	.113	.156	.206	.259	.312	.360	.396	.410	.392	.328	.204
	5	.000	.000	.000	.000	.000	.001	.002	.005	.010	.019	.031	.050	.078	.116	.168	.237	.328	.444	.590	.774
6	0	.941	.735	.531	.377	.262	.178	.118	.075	.047	.028	.016	.008	.004	.002	.001	.000	.000	.000	.000	.000
	1	.057	.232	.354	.399	.393	.356	.303	.244	.187	.136	.094	.061	.037	.020	.010	.004	.002	.000	.000	.000
	2	.001	.031	.098	.176	.246	.297	.324	.328	.311	.278	.234	.186	.138	.095	.060	.033	.015	.006	.001	.000
	3	.000	.002	.015	.042	.082	.132	.185	.236	.276	.303	.312	.303	.276	.236	.185	.132	.082	.042	.015	.002
	4	.000	.000	.001	.006	.015	.033	.060	.095	.138	.186	.234	.278	.311	.328	.324	.297	.246	.176	.098	.031
	5	.000	.000	.000	.000	.002	.004	.010	.020	.037	.061	.094	.136	.187	.244	.303	.356	.393	.399	.354	.232
	6	.000	.000	.000	.000	.000	.000	.001	.002	.004	.008	.016	.028	.047	.075	.118	.178	.262	.377	.531	.735
7	0	.932	.698	.478	.321	.210	.133	.082	.049	.028	.015	.008	.004	.002	.001	.000	.000	.000	.000	.000	.000
	1	.066	.257	.372	.396	.367	.311	.247	.185	.131	.087	.055	.032	.017	.008	.004	.001	.000	.000	.000	.000
	2	.002	.041	.124	.210	.275	.311	.318	.299	.261	.214	.164	.117	.077	.047	.025	.012	.004	.001	.000	.000
	3	.000	.004	.023	.062	.115	.173	.227	.268	.290	.292	.273	.239	.194	.144	.097	.058	.029	.011	.003	.000
	4	.000	.000	.003	.011	.029	.058	.097	.144	.194	.239	.273	.292	.290	.268	.227	.173	.115	.062	.023	.004
	5	.000	.000	.000	.001	.004	.012	.025	.047	.077	.117	.164	.214	.261	.299	.318	.311	.275	.210	.124	.041
	6	.000	.000	.000	.000	.000	.001	.004	.008	.017	.032	.055	.087	.131	.185	.247	.311	.367	.396	.372	.257
	7	.000	.000	.000	.000	.000	.000	.000	.001	.002	.004	.008	.015	.028	.049	.082	.133	.210	.321	.478	.698
8	0	.923	.663	.430	.272	.168	.100	.058	.032	.017	.008	.004	.002	.001	.000	.000	.000	.000	.000	.000	.000
	1	.075	.279	.383	.385	.336	.267	.198	.137	.090	.055	.031	.016	.008	.003	.001	.000	.000	.000	.000	.000
	2	.003	.051	.149	.238	.294	.311	.296	.259	.209	.157	.109	.070	.041	.022	.010	.004	.001	.000	.000	.000
	3	.000	.005	.033	.084	.147	.208	.254	.279	.279	.257	.219	.172	.124	.081	.047	.023	.009	.003	.000	.000
	4	.000	.000	.005	.018	.046	.087	.136	.188	.232	.263	.273	.263	.232	.188	.136	.087	.046	.018	.005	.000
	5	.000	.000	.000	.003	.009	.023	.047	.081	.124	.172	.219	.257	.279	.279	.254	.208	.147	.084	.033	.005
	6	.000	.000	.000	.000	.001	.004	.010	.022	.041	.070	.109	.157	.209	.259	.296	.311	.294	.238	.149	.051
	7	.000	.000	.000	.000	.000	.000	.001	.003	.008	.016	.031	.055	.090	.137	.198	.267	.336	.385	.383	.279
	8	.000	.000	.000	.000	.000	.000	.000	.000	.001	.002	.004	.008	.017	.032	.058	.100	.168	.272	.430	.663
9	0	.914	.630	.387	.232	.134	.075	.040	.021	.010	.005	.002	.001	.000	.000	.000	.000	.000	.000	.000	.000
	1	.083	.299	.387	.368	.302	.225	.156	.100	.060	.034	.018	.008	.004	.001	.000	.000	.000	.000	.000	.000
	2	.003	.063	.172	.260	.302	.300	.267	.216	.161	.111	.070	.041	.021	.010	.004	.001	.000	.000	.000	.000
	3	.000	.008	.045	.107	.176	.234	.267	.272	.251	.212	.164	.116	.074	.042	.021	.009	.003	.001	.000	.000
	4	.000	.001	.007	.028	.066	.117	.172	.219	.251	.260	.246	.213	.167	.118	.074	.039	.017	.005	.001	.000
	5	.000	.000	.001	.005	.017	.039	.074	.118	.167	.213	.246	.260	.251	.219	.172	.117	.066	.028	.007	.001
	6	.000	.000	.000	.001	.003	.009	.021	.042	.074	.116	.164	.212	.251	.272	.267	.234	.176	.107	.045	.008
	7	.000	.000	.000	.000	.000	.001	.004	.010	.021	.041	.070	.111	.161	.216	.267	.300	.302	.260	.172	.063
	8	.000	.000	.000	.000	.000	.000	.000	.001	.004	.008	.018	.034	.060	.100	.156	.225	.302	.368	.387	.299
	9	.000	.000	.000	.000	.000	.000	.000	.000	.000	.001	.002	.005	.010	.021	.040	.075	.134	.232	.387	.630

Binomial Probability Distribution, reprinted from Brase/Brase, *Understandable Statistics*, Sixth Edition. Copyright 1999 by Houghton Mifflin Company. Reprinted by permission.

Table 2—Binomial Distribution *(continued)*

n	x	.01	.05	.10	.15	.20	.25	.30	.35	.40	.45	.50	.55	.60	.65	.70	.75	.80	.85	.90	.95
10	0	.904	.599	.349	.197	.107	.056	.028	.014	.006	.003	.001	.000	.000	.000	.000	.000	.000	.000	.000	.000
	1	.091	.315	.387	.347	.268	.188	.121	.072	.040	.021	.010	.004	.002	.000	.000	.000	.000	.000	.000	.000
	2	.004	.075	.194	.276	.302	.282	.233	.176	.121	.076	.044	.023	.011	.004	.001	.000	.000	.000	.000	.000
	3	.000	.010	.057	.130	.201	.250	.267	.252	.215	.166	.117	.075	.042	.021	.009	.003	.001	.000	.000	.000
	4	.000	.001	.011	.040	.088	.146	.200	.238	.251	.238	.205	.160	.111	.069	.037	.016	.006	.001	.000	.000
	5	.000	.000	.001	.008	.026	.058	.103	.154	.201	.234	.246	.234	.201	.154	.103	.058	.026	.008	.001	.000
	6	.000	.000	.000	.001	.006	.016	.037	.069	.111	.160	.205	.238	.251	.238	.200	.146	.088	.040	.011	.001
	7	.000	.000	.000	.000	.001	.003	.009	.021	.042	.075	.117	.166	.215	.252	.267	.250	.201	.130	.057	.010
	8	.000	.000	.000	.000	.000	.000	.001	.004	.011	.023	.044	.076	.121	.176	.233	.282	.302	.276	.194	.075
	9	.000	.000	.000	.000	.000	.000	.000	.000	.002	.004	.010	.021	.040	.072	.121	.188	.268	.347	.387	.315
	10	.000	.000	.000	.000	.000	.000	.000	.000	.000	.001	.003	.006	.014	.028	.056	.107	.197	.349	.599
11	0	.895	.569	.314	.167	.086	.042	.020	.009	.004	.001	.000	.000	.000	.000	.000	.000	.000	.000	.000	.000
	1	.099	.329	.384	.325	.236	.155	.093	.052	.027	.013	.005	.002	.001	.000	.000	.000	.000	.000	.000	.000
	2	.005	.087	.213	.287	.295	.258	.200	.140	.089	.051	.027	.013	.005	.002	.001	.000	.000	.000	.000	.000
	3	.000	.014	.071	.152	.221	.258	.257	.225	.177	.126	.081	.046	.023	.010	.004	.001	.000	.000	.000	.000
	4	.000	.001	.016	.054	.111	.172	.220	.243	.236	.206	.161	.113	.070	.038	.017	.006	.002	.000	.000	.000
	5	.000	.000	.002	.013	.039	.080	.132	.183	.221	.236	.226	.193	.147	.099	.057	.027	.010	.002	.000	.000
	6	.000	.000	.000	.002	.010	.027	.057	.099	.147	.193	.226	.236	.221	.183	.132	.080	.039	.013	.002	.000
	7	.000	.000	.000	.000	.002	.006	.017	.038	.070	.113	.161	.206	.236	.243	.220	.172	.111	.054	.016	.001
	8	.000	.000	.000	.000	.000	.001	.004	.010	.023	.046	.081	.126	.177	.225	.257	.258	.221	.152	.071	.014
	9	.000	.000	.000	.000	.000	.000	.001	.002	.005	.013	.027	.051	.089	.140	.200	.258	.295	.287	.213	.087
	10	.000	.000	.000	.000	.000	.000	.000	.001	.002	.005	.013	.027	.052	.093	.155	.236	.325	.384	.329
	11	.000	.000	.000	.000	.000	.000	.000	.000	.000	.000	.001	.004	.009	.020	.042	.086	.167	.314	.569
12	0	.886	.540	.282	.142	.069	.032	.014	.006	.002	.001	.000	.000	.000	.000	.000	.000	.000	.000	.000	.000
	1	.107	.341	.377	.301	.206	.127	.071	.037	.017	.008	.003	.001	.000	.000	.000	.000	.000	.000	.000	.000
	2	.006	.099	.230	.292	.283	.232	.168	.109	.064	.034	.016	.007	.002	.001	.000	.000	.000	.000	.000	.000
	3	.000	.017	.085	.172	.236	.258	.240	.195	.142	.092	.054	.028	.012	.005	.001	.000	.000	.000	.000	.000
	4	.000	.002	.021	.068	.133	.194	.231	.237	.213	.170	.121	.076	.042	.020	.008	.002	.001	.000	.000	.000
	5	.000	.000	.004	.019	.053	.103	.158	.204	.227	.223	.193	.149	.101	.059	.029	.011	.003	.001	.000	.000
	6	.000	.000	.000	.004	.016	.040	.079	.128	.177	.212	.226	.212	.177	.128	.079	.040	.016	.004	.000	.000
	7	.000	.000	.000	.001	.003	.011	.029	.059	.101	.149	.193	.223	.227	.204	.158	.103	.053	.019	.004	.000
	8	.000	.000	.000	.000	.001	.002	.008	.020	.042	.076	.121	.170	.213	.237	.231	.194	.133	.068	.021	.002
	9	.000	.000	.000	.000	.000	.000	.001	.005	.012	.028	.054	.092	.142	.195	.240	.258	.236	.172	.085	.017
	10	.000	.000	.000	.000	.000	.000	.000	.001	.002	.007	.016	.034	.064	.109	.168	.232	.283	.292	.230	.099
	11	.000	.000	.000	.000	.000	.000	.000	.000	.000	.001	.003	.008	.017	.037	.071	.127	.206	.301	.377	.341
	12	.000	.000	.000	.000	.000	.000	.000	.000	.000	.000	.001	.002	.006	.014	.032	.069	.142	.282	.540
15	0	.860	.463	.206	.087	.035	.013	.005	.002	.000	.000	.000	.000	.000	.000	.000	.000	.000	.000	.000	.000
	1	.130	.366	.343	.231	.132	.067	.031	.013	.005	.002	.000	.000	.000	.000	.000	.000	.000	.000	.000	.000
	2	.009	.135	.267	.286	.231	.156	.092	.048	.022	.009	.003	.001	.000	.000	.000	.000	.000	.000	.000	.000
	3	.000	.031	.129	.218	.250	.225	.170	.111	.063	.032	.014	.005	.002	.000	.000	.000	.000	.000	.000	.000
	4	.000	.005	.043	.116	.188	.225	.219	.179	.127	.078	.042	.019	.007	.002	.001	.000	.000	.000	.000	.000
	5	.000	.001	.010	.045	.103	.165	.206	.212	.186	.140	.092	.051	.024	.010	.003	.001	.000	.000	.000	.000
	6	.000	.000	.002	.013	.043	.092	.147	.191	.207	.191	.153	.105	.061	.030	.012	.003	.001	.000	.000	.000
	7	.000	.000	.000	.003	.014	.039	.081	.132	.177	.201	.196	.165	.118	.071	.035	.013	.003	.001	.000	.000
	8	.000	.000	.000	.001	.003	.013	.035	.071	.118	.165	.196	.201	.177	.132	.081	.039	.014	.003	.000	.000
	9	.000	.000	.000	.000	.001	.003	.012	.030	.061	.105	.153	.191	.207	.191	.147	.092	.043	.013	.002	.000
	10	.000	.000	.000	.000	.000	.001	.003	.010	.024	.051	.092	.140	.186	.212	.206	.165	.103	.045	.010	.001
	11	.000	.000	.000	.000	.000	.000	.001	.002	.007	.019	.042	.078	.127	.179	.219	.225	.188	.116	.043	.005
	12	.000	.000	.000	.000	.000	.000	.000	.000	.002	.005	.014	.032	.063	.111	.170	.225	.250	.218	.129	.031
	13	.000	.000	.000	.000	.000	.000	.000	.000	.000	.001	.003	.009	.022	.048	.092	.156	.231	.286	.267	.135
	14	.000	.000	.000	.000	.000	.000	.000	.000	.000	.000	.000	.002	.005	.013	.031	.067	.132	.231	.343	.366
	15	.000	.000	.000	.000	.000	.000	.000	.000	.000	.000	.000	.000	.002	.005	.013	.035	.087	.206	.463

Table 2— Binomial Distribution *(continued)*

		p																			
n	x	.01	.05	.10	.15	.20	.25	.30	.35	.40	.45	.50	.55	.60	.65	.70	.75	.80	.85	.90	.95
16	0	.851	.440	.185	.074	.028	.010	.003	.001	.000	.000	.000	.000	.000	.000	.000	.000	.000	.000	.000	.000
	1	.138	.371	.329	.210	.113	.053	.023	.009	.003	.001	.000	.000	.000	.000	.000	.000	.000	.000	.000	.000
	2	.010	.146	.275	.277	.211	.134	.073	.035	.015	.006	.002	.001	.000	.000	.000	.000	.000	.000	.000	.000
	3	.000	.036	.142	.229	.246	.208	.146	.089	.047	.022	.009	.003	.001	.000	.000	.000	.000	.000	.000	.000
	4	.000	.006	.051	.131	.200	.225	.204	.155	.101	.057	.028	.011	.004	.001	.000	.000	.000	.000	.000	.000
	5	.000	.001	.014	.056	.120	.180	.210	.201	.162	.112	.067	.034	.014	.005	.001	.000	.000	.000	.000	.000
	6	.000	.000	.003	.018	.055	.110	.165	.198	.198	.168	.122	.075	.039	.017	.006	.001	.000	.000	.000	.000
	7	.000	.000	.000	.005	.020	.052	.101	.152	.189	.197	.175	.132	.084	.044	.019	.006	.001	.000	.000	.000
	8	.000	.000	.000	.001	.006	.020	.049	.092	.142	.181	.196	.181	.142	.092	.049	.020	.006	.001	.000	.000
	9	.000	.000	.000	.000	.001	.006	.019	.044	.084	.132	.175	.197	.189	.152	.101	.052	.020	.005	.000	.000
	10	.000	.000	.000	.000	.000	.001	.006	.017	.039	.075	.122	.168	.198	.198	.165	.110	.055	.018	.003	.000
	11	.000	.000	.000	.000	.000	.000	.001	.005	.014	.034	.067	.112	.162	.201	.210	.180	.120	.056	.014	.001
	12	.000	.000	.000	.000	.000	.000	.000	.001	.004	.011	.028	.057	.101	.155	.204	.225	.200	.131	.051	.006
	13	.000	.000	.000	.000	.000	.000	.000	.000	.001	.003	.009	.022	.047	.089	.146	.208	.246	.229	.142	.036
	14	.000	.000	.000	.000	.000	.000	.000	.000	.000	.001	.002	.006	.015	.035	.073	.134	.211	.277	.275	.146
	15	.000	.000	.000	.000	.000	.000	.000	.000	.000	.000	.000	.001	.003	.009	.023	.053	.113	.210	.329	.371
	16	.000	.000	.000	.000	.000	.000	.000	.000	.000	.000	.000	.000	.000	.001	.003	.010	.028	.074	.185	.440
20	0	.818	.358	.122	.039	.012	.003	.001	.000	.000	.000	.000	.000	.000	.000	.000	.000	.000	.000	.000	.000
	1	.165	.377	.270	.137	.058	.021	.007	.002	.000	.000	.000	.000	.000	.000	.000	.000	.000	.000	.000	.000
	2	.016	.189	.285	.229	.137	.067	.028	.010	.003	.001	.000	.000	.000	.000	.000	.000	.000	.000	.000	.000
	3	.001	.060	.190	.243	.205	.134	.072	.032	.012	.004	.001	.000	.000	.000	.000	.000	.000	.000	.000	.000
	4	.000	.013	.090	.182	.218	.190	.130	.074	.035	.014	.005	.001	.000	.000	.000	.000	.000	.000	.000	.000
	5	.000	.002	.032	.103	.175	.202	.179	.127	.075	.036	.015	.005	.001	.000	.000	.000	.000	.000	.000	.000
	6	.000	.000	.009	.045	.109	.169	.192	.171	.124	.075	.036	.015	.005	.001	.000	.000	.000	.000	.000	.000
	7	.000	.000	.002	.016	.055	.112	.164	.184	.166	.122	.074	.037	.015	.005	.001	.000	.000	.000	.000	.000
	8	.000	.000	.000	.005	.022	.061	.114	.161	.180	.162	.120	.073	.035	.014	.004	.001	.000	.000	.000	.000
	9	.000	.000	.000	.001	.007	.027	.065	.116	.160	.177	.160	.119	.071	.034	.012	.003	.000	.000	.000	.000
	10	.000	.000	.000	.000	.002	.010	.031	.069	.117	.159	.176	.159	.117	.069	.031	.010	.002	.000	.000	.000
	11	.000	.000	.000	.000	.000	.003	.012	.034	.071	.119	.160	.177	.160	.116	.065	.027	.007	.001	.000	.000
	12	.000	.000	.000	.000	.000	.001	.004	.014	.035	.073	.120	.162	.180	.161	.114	.061	.022	.005	.000	.000
	13	.000	.000	.000	.000	.000	.000	.001	.005	.015	.037	.074	.122	.166	.184	.164	.112	.055	.016	.002	.000
	14	.000	.000	.000	.000	.000	.000	.000	.001	.005	.015	.037	.075	.124	.171	.192	.169	.109	.045	.009	.000
	15	.000	.000	.000	.000	.000	.000	.000	.000	.001	.005	.015	.036	.075	.127	.179	.202	.175	.103	.032	.002
	16	.000	.000	.000	.000	.000	.000	.000	.000	.000	.001	.005	.014	.035	.074	.130	.190	.218	.182	.090	.013
	17	.000	.000	.000	.000	.000	.000	.000	.000	.000	.000	.001	.004	.012	.032	.072	.134	.205	.243	.190	.060
	18	.000	.000	.000	.000	.000	.000	.000	.000	.000	.000	.000	.001	.003	.010	.028	.067	.137	.229	.285	.189
	19	.000	.000	.000	.000	.000	.000	.000	.000	.000	.000	.000	.000	.000	.002	.007	.021	.058	.137	.270	.377
	20	.000	.000	.000	.000	.000	.000	.000	.000	.000	.000	.000	.000	.000	.000	.001	.003	.012	.039	.122	.358

Table 3 — Poisson Distribution

					μ					
x	0.1	0.2	0.3	0.4	0.5	0.6	0.7	0.8	0.9	1.0
0	.9048	.8187	.7408	.6703	.6065	.5488	.4966	.4493	.4066	.3679
1	.0905	.1637	.2222	.2681	.3033	.3293	.3476	.3595	.3659	.3679
2	.0045	.0164	.0333	.0536	.0758	.0988	.1217	.1438	.1647	.1839
3	.0002	.0011	.0033	.0072	.0126	.0198	.0284	.0383	.0494	.0613
4	.0000	.0001	.0003	.0007	.0016	.0030	.0050	.0077	.0111	.0153
5	.0000	.0000	.0000	.0001	.0002	.0004	.0007	.0012	.0020	.0031
6	.0000	.0000	.0000	.0000	.0000	.0000	.0001	.0002	.0003	.0005
7	.0000	.0000	.0000	.0000	.0000	.0000	.0000	.0000	.0000	.0001

					μ					
x	1.1	1.2	1.3	1.4	1.5	1.6	1.7	1.8	1.9	2.0
0	.3329	.3012	.2725	.2466	.2231	.2019	.1827	.1653	.1496	.1353
1	.3662	.3614	.3543	.3452	.3347	.3230	.3106	.2975	.2842	.2707
2	.2014	.2169	.2303	.2417	.2510	.2584	.2640	.2678	.2700	.2707
3	.0738	.0867	.0998	.1128	.1255	.1378	.1496	.1607	.1710	.1804
4	.0203	.0260	.0324	.0395	.0471	.0551	.0636	.0723	.0812	.0902
5	.0045	.0062	.0084	.0111	.0141	.0176	.0216	.0260	.0309	.0361
6	.0008	.0012	.0018	.0026	.0035	.0047	.0061	.0078	.0098	.0120
7	.0001	.0002	.0003	.0005	.0008	.0011	.0015	.0020	.0027	.0034
8	.0000	.0000	.0001	.0001	.0001	.0002	.0003	.0005	.0006	.0009
9	.0000	.0000	.0000	.0000	.0000	.0000	.0001	.0001	.0001	.0002

					μ					
x	2.1	2.2	2.3	2.4	2.5	2.6	2.7	2.8	2.9	3.0
0	.1225	.1108	.1003	.0907	.0821	.0743	.0672	.0608	.0550	.0498
1	.2572	.2438	.2306	.2177	.2052	.1931	.1815	.1703	.1596	.1494
2	.2700	.2681	.2652	.2613	.2565	.2510	.2450	.2384	.2314	.2240
3	.1890	.1966	.2033	.2090	.2138	.2176	.2205	.2225	.2237	.2240
4	.0992	.1082	.1169	.1254	.1336	.1414	.1488	.1557	.1622	.1680
5	.0417	.0476	.0538	.0602	.0668	.0735	.0804	.0872	.0940	.1008
6	.0146	.0174	.0206	.0241	.0278	.0319	.0362	.0407	.0455	.0504
7	.0044	.0055	.0068	.0083	.0099	.0118	.0139	.0163	.0188	.0216
8	.0011	.0015	.0019	.0025	.0031	.0038	.0047	.0057	.0068	.0081
9	.0003	.0004	.0005	.0007	.0009	.0011	.0014	.0018	.0022	.0027
10	.0001	.0001	.0001	.0002	.0002	.0003	.0004	.0005	.0006	.0008
11	.0000	.0000	.0000	.0000	.0000	.0001	.0001	.0001	.0002	.0002
12	.0000	.0000	.0000	.0000	.0000	.0000	.0000	.0000	.0000	.0001

					μ					
x	3.1	3.2	3.3	3.4	3.5	3.6	3.7	3.8	3.9	4.0
0	.0450	.0408	.0369	.0334	.0302	.0273	.0247	.0224	.0202	.0183
1	.1397	.1304	.1217	.1135	.1057	.0984	.0915	.0850	.0789	.0733
2	.2165	.2087	.2008	.1929	.1850	.1771	.1692	.1615	.1539	.1465
3	.2237	.2226	.2209	.2186	.2158	.2125	.2087	.2046	.2001	.1954
4	.1734	.1781	.1823	.1858	.1888	.1912	.1931	.1944	.1951	.1954
5	.1075	.1140	.1203	.1264	.1322	.1377	.1429	.1477	.1522	.1563
6	.0555	.0608	.0662	.0716	.0771	.0826	.0881	.0936	.0989	.1042
7	.0246	.0278	.0312	.0348	.0385	.0425	.0466	.0508	.0551	.0595
8	.0095	.0111	.0129	.0148	.0169	.0191	.0215	.0241	.0269	.0298
9	.0033	.0040	.0047	.0056	.0066	.0076	.0089	.0102	.0116	.0132
10	.0010	.0013	.0016	.0019	.0023	.0028	.0033	.0039	.0045	.0053
11	.0003	.0004	.0005	.0006	.0007	.0009	.0011	.0013	.0016	.0019
12	.0001	.0001	.0001	.0002	.0002	.0003	.0003	.0004	.0005	.0006
13	.0000	.0000	.0000	.0000	.0001	.0001	.0001	.0001	.0002	.0002
14	.0000	.0000	.0000	.0000	.0000	.0000	.0000	.0000	.0000	.0001

Reprinted with permission from W. H. Beyer, *Handbook of Tables for Probability and Statistics*, 2e, CRC Press, Boca Raton, Florida, 1986.

Table 3— Poisson Distribution *(continued)*

x	4.1	4.2	4.3	4.4	4.5	4.6	4.7	4.8	4.9	5.0
0	.0166	.0150	.0136	.0123	.0111	.0101	.0091	.0082	.0074	.0067
1	.0679	.0630	.0583	.0540	.0500	.0462	.0427	.0395	.0365	.0337
2	.1393	.1323	.1254	.1188	.1125	.1063	.1005	.0948	.0894	.0842
3	.1904	.1852	.1798	.1743	.1687	.1631	.1574	.1517	.1460	.1404
4	.1951	.1944	.1933	.1917	.1898	.1875	.1849	.1820	.1789	.1755
5	.1600	.1633	.1662	.1687	.1708	.1725	.1738	.1747	.1753	.1755
6	.1093	.1143	.1191	.1237	.1281	.1323	.1362	.1398	.1432	.1462
7	.0640	.0686	.0732	.0778	.0824	.0869	.0914	.0959	.1002	.1044
8	.0328	.0360	.0393	.0428	.0463	.0500	.0537	.0575	.0614	.0653
9	.0150	.0168	.0188	.0209	.0232	.0255	.0280	.0307	.0334	.0363
10	.0061	.0071	.0081	.0092	.0104	.0118	.0132	.0147	.0164	.0181
11	.0023	.0027	.0032	.0037	.0043	.0049	.0056	.0064	.0073	.0082
12	.0008	.0009	.0011	.0014	.0016	.0019	.0022	.0026	.0030	.0034
13	.0002	.0003	.0004	.0005	.0006	.0007	.0008	.0009	.0011	.0013
14	.0001	.0001	.0001	.0001	.0002	.0002	.0003	.0003	.0004	.0005
15	.0000	.0000	.0000	.0000	.0001	.0001	.0001	.0001	.0001	.0002

x	5.1	5.2	5.3	5.4	5.5	5.6	5.7	5.8	5.9	6.0
0	.0061	.0055	.0050	.0045	.0041	.0037	.0033	.0030	.0027	.0025
1	.0311	.0287	.0265	.0244	.0225	.0207	.0191	.0176	.0162	.0149
2	.0793	.0746	.0701	.0659	.0618	.0580	.0544	.0509	.0477	.0446
3	.1348	.1293	.1239	.1185	.1133	.1082	.1033	.0985	.0938	.0892
4	.1719	.1681	.1641	.1600	.1558	.1515	.1472	.1428	.1383	.1339
5	.1753	.1748	.1740	.1728	.1714	.1697	.1678	.1656	.1632	.1606
6	.1490	.1515	.1537	.1555	.1571	.1584	.1594	.1601	.1605	.1606
7	.1086	.1125	.1163	.1200	.1234	.1267	.1298	.1326	.1353	.1377
8	.0692	.0731	.0771	.0810	.0849	.0887	.0925	.0962	.0998	.1033
9	.0392	.0423	.0454	.0486	.0519	.0552	.0586	.0620	.0654	.0688
10	.0200	.0220	.0241	.0262	.0285	.0309	.0334	.0359	.0386	.0413
11	.0093	.0104	.0116	.0129	.0143	.0157	.0173	.0190	.0207	.0225
12	.0039	.0045	.0051	.0058	.0065	.0073	.0082	.0092	.0102	.0113
13	.0015	.0018	.0021	.0024	.0028	.0032	.0036	.0041	.0046	.0052
14	.0006	.0007	.0008	.0009	.0011	.0013	.0015	.0017	.0019	.0022
15	.0002	.0002	.0003	.0003	.0004	.0005	.0006	.0007	.0008	.0009
16	.0001	.0001	.0001	.0001	.0001	.0002	.0002	.0002	.0003	.0003
17	.0000	.0000	.0000	.0000	.0000	.0000	.0001	.0001	.0001	.0001

Table 3 — Poisson Distribution *(continued)*

x	6.1	6.2	6.3	6.4	6.5	6.6	6.7	6.8	6.9	7.0
					μ					
0	.0022	.0020	.0018	.0017	.0015	.0014	.0012	.0011	.0010	.0009
1	.0137	.0126	.0116	.0106	.0098	.0090	.0082	.0076	.0070	.0064
2	.0417	.0390	.0364	.0340	.0318	.0296	.0276	.0258	.0240	.0223
3	.0848	.0806	.0765	.0726	.0688	.0652	.0617	.0584	.0552	.0521
4	.1294	.1249	.1205	.1162	.1118	.1076	.1034	.0992	.0952	.0912
5	.1579	.1549	.1519	.1487	.1454	.1420	.1385	.1349	.1314	.1277
6	.1605	.1601	.1595	.1586	.1575	.1562	.1546	.1529	.1511	.1490
7	.1399	.1418	.1435	.1450	.1462	.1472	.1480	.1486	.1489	.1490
8	.1066	.1099	.1130	.1160	.1188	.1215	.1240	.1263	.1284	.1304
9	.0723	.0757	.0791	.0825	.0858	.0891	.0923	.0954	.0985	.1014
10	.0441	.0469	.0498	.0528	.0558	.0588	.0618	.0649	.0679	.0710
11	.0245	.0265	.0285	.0307	.0330	.0353	.0377	.0401	.0426	.0452
12	.0124	.0137	.0150	.0164	.0179	.0194	.0210	.0227	.0245	.0264
13	.0058	.0065	.0073	.0081	.0089	.0098	.0108	.0119	.0130	.0142
14	.0025	.0029	.0033	.0037	.0041	.0046	.0052	.0058	.0064	.0071
15	.0010	.0012	.0014	.0016	.0018	.0020	.0023	.0026	.0029	.0033
16	.0004	.0005	.0005	.0006	.0007	.0008	.0010	.0011	.0013	.0014
17	.0001	.0002	.0002	.0002	.0003	.0003	.0004	.0004	.0005	.0006
18	.0000	.0001	.0001	.0001	.0001	.0001	.0001	.0002	.0002	.0002
19	.0000	.0000	.0000	.0000	.0000	.0000	.0000	.0001	.0001	.0001

x	7.1	7.2	7.3	7.4	7.5	7.6	7.7	7.8	7.9	8.0
					μ					
0	.0008	.0007	.0007	.0006	.0006	.0005	.0005	.0004	.0004	.0003
1	.0059	.0054	.0049	.0045	.0041	.0038	.0035	.0032	.0029	.0027
2	.0208	.0194	.0180	.0167	.0156	.0145	.0134	.0125	.0116	.0107
3	.0492	.0464	.0438	.0413	.0389	.0366	.0345	.0324	.0305	.0286
4	.0874	.0836	.0799	.0764	.0729	.0696	.0663	.0632	.0602	.0573
5	.1241	.1204	.1167	.1130	.1094	.1057	.1021	.0986	.0951	.0916
6	.1468	.1445	.1420	.1394	.1367	.1339	.1311	.1282	.1252	.1221
7	.1489	.1486	.1481	.1474	.1465	.1454	.1442	.1428	.1413	.1396
8	.1321	.1337	.1351	.1363	.1373	.1382	.1388	.1392	.1395	.1396
9	.1042	.1070	.1096	.1121	.1144	.1167	.1187	.1207	.1224	.1241
10	.0740	.0770	.0800	.0829	.0858	.0887	.0914	.0941	.0967	.0993
11	.0478	.0504	.0531	.0558	.0585	.0613	.0640	.0667	.0695	.0722
12	.0283	.0303	.0323	.0344	.0366	.0388	.0411	.0434	.0457	.0481
13	.0154	.0168	.0181	.0196	.0211	.0227	.0243	.0260	.0278	.0296
14	.0078	.0086	.0095	.0104	.0113	.0123	.0134	.0145	.0157	.0169
15	.0037	.0041	.0046	.0051	.0057	.0062	.0069	.0075	.0083	.0090
16	.0016	.0019	.0021	.0024	.0026	.0030	.0033	.0037	.0041	.0045
17	.0007	.0008	.0009	.0010	.0012	.0013	.0015	.0017	.0019	.0021
18	.0003	.0003	.0004	.0004	.0005	.0006	.0006	.0007	.0008	.0009
19	.0001	.0001	.0001	.0002	.0002	.0002	.0003	.0003	.0003	.0004
20	.0000	.0000	.0001	.0001	.0001	.0001	.0001	.0001	.0001	.0002
21	.0000	.0000	.0000	.0000	.0000	.0000	.0000	.0000	.0001	.0001

Table 3— Poisson Distribution *(continued)*

x	8.1	8.2	8.3	8.4	8.5	8.6	8.7	8.8	8.9	9.0
0	.0003	.0003	.0002	.0002	.0002	.0002	.0002	.0002	.0001	.0001
1	.0025	.0023	.0021	.0019	.0017	.0016	.0014	.0013	.0012	.0011
2	.0100	.0092	.0086	.0079	.0074	.0068	.0063	.0058	.0054	.0050
3	.0269	.0252	.0237	.0222	.0208	.0195	.0183	.0171	.0160	.0150
4	.0544	.0517	.0491	.0466	.0443	.0420	.0398	.0377	.0357	.0337
5	.0882	.0849	.0816	.0784	.0752	.0722	.0692	.0663	.0635	.0607
6	.1191	.1160	.1128	.1097	.1066	.1034	.1003	.0972	.0941	.0911
7	.1378	.1358	.1338	.1317	.1294	.1271	.1247	.1222	.1197	.1171
8	.1395	.1392	.1388	.1382	.1375	.1366	.1356	.1344	.1332	.1318
9	.1256	.1269	.1280	.1290	.1299	.1306	.1311	.1315	.1317	.1318
10	.1017	.1040	.1063	.1084	.1104	.1123	.1140	.1157	.1172	.1186
11	.0749	.0776	.0802	.0828	.0853	.0878	.0902	.0925	.0948	.0970
12	.0505	.0530	.0555	.0579	.0604	.0629	.0654	.0679	.0703	.0728
13	.0315	.0334	.0354	.0374	.0395	.0416	.0438	.0459	.0481	.0504
14	.0182	.0196	.0210	.0225	.0240	.0256	.0272	.0289	.0306	.0324
15	.0098	.0107	.0116	.0126	.0136	.0147	.0158	.0169	.0182	.0194
16	.0050	.0055	.0060	.0066	.0072	.0079	.0086	.0093	.0101	.0109
17	.0024	.0026	.0029	.0033	.0036	.0040	.0044	.0048	.0053	.0058
18	.0011	.0012	.0014	.0015	.0017	.0019	.0021	.0024	.0026	.0029
19	.0005	.0005	.0006	.0007	.0008	.0009	.0010	.0011	.0012	.0014
20	.0002	.0002	.0002	.0003	.0003	.0004	.0004	.0005	.0005	.0006
21	.0001	.0001	.0001	.0001	.0001	.0002	.0002	.0002	.0002	.0003
22	.0000	.0000	.0000	.0000	.0001	.0001	.0001	.0001	.0001	.0001

x	9.1	9.2	9.3	9.4	9.5	9.6	9.7	9.8	9.9	10.0
0	.0001	.0001	.0001	.0001	.0001	.0001	.0001	.0001	.0001	.0000
1	.0010	.0009	.0009	.0008	.0007	.0007	.0006	.0005	.0005	.0005
2	.0046	.0043	.0040	.0037	.0034	.0031	.0029	.0027	.0025	.0023
3	.0140	.0131	.0123	.0115	.0107	.0100	.0093	.0087	.0081	.0076
4	.0319	.0302	.0285	.0269	.0254	.0240	.0226	.0213	.0201	.0189
5	.0581	.0555	.0530	.0506	.0483	.0460	.0439	.0418	.0398	.0378
6	.0881	.0851	.0822	.0793	.0764	.0736	.0709	.0682	.0656	.0631
7	.1145	.1118	.1091	.1064	.1037	.1010	.0982	.0955	.0928	.0901
8	.1302	.1286	.1269	.1251	.1232	.1212	.1191	.1170	.1148	.1126
9	.1317	.1315	.1311	.1306	.1300	.1293	.1284	.1274	.1263	.1251
10	.1198	.1210	.1219	.1228	.1235	.1241	.1245	.1249	.1250	.1251
11	.0991	.1012	.1031	.1049	.1067	.1083	.1098	.1112	.1125	.1137
12	.0752	.0776	.0799	.0822	.0844	.0866	.0888	.0908	.0928	.0948
13	.0526	.0549	.0572	.0594	.0617	.0640	.0662	.0685	.0707	.0729
14	.0342	.0361	.0380	.0399	.0419	.0439	.0459	.0479	.0500	.0521
15	.0208	.0221	.0235	.0250	.0265	.0281	.0297	.0313	.0330	.0347
16	.0118	.0127	.0137	.0147	.0157	.0168	.0180	.0192	.0204	.0217
17	.0063	.0069	.0075	.0081	.0088	.0095	.0103	.0111	.0119	.0128
18	.0032	.0035	.0039	.0042	.0046	.0051	.0055	.0060	.0065	.0071
19	.0015	.0017	.0019	.0021	.0023	.0026	.0028	.0031	.0034	.0037
20	.0007	.0008	.0009	.0010	.0011	.0012	.0014	.0015	.0017	.0019
21	.0003	.0003	.0004	.0004	.0005	.0006	.0006	.0007	.0008	.0009
22	.0001	.0001	.0002	.0002	.0002	.0002	.0003	.0003	.0004	.0004
23	.0000	.0001	.0001	.0001	.0001	.0001	.0001	.0001	.0002	.0002
24	.0000	.0000	.0000	.0000	.0000	.0000	.0000	.0001	.0001	.0001

Table 3— Poisson Distribution *(continued)*

x	11	12	13	14	15	16	17	18	19	20
					μ					
0	.0000	.0000	.0000	.0000	.0000	.0000	.0000	.0000	.0000	.0000
1	.0002	.0001	.0000	.0000	.0000	.0000	.0000	.0000	.0000	.0000
2	.0010	.0004	.0002	.0001	.0000	.0000	.0000	.0000	.0000	.0000
3	.0037	.0018	.0008	.0004	.0002	.0001	.0000	.0000	.0000	.0000
4	.0102	.0053	.0027	.0013	.0006	.0003	.0001	.0001	.0000	.0000
5	.0224	.0127	.0070	.0037	.0019	.0010	.0005	.0002	.0001	.0001
6	.0411	.0255	.0152	.0087	.0048	.0026	.0014	.0007	.0004	.0002
7	.0646	.0437	.0281	.0174	.0104	.0060	.0034	.0018	.0010	.0005
8	.0888	.0655	.0457	.0304	.0194	.0120	.0072	.0042	.0024	.0013
9	.1085	.0874	.0661	.0473	.0324	.0213	.0135	.0083	.0050	.0029
10	.1194	.1048	.0859	.0663	.0486	.0341	.0230	.0150	.0095	.0058
11	.1194	.1144	.1015	.0844	.0663	.0496	.0355	.0245	.0164	.0106
12	.1094	.1144	.1099	.0984	.0829	.0661	.0504	.0368	.0259	.0176
13	.0926	.1056	.1099	.1060	.0956	.0814	.0658	.0509	.0378	.0271
14	.0728	.0905	.1021	.1060	.1024	.0930	.0800	.0655	.0514	.0387
15	.0534	.0724	.0885	.0989	.1024	.0992	.0906	.0786	.0650	.0516
16	.0367	.0543	.0719	.0866	.0960	.0992	.0963	.0884	.0772	.0646
17	.0237	.0383	.0550	.0713	.0847	.0934	.0963	.0936	.0863	.0760
18	.0145	.0256	.0397	.0554	.0706	.0830	.0909	.0936	.0911	.0844
19	.0084	.0161	.0272	.0409	.0557	.0699	.0814	.0887	.0911	.0888
20	.0046	.0097	.0177	.0286	.0418	.0559	.0692	.0798	.0866	.0888

x	11	12	13	14	15	16	17	18	19	20
					μ					
21	.0024	.0055	.0109	.0191	.0299	.0426	.0560	.0684	.0783	.0846
22	.0012	.0030	.0065	.0121	.0204	.0310	.0433	.0560	.0676	.0769
23	.0006	.0016	.0037	.0074	.0133	.0216	.0320	.0438	.0559	.0669
24	.0003	.0008	.0020	.0043	.0083	.0144	.0226	.0328	.0442	.0557
25	.0001	.0004	.0010	.0024	.0050	.0092	.0154	.0237	.0336	.0446
26	.0000	.0002	.0005	.0013	.0029	.0057	.0101	.0164	.0246	.0343
27	.0000	.0001	.0002	.0007	.0016	.0034	.0063	.0109	.0173	.0254
28	.0000	.0000	.0001	.0003	.0009	.0019	.0038	.0070	.0117	.0181
29	.0000	.0000	.0001	.0002	.0004	.0011	.0023	.0044	.0077	.0125
30	.0000	.0000	.0000	.0001	.0002	.0006	.0013	.0026	.0049	.0083
31	.0000	.0000	.0000	.0000	.0001	.0003	.0007	.0015	.0030	.0054
32	.0000	.0000	.0000	.0000	.0001	.0001	.0004	.0009	.0018	.0034
33	.0000	.0000	.0000	.0000	.0000	.0001	.0002	.0005	.0010	.0020
34	.0000	.0000	.0000	.0000	.0000	.0000	.0001	.0002	.0006	.0012
35	.0000	.0000	.0000	.0000	.0000	.0000	.0000	.0001	.0003	.0007
36	.0000	.0000	.0000	.0000	.0000	.0000	.0000	.0001	.0002	.0004
37	.0000	.0000	.0000	.0000	.0000	.0000	.0000	.0000	.0001	.0002
38	.0000	.0000	.0000	.0000	.0000	.0000	.0000	.0000	.0000	.0001
39	.0000	.0000	.0000	.0000	.0000	.0000	.0000	.0000	.0000	.0001

Table 4 — Standard Normal Distribution

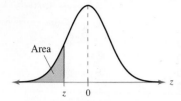

Area

z	.09	.08	.07	.06	.05	.04	.03	.02	.01	.00
−3.4	.0002	.0003	.0003	.0003	.0003	.0003	.0003	.0003	.0003	.0003
−3.3	.0003	.0004	.0004	.0004	.0004	.0004	.0004	.0005	.0005	.0005
−3.2	.0005	.0005	.0005	.0006	.0006	.0006	.0006	.0006	.0007	.0007
−3.1	.0007	.0007	.0008	.0008	.0008	.0008	.0009	.0009	.0009	.0010
−3.0	.0010	.0010	.0011	.0011	.0011	.0012	.0012	.0013	.0013	.0013
−2.9	.0014	.0014	.0015	.0015	.0016	.0016	.0017	.0018	.0018	.0019
−2.8	.0019	.0020	.0021	.0021	.0022	.0023	.0023	.0024	.0025	.0026
−2.7	.0026	.0027	.0028	.0029	.0030	.0031	.0032	.0033	.0034	.0035
−2.6	.0036	.0037	.0038	.0039	.0040	.0041	.0043	.0044	.0045	.0047
−2.5	.0048	.0049	.0051	.0052	.0054	.0055	.0057	.0059	.0060	.0062
−2.4	.0064	.0066	.0068	.0069	.0071	.0073	.0075	.0078	.0080	.0082
−2.3	.0084	.0087	.0089	.0091	.0094	.0096	.0099	.0102	.0104	.0107
−2.2	.0110	.0113	.0116	.0119	.0122	.0125	.0129	.0132	.0136	.0139
−2.1	.0143	.0146	.0150	.0154	.0158	.0162	.0166	.0170	.0174	.0179
−2.0	.0183	.0188	.0192	.0197	.0202	.0207	.0212	.0217	.0222	.0228
−1.9	.0233	.0239	.0244	.0250	.0256	.0262	.0268	.0274	.0281	.0287
−1.8	.0294	.0301	.0307	.0314	.0322	.0329	.0336	.0344	.0351	.0359
−1.7	.0367	.0375	.0384	.0392	.0401	.0409	.0418	.0427	.0436	.0446
−1.6	.0455	.0465	.0475	.0485	.0495	.0505	.0516	.0526	.0537	.0548
−1.5	.0559	.0571	.0582	.0594	.0606	.0618	.0630	.0643	.0655	.0668
−1.4	.0681	.0694	.0708	.0721	.0735	.0749	.0764	.0778	.0793	.0808
−1.3	.0823	.0838	.0853	.0869	.0885	.0901	.0918	.0934	.0951	.0968
−1.2	.0985	.1003	.1020	.1038	.1056	.1075	.1093	.1112	.1131	.1151
−1.1	.1170	.1190	.1210	.1230	.1251	.1271	.1292	.1314	.1335	.1357
−1.0	.1379	.1401	.1423	.1446	.1469	.1492	.1515	.1539	.1562	.1587
−0.9	.1611	.1635	.1660	.1685	.1711	.1736	.1762	.1788	.1814	.1841
−0.8	.1867	.1894	.1922	.1949	.1977	.2005	.2033	.2061	.2090	.2119
−0.7	.2148	.2177	.2206	.2236	.2266	.2296	.2327	.2358	.2389	.2420
−0.6	.2451	.2483	.2514	.2546	.2578	.2611	.2643	.2676	.2709	.2743
−0.5	.2776	.2810	.2843	.2877	.2912	.2946	.2981	.3015	.3050	.3085
−0.4	.3121	.3156	.3192	.3228	.3264	.3300	.3336	.3372	.3409	.3446
−0.3	.3483	.3520	.3557	.3594	.3632	.3669	.3707	.3745	.3783	.3821
−0.2	.3859	.3897	.3936	.3974	.4013	.4052	.4090	.4129	.4168	.4207
−0.1	.4247	.4286	.4325	.4364	.4404	.4443	.4483	.4522	.4562	.4602
−0.0	.4641	.4681	.4721	.4761	.4801	.4840	.4880	.4920	.4960	.5000

Critical Values

Level of Confidence c	z_c
0.80	1.28
0.90	1.645
0.95	1.96
0.99	2.575

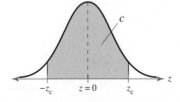

Table A-3, pp. 681–682 from *Probability and Statistics for Engineers and Scientists*, 6e by Walpole, Meyers, and Myers. Copyright 1997. Reprinted by permission of Pearson Prentice Hall, Upper Saddle River, N.J.

Table 4 — Standard Normal Distribution *(continued)*

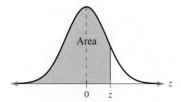

z	.00	.01	.02	.03	.04	.05	.06	.07	.08	.09
0.0	.5000	.5040	.5080	.5120	.5160	.5199	.5239	.5279	.5319	.5359
0.1	.5398	.5438	.5478	.5517	.5557	.5596	.5636	.5675	.5714	.5753
0.2	.5793	.5832	.5871	.5910	.5948	.5987	.6026	.6064	.6103	.6141
0.3	.6179	.6217	.6255	.6293	.6331	.6368	.6406	.6443	.6480	.6517
0.4	.6554	.6591	.6628	.6664	.6700	.6736	.6772	.6808	.6844	.6879
0.5	.6915	.6950	.6985	.7019	.7054	.7088	.7123	.7157	.7190	.7224
0.6	.7257	.7291	.7324	.7357	.7389	.7422	.7454	.7486	.7517	.7549
0.7	.7580	.7611	.7642	.7673	.7704	.7734	.7764	.7794	.7823	.7852
0.8	.7881	.7910	.7939	.7967	.7995	.8023	.8051	.8078	.8106	.8133
0.9	.8159	.8186	.8212	.8238	.8264	.8289	.8315	.8340	.8365	.8389
1.0	.8413	.8438	.8461	.8485	.8508	.8531	.8554	.8577	.8599	.8621
1.1	.8643	.8665	.8686	.8708	.8729	.8749	.8770	.8790	.8810	.8830
1.2	.8849	.8869	.8888	.8907	.8925	.8944	.8962	.8980	.8997	.9015
1.3	.9032	.9049	.9066	.9082	.9099	.9115	.9131	.9147	.9162	.9177
1.4	.9192	.9207	.9222	.9236	.9251	.9265	.9279	.9292	.9306	.9319
1.5	.9332	.9345	.9357	.9370	.9382	.9394	.9406	.9418	.9429	.9441
1.6	.9452	.9463	.9474	.9484	.9495	.9505	.9515	.9525	.9535	.9545
1.7	.9554	.9564	.9573	.9582	.9591	.9599	.9608	.9616	.9625	.9633
1.8	.9641	.9649	.9656	.9664	.9671	.9678	.9686	.9693	.9699	.9706
1.9	.9713	.9719	.9726	.9732	.9738	.9744	.9750	.9756	.9761	.9767
2.0	.9772	.9778	.9783	.9788	.9793	.9798	.9803	.9808	.9812	.9817
2.1	.9821	.9826	.9830	.9834	.9838	.9842	.9846	.9850	.9854	.9857
2.2	.9861	.9864	.9868	.9871	.9875	.9878	.9881	.9884	.9887	.9890
2.3	.9893	.9896	.9898	.9901	.9904	.9906	.9909	.9911	.9913	.9916
2.4	.9918	.9920	.9922	.9925	.9927	.9929	.9931	.9932	.9934	.9936
2.5	.9938	.9940	.9941	.9943	.9945	.9946	.9948	.9949	.9951	.9952
2.6	.9953	.9955	.9956	.9957	.9959	.9960	.9961	.9962	.9963	.9964
2.7	.9965	.9966	.9967	.9968	.9969	.9970	.9971	.9972	.9973	.9974
2.8	.9974	.9975	.9976	.9977	.9977	.9978	.9979	.9979	.9980	.9981
2.9	.9981	.9982	.9982	.9983	.9984	.9984	.9985	.9985	.9986	.9986
3.0	.9987	.9987	.9987	.9988	.9988	.9989	.9989	.9989	.9990	.9990
3.1	.9990	.9991	.9991	.9991	.9992	.9992	.9992	.9992	.9993	.9993
3.2	.9993	.9993	.9994	.9994	.9994	.9994	.9994	.9995	.9995	.9995
3.3	.9995	.9995	.9995	.9996	.9996	.9996	.9996	.9996	.9996	.9997
3.4	.9997	.9997	.9997	.9997	.9997	.9997	.9997	.9997	.9997	.9998

Table 5— *t*-Distribution

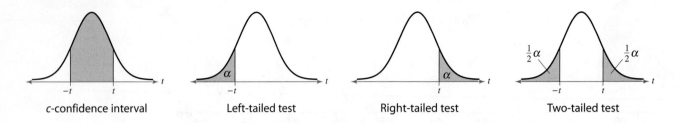

| c-confidence interval | Left-tailed test | Right-tailed test | Two-tailed test |

d.f.	Level of confidence, c	0.50	0.80	0.90	0.95	0.98	0.99
	One tail, α	0.25	0.10	0.05	0.025	0.01	0.005
	Two tails, α	0.50	0.20	0.10	0.05	0.02	0.01
1		1.000	3.078	6.314	12.706	31.821	63.657
2		.816	1.886	2.920	4.303	6.965	9.925
3		.765	1.638	2.353	3.182	4.541	5.841
4		.741	1.533	2.132	2.776	3.747	4.604
5		.727	1.476	2.015	2.571	3.365	4.032
6		.718	1.440	1.943	2.447	3.143	3.707
7		.711	1.415	1.895	2.365	2.998	3.499
8		.706	1.397	1.860	2.306	2.896	3.355
9		.703	1.383	1.833	2.262	2.821	3.250
10		.700	1.372	1.812	2.228	2.764	3.169
11		.697	1.363	1.796	2.201	2.718	3.106
12		.695	1.356	1.782	2.179	2.681	3.055
13		.694	1.350	1.771	2.160	2.650	3.012
14		.692	1.345	1.761	2.145	2.624	2.977
15		.691	1.341	1.753	2.131	2.602	2.947
16		.690	1.337	1.746	2.120	2.583	2.921
17		.689	1.333	1.740	2.110	2.567	2.898
18		.688	1.330	1.734	2.101	2.552	2.878
19		.688	1.328	1.729	2.093	2.539	2.861
20		.687	1.325	1.725	2.086	2.528	2.845
21		.686	1.323	1.721	2.080	2.518	2.831
22		.686	1.321	1.717	2.074	2.508	2.819
23		.685	1.319	1.714	2.069	2.500	2.807
24		.685	1.318	1.711	2.064	2.492	2.797
25		.684	1.316	1.708	2.060	2.485	2.787
26		.684	1.315	1.706	2.056	2.479	2.779
27		.684	1.314	1.703	2.052	2.473	2.771
28		.683	1.313	1.701	2.048	2.467	2.763
29		.683	1.311	1.699	2.045	2.462	2.756
∞		.674	1.282	1.645	1.960	2.326	2.576

Adapted from W. H. Beyer, *Handbook of Tables of Probability and Statistics*, 2e,
CRC Press, Boca Raton, Florida, 1986. Reprinted with permission.

Table 6 — Chi-Square Distribution

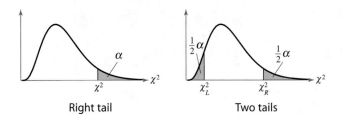

Right tail   Two tails

Degrees of freedom	α									
	0.995	0.99	0.975	0.95	0.90	0.10	0.05	0.025	0.01	0.005
1	—	—	0.001	0.004	0.016	2.706	3.841	5.024	6.635	7.879
2	0.010	0.020	0.051	0.103	0.211	4.605	5.991	7.378	9.210	10.597
3	0.072	0.115	0.216	0.352	0.584	6.251	7.815	9.348	11.345	12.838
4	0.207	0.297	0.484	0.711	1.064	7.779	9.488	11.143	13.277	14.860
5	0.412	0.554	0.831	1.145	1.610	9.236	11.071	12.833	15.086	16.750
6	0.676	0.872	1.237	1.635	2.204	10.645	12.592	14.449	16.812	18.548
7	0.989	1.239	1.690	2.167	2.833	12.017	14.067	16.013	18.475	20.278
8	1.344	1.646	2.180	2.733	3.490	13.362	15.507	17.535	20.090	21.955
9	1.735	2.088	2.700	3.325	4.168	14.684	16.919	19.023	21.666	23.589
10	2.156	2.558	3.247	3.940	4.865	15.987	18.307	20.483	23.209	25.188
11	2.603	3.053	3.816	4.575	5.578	17.275	19.675	21.920	24.725	26.757
12	3.074	3.571	4.404	5.226	6.304	18.549	21.026	23.337	26.217	28.299
13	3.565	4.107	5.009	5.892	7.042	19.812	22.362	24.736	27.688	29.819
14	4.075	4.660	5.629	6.571	7.790	21.064	23.685	26.119	29.141	31.319
15	4.601	5.229	6.262	7.261	8.547	22.307	24.996	27.488	30.578	32.801
16	5.142	5.812	6.908	7.962	9.312	23.542	26.296	28.845	32.000	34.267
17	5.697	6.408	7.564	8.672	10.085	24.769	27.587	30.191	33.409	35.718
18	6.265	7.015	8.231	9.390	10.865	25.989	28.869	31.526	34.805	37.156
19	6.844	7.633	8.907	10.117	11.651	27.204	30.144	32.852	36.191	38.582
20	7.434	8.260	9.591	10.851	12.443	28.412	31.410	34.170	37.566	39.997
21	8.034	8.897	10.283	11.591	13.240	29.615	32.671	35.479	38.932	41.401
22	8.643	9.542	10.982	12.338	14.042	30.813	33.924	36.781	40.289	42.796
23	9.260	10.196	11.689	13.091	14.848	32.007	35.172	38.076	41.638	44.181
24	9.886	10.856	12.401	13.848	15.659	33.196	36.415	39.364	42.980	45.559
25	10.520	11.524	13.120	14.611	16.473	34.382	37.652	40.646	44.314	46.928
26	11.160	12.198	13.844	15.379	17.292	35.563	38.885	41.923	45.642	48.290
27	11.808	12.879	14.573	16.151	18.114	36.741	40.113	43.194	46.963	49.645
28	12.461	13.565	15.308	16.928	18.939	37.916	41.337	44.461	48.278	50.993
29	13.121	14.257	16.047	17.708	19.768	39.087	42.557	45.722	49.588	52.336
30	13.787	14.954	16.791	18.493	20.599	40.256	43.773	46.979	50.892	53.672
40	20.707	22.164	24.433	26.509	29.051	51.805	55.758	59.342	63.691	66.766
50	27.991	29.707	32.357	34.764	37.689	63.167	67.505	71.420	76.154	79.490
60	35.534	37.485	40.482	43.188	46.459	74.397	79.082	83.298	88.379	91.952
70	43.275	45.442	48.758	51.739	55.329	85.527	90.531	95.023	100.425	104.215
80	51.172	53.540	57.153	60.391	64.278	96.578	101.879	106.629	112.329	116.321
90	59.196	61.754	65.647	69.126	73.291	107.565	113.145	118.136	124.116	128.299
100	67.328	70.065	74.222	77.929	82.358	118.498	124.342	129.561	135.807	140.169

Table 7— *F*-Distribution

$\alpha = 0.005$

d.f.$_N$: Degrees of freedom, numerator

d.f.$_D$: Degrees of freedom, denominator	1	2	3	4	5	6	7	8	9	10	12	15	20	24	30	40	60	120	∞
1	16211	20000	21615	22500	23056	23437	23715	23925	24091	24224	24426	24630	24836	24940	25044	25148	25253	25359	25465
2	198.5	199.0	199.2	199.2	199.3	199.3	199.4	199.4	199.4	199.4	199.4	199.4	199.4	199.5	199.5	199.5	199.5	199.5	199.5
3	55.55	49.80	47.47	46.19	45.39	44.84	44.43	44.13	43.88	43.69	43.39	43.08	42.78	42.62	42.47	42.31	42.15	41.99	41.83
4	31.33	26.28	24.26	23.15	22.46	21.97	21.62	21.35	21.14	20.97	20.70	20.44	20.17	20.03	19.89	19.75	19.61	19.47	19.32
5	22.78	18.31	16.53	15.56	14.94	14.51	14.20	13.96	13.77	13.62	13.38	13.15	12.90	12.78	12.66	12.53	12.40	12.27	12.14
6	18.63	14.54	12.92	12.03	11.46	11.07	10.79	10.57	10.39	10.25	10.03	9.81	9.59	9.47	9.36	9.24	9.12	9.00	8.88
7	16.24	12.40	10.88	10.05	9.52	9.16	8.89	8.68	8.51	8.38	8.18	7.97	7.75	7.65	7.53	7.42	7.31	7.19	7.08
8	14.69	11.04	9.60	8.81	8.30	7.95	7.69	7.50	7.34	7.21	7.01	6.81	6.61	6.50	6.40	6.29	6.18	6.06	5.95
9	13.61	10.11	8.72	7.96	7.47	7.13	6.88	6.69	6.54	6.42	6.23	6.03	5.83	5.73	5.62	5.52	5.41	5.30	5.19
10	12.83	9.43	8.08	7.34	6.87	6.54	6.30	6.12	5.97	5.85	5.66	5.47	5.27	5.17	5.07	4.97	4.86	4.75	4.64
11	12.23	8.91	7.60	6.88	6.42	6.10	5.86	5.68	5.54	5.42	5.24	5.05	4.86	4.76	4.65	4.55	4.44	4.34	4.23
12	11.75	8.51	7.23	6.52	6.07	5.76	5.52	5.35	5.20	5.09	4.91	4.72	4.53	4.43	4.33	4.23	4.12	4.01	3.90
13	11.37	8.19	6.93	6.23	5.79	5.48	5.25	5.08	4.94	4.82	4.64	4.46	4.27	4.17	4.07	3.97	3.87	3.76	3.65
14	11.06	7.92	6.68	6.00	5.56	5.26	5.03	4.86	4.72	4.60	4.43	4.25	4.06	3.96	3.86	3.76	3.66	3.55	3.44
15	10.80	7.70	6.48	5.80	5.37	5.07	4.85	4.67	4.54	4.42	4.25	4.07	3.88	3.79	3.69	3.58	3.48	3.37	3.26
16	10.58	7.51	6.30	5.64	5.21	4.91	4.69	4.52	4.38	4.27	4.10	3.92	3.73	3.64	3.54	3.44	3.33	3.22	3.11
17	10.38	7.35	6.16	5.50	5.07	4.78	4.56	4.39	4.25	4.14	3.97	3.79	3.61	3.51	3.41	3.31	3.21	3.10	2.98
18	10.22	7.21	6.03	5.37	4.96	4.66	4.44	4.28	4.14	4.03	3.86	3.68	3.50	3.40	3.30	3.20	3.10	2.99	2.87
19	10.07	7.09	5.92	5.27	4.85	4.56	4.34	4.18	4.04	3.93	3.76	3.59	3.40	3.31	3.21	3.11	3.00	2.89	2.78
20	9.94	6.99	5.82	5.17	4.76	4.47	4.26	4.09	3.96	3.85	3.68	3.50	3.32	3.22	3.12	3.02	2.92	2.81	2.69
21	9.83	6.89	5.73	5.09	4.68	4.39	4.18	4.01	3.88	3.77	3.60	3.43	3.24	3.15	3.05	2.95	2.84	2.73	2.61
22	9.73	6.81	5.65	5.02	4.61	4.32	4.11	3.94	3.81	3.70	3.54	3.36	3.18	3.08	2.98	2.88	2.77	2.66	2.55
23	9.63	6.73	5.58	4.95	4.54	4.26	4.05	3.88	3.75	3.64	3.47	3.30	3.12	3.02	2.92	2.82	2.71	2.60	2.48
24	9.55	6.66	5.52	4.89	4.49	4.20	3.99	3.83	3.69	3.59	3.42	3.25	3.06	2.97	2.87	2.77	2.66	2.55	2.43
25	9.48	6.60	5.46	4.84	4.43	4.15	3.94	3.78	3.64	3.54	3.37	3.20	3.01	2.92	2.82	2.72	2.61	2.50	2.38
26	9.41	6.54	5.41	4.79	4.38	4.10	3.89	3.73	3.60	3.49	3.33	3.15	2.97	2.87	2.77	2.67	2.56	2.45	2.33
27	9.34	6.49	5.36	4.74	4.34	4.06	3.85	3.69	3.56	3.45	3.28	3.11	2.93	2.83	2.73	2.63	2.52	2.41	2.29
28	9.28	6.44	5.32	4.70	4.30	4.02	3.81	3.65	3.52	3.41	3.25	3.07	2.89	2.79	2.69	2.59	2.48	2.37	2.25
29	9.23	6.40	5.28	4.66	4.26	3.98	3.77	3.61	3.48	3.38	3.21	3.04	2.86	2.76	2.66	2.56	2.45	2.33	2.24
30	9.18	6.35	5.24	4.62	4.23	3.95	3.74	3.58	3.45	3.34	3.18	3.01	2.82	2.73	2.63	2.52	2.42	2.30	2.18
40	8.83	6.07	4.98	4.37	3.99	3.71	3.51	3.35	3.22	3.12	2.95	2.78	2.60	2.50	2.40	2.30	2.18	2.06	1.93
60	8.49	5.79	4.73	4.14	3.76	3.49	3.29	3.13	3.01	2.90	2.74	2.57	2.39	2.29	2.19	2.08	1.96	1.83	1.69
120	8.18	5.54	4.50	3.92	3.55	3.28	3.09	2.93	2.81	2.71	2.54	2.37	2.19	2.09	1.98	1.87	1.75	1.61	1.43
∞	7.88	5.30	4.28	3.72	3.35	3.09	2.90	2.74	2.62	2.52	2.36	2.19	2.00	1.90	1.79	1.67	1.53	1.36	1.00

Table 7— *F*-Distribution *(continued)*

$\alpha = 0.01$

d.f.$_D$: Degrees of freedom, denominator	d.f.$_N$: Degrees of freedom, numerator																		
	1	2	3	4	5	6	7	8	9	10	12	15	20	24	30	40	60	120	∞
1	4052	4999.5	5403	5625	5764	5859	5928	5982	6022	6056	6106	6157	6209	6235	6261	6287	6313	6339	6366
2	98.50	99.00	99.17	99.25	99.30	99.33	99.36	99.37	99.39	99.40	99.42	99.43	99.45	99.46	99.47	99.47	99.48	99.49	99.50
3	34.12	30.82	29.46	28.71	28.24	27.91	27.67	27.49	27.35	27.23	27.05	26.87	26.69	26.60	26.50	26.41	26.32	26.22	26.13
4	21.20	18.00	16.69	15.98	15.52	15.21	14.98	14.80	14.66	14.55	14.37	14.20	14.02	13.93	13.84	13.75	13.65	13.56	13.46
5	16.26	13.27	12.06	11.39	10.97	10.67	10.46	10.29	10.16	10.05	9.89	9.72	9.55	9.47	9.38	9.29	9.20	9.11	9.02
6	13.75	10.92	9.78	9.15	8.75	8.47	8.26	8.10	7.98	7.87	7.72	7.56	7.40	7.31	7.23	7.14	7.06	6.97	6.88
7	12.25	9.55	8.45	7.85	7.46	7.19	6.99	6.84	6.72	6.62	6.47	6.31	6.16	6.07	5.99	5.91	5.82	5.74	5.65
8	11.26	8.65	7.59	7.01	6.63	6.37	6.18	6.03	5.91	5.81	5.67	5.52	5.36	5.28	5.20	5.12	5.03	4.95	4.86
9	10.56	8.02	6.99	6.42	6.06	5.80	5.61	5.47	5.35	5.26	5.11	4.96	4.81	4.73	4.65	4.57	4.48	4.40	4.31
10	10.04	7.56	6.55	5.99	5.64	5.39	5.20	5.06	4.94	4.85	4.71	4.56	4.41	4.33	4.25	4.17	4.08	4.00	3.91
11	9.65	7.21	6.22	5.67	5.32	5.07	4.89	4.74	4.63	4.54	4.40	4.25	4.10	4.02	3.94	3.86	3.78	3.69	3.60
12	9.33	6.93	5.95	5.41	5.06	4.82	4.64	4.50	4.39	4.30	4.16	4.01	3.86	3.78	3.70	3.62	3.54	3.45	3.36
13	9.07	6.70	5.74	5.21	4.86	4.62	4.44	4.30	4.19	4.10	3.96	3.82	3.66	3.59	3.51	3.43	3.34	3.25	3.17
14	8.86	6.51	5.56	5.04	4.69	4.46	4.28	4.14	4.03	3.94	3.80	3.66	3.51	3.43	3.35	3.27	3.18	3.09	3.00
15	8.68	6.36	5.42	4.89	4.56	4.32	4.14	4.00	3.89	3.80	3.67	3.52	3.37	3.29	3.21	3.13	3.05	2.96	2.87
16	8.53	6.23	5.29	4.77	4.44	4.20	4.03	3.89	3.78	3.69	3.55	3.41	3.26	3.18	3.10	3.02	2.93	2.84	2.75
17	8.40	6.11	5.18	4.67	4.34	4.10	3.93	3.79	3.68	3.59	3.46	3.31	3.16	3.08	3.00	2.92	2.83	2.75	2.65
18	8.29	6.01	5.09	4.58	4.25	4.01	3.84	3.71	3.60	3.51	3.37	3.23	3.08	3.00	2.92	2.84	2.75	2.66	2.57
19	8.18	5.93	5.01	4.50	4.17	3.94	3.77	3.63	3.52	3.43	3.30	3.15	3.00	2.92	2.84	2.76	2.67	2.58	2.49
20	8.10	5.85	4.94	4.43	4.10	3.87	3.70	3.56	3.46	3.37	3.23	3.09	2.94	2.86	2.78	2.69	2.61	2.52	2.42
21	8.02	5.78	4.87	4.37	4.04	3.81	3.64	3.51	3.40	3.31	3.17	3.03	2.88	2.80	2.72	2.64	2.55	2.46	2.36
22	7.95	5.72	4.82	4.31	3.99	3.76	3.59	3.45	3.35	3.26	3.12	2.98	2.83	2.75	2.67	2.58	2.50	2.40	2.31
23	7.88	5.66	4.76	4.26	3.94	3.71	3.54	3.41	3.30	3.21	3.07	2.93	2.78	2.70	2.62	2.54	2.45	2.35	2.26
24	7.82	5.61	4.72	4.22	3.90	3.67	3.50	3.36	3.26	3.17	3.03	2.89	2.74	2.66	2.58	2.49	2.40	2.31	2.21
25	7.77	5.57	4.68	4.18	3.85	3.63	3.46	3.32	3.22	3.13	2.99	2.85	2.70	2.62	2.54	2.45	2.36	2.27	2.17
26	7.72	5.53	4.64	4.14	3.82	3.59	3.42	3.29	3.18	3.09	2.96	2.81	2.66	2.58	2.50	2.42	2.33	2.23	2.13
27	7.68	5.49	4.60	4.11	3.78	3.56	3.39	3.26	3.15	3.06	2.93	2.78	2.63	2.55	2.47	2.38	2.29	2.20	2.10
28	7.64	5.45	4.57	4.07	3.75	3.53	3.36	3.23	3.12	3.03	2.90	2.75	2.60	2.52	2.44	2.35	2.26	2.17	2.06
29	7.60	5.42	4.54	4.04	3.73	3.50	3.33	3.20	3.09	3.00	2.87	2.73	2.57	2.49	2.41	2.33	2.23	2.14	2.03
30	7.56	5.39	4.51	4.02	3.70	3.47	3.30	3.17	3.07	2.98	2.84	2.70	2.55	2.47	2.39	2.30	2.21	2.11	2.01
40	7.31	5.18	4.31	3.83	3.51	3.29	3.12	2.99	2.89	2.80	2.66	2.52	2.37	2.29	2.20	2.11	2.02	1.92	1.80
60	7.08	4.98	4.13	3.65	3.34	3.12	2.95	2.82	2.72	2.63	2.50	2.35	2.20	2.12	2.03	1.94	1.84	1.73	1.60
120	6.85	4.79	3.95	3.48	3.17	2.96	2.79	2.66	2.56	2.47	2.34	2.19	2.03	1.95	1.86	1.76	1.66	1.53	1.38
∞	6.63	4.61	3.78	3.32	3.02	2.80	2.64	2.51	2.41	2.32	2.18	2.04	1.88	1.79	1.70	1.59	1.47	1.32	1.00

Table 7— F-Distribution (continued)

$\alpha = 0.025$

d.f.D: Degrees of freedom, denominator	\(d.f._N\): Degrees of freedom, numerator																		
	1	2	3	4	5	6	7	8	9	10	12	15	20	24	30	40	60	120	∞
1	647.8	799.5	864.2	899.6	921.8	937.1	948.2	956.7	963.3	968.6	976.7	984.9	993.1	997.2	1001	1006	1010	1014	1018
2	38.51	39.00	39.17	39.25	39.30	39.33	39.36	39.37	39.39	39.40	39.41	39.43	39.45	39.46	39.46	39.47	39.48	39.49	39.50
3	17.44	16.04	15.44	15.10	14.88	14.73	14.62	14.54	14.47	14.42	14.34	14.25	14.17	14.12	14.08	14.04	13.99	13.95	13.90
4	12.22	10.65	9.98	9.60	9.36	9.20	9.07	8.98	8.90	8.84	8.75	8.66	8.56	8.51	8.46	8.41	8.36	8.31	8.26
5	10.01	8.43	7.76	7.39	7.15	6.98	6.85	6.76	6.68	6.62	6.52	6.43	6.33	6.28	6.23	6.18	6.12	6.07	6.02
6	8.81	7.26	6.60	6.23	5.99	5.82	5.70	5.60	5.52	5.46	5.37	5.27	5.17	5.12	5.07	5.01	4.96	4.90	4.85
7	8.07	6.54	5.89	5.52	5.29	5.12	4.99	4.90	4.82	4.76	4.67	4.57	4.47	4.42	4.36	4.31	4.25	4.20	4.14
8	7.57	6.06	5.42	5.05	4.82	4.65	4.53	4.43	4.36	4.30	4.20	4.10	4.00	3.95	3.89	3.84	3.78	3.73	3.67
9	7.21	5.71	5.08	4.72	4.48	4.32	4.20	4.10	4.03	3.96	3.87	3.77	3.67	3.61	3.56	3.51	3.45	3.39	3.33
10	6.94	5.46	4.83	4.47	4.24	4.07	3.95	3.85	3.78	3.72	3.62	3.52	3.42	3.37	3.31	3.26	3.20	3.14	3.08
11	6.72	5.26	4.63	4.28	4.04	3.88	3.76	3.66	3.59	3.53	3.43	3.33	3.23	3.17	3.12	3.06	3.00	2.94	2.88
12	6.55	5.10	4.47	4.12	3.89	3.73	3.61	3.51	3.44	3.37	3.28	3.18	3.07	3.02	2.96	2.91	2.85	2.79	2.72
13	6.41	4.97	4.35	4.00	3.77	3.60	3.48	3.39	3.31	3.25	3.15	3.05	2.95	2.89	2.84	2.78	2.72	2.66	2.60
14	6.30	4.86	4.24	3.89	3.66	3.50	3.38	3.29	3.21	3.15	3.05	2.95	2.84	2.79	2.73	2.67	2.61	2.55	2.49
15	6.20	4.77	4.15	3.80	3.58	3.41	3.29	3.20	3.12	3.06	2.98	2.86	2.76	2.70	2.64	2.59	2.52	2.46	2.40
16	6.12	4.69	4.08	3.73	3.50	3.34	3.22	3.12	3.05	2.99	2.89	2.79	2.68	2.63	2.57	2.51	2.45	2.38	2.32
17	6.04	4.62	4.01	3.66	3.44	3.28	3.16	3.06	2.98	2.92	2.82	2.72	2.62	2.56	2.50	2.44	2.38	2.32	2.25
18	5.98	4.56	3.95	3.61	3.38	3.22	3.10	3.01	2.93	2.87	2.77	2.67	2.56	2.50	2.44	2.38	2.32	2.26	2.19
19	5.92	4.51	3.90	3.56	3.33	3.17	3.05	2.96	2.88	2.82	2.72	2.62	2.51	2.45	2.39	2.33	2.27	2.20	2.13
20	5.87	4.46	3.86	3.51	3.29	3.13	3.01	2.91	2.84	2.77	2.68	2.57	2.46	2.41	2.35	2.29	2.22	2.16	2.09
21	5.83	4.42	3.82	3.48	3.25	3.09	2.97	2.87	2.80	2.73	2.64	2.53	2.42	2.37	2.31	2.25	2.18	2.11	2.04
22	5.79	4.38	3.78	3.44	3.22	3.05	2.93	2.84	2.76	2.70	2.60	2.50	2.39	2.33	2.27	2.21	2.14	2.08	2.00
23	5.75	4.35	3.75	3.41	3.18	3.02	2.90	2.81	2.73	2.67	2.57	2.47	2.36	2.30	2.24	2.18	2.11	2.04	1.97
24	5.72	4.32	3.72	3.38	3.15	2.99	2.87	2.78	2.70	2.64	2.54	2.44	2.33	2.27	2.21	2.15	2.08	2.01	1.94
25	5.69	4.29	3.69	3.35	3.13	2.97	2.85	2.75	2.68	2.61	2.51	2.41	2.30	2.24	2.18	2.12	2.05	1.98	1.91
26	5.66	4.27	3.67	3.33	3.10	2.94	2.82	2.73	2.65	2.59	2.49	2.39	2.28	2.22	2.16	2.09	2.03	1.95	1.88
27	5.63	4.24	3.65	3.31	3.08	2.92	2.80	2.71	2.63	2.57	2.47	2.36	2.25	2.19	2.13	2.07	2.00	1.93	1.85
28	5.61	4.22	3.63	3.29	3.06	2.90	2.78	2.69	2.61	2.55	2.45	2.34	2.23	2.17	2.11	2.05	1.98	1.91	1.83
29	5.59	4.20	3.61	3.27	3.04	2.88	2.76	2.67	2.59	2.53	2.43	2.32	2.21	2.15	2.09	2.03	1.96	1.89	1.81
30	5.57	4.18	3.59	3.25	3.03	2.87	2.75	2.65	2.57	2.51	2.41	2.31	2.20	2.14	2.07	2.01	1.94	1.87	1.79
40	5.42	4.05	3.46	3.13	2.90	2.74	2.62	2.53	2.45	2.39	2.29	2.18	2.07	2.01	1.94	1.88	1.80	1.72	1.64
60	5.29	3.93	3.34	3.01	2.79	2.63	2.51	2.41	2.33	2.27	2.17	2.06	1.94	1.88	1.82	1.74	1.67	1.58	1.48
120	5.15	3.80	3.23	2.89	2.67	2.52	2.39	2.30	2.22	2.16	2.05	1.94	1.82	1.76	1.69	1.61	1.53	1.43	1.31
∞	5.02	3.69	3.12	2.79	2.57	2.41	2.29	2.19	2.11	2.05	1.94	1.83	1.71	1.64	1.57	1.48	1.39	1.27	1.00

Table 7— F-Distribution (continued)

$\alpha = 0.05$

d.f.$_D$: Degrees of freedom, denominator	d.f.$_N$: Degrees of freedom, numerator																		
	1	2	3	4	5	6	7	8	9	10	12	15	20	24	30	40	60	120	∞
1	161.4	199.5	215.7	224.6	230.2	234.0	236.8	238.9	240.5	241.9	243.9	245.9	248.0	249.1	250.1	251.1	252.2	253.3	254.3
2	18.51	19.00	19.16	19.25	19.30	19.33	19.35	19.37	19.38	19.40	19.41	19.43	19.45	19.45	19.46	19.47	19.48	19.49	19.50
3	10.13	9.55	9.28	9.12	9.01	8.94	8.89	8.85	8.81	8.79	8.74	8.70	8.66	8.64	8.62	8.59	8.57	8.55	8.53
4	7.71	6.94	6.59	6.39	6.26	6.16	6.09	6.04	6.00	5.96	5.91	5.86	5.80	5.77	5.75	5.72	5.69	5.66	5.63
5	6.61	5.79	5.41	5.19	5.05	4.95	4.88	4.82	4.77	4.74	4.68	4.62	4.56	4.53	4.50	4.46	4.43	4.40	4.36
6	5.99	5.14	4.76	4.53	4.39	4.28	4.21	4.15	4.10	4.06	4.00	3.94	3.87	3.84	3.81	3.77	3.74	3.70	3.67
7	5.59	4.74	4.35	4.12	3.97	3.87	3.79	3.73	3.68	3.64	3.57	3.51	3.44	3.41	3.38	3.34	3.30	3.27	3.23
8	5.32	4.46	4.07	3.84	3.69	3.58	3.50	3.44	3.39	3.35	3.28	3.22	3.15	3.12	3.08	3.04	3.01	2.97	2.93
9	5.12	4.26	3.86	3.63	3.48	3.37	3.29	3.23	3.18	3.14	3.07	3.01	2.94	2.90	2.86	2.83	2.79	2.75	2.71
10	4.96	4.10	3.71	3.48	3.33	3.22	3.14	3.07	3.02	2.98	2.91	2.85	2.77	2.74	2.70	2.66	2.62	2.58	2.54
11	4.84	3.98	3.59	3.36	3.20	3.09	3.01	2.95	2.90	2.85	2.79	2.72	2.65	2.61	2.57	2.53	2.49	2.45	2.40
12	4.75	3.89	3.49	3.26	3.11	3.00	2.91	2.85	2.80	2.75	2.69	2.62	2.54	2.51	2.47	2.43	2.38	2.34	2.30
13	4.67	3.81	3.41	3.18	3.03	2.92	2.83	2.77	2.71	2.67	2.60	2.53	2.46	2.42	2.38	2.34	2.30	2.25	2.21
14	4.60	3.74	3.34	3.11	2.96	2.85	2.76	2.70	2.65	2.60	2.53	2.46	2.39	2.35	2.31	2.27	2.22	2.18	2.13
15	4.54	3.68	3.29	3.06	2.90	2.79	2.71	2.64	2.59	2.54	2.48	2.40	2.33	2.29	2.25	2.20	2.16	2.11	2.07
16	4.49	3.63	3.24	3.01	2.85	2.74	2.66	2.59	2.54	2.49	2.42	2.35	2.28	2.24	2.19	2.15	2.11	2.06	2.01
17	4.45	3.59	3.20	2.96	2.81	2.70	2.61	2.55	2.49	2.45	2.38	2.31	2.23	2.19	2.15	2.10	2.06	2.01	1.96
18	4.41	3.55	3.16	2.93	2.77	2.66	2.58	2.51	2.46	2.41	2.34	2.27	2.19	2.15	2.11	2.06	2.02	1.97	1.92
19	4.38	3.52	3.13	2.90	2.74	2.63	2.54	2.48	2.42	2.38	2.31	2.23	2.16	2.11	2.07	2.03	1.98	1.93	1.88
20	4.35	3.49	3.10	2.87	2.71	2.60	2.51	2.45	2.39	2.35	2.28	2.20	2.12	2.08	2.04	1.99	1.95	1.90	1.84
21	4.32	3.47	3.07	2.84	2.68	2.57	2.49	2.42	2.37	2.32	2.25	2.18	2.10	2.05	2.01	1.96	1.92	1.87	1.81
22	4.30	3.44	3.05	2.82	2.66	2.55	2.46	2.40	2.34	2.30	2.23	2.15	2.07	2.03	1.98	1.94	1.89	1.84	1.78
23	4.28	3.42	3.03	2.80	2.64	2.53	2.44	2.37	2.32	2.27	2.20	2.13	2.05	2.01	1.96	1.91	1.86	1.81	1.76
24	4.26	3.40	3.01	2.78	2.62	2.51	2.42	2.36	2.30	2.25	2.18	2.11	2.03	1.98	1.94	1.89	1.84	1.79	1.73
25	4.24	3.39	2.99	2.76	2.60	2.49	2.40	2.34	2.28	2.24	2.16	2.09	2.01	1.96	1.92	1.87	1.82	1.77	1.71
26	4.23	3.37	2.98	2.74	2.59	2.47	2.39	2.32	2.27	2.22	2.15	2.07	1.99	1.95	1.90	1.85	1.80	1.75	1.69
27	4.21	3.35	2.96	2.73	2.57	2.46	2.37	2.31	2.25	2.20	2.13	2.06	1.97	1.93	1.88	1.84	1.79	1.73	1.67
28	4.20	3.34	2.95	2.71	2.56	2.45	2.36	2.29	2.24	2.19	2.12	2.04	1.96	1.91	1.87	1.82	1.77	1.71	1.65
29	4.18	3.33	2.93	2.70	2.55	2.43	2.35	2.28	2.22	2.18	2.10	2.03	1.94	1.90	1.85	1.81	1.75	1.70	1.64
30	4.17	3.32	2.92	2.69	2.53	2.42	2.33	2.27	2.21	2.16	2.09	2.01	1.93	1.89	1.84	1.79	1.74	1.68	1.62
40	4.08	3.23	2.84	2.61	2.45	2.34	2.25	2.18	2.12	2.08	2.00	1.92	1.84	1.79	1.74	1.69	1.64	1.58	1.51
60	4.00	3.15	2.76	2.53	2.37	2.25	2.17	2.10	2.04	1.99	1.92	1.84	1.75	1.70	1.65	1.59	1.53	1.47	1.39
120	3.92	3.07	2.68	2.45	2.29	2.17	2.09	2.02	1.96	1.91	1.83	1.75	1.66	1.61	1.55	1.50	1.43	1.35	1.25
∞	3.84	3.00	2.60	2.37	2.21	2.10	2.01	1.94	1.88	1.83	1.75	1.67	1.57	1.52	1.46	1.39	1.32	1.22	1.00

Table 7— *F*-Distribution (continued)

$\alpha = 0.10$

d.f._D: Degrees of freedom, denominator	\multicolumn{19}{c}{d.f._N: Degrees of freedom, numerator}
	1	2	3	4	5	6	7	8	9	10	12	15	20	24	30	40	60	120	∞
---	---	---	---	---	---	---	---	---	---	---	---	---	---	---	---	---	---	---	---
1	39.86	49.50	53.59	55.83	57.24	58.20	58.91	59.44	59.86	60.19	60.71	61.22	61.74	62.00	62.26	62.53	62.79	63.06	63.33
2	8.53	9.00	9.16	9.24	9.29	9.33	9.35	9.37	9.38	9.39	9.41	9.42	9.44	9.45	9.46	9.47	9.47	9.48	9.49
3	5.54	5.46	5.39	5.34	5.31	5.28	5.27	5.25	5.24	5.23	5.22	5.20	5.18	5.18	5.17	5.16	5.15	5.14	5.13
4	4.54	4.32	4.19	4.11	4.05	4.01	3.98	3.95	3.94	3.92	3.90	3.87	3.84	3.83	3.82	3.80	3.79	3.78	3.76
5	4.06	3.78	3.62	3.52	3.45	3.40	3.37	3.34	3.32	3.30	3.27	3.24	3.21	3.19	3.17	3.16	3.14	3.12	3.10
6	3.78	3.46	3.29	3.18	3.11	3.05	3.01	2.98	2.96	2.94	2.90	2.87	2.84	2.82	2.80	2.78	2.76	2.74	2.72
7	3.59	3.26	3.07	2.96	2.88	2.83	2.78	2.75	2.72	2.70	2.67	2.63	2.59	2.58	2.56	2.54	2.51	2.49	2.47
8	3.46	3.11	2.92	2.81	2.73	2.67	2.62	2.59	2.56	2.54	2.50	2.46	2.42	2.40	2.38	2.36	2.34	2.32	2.29
9	3.36	3.01	2.81	2.69	2.61	2.55	2.51	2.47	2.44	2.42	2.38	2.34	2.30	2.28	2.25	2.23	2.21	2.18	2.16
10	3.29	2.92	2.73	2.61	2.52	2.46	2.41	2.38	2.35	2.32	2.28	2.24	2.20	2.18	2.16	2.13	2.11	2.08	2.06
11	3.23	2.86	2.66	2.54	2.45	2.39	2.34	2.30	2.27	2.25	2.21	2.17	2.12	2.10	2.08	2.05	2.03	2.00	1.97
12	3.18	2.81	2.61	2.48	2.39	2.33	2.28	2.24	2.21	2.19	2.15	2.10	2.06	2.04	2.01	1.99	1.96	1.93	1.90
13	3.14	2.76	2.56	2.43	2.35	2.28	2.23	2.20	2.16	2.14	2.10	2.05	2.01	1.98	1.96	1.93	1.90	1.88	1.85
14	3.10	2.73	2.52	2.39	2.31	2.24	2.19	2.15	2.12	2.10	2.05	2.01	1.96	1.94	1.91	1.89	1.86	1.83	1.80
15	3.07	2.70	2.49	2.36	2.27	2.21	2.16	2.12	2.09	2.06	2.02	1.97	1.92	1.90	1.87	1.85	1.82	1.79	1.76
16	3.05	2.67	2.46	2.33	2.24	2.18	2.13	2.09	2.06	2.03	1.99	1.94	1.89	1.87	1.84	1.81	1.78	1.75	1.72
17	3.03	2.64	2.44	2.31	2.22	2.15	2.10	2.06	2.03	2.00	1.96	1.91	1.86	1.84	1.81	1.78	1.75	1.72	1.69
18	3.01	2.62	2.42	2.29	2.20	2.13	2.08	2.04	2.00	1.98	1.93	1.89	1.84	1.81	1.78	1.75	1.72	1.69	1.66
19	2.99	2.61	2.40	2.27	2.18	2.11	2.06	2.02	1.98	1.96	1.91	1.86	1.81	1.79	1.76	1.73	1.70	1.67	1.63
20	2.97	2.59	2.38	2.25	2.16	2.09	2.04	2.00	1.96	1.94	1.89	1.84	1.79	1.77	1.74	1.71	1.68	1.64	1.61
21	2.96	2.57	2.36	2.23	2.14	2.08	2.02	1.98	1.95	1.92	1.87	1.83	1.78	1.75	1.72	1.69	1.66	1.62	1.59
22	2.95	2.56	2.35	2.22	2.13	2.06	2.01	1.97	1.93	1.90	1.86	1.81	1.76	1.73	1.70	1.67	1.64	1.60	1.57
23	2.94	2.55	2.34	2.21	2.11	2.05	1.99	1.95	1.92	1.89	1.84	1.80	1.74	1.72	1.69	1.66	1.62	1.59	1.55
24	2.93	2.54	2.33	2.19	2.10	2.04	1.98	1.94	1.91	1.88	1.83	1.78	1.73	1.70	1.67	1.64	1.61	1.57	1.53
25	2.92	2.53	2.32	2.18	2.09	2.02	1.97	1.93	1.89	1.87	1.82	1.77	1.72	1.69	1.66	1.63	1.59	1.56	1.52
26	2.91	2.52	2.31	2.17	2.08	2.01	1.96	1.92	1.88	1.86	1.81	1.76	1.71	1.68	1.65	1.61	1.58	1.54	1.50
27	2.90	2.51	2.30	2.17	2.07	2.00	1.95	1.91	1.87	1.85	1.80	1.75	1.70	1.67	1.64	1.60	1.57	1.53	1.49
28	2.89	2.50	2.29	2.16	2.06	2.00	1.94	1.90	1.87	1.84	1.79	1.74	1.69	1.66	1.63	1.59	1.56	1.52	1.48
29	2.89	2.50	2.28	2.15	2.06	1.99	1.93	1.89	1.86	1.83	1.78	1.73	1.68	1.65	1.62	1.58	1.55	1.51	1.47
30	2.88	2.49	2.28	2.14	2.05	1.98	1.93	1.88	1.85	1.82	1.77	1.72	1.67	1.64	1.61	1.57	1.54	1.50	1.46
40	2.84	2.44	2.23	2.09	2.00	1.93	1.87	1.83	1.79	1.76	1.71	1.66	1.61	1.57	1.54	1.51	1.47	1.42	1.38
60	2.79	2.39	2.18	2.04	1.95	1.87	1.82	1.77	1.74	1.71	1.66	1.60	1.54	1.51	1.48	1.44	1.40	1.35	1.29
120	2.75	2.35	2.13	1.99	1.90	1.82	1.77	1.72	1.68	1.65	1.60	1.55	1.48	1.45	1.41	1.37	1.32	1.26	1.19
∞	2.71	2.30	2.08	1.94	1.85	1.77	1.72	1.67	1.63	1.60	1.55	1.49	1.42	1.38	1.34	1.30	1.24	1.17	1.00

From M. Merrington and C. M. Thompson (1943). Table of Percentage Points of the Inverted Beta (*F*) Distribution. *Biometrika* 33, pp. 74–87. Reprinted with permission from *Biometrika*.

Table 8 — Critical Values for the Sign Test

Reject the null hypothesis if the test statistic is less than or equal to the value in the table.

n	One-tailed, $\alpha = 0.005$ Two-tailed, $\alpha = 0.01$	$\alpha = 0.01$ $\alpha = 0.02$	$\alpha = 0.025$ $\alpha = 0.05$	$\alpha = 0.05$ $\alpha = 0.10$
8	0	0	0	1
9	0	0	1	1
10	0	0	1	1
11	0	1	1	2
12	1	1	2	2
13	1	1	2	3
14	1	2	3	3
15	2	2	3	3
16	2	2	3	4
17	2	3	4	4
18	3	3	4	5
19	3	4	4	5
20	3	4	5	5
21	4	4	5	6
22	4	5	5	6
23	4	5	6	7
24	5	5	6	7
25	5	6	6	7

Note: Table 8 is for one-tailed or two-tailed tests. The sample size n represents the total number of + and − signs. The test value is the smaller number of + or − signs..

From *Journal of American Statistical Association* Vol. 41 (1946), pp. 557–66. W. J. Dixon and A. M. Mood. Reprinted with permission.

Table 9 — Critical Values for the Wilcoxon Signed-Rank Test

Reject the null hypothesis if the value of the test statistic w_s is less than or equal to the value given in the table.

	One-tailed,			
	$\alpha = 0.05$	$\alpha = 0.025$	$\alpha = 0.01$	$\alpha = 0.005$
	Two-tailed,			
n	$\alpha = 0.10$	$\alpha = 0.05$	$\alpha = 0.02$	$\alpha = 0.01$
5	1	—	—	—
6	2	1	—	—
7	4	2	0	—
8	6	4	2	0
9	8	6	3	2
10	11	8	5	3
11	14	11	7	5
12	17	14	10	7
13	21	17	13	10
14	26	21	16	13
15	30	25	20	16
16	36	30	24	19
17	41	35	28	23
18	47	40	33	28
19	54	46	38	32
20	60	52	43	37
21	68	59	49	43
22	75	66	56	49
23	83	73	62	55
24	92	81	69	61
25	101	90	77	68
26	110	98	85	76
27	120	107	93	84
28	130	117	102	92
29	141	127	111	100
30	152	137	120	109

From *Some Rapid Approximate Statistical Procedures.* Copyright 1949, 1964 Lederle Laboratories, American Cyanamid Co., Wayne, N.J. Reprinted with permission.

Table 10 — Critical Values for the Spearman Rank Correlation

Reject H_0: $\rho_s = 0$ if the absolute value of r_s is greater than the value given in the table.

n	$\alpha = 0.10$	$\alpha = 0.05$	$\alpha = 0.01$
5	0.900	—	—
6	0.829	0.886	—
7	0.714	0.786	0.929
8	0.643	0.738	0.881
9	0.600	0.700	0.833
10	0.564	0.648	0.794
11	0.536	0.618	0.818
12	0.497	0.591	0.780
13	0.475	0.566	0.745
14	0.457	0.545	0.716
15	0.441	0.525	0.689
16	0.425	0.507	0.666
17	0.412	0.490	0.645
18	0.399	0.476	0.625
19	0.388	0.462	0.608
20	0.377	0.450	0.591
21	0.368	0.438	0.576
22	0.359	0.428	0.562
23	0.351	0.418	0.549
24	0.343	0.409	0.537
25	0.336	0.400	0.526
26	0.329	0.392	0.515
27	0.323	0.385	0.505
28	0.317	0.377	0.496
29	0.311	0.370	0.487
30	0.305	0.364	0.478

Reprinted with permission from the Institute of Mathematical Statistics.

Table 11— Critical Values for the Pearson Correlation Coefficient

Reject H_0: $\rho = 0$ if the absolute value of r is greater than the value given in the table.

n	$\alpha = 0.05$	$\alpha = 0.01$
4	0.950	0.990
5	0.878	0.959
6	0.811	0.917
7	0.754	0.875
8	0.707	0.834
9	0.666	0.798
10	0.632	0.765
11	0.602	0.735
12	0.576	0.708
13	0.553	0.684
14	0.532	0.661
15	0.514	0.641
16	0.497	0.623
17	0.482	0.606
18	0.468	0.590
19	0.456	0.575
20	0.444	0.561
21	0.433	0.549
22	0.423	0.537
23	0.413	0.526
24	0.404	0.515
25	0.396	0.505
26	0.388	0.496
27	0.381	0.487
28	0.374	0.479
29	0.367	0.471
30	0.361	0.463
35	0.334	0.430
40	0.312	0.403
45	0.294	0.380
50	0.279	0.361
55	0.266	0.345
60	0.254	0.330
65	0.244	0.317
70	0.235	0.306
75	0.227	0.296
80	0.220	0.286
85	0.213	0.278
90	0.207	0.270
95	0.202	0.263
100	0.197	0.256

The critical values in Table 11 were generated using Excel.

Table 12 — Critical Values for the Number of Runs

Reject the null hypothesis if the test statistic G is less than or equal to the smaller entry or greater than or equal to the larger entry.

Value of n_2	2	3	4	5	6	7	8	9	10	11	12	13	14	15	16	17	18	19	20
2	1	1	1	1	1	1	1	1	1	1	2	2	2	2	2	2	2	2	2
	6	6	6	6	6	6	6	6	6	6	6	6	6	6	6	6	6	6	6
3	1	1	1	2	2	2	2	2	2	2	2	2	3	3	3	3	3	3	3
	6	8	8	8	8	8	8	8	8	8	8	8	8	8	8	8	8	8	8
4	1	1	1	2	2	2	3	3	3	3	3	3	3	3	4	4	4	4	4
	6	8	9	9	9	10	10	10	10	10	10	10	10	10	10	10	10	10	10
5	1	1	2	2	3	3	3	3	3	4	4	4	4	4	4	4	5	5	5
	6	8	9	10	10	11	11	12	12	12	12	12	12	12	12	12	12	12	12
6	1	2	2	3	3	3	3	4	4	4	4	5	5	5	5	5	5	6	6
	6	8	9	10	11	12	12	13	13	13	13	14	14	14	14	14	14	14	14
7	1	2	2	3	3	3	4	4	5	5	5	5	5	6	6	6	6	6	6
	6	8	10	11	12	13	13	14	14	14	14	15	15	15	16	16	16	16	16
8	1	2	3	3	3	4	4	5	5	5	6	6	6	6	6	7	7	7	7
	6	8	10	11	12	13	14	14	15	15	16	16	16	16	17	17	17	17	17
9	1	2	3	3	4	4	5	5	5	6	6	6	7	7	7	7	8	8	8
	6	8	10	12	13	14	14	15	16	16	16	17	17	18	18	18	18	18	18
10	1	2	3	3	4	5	5	5	6	6	7	7	7	7	8	8	8	8	9
	6	8	10	12	13	14	15	16	16	17	17	18	18	18	19	19	19	20	20
11	1	2	3	4	4	5	5	6	6	7	7	7	8	8	8	9	9	9	9
	6	8	10	12	13	14	15	16	17	17	18	19	19	19	20	20	20	21	21
12	2	2	3	4	4	5	6	6	7	7	7	8	8	8	9	9	9	10	10
	6	8	10	12	13	14	16	16	17	18	19	19	20	20	21	21	21	22	22
13	2	2	3	4	5	5	6	6	7	7	8	8	9	9	9	10	10	10	10
	6	8	10	12	14	15	16	17	18	19	19	20	20	21	21	22	22	23	23
14	2	2	3	4	5	5	6	7	7	8	8	9	9	9	10	10	10	11	11
	6	8	10	12	14	15	16	17	18	19	20	20	21	22	22	23	23	23	24
15	2	3	3	4	5	6	6	7	7	8	8	9	9	10	10	11	11	11	12
	6	8	10	12	14	15	16	18	18	19	20	21	22	22	23	23	24	24	25
16	2	3	4	4	5	6	6	7	8	8	9	9	10	10	11	11	11	12	12
	6	8	10	12	14	16	17	18	19	20	21	21	22	23	23	24	25	25	25
17	2	3	4	4	5	6	7	7	8	9	9	10	10	11	11	11	12	12	13
	6	8	10	12	14	16	17	18	19	20	21	22	23	23	24	25	25	26	26
18	2	3	4	5	5	6	7	8	8	9	9	10	10	11	11	12	12	13	13
	6	8	10	12	14	16	17	18	19	20	21	22	23	24	25	25	26	26	27
19	2	3	4	5	6	6	7	8	8	9	10	10	11	11	12	12	13	13	13
	6	8	10	12	14	16	17	18	20	21	22	23	23	24	25	26	26	27	27
20	2	3	4	5	6	6	7	8	9	9	10	10	11	12	12	13	13	13	14
	6	8	10	12	14	16	17	18	20	21	22	23	24	25	25	26	27	27	28

Note: Table 12 is for a two-tailed test with $\alpha = 0.05$.

Reprinted with permission from the Institute of Mathematical Statistics.

APPENDIX C

C Normal Probability Plots and Their Graphs

What You SHOULD LEARN

▸ How to construct and interpret a normal probability plot

Normal Probability Plots

▸ Normal Probability Plots

For the majority of problems throughout this book, it has been assumed that a random sample of data is selected from a population that has a normal distribution. Suppose you select a random sample from a population with an unknown distribution. How can you determine if the sample was selected from a population that has a normal distribution?

You have already learned that a histogram or stem-and-leaf plot can reveal the shape of a distribution and any outliers, clusters, or gaps in a distribution. These data displays are useful for assessing large sets of data, but assessing small data sets in this manner can be difficult and unreliable. A reliable method for assessing normality in small data sets is to use a graph called a *normal probability plot*.

> **DEFINITION**
>
> A **normal probability plot** is a graph that plots each observed value from the data set along with its corresponding z-score. The observed values are usually plotted along the horizontal axis while the corresponding z-scores are plotted along the vertical axis.

If the plotted points in a normal probability plot are approximately linear, then you can conclude that the data come from a normal distribution. If the plotted points are not approximately linear or follow some type of pattern that is not linear, you can conclude that the data come from a distribution that is not normal. When examining a normal probability plot, look for deviations or clusters of points that stray from the line, which indicates a distribution that is not normal. Individual points that stray from the line in a normal probability plot may be outliers.

Constructing a normal probability plot by hand can be rather tedious. Technology tools such as Minitab or a TI-83/84 can be used to construct normal probability plots, as shown in Example 1.

Insight

A normal probability plot is also called a **normal quantile plot**.

> **EXAMPLE 1**
>
> ### Constructing a Normal Probability Plot
>
> The heights (in inches) of 12 current National Basketball Association players are listed. Use a technology tool to construct a normal probability plot to determine if the data come from a population that has a normal distribution. Identify any possible outliers.
>
> 74, 69, 78, 75, 73, 71, 80, 82, 81, 76, 86, 77

SOLUTION

Using a TI-83/84, begin by entering the data into List 1. Then use *Stat Plot* to construct the normal probability plot. The plot should look similar to the one shown below. From the scatter plot, it appears that there are no outliers and the points are approximately linear.

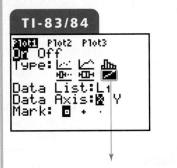

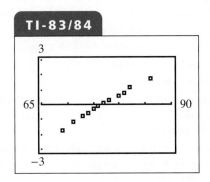

Normal probability plot

Interpretation   Because the points are approximately linear, you can conclude that the sample data come from a population that has a normal distribution.

▶ Try It Yourself 1

The balances (in dollars) on student loans for 18 randomly selected college seniors are listed.

29,150	16,980	12,470	19,235	15,875	8,960
16,105	14,575	39,860	20,170	9,710	19,650
21,590	8,200	18,100	25,530	9,285	10,075

a. *Use* a technology tool to construct a normal probability plot. Are the points approximately linear?
b. *Identify* any possible outliers.
c. *Interpret* your answer.   *Answer: Page A50*

To see that the points are approximately linear, you can graph the regression line for the original data values and their corresponding z-scores. The regression line for the heights and z-scores from Example 1 is shown in the graph. From the graph, you can see that the points lie along the regression line. You can also approximate the mean of the data set by determining where the line crosses the x-axis.

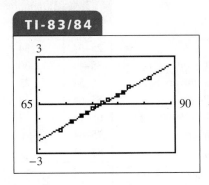

Try It Yourself Answers

CHAPTER 1

Section 1.1

1a. The population consists of the prices per gallon of regular gasoline at all gasoline stations in the United States.

b. The sample consists of the prices per gallon of regular gasoline at the 800 surveyed stations.

c. The data set consists of the 800 prices.

2a. Population **b.** Parameter

3a. Descriptive statistics involve the statement "76% of women and 60% of men had a physical examination within the previous year."

b. An inference drawn from the study is that a higher percentage of women had a physical examination within the previous year.

Section 1.2

1a. City names and city population

b. City name: Nonnumerical
City population: Numerical

c. City name: Qualitative
City population: Quantitative

2a. (1) The final standings represent a ranking of basketball teams.

(2) The collection of phone numbers represents labels. No mathematical computations can be made.

b. (1) Ordinal, because the data can be put in order.

(2) Nominal, because you cannot make calculations on the data.

3a. (1) The data set is the collection of body temperatures.

(2) The data set is the collection of heart rates.

b. (1) Interval, because the data can be ordered and meaningful differences can be calculated, but it does not make sense to write a ratio using the temperatures.

(2) Ratio, because the data can be ordered, meaningful differences can be calculated, the data can be written as a ratio, and the data set contains an inherent zero.

Section 1.3

1a. (1) Focus: Effect of exercise on relieving depression.

(2) Focus: Success rates of graduates of a large university finding a job within one year of graduation.

(1) Population: Collection of all people with depression.

(2) Population: Collection of all graduates of a large university.

(1) Experiment

(2) Survey

2a. There is no way to tell why the people quit smoking. They could have quit smoking either from the gum or from watching the DVD.

b. Two experiments could be done; one using the gum and the other using the DVD.

3a. Answers will vary. *Sample Answer:* start with the first digits 92630782 ...

b. 92│63│07│82│40│19│26 **c.** 63, 7, 40, 19, 26

4a. (1) The sample was selected by using only available students.

(2) The sample was selected by numbering each student in the school, randomly choosing a starting number, and selecting students at regular intervals from the starting number.

b. (1) Convenience sampling

(2) Systematic sampling

CHAPTER 2

Section 2.1

1a. 8 classes

b. Min = 15; Max = 89; Class width = 10

c.

Lower limit	Upper limit
15	24
25	34
35	44
45	54
55	64
65	74
75	84
85	94

e.

Class	Frequency, f
15–24	16
25–34	34
35–44	30
45–54	23
55–64	13
65–74	2
75–84	0
85–94	1

d. See part (e).

2a. See part (b).

b.

Class	Frequency, f	Midpoint	Relative frequency	Cumulative frequency
15–24	16	19.5	0.13	16
25–34	34	29.5	0.29	50
35–44	30	39.5	0.25	80
45–54	23	49.5	0.19	103
55–64	13	59.5	0.11	116
65–74	2	69.5	0.02	118
75–84	0	79.5	0.00	118
85–94	1	89.5	0.01	119
	$\Sigma f = 119$		$\Sigma \dfrac{f}{n} = 1$	

c. 86% of the teams scored fewer than 55 touchdowns. 3% of the teams scored more than 65 touchdowns. (Answers will vary.)

3 a.

Class boundaries
14.5–24.5
24.5–34.5
34.5–44.5
44.5–54.5
54.5–64.5
64.5–74.5
74.5–84.5
84.5–94.5

b. Use class midpoints for the horizontal scale and frequency for the vertical scale.

c.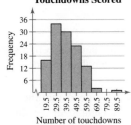

d. Same as 2c.

4 a. Same as 3b.

b. See part (c).

c.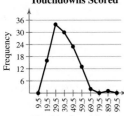

d. The number of touchdowns increases until 34.5 touchdowns, then decreases afterward.

5abc.

6 a. Use upper class boundaries for the horizontal scale and cumulative frequency for the vertical scale.

b. See part (c).

c.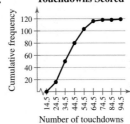

d. Approximately 80 teams scored 44 or fewer touchdowns.

e. Answers will vary.

7 a. Enter data.

b.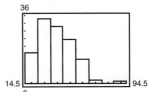

Section 2.2

1 a.
```
1 |
2 |
3 |
4 |
5 |
6 |
7 |
8 |
```

b.
```
1 | 7 5 8 8 5 5          Key 1|7 = 17
2 | 7 6 8 9 8 9 7 9 8 7 5 3 4 6 2 5 0 1 1 2 1 4 1
3 | 9 9 7 7 8 8 6 4 7 6 5 5 5 1 4 5 9 8 2 5 2 2 2 2 3 3 3 3 2 4 1 1 0
    4 2 1 2 1 0
4 | 9 8 6 8 7 8 6 4 8 5 4 6 6 7 1 1 5 4 5 3 2 2 8 3 0 4 0 5 3 0
5 | 9 4 5 4 3 5 9 0 2 3 5 7 0 5
6 | 8 5 1 3 3 1 1 0
7 |
8 | 9
```

c.
```
1 | 5 5 5 7 8 8          Key 1|7 = 17
2 | 0 1 1 1 2 2 3 4 4 5 5 6 6 7 7 7 8 8 8 9 9 9
3 | 0 0 1 1 1 1 2 2 2 2 2 2 2 3 3 3 3 4 4 4 4 5 5 5 5 5 5 6 6 7 7 7
    8 8 8 9 9 9
4 | 0 0 0 1 1 2 2 3 3 3 3 4 4 4 4 5 5 5 5 6 6 6 6 7 7 8 8 8 8 8 9
5 | 0 0 2 3 3 4 4 5 5 5 5 7 9 9
6 | 0 1 1 1 3 3 5 8
7 |
8 | 9
```

d. It seems that most of the teams scored under 54 touchdowns. (Answers will vary.)

2ab.

```
1  |                                    Key 1|7 = 17
1  | 5 5 5 7 8 8
2  | 0 1 1 1 1 2 2 3 4 4
2  | 5 5 6 6 7 7 7 8 8 8 9 9 9
3  | 0 0 1 1 1 1 1 2 2 2 2 2 2 2 2 3 3 3 4 4 4 4
3  | 5 5 5 5 5 6 6 7 7 7 8 8 8 9 9 9
4  | 0 0 0 1 1 2 2 3 3 3 4 4 4 4
4  | 5 5 5 5 6 6 6 6 7 7 8 8 8 8 8 9
5  | 0 0 2 3 3 4 4
5  | 5 5 5 5 7 9 9
6  | 0 1 1 1 3 3
6  | 5 8
7  |
7  |
8  |
8  | 9
```

3 a. Use number of touchdowns for the horizontal axis.

b. **Touchdowns Scored**

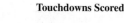
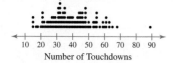

Number of Touchdowns

c. A large percentage of the teams scored under 50 touchdowns. (Answers will vary.)

4 a.

Vehicle type	Killed (frequency)	Relative frequency	Central angle
Cars	22,423	0.64	230°
Trucks	10,216	0.29	104°
Motorcycles	2,227	0.06	22°
Other	425	0.01	4°
	$\Sigma f = 35{,}291$	$\Sigma \dfrac{f}{n} = 1$	$\Sigma = 360°$

b. Motor Vehicle Occupants Killed in 1995

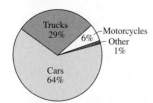

c. As a percentage of total motor vehicle deaths, car deaths decreased by 15%, truck deaths increased by 8%, and motorcycle deaths increased by 6%.

5 a.

Cause	Frequency, f
Auto Dealers	14,668
Auto Repair	9,728
Home Furnishing	7,792
Computer Sales	5,733
Dry Cleaning	4,649

b. **Causes of BBB Complaints**

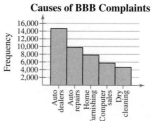

c. It appears that the auto industry (dealers and repair shops) account for the largest portion of complaints filed at the BBB. (Answers will vary.)

6ab. **Salaries**

c. It appears that the longer an employee is with the company, the larger his or her salary will be.

7ab. **Cellular Phone Bills**

c. From 1995 to 1998 the average bill decreased; the average bill increased from 1998 to 2004, and it decreased from 2004 to 2005.

Section 2.3

1 a. 578   **b.** 41.3

c. The mean age of an employee in a department is 41.3 years.

2 a. 18, 18, 19, 19, 19, 20, 21, 21, 21, 21, 23, 24, 24, 26, 27, 27, 29, 30, 30, 30, 33, 33, 34, 35, 38

b. 24

c. The median age for the sample of fans at the concert is 24.

3 a. 70, 80, 100, 130, 140, 150, 160, 200, 250, 270   **b.** 145

c. The median price of the sample of MP3 players is $145.

4 a. 0, 0, 1, 1, 1, 2, 3, 3, 3, 4, 5, 5, 5, 7, 9, 10, 12, 12, 13, 13, 13, 13, 13, 15, 16, 16, 17, 17, 18, 18, 18, 19, 19, 19, 20, 20, 21, 22, 23, 23, 24, 24, 25, 25, 26, 26, 26, 29, 33, 36, 37, 39, 39, 39, 39, 40, 40, 41, 41, 41, 42, 44, 44, 45, 47, 48, 49, 49, 49, 51, 53, 56, 58, 58, 59, 60, 67, 68, 68, 72

b. 13   **c.** The mode of the ages is 13 years old.

5 a. Yes   **b.** The mode of the responses to the survey is "Yes."

6 a. 21.6; 21; 20

b. The mean in Example 6 ($\bar{x} \approx 23.8$) was heavily influenced by the age 65. Neither the median nor the mode was affected as much by the age 65.

7ab.

Source	Score, x	Weight, w	$x \cdot w$
Test Mean	86	0.50	43.0
Midterm	96	0.15	14.4
Final	98	0.20	19.6
Computer Lab	98	0.10	9.8
Homework	100	0.05	5.0
		$\Sigma w = 1.00$	$\Sigma(x \cdot w) = 91.8$

c. 91.8

d. The weighted mean for the course is 91.8. So you did get an A.

8abc.

Class	Midpoint, x	Frequency, f	$x \cdot f$
15–24	19.5	16	312
25–34	29.5	34	1003
35–44	39.5	30	1185
45–54	49.5	23	1138.5
55–64	59.5	13	773.5
65–74	69.5	2	139
75–84	79.5	0	0
85–94	89.5	1	89.5
		$N = 119$	$\Sigma(x \cdot f) = 4640.5$

d. 39.0

Section 2.4

1 a. Min = 23, or $23,000; Max = 58, or $58,000

b. 35, or $35,000

c. The range of the starting salaries for Corporation B is 35, or $35,000 (much larger than the range of Corporation A).

2 a. 41.5, or $41,500

b.

Salary, x (1000s of dollars)	Deviation, $x - \mu$ (1000s of dollars)
23	−18.5
29	−12.5
32	−9.5
40	−1.5
41	−0.5
41	−0.5
49	7.5
50	8.5
52	10.5
58	16.5
$\Sigma x = 415$	$\Sigma(x - \mu) = 0$

3ab. $\mu = 41.5$, or $41,500

Salary, x	$x - \mu$	$(x - \mu)^2$
23	−18.5	342.25
29	−12.5	156.25
32	−9.5	90.25
40	−1.5	2.25
41	−0.5	0.25
41	−0.5	0.25
49	7.5	56.25
50	8.5	72.25
52	10.5	110.25
58	16.5	272.25
$\Sigma x = 415$	$\Sigma(x - \mu) = 0$	$\Sigma(x - \mu)^2 = 1102.5$

c. 110.3   **d.** 10.5, or $10,500

e. The population variance is 110.3 and the population standard deviation is 10.5, or $10,500.

4 a. See 3ab.   **b.** 122.5   **c.** 11.1, or $11,100

5 a. Enter data.   **b.** 37.89; 3.98

6 a. 7, 7, 7, 7, 7, 13, 13, 13, 13, 13   **b.** 3

7 a. 1 standard deviation   **b.** 34%

c. The estimated percent of the heights that are between 61.29 and 64 inches is 34%.

8 a. 0   **b.** 70.6

c. At least 75% of the data lie within 2 standard deviations of the mean. At least 75% of the population of Alaska is between 0 and 70.6 years old.

9 a.

x	f	xf
0	10	0
1	19	19
2	7	14
3	7	21
4	5	20
5	1	5
6	1	6
	$n = 50$	$\sum xf = 85$

b. 1.7

c.

$x - \bar{x}$	$(x - \bar{x})^2$	$(x - \bar{x})^2 \cdot f$
−1.70	2.8900	28.90
−0.70	0.4900	9.31
0.30	0.0900	0.63
1.30	1.6900	11.83
2.30	5.2900	26.45
3.30	10.8900	10.89
4.30	18.4900	18.49
		$\sum (x - \bar{x})^2 f = 106.5$

d. 1.5

10 a.

Class	x	f	xf
0–99	49.5	380	18,810
100–199	149.5	230	34,385
200–299	249.5	210	52,395
300–399	349.5	50	17,475
400–499	449.5	60	26,970
500+	650.0	70	45,500
		$n = 1000$	$\sum xf = 195,535$

b. 195.5

c.

$x - \bar{x}$	$(x - \bar{x})^2$	$(x - \bar{x})^2 f$
−146.0	21,316	8,100,080
−46.0	2,116	486,680
54.0	2,916	612,360
154.0	23,716	1,185,800
254.0	64,516	3,870,960
454.0	206,570.25	14,459,917.5
		$\sum (x - \bar{x})^2 f = 28,715,797.5$

d. 169.5

Section 2.5

1 a. 15, 15, 15, 17, 18, 18, 20, 21, 21, 21, 21, 22, 22, 23, 24, 24, 25, 25, 26, 26, 27, 27, 27, 28, 28, 28, 29, 29, 29, 30, 30, 31, 31, 31, 31, 31, 32, 32, 32, 32, 32, 32, 32, 33, 33, 33, 34, 34, 34, 34, 35, 35, 35, 35, 35, 36, 36, 37, 37, 37, 38, 38, 38, 39, 39, 39, 40, 40, 40, 41, 41, 42, 42, 43, 43, 43, 44, 44, 44, 44, 45, 45, 45, 45, 46, 46, 46, 46, 47, 47, 48, 48, 48, 48, 48, 49, 50, 50, 52, 53, 53, 54, 54, 55, 55, 55, 55, 57, 59, 59, 60, 61, 61, 61, 63, 63, 65, 68, 89

b. 37   **c.** 30, 47

2 a. Enter data.   **b.** 17, 23, 28.5

c. One quarter of the tuition costs is $17,000 or less, one half is $23,000 or less, and three quarters is $28,500 or less.

3 a. 30, 47   **b.** 17

c. The number of touchdowns scored in the middle half of the data set varies by at most 17.

4 a. min: 15, Q_1: 30, Q_2: 37, Q_3: 47, max: 89

bc.

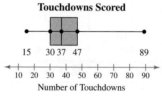
Touchdowns Scored

d. It appears that half of the teams scored between 30 and 47 touchdowns.

5 a. 50th percentile

b. 50% of the teams scored 40 or fewer touchdowns.

6 a. $\mu = 70$, $\sigma = 8$

b. $z_1 = \dfrac{60 - 70}{8} = -1.25$

$z_2 = \dfrac{71 - 70}{8} = 0.125$

$z_3 = \dfrac{92 - 70}{8} = 2.75$

c. From the z-score, $60 is 1.25 standard deviations below the mean, $71 is 0.125 standard deviation above the mean, and $92 is 2.75 standard deviations above the mean.

7 a. Best supporting actor: $\mu = 50.1$, $\sigma = 13.9$

Best supporting actress: $\mu = 39.7$, $\sigma = 14$

b. Alan Arkin: $z = 1.58$

Jennifer Hudson: $z = -1.05$

c. The age of Alan Arkin is 1.58 standard deviations above the mean and the age of Jennifer Hudson is 1.05 standard deviations below the mean. Neither actor's age is unusual. Comparing the two measures indicates that Alan Arkin is further above the average age of supporting actors than Jennifer Hudson is below the average age of supporting actresses. (Answers will vary.)

CHAPTER 3

Section 3.1

1ab. (1)

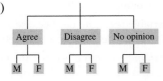

(2)

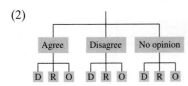

c. (1) 6   (2) 9

d. (1) Let A = Agree, D = Disagree,
N = No Opinion, M = Male, F = Female

Sample Space = $\{AM, AF, DM, DF, NM, NF\}$

(2) Let A = Agree, D = Disagree,
N = No Opinion, De = Democrat
R = Republican, O = Other

Sample Space =
$\{ADe, AR, AO, DDe, DR, DO, NDe, NR, NO\}$

2a. (1) 6   (2) 1

b. (1) Not a simple event   (2) Simple event

3a. Manufacturer: 4, Size: 3, Color: 6

b. 72

c.

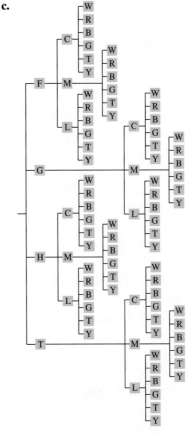

4a. (1) Each letter is an event (26 choices for each).

(2) Each letter is an event (26, 25, 24, 23, 22, and 21 choices).

(3) Each letter is an event (22, 26, 26, 26, 26, and 26 choices).

b. (1) 308,915,776   (2) 165,765,600   (3) 261,390,272

5a. (1) 52   (2) 52   (3) 52

b. (1) 1   (2) 13   (3) 52

c. (1) 0.019   (2) 0.25   (3) 1

6a. The event is "the next claim processed is fraudulent." The frequency is 4.

b. 100   **c.** 0.04

7a. 54   **b.** 1000   **c.** 0.054

8a. The event is "salmon successfully passing through a dam on the Columbia River."

b. Estimated   **c.** Empirical probability

9a. 0.18   **b.** 0.82   **c.** $\frac{41}{50}$ or 0.82

10a. 16   **b.** 5   **c.** 0.3125

11a. 10,000,000   **b.** $\dfrac{1}{10,000,000}$

Section 3.2

1a. (1) 30 and 102   (2) 11 and 50

b. (1) 0.294   (2) 0.22

2a. (1) Yes   (2) No

b. (1) Dependent   (2) Independent

3a. (1) Independent   (2) Dependent

b. (1) 0.723   (2) 0.059

4a. (1) Event   (2) Complement

b. (1) 0.729   (2) 0.999

5a. (1) and (2) $A = \{$is female$\}$, $B = \{$works in health field$\}$

b. (1) $P(A \text{ and } B) = P(A) \cdot P(B|A) = (0.65) \cdot (0.25)$

(2) $P(A \text{ and } B') = P(A) \cdot (1 - P(B|A))$
$$= (0.65) \cdot (0.75)$$

c. (1) 0.1625   (2) 0.4875

Section 3.3

1a. (1) None are true.   (2) None are true.

(3) All are true.

b. (1) Not mutually exclusive   (2) Not mutually exclusive

(3) Mutually exclusive

2a. (1) Mutually exclusive   (2) Not mutually exclusive

b. (1) $\frac{1}{6}, \frac{1}{2}$ (2) $\frac{12}{52}, \frac{13}{52}, \frac{3}{52}$

c. (1) 0.667   (2) 0.423

3a. $A = \{$sales between \$0 and \$24,999$\}$

$B = \{$sales between \$25,000 and \$49,000$\}$

b. A and B cannot occur at the same time.
A and B are mutually exclusive.

c. $\frac{3}{36}, \frac{5}{36}$ **d.** 0.222

4a. (1) Mutually exclusive   (2) Not mutually exclusive

b. (1) 0.149   (2) 0.910

5a. 0.169   **b.** 0.831

Section 3.4

1a. 6   **b.** 720

2a. 336

b. There are 336 possible ways that the subject can pick a first, second, and third activity.

3a. $n = 12, r = 4$ **b.** 11,880

4a. $n = 20, n_1 = 6, n_2 = 9, n_3 = 5$ **b.** 77,597,520

5a. $n = 20, r = 3$ **b.** 1140

c. There are 1140 different possible three-person committees that can be selected from 20 employees.

6a. 380   **b.** 0.003

7a. 1 outcome and 180 distinguishable permutations

b. 0.006

8a. 3003   **b.** 3,162,510   **c.** 0.0009

9a. 10   **b.** 220   **c.** 0.045

CHAPTER 4

Section 4.1

1a. (1) Measured   (2) Counted

b. (1) The random variable is continuous because x can be any amount of time needed to complete a test.

(2) The random variable is discrete because the number of songs played by a band at a rock festival is countable.

2ab.

x	f	$P(x)$
0	16	0.16
1	19	0.19
2	15	0.15
3	21	0.21
4	9	0.09
5	10	0.10
6	8	0.08
7	2	0.02
	$n = 100$	$\sum P(x) = 1$

c.

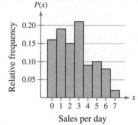

New Employee Sales

3a. Each $P(x)$ is between 0 and 1.   **b.** $\sum P(x) = 1$

c. Because both conditions are met, the distribution is a probability distribution.

4a. (1) Yes, each outcome is between 0 and 1.

(2) Yes, each outcome is between 0 and 1.

b. (1) Yes   (2) Yes

c. (1) A probability distribution

(2) A probability distribution

5ab.

x	$P(x)$	$xP(x)$
0	0.16	0.00
1	0.19	0.19
2	0.15	0.30
3	0.21	0.63
4	0.09	0.36
5	0.10	0.50
6	0.08	0.48
7	0.02	0.14
	$\sum P(x) = 1$	$\sum xP(x) = 2.60$

c. $\mu = 2.6$

On average, 2.6 sales are made per day.

6ab.

x	$P(x)$	$x - \mu$	$(x - \mu)^2$	$P(x)(x - \mu)^2$
0	0.16	-2.6	6.76	1.0816
1	0.19	-1.6	2.56	0.4864
2	0.15	-0.6	0.36	0.0540
3	0.21	0.4	0.16	0.0336
4	0.09	1.4	1.96	0.1764
5	0.10	2.4	5.76	0.5760
6	0.08	3.4	11.56	0.9248
7	0.02	4.4	19.36	0.3872
	$\Sigma P(x) = 1$			$\Sigma P(x)(x - \mu)^2 = 3.72$

c. 1.9

d. Most of the data values differ from the mean by no more than 1.9 sales per day.

7ab.

Gain, x	$1995	$995	$495	$245	$95	$-$5
Probability, $P(x)$	$\frac{1}{2000}$	$\frac{1}{2000}$	$\frac{1}{2000}$	$\frac{1}{2000}$	$\frac{1}{2000}$	$\frac{1995}{2000}$

c. $-$3.08

d. Because the expected value is negative, you can expect to lose an average of $3.08 for each ticket you buy.

Section 4.2

1a. Trial: answering a question

Success: question answered correctly

b. Yes

c. It is a binomial experiment; $n = 10$, $p = 0.25$, $q = 0.75$, $x = 0, 1, 2, \ldots, 9, 10$

2a. Trial: drawing a card with replacement

Success: card drawn is a club

Failure: card drawn is not a club

b. $n = 5$, $p = 0.25$, $q = 0.75$, $x = 3$

c. $P(3) = \dfrac{5!}{2! \, 3!} (0.25)^3 (0.75)^2 \approx 0.088$

3a. Trial: selecting a worker and asking a question

Success: selecting a worker who will rely on pension

Failure: selecting a worker who will not rely on pension

b. $n = 7$, $p = 0.26$, $q = 0.74$, $x = 0, 1, 2, \ldots, 6, 7$

c. $P(0) = {}_7C_0 \, (0.26)^0 \, (0.74)^7 = 0.1215$

$P(1) = {}_7C_1 \, (0.26)^1 \, (0.74)^6 = 0.2989$

$P(2) = {}_7C_2 \, (0.26)^2 \, (0.74)^5 = 0.3150$

$P(3) = {}_7C_3 \, (0.26)^3 \, (0.74)^4 = 0.1845$

$P(4) = {}_7C_4 \, (0.26)^4 \, (0.74)^3 = 0.0648$

$P(5) = {}_7C_5 \, (0.26)^5 \, (0.74)^2 = 0.0137$

$P(6) = {}_7C_6 \, (0.26)^6 \, (0.74)^1 = 0.0016$

$P(7) = {}_7C_7 \, (0.26)^7 \, (0.74)^0 = 0.0001$

d.

x	$P(x)$
0	0.1215
1	0.2989
2	0.3150
3	0.1845
4	0.0648
5	0.0137
6	0.0016
7	0.0001
	$\Sigma P(x) \approx 1$

4a. $n = 250$, $p = 0.71$, $x = 178$ **b.** 0.056

c. The probability that exactly 178 people from a random sample of 250 people in the United States will use more than one topping on their hotdog is about 0.056.

5a. (1) $x = 2$ (2) $x = 2, 3, 4$, or 5 (3) $x = 0$ or 1

b. (1) 0.217 (2) 0.217, 0.058, 0.008, 0.0004; 0.283

(3) 0.308, 0.409; 0.717

c. (1) The probability that exactly two of the five men consider fishing their favorite leisure-time activity is about 0.217.

(2) The probability that at least two of the five men consider fishing their favorite leisure-time activity is about 0.283.

(3) The probability that fewer than two of the five men consider fishing their favorite leisure-time activity is about 0.717.

6a. Trial: selecting a business and asking if it has a Web site

Success: selecting a business with a Web site

Failure: selecting a business without a Web site

b. $n = 10$, $p = 0.45$, $x = 4$ **c.** 0.238

d. The probability that exactly four of the 10 small businesses have a Web site is 0.238.

7a. 0.003, 0.029, 0.120, 0.262, 0.320, 0.209, 0.057

b.

x	$P(x)$
0	0.003
1	0.029
2	0.120
3	0.262
4	0.320
5	0.209
6	0.057

c.

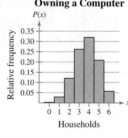

Owning a Computer

8a. Success: selecting a clear day
  $n = 31$, $p = 0.44$, $q = 0.56$

b. 13.6   **c.** 7.6   **d.** 2.8

e. On average, there are about 14 clear days during the month of May. A May with fewer than 8 sunny days or more than 19 sunny days would be unusual.

Section 4.3

1a. 0.23, 0.177, 0.136   **b.** 0.543

c. The probability that your first sale will occur before your fourth sales call is 0.543.

2a. $P(0) \approx 0.050$
  $P(1) \approx 0.149$
  $P(2) \approx 0.224$
  $P(3) \approx 0.224$
  $P(4) \approx 0.168$

b. 0.815   **c.** 0.185

d. The probability that more than four accidents will occur in any given month at the intersection is 0.185.

3a. 0.10   **b.** 0.10, 3   **c.** 0.0002

d. The probability of finding three brown trout in any given cubic meter of the lake is 0.0002.

CHAPTER 5

Section 5.1

1a. A: 45, B: 60, C: 45; B has the greatest mean.

b. Curve C is more spread out, so curve C has the greatest standard deviation.

2a. 3.5 feet   **b.** 3.3, 3.7; 0.2 foot

3. (1) 0.0143   (2) 0.9850

4a.

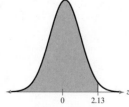

b. 0.9834

5a.

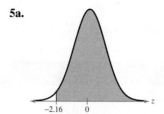

b. 0.0154

c. 0.9846

6a. 0.0885   **b.** 0.0154   **c.** 0.0731

Section 5.2

1a.

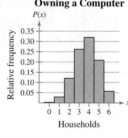

b. 2.5

c. 0.0062

d. The probability that a randomly selected manual transmission Focus will get more than 28 miles per gallon in city driving is 0.0062.

2a.

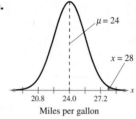

b. -1, 1.25

c. 0.1587; 0.8944; 0.7357

d. If 150 shoppers enter the store, then you would expect $150(0.7357) = 110.355$ (or about 110) shoppers to be in the store between 33 and 60 minutes.

3a. Read user's guide for the technology tool.

b. 0.4968

c. The probability that a randomly selected U.S. man's cholesterol is between 190 and 225 is 0.4968.

Section 5.3

1a. (1) 0.0384   (2) 0.0250 and 0.9750
bc. (1) -1.77 (2) ± 1.96
2a. (1) Area $= 0.10$ (2) Area $= 0.20$
  (3) Area $= 0.99$
bc. (1) -1.28 (2) -0.84 (3) 2.33
3a. $\mu = 70$, $\sigma = 8$ **b.** 64; 104.32; 55.44

c. 64 is below the mean, 104.32 is above the mean, and 55.44 is below the mean.

4ab.

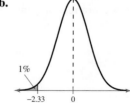

c. 126.83

d. So, the longest braking distance a Honda Accord could have and still be in the top 1% is about 127 feet.

5ab.

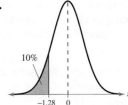

10%

−1.28 0 z

c. 8.512

d. So, the maximum length of time an employee could have worked and still be laid off is about 8 years.

c. $\mu_{\bar{x}} = \mu = 4$

$(\sigma_{\bar{x}})^2 = \dfrac{\sigma^2}{n} = \dfrac{5}{3} = 1.667;\ \sigma_{\bar{x}} = \dfrac{\sigma}{\sqrt{n}} = \dfrac{\sqrt{5}}{\sqrt{3}} = 1.291$

2a. 64, 0.9

b. $n = 100$

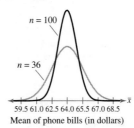

$n = 100$

$n = 36$

59.5 61.0 62.5 64.0 65.5 67.0 68.5
Mean of phone bills (in dollars)

c. With a larger sample size, the mean stays the same but the standard deviation decreases.

3a. 3.5, 0.05

b.

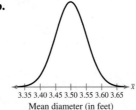

3.35 3.40 3.45 3.50 3.55 3.60 3.65
Mean diameter (in feet)

4a. 25; 0.15   **b.** −2, 3.33   **c.** 0.9768

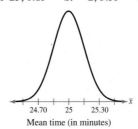

24.70   25   25.30
Mean time (in minutes)

5a. 306,258; 12,701.71

280,855   306,258   331,661
Mean sales price (in dollars)

b. −2.07   **c.** 0.9808 (*Tech*: 0.9806)

6a. 0.5, 1.58   **b.** 0.6915, 0.9429

c. There is a 69% chance an individual receiver will cost less than $700. There is a 94% chance that the mean of a sample of 10 receivers is less than $700.

Section 5.5

1a. $n = 70$, $p = 0.80$, $q = 0.20$ **b.** 56, 14

c. Normal distribution can be used.

d. 56, 3.35

Section 5.4

1a.

Sample	Mean	Sample	Mean	Sample	Mean
1, 1, 1	1	3, 3, 5	3.67	5, 7, 1	4.33
1, 1, 3	1.67	3, 3, 7	4.33	5, 7, 3	5
1, 1, 5	2.33	3, 5, 1	3	5, 7, 5	5.67
1, 1, 7	3	3, 5, 3	3.67	5, 7, 7	6.33
1, 3, 1	1.67	3, 5, 5	4.33	7, 1, 1	3
1, 3, 3	2.33	3, 5, 7	5	7, 1, 3	3.67
1, 3, 5	3	3, 7, 1	3.67	7, 1, 5	4.33
1, 3, 7	3.67	3, 7, 3	4.33	7, 1, 7	5
1, 5, 1	2.33	3, 7, 5	5	7, 3, 1	3.67
1, 5, 3	3	3, 7, 7	5.67	7, 3, 3	4.33
1, 5, 5	3.67	5, 1, 1	2.33	7, 3, 5	5
1, 5, 7	4.33	5, 1, 3	3	7, 3, 7	5.67
1, 7, 1	3	5, 1, 5	3.67	7, 5, 1	4.33
1, 7, 3	3.67	5, 1, 7	4.33	7, 5, 3	5
1, 7, 5	4.33	5, 3, 1	3	7, 5, 5	5.67
1, 7, 7	5	5, 3, 3	3.67	7, 5, 7	6.33
3, 1, 1	1.67	5, 3, 5	4.33	7, 7, 1	5
3, 1, 3	2.33	5, 3, 7	5	7, 7, 3	5.67
3, 1, 5	3	5, 5, 1	3.67	7, 7, 5	6.33
3, 1, 7	3.67	5, 5, 3	4.33	7, 7, 7	7
3, 3, 1	2.33	5, 5, 5	5		
3, 3, 3	3	5, 5, 7	5.67		

b.

$\bar{x}$	f	Probability
1	1	0.0156
1.67	3	0.0469
2.33	6	0.0938
3	10	0.1563
3.67	12	0.1875
4.33	12	0.1875
5	10	0.1563
5.67	6	0.0938
6.33	3	0.0469
7	1	0.0156

$\mu_{\bar{x}} = 4$
$(\sigma_{\bar{x}})^2 = 1.667$
$\sigma_{\bar{x}} = 1.291$

2a. (1) $57, 58, \ldots, 83$ (2) $\ldots, 52, 53, 54$

b. (1) $56.5 < x < 83.5$ (2) $x < 54.5$

3a. Normal distribution can be used. **b.** $56, 3.35$

c.

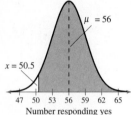

d. -1.64 **e.** 0.9495

4a. Normal distribution can be used. **b.** $76, 6.86$

c. $P(x \le 85.5)$ **d.** 1.38 **e.** 0.9162

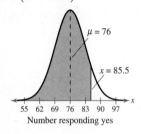

5a. Normal distribution can be used. **b.** $172, 4.91$

c. $P(169.5 < x < 170.5)$ **d.** $-0.51, -0.31$ **e.** 0.0733

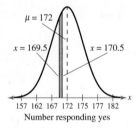

CHAPTER 6

Section 6.1

1a. $\bar{x} = 14.8$

b. The mean number of sentences per magazine advertisement is 14.8.

2a. $z_c = 1.96, n = 30, s \approx 16.5$ **b.** $E = 5.9$

c. You are 95% confident that the maximum error of the estimate is about 5.9 sentences per magazine advertisement.

3a. $\bar{x} = 14.8, E = 5.9$ **b.** $8.9, 20.7$

c. You are 95% confident that the mean number of sentences per magazine advertisement is between 8.8 and 20.7.

4a. Enter the data. **b.** $(11.6, 13.2)$; $(11.4, 13.4)$; $(10.6, 14.2)$

c. As the confidence level increases, so does the width of the interval.

5a. $n = 30, \bar{x} = 22.9, \sigma = 1.5, z_c = 1.645, E = 0.5$

b. $(22.4, 23.4)$ [*Tech:* $(22.5, 23.4)$]

c. You are 90% confident that the mean age of the students is between 22.4 (*Tech:* 22.5) and 23.4 years. Because of the larger sample size, the confidence interval is slightly smaller.

6a. $z_c = 1.96, E = 2, s \approx 5.0$ **b.** $n = 25$

c. You should have at least 25 magazine advertisements in your sample. Because of the larger margin of error, the number of samples needed is much smaller.

Section 6.2

1a. d.f. $= 21$ **b.** $c = 0.90$ **c.** $t_c = 1.721$

2a. $t_c = 1.753; E = 4.4; t_c = 2.947; E = 7.4$

b. $(157.6, 166.4)$; $(154.6, 169.4)$

c. You are 90% confident that the mean temperature of coffee sold is between 157.6°F and 166.4°F.

You are 99% confident that the mean temperature of coffee sold is between 154.6°F and 169.4°F.

3a. $t_c = 1.729; E = 0.16; t_c = 2.093; E = 0.20$

b. $(6.06, 6.38)$; $(6.02, 6.42)$

c. You are 90% confident that the mean mortgage interest rate is contained between 6.06% and 6.38%.

You are 95% confident that the mean mortgage interest rate is contained between 6.02% and 6.42%.

The 90% confidence interval is slightly narrower.

4. No; Yes; No; Use t-distribution.

Section 6.3

1a. $x = 181, n = 1006$ **b.** $\hat{p} = 0.180$

2a. $\hat{p} = 0.180, \hat{q} = 0.820$

b. $n\hat{p} = 181 > 5$ and $n\hat{q} = 825 > 5$

c. $z_c = 1.645; E = 0.020$ **d.** $(0.160, 0.200)$

e. You are 90% confident that the proportion of adults who think Abraham Lincoln was the greatest president is contained between 16.0% and 20.0%.

3a. $n = 900, \hat{p} = 0.33$ **b.** $\hat{q} = 0.67$

c. $n\hat{p} = 297 > 5$ and $n\hat{q} = 603 > 5$

d. $z_c = 2.575$ **e.** $(0.290, 0.370)$

f. You are 99% confident that the proportion of adults who think that people over 75 are the more dangerous drivers is contained between 29.0% and 37.0%.

4a. (1) $\hat{p} = 0.5, \hat{q} = 0.5, z_c = 1.645, E = 0.02$

(2) $\hat{p} = 0.064, \hat{q} = 0.936, z_c = 1.645, E = 0.02$

b. (1) $n = 1691.27$ (2) $n = 405.25$

c. (1) $n = 1692$ males (2) $n = 406$ males

Section 6.4

1a. d.f. $= 24, c = 0.95$ **b.** $0.025, 0.975$ **c.** $39.364, 12.401$

2a. $42.557, 17.708; 45.722, 16.047$

b. $(0.98, 2.36)$; $(0.91, 2.60)$ **c.** $(0.99, 1.54)$; $(0.96, 1.61)$

d. You are 90% confident that the population variance is between 0.98 and 2.36 and that the population standard deviation is between 0.99 and 1.54. You are 95% confident that the population variance is between 0.91 and 2.60 and that the population standard deviation is between 0.96 and 1.61.

CHAPTER 7

Section 7.1

1a. (1) The mean life of a certain type of automobile battery is not 74 months.

$\mu \neq 74$

(2) The variance of the life of a certain type of television is less than or equal to 3.5.

$\sigma^2 \leq 3.5$

(3) The proportion of the total listening audience is greater than 39%.

$p > 0.39$

b. (1) $\mu = 74$ (2) $\sigma^2 > 3.5$ (3) $p \leq 0.39$

c. (1) $H_0: \mu = 74$; $H_a: \mu \neq 74$ (claim)

(2) $H_0: \sigma^2 \leq 3.5$ (claim); $H_a: \sigma^2 > 3.5$

(3) $H_0: p \leq 0.39$; $H_a: p > 0.39$ (claim)

2a. $H_0: p \leq 0.01$; $H_a: p > 0.01$

b. A type I error will occur if the actual proportion is less than or equal to 0.01, but you reject H_0.

A type II error will occur if the actual proportion is greater than 0.01, but you fail to reject H_0.

c. A type II error is more serious because you would be misleading the consumer, possibly causing serious injury or death.

3a. (1) $H_0: \mu = 74$; $H_a: \mu \neq 74$

(2) $H_0: p \leq 0.39$; $H_a: p > 0.39$

b. (1) Two-tailed (2) Right-tailed

c. (1) 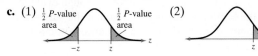 (2)

4a. There is enough evidence to support the radio station's claim that its proportion of the local listening audience is greater than 39%.

b. There is not enough evidence to support the radio station's claim that its proportion of the local listening audience is greater than 39%.

5a. (1) Support claim. (2) Reject claim.

b. (1) $H_0: \mu \geq 650$; $H_a: \mu < 650$ (claim)

(2) $H_0: \mu = 98.6$ (claim); $H_a: \mu \neq 98.6$

Section 7.2

1a. (1) $0.0347 > 0.01$ (2) $0.0347 < 0.05$

b. (1) Fail to reject H_0. (2) Reject H_0.

2ab. 0.0526

c. Fail to reject H_0 because $0.0526 > 0.05$.

3a. 0.9896 **b.** 0.0208

c. Fail to reject H_0 because $0.0208 > 0.01$.

4a. The claim is "the mean speed is greater than 35 miles per hour."

$H_0: \mu \leq 35$; $H_a: \mu > 35$ (claim)

b. $\alpha = 0.05$ **c.** 2.5 **d.** 0.0062 **e.** Reject H_0.

f. At the 5% significance level, there is enough evidence to conclude the average speed is greater than 35 miles per hour.

5a. The claim is "one of your distributors reports an average of 150 sales per day."

$H_0: \mu = 150$ (claim); $H_a: \mu \neq 150$

b. $\alpha = 0.01$ **c.** -2.76 **d.** 0.0058

e. Reject H_0 because $0.0058 < 0.01$.

f. At the 1% significance level, there is enough evidence to reject the claim that the distributorship averages 150 sales per day.

6a. $0.0440 > 0.01$ **b.** Fail to reject H_0.

7a.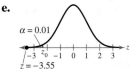

b. 0.1003

c. $z_0 = -1.28$

d. Rejection region: $z < -1.28$

8a.

b. $0.0401, 0.9599$

c. $-z_0 = -1.75$, $z_0 = 1.75$

d. Rejection regions: $z < -1.75$, $z > 1.75$

9a. The claim is "the mean work day of the firm's accountants is less than 8.5 hours."

$H_0: \mu \geq 8.5$; $H_a: \mu < 8.5$ (claim)

b. $\alpha = 0.01$

c. $z_0 = -2.33$; Rejection region: $z < -2.33$

d. -3.55

e.

Because $-3.55 < -2.33$, reject H_0.

f. At the 1% significance level, there is enough evidence to support the claim that the mean work day is less than 8.5 hours.

10a. $\alpha = 0.01$

b. $-z_0 = -2.575$, $z_0 = 2.575$

Rejection regions: $z < -2.575$, $z > 2.575$

c. Fail to reject H_0.

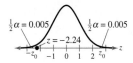

d. At the 1% significance level, there is not enough evidence to support the claim that the mean cost is significantly different from $10,460.

Section 7.3

1a. 2.650   **b.** −2.650

2ab. 1.860

3a. 2.947   **b.** −2.947, 2.947

4a. The claim is "the mean cost of insuring a 2005 Honda Pilot LX is at least $1350."

$H_0: \mu \geq \$1350$ (claim); $H_a: \mu < \$1350$

b. $\alpha = 0.01$, d.f. $= 8$

c. $t_0 = -2.896$; Rejection region: $t < -2.896$ **d.** −2.571

e. Fail to reject H_0.

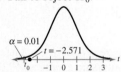

f. At the 1% significance level, there is not enough evidence to reject the insurance agent's claim that the mean cost of insuring a 2005 Honda Pilot LX is at least $1350.

5a. The claim is "the mean conductivity of the river is 1890 milligrams per liter."

$H_0: \mu = 1890$ (claim); $H_a: \mu \neq 1890$

b. $\alpha = 0.01$, d.f. $= 18$

c. $-t_0 = -2.878$, $t_0 = 2.878$

Rejection regions: $t < -2.878$, $t > 2.878$

d. 3.798

e. Reject H_0.

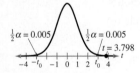

f. At the 1% significance level, there is enough evidence to reject the company's claim that the mean conductivity of the river is 1890 milligrams per liter.

6a. 0.0436   **b.** $0.0436 < 0.05$ **c.** Reject H_0.

d. At the 5% significance level, there is enough evidence to reject the claim that the mean nightly lodging rate is at least $185.

Section 7.4

1a. $np = 25.8 > 5$, $nq = 60.2 > 5$

b. The claim is "less than 30% of cellular phone users whose phone can connect to the Internet have done so while at home."

$H_0: p \geq 0.30$; $H_a: p < 0.30$ (claim)   **c.** $\alpha = 0.05$

d. $z_0 = -1.645$; Rejection region: $z < -1.645$

e. −2.024   **f.** Reject H_0.

g. At the 5% significance level, there is enough evidence to support the research center's claim that less than 30% of cellular phone users whose phone can connect to the Internet have done so while at home.

2a. $np = 12.5 > 5$, $nq = 237.5 > 5$

b. The claim is "5% of U.S. adults have had vivid dreams about UFOs."

$H_0: p = 0.05$ (claim); $H_a: p \neq 0.05$ **c.** $\alpha = 0.01$

d. $-z_0 = -2.575$, $z_0 = 2.575$

Rejection regions: $z < -2.575$, $z > 2.575$

e. 2.176   **f.** Fail to reject H_0.

g. At the 1% significance level, there is not enough evidence to reject the Roper Poll's claim that 5% of U.S. adults have had vivid dreams about UFOs.

3a. $np = 22.5 > 5$, $nq = 52.5 > 5$

b. The claim is "more than 30% of U.S. adults regularly watch the Weather Channel."

$H_0: p \leq 0.30$; $H_a: p > 0.30$ (claim)   **c.** $\alpha = 0.01$

d. $z_0 = 2.33$; Rejection region: $z > 2.33$ **e.** 1.13

f. Fail to reject H_0.

g. At the 1% significance level, there is not enough evidence to support the Pew Research Center's claim that more than 30% of U.S. adults regularly watch the Weather Channel.

Section 7.5

1. 33.409   **2.** 17.708   **3a.** 31.526   **b.** 8.231

4a. The claim is "the variance of the amount of sports drink in a 12-ounce bottle is no more than 0.40."

$H_0: \sigma^2 \leq 0.40$ (claim); $H_a: \sigma^2 > 0.40$

b. $\alpha = 0.01$, d.f. $= 30$

c. $\chi_0^2 = 50.892$; Rejection region: $\chi^2 > 50.892$

d. 56.250   **e.** Reject H_0.

f. At the 1% significance level, there is enough evidence to reject the bottling company's claim that the variance of the amount of sports drink in a 12-ounce bottle is no more than 0.40.

5a. The claim is "the standard deviation in the length of response times is less than 3.7 minutes."

$H_0: \sigma \geq 3.7$; $H_a: \sigma < 3.7$ (claim)   **b.** $\alpha = 0.05$, d.f. $= 8$

c. $\chi_0^2 = 2.733$; Rejection region: $\chi^2 < 2.733$

d. 5.259   **e.** Fail to reject H_0.

f. At the 5% significance level, there is not enough evidence to support the police chief's claim that the standard deviation in the length of response times is less than 3.7 minutes.

6a. The claim is "the variance of the diameters in a certain tire model is 8.6."

$H_0: \sigma^2 = 8.6$ (claim); $H_a: \sigma^2 \neq 8.6$

b. $\alpha = 0.01$, d.f. $= 9$

c. $\chi_L^2 = 1.735, \chi_R^2 = 23.589$

Rejection regions: $\chi^2 < 1.735, \chi^2 > 23.589$

d. 4.50   **e.** Fail to reject H_0.

f. At the 1% significance level, there is not enough evidence to reject the tire manufacturer's claim that the variance of the diameters in a certain tire model is 8.6.

CHAPTER 8

Section 8.1

1. (1) Independent   (2) Dependent

2a. The claim is "there is a difference in the mean credit card charges for residents of New Hampshire and New York."

$H_0: \mu_1 = \mu_2; H_a: \mu_1 \neq \mu_2$ (claim)

b. $\alpha = 0.01$

c. $-z_0 = -2.575, z_0 = 2.575$

Rejection regions: $z < -2.575, z > 2.575$

d. 2.747   **e.** Reject H_0.

f. At the 1% significance level, there is enough evidence to support the claim that there is a difference in the mean per capita credit card charges for residents of New Hampshire and New York.

3a. $z \approx 3.00; p \approx 0.0014$

b. Reject H_0. At the 5% significance level, there is enough evidence to support the American Automobile Association's claim that the average daily meal and lodging costs for vacationing in Maryland are greater than the same average costs for vacationing in Colorado.

Section 8.2

1a. The claim is "the mean braking distances are different."

$H_0: \mu_1 = \mu_2; H_a: \mu_1 \neq \mu_2$ (claim)

b. $\alpha = 0.05$ **c.** d.f. = 7

d. $-t_0 = -2.365, t_0 = 2.365$; Rejection regions: $t < -2.365$, $t > 2.365$

e. -3.757 **f.** Reject H_0.

g. At the 5% significance level, there is enough evidence to support the claim that the mean braking distances are different.

2a. The claim is "the watt usage of a manufacturer's 17-inch flat panel monitors is less than that of its leading competitor."

$H_0: \mu_1 \geq \mu_2; H_a: \mu_1 < \mu_2$ (claim)

b. $\alpha = 0.10$ **c.** d.f. = 25

d. $t_0 = -1.316$; Rejection region: $t < -1.316$

e. -3.997 **f.** Reject H_0.

g. At the 10% significance level, there is enough evidence to support the manufacturer's claim that the watt usage is less than that of its leading competitor.

Section 8.3

1a. The claim is "an experimental medication increases an individual's heart rate."

$H_0: \mu_d \geq 0; H_a: \mu_d < 0$ (claim)

b. $\alpha = 0.05$, d.f. = 11

c. $t_0 = -1.796$; Rejection region: $t < -1.796$

d. $\bar{d} = -1; s_d \approx 2.374$ **e.** -1.459

f. Fail to reject H_0.

g. At the 5% significance level, there is not enough evidence to support the physician's claim that experimental medication increases an individual's heart rate.

2a. The claim is "that the drug changes the body's temperature."

$H_0: \mu_d = 0; H_a: \mu_d \neq 0$ (claim)

b. $\alpha = 0.05$, d.f. = 6

c. $-t_0 = -2.447, t_0 = 2.447$

Rejection regions: $t < -2.447, t > 2.447$

d. $\bar{d} \approx 0.557; s_d \approx 0.924$

e. 1.596   **f.** Fail to reject H_0.

g. At the 5% significance level, there is not enough evidence to support the claim that the drug changes the body's temperature.

Section 8.4

1a. The claim is "there is a difference between the proportion of male high school students who smoke cigarettes and the proportion of female high school students who smoke cigarettes."

$H_0: p_1 = p_2; H_a: p_1 \neq p_2$ (claim)

b. $\alpha = 0.05$

c. $-z_0 = -1.96, z_0 = 1.96$

Rejection regions: $z < -1.96, z > 1.96$

d. $\bar{p} \approx 0.217; \bar{q} \approx 0.783$

e. $n_1\bar{p} = 1490.5 > 5, n_1\bar{q} = 5378.5 > 5,$
$n_2\bar{p} \approx 1490.5 > 5,$ and $n_2\bar{q} = 5378.5 > 5.$

f. -0.28 **g.** Fail to reject H_0.

h. At the 5% significance level, there is not enough evidence to support the claim that there is a difference between the proportion of male high school students who smoke cigarettes and the proportion of female high school students who smoke cigarettes.

2a. The claim is "the proportion of male high school students who smoke cigars is greater than the proportion of female high school students who smoke cigars."

$H_0: p_1 \leq p_2; H_a: p_1 > p_2$ (claim)

b. $\alpha = 0.05$ **c.** $z_0 = 1.645$; Rejection region: $z > 1.645$

d. $\bar{p} \approx 0.130; \bar{q} \approx 0.870$

e. $n_1\bar{p} = 893 > 5, n_1\bar{q} = 5976 > 5, n_2\bar{p} = 893 > 5,$ and $n_2\bar{q} = 5976 > 5$

f. 18.820   **g.** Reject H_0.

h. At the 5% significance level, there is enough evidence to support the claim that the proportion of male high school students who smoke cigars is greater than the proportion of female high school students who smoke cigars.

CHAPTER 9

Section 9.1

1ab.

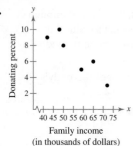

Family income
(in thousands of dollars)

c. Yes, it appears that there is a negative linear correlation. As family income increases, the percent of income donated to charity decreases.

2ab.

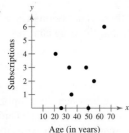

Age (in years)

c. No, it appears that there is no linear correlation between age and subscriptions.

3ab.

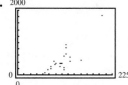

c. Yes, it appears that there is a positive linear correlation. As the budget increases, the worldwide gross increases.

4a. 6

b. $\Sigma x = 336$, $\Sigma y = 41$, $\Sigma xy = 2159$, $\Sigma x^2 = 19{,}458$, $\Sigma y^2 = 315$

c. -0.916

d. Because r is close to -1, this suggests a strong negative linear correlation between income level and donating percent.

5ab. 0.838

c. Because r is close to 1, this suggests a strong positive linear correlation between the movies' budgets and the worldwide grosses.

6a. 6   **b.** 0.01   **c.** 0.917

d. $|r| \approx 0.916 < 0.917$; the correlation is not significant.

e. At the 1% significance level, there is not enough evidence to conclude that there is a significant linear correlation between income level and donating percent.

7a. $H_0: \rho = 0$ and $H_a: \rho \neq 0$ **b.** 0.01   **c.** 23

d. $-t_0 = -2.807$ and $t_0 = 2.807$
Rejection regions: $t < -2.807$, $t > 2.807$

e. 7.357   **f.** Reject H_0.

g. At the 1% significance level, there is enough evidence to conclude that there is a significant linear correlation between the movies' budgets and the worldwide grosses.

Section 9.2

1a. $n = 6$, $\Sigma x = 336$, $\Sigma y = 41$, $\Sigma xy = 2159$, $\Sigma x^2 = 19{,}458$

b. $m \approx -0.2133956$ **c.** $b \approx 18.78349$

d. $\hat{y} = -0.213x + 18.783$

2a. Enter data.   **b.** $m \approx 10.93477$; $b \approx -710.61551$

c. $\hat{y} = 10.935x - 710.616$

3a. (1) $\hat{y} = 12.481(2) + 33.683$
(2) $\hat{y} = 12.481(3.32) + 33.683$

b. (1) 58.645   (2) 75.120

c. (1) 58.645 minutes   (2) 75.120 minutes

Section 9.3

1a. 0.979   **b.** 0.958

c. 95.8% of the variation in the times is explained.
4.2% of the variation is unexplained.

2a.

x_i	y_i	$\hat{y}_i$	$(y_i - \hat{y}_i)^2$
15	26	28.386	5.692996
20	32	35.411	11.634921
20	38	35.411	6.702921
30	56	49.461	42.758521
40	54	63.511	90.459121
45	78	70.536	55.711296
50	80	77.561	5.948721
60	88	91.611	13.039321
			$\Sigma = 231.947818$

b. 8   **c.** 6.218

d. The standard error of estimate of the weekly sales for a specific radio ad time is about $621.80.

3a. $n = 8$, d.f. $= 6$, $t_c = 2.447$, $s_e \approx 10.290$

b. 230.884   **c.** 29.236   **d.** $201.648 < y < 260.120$

e. You can be 95% confident that when advertising expenses are $2500 the company sales will be between $201,648 and $260,120.

Section 9.4

1a. Enter data.

b. $\hat{y} = 46.385 + 0.540x_1 - 4.897x_2$

2ab. (1) $\hat{y} = 46.385 + 0.540(89) - 4.897(1)$
 (2) $\hat{y} = 46.385 + 0.540(78) - 4.897(3)$
 (3) $\hat{y} = 46.385 + 0.540(83) - 4.897(2)$

c. (1) $\hat{y} = 89.548$ (2) $\hat{y} = 73.814$ (3) $\hat{y} = 81.411$

d. (1) 90 (2) 74 (3) 81

CHAPTER 10

Section 10.1

1.

Music	% of listeners	Expected frequency
Classical	4%	12
Country	36%	108
Gospel	11%	33
Oldies	2%	6
Pop	18%	54
Rock	29%	87

2a. The expected frequencies are 64, 80, 32, 56, 60, 48, 40, and 20, all of which are at least 5.

b. Claimed distribution:

Ages	Distribution
0–9	16%
10–19	20%
20–29	8%
30–39	14%
40–49	15%
50–59	12%
60–69	10%
70+	5%

H_0: Distribution of ages is as shown in table above.

H_a: Distribution of ages differs from the claimed distribution. (claim)

c. 0.05 **d.** 7

e. $\chi_0^2 = 14.067$; Rejection region: $\chi^2 > 14.067$

f. 6.694 **g.** Fail to reject H_0.

h. At the 5% significance level, there is not enough evidence to support the sociologist's claim that the age distribution differs from the age distribution 10 years ago.

3a. The expected frequencies are 123, 138, and 39, all of which are at least 5.

b. Claimed distribution:

Response	Distribution
Retirement	41%
Children's college education	46%
Not sure	13%

H_0: Distribution of responses is as shown in table above. (claim)

H_a: Distribution of responses differs from the claimed distribution.

c. 0.01 **d.** 2

e. $\chi_0^2 = 9.210$; Rejection region: $\chi^2 > 9.210$

f. 8.580 **g.** Fail to reject H_0.

h. At the 1% significance level, there is not enough evidence to dispute the claimed distribution of women's opinions.

4a. The expected frequency for each category is 30, which is at least 5.

b. Claimed distribution:

Color	Distribution
Brown	$16.\overline{6}\%$
Yellow	$16.\overline{6}\%$
Red	$16.\overline{6}\%$
Blue	$16.\overline{6}\%$
Orange	$16.\overline{6}\%$
Green	$16.\overline{6}\%$

H_0: The distribution of colors is uniform as shown in the table above. (claim)

H_a: The distribution of colors is not uniform.

c. 0.05 **d.** 5

e. $\chi_0^2 = 11.071$; Rejection region: $\chi^2 > 11.071$

f. 12.933 **g.** Reject H_0.

h. At the 5% significance level, there is enough evidence to dispute the claim that the distribution of different-colored candies in bags of peanut M&M's is uniform.

Section 10.2

1a. Marginal frequencies: Row 1: 180; Row 2: 120; Column 1: 74; Column 2: 162; Column 3: 28; Column 4: 36

b. 300

c. $E_{1,1} = 44.4$, $E_{1,2} = 97.2$, $E_{1,3} = 16.8$, $E_{1,4} = 21.6$, $E_{2,1} = 29.6$, $E_{2,2} = 64.8$, $E_{2,3} = 11.2$, $E_{2,4} = 14.4$

2a. H_0: Travel concern is independent of travel purpose.

H_a: Travel concern is dependent on travel purpose. (claim)

b. 0.01 **c.** 3

d. $\chi_0^2 = 11.345$; Rejection region: $\chi^2 > 11.345$

e. 8.158 **f.** Fail to reject H_0.

g. No, at the 1% significance level, there is not enough evidence for the consultant to conclude that travel concern is dependent on travel purpose.

3 a. H_0: The number of minutes adults spend online per day is independent of gender.

H_a: The number of minutes adults spend online per day is dependent on gender. (claim)

b. Enter the data.

c. $\chi_0^2 = 9.488$; Rejection region: $\chi^2 > 9.488$

d. 65.619   **e.** Reject H_0.

f. Yes, at the 5% significance level, there is enough evidence to conclude that the number of minutes spent online per day is dependent on gender.

Section 10.3

1 a. 0.01   **b.** 5.42

2 a. 0.01   **b.** 18.31

3 a. H_0: $\sigma_1^2 \leq \sigma_2^2$; H_a: $\sigma_1^2 > \sigma_2^2$ (claim)

b. 0.01   **c.** d.f.$_N$ = 24, d.f.$_D$ = 19

d. $F_0 = 2.92$; Rejection region: $F > 2.92$

e. 3.21   **f.** Reject H_0.

g. Yes, at the 1% significance level, there is enough evidence to support the researcher's claim that a specially treated intravenous solution decreases the variance of the time required for nutrients to enter the bloodstream.

4 a. H_0: $\sigma_1 = \sigma_2$ (claim); H_a: $\sigma_1 \neq \sigma_2$

b. 0.01   **c.** d.f.$_N$ = 15, d.f.$_D$ = 21

d. $F_0 = 3.43$; Rejection region: $F > 3.43$

e. 1.48   **f.** Fail to reject H_0.

g. No, at the 1% significance level, there is not enough evidence to reject the the biologist's claim that the pH levels of the soil in two geographic locations have equal standard deviations.

Section 10.4

1 a. H_0: $\mu_1 = \mu_2 = \mu_3 = \mu_4$

H_a: At least one mean is different from the others. (claim)

b. 0.05   **c.** d.f.$_N$ = 3, d.f.$_D$ = 14

d. $F_0 = 3.34$; Rejection region: $F > 3.34$

e. 4.22   **f.** Reject H_0.

g. Yes, at the 5% significance level, there is enough evidence for the analyst to conclude that there is a difference in the mean monthly sales among the sales regions.

2 a. Enter the data.

b. $F \approx 1.34$; P-value ≈ 0.280

c. $0.280 > 0.05$

d. Fail to reject H_0. No, at the 5% significance level, there is not enough evidence to conclude that there is a difference in the means of the GPAs.

CHAPTER 11

Section 11.1

1 a. H_0: median ≤ 2500; H_a: median > 2500 (claim)

b. 0.025   **c.** 22   **d.** 5   **e.** 10   **f.** Fail to reject H_0.

g. No, at the 2.5% significance level, there is not enough evidence to support the manager's claim that the median number of customers per day is greater than 2500.

2 a. H_0: median $= \$134{,}500$ (claim); H_a: median $\neq \$134{,}500$

b. 0.10   **c.** 81   **d.** -1.645 **e.** -2.22 **f.** Reject H_0.

g. Yes, at the 10% significance level, there is enough evidence to reject the realtor's claim that the median sales price of houses sold in a certain region is $134,500.

3 a. H_0: The number of colds will not decrease.

H_a: The number of colds will decrease. (claim)

b. 0.05   **c.** 11   **d.** 2   **e.** 2   **f.** Reject H_0.

g. Yes, at the 5% significance level, there is enough evidence to support the researcher's claim that a new vaccine will decrease the number of colds in adults.

Section 11.2

1 a. H_0: There is no difference in the amount of water repelled.

H_a: There is a difference in the amount of water repelled. (claim)

b. 0.01   **c.** 11   **d.** 5

e.

No repellent	Repellent applied	Differ-ence	Absolute value	Rank	Signed rank
8	15	-7	7	11	-11
7	12	-5	5	9	-9
7	11	-4	4	7.5	-7.5
4	6	-2	2	3.5	-3.5
6	6	0	0		
10	8	2	2	3.5	3.5
9	8	1	1	1.5	1.5
5	6	-1	1	1.5	-1.5
9	12	-3	3	5.5	-5.5
11	8	3	3	5.5	5.5
8	14	-6	6	10	-10
4	8	-4	4	7.5	-7.5

$w_s = 10.5$

f. Fail to reject H_0.

g. No, at the 1% significance level, there is not enough evidence for the quality control inspector to conclude that the spray-on water repellent is effective.

2 a. H_0: There is no difference in the claims paid by the companies.

H_a: There is a difference in the claims paid by the companies. (claim)

b. 0.05   **c.** ±1.96   **d.** $n_1 = 12$ and $n_2 = 12$

e.

Ordered data	Sample	Rank	Ordered data	Sample	Rank
1.7	B	1	5.3	B	13
1.8	B	2	5.6	B	14
2.2	B	3	5.8	A	15
2.5	A	4	6.0	A	16
3.0	A	5.5	6.2	A	17
3.0	B	5.5	6.3	A	18
3.4	B	7	6.5	A	19
3.9	A	8	7.3	B	20
4.1	B	9	7.4	A	21
4.4	B	10	9.9	A	22
4.5	A	11	10.6	A	23
4.7	B	12	10.8	B	24

$R = 120.5$ (*or* $R = 179.5$)

f. −1.703 (*or* 1.703)   **g.** Fail to reject H_0.

h. No, at the 5% significance level, there is not enough evidence to conclude that there is a difference in the claims paid by the companies.

Section 11.3

1 a. H_0: There is no difference in the salaries in the three states.

H_a: There is a difference in the salaries in the three states. (claim)

b. 0.10   **c.** 2

d. $\chi_0^2 = 4.605$; Rejection region: $\chi^2 > 4.605$

e.

Ordered data	State	Rank	Ordered data	State	Rank
86.85	MI	1	94.72	NC	16
87.25	NC	2	94.75	NC	17
87.70	CO	3	95.10	MI	18
89.65	MI	4	95.36	NC	19
89.75	CO	5	96.02	NC	20
89.92	NC	6	96.24	CO	21
91.17	CO	7	96.31	MI	22
91.55	CO	8	97.35	CO	23
92.85	CO	9	98.21	MI	24
93.12	CO	10	98.34	NC	25
93.76	MI	11	98.99	CO	26
93.92	MI	12	100.27	NC	27
94.42	MI	13	105.77	NC	28
94.45	MI	14	106.78	MI	29
94.55	CO	15	110.99	NC	30

$R_1 = 127$
$R_2 = 148$
$R_3 = 190$

f. 2.655   **g.** Fail to reject H_0.

h. No, at the 10% significance level, there is not enough evidence to conclude that the distributions of the pharmacists' salaries in these three states are different.

Section 11.4

1 a. H_0: $\rho_s = 0$; H_a: $\rho_s \neq 0$ (claim)

b. 0.05   **c.** 0.700

d.

Oat	Rank	Wheat	Rank	d	d^2
1.10	1.5	2.65	3	−1.5	2.25
1.12	3	2.48	1	2	4
1.10	1.5	2.62	2	−0.5	0.25
1.59	6	2.78	4	2	4
1.81	8	3.56	8	0	0
1.48	4.5	3.40	5.5	−1	1
1.48	4.5	3.40	5.5	−1	1
1.63	7	3.42	7	0	0
1.85	9	4.25	9	0	0
					$\Sigma = 12.5$

$\Sigma d^2 = 12.5$

e. 0.896   **f.** Reject H_0.

g. Yes, at the 5% significance level, there is enough evidence to conclude that a significant correlation exists between oat and wheat prices.

Section 11.5

1a. *P P P   F   P   F   P P P P   F F   P   F   P P*
     F F F   P P P   F   P P P

b. 13

c. 3, 1, 1, 1, 4, 2, 1, 1, 2, 3, 3, 1, 3

2a. H_0: The sequence of genders is random.

 H_a: The sequence of genders is not random. (claim)

b. 0.05

c. n_1 = number of *F*s = 9

 n_2 = number of *M*s = 5

 G = number of runs = 7

d. lower critical value = 3

 upper critical value = 12

e. 7   **f.** Fail to reject H_0.

g. No, at the 5% significance level, there is not enough evidence to support the claim that the sequence of genders is not random.

3a. H_0: The sequence of weather conditions is random.

 H_a: The sequence of weather conditions is not random. (claim)

b. 0.05

c. n_1 = number of *N*s = 21

 n_2 = number of *S*s = 10

 G = number of runs = 17

d. ±1.96   **e.** 1.03   **f.** Fail to reject H_0.

g. No, at the 5% significance level, there is not enough evidence to support the claim that the sequence of weather conditions is not random.

APPENDIX A

1. (1) 0.4857

 (2) $z = \pm 2.17$

2a.

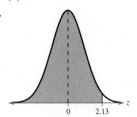

b. 0.4834   **c.** 0.9834

3a.

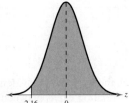

b. 0.4846   **c.** 0.9846

4a.

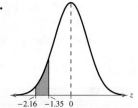

b. 0.4846; 0.4115   **c.** 0.0731

APPENDIX C

1a.

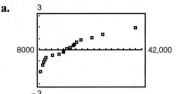

The points do not appear to be approximately linear.

b. 39,860 is a possible outlier because it is far removed from the other entries in the data set.

c. Because the points do not appear to be approximately linear and there is an outlier, you can conclude that the sample data do not come from a population that has a normal distribution.

A50

Odd Answers

CHAPTER 1

Section 1.1   *(page 8)*

1. A sample is a subset of a population.

3. A parameter is a numerical description of a population characteristic. A statistic is a numerical description of a sample characteristic.

5. False. A statistic is a numerical measure that describes a sample characteristic.

7. True

9. False. A population is the collection of *all* outcomes, responses, measurements, or counts that are of interest.

11. Population, because it is a collection of the ages of all the members of the House of Representatives.

13. Sample, because the collection of the 500 spectators is a subset within the population.

15. Sample, because the collection of the 20 patients is a subset within the population.

17. Population: Party of registered voters in Warren County

Sample: Party of Warren County voters responding to phone survey

19. Population: Ages of adults in the U.S. who own computers

Sample: Ages of adults in the U.S. who own Dell computers

21. Population: Collection of all adults in the United States

Sample: Collection of the 1000 adults surveyed

23. Population: Collection of all households in the United States

Sample: Collection of the 1906 households surveyed

25. Population: Collection of all registered voters

Sample: Collection of the 1045 registered voters surveyed

27. Population: Collection of all women in the U.S.

Sample: Collection of the 546 U.S. women surveyed

29. Statistic. The value $68,000 is a numerical description of a sample of annual salaries.

31. Parameter. The 62 surviving passengers out of 97 total passengers is a numerical description of all of the passengers of the Hindenburg that survived.

33. Statistic. 8% is a numerical description of a sample of computer users.

35. Statistic. 53% is a numerical description of a sample of all adults in the United States

37. The statement "56% are the primary investor in their household" is an application of descriptive statistics.

An inference drawn from the sample is that an association exists between U.S. women and being the primary investor in their household.

39. Answers will vary.

41. (a) An inference drawn from the sample is that senior citizens who live in Florida have better memories than senior citizens who do not live in Florida.

(b) This inference may incorrectly imply that if you live in Florida you will have a better memory.

43. Answers will vary.

Section 1.2   *(page 15)*

1. Nominal and ordinal

3. False. Data at the ordinal level can be qualitative or quantitative.

5. False. More types of calculations can be performed with data at the interval level than with data at the nominal level.

7. Qualitative   **9.** Quantitative   **11.** Qualitative

13. Qualitative. Ordinal. Data can be arranged in order, but the differences between data entries make no sense.

15. Qualitative. Nominal. No mathematical computations can be made and data are categorized by region.

17. Qualitative. Ordinal. Data can be arranged in order, but the differences between data entries are not meaningful.

19. Ordinal   **21.** Nominal

23. (a) Interval   (b) Nominal   (c) Ratio   (d) Ordinal

25. An inherent zero is a zero that implies "none." Answers will vary.

Section 1.3   *(page 25)*

1. In an experiment, a treatment is applied to part of a population and responses are observed. In an observational study, a researcher measures characteristics of interest of a part of a population but does not change existing conditions.

3. Assign numbers to each member of the population and use a random number table or use a random number generator.

5. True

7. False. Using stratified sampling guarantees that members of each group within a population will be sampled.

9. False. A systematic sample is selected by ordering a population in some way and then selecting members of the population at regular intervals.

11. Perform an experiment because you want to measure the effect of a treatment on the human digestive system.

13. Use a simulation because the situation is impractical.

15. (a) The experimental units are the 30-35 year old females being given the treatment.

(b) One treatment is used.

(c) A problem with the design is that there may be some bias on the part of the researchers if he or she knows which patients were given the real drug. A way to eliminate this problem would be to make the study into a double-blind experiment.

(d) The study would be a double-blind study if the researcher did not know which patients received the real drug or the placebo.

17. Simple random sampling is used because each telephone number has an equal chance of being dialed, and all samples of 1599 phone numbers have an equal chance of being selected. The sample may be biased because only homes with telephones will be sampled.

19. Convenience sampling is used because the students were chosen due to their convenience of location. Bias may enter into the sample because the students sampled may not be representative of the population of students.

21. Simple random sampling is used because each outpatient had an equal chance of being contacted, and all samples of 1210 outpatients had an equal chance of being selected.

23. Stratified sampling is used because a sample is taken from each one-acre subplot.

25. Systematic sampling is used because every ninth name on a list is being selected.

27. Answers will vary. *Sample Answer:* Treatment group: Jake, Maria, Lucy, Adam, Bridget, Vanessa, Rick, Dan, and Mary. Control group: Mike, Ron, Carlos, Steve, Susan, Kate, Pete, Judy, and Connie. A random number table was used.

29. Census, because it is relatively easy to obtain the salaries of the 50 employees.

31. The question is biased because it already suggests that drinking fruit juice is good for you. The question might be rewritten as "How does drinking fruit juice affect your health?"

33. The survey question is unbiased.

35. The households sampled represent various locations, ethnic groups, and income brackets. Each of these variables is considered a stratum.

37. Open Question
Advantage: Allows respondent to express some depth and shades of meaning in the answer.
Disadvantage: Not easily quantified and difficult to compare surveys.
Closed Question
Advantage: Easy to analyze results.
Disadvantage: May not provide appropriate alternatives and may influence the opinion of the respondent.

39. *Sample Answer:* Confounding would occur in a study to see the effectiveness of a billboard as an advertisement for a hotel if the billboard was put up just prior to a busy travel holiday.

41. The Hawthorne effect occurs when a subject changes behavior because he or she is in an experiment. However, the placebo effect occurs when a subject reacts favorably to a placebo he or she has been given.

43. Answers will vary.

Section 1.3 Activity   (page 28)

1. Answers will vary. The list contains one number at least twice.

2. The minimum is 1, the maximum is 731, and the number of samples is 8. Answers will vary.

Uses and Abuses for Chapter 1   (page 29)

1. Answers will vary.   **2.** Answers will vary.

Review Answers for Chapter 1   (page 31)

1. Population: Collection of all U.S. adults
Sample: Collection of the 1000 U.S. adults surveyed

3. Population: Collection of all credit cards
Sample: Collection of the 146 credit cards sampled

5. Parameter   **7.** Parameter

9. The statement "the average late fee charged by credit cards is $27.46" is an application of descriptive statistics. An inference drawn from the sample is that all credit cards charge a late fee of $27.46.

11. Quantitative, because monthly salaries are numerical measurements.

13. Quantitative, because ages are numerical measurements.

15. Interval. It makes no sense saying that 100 degrees is twice as hot as 50 degrees.

17. Nominal. The data are qualitative and cannot be arranged in a meaningful order.

19. Take a census because CEOs keep accurate records of charitable donations.

21. Perform an experiment because you want to measure the effect of a treatment on a soybean crop.

23. The subjects could be split into male and female and then be randomly assigned to each of the five treatment groups.

25. Simple random sampling is used because random telephone numbers were generated and called.

27. Cluster sampling is used because each community is considered a cluster and every pregnant woman in a selected community is surveyed.

29. Stratified sampling is used because 25 students are randomly selected from each grade level.

31. Telephone sampling samples only individuals who have telephones, are available, and are willing to respond.

33. The selected communities may not be representative of the entire area.

Chapter Quiz for Chapter 1   (page 33)

1. Population: Collection of all individuals with anxiety disorders
Sample: Collection of 372 patients in study

2. (a) Statistic   (b) Parameter   (c) Statistic

3. (a) Qualitative   (b) Quantitative

4. (a) Nominal, because no mathematical computations can be made.

(b) Ratio, because one data value can be expressed as a multiple of another.

(c) Interval, because meaningful differences between entries can be calculated but a zero entry is not an inherent zero.

5. (a) Perform an experiment because you want to measure the effect of a treatment on lead levels in adults.

(b) Use a survey because it would be impossible to question everyone in the population.

6. Randomized Block Design

7. (a) Convenience sampling, because all of the people sampled are in one convenient location.

(b) Systematic sampling, because every tenth machine is sampled.

(c) Stratified sampling, because the population is first stratified and then a sample is collected from each stratum.

8. Convenience

Real Statistics–Real Decisions for Chapter 1   *(page 34)*

1. (a) Answers will vary.   (b) Yes   (c) Use surveys.

(d) You may take too large of a percentage of your sample from a subgroup of the population that is relatively small.

2. (a) Response: qualitative and quantitative; Percent responding: quantitative

(b) Response: nominal; Percent responding: ratio
Method: nominal; Percent responding: ratio

(c) Sample   (d) Statistics

3. (a) Answers will vary. *Sample Answer:* Sample only includes members of the population with access to the Internet.

(b) Answers will vary

CHAPTER 2

Section 2.1   *(page 49)*

1. Organizing the data into a frequency distribution may make patterns within the data more evident.

3. Class limits determine which numbers can belong to that class.

Class boundaries are the numbers that separate classes without forming gaps between them.

5. False. Class width is the difference between lower or upper limits of consecutive classes.

7. False. An ogive is a graph that displays cumulative frequency.

9. Class width = 9; Lower class limits: 7, 16, 25, 34, 43, 52;
Upper class limits: 15, 24, 33, 42, 51, 60

11. Class width = 19; Lower class limits: 15, 34, 53, 72, 91, 110;
Upper class limits: 33, 52, 71, 90, 109, 128

13. (a) Class width = 11

(b) and (c)

Class	Midpoint	Class boundaries
20–30	25	19.5–30.5
31–41	36	30.5–41.5
42–52	47	41.5–52.5
53–63	58	52.5–63.5
64–74	69	63.5–74.5
75–85	80	74.5–85.5
86–96	91	85.5–96.5

15.

Class	Frequency, f	Midpoint	Relative frequency	Cumulative frequency
20–30	19	25	0.05	19
31–41	43	36	0.12	62
42–52	68	47	0.19	130
53–63	69	58	0.19	199
64–74	74	69	0.20	273
75–85	68	80	0.19	341
86–96	24	91	0.07	365
	$\Sigma f = 365$		$\Sigma \dfrac{f}{n} \approx 1$	

17. (a) Number of classes = 7   (b) Least frequency ≈ 10

(c) Greatest frequency ≈ 300   (d) Class width = 10

19. (a) 50   (b) 22.5–24.5 pounds

21. (a) 24   (b) 29.5 pounds

23. (a) Class with greatest relative frequency: 8–9 inches
Class with least relative frequency: 17–18 inches

(b) Greatest relative frequency ≈ 0.195
Least relative frequency ≈ 0.005

(c) Approximately 0.015

25. Class with greatest frequency: 500–550
Classes with least frequency: 250–300 and 700–750

27.

Class	Frequency, f	Midpoint	Relative frequency	Cumulative frequency
0–7	8	3.5	0.32	8
8–15	8	11.5	0.32	16
16–23	3	19.5	0.12	19
24–31	3	27.5	0.12	22
32–39	3	35.5	0.12	25
	$\Sigma f = 25$		$\Sigma \dfrac{f}{n} = 1$	

Classes with greatest frequency: 0–7, 8–15

Classes with least frequency: 16–23, 24–31, 32–39

29.

Class	Frequency, f	Mid-point	Relative frequency	Cumulative frequency
1000–2019	12	1509.5	0.5455	12
2020–3039	3	2529.5	0.1364	15
3040–4059	2	3549.5	0.0909	17
4060–5079	3	4569.5	0.1364	20
5080–6099	1	5589.5	0.0455	21
6100–7119	1	6609.5	0.0455	22
	$\Sigma f = 22$		$\Sigma\dfrac{f}{N} \approx 1$	

July Sales for Representatives

The graph shows that most of the sales representatives at the company sold between $1000 and $2019. (Answers will vary.)

31.

Class	Frequency, f	Mid-point	Relative frequency	Cumulative frequency
291–318	5	304.5	0.1667	5
319–346	4	332.5	0.1333	9
347–374	3	360.5	0.1000	12
375–402	5	388.5	0.1667	17
403–430	6	416.5	0.2000	23
431–458	4	444.5	0.1333	27
459–486	1	472.5	0.0333	28
487–514	2	500.5	0.0667	30
	$\Sigma f = 30$		$\Sigma\dfrac{f}{n} = 1$	

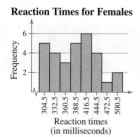

Reaction Times for Females

The graph shows that the most frequent response time was between 403 and 430 milliseconds. (Answers will vary.)

33.

Class	Frequency, f	Mid-point	Relative frequency	Cumulative frequency
146–169	6	157.5	0.2308	6
170–193	9	181.5	0.3462	15
194–217	3	205.5	0.1154	18
218–241	6	229.5	0.2308	24
242–265	2	253.5	0.0769	26
	$\Sigma f = 26$		$\Sigma\dfrac{f}{n} \approx 1$	

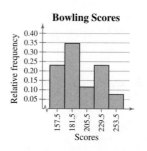

Bowling Scores

Class with greatest relative frequency: 170–193

Class with least relative frequency: 242–265

35.

Class	Frequency, f	Mid-point	Relative frequency	Cumulative frequency
33–36	8	34.5	0.3077	8
37–40	6	38.5	0.2308	14
41–44	5	42.5	0.1923	19
45–48	2	46.5	0.0769	21
49–52	5	50.5	0.1923	26
	$\Sigma f = 26$		$\Sigma\dfrac{f}{n} \approx 1$	

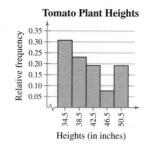

Tomato Plant Heights

Class with greatest relative frequency: 33–36

Class with least relative frequency: 45–48

37.

Class	Frequency, f	Relative frequency	Cumulative frequency
52–55	3	0.125	3
56–59	3	0.125	6
60–63	9	0.375	15
64–67	4	0.167	19
68–71	4	0.167	23
72–75	1	0.042	24
	$\Sigma f = 24$	$\Sigma \dfrac{f}{n} \approx 1$	

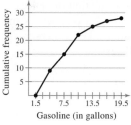

Location of the greatest increase in frequency: 60–63

39.

Class	Frequency, f	Relative frequency	Cumulative frequency
2–4	9	0.3214	9
5–7	6	0.2143	15
8–10	7	0.2500	22
11–13	3	0.1071	25
14–16	2	0.0714	27
17–19	1	0.0357	28
	$\Sigma f = 28$	$\Sigma \dfrac{f}{n} \approx 1$	

Gallons of Gasoline Purchased

Location of the greatest increase in frequency: 2–4

41.

Class	Frequency, f	Mid-point	Relative frequency	Cumulative frequency
47–57	1	52	0.05	1
58–68	1	63	0.05	2
69–79	5	74	0.25	7
80–90	8	85	0.40	15
91–101	5	96	0.25	20
	$\Sigma f = 20$		$\Sigma \dfrac{f}{N} = 1$	

The graph shows that the most frequent exam scores were between 80 and 90. (Answers will vary.)

43. (a)

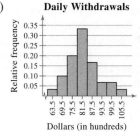

(b) 16.7%, because the sum of the relative frequencies for the last three classes is 0.167.

(c) $9600, because the sum of the relative frequencies for the last two classes is 0.10.

45.

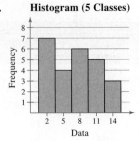

Histogram (5 Classes)

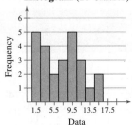

Histogram (10 Classes)

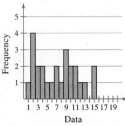

Histogram (20 Classes)

In general, a greater number of classes better preserves the actual values of the data set but is not as helpful for observing general trends and making conclusions. In choosing the number of classes, an important consideration is the size of the data set. For instance, you would not want to use 20 classes if your data set contained 20 entries. In this particular example, as the number of classes increases, the histogram shows more fluctuation. The histograms with 10 and 20 classes have classes with zero frequencies. Not much is gained by using more than five classes. Therefore, it appears that five classes would be best.

Section 2.2 *(page 62)*

1. Quantitative: stem-and-leaf plot, dot plot, histogram, scatter plot, time series chart

Qualitative: pie chart, Pareto chart

3. Both the stem and leaf plot and the dot plot allow you to see how data are distributed, determine specific data entries, and identify unusual data values.

5. b   **6.** d   **7.** a   **8.** c

9. 27, 32, 41, 43, 43, 44, 47, 47, 48, 50, 51, 51, 52, 53, 53, 53, 54, 54, 54, 54, 55, 56, 56, 58, 59, 68, 68, 68, 73, 78, 78, 85

Max: 85; Min: 27

11. 13, 13, 14, 14, 14, 15, 15, 15, 15, 15, 16, 17, 17, 18, 19

Max: 19; Min: 13

13. Anheuser-Busch spends the most on advertising and Coors spends the least. (Answers will vary.)

15. Tailgaters irk drivers the most, and too-cautious drivers irk drivers the least. (Answers will vary.)

17. Key: 6|7 = 67

```
6 | 7 8
7 | 3 5 5 6 9
8 | 0 0 2 3 5 5 7 7 8
9 | 0 1 1 1 2 4 5 5
```

It appears that most grades for the biology midterm were in the 80s or 90s. (Answers will vary.)

19. Key: 4|3 = 4.3

```
4 | 3 9
5 | 1 8 8 8 9
6 | 4 8 9 9 9
7 | 0 0 2 2 2 5
8 | 0 1
```

It appears that most ice had a thickness of 5.8 centimeters to 7.2 centimeters. (Answers will vary.)

21.

Advertisements

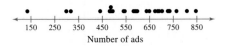

It appears that most of the 30 people from the U.S. see or hear between 450 and 750 advertisements per week. (Answers will vary.)

23.   **Countries in the United Nations**

Most countries in the United Nations come from Africa and the least amount come from South America. (Answers will vary.)

25.   **Airline Baggage Delay**

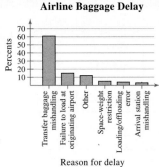

It appears that the biggest reason for baggage delay comes from transfer baggage mishandling. (Answers will vary.)

27.   **Hourly Wages**

It appears that there is no relation between wages and hours worked. (Answers will vary.)

29.   **Ultraviolet Index**

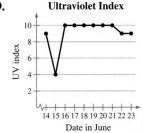

During the period from June 14–23 in Memphis, TN, the ultraviolet index was highest from June 16–21. (Answers will vary.)

31.

It appears the price of eggs peaked in 2003. (Answers will vary.)

33. (a) When data are taken at regular intervals over a period of time, a time series chart should be used. (Answers will vary.)

(b)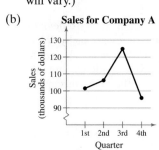

35. (a) At Law Firm A the lowest salary was $90,000 and the highest salary was $203,000; at Law Firm B the lowest salary was $90,000 and the highest salary was $190,000.

(b) There are 30 lawyers at Law Firm A and 32 lawyers at Law Firm B.

(c) At Law Firm A the salaries tend to be clustered at the far ends of the distribution range and at Law Firm B the salaries tend to fall in the middle of the distribution range.

Section 2.3 *(page 74)*

1. True

3. False. All quantitative data sets have a median.

5. False. When each data class has the same frequency, the distribution is uniform.

7. 3, 5, 4, 3, 14, 13, 12, 18 (Answers will vary.)

9. The shape of the distribution is skewed right because the bars have a "tail" to the right.

11. The shape of the distribution is uniform because the bars are approximately the same height.

13. (11), because the distribution of values ranges from 1 to 12 and has (approximately) equal frequencies.

15. (12), because the distribution has a maximum value of 90 and is skewed left due to a few students' scoring much lower than the majority of the students.

17. $\bar{x} \approx 6.2$; median = 6; mode = 5

19. $\bar{x} \approx 4.57$; median = 4.8; mode = 4.8

21. $\bar{x} \approx 20.66$; median = 20.05; mode = 18.8, 22.1, 26.7

23. $\bar{x}$ = not possible; median = not possible; mode = "Worse"; The mean and median cannot be found because the data are at the nominal level of measurement.

25. $\bar{x} \approx 170.63$; median = 169.3; mode = none; The mode cannot be found because no data points are repeated.

27. $\bar{x} = 22.6$; median = 19; mode = 14; The mode does not represent the center of the data because 14 is the smallest number in the data set.

29. $\bar{x} \approx 14.11$; median = 14.25; mode = 2.5; The mode does not represent the center of the data because 2.5 is much smaller than most of the data in the set.

31. $\bar{x} = 41.3$; median = 39.5; mode = 45

33. $\bar{x} \approx 19.5$; median = 20; mode = 15

35. The data are skewed right.

A = mode, because it is the data entry that occurred most often.

B = median, because the median is to the left of the mean in a skewed-right distribution.

C = mean, because the mean is to the right of the median in a skewed-right distribution.

37. Mode, because the data are at the nominal level of measurement.

39. Mean, because there are no outliers.

41. 89   **43.** $612.73   **45.** 2.8   **47.** 65 inches

49. 35.76 years old

51.

Class	Frequency, f	Midpoint
3–4	3	3.5
5–6	8	5.5
7–8	4	7.5
9–10	2	9.5
11–12	2	11.5
13–14	1	13.5
	$\Sigma f = 20$	

Positively skewed

A57

53.

Class	Frequency, f	Midpoint
62–64	3	63
65–67	7	66
68–70	9	69
71–73	8	72
74–76	3	75
	$\Sigma f = 30$	

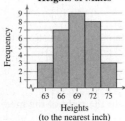

Heights of Males   Symmetric

Frequency

Heights
(to the nearest inch)

55. (a) $\bar{x} = 6.005$ (b) $\bar{x} = 5.945$

median = 6.01 median = 6.01

(c) Mean

57. (a) $\bar{x} = 358$, median = 375

(b) $\bar{x} = 1074$, median = 1125

(c) The mean and median in part (b) are three times the mean and median in part (a).

(d) If you multiply the mean and median from part (b) by 12, you will get the mean and median of the data set in inches.

59. Car A, because the midrange is the largest.

61. (a) 49.2

(b) $\bar{x} \approx 49.2$; median = 46.5; mode = 36, 37, 51; midrange = 50.5

(c) Using the trimmed mean eliminates potential outliers that could affect the mean of the entries.

Section 2.3 Activity *(page 81)*

1. The distribution is symmetric. The mean and median both decrease slightly. The median will decrease dramatically and the mean will also decrease, but to a lesser extent.

2. Neither the mean nor the median can be any of the points that were plotted. Since there are 10 points in each output region, the mean will fall somewhere between the two regions. By the same logic, the median will be the average of the greatest point between 0 and 0.75 and the smallest point between 20 and 25.

Section 2.4 *(page 92)*

1. Range = 8, $\mu = 7.9$, $\sigma^2 = 6.1$, $\sigma \approx 2.5$

3. Range = 12, $\bar{x} \approx 11.9$, $s^2 \approx 17.1$, $s \approx 4.1$

5. 73

7. The range is the difference between the maximum and minimum values of a data set. The advantage of the range is that it is easy to calculate. The disadvantage is that it uses only two entries from the data set.

9. The units of variance are squared. Its units are meaningless. (Example: dollars^2)

11. (a) Range = 24.3 (b) Range = 44.3

(c) Changing the maximum value of the data set greatly affects the range.

13. (a) has a standard deviation of 24 and (b) has a standard deviation of 16, because the data in (a) have more variability.

15. When calculating the population standard deviation, you divide the sum of the squared deviations by N then take the square root of that value. When calculating the sample standard deviation, you divide the sum of the squared deviations by $n - 1$, then take the square root of that value.

17. Company B

19. (a) Los Angeles: Range = 17.6; $s^2 \approx 37.35$; $s \approx 6.11$

Long Beach: Range = 8.7; $s^2 \approx 8.71$; $s \approx 2.95$

(b) It appears from the data that the annual salaries in Los Angeles are more variable than the salaries in Long Beach.

21. (a) Males: Range = 405; $s^2 \approx 16,225.3$; $s \approx 127.4$

Females: Range = 552; $s^2 \approx 34,575.1$; $s \approx 185.9$

(b) It appears from the data that the SAT scores for females are more variable than the SAT scores for males.

23. (a) Greatest sample standard deviation: (ii)

Data set (ii) has more entries that are farther away from the mean.

Least sample standard deviation: (iii)

Data set (iii) has more entries that are close to the mean.

(b) The three data sets have the same mean but have different standard deviations.

25. (a) Greatest sample standard deviation: (ii)

Data set (ii) has more entries that are farther away from the mean.

Least sample standard deviation: (iii)

Data set (iii) has more entries that are close to the mean.

(b) The three data sets have the same mean, median, and mode but have different standard deviations.

27. Similarity: Both estimate proportions of the data contained within k standard deviations of the mean.

Difference: The Empirical Rule assumes the distribution is bell-shaped; Chebychev's Theorem makes no such assumption.

29. 68% **31.** (a) 51 (b) 17

33. $1000, $2000 **35.** 24

37. $\bar{x} \approx 2.1$
$s \approx 1.3$

39.

Class	Midpoint, x	f	xf
2–4	3	4	12
5–7	6	8	48
8–10	9	15	135
11–13	12	4	48
14–16	15	1	15
		$N = 32$	$\Sigma xf = 258$

$x - \mu$	$(x - \mu)^2$	$(x - \mu)^2 f$
−5.1	26.01	104.04
−2.1	4.41	35.28
0.9	0.81	12.15
3.9	15.21	50.84
6.9	47.61	47.61
		$\Sigma(x - \mu)^2 f = 249.92$

$\mu \approx 8.1$
$\sigma \approx 2.8$

41.

f	Mid-point x	xf	$x - \bar{x}$	$(x - \bar{x})^2$	$(x - \bar{x})^2 f$
1	70.5	70.5	−44	1936	1936
12	92.5	1110.0	−22	484	5808
25	114.5	2862.5	0	0	0
10	136.5	1365.0	22	484	4840
2	158.5	317.0	44	1936	3872
$n = 50$		$\Sigma xf = 5725$			$\Sigma(x - \bar{x})^2 f = 16,456$

$\bar{x} = 114.5$
$s \approx 18.33$

43.

Class	f	Midpoint, x	xf
0–4	20.3	2.0	40.60
5–13	35.5	9.0	319.50
14–17	16.5	15.5	255.75
18–24	30.4	21.0	638.40
25–34	39.4	29.5	1162.30
35–44	39.0	39.5	1540.50
45–64	80.8	54.5	4403.60
65+	40.4	70.0	2828.00
	$n = 302.3$		$\Sigma xf = 11,188.65$

$x - \bar{x}$	$(x - \bar{x})^2$	$(x - \bar{x})^2 f$
−35.01	1225.70	24,881.71
−28.01	784.56	27,851.88
−21.51	462.68	7634.22
−16.01	256.32	7792.13
−7.51	56.40	2222.16
2.49	6.20	241.80
17.49	305.90	24,716.72
32.99	1088.34	43,968.94
		$\Sigma(x - \bar{x})^2 f = 139,309.56$

$\bar{x} \approx 37.01$
$s \approx 21.50$

45. $CV_{\text{heights}} = \dfrac{3.44}{72.75} \cdot 100 \approx 4.7$

$CV_{\text{weights}} = \dfrac{18.47}{187.83} \cdot 100 \approx 9.8$

It appears that weight is more variable than height.

47. (a) $\bar{x} \approx 41.5$, $s \approx 5.3$
(b) $\bar{x} \approx 43.6$, $s \approx 5.6$
(c) $\bar{x} \approx 3.5$, $s \approx 0.4$
(d) When each entry is multiplied by a constant k, the new sample mean is $k \cdot \bar{x}$, and the new sample standard deviation is $k \cdot s$.

49. (a) Males: 99.9, Females: 154.8; The mean absolute deviation is less than the sample standard deviation.
(b) Public: 1.45, Private: 1.11; The mean absolute deviation is less than the sample standard deviation.

51. (a) $P \approx -2.61$
The data are skewed left.
(b) $P \approx 4.12$
The data are skewed right.

Section 2.4 Activity *(page 100)*

1. When a point with a value of 15 is added, the mean remains constant and the standard deviation decreases; When a point with a value of 20 is added, the mean is raised and the standard deviation increases. (Answers will vary.)

2. To get the largest standard deviation, plot four of the points at 30 and four of the points at 40; To get the smallest standard deviation, plot all of the points at the same value.

Section 2.5 *(page 109)*

1. (a) $Q_1 = 4.5$, $Q_2 = 6$, $Q_3 = 7.5$

(b)

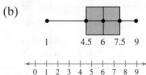

3. The soccer team scored fewer points per game than 75% of the teams in the league.

5. The student scored higher than 78% of the students who took the actuarial exam.

7. True

9. False. The 50th percentile is equivalent to Q_2.

11. (a) Min = 10   (b) Max = 20
    (c) $Q_1 = 13$ (d) $Q_2 = 15$
    (e) $Q_3 = 17$ (f) IQR = 4

13. (a) Min = 900   (b) Max = 2100
    (c) $Q_1 = 1250$ (d) $Q_2 = 1500$
    (e) $Q_3 = 1950$ (f) IQR = 700

15. (a) Min = −1.9   (b) Max = 2.1
    (c) $Q_1 = -0.5$ (d) $Q_2 = 0.1$
    (e) $Q_3 = 0.7$ (f) IQR = 1.2

17. None. The data are not skewed or symmetric.

19. Skewed left. Most of the data lie to the right on the box plot.

21. $Q_1 = B$, $Q_2 = A$, $Q_3 = C$, because about one quarter of the data fall on or below 17, 18.5 is the median of the entire data set, and about three quarters of the data fall on or below 20.

23. (a) $Q_1 = 2$, $Q_2 = 4$, $Q_3 = 5$

(b) **Watching Television**

Hours

25. (a) $Q_1 = 3$, $Q_2 = 3.85$, $Q_3 = 5.28$

(b) **Airline Distances**

Distances (in miles)

27. (a) 5   (b) 50%   (c) 25%

29. A → $z = -1.43$
B → $z = 0$
C → $z = 2.14$
A z-score of 2.14 would be unusual.

31. (a) Statistics: $z = \dfrac{73 - 63}{7} \approx 1.43$

Biology: $z = \dfrac{26 - 23}{3.9} \approx 0.77$

(b) The student did better on the statistics test.

33. (a) Statistics: $z = \dfrac{78 - 63}{7} \approx 2.14$

Biology: $z = \dfrac{29 - 23}{3.9} \approx 1.54$

(b) The student did better on the statistics test.

35. (a) $z_1 = \dfrac{34{,}000 - 35{,}000}{2250} \approx -0.44$

$z_2 = \dfrac{37{,}000 - 35{,}000}{2250} \approx 0.89$

$z_3 = \dfrac{31{,}000 - 35{,}000}{2250} \approx -1.78$

None of the selected tires have unusual life spans.

(b) For 30,500, 2.5th percentile
For 37,250, 84th percentile
For 35,000, 50th percentile

37. About 68.5 inches; 40% of the heights are below 68.5 inches.

39. $z_1 = \dfrac{74 - 69.6}{3.0} \approx 1.47$

$z_2 = \dfrac{62 - 69.6}{3.0} \approx -2.53$

$z_3 = \dfrac{80 - 69.6}{3.0} \approx 3.47$

The heights that are 62 and 80 inches are unusual.

41. $z = \dfrac{71.1 - 69.6}{3.0} \approx 0.5$

About the 70th percentile

43. (a) $Q_1 = 42$, $Q_2 = 49$, $Q_3 = 56$

(b) **Ages of Executives**

Ages

(c) Half of the ages are between 42 and 56 years.

(d) 49, because half of the executives are older and half are younger.

(e) The age groups 20–29, 70–79, and 80–89 would all be considered unusual because they lie more than two standard deviations from the mean.

45. 33.75   **47.** 19.8

49. The shape of your bill is symmetric and the shape of your friend's bill is uniform.

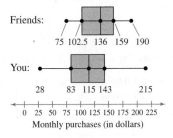

Credit Card Purchases

Friends:

75 102.5 136 159 190

You:

28   83   115 143   215

0   25   50   75   100 125 150 175 200 225

Monthly purchases (in dollars)

51. 94th percentile

Uses and Abuses for Chapter 2 *(page 115)*

1. Answers will vary.

2. The salaries of employees at a business could contain an outlier.

The median is not affected by an outlier because the median does not take into account the outlier's numerical value.

Review Answers for Chapter 2 *(page 117)*

1.

Class	Mid-point	Boundaries	Frequency, f	Rel freq	Cum freq
20–23	21.5	19.5–23.5	1	0.05	1
24–27	25.5	23.5–27.5	2	0.10	3
28–31	29.5	27.5–31.5	6	0.30	9
32–35	33.5	31.5–35.5	7	0.35	16
36–39	37.5	35.5–39.5	4	0.20	20
			$\Sigma f = 20$	$\Sigma \dfrac{f}{n} = 1$	

3. **Liquid Volume 12-oz Cans**

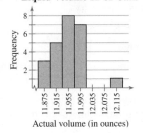

Frequency

11.875 11.915 11.955 11.995 12.035 12.075 12.115

Actual volume (in ounces)

5.

Class	Midpoint	Frequency, f
79–93	86	9
94–108	101	12
109–123	116	5
124–138	131	3
139–153	146	2
154–168	161	1
		$\Sigma f = 32$

Rooms Reserved

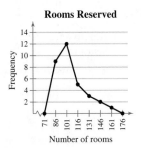

Frequency

71   86   101   116   131   146   161   176

Number of rooms

7.
1	3 7 8 9
2	0 1 2 3 3 3 3 4 4 5 5 5 7 8 8 9
3	1 1 2 3 4 5 7 8
4	3 4 7
5	1

9. **Height of Buildings**

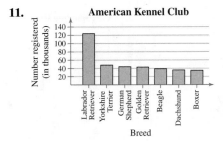

Number of stories

60
55
50
45
40
35
30
25
20

400   500   600   700   800

Height (in feet)

The number of stories appears to increase with height.

11. **American Kennel Club**

Number registered (in thousands)

140
120
100
80
60
40
20

Labrador Retriever, Yorkshire Terrier, German Shepherd, Golden Retriever, Beagle, Dachshund, Boxer

Breed

13. $\bar{x} = 9.1$; median $= 8.5$; mode $= 7$ **15.** 31.7   **17.** 82.1

19. Skewed   **21.** Skewed left   **23.** Median   **25.** 2.8

27. $\mu \approx 6.9$; $\sigma \approx 4.6$ **29.** $\bar{x} = 2453.4$; $s \approx 306.1$

31. Between \$41.50 and \$56.50   **33.** 30 customers

35. $\bar{x} \approx 2.5$; $s \approx 1.2$ **37.** 56 inches   **39.** 12 inches

41. 4   **43.** 23% scored higher than 68.

45. not unusual   **47.** not unusual

Chapter Quiz for Chapter 2 *(page 121)*

1. (a)

Class	Mid-point	Class boundaries	Frequency, f	Rel freq	Cum freq
101–112	106.5	100.5–112.5	3	0.12	3
113–124	118.5	112.5–124.5	11	0.44	14
125–136	130.5	124.5–136.5	7	0.28	21
137–148	142.5	136.5–148.5	2	0.08	23
149–160	154.5	148.5–160.5	2	0.08	25

(b) Frequency histogram and polygon

(c) Relative frequency histogram

(d) Skewed

(e)

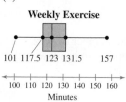

(f)

2. 125.2, 13.0

3. (a)

(b)

4. (a) $\bar{x} \approx 751.6$, median = 784.5, there is no mode

The mean best describes a typical salary because there are no outliers.

(b) 575; 48,135.1; 219.4

5. Between \$125,000 and \$185,000

6. (a) $z = 3.0$, unusual

(b) $z \approx -6.67$, very unusual

(c) $z \approx 1.33$

(d) $z = -2.2$, unusual

7. (a) $Q_1 = 76$, $Q_2 = 80$, $Q_3 = 88$ **(b)** 12

(c)

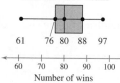

Real Statistics–Real Decisions for Chapter 2 *(page 122)*

1. (a) Find the average price of automobile insurance for each city and do a comparison.

(b) Find the mean, range, and sample standard deviation for each city.

2. (a) Construct a Pareto chart because the data are quantitative and a Pareto chart positions data in order of decreasing height, with the tallest bar positioned at the left.

(b)

Price of Insurance per City

(c) Yes. From the Pareto chart you can see that City A has the highest average automobile insurance premium followed by City B, City D, and City C.

3. (a) Find the mean, range, and sample standard deviation for each city.

(b)

City A	*City B*
$\bar{x} = \$2191.00$	$\bar{x} = \$2029.20$
$\sigma \approx \$351.86$	$\sigma \approx \$437.54$
range = \$1015.00	range = \$1336.00

City C	*City D*
$\bar{x} = \$1772.00$	$\bar{x} = \$1909.30$
$\sigma \approx \$418.52$	$\sigma \approx \$361.14$
range = \$1347.00	range = \$1125.00

(c) Yes. City A has the highest mean and lowest range and standard deviation.

4. (a) Tell your readers that on average, the price of automobile insurance premiums is higher in this city than in other cities.

(b) Location, weather, population

Cumulative Review Answers for Chapters 1–2 *(page 126)*

1. Systematic sample. A bias may enter this study if the machine makes a consistent error.

2. Random sample. A bias of this type of study is that the researchers did not include people without telephones.

3.

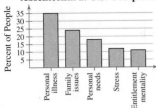

Absenteeism at U.S. Companies

4. Parameter. All of the company's employees are included.

5. Statistic. The 28% is a numerical description of the 1000 adults surveyed in the United States.

6. (a) 95%   (b) 38

7. Population: Collection of all adults in the United States

   Sample: Collection of the 1498 adults surveyed

8. Population: Collection of all people.

   Sample: Collection of the 232,606 people in the study.

9. Survey. A census would be a good way to investigate the years of service characteristic of all the 100 members of the Senate.

10. Experiment. An experiment could have a control group that has recess and a treatment group that has recess removed and a comparison of the differences.

11. Quantitative. The data are at the ratio level.

12. Qualitative. The data are at the nominal level.

13. $Q_1 = 2$, $Q_2 = 12.5$, $Q_3 = 39$

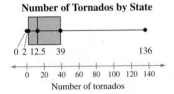

Number of Tornados by State

14. 88.9

15. (a) $\overline{x} \approx 5.49$, median $= 5.4$, no mode; Both the mean and the median accurately describe a typical American alligator tail length. (Answers will vary.)

   (b) range $= 4.1$, $s^2 = 2.34$, $s = 1.53$; The maximum difference in alligator tail lengths is about 4.1 feet and about 67% of alligator tail lengths will fall between 3.96 feet and 7.02 feet.

16. (a) An inference drawn from the sample is that the number of deaths due to heart disease for women will continue to decrease.

   (b) This inference may incorrectly imply that women will have less of a chance of dying of heart disease in the future.

17.

Class	Frequency, f	Mid-point	Relative frequency	Cumulative frequency
0–10	8	5	0.30	8
11–21	8	16	0.30	16
22–32	1	27	0.04	17
33–43	1	38	0.04	18
44–54	1	49	0.04	19
55–65	4	60	0.15	23
66–76	0	71	0.00	23
77–87	4	82	0.15	27
	$\Sigma f = 27$		$\Sigma \dfrac{f}{n} = 1$	

18. The distribution is skewed right.

19.

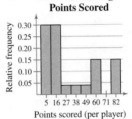

Detroit Redwings Points Scored

Classes with greatest frequency: 0–10 and 11–21

Class with least frequency: 66–76

CHAPTER 3

Section 3.1   *(page 142)*

1. (a) Could represent the probability of an event. The probability of an event occurring must be contained in the interval $[0, 1]$ or $[0\%, 100\%]$.

   (b) Could represent the probability of an event. The probability of an event occurring must be contained in the interval $[0, 1]$ or $[0\%, 100\%]$.

   (c) Could not represent the probability of an event. The probability of an event occurring cannot be less than 0.

   (d) Could represent the probability of an event. The probability of an event occurring must be contained in the interval $[0, 1]$ or $[0\%, 100\%]$.

   (e) Could represent the probability of an event. The probability of an event occurring must be contained in the interval $[0, 1]$ or $[0\%, 100\%]$.

   (f) Could not represent the probability of an event. The probability of an event occurring cannot be greater than 1.

3. The Fundamental Counting Principle counts the number of ways that two or more events can occur in sequence.

5. {A, B, C, D, E, F, G, H, I, J, K, L, M, N, O, P, Q, R, S, T, U, V, W, X, Y, Z}; 26

7. 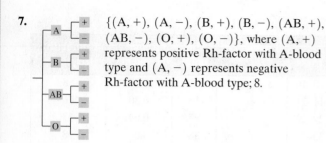 {(A, +), (A, −), (B, +), (B, −), (AB, +), (AB, −), (O, +), (O, −)}, where (A, +) represents positive Rh-factor with A-blood type and (A, −) represents negative Rh-factor with A-blood type; 8.

9. 1; Simple event because it is an event that consists of a single outcome.

11. 4; Not a simple event because it is an event that consists of more than a single outcome.

13. 135   **15.** 4500

17. False. If you roll a six-sided die six times, the probability of rolling an even number at least once is approximately 0.9844.

19. False. A probability of less than 0.05 indicates an unusual event.

21. b   **22.** d   **23.** c   **24.** a

25. Empirical probability because company records were used to calculate the frequency of a washing machine breaking down.

27. 0.159   **29.** 0.000953   **31.** 0.042   **33.** 0.208

35. (a) 1000   (b) 0.001   (c) 0.999

37. {(SSS), (SSR), (SRS), (SRR), (RSS), (RSR), (RRS), (RRR)}

39. {(SSR), (SRS), (RSS)}

41. (a)
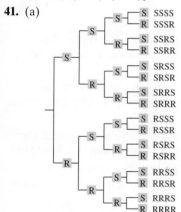

(b) {(SSSS), (SSSR), (SSRS), (SSRR), (SRSS), (SRSR), (SRRS), (SRRR), (RSSS), (RSSR), (RSRS), (RSRR), (RRSS), (RRSR), (RRRS), (RRRR)}

(c) {(SSSR), (SSRS), (SRSS), (RSSS)}

43. 0.500   **45.** 0.060   **47.** 0.959

49. 0.090   **51.** 0.236

53. (a) 0.5   (b) 0.25   (c) 0.25

55. 0.785   **57.** 0.215

59. (a) 0.739   (b) 0.269   (c) 0.008

61. The probability of choosing a tea drinker who does not have a college degree.

63. (a)

Sum	Probability
2	0.028
3	0.056
4	0.083
5	0.111
6	0.139
7	0.167
8	0.139
9	0.111
10	0.083
11	0.056
12	0.028

(b) Answers will vary.

(c) Answers will vary.

65. (a) 0.444   (b) 0.556   **67.** 3 : 1

Section 3.1 Activity   *(page 148)*

1–2. Answers will vary.

Section 3.2   *(page 154)*

1. Two events are independent if the occurrence of one of the events does not affect the probability of the occurrence of the other event.

If $P(B|A) = P(B)$ or $P(A|B) = P(A)$, then events A and B are independent.

3. False. If two events are independent, then $P(A|B) = P(A)$.

5. Independent. The outcome of the 1st card drawn does not affect the outcome of the 2nd card drawn.

7. Dependent. The sum of the rolls depends on which numbers were rolled first and second.

9. Events: depression, breathing-related sleep disorder; Dependent. People with depression are more likely to have a breathing-related sleep disorder.

11. Events: memory loss, use of Aspartame; Independent. The use of Aspartame does not cause memory loss.

13. (a) 0.8   (b) 0.0013

(c) Dependent.

$P(\text{developing breast cancer}|\text{gene})$

$\neq P(\text{developing breast cancer})$

15. (a) 0.308   (b) 0.390   (c) 0.807   (d) 0.315

(e) Dependent.

$P(\text{taking a summer vacation}|\text{family owns a computer})$

$\neq P(\text{taking a summer vacation})$

17. (a) 0.098

(b) 0.72

(c) No, the probability is not unusual because it is not less than or equal to 0.05.

19. 0.546

21. (a) 0.014   (b) 0.774   (c) 0.226

23. (a) 0.481 (b) 0.465 (c) 0.449

(d) Dependent.

$P($having less than one month's income saved$|$being male$)$

$\neq P($having less than one month's income saved$)$

25. (a) 0.0000000243 (b) 0.859 (c) 0.141

27. (a) 0.2 (b) 0.04 (c) 0.008 (d) 0.512 (e) 0.488

29. 0.011 **31.** 0.444 **33.** 0.167

35. (a) 0.074 (b) 0.999 **37.** 0.954

Section 3.3 *(page 165)*

1. $P(A \text{ and } B) = 0$ because A and B cannot occur at the same time.

3. True

5. False. The probability that event A or event B will occur is $P(A \text{ or } B) = P(A) + P(B) - P(A \text{ and } B)$.

7. Not mutually exclusive. The student can be taking both economics and statistics.

9. Not mutually exclusive. The worker can be female and have a college degree.

11. Mutually exclusive. The person cannot be in both age classes.

13. (a) Not mutually exclusive. For five weeks the events overlap.

(b) 0.423

15. (a) Not mutually exclusive. A carton can have a puncture and a smashed corner.

(b) 0.126

17. (a) 0.308 (b) 0.538 (c) 0.308

19. (a) 0.068 (b) 0.853 (c) 0.229

21. (a) 0.900 (b) 0.450

23. (a) 0.512 (b) 0.973 (c) 0.512

(d) Not mutually exclusive. A male can be a nursing major.

25. (a) 0.461 (b) 0.762 (c) 0.589 (d) 0.922

(e) Not mutually exclusive. A female can be frequently involved in charity work.

27. Answers will vary. **29.** 0.55

Section 3.3 Activity *(page 170)*

1. 0.3333 **2.** Answers will vary.

3. The theoretical probability is 0.5, so the green line should be placed there.

Section 3.4 *(page 178)*

1. The number of ordered arrangements of n objects taken r at a time. An example of a permutation is the number of seating arrangements of you and three of your friends.

3. False. A permutation is an ordered arrangement of objects.

5. True **7.** 210 **9.** 35 **11.** 134,596 **13.** 0.0060

15. Permutation. The order of the 15 people in line matters.

17. Combination. The order does not matter because the position of one captain is the same as the other.

19. 6240 **21.** 720 **23.** 20,358,520

25. 9,189,180 **27.** 50,400

29. (a) 720 (b) sample (c) 0.0014

31. (a) 12 (b) tree (c) 0.0833

33. (a) 907,200 (b) population (c) 0.000001

35. 0.0045

37. (a) 0.0164 (b) 0.385

39. (a) 70 (b) 16 (c) 0.086

41. (a) 67,600,000 (b) 19,656,000 (c) 0.000000015

43. (a) 120 (b) 12 (c) 12 (d) 0.4

45. 0.000039 **47.** 5.03×10^{-18}

49. (a) 658,008 (b) 0.00000152

51. (a) 0.0002 (b) 0.0014 (c) 0.0211 (d) 0.0659

53. 1001; 1000

55.

Team (worst team first)	1	2	3	4	5
Probability	0.250	0.199	0.156	0.119	0.088

Team (worst team first)	6	7	8	9	10
Probability	0.063	0.043	0.028	0.017	0.011

Team (worst team first)	11	12	13	14
Probability	0.008	0.007	0.006	0.005

57. 0.314

Uses and Abuses for Chapter 3 *(page 183)*

1. (a) 0.000001 (b) 0.001 (c) 0.001

2. Answers will vary.

1. Sample space:

   {HHHH, HHHT, HHTH, HHTT, HTHH, HTHT, HTTH,
   HTTT, THHH, THHT, THTH, THTT, TTHH, TTHT,
   TTTH, TTTT}; 4

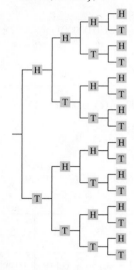

3. Sample space:

   {January, February, March, April, May, June, July, August,
   September, October, November, December}; 3

5. 84   **7.** Empirical probability

9. Subjective probability   **11.** Classical probability

13. 0.215   **15.** 1.25×10^{-7} **17.** 0.92

19. Independent   **21.** 0.025   **23.** Mutually exclusive

25. 0.60   **27.** 0.538   **29.** 0.583   **31.** 0.498

33. 0.23   **35.** 2730   **37.** 2380   **39.** 0.00000923

41. (a) 0.955   (b) 0.000000761   (c) 0.045

   (d) 0.999999239

Chapter Quiz for Chapter 3 *(page 189)*

1. (a) 0.524   (b) 0.515   (c) 0.536   (d) 0.773

   (e) 0.023   (f) 0.671   (g) 0.097   (h) 0.575

2. Not mutually exclusive. A golfer can score the best round
   in a four-round tournament and still lose the tournament.

   Dependent. One event can affect the occurrence of the
   second event.

3. (a) 518,665   (b) 1   (c) 551,299

4. (a) 0.941   (b) 0.00000181   (c) 0.999998

5. 450,000   **6.** 657,720

Real Statistics–Real Decisions for Chapter 3 *(page 190)*

1. (a) Answers will vary.

   (b) Use the Multiplication Rule, Fundamental Counting
   Principle, and Combinations.

2. If you played only the red ball, the probability of matching
   it is $\frac{1}{42}$. However, because you must pick five white balls,
   you must get the white balls wrong. So, using the
   Multiplication Rule, you get

   P(matching only the red ball and not matching any of the
   five white balls)

   $$= \tfrac{1}{42} \cdot \tfrac{50}{55} \cdot \tfrac{49}{54} \cdot \tfrac{48}{53} \cdot \tfrac{47}{52} \cdot \tfrac{46}{51}$$

   $$\approx 0.015$$

   $$\approx \tfrac{1}{69}.$$

3. The overall probability of winning a prize is determined by
   calculating the number of ways to win and dividing by the
   total number of outcomes.

   To calculate the number of ways to win something, you
   must use combinations.

CHAPTER 4

Section 4.1 *(page 201)*

1. A random variable represents a numerical value assigned
   to an outcome of a probability experiment.

   Examples: Answers will vary.

3. An expected value of 0 represents the break-even point,
   so the accountant will not gain or lose any money.

5. False. In most applications, discrete random variables
   represent counted data, whereas continuous random
   variables represent measured data.

7. True

9. Discrete because home attendance is a random variable
   that is countable.

11. Continuous because annual vehicle-miles driven is a
   random variable that cannot be counted.

13. Discrete because number of motorcycle accidents in one
   year in California is a random variable that is countable.

15. Continuous because volume of blood drawn for a blood
   test is a random variable that cannot be counted.

17. Discrete because number of home theater systems sold per
   month at an electronics store is a random variable that is
   countable.

19. Continuous because the amount of snow that fell in Nome,
   Alaska last winter is a random variable that cannot be
   counted.

21. (a) 0.35   (b) 0.90   **23.** 0.22   **25.** Yes

27. No, $\sum P(x) = 0.95$ and $P(5) < 0$.

29. (a)

x	P(x)
0	0.686
1	0.195
2	0.077
3	0.022
4	0.013
5	0.006
	$\sum P(x) \approx 1$

(b) 0.5   (c) 0.8   (d) 0.9

(e) A household on average has 0.5 dog with a standard deviation of 0.9 dog.

31. (a)

x	P(x)
0	0.432
1	0.403
2	0.137
3	0.029
	$\sum P(x) \approx 1$

(b) 0.8   (c) 0.6   (d) 0.8

(e) A household on average has 0.8 computer with a standard deviation of 0.8 computer.

33. (a)

x	P(x)
0	0.031
1	0.063
2	0.151
3	0.297
4	0.219
5	0.156
6	0.083
	$\sum P(x) = 1$

(b) 3.4   (c) 2.1   (d) 1.5

(e) An employee works an average of 3.4 overtime hours per week with a standard deviation of 1.5 hours.

35. (a) 5.3   (b) 3.3   (c) 1.8   (d) 5.3

(e) The expected number of questions answered correctly is 5.3 with a standard deviation of 1.8 questions.

37. (a) 2.0   (b) 1.0   (c) 1.0   (d) 2.0

(e) The expected category of hurricane that hit the U.S. is 2.0 with a standard deviation of 1.0.

39. (a) 2.5   (b) 1.9   (c) 1.4   (d) 2.5

(e) The expected number of persons in a household is 2.5 with a standard deviation of 1.4 persons.

41. (a) 0.881   (b) 0.314   (c) 0.294

43. A household with three dogs is unusual because the probability of this event is 0.022.

45. −$0.05   **47.** $38,800   **49.** 3038; 26

Section 4.2 *(page 215)*

1. (a) $p = 0.50$ (b) $p = 0.20$ (c) $p = 0.80$

3. (a) $n = 12$ (b) $n = 4$ (c) $n = 8$

As n increases, the distribution becomes more symmetric.

5. (a) $x = 0, 1$ (b) $x = 0, 5$ (c) $x = 4, 5$

7. Binomial experiment

Success: baby recovers

$n = 5, p = 0.80, q = 0.20, x = 0, 1, 2, \ldots, 5$

9. Binomial experiment

Success: selecting an adult who thinks tax cuts hurt the economy

$n = 15, p = 0.21, q = 0.79, x = 0, 1, 2, \ldots, 15$

11. 24; 16.8; 4.1   **13.** 32.2; 23.9; 4.9

15. (a) 0.088   (b) 0.104   (c) 0.896

17. (a) 0.111   (b) 0.152   (c) 0.848

19. (a) 0.213   (b) 0.139   (c) 0.861

21. (a) 0.028   (b) 0.964   (c) 0.008

23. (a) 0.255   (b) 0.562   (c) 0.783

25. (a) $n = 6, p = 0.37$ (b)

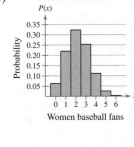
Women Baseball Fans

x	P(x)
0	0.063
1	0.220
2	0.323
3	0.253
4	0.112
5	0.026
6	0.003

(c) Skewed right   (d) 2.2   (e) 1.4   (f) 1.2

(g) On average, 2.2 out of 6 women would consider themselves baseball fans, with a standard deviation of 1.2 women. The values $x = 5$ and $x = 6$ would be unusual because their probabilities are less than 0.05.

27. (a) $n = 4, p = 0.05$ (b)

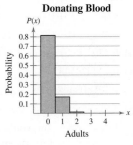
Donating Blood

x	P(x)
0	0.814506
1	0.171475
2	0.013537
3	0.000475
4	0.000006

(c) Skewed right   (d) 0.2   (e) 0.2   (f) 0.4

(g) On average, 0.2 eligible adult out of every 4 give blood. The standard deviation is 0.4 adult.

$x = 2, 3$, and 4 would be unusual because of their low probabilities.

29. (a) $n = 6$, $p = 0.29$ (b) 0.321   (c) 0.010

x	$P(x)$
0	0.128
1	0.314
2	0.321
3	0.175
4	0.053
5	0.009
6	0.001

31. 1.7; 1.1

On average, 1.7 out of 6 drivers name talking on cell phones as the most annoying habit of other drivers.

Five of the six or all of the six randomly selected drivers naming talking on cell phones as the most annoying habit of other drivers would be unusual because their probabilities are less than 0.05.

33. 0.033

4.2 Activity   *(page 220)*

1–3. Answers will vary.

Section 4.3   *(page 226)*

1. 0.24   **3.** 0.056   **5.** 0.195   **7.** 0.251

9. In a binomial distribution, the value of x represents the number of successes in n trials and in a geometric distribution the value of x represents the first trial that results in a success.

11. Geometric. You are interested in counting the number of trials until the first success.

13. Poisson. You are interested in counting the number of occurrences that take place within a given unit of space.

15. Binomial. You are interested in counting the number of successes out of n trials.

17. (a) 0.082   (b) 0.469   (c) 0.531

19. (a) 0.002   (b) 0.006   (c) 0.980

21. (a) 0.101   (b) 0.185   (c) 0.084

23. (a) 0.329   (b) 0.878   (c) 0.122

25. (a) 0.1254235482

(b) 0.1254084986; The results are approximately the same.

27. (a) 1000; 999,000; 999.5

On average you would have to play 1000 times until you won the lottery. The standard deviation is 999.5 times.

(b) 1000 times

Lose money. On average you would win $500 every 1000 times you play the lottery. So, the net gain would be −$500.

29. (a) 3.8; 1.9; The standard deviation is 1.9 strokes.

(b) 0.305

Uses and Abuses for Chapter 4   *(page 229)*

1. 40, 0.081

2. 0.739; Answers will vary.

3. The probability of finding 36 adults out of 100 who prefer Brand A is 0.059. So, the manufacturer's claim is hard to believe.

4. The probability of finding 25 adults out of 100 who prefer Brand A is 0.000627. So, the manufacturer's claim is not believable.

Review Answers for Chapter 4   *(page 231)*

1. Discrete   **3.** Continuous   **5.** No, $\sum P(x) \neq 1$.

7. Yes   **9.** Yes

11. (a)

x	f	$P(x)$
2	3	0.005
3	12	0.018
4	72	0.111
5	115	0.177
6	169	0.260
7	120	0.185
8	83	0.128
9	48	0.074
10	22	0.034
11	6	0.009
	$n = 650$	$\sum P(x) \approx 1$

(b)

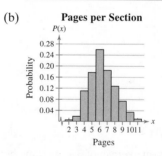

Pages per Section

(c) 6.4, 2.9, 1.7

13. (a)

x	f	$P(x)$
0	3	0.015
1	38	0.190
2	83	0.415
3	52	0.260
4	18	0.090
5	5	0.025
6	1	0.005
	$n = 200$	$\sum P(x) = 1$

(b)

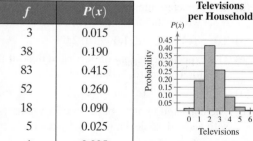

Televisions per Household

(c) 2.3, 1.1, 1.0

A68

15. 3.4

17. Yes, $n = 12$, $p = 0.24$, $q = 0.76$, $x = 0, 1, \ldots, 12$

19. (a) 0.208   (b) 0.322 (*Tech:* 0.321)   (c) 0.114

21. (a) 0.294   (b) 0.644   (c) 0.350

23. (a)

x	P(x)
0	0.007
1	0.059
2	0.201
3	0.342
4	0.291
5	0.099

(b)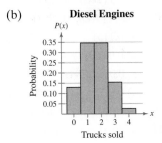

Renting Movies

(c) 3.2, 1.2, 1.1

25. (a)

x	P(x)
0	0.130
1	0.346
2	0.346
3	0.154
4	0.026

(b)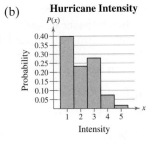

Diesel Engines

(c) 1.6, 1.0, 1.0

27. (a) 0.096   (b) 0.518   (c) 0.579

29. (a) 0.830 (*Tech:* 0.829)   (b) 0.155   (c) 0.015

Chapter Quiz for Chapter 4   *(page 235)*

1. (a) Discrete because the random variable is countable.

(b) Continuous because the random variable has an infinite number of possible outcomes and cannot be counted.

2. (a)

x	f	P(x)
1	70	0.398
2	41	0.233
3	49	0.278
4	13	0.074
5	3	0.017
	$n = 176$	$\sum P(x) = 1$

(b) Hurricane Intensity

(c) 2.1, 1.1, 1.1

On average, the intensity of a hurricane will be 2.1 with a standard deviation of 1.1.

(d) 0.091

3. (a) $n = 8$, $p = 0.80$

x	P(x)
0	0.000003
1	0.000082
2	0.001147
3	0.009175
4	0.045875
5	0.146801
6	0.293601
7	0.335544
8	0.167772

(b)

Successful Surgeries

(c) 6.4, 1.3, 1.1; The average number of successful surgeries out of 8 is 6.4, with a standard deviation of 1.1 surgeries.

(d) 0.001

(e) 0.000084

4. (a) 0.176   (b) 0.440   (c) 0.007

Real Statistics–Real Decisions for Chapter 4   *(page 236)*

1. (a) Answers will vary. For example, calculate the probability of obtaining zero clinical pregnancies out of 10 randomly selected ART cycles.

(b) Binomial. The distribution is discrete because the number of clinical pregnancies is countable.

2. $n = 10$, $p = 0.337$, $P(0) = 0.0164$

x	P(x)
0	0.0164
1	0.0834
2	0.1908
3	0.2586
4	0.2300
5	0.1403
6	0.0594
7	0.0173
8	0.0033
9	0.0004
10	0.00002

3. (a) Suspicious, because the probability is very small.

(b) Not suspicious, because the probability is not that small.

CHAPTER 5

Section 5.1   *(page 248)*

1. Answers will vary.

3. Answers will vary.

Similarities: The two curves will have the same line of symmetry.

Differences: One curve will be more spread out than the other.

5. $\mu = 0$, $\sigma = 1$

7. "The" standard normal distribution is used to describe one specific normal distribution ($\mu = 0$, $\sigma = 1$). "A" normal distribution is used to describe a normal distribution with any mean and standard deviation.

9. No, the graph crosses the x-axis.

11. Yes, the graph fulfills the properties of the normal distribution.

13. No, the graph is skewed right.

15. It is normal because it is bell-shaped and symmetric.

17. 0.3849   **19.** 0.6247   **21.** 0.9131   **23.** 0.975

25. 0.7422   **27.** 0.1003   **29.** 0.005   **31.** 0.0532

33. 0.4382   **35.** 0.437   **37.** 0.95

39. 0.2006 (*Tech:* 2005)

41. (a)

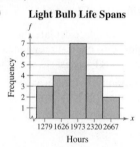

Light Bulb Life Spans

It is reasonable to assume that the life span is normally distributed because the histogram is nearly symmetric and bell-shaped.

(b) 1941.35, 432.385

(c) The sample mean of 1941.35 hours is less than the claimed mean, so, on average, the bulbs in the sample lasted for a shorter time. The sample standard deviation of 432 hours is greater than the claimed standard deviation, so the bulbs in the sample had a greater variation in life span than the manufacturer's claim.

43. (a) A = 92.994; B = 93.004; C = 93.014; D = 93.018

(b) 0.8; 1.6; −1.2; −3.2

(c) $x = 92.994$ is very unusual due to a relatively small z-score (−3.2).

45. (a) A = 1186; B = 1406; C = 1848; D = 2177

(b) −0.36; 1.07; 2.14; −1.08

(c) $x = 2177$ is unusual due to a relatively large z-score (2.14).

47. 0.6915   **49.** 0.05   **51.** 0.5328   **53.** 0.9265

55. 0.8289   **57.** 0.3133   **59.** 0.901 (*Tech:* 0.9011)

61. 0.0098 (*Tech:* 0.0099)

63.

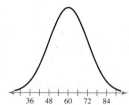

The normal distribution curve is centered at its mean (60) and has 2 points of inflection (48 and 72) representing $\mu \pm \sigma$.

65. (a) Answers will vary. *Sample answer:*

Area under curve = area of rectangle = (1)(1) = 1

(b) 0.25   (c) 0.4

Section 5.2   (*page 256*)

1. 0.1151   **3.** 0.1151   **5.** 0.1144

7. 0.3155 (*Tech:* 0.3159)   **9.** 0.2789 (*Tech:* 0.2785)

11. 0.1989 (*Tech:* 0.1987)

13. (a) 0.1151   (b) 0.673 (*Tech:* 0.6731)   (c) 0.2119

15. (a) 0.0475 (*Tech:* 0.0470)   (b) 0.7051 (*Tech:* 0.7035)

(c) 0.0351 (*Tech:* 0.0348)

17. (a) 0.0228   (b) 0.927   (c) 0.0013

19. (a) 0.0073   (b) 0.7215 (*Tech:* 0.7218)   (c) 0.0228

21. (a) 80.51% (*Tech:* 80.47%)

(b) 337 scores (*Tech:* 339 scores)

23. (a) 65.17% (*Tech:* 65.21%)   (b) 16 women

25. (a) 30.85%   (b) 32 fish

27. (a) 99.87%   (b) 1 adult

29. 1.5% (*Tech:* 1.51%); It is unusual for a battery to have a life span that is more than 2065 hours because of the relatively large z-score (2.17).

31. Out of control, because there is a point more than three standard deviations beyond the mean.

33. Out of control, because there are nine consecutive points below the mean, and two out of three consecutive points lie more than two standard deviations from the mean.

Section 5.3   (*page 266*)

1. 0.70   **3.** 0.34   **5.** −0.16   **7.** 2.39

9. −1.645   **11.** 1.555   **13.** −2.33   **15.** −0.84

17. 1.175   **19.** −0.67   **21.** 0.67   **23.** −0.39

25. −0.38   **27.** −0.58   **29.** −1.645, 1.645

31. −1.18   **33.** 1.18   **35.** −1.28, 1.28   **37.** −0.06, 0.06

39. (a) 68.56 inches   (b) 62.28 inches (*Tech:* 62.27 inches)

41. (a) 11.98 pounds (*Tech:* 11.97 pounds)

(b) 19.78 pounds (*Tech:* 19.80 pounds)

43. (a) 139.22 days (*Tech:* 139.32 days)

(b) 96.92 days (*Tech:* 96.88 days)

45. 19.88 ounces

47. Tires that wear out by 26,800 miles (*Tech:* 26,796 miles) will be replaced free of charge.

49. 7.93 ounces

Section 5.4 *(page 278)*

1. 100, 2.121　**3.** 100, 0.949

5. False. As the size of a sample increases, the mean of the distribution of sample means does not change.

7. False. A sampling distribution is normal if either $n \geq 30$ or the population is normal.

9.

Sample	Mean	Sample	Mean	Sample	Mean
0, 0, 0	0	2, 2, 4	2.67	4, 8, 0	4
0, 0, 2	0.67	2, 2, 8	4	4, 8, 2	4.67
0, 0, 4	1.33	2, 4, 0	2	4, 8, 4	5.33
0, 0, 8	2.67	2, 4, 2	2.67	4, 8, 8	6.67
0, 2, 0	0.67	2, 4, 4	3.33	8, 0, 0	2.67
0, 2, 2	1.33	2, 4, 8	4.67	8, 0, 2	3.33
0, 2, 4	2	2, 8, 0	3.33	8, 0, 4	4
0, 2, 8	3.33	2, 8, 2	4	8, 0, 8	5.33
0, 4, 0	1.33	2, 8, 4	4.67	8, 2, 0	3.33
0, 4, 2	2	2, 8, 8	6	8, 2, 2	4
0, 4, 4	2.67	4, 0, 0	1.33	8, 2, 4	4.67
0, 4, 8	4	4, 0, 2	2	8, 2, 8	6
0, 8, 0	2.67	4, 0, 4	2.67	8, 4, 0	4
0, 8, 2	3.33	4, 0, 8	4	8, 4, 2	4.67
0, 8, 4	4	4, 2, 0	2	8, 4, 4	5.33
0, 8, 8	5.33	4, 2, 2	2.67	8, 4, 8	6.67
2, 0, 0	0.67	4, 2, 4	3.33	8, 8, 0	5.33
2, 0, 2	1.33	4, 2, 8	4.67	8, 8, 2	6
2, 0, 4	2	4, 4, 0	2.67	8, 8, 4	6.67
2, 0, 8	3.33	4, 4, 2	3.33	8, 8, 8	8
2, 2, 0	1.33	4, 4, 4	4		
2, 2, 2	2	4, 4, 8	5.33		

$\mu = 3.5$, $\sigma = 2.958$

$\mu_{\bar{x}} = 3.5$, $\sigma_{\bar{x}} = 1.708$

The means are equal but the standard deviation of the sampling distribution is smaller.

11. (c), because $\mu_{\bar{x}} = 16.5$, $\sigma_{\bar{x}} = 1.19$, and the graph approximates a normal curve.

13. 0.8962 (*Tech:* 0.8967); not unusual　**15.** 0.0132; unusual

17. 87.5, 1.804

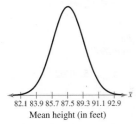

Mean height (in feet)

19. 224, 1.265

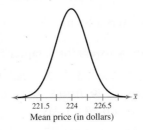

Mean price (in dollars)

21. 110, 8.609

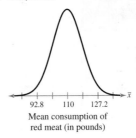

Mean consumption of red meat (in pounds)

23. 87.5, 1.276; 87.5, 1.042

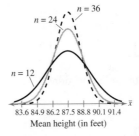

Mean height (in feet)

As the sample size increases, the standard error decreases, while the mean of the sample means remains constant.

25. 0.0009　**27.** ≈ 1　**29.** ≈ 0

31. It is more likely to select a sample of 20 women with a mean height less than 70 inches because the sample of 20 has a higher probability.

33. Yes, it is very unlikely that you would have randomly sampled 40 cans with a mean equal to 127.9 ounces, because it is more than 2 standard deviations from the mean of the sample means.

35. (a) 0.0008　(b) Claim is inaccurate.

(c) No, assuming the manufacturer's claim is true, because 96.25 is within 1 standard deviation of the mean for an individual board.

37. (a) 0.0002　(b) Claim is inaccurate.

(c) No, assuming the manufacturer's claim is true, because 49,721 is within 1 standard deviation of the mean for an individual tire.

39. No, because the z-score (0.74) is not unusual.

41. Yes the finite correction factor should be used; ≈ 0 (*Tech:* 0.00001)

43.

Sample	Number of boys from 3 births	Proportion of boys from 3 births
bbb	3	1
bbg	2	$\frac{2}{3}$
bgb	2	$\frac{2}{3}$
gbb	2	$\frac{2}{3}$
bgg	1	$\frac{1}{3}$
gbg	1	$\frac{1}{3}$
ggb	1	$\frac{1}{3}$
ggg	0	0

45.

Sample	Numerical representation	Sample mean
bbb	111	1
bbg	110	$\frac{2}{3}$
bgb	101	$\frac{2}{3}$
gbb	011	$\frac{2}{3}$
bgg	100	$\frac{1}{3}$
gbg	010	$\frac{1}{3}$
ggb	001	$\frac{1}{3}$
ggg	000	0

The sample means are equal to the proportions.

47. 0.1357 (*Tech:* 0.1367)

Section 5.4 Activity   *(page 284)*

1–2. Answers will vary.

Section 5.5   *(page 291)*

1. Cannot use normal distribution.

3. Cannot use normal distribution.

5. Cannot use normal distribution because $nq < 5$.

7. Cannot use normal distribution because $nq < 5$.

9. d   **10.** b   **11.** a   **12.** c

13. a   **14.** d   **15.** c   **16.** b

17. Binomial: 0.549 (*Tech:* 0.5495); Normal: 0.5463 (*Tech:* 0.5466)

19. Cannot use normal distribution for (a)–(c) because $np < 5$.
   (a) 0.0000199   (b) 0.000023   (c) 0.999977
   (d) 0.1635 (*Tech:* 0.1636)

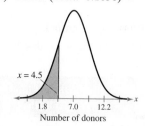

21. Can use normal distribution.
   (a) 0.0692 (*Tech:* 0.0691)   (b) 0.8770 (*Tech:* 0.8771)

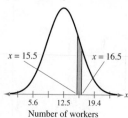

(c) 0.8078 (*Tech:* 0.8080)   (d) 0.8212 (*Tech:* 0.8221)

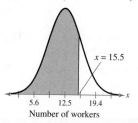
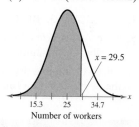

23. Can use normal distribution.
   (a) 0.8023 (*Tech:* 0.8036)   (b) 0.8508 (*Tech:* 0.8518)

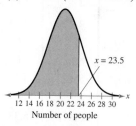
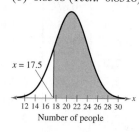

(c) 0.5359 (*Tech:* 0.5378)   (d) 0.1635 (*Tech:* 0.1632)

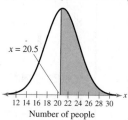
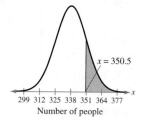

25. (a) $np = 6 \geq 5$
      $nq = 19 \geq 5$
   (b) 0.121 (*Tech:* 0.1209)
   (c) No, because the z-score (0.94) is within one standard deviation of the mean.

27. Highly unlikely. Answers will vary.

29. 0.1020

Uses and Abuses for Chapter 5   *(page 295)*

1. (a) Not unusual; A sample mean of 115 is less than 2 standard deviations from the population mean.
   (b) Not unusual; A sample mean of 105 lies within 2 standard deviations of the population mean.

2. The ages of students at a high school may not be normally distributed.

3. Answers will vary.

Review Answers for Chapter 5   *(page 297)*

1. $\mu = 15, \sigma = 3$ **3.** $-2.25; 0.5; 2; 3.5$ **5.** 0.6293

7. 0.3936   **9.** 0.0465   **11.** 0.4495

13. 0.4365 (*Tech:* 0.4364)

15. 0.1336   **17.** 0.8997   **19.** 0.9236 (*Tech:* 0.9237)

21. 0.0124   **23.** (a) 0.3156   (b) 0.3099   (c) 0.3446
25. −0.07   **27.** 1.13   **29.** 1.04   **31.** 46 meters
33. 56.113 meters (*Tech:* 56.112 meters)
35. 55.2 meters (*Tech:* 55.204 meters)
37. $\mu = 176$, $\sigma = 73.919$

$\mu_{\bar{x}} = 176$, $\sigma_{\bar{x}} \approx 42.677$

The means are the same, but $\sigma_{\bar{x}}$ is less than σ.

39. 144.3, 8.722

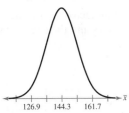

Mean consumption (in pounds)

41. (a) 0.0485 (*Tech:* 0.0482)

(b) 0.8180

(c) 0.0823 (*Tech:* 0.0829)

(a) and (c) are smaller, (b) is larger. This is to be expected because the standard error of the sample means is smaller.

43. (a) 0.1867 (*Tech:* 0.1855)   (b) ≈ 0

45. 0.0019 (*Tech:* 0.0018)

47. Cannot use normal distribution because $nq < 5$.

49. $P(x > 24.5)$ **51.** $P(44.5 < x < 45.5)$

53. Can use normal distribution.

≈ 0 (*Tech:* 0.0002)

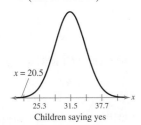

$x = 20.5$

Children saying yes

Chapter Quiz for Chapter 5   (*page 301*)

1. (a) 0.9821   (b) 0.9994
(c) 0.9802   (d) 0.8135 (*Tech:* 0.8134)

2. (a) 0.9198 (*Tech:* 0.9199)   (b) 0.1940 (*Tech:* 0.1938)
(c) 0.0456 (*Tech:* 0.0455)

3. 0.2090 (*Tech:* 0.2087)   **4.** 0.4663 (*Tech:* 0.4667)

5. 85.99% (*Tech:* 86.02%)   **6.** 787 students

7. 351   **8.** 265   **9.** 0.0183 (*Tech:* 0.0182)

10. More likely to select one student with a test score greater than 300 because the standard error of the mean is less than the standard deviation.

11. Can use normal distribution.

$\mu = 18$, $\sigma \approx 2.121$

12. 0.1190 (*Tech:* 0.1193)

Real Statistics–Real Decisions for Chapter 5   (*page 302*)

1. (a) 0.4207   (b) 0.9988 (*Tech:* 0.9990)

2. (a) 0.3264 (*Tech:* 0.3274)   (b) 0.6944 (*Tech:* 0.6957)
(c) mean

3. Answers will vary.

Cumulative Review Answers for Chapter 3–5   (*page 304*)

1. (a) Answers will vary. *Sample answer:* $np = 16.8 > 5$, $nq = 13.2 > 5$

(b) 0.1977 (*Tech:* 0.1988)

(c) No, because the probability is greater than 0.05.

2. (a) 3.1   (b) 1.5   (c) 1.2   (d) 3.1

(e) A family household size on average is 3.1 persons with a standard deviation of 1.2 persons.

3. (a) 3.6   (b) 1.9   (c) 1.4   (d) 3.6

(e) The number of fouls for a player in a game on average is 3.6 fouls with a standard deviation of 1.4 fouls.

4. (a) 0.476   (b) 0.78   (c) 0.659

5. (a) 43,680   (b) 0.0192

6. 0.9382   **7.** 0.0010   **8.** 0.7995

9. 0.4990   **10.** 0.2862   **11.** 0.5905

12. (a) 0.1108   (b) 0.9521   (c) 0.0479

13. (a) 0.0048   (b) 0.0149   (c) 0.9511

14. (a) 0.2240   (b) 0.8785

(c) Dependent. $P($being a public school teacher $|$ having 20 years or more of full-time teaching experience$) \neq P($being a public school teacher$)$

(d) 0.9084   (e) 0.4099

15. (a) 70, 0.1897   (b) 0.0006

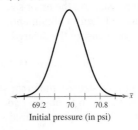

Initial pressure (in psi)

16. (a) 0.0548   (b) 0.6547   (c) 52.2 months

17. (a) 495   (b) 0.0020

18. (a) 0.1790   (b) 0.8921   (c) 0.9916

CHAPTER 6

Section 6.1   (*page 317*)

1. You are more likely to be correct using an interval estimate because it is unlikely that a point estimate will exactly equal the population mean.

3. d; As the level of confidence increases, z_c increases causing wider intervals.

5. 1.28 **7.** 1.15 **9.** -0.47 **11.** 1.76 **13.** -0.6

15. 0.685 **17.** 0.192 **19.** c **20.** d **21.** b **22.** a

23. (14.8, 15.6) **25.** (4.18, 4.36) **27.** 0.115, 0.379

29. 0.165, 1.88 **31.** 126 **33.** 7 **35.** 0.7, 2.8

37. (614.41, 647.39); (611.25, 650.55)

The 95% CI is wider.

39. (87.0, 111.6); (84.7, 113.9)

The 95% CI is wider.

41. (114.58, 125.42)

43. (116.17, 123.83)

The $n = 40$ CI is wider because a smaller sample is taken, giving less information about the population.

45. (3.09, 3.15)

47. (3.10, 3.14)

The $s = 0.09$ CI is wider because of the increased variability within the sample.

49. (a) An increase in the level of confidence will widen the confidence interval.

(b) An increase in the sample size will narrow the confidence interval.

(c) An increase in the standard deviation will widen the confidence interval.

51. (8.4, 9.7); (8.1, 10.1) **53.** 89

The 99% CI is wider.

55. (a) 121 servings (b) 208 servings

The 99% CI requires a larger sample because more information is needed from the population to be 99% confident.

57. (a) 32 cans (b) 87 cans

$E = 0.15$ requires a larger sample size. As the error size decreases, a larger sample must be taken to obtain enough information from the population to ensure the desired accuracy.

59. (a) 16 sheets (b) 62 sheets

$E = 0.0625$ requires a larger sample size. As the error size decreases, a larger sample must be taken to obtain enough information from the population to ensure the desired accuracy.

61. (a) 42 soccer balls (b) 60 soccer balls

$\sigma = 0.3$ requires a larger sample size. Due to the increased variability in the population, a larger sample size is needed to ensure the desired accuracy.

63. (a) An increase in the level of confidence will increase the minimum sample size required.

(b) An increase (larger E) in the error tolerance will decrease the minimum sample size required.

(c) An increase in the population standard deviation will increase the minimum sample size required.

65. (234.1, 243.4)

With 95% confidence, you can say that the population mean airfare price for a one-way ticket from Atlanta, GA to Pittsburgh, PA is between $234.10 and $243.40.

67. (14.902, 16.665)

With 95% confidence, you can say that the population mean annual precipitation for Anchorage, Alaska is between 14.902 inches and 16.665 inches.

69. (a) 0.707 (b) 0.949 (c) 0.962 (d) 0.975

(e) The finite population correction factor approaches 1 when the sample size decreases and the population size remains the same.

71. *Sample Answer:*

$$E = \frac{z_c \sigma}{\sqrt{n}} \qquad \text{Write original equation}$$

$$E\sqrt{n} = z_c \sigma \qquad \text{Multiply each side by } \sqrt{n}.$$

$$\sqrt{n} = \frac{z_c \sigma}{E} \qquad \text{Divide each side by } E.$$

$$n = \left(\frac{z_c \sigma}{E}\right)^2 \qquad \text{Square each side.}$$

Section 6.2 *(page 330)*

1. 1.833 **3.** 2.947 **5.** 2.7 **7.** 1.2

9. (a) (10.9, 14.1) (b) The t-CI is wider.

11. (a) (4.1, 4.5)

(b) When rounded to the nearest tenth, the normal CI and the t-CI have the same width.

13. (59.48, 90.52); 15.52

15. (61.85, 88.15); 13.15

The t-CI is wider.

17. (a) (3.84, 5.24) (b) (4.45, 4.63); The t-CI is wider.

19. (a) 4460.16

(b) 146.143

(c) (4309.96, 4610.36) [*Tech:* (4310, 4610.3)]

21. (a) 1767.7 (b) 252.2 (c) (1541.5, 1993.8)

23. Use normal distribution because $n \geq 30$.

(1.24, 1.26)

25. Use t-distribution because $n < 30$, the miles per gallon are normally distributed, and σ is unknown.

(20.5, 23.3) [*Tech:* (20.5, 23.4)]

27. Cannot use normal or t-distribution because $n < 30$ and the times are not normally distributed.

29. No; They are not making good tennis balls because the desired bounce height of 55.5 inches is not contained between 55.9 and 56.1 inches.

Activity 6.2 *(page 333)*

1–2. Answers will vary.

Section 6.3 *(page 339)*

1. False. To estimate the value of p, the population proportion of successes, use the point estimate $\hat{p} = x/n$.

3. $0.750, 0.250$ **5.** $0.663, 0.337$ **7.** $0.170, 0.830$

9. $0.718, 0.282$ **11.** $0.23, 0.77$ **13.** $(0.45, 0.51)$

15. $(0.724, 0.777); (0.715, 0.786)$
   The 99% CI is wider.

17. $(0.649, 0.677); (0.645, 0.681)$
   The 99% CI is wider.

19. $(0.145, 0.195); (0.137, 0.203)$
   The 99% CI is wider.

21. (a) 1068 vacationers   (b) 822 vacationers
   (c) Having an estimate of the proportion reduces the minimum sample size needed.

23. (a) 1681 camcorders   (b) 1261 camcorders
   (c) Having an estimate of the proportion reduces the minimum sample size needed.

25. (a) $(0.298, 0.422)$
   (b) $(0.260, 0.380)$
   It is possible that the two proportions are equal because the confidence intervals estimating the proportions overlap.

27. (a) $(0.626, 0.674)$ (b) $(0.855, 0.905)$ (c) $(0.899, 0.941)$

29. $(0.304, 0.324)$ is approximately a 95.2% CI.

31. If $n\hat{p} < 5$ or $n\hat{q} < 5$, the sampling distribution of $\hat{p}$ may not be normally distributed, therefore preventing the use of z_c when calculating the confidence interval.

33.

$\hat{p}$	$\hat{q} = 1 - \hat{p}$	$\hat{p}\hat{q}$	$\hat{p}$	$\hat{q} = 1 - \hat{p}$	$\hat{p}\hat{q}$
0.0	1.0	0.00	0.45	0.55	0.2475
0.1	0.9	0.09	0.46	0.54	0.2484
0.2	0.8	0.16	0.47	0.53	0.2491
0.3	0.7	0.21	0.48	0.52	0.2496
0.4	0.6	0.24	0.49	0.51	0.2499
0.5	0.5	0.25	0.50	0.50	0.2500
0.6	0.4	0.24	0.51	0.49	0.2499
0.7	0.3	0.21	0.52	0.48	0.2496
0.8	0.2	0.16	0.53	0.47	0.2491
0.9	0.1	0.09	0.54	0.46	0.2484
1.0	0.0	0.00	0.55	0.45	0.2475

$\hat{p} = 0.5$ gives the maximum value of $\hat{p}\hat{q}$.

Activity 6.3 *(page 343)*

1–2. Answers will vary.

Section 6.4 *(page 348)*

1. $16.919, 3.325$ **3.** $35.479, 10.283$ **5.** $52.336, 13.121$

7. (a) $(0.0000413, 0.000157)$ (b) $(0.00643, 0.0125)$

9. (a) $(0.0305, 0.191)$ (b) $(0.175, 0.438)$

11. (a) $(4.34, 44.64)$ (b) $(2.08, 6.68)$

13. (a) $(359.6, 1829.8)$ (b) $(19.0, 42.8)$

15. (a) $(128, 492)$ (b) $(11, 22)$

17. (a) $(61,470, 303,560)$ (b) $(248, 551)$

19. (a) $(7.0, 30.6)$ (b) $(2.6, 5.5)$

21. Yes, because the entire confidence interval is below 0.015.

Uses and Abuses for Chapter 6 *(page 351)*

1–2. Answers will vary.

Review Answers for Chapter 6 *(page 353)*

1. (a) 103.5 (b) 9.0 **3.** $(10.2, 10.4)$ **5.** 47 people

7. 49 people   **9.** 2.365 **11.** 2.624 **13.** 11.2

15. 0.7 **17.** $(60.9, 83.3)$ **19.** $(6.1, 7.5)$ **21.** $(74, 86)$

23. $0.28, 0.72$ **25.** $0.220, 0.780$ **27.** $0.180, 0.820$

29. $0.420, 0.580$ **31.** $(0.260, 0.300)$ **33.** $(0.205, 0.235)$

35. $(0.141, 0.219)$ **37.** $(0.406, 0.434)$

39. (a) 385 adults (b) 359 adults
   (c) Having an estimate of the proportion reduces the minimum sample size needed.

41. $23.337, 4.404$ **43.** $14.067, 2.167$

45. $(0.0029, 0.0127); (0.0537, 0.1125)$

47. $(0.83, 2.22); (0.91, 1.49)$

Chapter Quiz for Chapter 6 *(page 357)*

1. (a) 98.11 (b) 8.847
   (c) $(89.263, 106.957)$ [*Tech:* $(89.263, 106.96)$]
   With 95% confidence, you can say that the population mean repair cost is between $89.26 and $106.96.

2. 34 dishwashers

3. (a) 12.96 (b) 1.351 (c) $(12.18, 13.74)$
   With 90% confidence, you can say that the population mean number of yards per catch is between 12.18 and 13.74 yards.
   (d) $(11.59, 14.33)$
   With 90% confidence, you can say that the population mean number of yards per catch is between 11.59 and 13.74 yards.
   The interval from part (d) is wider than the interval from part (c).

4. $(6510, 7138)$

5. (a) 0.620 (b) $(0.595, 0.645)$ (c) 977 adults

6. (a) $(387.663, 1104.552)$ (b) $(19.689, 33.234)$

1. (a) No, there has not been a change in the mean concentration levels because the confidence interval for year 1 overlaps with the confidence interval for year 2.

(b) Yes, there has been a change in the mean concentration levels because the confidence interval for year 2 does not overlap with the confidence interval for year 3.

(c) Yes, there has been a change in the mean concentration levels because the confidence interval for year 1 does not overlap with the confidence interval for year 3.

2. The efforts to reduce the formaldehyde concentration are significant over the three-year period.

3. (a) The sampling distribution of the sample means was used because the "mean concentration" was used. The point estimate is the most unbiased estimate of the population mean.

(b) No, because typically σ is unknown. They could have used the sample standard deviation.

CHAPTER 7

Section 7.1 *(page 375)*

1. The two types of hypotheses used in a hypothesis test are the null hypothesis and the alternative hypothesis.

The alternative hypothesis is the complement of the null hypothesis.

3. False. In a hypothesis test, you assume the null hypothesis is true.

5. True

7. False. A small P-value in a test will favor a rejection of the null hypothesis.

9. H_0: $\mu \leq 645$ (claim); H_a: $\mu > 645$

11. H_0: $\sigma = 5$; H_a: $\sigma \neq 5$ (claim)

13. H_0: $p \geq 0.45$: H_a: $p < 0.45$ (claim)

15. c; H_0: $\mu \leq 3$ **16.** d; H_0: $\mu \geq 3$

17. b; H_0: $\mu = 3$ **18.** a; H_0: $\mu \leq 2$

19. Right-tailed **21.** Two-tailed

23. $\mu > 750$

H_0: $\mu \leq 750$; H_a: $\mu > 750$ (claim)

25. $\sigma \leq 320$

H_0: $\sigma \leq 320$ (claim); H_a: $\sigma > 320$

27. $p = 0.81$

H_0: $p = 0.81$ (claim); H_a: $p \neq 0.81$

29. A type I error will occur if the actual proportion of new customers that return to buy their next piece of furniture is at least 0.60, but you reject H_0: $p \geq 0.60$.

A type II error will occur if the actual proportion of new customers that return to buy their next piece of furniture is less than 0.60, but you fail to reject H_0: $p \geq 0.60$.

31. A type I error will occur if the actual standard deviation of the length of time to play a game is less than or equal to 12 minutes, but you reject H_0: $\sigma \leq 12$.

A type II error will occur if the actual standard deviation of the length of time to play a game is greater than 12 minutes, but you fail to reject H_0: $\sigma \leq 12$.

33. A type I error will occur if the actual proportion of college students who own a computer is 0.88, but you reject H_0: $p = 0.88$.

A type II error will occur if the actual proportion of college students who own a computer is not 0.88, but you fail to reject H_0: $p = 0.88$.

35. Left-tailed because the alternative hypothesis contains $<$.

37. Two-tailed because the alternative hypothesis contains $\neq$.

39. Two-tailed because the alternative hypothesis contains $\neq$.

41. (a) There is enough evidence to support the film company's claim that the mean number of pictures developed for a single-use camera with 24 exposures is more than 22.

(b) There is not enough evidence to support the film company's claim that the mean number of pictures developed for a single-use camera with 24 exposures is more than 22.

43. (a) There is enough evidence to support the U.S. Department of Labor's claim that the proportion of hourly workers earning over $11.55 per hour is greater than 75%.

(b) There is not enough evidence to support the U.S. Department of Labor's claim that the proportion of hourly workers earning over $11.55 per hour is greater than 75%.

45. (a) There is enough evidence to support the automotive manufacturer's claim that the mean price of a small SUV is less than $26,860.

(b) There is not enough evidence to support the automotive manufacturer's claim that the mean price of a small SUV is less than $26,860.

47. H_0: $\mu \geq 60$; H_a: $\mu < 60$

49. (a) H_0: $\mu \geq 15$; H_a: $\mu < 15$

(b) H_0: $\mu \leq 15$; H_a: $\mu > 15$

51. If you decrease α, you are decreasing the probability that you will reject H_0. Therefore, you are increasing the probability of failing to reject H_0. This could increase β, the probability of failing to reject H_0 when H_0 is false.

53. (a) Fail to reject H_0 because the confidence interval includes values greater than 70.

(b) Reject H_0 because the confidence interval is located entirely to the left of 70.

(c) Fail to reject H_0 because the confidence interval includes values greater than 70.

55. (a) Reject H_0 because the confidence interval is located entirely to the right of 0.20.

(b) Fail to reject H_0 because the confidence interval includes values less than 0.20.

(c) Fail to reject H_0 because the confidence interval includes values less than 0.20.

Section 7.2   *(page 389)*

1. $P = 0.1151$; Fail to reject H_0.

3. $P = 0.0096$; Reject H_0.

5. $P = 0.1188$; Fail to reject H_0.

7. c   **8.** d   **9.** e   **10.** f   **11.** b   **12.** a

13. (a) Fail to reject H_0.   (b) Reject H_0.

15. 1.645   **17.** -1.88 **19.** $-2.33, 2.33$

21. (a) right-tailed   (b) 0.01

23. (a) two-tailed   (b) 0.10

25. (a) Fail to reject H_0 because $-1.645 < z < 1.645$.

(b) Reject H_0 because $z > 1.645$.

(c) Fail to reject H_0 because $-1.645 < z < 1.645$.

(d) Reject H_0 because $z < -1.645$.

27. (a) Fail to reject H_0 because $z < 1.285$.

(b) Fail to reject H_0 because $z < 1.285$.

(c) Fail to reject H_0 because $z < 1.285$.

(d) Reject H_0 because $z > 1.285$.

29. Reject H_0. At the 5% significance level, there is enough evidence to reject the claim.

31. Reject H_0. At the 1% significance level, there is enough evidence to support the claim.

33. (a) $H_0: \mu \le 275$; $H_a: \mu > 275$ (claim)

(b) 1.84; 0.9671 (*Tech:* 0.9674)

(c) 0.0329 (*Tech:* 0.0326)   (d) Reject H_0.

(e) At the 4% significance level, there is enough evidence to support the administrator's claim that the mean score for Illinois' eighth graders on the examination is more than 275.

35. (a) $H_0: \mu \le 8$; $H_a: \mu > 8$ (claim)

(b) -0.37; 0.3557 (*Tech:* 0.3540)

(c) 0.6443 (*Tech:* 0.6460)   (d) Fail to reject H_0.

(e) At the 7% significance level, there is not enough evidence to support the tea drinker's society's claim that the mean consumption of tea by a person in the United States is more than 8 gallons per year.

37. (a) $H_0: \mu = 15$ (claim); $H_a: \mu \ne 15$

(b) -0.22; 0.4129 (*Tech:* 0.4135)

(c) 0.8258 (*Tech:* 0.8270)   (d) Fail to reject H_0.

(e) At the 5% significance level, there is insufficient evidence to reject the claim that the mean time it takes smokers to quit smoking permanently is 15 years.

39. (a) $H_0: \mu = 40$ (claim); $H_a: \mu \ne 40$

(b) $-z_0 = -2.575$, $z_0 = 2.575$

Rejection regions: $z < -2.575$, $z > 2.575$

(c) -0.584 (d) Fail to reject H_0.

(e) At the 1% significance level, there is insufficient evidence to reject the company's claim that the mean caffeine content per one 12-ounce bottle of cola is 40 milligrams.

41. (a) $H_0: \mu \ge 750$ (claim); $H_a: \mu < 750$

(b) $z_0 = -2.05$; Rejection region: $z < -2.05$

(c) -0.5 (d) Fail to reject H_0.

(e) At the 2% significance level, there is insufficient evidence to reject the light bulb manufacturer's claim that the mean life of the bulb is at least 750 hours.

43. (a) $H_0: \mu \le 32$; $H_a: \mu > 32$ (claim)

(b) $z_0 = 1.555$; Rejection region: $z > 1.555$

(c) -1.478 (d) Fail to reject H_0.

(e) At the 6% significance level, there is not enough evidence to support the scientist's claim that the mean nitrogen dioxide level in Calgary is greater than 32 parts per billion.

45. (a) $H_0: \mu \ge 10$ (claim); $H_a: \mu < 10$

(b) $z_0 = -1.88$; Rejection region: $z < -1.88$

(c) -0.51 (d) Fail to reject H_0.

(e) At the 3% significance level, there is insufficient evidence to reject the weight loss program's claim that the mean weight loss after one month is at least 10 pounds.

47. Fail to reject H_0 because the standardized test statistic $z = -1.71$ is not in the rejection region ($z < -2.33$).

49. b, d

51. In the classical z-test, the test statistic is compared with critical values. The z-test using a P-value compares the P-value with the level of significance α.

Section 7.2 Activity   *(page 395)*

1–3. Answers will vary.

Section 7.3   *(page 403)*

1. Identify the level of significance α and the degrees of freedom, d.f. $= n - 1$. Find the critical value(s) using the t-distribution table in the row with $n - 1$ d.f. If the hypothesis test is

(1) left-tailed, use "One Tail, α" column with a negative sign.

(2) right-tailed, use "One Tail, α" column with a positive sign.

(3) two-tailed, use "Two Tail, α" column with a negative and a positive sign.

3. 1.717   **5.** -2.101 **7.** $-2.779, 2.779$

9. 1.328   **11.** -2.473 **13.** $-3.747, 3.747$

15. (a) Fail to reject H_0 because $t > -2.086$.
(b) Fail to reject H_0 because $t > -2.086$.
(c) Fail to reject H_0 because $t > -2.086$.
(d) Reject H_0 because $t < -2.086$.

17. (a) Fail to reject H_0 because $-2.602 < t < 2.602$.
(b) Fail to reject H_0 because $-2.602 < t < 2.602$.
(c) Reject H_0 because $t > 2.602$.
(d) Reject H_0 because $t < -2.602$.

19. Fail to reject H_0. At the 1% significance level, there is not enough evidence to reject the claim.

21. Reject H_0. At the 1% significance level, there is enough evidence to reject the claim.

23. (a) H_0: $\mu \geq 100$; H_a: $\mu < 100$ (claim)
(b) $t_0 = -3.747$; Rejection region: $t < -3.747$
(c) -4.472 (d) Reject H_0.
(e) At the 1% significance level, there is sufficient evidence to support the microwave oven repairer's claim that the mean repair cost for damaged microwave ovens is less than \$100.

25. (a) H_0: $\mu \leq 1$; H_a: $\mu > 1$ (claim)
(b) $t_0 = 1.796$; Rejection region: $t > 1.796$
(c) 5.691   (d) Reject H_0.
(e) At the 5% significance level, there is sufficient evidence to support the environmentalist's claim that the mean waste recycled by adults in the United States is more than 1 pound per person per day.

27. (a) H_0: $\mu = \$25,000$ (claim); H_a: $\mu \neq \$25,000$
(b) $-t_0 = -2.262$, $t_0 = 2.262$
Rejection regions: $t < -2.262$, $t > 2.262$
(c) 0.843   (d) Fail to reject H_0.
(e) At the 5% significance level, there is insufficient evidence to reject the employment information service's claim that the mean salary for full-time male workers over age 25 without a high school diploma is \$25,000.

29. (a) H_0: $\mu \geq 3$; H_a: $\mu < 3$ (claim)
(b) ≈ 0 (c) Reject H_0.
(d) At the 5% significance level, there is sufficient evidence to support the claim that teenage males drink fewer than three 12-ounce servings of soda per day.

31. (a) H_0: $\mu \geq 32$; H_a: $\mu < 32$ (claim)
(b) 0.0344   (c) Fail to reject H_0.
(d) At the 1% significance level, there is insufficient evidence to support the brochure's claim that the mean class size for full-time faculty is fewer than 32 students.

33. (a) H_0: $\mu = \$2634$ (claim); H_a: $\mu \neq \$2634$
(b) 0.5036   (c) Fail to reject H_0.
(d) At the 2% significance level, there is insufficient evidence to reject the restaurant association's claim that the typical household in the United States spends a mean amount of \$2634 per year on food away from home.

35. Because the P-value $= 0.096 > 0.01$, fail to reject H_0.

37. Use the t-distribution because the population is normal, $n < 30$, and σ is unknown.
Fail to reject H_0. At the 5% significance level, there is insufficient evidence to reject the car company's claim that the mean gas mileage for the luxury sedan is at least 23 miles per gallon.

Section 7.4   (page 411)

1. Verify that $np \geq 5$ and $nq \geq 5$. State H_0 and H_a. Specify the level of significance α. Determine the critical value(s) and rejection region(s). Find the standardized test statistic. Make a decision and interpret in the context of the original claim.

3. Can use normal distribution.
Fail to reject H_0. At the 5% significance level, there is not enough evidence to support the claim.

5. Cannot use normal distribution.

7. Can use normal distribution.
Reject H_0. At the 10% significance level, there is enough evidence to reject the claim.

9. (a) H_0: $p \geq 0.20$ (claim); H_a: $p < 0.20$
(b) $z_0 = -2.33$; Rejection region: $z < -2.33$
(c) -0.53 (d) Fail to reject H_0.
(e) At the 1% significance level, there is insufficient evidence to reject the medical researcher's claim that at least 20% of U.S. adults are smokers.

11. (a) H_0: $p \leq 0.30$; H_a: $p > 0.30$ (claim)
(b) $z_0 = 1.88$; Rejection region: $z > 1.88$
(c) 1.41   (d) Fail to reject H_0.
(e) At the 3% significance level, there is insufficient evidence to support the claim that more than 30% of U.S. consumers have stopped buying the product because the manufacturing of the product pollutes the environment.

13. (a) H_0: $p = 0.44$ (claim); H_a: $p \neq 0.44$
(b) $-z_0 = -2.33$, $z_0 = 2.33$
Rejection regions: $z < -2.33$, $z > 2.33$
(c) -2.56 (d) Reject H_0.
(e) At the 2% significance level, there is sufficient evidence to reject the claim that 44% of home buyers found their real estate agent through a friend.

15. Fail to reject H_0. At the 5% significance level, there is not enough evidence to reject the claim that at least 52% of the adults are more likely to buy a product when there are free samples.

17. (a) H_0: $p = 0.44$ (claim); H_a: $p \neq 0.44$

(b) $-z_0 = -2.33$, $z_0 = 2.33$; Rejection regions: $z < -2.33$, $z > 2.33$

(c) -2.56 (d) Reject H_0.

(e) At the 2% significance level, there is sufficient evidence to reject the claim that 44% of home buyers found their real estate agent through a friend.

The results are the same.

Section 7.4 Activity   *(page 413)*

1–2. Answers will vary.

Section 7.5   *(page 420)*

1. Specify the level of significance α. Determine the degrees of freedom. Determine the critical values using the χ^2 distribution. If (a) right-tailed test, use the value that corresponds to d.f. and α; (b) left-tailed test, use the value that corresponds to d.f. and $1 - \alpha$; (c) two-tailed test, use the value that corresponds to d.f. and $\frac{1}{2}\alpha$ and $1 - \frac{1}{2}\alpha$.

3. 38.885   **5.** 0.872   **7.** 7.261, 24.996

9. (a) Fail to reject H_0.   (b) Fail to reject H_0.

(c) Fail to reject H_0.   (d) Reject H_0.

11. (a) Fail to reject H_0.   (b) Reject H_0.

(c) Reject H_0.   (d) Fail to reject H_0.

13. Fail to reject H_0. At the 5% significance level, there is not enough evidence to reject the claim.

15. (a) H_0: $\sigma^2 = 3$ (claim); H_a: $\sigma^2 \neq 3$

(b) $\chi_L^2 = 13.844$, $\chi_R^2 = 41.923$

Rejection regions: $\chi^2 < 13.844$, $\chi^2 > 41.923$

(c) 24.267   (d) Fail to reject H_0.

(e) At the 5% significance level, there is insufficient evidence to reject the large appliance company's claim that the variance of the life of the appliances is 3.

17. (a) H_0: $\sigma \geq 36$; H_a: $\sigma < 36$ (claim)

(b) $\chi_0^2 = 13.240$; Rejection region: $\chi^2 < 13.240$

(c) 18.076   (d) Fail to reject H_0.

(e) At the 10% significance level, there is insufficient evidence to support the test administrator's claim that the standard deviation for eighth graders on the examination is less than 36 points.

19. (a) H_0: $\sigma \leq 0.5$ (claim); H_a: $\sigma > 0.5$

(b) $\chi_0^2 = 33.196$; Rejection region: $\chi^2 > 33.196$

(c) 47.04   (d) Reject H_0.

(e) At the 10% significance level, there is sufficient evidence to reject the hospital spokesperson's claim that the standard deviation of the waiting times is no more than 0.5 minute.

21. (a) H_0: $\sigma \geq \$3500$; H_a: $\sigma < \$3500$ (claim)

(b) $\chi_0^2 = 18.114$; Rejection region: $\chi^2 < 18.114$

(c) 37.051   (d) Fail to reject H_0.

(e) At the 10% significance level, there is insufficient evidence to support the insurance agent's claim that the standard deviation of the total charge for patients involved in a crash in which the vehicle struck a construction barricade is less than \$3500.

23. (a) H_0: $\sigma \leq \$20,000$; H_a: $\sigma > \$20,000$ (claim)

(b) $\chi_0^2 = 24.996$; Rejection region: $\chi^2 > 24.996$

(c) 16.265   (d) Fail to reject H_0.

(e) At the 5% significance level, there is insufficient evidence to support the claim that the standard deviation of the annual salaries for actuaries is more than \$20,000.

25. *P*-value = 0.9059   **27.** *P*-value = 0.3647

Fail to reject H_0.   Fail to reject H_0.

Uses and Abuses for Chapter 7   *(page 423)*

1. Answers will vary.

2. H_0: $p = 0.57$; Answers will vary.

3. Answers will vary.

4. Answers will vary.

Review Answers for Chapter 7   *(page 427)*

1. H_0: $\mu \leq 1479$ (claim); H_a: $\mu > 1479$

3. H_0: $p \geq 0.205$; H_a: $p < 0.205$ (claim)

5. H_0: $\sigma \leq 6.2$; H_a: $\sigma > 6.2$ (claim)

7. (a) H_0: $p = 0.63$ (claim); H_a: $p \neq 0.63$

(b) A type I error will occur if the actual proportion of college students that occasionally or frequently come late to class is 63%, but you reject H_0: $p = 0.63$.

A type II error will occur if the actual proportion of college students that occasionally or frequently come late to class is not 63%, but you fail to reject H_0: $p = 0.63$.

(c) Two-tailed because the alternative hypothesis contains $\neq$.

(d) There is enough evidence to reject the research center's claim that the proportion of college students that occasionally or frequently come late to class is 63%.

(e) There is not enough evidence to reject the research center's claim that the proportion of college students that occasionally or frequently come late to class is 63%.

9. (a) H_0: $\sigma \leq 50$ (claim); H_a: $\sigma > 50$

(b) A type I error will occur if the actual standard deviation of the sodium content in one serving of a certain soup is no more than 50 milligrams, but you reject H_0: $\sigma \leq 50$.

A type II error will occur if the actual standard deviation of the sodium content in one serving of a certain soup is more than 50 milligrams, but you fail to reject H_0: $\sigma \leq 50$.

(c) Right-tailed because the alternative hypothesis contains $>$.

(d) There is enough evidence to reject the soup maker's claim that the standard deviation of the sodium content in one serving of a certain soup is no more than 50 milligrams.

(e) There is not enough evidence to reject the soup maker's claim that the standard deviation of the sodium content in one serving of a certain soup is no more than 50 milligrams.

11. -2.05 **13.** 1.96

15. Reject H_0. At the 5% significance level, there is enough evidence to reject the claim.

17. Fail to reject H_0. At the 1% significance level, there is not enough evidence to support the claim.

19. H_0: $\mu \leq 0.05$ (claim); H_a: $\mu > 0.05$

$z = 2.20$; P-value $= 0.0139$

$\alpha = 0.10 \Rightarrow$ Reject H_0.

$\alpha = 0.05 \Rightarrow$ Reject H_0.

$\alpha = 0.01 \Rightarrow$ Fail to reject H_0.

21. Yes; At the 5% significance level, there is sufficient evidence to reject the tourist agency's claim that mean daily cost of meals and lodging for a family of 4 traveling in New York is $326.

23. $-2.093, 2.093$ **25.** -1.345

27. Fail to reject H_0. At the 5% significance level, there is not enough evidence to support the claim.

29. Fail to reject H_0. At the 10% significance level, there is not enough evidence to reject the claim.

31. Reject H_0. At the 1% significance level, there is enough evidence to reject the claim.

33. No; At the 10% significance level, there is not enough evidence to reject the advertisement's claim that the mean monthly cost of joining a health club is $25.

35. No; At the 1% significance level, there is not enough evidence to reject the education publication's claim that the mean expenditure per student in public elementary and secondary schools is at least $10,200.

37. Can use normal distribution.

Fail to reject H_0. At the 5% significance level, there is not enough evidence to reject the claim.

39. Cannot use normal distribution.

41. Cannot use normal distribution.

43. Can use normal distribution.

Fail to reject H_0. At the 1% significance level, there is not enough evidence to support the claim.

45. Reject H_0. At the 10% significance level, there is enough evidence to support the polling agency's claim that over 40% of adults shop for a gift within 1 week of an event.

47. 30.144 **49.** 33.196

51. Reject H_0. At the 10% significance level, there is enough evidence to support the claim.

53. Fail to reject H_0. At the 5% significance level, there is not enough evidence to reject the claim.

55. Reject H_0. At the 0.5% significance level, there is enough evidence to reject the bolt manufacturer's claim that the variance is at most 0.01.

Chapter Quiz for Chapter 7   *(page 431)*

1. (a) H_0: $\mu \geq 22$ (claim); H_a: $\mu < 22$

(b) One-tailed because the alternative hypothesis contains $<$; z-test because $n \geq 30$

(c) $z_0 = -2.05$; Rejection region: $z < -2.05$

(d) -0.58

(e) Fail to reject H_0. At the 2% significance level, there is not enough evidence to reject the citrus growers association's claim that the mean utilization of fresh citrus fruits by people in the United States is at least 22 pounds per year.

2. (a) H_0: $\mu \geq 20$ (claim); H_a: $\mu < 20$

(b) One-tailed because the alternative hypothesis contains $<$; t-test because $n < 30$, σ is unknown, and the population is normally distributed

(c) $t_0 = -1.895$; Rejection region: $t < -1.895$

(d) -1.131

(e) Fail to reject H_0. At the 5% significance level, there is not enough evidence to reject the auto maker's claim that the mean gas mileage of its sports utility vehicle is at least 20 miles per gallon.

3. (a) H_0: $p \leq 0.10$ (claim); H_a: $p > 0.10$

(b) One-tailed because the alternative hypothesis contains $>$; z-test because $np > 5$ and $nq > 5$

(c) $z_0 = 1.75$; Rejection region: $z > 1.75$

(d) 0.75

(e) Fail to reject H_0. At the 4% significance level, there is not enough evidence to reject the microwave oven maker's claim that no more than 10% of its microwaves need repair during the first 5 years of use.

4. (a) H_0: $\sigma = 113$ (claim); H_a: $\sigma \neq 113$

(b) Two-tailed because the alternative hypothesis contains $\neq$; χ^2-test because the population is normally distributed

(c) $\chi_L^2 = 3.565$, $\chi_R^2 = 29.819$

Rejection regions: $\chi^2 < 3.565$, $\chi^2 > 29.819$

(d) 11.875

(e) Fail to reject H_0. At the 1% significance level, there is not enough evidence to reject the state school administrator's claim that the standard deviation of SAT critical reading scores is 113.

5. (a) H_0: $\mu = \$48{,}718$ (claim); H_a: $\mu \neq \$48{,}718$

(b) Two-tailed because the alternative hypothesis contains $\neq$; t-test because $n < 30$, σ is unknown, and the population is normally distributed

(c) Not necessary   (d) -0.828; 0.4252

(e) Fail to reject H_0. At the 5% significance level, there is not enough evidence to reject the employment information service report's claim that the mean annual salary for full-time male workers ages 25 to 34 with a bachelor's degree is $48,718.

6. (a) H_0: $\mu = \$201$ (claim); H_a: $\mu \neq \$201$

(b) Two-tailed because the alternative hypothesis contains $\neq$; z-test because $n \geq 30$

(c) Not necessary   (d) 0.0030 (*Tech:* 0.0031)

(e) Reject H_0. At the 5% significance level, there is enough evidence to reject the tourist agency's claim that the mean daily cost of meals and lodging for a family of 4 traveling in the state of Kansas is $201.

Real Statistics–Real Decisions for Chapter 7   *(page 432)*

1. (a) *Sample Answer:* Take a random sample to get a diverse group of people. Stratified random sampling.

(b) Random sample   (c) Answers will vary.

2. Fail to reject H_0. At the 10% significance level, there is not enough evidence to support the claim that less than 40% of people in the United States think the Social Security system will have money available to provide the benefits they expect for their retirements.

3. Reject H_0. At the 10% significance level, there is enough evidence to reject the claim that the mean age of people in the United States who would say yes to the survey question is 60 years or older.

4. Answers will vary.

CHAPTER 8

Section 8.1   *(page 444)*

1. Two samples are dependent if each member of one sample corresponds to a member of the other sample. Example: The weights of 22 people before starting an exercise program and the weights of the same 22 people 6 weeks after starting the exercise program.

   Two samples are independent if the sample selected from one population is not related to the sample selected from the second population. Example: The weights of 25 cats and the weights of 20 dogs.

3. Use P-values.

5. Independent because different students were sampled.

7. Dependent because the same adults were sampled.

9. Independent because different boats were sampled.

11. Dependent because the same tire sets were sampled.

13. (a) 2   (b) 7.60   (c) In the rejection region.

(d) Reject H_0. At the 5% significance level, there is enough evidence to reject the claim.

15. (a) 30   (b) 1.84   (c) Not in the rejection region.

(d) Fail to reject H_0. At the 1% significance level, there is not enough evidence to support the claim.

17. Fail to reject H_0. At the 1% significance level, there is not enough evidence to support the claim.

19. (a) The claim is "the mean braking distance is different for the two types of tires."

   H_0: $\mu_1 = \mu_2$; H_a: $\mu_1 \neq \mu_2$ (claim)

(b) $-z_0 = -1.645$, $z_0 = 1.645$

   Rejection regions: $z < -1.645$, $z > 1.645$

(c) -2.786 (d) Reject H_0.

(e) At the 10% significance level, there is sufficient evidence to support the safety engineer's claim that the mean braking distance is different for the two types of tires.

21. (a) The claim is "Model A's repair costs are lower than Model B's."

   H_0: $\mu_1 \geq \mu_2$; H_a: $\mu_1 < \mu_2$ (claim)

(b) $z_0 = -2.33$; Rejection region: $z < -2.33$

(c) -1.54 (d) Fail to reject H_0.

(e) No, at the 1% significance level, there is insufficient evidence to conclude that the repair costs for Model A are lower than for Model B.

23. (a) The claim is "male and female high school students have equal ACT scores."

   H_0: $\mu_1 = \mu_2$ (claim); H_a: $\mu_1 \neq \mu_2$

(b) $-z_0 = -2.575$, $z_0 = 2.575$

   Rejection regions: $z < -2.575$, $z > 2.575$

(c) 0.202 (d) Fail to reject H_0.

(e) At the 1% significance level, there is insufficient evidence to reject the claim that male and female high school students have equal ACT scores.

25. (a) The claim is "the mean daily lodging cost for a family traveling in North Carolina is the same as in South Carolina."

   H_0: $\mu_1 = \mu_2$ (claim); H_a: $\mu_1 \neq \mu_2$

(b) $-z_0 = -1.645$, $z_0 = 1.645$

   Rejection regions: $z < -1.645$, $z > 1.645$

(c) -0.919 (d) Fail to reject H_0.

(e) At the 10% significance level, there is insufficient evidence to reject the travel association's claim that the lodging cost for a family traveling in North Carolina is the same as in South Carolina.

27. (a) The claim is "the mean daily lodging cost for a family traveling in North Carolina is the same as in South Carolina."

H_0: $\mu_1 = \mu_2$ (claim); H_a: $\mu_1 \neq \mu_2$

(b) $-z_0 = -1.645$, $z_0 = 1.645$

Rejection regions: $z < -1.645$, $z > 1.645$

(c) 1.342 (d) Fail to reject H_0.

(e) At the 10% significance level, there is insufficient evidence to reject the travel association's claim that the lodging cost for a family traveling in North Carolina is the same as in South Carolina.

The new samples do not lead to a different conclusion.

29. (a) The claim is "children ages 6–17 spent more time watching television in 1981 than children ages 6–17 do today."

H_0: $\mu_1 \leq \mu_2$; H_a: $\mu_1 > \mu_2$ (claim)

(b) $z_0 = 1.96$; Rejection region: $z > 1.96$

(c) 3.01 (d) Reject H_0.

(e) At the 2.5% significance level, there is sufficient evidence to support the sociologist's claim that children ages 6–17 spent more time watching television in 1981 than children ages 6–17 do today.

31. (a) The claim is "there is no difference in the mean washer diameter manufactured by two different methods."

H_0: $\mu_1 = \mu_2$ (claim); H_a: $\mu_1 \neq \mu_2$

(b) $-z_0 = -2.575$, $z_0 = 2.575$

Rejection regions: $z < -2.575$, $z > 2.575$

(c) 64.978 (d) Reject H_0.

(e) At the 1% significance level, there is sufficient evidence to reject the production engineer's claim that there is no difference in the mean washer diameter manufactured by two different methods.

33. They are equivalent through algebraic manipulation of the equation.

$\mu_1 = \mu_2 \Rightarrow \mu_1 - \mu_2 = 0$

35. H_0: $\mu_1 - \mu_2 = -9$ (claim); H_a: $\mu_1 - \mu_2 \neq -9$

Fail to reject H_0. At the 1% significance level, there is not enough evidence to reject the claim that children spend 9 hours a week more in day care or preschool.

37. H_0: $\mu_1 - \mu_2 \leq 6000$; H_a: $\mu_1 - \mu_2 > 6000$ (claim)

Fail to reject H_0. At the 10% significance level, there is not enough evidence to support the claim that the difference in mean annual salaries of statisticians in Massachusetts and North Carolina is more than $6000.

39. $-3.6 < \mu_1 - \mu_2 < -0.2$

41. H_0: $\mu_1 \geq \mu_2$; H_a: $\mu_1 < \mu_2$ (claim)

Reject H_0. At the 5% significance level, there is enough evidence to support the claim. You should recommend using the DASH diet and exercise program over using the traditional diet and exercise program because the mean systolic blood pressure was significantly lower in the DASH program.

43. The 95% CI for $\mu_1 - \mu_2$ in Exercise 39 contained only values less than zero and, as found in Exercise 41, there was enough evidence at the 5% significance level to support the claim.

If the CI for $\mu_1 - \mu_2$, contains only negative numbers, you reject H_0 because the null hypothesis states that $\mu_1 - \mu_2$ is greater than or equal to zero.

Section 8.2 *(page 456)*

1. State hypotheses and identify the claim. Specify the level of significance. Determine the degrees of freedom. Find the critical value(s) and identify the rejection region(s). Find the standardized test statistic. Make a decision and interpret in the context of the original claim.

3. (a) $-t_0 = -1.714$, $t_0 = 1.714$

(b) $-t_0 = -1.812$, $t_0 = 1.812$

5. (a) $t_0 = -2.074$ (b) $t_0 = -2.306$

7. (a) $t_0 = 1.729$ (b) $t_0 = 1.895$

9. (a) $-t_0 = -2.771$, $t_0 = 2.771$

(b) $-t_0 = -3.106$, $t_0 = 3.106$

11. (a) -1.8 (b) -1.199

(c) Not in the rejection region. (d) Fail to reject H_0.

13. (a) -55 (b) -1.073

(c) Not in the rejection region. (d) Fail to reject H_0.

15. (a) The claim is "the mean footwell intrusions for small and midsize cars are equal."

H_0: $\mu_1 = \mu_2$ (claim); H_a: $\mu_1 \neq \mu_2$

(b) $-t_0 = -1.703$, $t_0 = 1.703$

Rejection regions: $t < -1.703$, $t > 1.703$

(c) 1.177 (d) Fail to reject H_0.

(e) At the 10% significance level, there is not enough evidence to reject the insurance actuary's claim that the mean footwell intrusions for small and midsize cars are equal.

17. (a) The claim is "the mean bumper repair cost is less for small cars than it is for midsize cars."

H_0: $\mu_1 \geq \mu_2$; H_a: $\mu_1 < \mu_2$ (claim)

(b) $t_0 = -1.282$; Rejection region: $t < -1.282$

(c) -3.962 (d) Reject H_0.

(e) At the 10% significance level, there is enough evidence to support the claim that the mean bumper repair cost is less for small cars than it is for midsize cars.

19. (a) The claim is "the mean annual income is greater in Allegheny County than it is in Erie County."

$H_0: \mu_1 \leq \mu_2$; $H_a: \mu_1 > \mu_2$ (claim)

(b) $t_0 = 1.345$; Rejection region: $t > 1.345$

(c) 1.769   (d) Reject H_0.

(e) At the 10% significance level, there is enough evidence to support the personnel director's claim that the mean annual income is greater in Allegheny County than it is in Erie County.

21. (a) The claim is "the new treatment makes a difference in the tensile strength of steel bars."

$H_0: \mu_1 = \mu_2$; $H_a: \mu_1 \neq \mu_2$ (claim)

(b) $-t_0 = -2.831$, $t_0 = 2.831$

Rejection regions: $t < -2.831$, $t > 2.831$

(c) -6.410 (d) Reject H_0.

(e) At the 1% significance level, there is enough evidence to support the claim that the new treatment makes a difference in the tensile strength of steel bars.

23. (a) The claim is "the new method of teaching reading produces higher reading test scores than the old method."

$H_0: \mu_1 \geq \mu_2$; $H_a: \mu_1 < \mu_2$ (claim)

(b) $t_0 = -1.282$; Rejection region: $t < -1.282$

(c) -4.295 (d) Reject H_0.

(e) At the 10% significance level, there is enough evidence to support the claim that the new method of teaching reading produces higher reading test scores than the old method and to recommend changing to the new method.

25. $24 < \mu_1 - \mu_2 < 36$

27. $3 < \mu_1 - \mu_2 < 7$

Section 8.3   *(page 466)*

1. (1) Each sample must be randomly selected from a normal population.

(2) Each member of the first sample must be paired with a member of the second sample.

3. Left-tailed test; Fail to reject H_0.

5. Right-tailed test; Reject H_0.

7. Left-tailed test; Reject H_0.

9. (a) The claim is "the students' critical reading SAT scores improved the second time they took the SAT."

$H_0: \mu_d \geq 0$; $H_a: \mu_d < 0$ (claim)

(b) $t_0 = -2.650$; Rejection region: $t < -2.650$

(c) $\bar{d} \approx -33.714$; $s_d \approx 42.034$

(d) -3.001 (e) Reject H_0.

(f) At the 1% significance level, there is enough evidence to support the claim that the students' critical reading SAT scores improved the second time they took the SAT.

11. (a) The claim is "the fuel additive improved gas mileage."

$H_0: \mu_d \geq 0$; $H_a: \mu_d < 0$ (claim)

(b) $t_0 = -1.415$; Rejection region: $t < -1.415$

(c) $\bar{d} = -1.575$; $s_d \approx 0.803$

(d) -5.547 (e) Reject H_0.

(f) At the 10% significance level, there is enough evidence to support the claim that the fuel additive improved gas mileage.

13. (a) The claim is "a particular exercise program will help participants lose weight after one month." $H_0: \mu_d \leq 0$; $H_a: \mu_d > 0$ (claim)

(b) $t_0 = 1.363$; Rejection region: $t > 1.363$

(c) $\bar{d} = 3.75$; $s_d \approx 7.841$

(d) 1.657   (e) Reject H_0.

(f) At the 10% significance level, there is enough evidence to support the nutritionist's claim that the exercise program helps participants lose weight after one month.

15. (a) The claim is "soft tissue therapy and spinal manipulation help to reduce the length of time patients suffer from headaches."

$H_0: \mu_d \leq 0$; $H_a: \mu_d > 0$ (claim)

(b) $t_0 = 2.764$; Rejection region: $t > 2.764$

(c) $\bar{d} \approx 1.255$; $s_d \approx 0.441$

(d) 9.429   (e) Reject H_0.

(f) At the 1% significance level, there is enough evidence to support the physical therapist's claim that soft tissue therapy and spinal manipulation help reduce the length of time patients suffer from headaches.

17. (a) The claim is "the new drug reduces systolic blood pressure."

$H_0: \mu_d \leq 0$; $H_a: \mu_d > 0$ (claim)

(b) $t_0 = 1.895$; Rejection region: $t > 1.895$

(c) $\bar{d} = 14.75$; $s_d \approx 6.861$

(d) 6.081   (e) Reject H_0.

(f) At the 5% significance level, there is enough evidence to support the pharmaceutical company's claim that its new drug reduces systolic blood pressure.

19. (a) The claim is "the product ratings have changed from last year to this year."

$H_0: \mu_d = 0$; $H_a: \mu_d \neq 0$ (claim)

(b) $-t_0 = -2.365$, $t_0 = 2.365$

Rejection regions: $t < -2.365$, $t > 2.365$

(c) $\bar{d} = -1$; $s_d \approx 1.309$

(d) -2.160 (e) Fail to reject H_0.

(f) At the 5% significance level, there is not enough evidence to support the claim that the product ratings have changed from last year to this year.

21. $-1.76 < \mu_d < -1.29$

Section 8.4 *(page 475)*

1. State the hypotheses and identify the claim. Specify the level of significance. Find the critical value(s) and rejection region(s). Find $\bar{p}$ and $\bar{q}$. Find the standardized test statistic. Make a decision and interpret in the context of the claim.

3. Two-tailed test; Fail to reject H_0.

5. Right-tailed test; Fail to reject H_0.

7. (a) The claim is "the proportion of adults using alternative medicines has not changed since 1991."

   H_0: $p_1 = p_2$ (claim); H_a: $p_1 \neq p_2$

   (b) $-z_0 = -1.96$, $z_0 = 1.96$

   Rejection regions: $z < -1.96$, $z > 1.96$

   (c) -5.06 (d) Reject H_0.

   (e) At the 5% significance level, there is sufficient evidence to reject the claim that the proportion of adults using alternative medicines has not changed since 1991.

9. (a) The claim is "the proportions of senior citizens who said they eat the daily recommended number of servings of vegetables are the same for the two groups."

   H_0: $p_1 = p_2$ (claim); H_a: $p_1 \neq p_2$

   (b) $-z_0 = -1.645$, $z_0 = 1.645$

   Rejection regions: $z < -1.645$, $z > 1.645$

   (c) 4.362 (d) Reject H_0.

   (e) At the 10% significance level, there is sufficient evidence to reject the claim that the proportions of male and female senior citizens who eat the daily recommended number of servings of vegetables are the same.

11. (a) The claim is "the proportion of adults who are smokers is greater in Alabama than in Missouri."

    H_0: $p_1 \leq p_2$; H_a: $p_1 > p_2$ (claim)

    (b) $z_0 = 2.33$; Rejection region: $z > 2.33$

    (c) 1.04 (d) Fail to reject H_0.

    (e) At the 1% significance level, there is insufficient evidence to support the claim that the proportion of adults who are smokers is greater in Alabama than in Missouri.

13. (a) The claim is "the proportion of twelfth grade males who said they had smoked in the last 30 days is less than the proportion of twelfth grade females."

    H_0: $p_1 \geq p_2$; H_a: $p_1 < p_2$ (claim)

    (b) $z_0 = -2.33$; Rejection region: $z < -2.33$

    (c) 3.16 (d) Fail to reject H_0.

    (e) At the 1% significance level, there is insufficient evidence to support the claim that the proportion of twelfth grade males who said they had smoked in the last 30 days is less than the proportion of twelfth grade females.

15. (a) The claim is "the proportions of Internet users are the same for the two groups."

    H_0: $p_1 = p_2$ (claim); H_a: $p_1 \neq p_2$

    (b) $-z_0 = -1.96$, $z_0 = 1.96$

    Rejection regions: $z < -1.96$, $z > 1.96$

    (c) -0.54 (d) Fail to reject H_0.

    (e) At the 5% significance level, there is not enough evidence to reject the claim that the proportions of Internet users are the same for males and females.

17. No, at the 1% significance level, there is insufficient evidence to support the claim that the proportions of teens who watch less than 1 hour of TV per week is greater for girls than for boys.

19. Yes, at the 5% significance level, there is sufficient evidence to support the organization's claim that the proportions of teens who watch 1 to 5 hours of TV per week is greater for girls than for boys.

21. Yes, at the 5% significance level, there is sufficient evidence to support the claim that the proportions of men ages 18 to 24 living in parents' homes was greater in 2000 than in 2006.

23. Yes, at the 1% significance level, there is sufficient evidence to reject the claim that the proportions of 18- to 24-year-olds living in parents' homes in 2000 was the same for men and women.

25. $0.004 < p_1 - p_2 < 0.006$

Uses and Abuses for Chapter 8   *(page 479)*

1. Answers will vary.

2. Blind: The patients do not know which group (medicine or placebo) they belong to.

   Double Blind: Both the researcher and patient do not know which group (medicine or placebo) that the patient belongs to.

Review Answers for Chapter 8   *(page 481)*

1. Independent because different laboratory mice were sampled.

3. Fail to reject H_0. At the 5% significance level, there is not enough evidence to reject the claim.

5. Reject H_0. At the 10% level of significance, there is enough evidence to support the claim.

7. (a) The claim is "the Long John Silver's sandwich has fewer calories than the Wendy's sandwich."

   H_0: $\mu_1 \leq \mu_2$; H_a: $\mu_1 > \mu_2$ (claim)

   (b) $z_0 = 1.645$; Rejection region: $z > 1.645$

   (c) 1.002 (d) Fail to reject H_0.

   (e) At the 5% significance level, there is not enough evidence to support the claim that the Long John Silver's sandwich has fewer calories than the Wendy's sandwich.

9. Fail to reject H_0. At the 5% significance level, there is not enough evidence to reject the claim.

11. Fail to reject H_0. At the 5% significance level, there is not enough evidence to reject the claim.

13. Reject H_0. At the 1% significance level, there is enough evidence to support the claim.

15. (a) The claim is "third graders taught with the directed reading activities scored higher than those taught without the activities."

$H_0: \mu_1 \leq \mu_2$; $H_a: \mu_1 > \mu_2$ (claim)

(b) $t_0 = 1.645$; Rejection region: $t > 1.645$

(c) 2.267   (d) Reject H_0.

(e) At the 5% significance level, there is sufficient evidence to support the claim that third graders taught with the directed reading activities scored higher than those taught without the activities.

17. Two-tailed test; Reject H_0.

19. Right-tailed test; Reject H_0.

21. (a) The claim is "the men's systolic blood pressure decreased."

$H_0: \mu_d \leq 0$; $H_a: \mu_d > 0$ (claim)

(b) $t_0 = 1.383$; Rejection region: $t > 1.383$

(c) $\bar{d} = 5$; $s_d \approx 8.743$ (d) 1.808   (e) Reject H_0.

(f) At the 10% significance level, there is enough evidence to support the claim that the men's systolic blood pressure decreased.

23. Two-tailed test; Fail to reject H_0.

25. Right-tailed test; Reject H_0.

27. (a) The claim is "the proportions of U.S. adults who considered the amount of federal income tax they had to pay to be too high were the same for the two years."

$H_0: p_1 = p_2$ (claim); $H_a: p_1 \neq p_2$

(b) $-z_0 = -1.645$, $z_0 = 1.645$

Rejection regions: $z < -1.645$, $z > 1.645$

(c) -1.371 (d) Fail to reject H_0.

(e) At the 10% significance level, there is not enough evidence to reject the claim that the proportions of U.S. adults who considered the amount of federal income tax they had to pay to be too high were the same for the two years.

Chapter Quiz for Chapter 8   *(page 485)*

1. (a) $H_0: \mu_1 \leq \mu_2$; $H_a: \mu_1 > \mu_2$ (claim)

(b) One-tailed because H_a contains >; z-test because n_1 and n_2 are each greater than 30.

(c) $z_0 = 1.645$; Rejection region: $z > 1.645$

(d) 0.585   (e) Fail to reject H_0.

(f) At the 5% level of significance, there is not enough evidence to support the claim that the mean score on the science assessment for the male high school students was higher than for the female high school students.

2. (a) $H_0: \mu_1 = \mu_2$ (claim); $H_a: \mu_1 \neq \mu_2$

(b) Two-tailed because H_a contains $\neq$; t-test because n_1 and n_2 are less than 30, the samples are independent, and the populations are normally distributed.

(c) $-t_0 = -2.779$, $t_0 = 2.779$

Rejection regions: $t < -2.779$, $t > 2.779$

(d) 0.341   (e) Fail to reject H_0.

(f) At the 1% level of significance, there is not enough evidence to reject the teacher's claim that the mean scores on the science assessment test are the same for fourth grade boys and girls.

3. (a) $H_0: p_1 \leq p_2$; $H_a: p_1 > p_2$ (claim)

(b) One-tailed because H_a contains >; z-test because you are testing proportions and $n_1 \bar{p}$, $n_2 \bar{p}$, $n_1 \bar{q}$, and $n_2 \bar{q} \geq 5$ and the samples are independent.

(c) $z_0 = 1.28$; Rejection region: $z > 1.28$

(d) 7.04   (e) Reject H_0.

(f) At the 10% level of significance, there is enough evidence to support the claim that the proportion of drivers involved in fatal crashes with blood alcohol concentration of 0.08% or greater is higher for drivers ages 21 to 24 than for drivers ages 25 to 34.

4. (a) $H_0: \mu_d \geq 0$; $H_a: \mu_d < 0$ (claim)

(b) One-tailed because H_a contains <; t-test because both populations are normally distributed and the samples are dependent.

(c) $t_0 = -1.796$; Rejection region: $t < -1.796$

(d) -9.016 (e) Reject H_0.

(f) At the 5% level of significance, there is sufficient evidence to conclude that the students' SAT scores improved on the second test.

Real Statistics–Real Decisions for Chapter 8   *(page 486)*

1. (a) *Sample answer:* Take a simple random sample of records today and 10 years ago from a random sample of hospitals.

Use a cluster sample.

(b) Answers will vary.

(c) Answers will vary.

2. Use a t-test; independent; yes, you need to know if the population distributions are normal or not; yes, you need to know if the population variances are equal or not.

3. At the 5% significance level, there is not enough evidence to support the claim that there is a difference in the mean length of hospital stays for patients (ages 17 and younger) diagnosed with pneumonia.

This decision does not support your department's claim.

Cumulative Review Chapters 6–8   *(page 490)*

1. (a) (0.539, 0.601)

(b) No, at the 5% significance level, there is not enough evidence to support the researcher's claim that more than 60% of adults believe it is somewhat or very likely that life exists on other planets.

2. Reject H_0. At the 5% significance level, there is enough evidence to support the pulmonologist's claim that a smoking ban in bars will reduce the amount of nitric oxide exhaled by asthmatic bar workers.

3. (25.94, 28.00); z-distribution

4. (2.75, 4.17); t-distribution

5. (10.7, 13.5); t-distribution

6. (7.69, 8.73); t-distribution

7. Yes, at the 10% significance level, there is enough evidence to support the pediatrician's claim that the mean birth weight for a single-birth baby is greater than the mean birth weight of a baby that has a twin.

8. H_0: $\mu \geq 33$; H_a: $\mu < 33$ (claim)

9. H_0: $p \geq 0.19$ (claim); H_a: $p < 0.19$

10. H_0: $\sigma = 0.63$ (claim); H_a: $\sigma \neq 0.63$

11. H_0: $\mu = 2.28$; H_a: $\mu \neq 2.28$ (claim)

12. (a) (5.1, 22.8) (b) (2.3, 4.8)

(c) No, at the 1% significance level, there is not enough evidence to support the pharmacist's claim that the standard deviation of the mean number of chronic medications taken by elderly adults in the community is less than 2.5 medications.

13. Yes, at the 5% significance level, there is enough evidence to support the tennis instructor's claim that the string tension of racquets used for power is less than the string tension of racquets used for control.

14. (a) (251.2, 341.3)

(b) No, at the 10% significance level, there is not enough evidence to support the physical therapist's claim that the mean distance walked is less than 280 meters.

15. No, at the 10% significance level, there is not enough evidence to reject the claim that the proportions of players sustaining head and neck injuries are the same for the two groups.

16. (a) (145, 155)

(b) No, at the 5% significance level, there is not enough evidence to reject the school administrator's claim that the mean score for all twelfth grade students who took the test is at least 145.

CHAPTER 9

Section 9.1   *(page 507)*

1. $r = -0.925$ represents a stronger correlation because $|-0.925| > |0.834|$.

3. A table can be used to compare r with a critical value or a hypothesis test can be performed using a t-test.

5. Negative linear correlation

7. No linear correlation

9. c; You would expect a positive linear correlation between age and income.

10. d; You would not expect age and height to be correlated.

11. b; You would expect a negative linear correlation between age and balance on student loans.

12. a; You would expect the relationship between age and body temperature to be fairly constant.

13. Explanatory variable: Amount of water consumed

Response variable: Weight loss

15. (a)

(b) 0.908   (c) Strong positive linear correlation

17. (a)

(b) 0.923   (c) Strong positive linear correlation

19. (a)

(b) 0.427   (c) Weak positive linear correlation

21. (a)

(b) −0.030   (c) No linear correlation

23. No, at the 1% significance level, there is not enough evidence to conclude that there is a significant linear correlation between vehicle weight and the variability in braking distance.

25. Yes, at the 1% significance level, there is enough evidence to conclude that there is a significant linear correlation between the number of hours spent studying for a test and the score received on the test.

27. No, at the 1% significance level, there is not enough evidence to conclude that there is a significant linear correlation between earnings per share and dividends per share.

29. 0.883; 0.883; The correlation coefficient remains unchanged when the x-values and y-values are switched.

31. Answers will vary.

Activity 9.1 *(page 512)*

1–4. Answers will vary.

Section 9.2 *(page 517)*

1. c   **2.** a   **3.** d   **4.** b   **5.** g   **6.** e   **7.** h

8. f   **9.** c   **10.** b   **11.** a   **12.** d

13. $\hat{y} = 0.062x + 7.535$

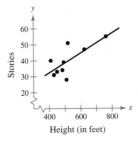

  (a) 39 stories   (b) 48 stories

  (c) It is not meaningful to predict the value of y for $x = 310$ because $x = 310$ is outside the range of the original data.

  (d) 52 stories

15. $\hat{y} = 7.350x + 34.617$

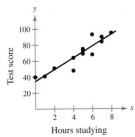

  (a) 56.7   (b) 82.4

  (c) It is not meaningful to predict the value of y for $x = 13$ because $x = 13$ is outside the range of the original data.

  (d) 67.7

17. $\hat{y} = 2.472x + 80.813$

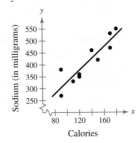

  (a) 501.053 milligrams   (b) 328.013 milligrams

  (c) 426.893 milligrams

  (d) It is not meaningful to predict the value of y for $x = 210$ because $x = 210$ is outside the range of the original data.

19. $\hat{y} = 1.870x + 51.360$

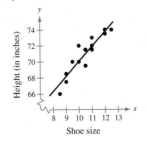

  (a) 72.865 inches   (b) 66.32 inches

  (c) It is not meaningful to predict the value of y for $x = 15.5$ because $x = 15.5$ is outside the range of the original data.

  (d) 70.06 inches

21. $\hat{y} = 0.000447x - 0.425$

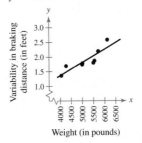

  (a) 1.587 feet   (b) 2.257 feet

  (c) It is not meaningful to predict the value of y for $x = 7500$ because $x = 7500$ is outside the range of the original data.

  (d) 2.145 feet

23. Substitute a value x into the equation of a regression line and solve for y.

25. Strong positive linear correlation; As the ages of the engineers increase, the salaries of the engineers tend to increase.

27. No, it is not meaningful to predict a salary for a 74-year-old engineer because $x = 74$ is outside the range of the original data.

29. *Sample Answer:* Although there is a strong positive linear correlation between an engineer's annual salary and age, a cause-and-effect relationship should not be inferred. The correlation could be caused by other factors such as work experience, level of education, or the number of years at a company.

31. (a) $\hat{y} = -4.297x + 94.200$

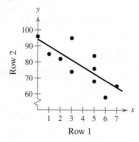

(b) $\hat{y} = -0.141x + 14.763$

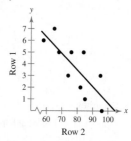

(c) The sign of m is unchanged, but the values of m and b change.

33. (a) $\hat{y} = 0.139x + 21.024$

(b)

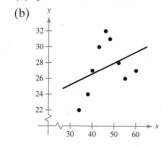

(c)

(d) The residual plot shows a pattern because the residuals do not fluctuate about 0. This implies that the regression line is not a good representation of the relationship between the two variables.

35. (a)

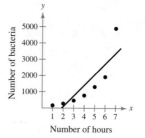

(b) The point $(44, 8)$ may be an outlier.

(c) The point $(44, 8)$ is not an influential point because the slopes and y-intercepts of the regression lines with the point included and without the point included are not significantly different.

37. $\hat{y} = 654.536x - 1214.857$

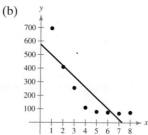

39. $y = 93.028(1.712)^x$

41. (a) $\hat{y} = -78.929x + 576.179$

(b)

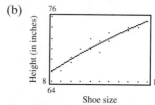

43. $y = 782.300x^{-1.251}$

45. (a) $y = 25.035 + 19.599 \ln(x)$

(b)

47. The logarithmic equation is a better model for the data. The logarithmic equation's error is smaller.

Activity 9.2 *(page 523)*

1–4. Answers will vary.

A88

Section 9.3 *(page 531)*

1. The total variation is the sum of the squares of the differences between the y-values of each ordered pair and the mean of the y-values of the ordered pairs, or $\sum (y_i - \bar{y})^2$.

3. The unexplained variation is the sum of the squares of the differences between the observed y-values and the predicted y-values, or $\sum (y_i - \hat{y}_i)^2$.

5. 0.123; 12.3% of the variation is explained. 87.7% of the variation is unexplained.

7. 0.794; 79.4% of the variation is explained. 20.6% of the variation is unexplained.

9. (a) 0.233; 23.3% of the variation in proceeds can be explained by the variation in the number of issues, and 76.7% of the variation is unexplained.

   (b) 15,349.725; The standard error of estimate of the proceeds for a specific number of issues is about $15,349,725,000.

11. (a) 0.981; 98.1% of the variation in sales can be explained by the variation in the total square footage, and 1.9% of the variation is unexplained.

    (b) 30.576; The standard error of estimate of the sales for a specific total square footage is about $30,576,000,000.

13. (a) 0.994; 99.4% of the variation in the median weekly earnings of female workers can be explained by the variation in the median weekly earnings of male workers, and 0.6% of the variation is unexplained.

    (b) 2.719; The standard error of estimate of the median weekly earnings of female workers for a specific median weekly earnings of male workers is about $2.72.

15. (a) 0.994; 99.4% of the variation in the money spent can be explained by the variation in the money raised, and 0.6% of the variation is unexplained.

    (b) 18.869; The standard error of estimate of the money spent for a specified amount of money raised is about $18,869,000.

17. $9,415,215,000 < y < $91,300,741,000

    You can be 95% confident that the proceeds will be between $9,415,215,000 and $91,300,741,000 when the number of initial offerings is 712 issues.

19. $513,641,000,000 < y < $668,003,000,000

    You can be 90% confident that the sales will be between $513,641,000,000 and $668,003,000,000 when the total square footage is 4.5 billion.

21. $463.15 < y < $511.18

    You can be 99% confident that the median weekly earnings of female workers will be between $463.15 and $511.18 when the median weekly earnings of male workers is $650.

23. $703,957,000 < y < $802,283,000

    You can be 95% confident that the money spent for congressional campaigns will be between $703,957,000 and $802,283,000 when the money raised is $775,800,000.

25.

27.

x_i	y_i	$\hat{y}_i$	$\hat{y}_i - \bar{y}$	$y_i - \hat{y}_i$	$y_i - \bar{y}$
9.2	6.9	6.9624	0.3764	−0.0624	0.314
9.0	6.8	6.919	0.333	−0.119	0.214
8.4	6.8	6.7888	0.2028	0.0112	0.214
8.3	6.9	6.7671	0.1811	0.1329	0.314
6.5	6.5	6.3765	−0.2095	0.1235	−0.086
6.0	6.3	6.268	−0.318	0.032	−0.286
4.9	5.9	6.0293	−0.5567	−0.1293	−0.686

29. 0.921; 92.1% of the variation in the median age of trucks can be explained by the variation in the median age of cars, and 7.9% of the variation is unexplained.

31. $6.5 < y < 7.164$

33. Fail to reject H_0. At the 1% significance level, there is not enough evidence to support the claim that there is a linear relationship between weight and hours slept.

35. $58.435 < B < 149.687$; $28.071 < M < 73.387$

Section 9.4 *(page 539)*

1. (a) 710.5 pounds   (b) 739 pounds
   (c) 844 pounds   (d) 729.5 pounds

3. (a) 7.5 cubic feet   (b) 16.8 cubic feet
   (c) 51.9 cubic feet   (d) 62.1 cubic feet

5. $\hat{y} = -2518.4 + 126.8x_1 + 66.4x_2$

   (a) 28.489   (b) 0.985

   (c) The standard error of estimate of the predicted sales given a specific total square footage and number of shopping centers is $28.489 billion. The multiple regression model explains 98.5% of the variation in y.

7. 0.981; 98.1% of the variation in y can be explained by the relationship between variables; $r^2_{\text{adj}} < r^2$.

Uses and Abuses for Chapter 9 *(page 541)*

1. Answers will vary.   2. Answers will vary.

Review Answers for Chapter 9   (page 543)

1.

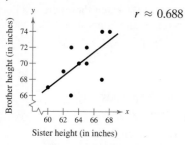

−0.939; strong negative linear correlation; milk production decreases as age increases.

3.

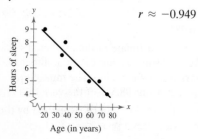

0.338; weak positive linear correlation; brain size increases as IQ increases.

5. At the 1% significance level, there is not enough evidence to conclude that there is a significant linear correlation.

7. At the 5% significance level, there is enough evidence to conclude that there is a significant linear correlation between the age of a cow and its milk production.

9. At the 1% significance level, there is not enough evidence to conclude that there is a significant linear correlation between IQ and brain size.

11. $\hat{y} = 0.757x + 21.525$

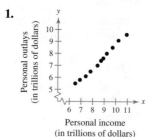

$r \approx 0.688$

13. $\hat{y} = -0.086x + 10.450$

$r \approx -0.949$

15. (a) 67.702 inches   (b) 71.487 inches

(c) It is not meaningful to predict the value of y for $x = 75$ because $x = 75$ is outside the range of the original data.

(d) It is not meaningful to predict the value of y for $x = 50$ because $x = 50$ is outside the range of the original data.

17. (a) 8.902 hours

(b) 8.3 hours

(c) It is not meaningful to predict the value of y for $x = 85$ because $x = 85$ is outside the range of the original data.

(d) 6.15 hours

19. 0.306; 30.6% of the variation is explained. 69.4% of the variation is unexplained.

21. 0.033; 3.3% of the variation is explained. 96.7% of the variation is unexplained.

23. (a) 0.897; 89.7% of the variation in the cooling capacity of an air conditioner can be explained by the variation in the living area, and 10.3% of the variation is unexplained.

(b) 568.011; The standard error of estimate of the cooling capacity for a specific living area is 568.0 Btu per hour.

25. $65.742 < y < 74.204$; You can be 90% confident that the height of a male will be between 65.742 inches and 74.204 inches when his sister is 64 inches tall.

27. $4.865 < y < 8.295$; You can be 95% confident that the hours slept will be between 4.865 and 8.295 hours for a person who is 45 years old.

29. $7342.007 < y < 12,297.895$; You can be 99% confident that the cooling capacity will be between 7342.007 Btu per hour and 12,297.895 Btu per hour when the living area is 720 square feet.

31. $\hat{y} = 3.674 + 1.287x_1 - 7.531x_2$

33. (a) 21.705   (b) 25.21   (c) 30.1   (d) 25.86

Chapter Quiz for Chapter 9   (page 547)

1.

The data appear to have a positive linear correlation. The outlays increase as the incomes increase.

2. 0.996; strong positive linear correlation

3. At the 5% significance level, there is enough evidence to conclude that a significant linear correlation exists between personal income and personal outlays for Americans.

4. $\hat{y} = 0.976x - 1.018$

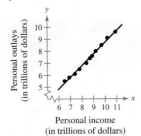

5. $5.033 trillion

6. 0.993; 99.3% of the variation in personal outlays can be explained by the variation in personal income, and 0.7% of the variation is unexplained.

7. 0.121; The standard deviation of personal outlays for a specified personal income is $0.121 trillion.

8. $6.110 < y < $6.690

You can be 95% confident that the personal outlays will be between $6.110 trillion and $6.690 trillion when personal income is $7.6 trillion.

9. (a) 1374.762 pounds   (b) 1556.755 pounds

  (c) 1183.262 pounds   (d) 1294.385 pounds

  x_2 has the greater influence on y.

Real Statistics–Real Decisions for Chapter 9   *(page 548)*

1. (a)

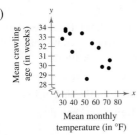

There appears to be a negative linear correlation between mean crawling age and the mean monthly temperature.

  (b) −0.700

  (c) At the 5% significance level, there is enough evidence to conclude that there is a significant linear correlation between mean crawling age and the mean monthly temperature.

  (d) $\hat{y} = -0.078x + 35.678$

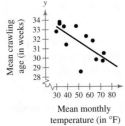

The regression line appears to be a good fit.

  (e) Answers will vary.

(f) 0.490; 49.0% of the variation in mean crawling age can be explained by the variation in the mean monthly temperature, and 51.0% of the variation is unexplained; The standard error of estimate of mean crawling age for a specific mean monthly temperature is 1.319 weeks.

2. Answers will vary.

CHAPTER 10

Section 10.1   *(page 560)*

1. A multinomial experiment is a probability experiment consisting of a fixed number of trials in which there are more than two possible outcomes for each independent trial.

3. 45   **5.** 57.5

7. (a) H_0: The distribution of motivations is 28% reward program, 24% low interest rate, 22% cash back, 8% special store discounts, and 18% other.

  H_a: The distribution of motivations differs from the claimed or expected distribution. (claim)

  (b) $\chi_0^2 = 9.488$; Rejection region: $\chi^2 > 9.488$

  (c) 9.501

  (d) Reject H_0. Yes, at the 5% significance level, there is enough evidence to conclude that the distribution of motivations differs from the claimed or expected distribution.

9. (a) H_0: The distribution of responses is 77% keeping Medicare, Social Security and Medicaid, 15% tax cuts, and 8% not sure.

  H_a: The distribution of responses differs from the claimed or expected distribution. (claim)

  (b) $\chi_0^2 = 9.210$; Rejection region: $\chi^2 > 9.210$ (c) 9.375

  (d) Reject H_0. Yes, at the 1% significance level, there is enough evidence to conclude that the distribution of responses differs from the claimed or expected distribution.

11. (a) H_0: The distribution of fatal bicycle accidents throughout the week is uniform. (claim)

  H_a: The distribution of fatal bicycle accidents throughout the week is not uniform.

  (b) $\chi_0^2 = 10.645$; Rejection region: $\chi^2 > 10.645$

  (c) 2.430

  (d) Fail to reject H_0. No, at the 10% significance level, there is not enough evidence to reject the claim that the distribution of fatal bicycle accidents throughout the week is uniform.

13. (a) H_0: The distribution of objects struck is 50% trees, 20% other, 14% utility poles, 6% embankments, 5% guardrails, 3% ditches, and 2% culverts.

  H_a: The distribution of objects struck has changed from the claimed or expected distribution. (claim)

  (b) $\chi_0^2 = 16.812$; Rejection region: $\chi^2 > 16.812$

(c) 28.501

(d) Reject H_0. Yes, at the 1% significance level, there is enough evidence to conclude that the distribution of objects struck has changed from the claimed or expected distribution.

15. (a) H_0: The distribution of educational attainment responses is uniform. (claim)

H_a: The distribution of educational attainment responses is not uniform.

(b) $\chi_0^2 = 7.378$; Rejection region: $\chi^2 > 7.378$

(c) 5.636

(d) Fail to reject H_0. No, at the 2.5% significance level, there is not enough evidence to reject the claim that the distribution of educational attainment responses is uniform.

17. (a) H_0: The national distribution of fatal work injuries is 43% transportation accidents, 18% contacts with objects/equipment, 14% assault/violent acts, 13% falls, 9% exposure to harmful substances/environments, and 3% fires/explosions.

H_a: The distribution of fatal work injuries differs from the claimed or expected distribution. (claim)

(b) $\chi_0^2 = 11.071$; Rejection region: $\chi^2 > 11.071$

(c) 76.992

(d) Reject H_0. Yes, at the 5% significance level, there is enough evidence to conclude that the western distribution of fatal work injuries differs from the national distribution.

19. (a) The expected frequencies are 17, 63, 79, 34, and 5.

(b) $\chi_0^2 = 13.277$; Rejection region: $\chi^2 > 13.277$

(c) 0.613

(d) Fail to reject H_0. At the 1% significance level, there is not enough evidence to reject the claim that the test scores are normally distributed.

Section 10.2 *(page 571)*

1. Find the sum of the row and the sum of the column in which the cell is located. Find the product of these sums. Divide the product by the sample size.

3. False. To use the chi-square independence test, each expected frequency must be greater than or equal to 5.

5. False. If the two variables of a chi-square test for independence are dependent, then you can expect a large difference between the observed frequencies and the expected frequencies.

7. (a)–(b)

Result	Athlete has		
	Stretched	Not stretched	Total
Injury	18 (20.82)	22 (19.18)	40
No injury	211 (208.18)	189 (191.82)	400
Total	229	211	440

9. (a)–(b)

Result	Treatment			
	Brand-name	Generic	Placebo	Total
Improvement	24 (15.84)	21 (14.96)	10 (24.2)	55
No change	12 (20.16)	13 (19.04)	45 (30.8)	70
Total	36	34	55	125

11. (a)–(b)

Gender	Type of car				
	Compact	Full-size	SUV	Truck/Van	Total
Male	28 (28.6)	39 (39.05)	21 (22.55)	22 (19.8)	110
Female	24 (23.4)	32 (31.95)	20 (18.45)	14 (16.2)	90
Total	52	71	41	36	200

13. (a) H_0: Skill level in a subject is independent of location. (claim)

H_a: Skill level in a subject is dependent on location.

(b) d.f. $= 2$; $\chi_0^2 = 9.210$; Rejection region: $\chi^2 > 9.210$

(c) 0.297

(d) Fail to reject H_0. At the 1% significance level, there is not enough evidence to reject the claim that skill level in a subject is independent of location.

15. (a) H_0: Grades are independent of the institution.

H_a: Grades are dependent on the institution. (claim)

(b) d.f. $= 8$; $\chi_0^2 = 15.507$; Rejection region: $\chi^2 > 15.507$

(c) 48.488

(d) Reject H_0. Yes, at the 5% significance level, there is enough evidence to conclude that grades are dependent on the institution.

17. (a) H_0: Results are independent of the type of treatment.

H_a: Results are dependent on the type of treatment. (claim)

(b) d.f. $= 1$; $\chi_0^2 = 2.706$; Rejection region: $\chi^2 > 2.706$

(c) 5.106

(d) Reject H_0. Yes, at the 10% significance level, there is enough evidence to conclude that results are dependent on the type of treatment. Answers will vary.

19. (a) H_0: Reasons are independent of the type of worker.

H_a: Reasons are dependent on the type of worker. (claim)

(b) d.f. $= 2$; $\chi_0^2 = 9.210$; Rejection region: $\chi^2 > 9.210$

(c) 7.326

(d) Fail to reject H_0. No, at the 1% significance level, there is not enough evidence to conclude that reasons for continuing education are dependent on the type of worker. On the basis of these results, marketing strategies should not differ between technical and nontechnical audiences in regard to reasons for continuing education.

21. (a) H_0: Type of crash is independent of the type of vehicle.

H_a: Type of crash is dependent on the type of vehicle. (claim)

(b) d.f. = 2; $\chi_0^2 = 5.991$; Rejection region: $\chi^2 > 5.991$

(c) 108.913

(d) Reject H_0. Yes, at the 5% significance level, there is enough evidence to conclude that the type of crash is dependent on the type of vehicle.

23. (a) H_0: Coauthorship and subject are independent.

H_a: Coauthorship and subject are dependent. (claim)

(b) d.f. = 4; $\chi_0^2 = 7.779$; Rejection region: $\chi^2 > 7.779$

(c) 5.610

(d) Fail to reject H_0. No, at the 10% significance level, there is not enough evidence to conclude that subject matter and coauthorship are related.

25. Fail to reject H_0. At the 5% significance level, there is not enough evidence to reject the claim that the proportions of motor vehicle crash deaths involving males or females are the same for each age group.

27.

	Educational Attainment			
Status	Not a high school graduate	High school graduate	Some college, no degree	Associate's, bachelor's, or advanced degree
Employed	0.061	0.190	0.113	0.273
Unemployed	0.006	0.011	0.005	0.007
Not in the labor force	0.082	0.120	0.050	0.082

29. 8.2%   **31.** 63.7%

33. Several of the expected frequencies are less than 5.

35. 29.9%

37.

	Educational Attainment			
Status	Not a high school graduate	High school graduate	Some college, no degree	Associate's, bachelor's, or advanced degree
Employed	0.411	0.591	0.672	0.754
Unemployed	0.039	0.035	0.032	0.021
Not in the labor force	0.55	0.374	0.297	0.226

39. 3.9%

41. *Sample Answer:* As educational attainment increases, employment increases.

Section 10.3   (page 585)

1. Specify the level of significance α. Determine the degrees of freedom for the numerator and denominator. Use Table 7 in Appendix B to find the critical value F.

3. (1) The samples must be randomly selected, (2) the samples must be independent, and (3) each population must have a normal distribution.

5. 2.54   **7.** 4.86   **9.** 2.06

11. Fail to reject H_0. At the 10% significance level, there is not enough evidence to support the claim.

13. Fail to reject H_0. At the 1% significance level, there is not enough evidence to reject the claim.

15. Reject H_0. At the 1% significance level, there is enough evidence to reject the claim.

17. (a) H_0: $\sigma_1^2 \leq \sigma_2^2$; H_a: $\sigma_1^2 > \sigma_2^2$ (claim)

(b) $F_0 = 2.11$; Rejection region: $F > 2.11$

(c) 1.08

(d) Fail to reject H_0.

(e) No, at the 5% significance level, there is not enough evidence to support Company A's claim that the variance of the life of its appliances is less than the variance of the life of Company B's appliances.

19. (a) H_0: $\sigma_1^2 = \sigma_2^2$ (claim); H_a: $\sigma_1^2 \neq \sigma_2^2$

(b) $F_0 = 2.635$; Rejection region: $F > 2.635$

(c) 1.282

(d) Fail to reject H_0.

(e) No, at the 10% significance level, there is not enough evidence to reject the administrator's claim that the standard deviations of science assessment test scores for eighth grade students are the same in Districts 1 and 2.

21. (a) H_0: $\sigma_1^2 \leq \sigma_2^2$; H_a: $\sigma_1^2 > \sigma_2^2$ (claim)

(b) $F_0 = 1.77$; Rejection region: $F > 1.77$

(c) 1.96

(d) Reject H_0.

(e) Yes, at the 10% significance level, there is enough evidence to support the hospital's claim that the standard deviation of waiting times has decreased.

23. (a) H_0: $\sigma_1^2 \leq \sigma_2^2$; H_a: $\sigma_1^2 > \sigma_2^2$ (claim)

(b) $F_0 = 2.35$; Rejection region: $F > 2.35$ (c) 2.41

(d) Reject H_0.

(e) Yes, at the 5% significance level, there is enough evidence to conclude that the standard deviation of the annual salaries for actuaries is greater in New York than in California.

25. Right-tailed: 14.73   **27.** (0.375, 3.774)

Left-tailed: 0.15

Section 10.4 *(page 595)*

1. H_0: $\mu_1 = \mu_2 = \mu_3 = \ldots = \mu_k$

H_a: At least one of the means is different from the others.

3. The MS_B measures the differences related to the treatment given to each sample. The MS_W measures the differences related to entries within the same sample.

5. (a) H_0: $\mu_1 = \mu_2 = \mu_3$

H_a: At least one mean is different from the others. (claim)

(b) d.f.$_N$ = 2; d.f.$_D$ = 26; F_0 = 3.37

Rejection region: $F > 3.37$

(c) 1.02

(d) Fail to reject H_0. No, at the 5% significance level, there is not enough evidence to conclude that the mean costs per ounce are different.

7. (a) H_0: $\mu_1 = \mu_2 = \mu_3$ (claim)

H_a: At least one mean is different from the others.

(b) d.f.$_N$ = 2; d.f.$_D$ = 12; F_0 = 2.81

Rejection region: $F > 2.81$

(c) 1.77

(d) Fail to reject H_0. No, at the 10% significance level, there is not enough evidence to reject the claim that the mean price is the same for the three types of treatments.

9. (a) H_0: $\mu_1 = \mu_2 = \mu_3 = \mu_4$ (claim)

H_a: At least one mean is different from the others.

(b) d.f.$_N$ = 3; d.f.$_D$ = 29; F_0 = 4.54

Rejection region: $F > 4.54$

(c) 0.56

(d) Fail to reject H_0. No, at the 1% significance level, there is not enough evidence for the company to reject the claim that the mean number of days patients spend in the hospital is the same for all four regions.

11. (a) H_0: $\mu_1 = \mu_2 = \mu_3 = \mu_4$ (claim)

H_a: At least one mean is different from the others.

(b) d.f.$_N$ = 3; d.f.$_D$ = 40; F_0 = 2.23

Rejection region: $F > 2.23$

(c) 2.76

(d) Reject H_0. Yes, at the 10% significance level, there is enough evidence for the realtor to reject the claim that the mean price is the same for all four cities.

13. (a) H_0: $\mu_1 = \mu_2 = \mu_3 = \mu_4$

H_a: At least one mean is different from the others. (claim)

(b) d.f.$_N$ = 3; d.f.$_D$ = 26; F_0 = 2.98

Rejection region: $F > 2.98$

(c) 16.20

(d) Reject H_0. Yes, at the 10% significance level, there is enough evidence to conclude that at least one of the mean prices is different from the others.

15. (a) H_0: $\mu_1 = \mu_2 = \mu_3 = \mu_4$ (claim)

H_a: At least one mean is different from the others.

(b) d.f.$_N$ = 3; d.f.$_D$ = 28; F_0 = 4.57

Rejection region: $F > 4.57$

(c) 0.46

(d) Fail to reject H_0. No, at the 1% significance level, there is not enough evidence to reject the claim that the mean numbers of female students are equal for all grades.

17. Fail to reject all null hypotheses. The interaction between advertising medium and the length of the ad has no effect on the rating and therefore there is no significant difference in the means of the ratings.

19. Fail to reject all null hypotheses. The interaction between age and gender has no effect on GPA and therefore there is no significant difference in the means of the GPAs.

21. $CV_{\text{Scheffé}}$ = 6.615

$(1, 2) \rightarrow 6.212 \rightarrow$ No difference

$(1, 3) \rightarrow 7.620 \rightarrow$ Significant difference

$(1, 4) \rightarrow 8.330 \rightarrow$ Significant difference

$(2, 3) \rightarrow 0.049 \rightarrow$ No difference

$(2, 4) \rightarrow 0.121 \rightarrow$ No difference

$(3, 4) \rightarrow 0.016 \rightarrow$ No difference

23. $CV_{\text{Scheffé}}$ = 8.94

$(1, 2) \rightarrow 2.91 \rightarrow$ No difference

$(1, 3) \rightarrow 11.19 \rightarrow$ Significant difference

$(1, 4) \rightarrow 12.70 \rightarrow$ Significant difference

$(2, 3) \rightarrow 2.17 \rightarrow$ No difference

$(2, 4) \rightarrow 25.45 \rightarrow$ Significant difference

$(3, 4) \rightarrow 45.36 \rightarrow$ Significant difference

Uses and Abuses for Chapter 10 *(page 601)*

1–2. Answers will vary.

Review Answers for Chapter 10 *(page 603)*

1. Reject H_0. At the 5% significance level, there is enough evidence to reject the claim about the distribution of health care visits by people in the United States.

3. Fail to reject H_0. At the 10% significance level, there is not enough evidence to support the executive's claim that the distribution of the percent of adults who plan to use vacation days during the summer is different from the claimed or expected distribution.

5. (a) $E_{1,1} \approx 663.49$, $E_{1,2} \approx 1440.47$, $E_{1,3} \approx 1137.54$, $E_{1,4} \approx 1237.50$, $E_{2,1} \approx 856.51$, $E_{2,2} \approx 1859.53$, $E_{2,3} \approx 1468.46$, $E_{2,4} \approx 1597.50$

(b) Reject H_0.

(c) At the 10% significance level, there is enough evidence to conclude that the educational attainment of people in the United States is dependent on age.

7. (a) $E_{1,1} \approx 143.76$, $E_{1,2} \approx 284.17$, $E_{1,3} \approx 274.14$,
$E_{1,4} \approx 237.37$, $E_{1,5} \approx 147.10$, $E_{1,6} \approx 43.46$,
$E_{2,1} \approx 71.24$, $E_{2,2} \approx 140.83$, $E_{2,3} \approx 135.86$,
$E_{2,4} \approx 117.63$, $E_{2,5} \approx 72.90$, $E_{2,6} \approx 21.54$

(b) Fail to reject H_0.

(c) At the 5% significance level, there is not enough evidence to conclude that the age group is dependent on gender.

9. 2.295 **11.** 2.39

13. Fail to reject H_0. At the 1% significance level, there is not enough evidence to reject the claim.

15. Fail to reject H_0. At the 10% significance level, there is not enough evidence to support the claim that the variation in wheat production is greater in Garfield County than in Kay County.

17. Fail to reject H_0. At the 1% significance level, there is not enough evidence to support the claim that the test score variance for females is different from that for males.

19. Reject H_0. At the 10% significance level, there is enough evidence to conclude that at least one of the mean costs is different from the others.

Chapter Quiz for Chapter 10   *(page 607)*

1. (a) $H_0: \sigma_1^2 = \sigma_2^2$; $H_a: \sigma_1^2 \neq \sigma_2^2$ (claim)

(b) 0.01   (c) $F_0 = 4.25$

(d) Rejection region: $F > 4.25$

(e) 3.57   (f) Fail to reject H_0.

(g) No, at the 1% significance level, there is not enough evidence to conclude that the variances in annual wages for San Jose, CA and Dallas, TX are different.

2. (a) $H_0: \mu_1 = \mu_2 = \mu_3$ (claim)
H_a: At least one mean is different from the others.

(b) 0.10   (c) $F_0 = 2.44$

(d) Rejection region: $F > 2.44$

(e) 12.21   (f) Reject H_0.

(g) No, at the 10% significance level, there is enough evidence to reject the claim that the mean annual wages are equal for all three cities.

3. (a) H_0: The distribution of educational achievement for people in the United States ages 35–44 is 14.8% not a high school graduate, 32.2% high school graduate, 16.8% some college, no degree; 8.6% associate degree, 18.1% bachelor's degree, and 9.5% advanced degree.

H_a: Distribution of educational achievement for people in the United States ages 35–44 differs from the claimed distribution. (claim)

(b) 0.01   (c) $\chi_0^2 = 15.086$

(d) Rejection region: $\chi^2 > 15.086$

(e) 3.528   (f) Fail to reject H_0.

(g) No, at the 1% significance level, there is not enough evidence to conclude that the distribution for people in the United States ages 25 and older differs from the distribution for people ages 35–44.

4. (a) H_0: The distribution of educational achievement for people in the United States ages 65–74 is 14.8% not a high school graduate, 32.2% high school graduate, 16.8% some college, no degree; 8.6% associate degree, 18.1% bachelor's degree, and 9.5% advanced degree.

H_a: Distribution of educational achievement for people in the United States ages 65–74 differs from the claimed distribution. (claim)

(b) 0.05   (c) $\chi_0^2 = 11.071$

(d) Rejection region: $\chi^2 > 11.071$

(e) 32.950   (f) Reject H_0.

(g) Yes, at the 5% significance level, there is enough evidence to conclude that the distribution for people in the United States ages 25 and older differs from the distribution for people ages 65–74.

Real Statistics–Real Decisions for Chapter 10   *(page 608)*

1. Reject H_0. At the 1% significance level, there is enough evidence to conclude that the distribution of responses differs from the claimed or expected distribution.

2. (a) $E_{1,1} = 15$, $E_{1,2} = 120$, $E_{1,3} = 165$, $E_{1,4} = 185$,
$E_{1,5} = 135$, $E_{1,6} = 115$, $E_{1,7} = 155$, $E_{1,8} \approx 110$,
$E_{2,1} = 15$, $E_{2,2} = 120$, $E_{2,3} = 165$, $E_{2,4} = 185$,
$E_{2,5} = 135$, $E_{2,6} = 115$, $E_{2,7} = 155$, $E_{2,8} \approx 110$

(b) Yes, at the 1% significance level, there is enough evidence to conclude that the ages of the victims is related to the type of fraud.

CHAPTER 11

Section 11.1   *(page 618)*

1. A nonparametric test is a hypothesis test that does not require any specific conditions concerning the shape of populations or the value of any population parameters.

A nonparametric test is usually easier to perform than its corresponding parametric test, but the nonparametric test is usually less efficient.

3. (a) H_0: median $\leq \$300$; H_a: median $> \$300$ (claim)

(b) 1   (c) 5   (d) Fail to reject H_0.

(e) No, at the 1% significance level, there is not enough evidence for the accountant to conclude that the median amount of new credit card charges for the previous month was more than $300.

5. (a) H_0: median $\leq \$210{,}000$ (claim)
H_a: median $> \$210{,}000$

(b) 1   (c) 3   (d) Fail to reject H_0.

(e) No, at the 5% significance level, there is not enough evidence to reject the agent's claim that the median sales price of new privately owned one-family homes sold in the past year is $210,000 or less.

7. (a) H_0: median $\geq$ $2200 (claim); H_a: median < $2200

(b) −2.05   (c) −1.47   (d) Fail to reject H_0.

(e) No, at the 2% significance level, there is not enough evidence to reject the institution's claim that the median amount of credit card debt for families holding such debts is at least $2200.

9. (a) H_0: median $\leq$ 30; H_a: median > 30 (claim)

(b) 2   (c) 4   (d) Fail to reject H_0.

(e) At the 1% significance level, there is not enough evidence to support the association's claim that the median age of recipients of engineering doctorates is greater than 30 years.

11. (a) H_0: median = 4 (claim); H_a: median $\neq$ 4

(b) −1.96   (c) −1.04   (d) Fail to reject H_0.

(e) No, at the 5% significance level, there is not enough evidence to reject the organization's claim that the median number of rooms in renter-occupied units is 4.

13. (a) H_0: median = $12.16 (claim); H_a: median $\neq$ $12.16

(b) −2.575   (c) −0.961   (d) Fail to reject H_0.

(e) No, at the 1% significance level, there is not enough evidence to reject the organization's claim that the median hourly earnings of male workers paid hourly rates is $12.16.

15. (a) H_0: The lower back pain intensity scores have not decreased.

H_a: The lower back pain intensity scores have decreased. (claim)

(b) 1   (c) 0   (d) Reject H_0.

(e) Yes, at the 5% significance level, there is enough evidence to conclude that the lower back pain intensity scores were lower after the acupuncture.

17. (a) H_0: The SAT scores have not improved.

H_a: The SAT scores have improved. (claim)

(b) 2   (c) 4   (d) Fail to reject H_0.

(e) No, at the 5% significance level, there is not enough evidence to conclude that verbal SAT scores improved.

19. (a) Fail to reject H_0.

(b) At the 5% significance level, there is not enough evidence to reject the claim that the proportion of adults who prefer unplanned travel activities is equal to the proportion of adults who prefer planned travel activities.

21. (a) H_0: median $\leq$ $585 (claim); H_a: median > $585

(b) 2.33   (c) 1.46   (d) Fail to reject H_0.

(e) No, at the 1% significance level, there is not enough evidence to reject the organization's claim that the median weekly earnings of female workers is less than or equal to $585.

23. (a) H_0: median $\leq$ 25.5; H_a: median > 25.5 (claim)

(b) 1.645   (c) 1.936   (d) Reject H_0.

(e) Yes, at the 5% significance level, there is enough evidence to support the counselor's claim that the median age of brides at the time of their first marriage is greater than 25.5 years.

Section 11.2   *(page 629)*

1. If the samples are dependent, use a Wilcoxon signed-rank test. If the samples are independent, use a Wilcoxon rank sum test.

3. (a) H_0: There is no reduction in diastolic blood pressure. (claim)

H_a: There is a reduction in diastolic blood pressure.

(b) Wilcoxon signed-rank test

(c) 10   (d) 17   (e) Fail to reject H_0.

(f) No, at the 1% significance level, there is not enough evidence to reject the claim that there was no reduction in diastolic blood pressure.

5. (a) H_0: There is no difference in the earnings.

H_a: There is a difference in the earnings. (claim)

(b) Wilcoxon rank sum test

(c) ±1.96   (d) −3.66   (e) Reject H_0.

(f) Yes, at the 5% significance level, there is enough evidence to support the administrator's belief that there is a difference in the earnings of people with bachelor's degrees and those with associate's degrees.

7. (a) H_0: There is no difference in salaries.

H_a: There is a difference in salaries. (claim)

(b) Wilcoxon rank sum test

(c) ±1.96   (d) −1.91 (or 1.91)   (e) Fail to reject H_0.

(f) No, at the 5% significance level, there is not enough evidence to support the representative's claim that there is a difference in the salaries earned by teachers in Massachusetts and Connecticut.

9. Yes, at the 10% significance level, there is enough evidence for the engineer to conclude that the gas mileage is improved.

Section 11.3   *(page 637)*

1. The conditions for using a Kruskal-Wallis test are that each sample must be randomly selected and the size of each sample must be at least 5.

3. (a) H_0: There is no difference in the premiums.

H_a: There is a difference in the premiums. (claim)

(b) 5.991   (c) 13.091   (d) Reject H_0.

(e) Yes, at the 5% significance level, there is enough evidence to conclude that the distributions of the annual premiums of the three states are different.

5. (a) H_0: There is no difference in the salaries.

H_a: There is a difference in the salaries. (claim)

(b) 6.251 (c) 1.024 (d) Fail to reject H_0.

(e) No, at the 10% significance level, there is not enough evidence to conclude that the distributions of the annual salaries in the four states are different.

7. (a) Fail to reject H_0. (b) Fail to reject H_0.

(c) Both tests come to the same decision, which is that there is not enough evidence to support the claim that there is a difference in the number of days spent in the hospital.

Section 11.4 *(page 642)*

1. The Spearman rank correlation coefficient can be used to describe the relationship between linear or nonlinear data. Also, it can be used for data at the ordinal level and it is easier to calculate by hand than the Pearson correlation coefficient.

3. (a) H_0: $\rho_s = 0$; H_a: $\rho_s \neq 0$ (claim)

(b) 0.929 (c) 0.857 (d) Fail to reject H_0.

(e) No, at the 1% significance level, there is not enough evidence to support the claim that there is a correlation between debt and income in the farming business.

5. (a) H_0: $\rho_s = 0$; H_a: $\rho_s \neq 0$ (claim)

(b) 0.881 (c) 0.208 (d) Fail to reject H_0.

(e) No, at the 1% significance level, there is not enough evidence to conclude that there is a correlation between the overall score and the price.

7. Fail to reject H_0. No, at the 5% significance level, there is not enough evidence to conclude that there is a correlation between science achievement scores and GNP.

9. Reject H_0. Yes, at the 5% significance level, there is enough evidence to conclude that there is a correlation between science and mathematics achievement scores.

11. Fail to reject H_0. No, at the 5% significance level, there is not enough evidence to conclude that there is a correlation between average hours worked and the number of on-the-job injuries.

Section 11.5 *(page 651)*

1. Number of runs: 8

Run lengths: 1, 1, 1, 1, 3, 3, 1, 1

3. Number of runs: 9

Run lengths: 1, 1, 1, 1, 1, 6, 3, 2, 4

5. n_1 = number of Ts = 6

n_2 = number of Fs = 6

7. n_1 = number of Ms = 10

n_2 = number of Fs = 10

9. too high: 11 **11.** too high: 14

too low: 3 too low: 5

13. (a) H_0: The coin tosses were random.

H_a: The coin tosses were not random. (claim)

(b) lower critical value = 4

upper critical value = 14

(c) 9 (d) Fail to reject H_0.

(e) At the 5% significance level, there is not enough evidence to support the claim that the coin tosses were not random.

15. (a) H_0: The sequence of digits was randomly generated.

H_a: The sequence of digits was not randomly generated. (claim)

(b) lower critical value = 11

upper critical value = 23

(c) 9 (d) Reject H_0.

(e) At the 5% significance level, there is enough evidence to support the claim that the sequence of digits was not randomly generated.

17. (a) H_0: The sequence is random.

H_a: The sequence is not random. (claim)

(b) ± 1.96 (c) -0.83 (d) Fail to reject H_0.

(e) At the 5% significance level, there is not enough evidence to support the claim that the sequence is not random.

19. Fail to reject H_0. At the 5% significance level, there is not enough evidence to support the claim that the daily high temperatures do not occur randomly.

21. Answers will vary.

Uses and Abuses for Chapter 11 *(page 653)*

1. Answers will vary.

2. Sign test $\rightarrow$ z-test

Paired-sample sign test $\rightarrow$ t-test

Wilcoxon signed-rank test $\rightarrow$ t-test

Wilcoxon rank sum test $\rightarrow$ z or t-test

Kruskal-Wallis test $\rightarrow$ one-way ANOVA

Spearman rank correlation coefficient $\rightarrow$ Pearson correlation coefficient

Review Answers for Chapter 11 *(page 655)*

1. (a) H_0: median = \$24,300 (claim)

H_a: median $\neq$ \$24,300

(b) 2 (c) 7 (d) Fail to reject H_0.

(e) No, at the 1% significance level, there is not enough evidence to reject the institution's claim that the median value of stock among families that own stock is \$24,300.

3. (a) H_0: median ≤ 6 (claim); H_a: median > 6

(b) -1.28 (c) -2.03 (d) Reject H_0.

(e) Yes, at the 10% significance level, there is enough evidence to reject the company's claim that the median turnover time is 6 hours or less.

5. (a) H_0: There is no reduction in diastolic blood pressure. (claim)

H_a: There is a reduction in diastolic blood pressure.

(b) 2   (c) 3   (d) Fail to reject H_0.

(e) No, at the 5% significance level, there is not enough evidence to reject the claim that there was no reduction in diastolic blood pressure.

7. (a) Independent; Wilcoxon rank sum test

(b) H_0: There is no difference in the total time to earn a doctorate degree by female and male graduate students.

H_a: There is a difference in the total time to earn a doctorate degree by female and male graduate students. (claim)

(c) ±2.575   (d) −1.357 (or 1.357)

(e) Fail to reject H_0.

(f) No, at the 1% significance level, there is not enough evidence to support the claim that there is a difference in the total time to earn a doctorate degree by female and male graduate students.

9. (a) H_0: There is no difference in salaries between the fields of study.

H_a: There is a difference in salaries between the fields of study. (claim)

(b) 5.991   (c) 21.695   (d) Reject H_0.

(e) Yes, at the 5% significance level, there is enough evidence to conclude that the distributions of the starting salaries in the three fields of study are different.

11. (a) H_0: $\rho_s = 0$; H_a: $\rho_s \neq 0$ (claim)

(b) 0.881   (c) 0.321   (d) Fail to reject H_0.

(e) No, at the 1% significance level, there is not enough evidence to support the claim that there is a correlation between overall score and price.

13. (a) H_0: The traffic stops were random by gender.

H_a: The traffic stops were not random by gender. (claim)

(b) lower critical value = 8

upper critical value = 19

(c) 14   (d) Fail to reject H_0.

(e) No, at the 5% significance level, there is not enough evidence to support the claim that the stops were not random by gender.

Chapter Quiz for Chapter 11   (page 659)

1. (a) H_0: There is no difference in the salaries between genders.

H_a: There is a difference in the salaries between genders. (claim)

(b) Wilcoxon rank sum test

(c) ±1.645   (d) −2.835 (or 2.835)   (e) Reject H_0.

(f) Yes, at the 10% significance level, there is enough evidence to support the organization's claim that there is a difference in the salaries earned by female and male employees of state and local governments.

2. (a) H_0: median = 50 (claim); H_a: median ≠ 50

(b) Sign test   (c) 5   (d) 9   (e) Fail to reject H_0.

(f) No, at the 5% significance level, there is not enough evidence to reject the organization's claim that the median number of annual volunteer hours for volunteers is 50 hours.

3. (a) H_0: There is no difference in the monthly rent between the regions.

H_a: There is a difference in the monthly rent between the regions. (claim)

(b) Kruskal-Wallis test

(c) 7.815   (d) 11.826   (e) Reject H_0.

(f) Yes, at the 5% significance level, there is enough evidence for the association to conclude that the distributions of the monthly rent prices in these regions are different.

4. (a) H_0: The days with rain are random.

H_a: The days with rain are not random. (claim)

(b) Runs test

(c) lower critical value = 10

upper critical value = 22

(d) 16   (e) Fail to reject H_0.

(f) No, at the 5% significance level, there is not enough evidence for the meteorologist to conclude that days with rain are not random.

Real Statistics–Real Decisions for Chapter 11   (page 660)

1. (a) random sample

(b) Answers will vary.

(c) Answers will vary.

2. (a) Answers will vary.

(b) Sign test; You need to use the nonparametric test because nothing is known about the shape of the population.

(c) H_0: median ≥ 4.0; H_a: median < 4.0 (claim)

(d) Fail to reject H_0. At the 5% significance level, there is not enough evidence to support the claim that the median tenure for workers from the representative's district is less than 4.0 years.

3. (a) Wilcoxon rank sum test; You need to use the nonparametric test because nothing is known about the shape of the population.

(b) H_0: The median tenure for male workers is less than or equal to the median tenure for female workers.

H_a: The median tenure for male workers is greater than the median tenure for female workers. (claim)

(c) Fail to reject H_0. At the 5% significance level, there is not enough evidence to support the claim that the median tenure for male workers is greater than the median tenure for female workers.

Cumulative Review for Chapters 9–11 *(page 662)*

1. (a)

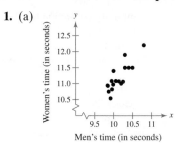

0.828; Strong positive linear correlation

(b) At the 5% significance level, there is enough evidence to conclude that there is a significant linear correlation between the winning times for the men's and women's 100-meter runs in the Summer Olympics from 1928 to 2004.

(c) $\hat{y} = 1.423x - 3.204$

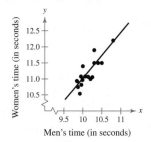

(d) 10.884 seconds

2. Yes, at the 5% significance level, there is enough evidence to support the agency's claim that there is a difference in the weekly earnings of workers who are union members and workers who are not union members.

3. No, at the 1% significance level, there is not enough evidence to reject the company's claim that the median age of people with mutual funds is 48 years.

4. Yes, at the 10% significance level, there is enough evidence to reject the claim that the mean expenditures are equal for all four regions.

5. No, at the 10% significance level, there is not enough evidence to reject the administrator's claim that the standard deviations of reading test scores for eighth grade students are the same in Colorado and Utah.

6. Yes, at the 1% significance level, there is enough evidence for the representative to conclude that the distributions of annual household incomes in these regions are different.

7. At the 5% significance level, there is not enough evidence to reject the claim about the distribution of physician practices in the United States and the number of physicians.

8. (a) 0.733; About 73.3% of the variation in height can be explained by the variation in metacarpal bone length; About 26.7% of the variation is unexplained.

(b) 4.255; The standard error of estimate of the height for a specific metacarpal bone length is about 4.255 centimeters.

(c) $168.026 < y < 190.83$; You can be 95% confident that the height will be between 168.026 centimeters and 190.83 centimeters when the metacarpal bone length is 50 centimeters.

9. No, at the 10% significance level, there is not enough evidence to conclude that there is a correlation between the overall score and the price.

10. (a) 64.763 bushels (b) 61.447 bushels

Index

A

Addition Rule, 193
  for the probability of A
    and B, 161, 164
alternative formula
  for the standardized test
    statistic for a proportion,
    412
  for variance and standard
    deviation, 98
alternative hypothesis
  one-sample, 365
  two-sample, 440
analysis of variance
  (ANOVA) test
  one-way, 588, 589
  two-way, 594
approximating binomial
  probabilities, 288
area of a region
  under a probability curve,
    243
  under a standard normal
    curve, 243

B

back-to-back stem-and-leaf
  plot, 66
Bayes's Theorem, 158
biased sample, 22
bimodal, 69
binomial distribution, 225
  mean of a, 214
  normal approximation to a,
    285
  population parameters of a,
    214
  standard deviation of a, 214
  variance of a, 214
binomial experiment, 206, 552
  notation for, 206
binomial probabilities, using
  the normal distribution to
    approximate, 288
binomial probability
  distribution, 209, 225
binomial probability formula,
  208
bivariate normal distribution,
  529
blinding, 20
blocks, 20
box-and-whisker plot, 104
  side-by-side, 114

C

calculating a correlation
  coefficient, 499
categories, 552
c-confidence interval
  for the population mean,
    313
  for the population
    proportion, 335
cell, 565
census, 5, 22
center, 40
central angle, 58
Central Limit Theorem, 272
chart
  control, 260
  Pareto, 59
  pie, 58
  time series, 61
Chebychev's Theorem, 89
chi-square distribution, 344
chi-square goodness-of-fit test,
  552, 554
chi-square independence test,
  567
chi-square test
  finding critical values for,
    414
  for independence, 567
  for standard deviation, 416,
    425
  for variance, 416, 425
  test statistic for, 416
class, 40
  boundaries, 44
  mark, 42
  width, 40
class limit
  lower, 40
  upper, 40
classical probability, 136, 164
cluster sample, 23
clusters, 23
  of data, 73
coefficient
  correlation, 499
    t-test for, 504
  of determination, 526
  of variation, 98
combination
  of n objects taken r at a
    time, 174, 175
complement of event E, 140
complementary events, 164

completely randomized
  design, 20
conditional probability, 149
conditional relative frequency,
  577
confidence interval, 313
  for a population mean,
    finding a, 313
  for a population proportion,
    constructing a, 335
  for a population standard
    deviation, 346
  for a population variance,
    346
  for slope, 535
  for the difference between
    means, 450
  for the difference between
    two population
    proportions, 478
  for the mean of the
    differences of paired
    data, 470
  for y-intercept, 535
confidence, level of, 311
confounding variable, 20
constructing
  a confidence interval for a
    population proportion,
    335
  a confidence interval for a
    population standard
    deviation, 346
  a confidence interval for a
    population variance, 346
  a confidence interval for the
    difference between
    means, 450, 459, 460
  a confidence interval for the
    difference between two
    population proportions,
    478
  a confidence interval for the
    mean of the differences
    of paired data, 470
  a confidence interval for the
    mean: t-distribution, 327
  a discrete probability
    distribution, 196
  a frequency distribution
    from a data set, 40
  an ogive, 47
  a prediction interval for y
    for a specific value of x,
    529

contingency table, 565
contingency table cells, finding
  the expected frequency
  for, 565
continuity, correction for, 287
continuous probability
  distribution, 240
continuous random variable,
  194, 240
control
  chart, 260
  group, 18
convenience sample, 24
correction factor
  finite, 282
  finite population, 323
correction for continuity, 287
correlation, 496
correlation coefficient, 499
  Pearson product moment,
    499
  Spearman rank, 639
  t-test for, 504
  using a table for, 502
counting principle
  fundamental, 134, 175
c-prediction interval, 529
critical region, 384
critical value, 311, 384
  in a normal distribution,
    finding, 384
  in a t-distribution, finding,
    397
cumulative frequency, 42
  graph, 46
curve, normal, 240

D

data, 4
  qualitative, 11
  quantitative, 11
data sets
  center of, 40
  paired, 60
  shape of, 40
  variability of, 40
decision rule
  based on P-value, 372, 379
  based on rejection region,
    386
degrees of freedom, 325
  corresponding to the
    variance in the
    denominator, 579

corresponding to the variance in the numerator, 579
density function, probability, 240
dependent
  event, 150
  random variable, 205
  sample, 438
  variable, 496
descriptive statistics, 7
designing a statistical study, 18
determination, coefficient of, 526
deviation, 83
  explained, 525
  total, 525
  unexplained, 525
d.f.$_D$, 579
d.f.$_N$, 579
diagram, tree, 132
discrete probability distribution, 195
discrete random variable, 194
  expected value of a, 200
  mean of a, 198
  standard deviation of a, 199
  variance of a, 199
distinguishable permutation, 173
distribution
  binomial, 225
  binomial probability, 209, 225
  bivariate normal, 529
  chi-square, 344
  continuous probability, 240
  discrete probability, 195
  frequency, 40
  F-, 579
  geometric, 222, 225
  hypergeometric, 228
  normal, 240
    finding critical values in, 384
    properties of a, 240
  Poisson, 223, 225
  sampling, 270
  standard normal, 243, A1, A2
    properties of, 243, A2
  t-, 325
    finding critical values in, 397
  uniform, 252
dot plot, 57
double-blind experiment, 20
drawing a box-and-whisker plot, 105

E

e, 223
effect
  interaction, 594
  main, 594

elements of well-designed experiment, 20
empirical probability, 137, 164
Empirical Rule (or 68-95-99.7 Rule), 88
equation
  exponential, 522
  logarithmic, 522
  multiple regression, 536
  of a regression line, 514
  power, 522
error
  margin of, 312
  of estimate
    standard, 527
  of the mean
    standard, 270, 272
  sampling, 270, 312
  tolerance, 312
  type I, 367
  type II, 367
estimate
  interval, 311
  point, 310
  pooled, of the standard deviation, 452
  standard error of, 527
estimating p by minimum sample size, 338
event, 132
  complement of an, 140
  dependent, 150
  independent, 150, 164
  mutually exclusive, 160, 164
  simple, 133
expected frequency, 553
  finding for contingency table cells, 565
expected value, 200
  of a discrete random variable, 200
experiment, 18
  binomial, 206, 552
  double-blind, 20
  multinomial, 219, 552
  probability, 132
  well designed, elements of, 20
experimental design
  completely randomized, 20
  matched-pairs, 21
  randomized block, 20
experimental unit, 18
explained deviation, 525
explained variation, 525
explanatory variable, 496
exploratory data analysis (EDA), 55
exponential equation, 522

F

factorial, 172
false positive, 159
F-distribution, 579

finding a confidence interval for a population mean, 313
finding a minimum sample size
  to estimate μ, 316
  to estimate p, 338
finding areas under the standard normal curve, 245, A4
finding critical values
  for the chi-square test, 414
  for the F-distribution, 580
  in a normal distribution, 384
  in a t-distribution, 397
finding the expected frequency for contingency table cells, 565
finding the mean of a frequency distribution, 72
finding the P-value for a hypothesis test, 379
finding the standard error of estimate, 527
finding the test statistic for the one-way ANOVA test, 589
finite correction factor, 282
finite population correction factor, 323
first quartile, 102
five-number summary, 105
formula, binomial probability, 208
fractiles, 102
frequency, 40
  conditional relative, 577
  cumulative, 42
  expected, 553
  joint, 565
  marginal, 565
  observed, 553
  relative, 42
frequency distribution, 40
  mean of, 72
  rectangular, 73
  skewed left (negatively skewed), 73
  skewed right (positively skewed), 73
  symmetric, 73
  uniform, 73
frequency histogram, 44
  relative, 46
frequency polygon, 45
F-test for variances, two-sample, 582
function, probability density 240
Fundamental Counting Principle, 134, 175

G

gaps, 70
geometric distribution, 222, 225

mean of a, 228
variance of a, 228
geometric probability, 222
goodness-of-fit test, chi-square, 552, 554
graph, cumulative frequency, 46

H

Hawthorne effect, 20
histogram
  frequency, 44
  relative frequency, 46
history of statistics timeline, 35
homogeneity of proportions test, 575
hypergeometric distribution, 228
hypothesis
  alternative, 365, 440
  null, 365, 440
  statistical, 365
hypothesis test, 364
  finding the P-value for, 379
hypothesis testing
  for slope, 535
  steps for, 373
  summary of 424, 425

I

independence test, chi-square, 567
independent, 565
  event, 150, 164
  random variable, 205
  sample, 438
  variable, 496
inferential statistics, 7
inflection points, 240, 241
influential point, 521
inherent zero, 13
interaction effect, 594
interquartile range (IQR), 104
interval estimate, 311
interval level of measurement, 13, 14
interval, c-prediction, 529
intervals, 40

J

joint frequency, 565

K

Kruskal-Wallis test, 633
  test statistic for, 633

L

law of large numbers, 138
leaf, 55
left, skewed, 73
left-tailed test, 370
  for a population correlation coefficient, 504
length of a run, 645

level of confidence, 311
level of significance, 369, 502
levels of measurement
    interval, 13, 14
    nominal, 12, 14
    ordinal, 12, 14
    ratio, 13, 14
limit
    lower class, 40
    upper class, 40
linear transformation of a
    random variable, 205
line
    of best fit, 513
    regression, 502, 513
logarithmic
    equation, 522
    transformation, 522
lower class limit, 40

M

main effect, 594
making an interval estimate,
    311
margin of error, 312
marginal frequency, 565
matched-pairs design, 21
matched samples, 438
maximum error of estimate,
    312
mean, 67
    difference between
        two-sample t-test for, 452
        two-sample z-test for, 441
    of a binomial distribution,
        214
    of a discrete random
        variable, 198
    of a frequency distribution,
        72
    of a geometric distribution,
        228
    standard error, 270, 272
    t-test for, 399
    trimmed, 80
    weighted, 71
mean absolute deviation
    (MAD), 99
mean square
    between, 588
    within, 588
means, sampling distribution
    of sample, 270
measure of central tendency,
    67
measurement
    interval level of, 13, 14
    nominal level of, 12, 14
    ordinal level of, 12, 14
    ratio level of, 13, 14
median, 68
midpoint, 42
midquartile, 114
midrange, 80

minimum sample size
    to estimate μ, 316
    to estimate p, 338
mode, 69
multinomial experiment, 219,
    552
multiple regression equation,
    536
Multiplication Rule for the
    probability of A and B,
    151, 164
mutually exclusive, 160, 164

N

n factorial, 172
negative linear correlation,
    496
negatively skewed, 73
no correlation, 496
nominal level of
    measurement, 12, 14
nonlinear correlation, 496
nonparametric test, 612
normal approximation to a
    binomial distribution, 285
normal curve, 240
normal distribution, 240
    bivariate, 529
    finding critical values in, 384
    properties of a, 240
    standard, 243, A1, A2
        finding areas under, 245,
        A4
        properties of, 243, A2
normal probability plot, A30
normal quantile plot, A30
notation for binomial
    experiment, 206
null hypothesis
    one-sample, 365
    two-sample, 440

O

observational study, 18
observed frequency, 553
odds, 147
    of winning, 147
    of losing, 147
ogive, 46
one-way analysis of variance,
    588
    test, 588, 589
        finding the test statistic
        for, 589
ordered stem-and-leaf plot, 55
ordinal level of measurement,
    12, 14
outcome, 132
outlier, 55, 70

P

paired data sets, 60
paired samples, 438
    sign test, performing a, 616

parameter, 6
    Population
        binomial distribution, 214
Pareto chart, 59
Pearson product moment
    correlation coefficient,
    499
Pearson's index of skewness,
    99
performing a chi-square
    goodness-of-fit test, 554
performing a chi-square test
    for independence, 568
performing a Kruskal-Wallis
    test, 634
performing a one-way analysis
    of variance test, 590
performing a paired-sample
    sign test, 616
performing a runs test for
    randomness, 647
performing a sign test for a
    population median, 613
performing a Wilcoxon rank
    sum test, 626
performing a Wilcoxon signed-
    rank test, 623
permutation, 172, 175
    distinguishable, 173, 175
    of n objects taken r at a
        time, 172, 175
pie chart, 58
placebo, 18
    effect, 20
plot
    box-and-whisker, 104
    dot, 57
    normal probability, A30
    normal quantile, A30
    residual, 521
    scatter, 60, 496
    stem-and-leaf, 55
point, influential, 521
point estimate, 310
    for σ, 344
    for σ^2, 344
    for p, 334
Poisson distribution, 223, 225
    variance of a, 228
polygon, frequency, 45
pooled estimate of the
    standard deviation, 452
population, 5
    correlation coefficient
        using Table 11 for the, 502
        using the t-test for the,
        504
    mean, finding a confidence
        interval for, 313
    parameters
        of a binomial
            distribution, 214
    proportion, 334
        constructing a confidence
        interval for, 335

standard deviation, 84
    variance, 83, 84
positive linear correlation, 496
positively skewed, 73
power equation, 522
power of the test, 369
principle, fundamental
    counting, 134, 175
probability
    Addition Rule for, 161, 164
    classical, 136, 164
    conditional, 149
    curve, area of a region
        under, 243
    density function, 240
    empirical, 137, 164
    experiment, 132
    formula, binomial, 208
    geometric, 222
    Multiplication Rule for, 151,
        164
    rule, range of, 139, 164
    statistical, 137
    subjective, 138
    that the first success will
        occur on trial number
        x, 222, 225
    theoretical, 136
    value, 369
probability distribution
    binomial, 209, 225
    chi-square, 344
    continuous, 240
    discrete, 195
    geometric, 222, 225
    normal properties of a, 240
    Poisson, 223, 225
    sampling, 270
    standard normal, 243
probability plot, normal, A30
properties
    of a normal distribution, 240
    of sampling distributions of
        sample means, 270
    of the standard normal
        distribution, 243, A2
proportion
    population, 334
        confidence interval for,
        335
        z-test for, 407
    sample, 283
proportions, sampling
    distribution of sample,
    283
proportions test, homogeneity
    of, 575
P-value, 369
    decision rule based on, 372,
    379
    for a hypothesis test, finding
        the, 379

Q

qualitative data, 11

quantile plot, normal, A30
quantitative data, 11
quartile, 102
  first, 102
  second, 102
  third, 102

R

random sample, simple, 22
random selection, 5
random variable, 194
  continuous, 194, 240
  dependent, 205
  discrete, 194
    expected value of a, 200
    mean of a, 198
    standard deviation of a, 199
    variance of a, 199
  independent, 205
  linear transformation of a, 205
randomization, 20
randomized block design, 20
randomness, runs test for, 646
range, 40, 82
  interquartile, 104
  of probabilities rule, 139, 164
rank correlation coefficient, Spearman, 639
rank sum test, Wilcoxon, 625
ratio level of measurement, 13, 14
rectangular, frequency distribution, 73
region
  critical, 384
  rejection, 384
regression line, 502, 513
  deviation about, 525
  equation of, 514
  variation about, 525
regression, multiple, 536
rejection region, 384
  decision rule based on, 386
relative frequency, 42
  conditional, 577
  histogram, 46
replacement
  with, 23
  without, 23, 207
replication, 21
residual plot, 521
residuals, 513
response variable, 496
right, skewed, 73
right-tailed test, 370
  for a population correlation coefficient, 504
rule
  addition, 161, 164
  decision
    based on *P*-value, 372, 379
    based on rejection region, 386

  empirical, 88
  multiplication, 151, 164
  range of probabilities, 139, 164
run, 645
runs test for randomness, 646

S

sample, 5
  biased, 22
  cluster, 23
  convenience, 24
  dependent, 438
  independent, 438
  matched, 438
  paired, 438
  random, 22
    simple, 22
  stratified, 23
  systematic, 24
sample means
  sampling distribution for the difference of, 440
  sampling distribution of, 270
sample proportion, 283
sample proportions, sampling distribution of, 283
sample size
  minimum to estimate p, 338
  minimum to estimate μ, 316
sample space, 132
sample standard deviation, 85
  for grouped data, 90
sample variance, 85
sampling, 22
sampling distribution, 270
  for the difference of the sample means, 440
  for the difference between the sample proportions, 471
  of sample means, 270
  of sample proportions, 283
  properties of, 270
sampling error, 22, 270, 312
sampling process
  with replacement, 23
  without replacement, 23
scatter plot, 60, 496
Scheffé Test, 600
score, standard, 107
second quartile, 102
shape, 40
side-by-side box-and-whisker plot, 114
sigma, 41
significance, level of, 369, 502
sign test, 612
  performing a paired-sample, 616
  test statistic for, 613
signed-rank test, Wilcoxon, 623
simple event, 133
simple random sample, 22

simulation, 19
skewed
  left, 73
  negatively, 73
  positively, 73
  right, 73
slope
  confidence interval for, 535
  hypothesis testing for, 535
Spearman rank correlation coefficient, 639
standard deviation
  chi-square test for, 416, 425
  confidence intervals for, 346
  of a binomial distribution, 214
  of a discrete random variable, 199
  point estimate for, 344
  pooled estimate of, 452
  population, 84
  sample 85
standard error
  of estimate, 527
  of the mean, 270, 272
standard normal curve, finding areas under, 245, A4
standard normal distribution, 243, A1, A2
  properties of, 243, A2
standard score, 107
standardized test statistic,
  for a chi-square test,
    for standard deviation, 416, 425
    for variance, 416, 425
  for the correlation coefficient
    t-test, 504
  for the difference between means
    t-test, 462
    z-test, 441
  for the difference between proportions
    z-test, 472
  for a *t*-test
    for a mean 399, 425
  for a *z*-test
    for a mean, 381, 425
    for a proportion, 407, 425
    two-sample, 441
statistic, 6
statistical hypothesis, 365
statistical probability, 137
statistical process control (SPC), 260
statistical study, designing a, 18
statistics, 4
  descriptive, 7
  history of, timeline, 35
  inferential, 7
status, 4
stem, 55

stem-and-leaf plot, 55
  back-to-back, 66
  ordered, 55
  unordered, 55
steps for hypothesis testing, 373
strata, 23
stratified sample, 23
study
  observational, 18
  statistical, designing a, 18
subjective probability, 138
success, population proportion of, 334
summary
  five-number, 105
  of counting principles, 175
  of discrete probability distributions, 225
  of four levels of measurement, 14
  of hypothesis testing, 424, 425
  of probability, 164
sum of squares, 83–85
sum test, Wilcoxon rank, 625
survey, 19
survey questions
  open question, 27
  closed question, 27
symmetric, frequency distribution, 73
systematic sample, 24

T

table, contingency, 565
t-distribution, 325
  constructing a confidence interval for the mean, 327
  finding critical values in, 397
test
  chi-square
    goodness-of-fit, 552, 554
    independence, 567
  for randomness, runs, 646
  hypothesis, 364
  Kruskal-Wallis, 633
  left-tailed, 370
  nonparametric, 612
  one-way analysis of variance, 588, 589
  paired-sample sign, 616
  power of the, 369
  right-tailed, 370
  Scheffé, 600
  sign, 612
  two-tailed, 370
  two-way analysis of variance, 594
  Wilcoxon rank sum, 625
  Wilcoxon signed-rank, 623
test statistic, 369
  for a chi-square test, 416, 425

for the correlation
coefficient, 504
for the difference between
means, 462
for the difference between
proportions, 472
for the Kruskal-Wallis test,
633
for a mean
large sample, 381, 425
small sample, 399, 425
for a proportion, 407, 425
for the runs test, 647
for the sign test, 613
for a two-sample z-test, 441
for the Wilcoxon rank sum
test, 626
testing the significance of the
Spearman rank
correlation coefficient,
640
Theorem
Bayes's, 158
Central Limit, 272
Chebychev's, 89
theoretical probability, 136
third quartile, 102
time series, 61
chart, 61
timeline, history of statistics, 35
total deviation, 525
total variation, 525
transformation, logarithmic, 522
transformations to achieve
linearity, 522
transforming a z-score to an
x-value, 263
treatment, 18
tree diagram, 132
trimmed mean, 80
t-test
for the correlation
coefficient, 504
for the difference between
means, 462
for a mean, 399, 425
two-sample
for the difference
between means, 452
two-sample
F-test for variances, 582
t-test, 452
z-test
for the difference
between means, 441
for the difference
between proportions, 472
two-tailed test, 370
for a population correlation
coefficient, 504
two-way analysis of variance
test, 594
type I error, 367
type II error, 367

U
unexplained deviation, 525
unexplained variation, 525
uniform distribution, 252
uniform, frequency
distribution, 73
upper class limit, 40
using the chi-square test for a
variance or standard
deviation, 416
using the normal distribution
to approximate binomial
probabilities, 288
using P-values for a z-test for
a mean, 381
using rejection regions for a
z-test for a mean, 386
using Table 11 for the
correlation coefficient,
502
using the t-test
for the correlation
coefficient ρ, 504
for the difference between
means, 462
for a mean, 399
using a two-sample F-test to
compare σ₁² and σ₂², 582
using a two-sample t-test for
the difference between
means, 453
using a two-sample z-test
for the difference
between means, 441
for the difference
between proportions,
472
using a z-test for a proportion,
407

V
value
critical 311, 384
expected, 200
probability 369
variable
confounding, 20
dependent, 496
explanatory, 496
independent, 496
random, 194
continuous, 194, 240
response, 496
variability, 40
variance
chi-square test for, 416, 425
confidence intervals for, 346
mean square
between, 588
within, 588
of a binomial distribution,
214
of a discrete random
variable, 199

of a geometric distribution,
228
of a Poisson distribution,
228
one-way analysis of, 588
point estimate for, 344
population, 83, 84
sample, 85
two-sample F-test for, 582
two-way analysis of, 594
variation
explained, 525
total, 525
unexplained, 525

W
weighted mean, 71
Wilcoxon rank sum test, 625
test statistic for, 626
Wilcoxon signed-rank test, 623
with replacement, 23
without replacement, 23, 207

X
x, random variable, 194

Y
y-intercept, confidence
interval for, 535

Z
z-score, 107
z-test
for a mean, 381, 425
test statistic for, 381, 425
using P-values for, 381
using rejection regions
for, 386
for a proportion, 407, 425
test statistic for, 407, 425
two-sample
difference between
means, 441
difference between
proportions, 472
zero, inherent, 13

Photo Credits

SINGLE PC LICENSE AGREEMENT AND LIMITED WARRANTY

READ THIS LICENSE CAREFULLY BEFORE OPENING THIS PACKAGE. BY OPENING THIS PACKAGE, YOU ARE AGREEING TO THE TERMS AND CONDITIONS OF THIS LICENSE. IF YOU DO NOT AGREE, DO NOT OPEN THE PACKAGE. PROMPTLY RETURN THE UNOPENED PACKAGE AND ALL ACCOMPANYING ITEMS TO THE PLACE YOU OBTAINED THEM [[FOR A FULL REFUND OF ANY SUMS YOU HAVE PAID FOR THE SOFTWARE]]. *THESE TERMS APPLY TO ALL LICENSED SOFTWARE ON THE DISK EXCEPT THAT THE TERMS FOR USE OF ANY SHAREWARE OR FREEWARE ON THE DISKETTES ARE AS SET FORTH IN THE ELECTRONIC LICENSE LOCATED ON THE DISK:*

1. **GRANT OF LICENSE and OWNERSHIP:** The enclosed computer programs and data ("Software") are licensed, not sold, to you by Pearson Education, Inc. publishing as Prentice-Hall, Inc. ("We" or the "Company") in consideration of your purchase or adoption of the accompanying Company textbooks and/or other materials, and your agreement to these terms. We reserve any rights not granted to you. You own only the disk(s) but we and/or our licensors own the Software itself. This license allows individuals who have purchased the accompanying Company textbook to use and display their copy of the Software on a single computer (i.e., with a single CPU) at a single location for *academic* use only, so long as you comply with the terms of this Agreement. You may make one copy for back up, or transfer your copy to another CPU, provided that the Software is usable on only one computer.

2. **RESTRICTIONS:** You may *not* transfer or distribute the Software or documentation to anyone else. Except for backup, you may *not* copy the documentation or the Software. You may *not* network the Software or otherwise use it on more than one computer or computer terminal at the same time. You may *not* reverse engineer, disassemble, decompile, modify, adapt, translate, or create derivative works based on the Software or the Documentation. You may be held legally responsible for any copying or copyright infringement that is caused by your failure to abide by the terms of these restrictions.

3. **TERMINATION:** This license is effective until terminated. This license will terminate automatically without notice from the Company if you fail to comply with any provisions or limitations of this license. Upon termination, you shall destroy the Documentation and all copies of the Software. All provisions of this Agreement as to limitation and disclaimer of warranties, limitation of liability, remedies or damages, and our ownership rights shall survive termination.

4. **LIMITED WARRANTY AND DISCLAIMER OF WARRANTY:** Company warrants that for a period of 60 days from the date you purchase this SOFTWARE (or purchase or adopt the accompanying textbook), the Software, when properly installed and used in accordance with the Documentation, will operate in substantial conformity with the description of the Software set forth in the Documentation, and that for a period of 30 days the disk(s) on which the Software is delivered shall be free from defects in materials and workmanship under normal use. The Company does *not* warrant that the Software will meet your requirements or that the operation of the Software will be uninterrupted or error-free. Your only remedy and the Company's only obligation under these limited warranties is, at the Company's option, return of the disk for a refund of any amounts paid for it by you or replacement of the disk. THIS LIMITED WARRANTY IS THE ONLY WARRANTY PROVIDED BY THE COMPANY AND ITS LICENSORS, AND THE COMPANY AND ITS LICENSORS DISCLAIM ALL OTHER WARRANTIES, EXPRESS OR IMPLIED, INCLUDING WITHOUT LIMITATION, THE IMPLIED WARRANTIES OF MERCHANTABILITY AND FITNESS FOR A PARTICULAR PURPOSE. THE COMPANY DOES NOT WARRANT, GUARANTEE OR MAKE ANY REPRESENTATION REGARDING THE ACCURACY, RELIABILITY, CURRENTNESS, USE, OR RESULTS OF USE, OF THE SOFTWARE.

5. **LIMITATION OF REMEDIES AND DAMAGES:** IN NO EVENT, SHALL THE COMPANY OR ITS EMPLOYEES, AGENTS, LICENSORS, OR CONTRACTORS BE LIABLE FOR ANY INCIDENTAL, INDIRECT, SPECIAL, OR CONSEQUENTIAL DAMAGES ARISING OUT OF OR IN CONNECTION WITH THIS LICENSE OR THE SOFTWARE, INCLUDING FOR LOSS OF USE, LOSS OF DATA, LOSS OF INCOME OR PROFIT, OR OTHER LOSSES, SUSTAINED AS A RESULT OF INJURY TO ANY PERSON, OR LOSS OF OR DAMAGE TO PROPERTY, OR CLAIMS OF THIRD PARTIES, EVEN IF THE COMPANY OR AN AUTHORIZED REPRESENTATIVE OF THE COMPANY HAS BEEN ADVISED OF THE POSSIBILITY OF SUCH DAMAGES. IN NO EVENT SHALL THE LIABILITY OF THE COMPANY FOR DAMAGES WITH RESPECT TO THE SOFTWARE EXCEED THE AMOUNTS ACTUALLY PAID BY YOU, IF ANY, FOR THE SOFTWARE OR THE ACCOMPANYING TEXTBOOK. BECAUSE SOME JURISDICTIONS DO NOT ALLOW THE LIMITATION OF LIABILITY IN CERTAIN CIRCUMSTANCES, THE ABOVE LIMITATIONS MAY NOT ALWAYS APPLY TO YOU.

6. **GENERAL:** THIS AGREEMENT SHALL BE CONSTRUED IN ACCORDANCE WITH THE LAWS OF THE UNITED STATES OF AMERICA AND THE STATE OF NEW YORK, APPLICABLE TO CONTRACTS MADE IN NEW YORK, AND SHALL BENEFIT THE COMPANY, ITS AFFILIATES AND ASSIGNEES. HIS AGREEMENT IS THE COMPLETE AND EXCLUSIVE STATEMENT OF THE AGREEMENT BETWEEN YOU AND THE COMPANY AND SUPERSEDES ALL PROPOSALS OR PRIOR AGREEMENTS, ORAL, OR WRITTEN, AND ANY OTHER COMMUNICATIONS BETWEEN YOU AND THE COMPANY OR ANY REPRESENTATIVE OF THE COMPANY RELATING TO THE SUBJECT MATTER OF THIS AGREEMENT. If you are a U.S. Government user, this Software is licensed with "restricted rights" as set forth in subparagraphs (a)-(d) of the Commercial Computer-Restricted Rights clause at FAR 52.227-19 or in subparagraphs (c)(1)(ii) of the Rights in Technical Data and Computer Software clause at DFARS 252.227-7013, and similar clauses, as applicable.

Should you have any questions concerning this agreement or if you wish to contact the Company for any reason, please contact in writing:

Director, Media Production
Pearson Education
1 Lake Street
Upper Saddle River, NJ 07458